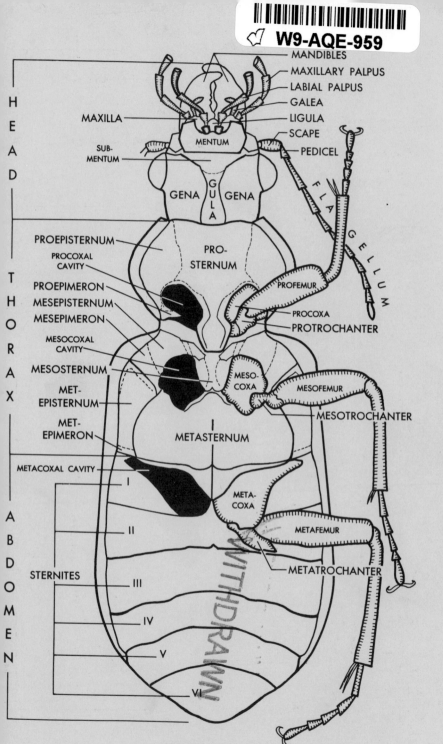

MANDIBLES
MAXILLARY PALPUS
LABIAL PALPUS
GALEA
MAXILLA
LIGULA
SCAPE
MENTUM
PEDICEL
SUB-MENTUM
GENA
GULA
GENA
FLAGELLUM
PROEPISTERNUM
PRO-STERNUM
PROCOXAL CAVITY
PROEPIMERON
PROFEMUR
MESEPISTERNUM
MESEPIMERON
PROCOXA
PROTROCHANTER
MESOCOXAL CAVITY
MESOSTERNUM
MESO-COXA
MESOFEMUR
MET-EPISTERNUM
MESOTROCHANTER
MET-EPIMERON
METASTERNUM
METACOXAL CAVITY
META-COXA
I
METAFEMUR
II
METATROCHANTER
STERNITES
III
IV
V
VI

HEAD
THORAX
ABDOMEN

PLATE II

A Manual of Common Beetles of Eastern North America

by

ELIZABETH S. DILLON

and

LAWRENCE S. DILLON

Associate Professor of Biology, A. & M. College of Texas

ROW, PETERSON AND COMPANY

Evanston, Illinois   Elmsford, New York

To

HENRY DIETRICH

Curator of Insects
Cornell University

1961
Copyright © 1961 by Row, Peterson and Company

Library of Congress catalog card number 60-8281

Printed in the United States of America

22 6 10

TABLE OF CONTENTS

PREFACE

This book is intended for anyone interested in North American beetles—
the casual naturalist, the amateur collector, the serious student, and the
professional who needs a ready reference work.

As we worked with young and with more mature naturalists for many
years, a need for a handbook of the commoner beetles became apparent.
This need has increased in recent years and exists among college students
and professional entomologists as well as amateurs. At present, Blatchley's
Coleoptera of Indiana, published in 1910 and currently selling for one
hundred dollars per copy when available, is the sole North American descriptive work covering the beetles of one state, Indiana, comprehensively.
Jacques' *How to Know the Beetles* presents a key to a number of beetles
of the area, but the forms are not described in detail, nor are they thoroughly
figured. While a number of good guides to insects in general are available,
such as Lutz's *Field Guide to the Insects,* there is nothing extant that will
enable an individual who is particularly interested in beetles to identify
those that come to hand. Numerous well-illustrated manuals have helped
"bird watching" become a widespread hobby. Similarly, snakes and lizards,
toads and frogs, sea shells, flowers, trees, stars, and even spiders can be
identified with ease by appropriate, up-to-date books with ample pictures.
But beetles, those interesting, active, often prettily colored insects, which
make up about 20 per cent of the living species of animals and which insist
frequently on coming to everyone's attention by some means or other, pleas-
ant or unpleasant, have largely been neglected.

The area covered by the book is approximately the eastern half of North
America, west as far as the 100th meridian and south to Mexico. In general
the species included here are found throughout this entire range or virtually so; in a few instances some are restricted to, or are more abundant in,
particular sections. In each of these exceptional cases an appropriate note
on their distribution is made.

As nearly 10,000 species, arranged in anywhere from 109 to over 200
families, depending on the specialist, probably occur within the area covered by this book, it was planned to include only the common, widespread
forms in the principal families in order to make the book more easily usable,
not to mention keeping its size within reason. Accordingly, nearly 1,200
species in 64 families were selected which are frequent in occurrence
throughout the area or a large portion of it or which because of their size

(such as *Dynastes*), attractive coloration, or form are most apt to come to the collector's attention. It must not be anticipated that *all* species (or even all families) of beetles commonly encountered in any given locality shall have been included here; it must be remembered that many generally rare forms may be quite abundant locally under unusual conditions. But it may be expected that the student should be able to identify to species the vast majority of specimens he collects, and a large number of others to genus or family.

While numerous persons have offered criticisms and suggestions, the final decisions have rested in our hands, and we assume all responsibility for any errors and omissions. Some errors in judgment have certainly been made, both in regard to species which have been excluded and in various items concerning nomenclature. For example, in a few cases the sole distinction between two genera lies in the shape of the male genitalia. Since females are usually of as frequent occurrence as the opposite sex, the authors felt compelled to combine the two, out of sympathy for the nonspecialist as well as in a sincere belief that genera should indicate real differences between groups of species based on whole constellations of distinctions. Family delimitations, too, have occasionally received arbitrary treatment, but few specialists are in agreement on this subject themselves. The family Chrysomelidae, for example, is subdivided into nine separate families by some, the Scarabaeidae into four by others, the Erotylidae into at least three, and the Silphidae into five or six. Others prefer a more conservative treatment, a course that in general has been followed here.

During the preparation of the manuscript, portions were examined by a number of specialists. Those who graciously consented to read and criticize sections include Dr. Mont Cazier, Mr. Warren S. Fisher, Dr. O. L. Cartwright, Professor Josef N. Knull, Mr. J. Wagener Green, the late Dr. E. A. Chapin, Dr. P. J. Darlington, Mr. Rupert L. Wenzel, and Dr. E. S. Ross.

In order to provide as high a degree of accuracy in the illustrations and descriptions as possible, specimens determined by specialists were secured from a number of museums and private collections. Dr. Mont Cazier, Mrs. Patricia Vaurie, and Mr. John Pallister made several portions of the collections of the American Museum of Natural History available to us. Several specimens were received from the United States National Museum through the kindness of Mr. George N. Vogt, and Dr. William Stehr of Ohio University loaned or donated the representatives of the Carabidae from his personal collection. A number of small-family examples from the Chicago Natural History Museum were obtained through Mr. Rupert L. Wenzel, and from his personal collection Mr. J. Wagener Green sent the required lampyrids, cantharids, and lycids. To all of these persons and institutions we are most appreciative.

Besides sending urgently needed specimens from time to time from the collections of the Illinois Natural History Survey, Dr. Milton W. Sanderson has been very helpful in many ways during the course of the preparation of this book, and to him we are deeply grateful.

Dr. V. A. Little, of A. & M. College of Texas, has always been ready with a helping hand and a friendly word of encouragement, and we would like to extend our thanks to him.

And to Dr. Henry Dietrich from Cornell University, who not only sent several thousand specimens for our use but who also gave us much needed encouragement and advice on frequent occasions, we are especially indebted.

During the earlier portion of the work on the manuscript the facilities and collections of the Reading Public Museum were freely drawn upon; and the summer nature-study classes of the same institution, upon which the eyeteeth of this book were cut, so to speak, were helpful in more ways than can be expressed. To these persons and to the staff we are much indebted.

Many others, too numerous to mention individually, have contributed records, specimens, literature, or suggestions, and to each of these we extend our warm thanks.

E. S. D.
L. S. D.

Calosoma scrutator Fabricius

COLOR PLATE A

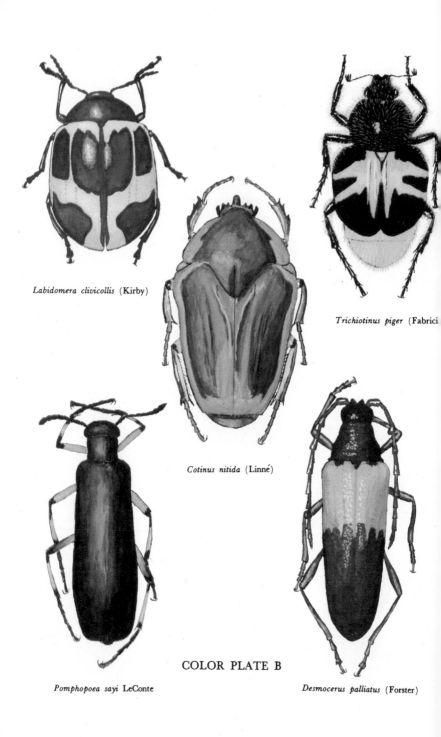

Labidomera clivicollis (Kirby)

Trichiotinus piger (Fabrici

Cotinus nitida (Linné)

Pomphopoea sayi LeConte

COLOR PLATE B

Desmocerus palliatus (Forster)

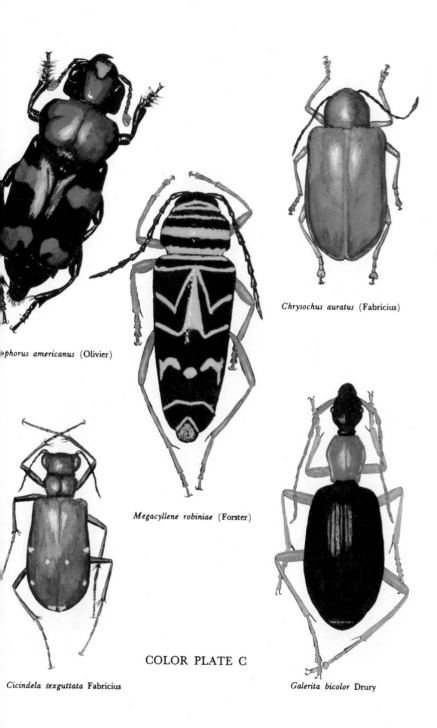

Chrysochus auratus (Fabricius)

...phorus americanus (Olivier)

Megacyllene robiniae (Forster)

COLOR PLATE C

Cicindela sexguttata Fabricius

Galerita bicolor Drury

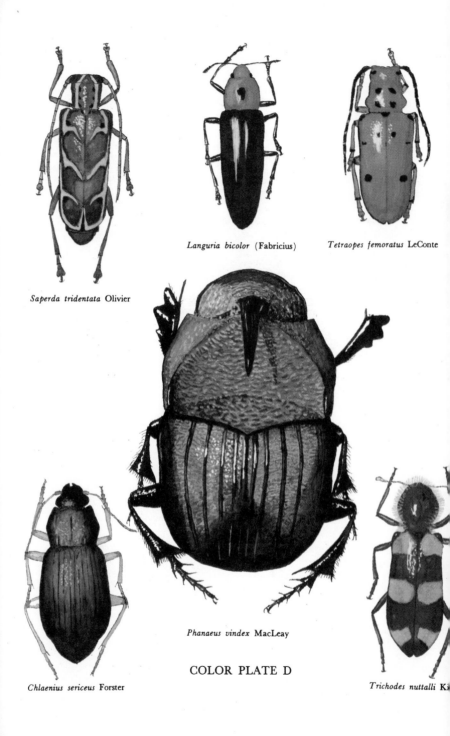

Saperda tridentata Olivier

Languria bicolor (Fabricius)

Tetraopes femoratus LeConte

Phanaeus vindex MacLeay

COLOR PLATE D

Chlaenius sericeus Forster

Trichodes nuttalli K

INTRODUCTION

Nearly a million species of insects are known to exist at the present time, by far the largest group of animals. Of these, the beetles form the largest portion—possibly over 600,000 species have already been described. In a series of catalogues published between 1910 and 1940, the lists of names of beetles fill thirty-one volumes, totaling around 25,000 pages. In fact, one family, the Curculionidae, includes some 50,000 species, more than all the species of birds, mammals, reptiles, and amphibia of the world combined. It has been estimated that about 150,000 to 200,000 species remain to be described in this one family alone.

Beetles may be easily distinguished from other insects by having the mouthparts adapted for chewing (Plate II) and the anterior pair of wings (elytra) stiffened to form a protecting sheath for the membranous hind wings that are folded beneath them. The prothorax is highly developed and its notum enlarged (Plate I) and usually mobile, while the meso- and meta-thorax are fused.

COLLECTING

Knowing when, where, and how to collect is a prerequisite for making a good collection of beetles, and knowing how to identify them a requirement for an orderly and scientific one. The "when" of collecting Coleoptera in general is simple, for many of these insects may be found the year round, if one only knows where to look. Water beetles, such as the Hydrophilidae, Haliplidae, and Dytiscidae, for example, are active all winter and can even be observed swimming beneath the ice of frozen ponds and lakes. In addition, a great many forms hibernate in the adult stage. Some of the latter, with the coming of winter, crawl beneath the bark of fallen logs or into crevices of tree trunks; others seek shelter under stones or boards or in sod. Some find protection in decaying wood; still others, especially weevils, rest during the winter months between mullein leaves. Then on warm days during March or April, certain of the smaller scarabs, curculios, and cara-bids fly by the thousands, to usher in the really active collecting season.

April through July are, generally speaking, the very best months for beetles, as it is then that the majority of species are active; however, August and into October are still quite prolific in yield of specimens, and even into November or December in the South. While numerous forms occur at any time of the year, some, on the other hand, live only a short season as adults. For example, the locust borer, *Megacyllene caryae*, may be found during June and July, while its more abundant relative, *M. robiniae*, is common on goldenrod from the end of August to the middle of October, the exact dates varying in different localities and with the weather. Consequently, while it is easy to know when to collect beetles in general, the collector, if interested in obtaining particular species, should know during which months to look for them—and the best way to get this information is by personal observation.

As to the "where" of collecting, much must be left for the collector himself to discover through experience in the field. He should, however, acquaint himself with the food habits of the different groups and species. The "soldier beetles" of the family Cantharidae live almost exclusively on flowers, while many of the Staphylinidae and most Silphidae will be found in carrion. Certain species of the Scarabaeidae and Cerambycidae also occur on flowers, while other members of the same families live in decayed logs, and some of the former in dung. Old fungi generally harbor Erotylidae, Cryptophagidae, Staphylinidae, and Tenebrionidae as well. Underneath logs, stones, and debris Carabidae, or the ground beetles, are quite common. Along sandy banks of rivers and lakes as well as on woodland paths are to be found the tiger beetles (Cicindelidae). Leaves of trees in sunny situations are favorite basking places of the Buprestidae. Other beetles, such as Lucanidae, Scarabaeidae, Pyrochroidae, and Lampyridae are nocturnal and often are attracted to bright lights. Underneath close-fitting bark live the Cucujidae, and fresh sap attracts the Nitidulidae. Certain species are highly specific in choice of food plants and are to be found nowhere else. A good example of this among the well-known forms is to be found in the species of *Tetraopes,* which occur solely on milkweed.

"How" to collect depends largely upon the purposes and desires of the individual. The simplest and quite a successful method is that of hand-picking. Flowers, plants, leaves, carrion, dung, bark of trees, logs, stones, and so forth are examined and the beetles picked up by hand and placed in the killing jar. While this is a slow procedure, it has a distinct advantage in that the habits of each species can be most easily observed. Handpicking from foliage can be facilitated by "beating." A net is held beneath the leaves (an open umbrella or piece of white cloth will do); into this, when the branches are shaken or sharply beaten by means of a stick, drop whatever insects happen to be on the tree. For collecting specimens in numbers without learning much of their habits, or for other ecological purposes, "sweeping" is of great value. A strong, durable net mounted on a rather short handle is necessary for this method. In use, it is swung quickly from side to side in front of the collector through tall grasses and brush. When there is considerable debris in the bottom of the net, the contents may be carefully sorted and examined and the beetles removed to the killing jar.

A number of species which conceal themselves among fallen leaves and ground cover can be most readily taken by sifting debris collected from the top of the ground. In this method the very top layer of soil and its cover are placed in a large, coarse sieve, which is then shaken over a piece of white cloth. The small forms that fall through the screening can easily be seen and captured. Sod or clods of grass with adhering earth can be treated similarly to leaves. It is well, after some soil has been sifted out, to pause a few minutes and watch for any sign of movement, for many forms of

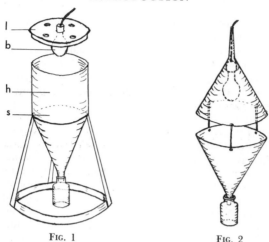

FIG. 1   FIG. 2

Fig. 1. Berlese-type funnel. In use, the hopper (*h*) is partly filled with
decaying leaves, forest soil, or the like, and the vented lid
(*l*), with a bright light-bulb (*b*), is placed over it. The light and
heat stimulate any beetles which may be present to escape
through the 1/8-inch mesh screening (*s*), down the funnel, and into
the bottle.

Fig. 2. An easily constructed light trap.

beetles "play dead" for a few moments when they have been disturbed.
Another type of sifting is the use of an adaptation of the Berlese-type funnel (Fig. 1), which is an excellent way to secure many of these small
debris- or topsoil-inhabiting forms during any season. The debris or soil
is placed on the screen in the top metal container, and the tight-fitting
lid with the light (25–40-watt bulb) is placed on the container. Most of the
insects in this type of habitat are negatively phototropic (move away from
light) and will burrow down through the soil toward the screen and drop
through it to the alcohol in the jar below the funnel. The heat also will
activate those which are dormant in cold weather.

Traps of various kinds are of great value in collecting certain families
and are of several types. Light traps are used for night-flying forms and
are easily made in the following manner (Fig. 2). Two rather large metal
funnels, painted white inside, are needed. One should be inverted, and
an electric-light cord carrying a socket should be passed through the small
end and a 100–200-watt bulb inserted in the socket. The other funnel is
suspended below the first, the narrow end being cut off short and secured
to a killing jar or a cloth bag.

A second type of trap is the carrion trap. This is merely a tin can sunk
into the ground to its top rim, with a piece of old meat, a dead mouse, or,
preferably, a fish head inside. Fine holes previously punched in the bottom of the can provide drainage for rain water, but they must not be so
large that small beetles will be able to leave the trap through them. Staph-

ylinids, silphids, histerids, and scarabs are very easily obtained this way, and, the "riper" the bait, the better the results.

Another useful trap uses brown sugar. To make it, use fairly large tin cans which have wire handles by means of which they may be suspended in trees. In the tins, place a solution of brown sugar mixed in the proportion of one pound of sugar to a gallon of water, being careful to fill them not more than one-third full; otherwise the beetles may be able to crawl out. Various species of forest trees and shrubs should be selected and the traps suspended in them at not too great a height. A variety of forms will be attracted to this bait, some of which are not easily obtainable any other way. Included among them will be cerambycids, carabids, and elaters when the sugar solution is fresh, and later, as fermentation proceeds, staphylinids, histerids, and scarabs. The beetles should be removed at frequent intervals, washed off, killed if necessary, and mounted. The bait should be replaced after it becomes too ripe. Another very simple form of trap useful for capturing carabids and other ground-dwelling beetles is formed by sinking cans or jars into the earth in meadows, fields, or open woods. A little molasses can be placed in the containers, but while adding to the efficiency of the method, this is not essential to its success.

Two unique and very successful methods for collecting wood-boring beetles have been described by L. M. Gardinier (1957). The first is by the use of turpentine in a small, shallow, screen-covered metal pan, suspended about four feet above the ground. The pan should be placed near a landing surface, such as a tree or a wall, because the beetles tend to alight two to ten feet away rather than on the pan. Warm, humid days give the best results, and the beetles come soon after the bait is set out. Curculios, cerambycids, buprestids, clerids, and scolytids can be collected this way. The second method is by using smoke as bait. A small fire of pine chips is made in a metal pail and fed with resin and coniferous foliage to make plenty of smoke. Cerambycids and scolytids are especially attracted in large numbers by this method. Gardinier claims that, when this method was used, beetles were seen to fly in direct paths from a distance of about 75 feet, and he thinks that this probably partly explains the huge populations of wood-boring insects found in forest areas devastated by fire.

Finally, a means of collecting should be mentioned which, while slow and in proportion to effort expended yields only a relatively few specimens, is one that should be more widely used—the rearing of larvae. Equipment needed varies according to the habits of the species raised. For plant- or leaf-eating kinds, a box with screen sides and top is useful. After the bottom is covered with earth, the plants or leaves containing the larvae or eggs are placed inside, and fresh food is supplied daily. The fresh food must be of the same species of plant on which the specimens were first found or else the larvae will die of starvation. Often, while the collector is searching under bark or in dead logs for beetles, he will find larvae of woodborers and bark beetles. These can be taken home on small pieces of the wood and kept in the boxes, as above. Care must be taken to keep the earth moist but not wet. In lieu of screened-in cages, large cans, jars, etc., can be made to serve if muslin is securely fastened over the opening and a little moist earth is placed in the bottom. It is only fair at this point to warn the student that many wood-dwelling species require two or more years to mature; consequently much patience needs to be exerted to secure good results. But the amateur can render valuable service to entomology by carefully rearing specimens in this manner, especially if sufficient quantities are reared so that examples of the larvae in the different stages of growth are preserved as permanent specimens. They should be placed in vials of 70 per cent alcohol, sealed tightly, and labeled with the date collected, locality, and habitat. Then, after some have attained maturity, a complete life history of the species will have been obtained. Of a great many of our commonest forms the biology is, at present, practically unknown.

Methods and Materials for Collecting, Killing, and Preserving

The list of materials needed to collect beetles is not an imposing one. Killing jars are absolutely essential and may be manufactured in various ways. Small vials and jars up to eight ounces may be used, but the smaller the container, the more practical. The most rapid killing compound is potassium cyanide. Enough cyanide is placed in the jar to cover the bottom of it to a depth of about one-quarter inch. Then dry plaster of Paris is added to a thickness of one inch. After the two ingredients have been thoroughly mixed by shaking or stirring, the surface of the plaster is made smooth and firm by lightly tamping it with a flat-ended piece of wood. When enough water to moisten just the surface has been added, the jar is ready for use. The dry plaster in the bottom serves to absorb any moisture which may subsequently collect. In case cyanide is not available, ammonium carbonate may be substituted. A word of warning on the use of cyanide: it is *extremely* toxic to vertebrate animals and must be handled with extreme care. *Do not touch with the hands or breathe the fumes.*

Another and much safer method for killing and preserving, which is fast becoming widely used, has been described at some length by J. M. Valentine (1942). In this procedure ethyl acetate (acetic ether), which is available in drugstores or hardware stores, is used as the killing agent. Tightly corked glass vials or small jars are filled about one-third full of dry, clean, coarse, hardwood sawdust. Then, just before the collecting starts, about ten drops of the ethyl acetate are poured into the tube—the sawdust should be kept just damp, not wet. An extra supply of the acetate may be carried along on a collecting trip so as to recharge the collecting vessel if too much of the liquid has evaporated by continuous use. Several vials should be carried so as to keep beetles from different localities separate. In this way, when collecting is finished in one area, the bottle may be labeled with locality and date and other collecting data and the sample stored as it is. If the stopper fits tightly, the beetles will remain fresh for a year or more and may be pinned without further relaxing of the specimens.

A modification of the preceding method is made by putting a layer of

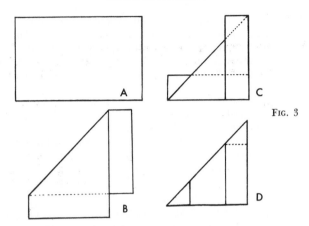

Fig. 3

Fig. 3. An envelope for temporary storage of beetles. Paper of any dimensions may be used, but it must be about one inch longer than wide (*A*). After the sheet is folded obliquely across the middle (*B*), the long ends are folded (*C*), and finally the corners (*D*).

wet plaster of Paris in a jar or vial, then placing it in an oven until dry. When dry, it is saturated with ethyl acetate and the excess poured off; when corked tightly, it is ready for use. One such charge should last for at least a few weeks. Then, when the jar ceases to be effective, it may be dried in the oven again and recharged with the ethyl acetate. In either case, the beetles should be left in at least overnight to insure complete relaxing effects.

Carbon tetrachloride may be used in much the same manner as ethyl acetate; it may also be poured over crumpled paper toweling, pieces of blotter, or pieces of rubber (chopped rubber bands) in jars or vials. Since the fumes are heavier than air, they remain in the bottom of the container for some time.

In addition to killing jars, small forceps are often of invaluable assistance, especially in collecting dung and carrion beetles or in extracting small forms from crevices in trees and the like. A strong screw driver or chisel aids in prying bark off logs as well as in breaking up decaying wood. For sweeping, a sturdy, short-handled net is needed, and, when beating foliage, a net or umbrella is used as previously described. A coarse screen for sifting leaves or other debris is the last necessary article. Sometimes, if the collector finds a desirable specimen and by chance does not have a killing jar with him, he may still be able to get it home safely by making an envelope out of paper as shown in the diagram (Fig. 3), or the insect may be tied into a corner of a handkerchief, though this latter method should be used only when necessary. An ardent collector is practically never without at least a small collecting vial somewhere about his person.

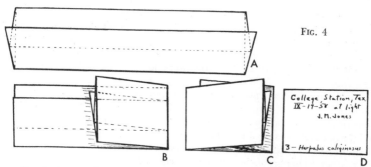

Fig. 4

Fig. 4. An envelope for permanent storage. To make a finished envelope 1½″ × 2″, which is a very convenient size, a piece of paper nearly three times as wide as long is folded in thirds lengthwise (A) and then folded in thirds crosswise (B and C), and the necessary data written on the smooth central portion (D). The specimens are laid between layers of cellucotton, and one folded end of the envelope is then inserted into the other.

PINNING AND LABELING

After the beetles have been caught, the next problem that confronts the collector is the pinning, labeling, and arranging of the insects in whatever container he chooses to keep his specimens. The best time for pinning a beetle is as soon as possible after it has been removed from the killing jar. Care must be taken to leave the insects in the killing jar long enough for them to be completely killed; overnight is best. Otherwise the specimens may come alive again, because some beetles are able to live on the supply of air they carry under their elytra and others close their spiracles (breathing pores on the sides of the abdomen) and "play dead" for some time. This latter habit is especially true of the weevils. If the specimens cannot be pinned for several weeks, they should be placed in small envelopes, as shown in Figure 4, with the date, place of collection, habitat, and name of collector written on the outside, and the envelopes should be placed preferably in a tin box with napthalene flakes or paradichlorobenzene in it to keep out the pests which attack dried insects.

When the time comes to pin these dry beetles, they may be relaxed by the following methods. A quick but not necessarily the best way is to drop the insects into hot water, let them stand several minutes, remove to a blotter, and pin. A second and much more desirable method, because it completely relaxes the entire beetle and preserves it in a relaxed state for an indefinite period, is the use of Barber's fluid. This is made by mixing 53 parts ethyl alcohol (95%; and denatured can be used as long as it is ethyl), 49 parts water, 19 parts ethyl acetate (acetic ether), 7 parts benzol (benzene), by volume. Immersion in this solution produces rapid relaxation of appendages, and it may also be used on mounted specimens by applying only to that appendage which needs to be moved. A third and somewhat slower method of relaxing and which is within the reach of any collector is the use of moist sand treated with a few drops of carbolic acid in the bottom of a container and covered with a piece of absorbent paper, blotter, or cardboard. The insects are placed on the paper or cardboard and the receptacle covered so it is airtight. After 12 to 48 hours most specimens are relaxed so that the appendages can be moved without breaking.

A step which should precede mounting, and which is especially desirable when beetles of the families Carabidae, Cicindelidae, and Scarabaeidae are concerned, is degreasing. These families in particular have large amounts of internal fatty tissue, and, when specimens are pinned, the grease tends to come to the surface. The beetles are immersed usually in commercial ether, several changes of which may be needed until there is no discoloration of the ether, for the dissolved fatty substances tend to impart a yellowish color. Other solvents which may be used in place of ether are diethyl carbonate, xylol, and benzol.

In the pinning of specimens, these materials are necessary: insect pins (preferably black or blue steel) from numbers 0 to 4 in size, a pair of forceps, glue or Duco lacquer cement (to mend broken parts and mount the smaller beetles), and paper triangles (for mounting specimens too small to pin) three-eighths of an inch long and one-eighth of an inch wide at the widest part. The latter may be cut from a good heavy paper (100 per cent rag linen ledger is best). The size of pin to use for the various sizes of insects must be left to the discretion of the pinner, a pin as large as possible without breaking the beetle being the general rule. The size of pin having been decided upon, the beetle should then be held firmly between the fingers of one hand and the pin inserted in the middle of the right elytron at about the basal quarter. For the very small beetles a size 3 or 4 pin should be pushed through the wide end of a paper triangle until it is within one-quarter of the distance from the top of the pin; the tip of the triangle should then be bent downward and an adhesive placed on the bent portion and applied to the right side of the beetle between the meso- and metasternum (Fig. 5). This method leaves the sterna free for structural examination during identification. Several adhesives may be used: Duco or lacquer cement (airplane cement) thinned with amyl acetate or equal parts of amyl and ethyl acetate, orange shellac dissolved in absolute alcohol, or glue (LePage's).

All specimens should bear labels giving information as to the locality and date of collection, habitat, and name of collector. For the locality and date labels, a good size for the printed ones is three-eighths to one-half inch by three-sixteenths to one-quarter inch; for the handwritten labels a slightly larger size is used. The locality should be placed at the top; this should include the nearest city or town, or the township, and state (Fig. 6). The date should come next, with the month expressed first, in Roman numerals, then the day, and then the year, abbreviated; e.g., V-26-58. Sometimes the collector's name may be placed at the bottom, but more often it is put on a separate label, as is also the habitat from which the specimen was collected; both of these labels are placed underneath the date and locality label on the pin below the specimen (Fig. 6). When the insect

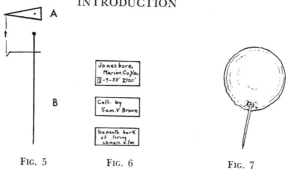

FIG. 5   FIG. 6   FIG. 7

Fig. 5. Paper triangle (*A*) used in pinning small specimens. The tip of the triangle (*t*) is bent downward, as in *B*; the adhesive is applied to this bent portion.

Fig. 6. Labels commonly used and the sort of data which is especially valuable. Elevation is especially desired in mountainous regions.

Fig. 7. Moth ball into which an ordinary pin, its head-end first heated red hot, has been pushed.

has been identified, the name should be printed or written on a slightly larger label and pinned to the bottom of the drawer or box near the insect. Black waterproof India ink for the writing of the labels is most satisfactory and permanent. While printed labels make a better appearance, they are an additional expense, so, if a plate camera is available, satisfactory labels can be made by means of photography. The locality is typed repeatedly in columns on a sheet of white paper, allowing sufficient space for other data (date, etc.). Photographing it then can reduce the lettering to the proper size. Once a plate has been made, as many labels as desired can be printed from it. Care should be taken to have the photographed labels properly fixed so that there is no danger of their becoming faded.

Housing specimens is the next consideration. There are many excellent boxes on the market, ranging from the small Schmidt boxes to the large Cornell-type drawers with glass tops. If one desires only a small collection, the Schmidt box or one of a similar type is satisfactory; but if a collection of any size is contemplated, the larger drawers will be found to be of greater value. However, for the beginner, good insect boxes can be made out of the deep cigar boxes, with either a layer of Celotex (a composition board) or cork in the bottom. Naphthalene flakes or paradichlorobenzene crystals should be kept in the boxes to keep out the beetles, such as the Dermestidae and Ptinidae, which attack dried specimens. These compounds should either be sprinkled around loosely or put in small cheese-cloth bags anchored by pins; the cone or ball form of the naphthalene may be used by heating the head of a pin, inserting this into the cone or ball (Fig. 7), and then sticking the pointed end of the pin into the bottom of the box.

For a list of dealers who can supply entomological supplies and books see the Appendix.

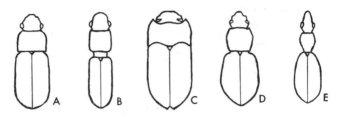

Fig. 8

Fig. 8. Body shapes of beetles frequently encountered. *A,* elongate-oblong, moderately robust; *B,* elongate-oblong, slender; *C,* broadly oblong, robust; *D,* ovate, robust; *E,* elongate-ovate, slender.

STRUCTURE
(Plates I, II)

Many species of beetles can be readily and accurately identified by means of the illustrations, and much time may be saved by making use of them. However, there are numerous species which so closely resemble others that it is always a wise procedure to check determinations of specimens with the written descriptions to avoid error as far as possible. At first this will be rather a tedious process to the beginner because of the unfamiliarity of the terms, but, as the meanings of these are learned, the task will become increasingly easier. In order that the process of becoming familiar with the terminology may be as brief and simple as possible, the following explanations are made.

The groupings of the various forms of beetles, or other animals for that matter, into species, genera, families, and the like to a large extent are man-made devices. Except for the species, these groupings do not exist as such in nature; they are created by taxonomists for the sake of convenience in identification of forms. As the basis for the larger groups—genera, tribes, families—structure is always used; and, ideally, structure is the basis for separation of species also, but color is frequently employed. Color, while easy to see, is often variable and inconstant; moreover, it is impossible to describe differences in shades of color. Hence, structure is the more desirable basis for speciation.

Such terms as "oblong," "elongate," and "ovate" refer to the general outline of the insect when viewed from above; the accompanying figure (Fig. 8) attempts to illustrate the shades of meanings employed. "Convex" or "depressed" refers to the general surface when viewed from behind or from the front; "cylindrical" means that both upper and lower surfaces are convex, so that in cross section the body wall looks somewhat circular.

The bodies of beetles, like other insects, are divided anatomically into three general regions: the *head,* the *thorax,* and the *abdomen.* Aside from

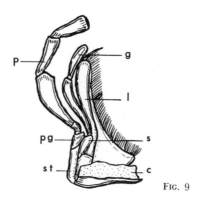

Fig. 9. Maxilla of a beetle (*Pasimachus* sp.). *c*, cardo; *g*, galea; *l*, lacinia;
p, palpus; *pg*, palpiger; *s*, subgalea; *st*, stipes.

the appendages (antennae and mouthparts), the head bears several distinct characters that are of importance in identification. These include, primarily, the head regions, the position and shape of the eyes, and the locus of attachment of the antennae. The head regions include, first of all, the *front*, or frontal region, which is, as the name implies, the fore position, or the insect's face. Connecting above with the front is the *vertex*, the top portion between the eyes extending to the *occiput*, which is the extreme back of the head. Sometimes where the vertex and front join each other there is formed a distinct angle; often, however, the two are nearly in the same plane and there is no definite line of demarcation. When such is the case, the reader must use his own judgment as to where one ends and the other begins. On each side, immediately below and behind the eye, is found the *gena*, or check, while basally, at the extreme lower part, is the *gula*, the throat. Anterior to the gula is the *submentum*, which bears the lower lip, or *labium*.

The mouthparts are, unlike those of moths, butterflies, and true bugs, which suck nectar or plant juices, adapted for chewing and consist of four different parts, the middle two of these being paired. The uppermost part is the *labrum*, or upper lip, which is merely a flap of sclerotized material, used to help in grasping food. It is attached to the front by an intermediate piece, the *clypeus*. Immediately below it lies a pair of jaws, the *mandibles*, which move from side to side instead of vertically, as do our own; however, they do not differ functionally from man's, for they serve as the principal organ of mastication and often are equipped with teeth on the inner edges to aid the process. Moreover, they are, in many cases, a means of defense as well. Beneath them are located the other paired mouthparts, the *maxillae;* these are very complex in structure, being composed of a number of segments (Fig. 9). While these are somewhat like the mandibles in appearance, their function is more to hold and turn the food than to chew it. They differ further in that each bears a *palpus,* a supposedly tactile

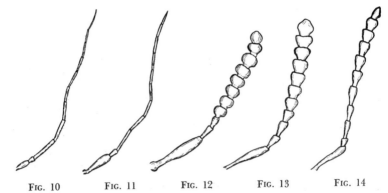

FIG. 10   FIG. 11   FIG. 12   FIG. 13   FIG. 14

Figs. 10–14. Types of antennae. Filiform (10 and 11). Moniliform (12). Clavate (13 and 14).

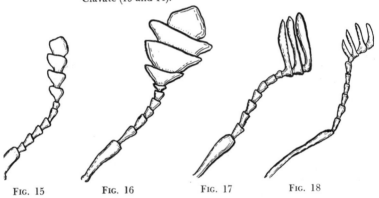

FIG. 15   FIG. 16   FIG. 17   FIG. 18

Figs. 15–18. Types of antennae. Capitate (15 and 16). Lamellate (17 and 18).

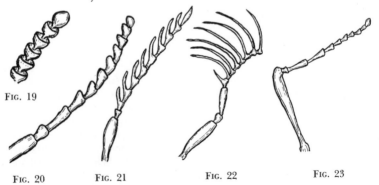

FIG. 19

FIG. 20   FIG. 21   FIG. 22   FIG. 23

Figs. 19–23. Types of antennae. A portion of a perfoliate antenna (19). Serrate (20). Pectinate (21). Flabellate (22). Geniculate (23).

organ composed of two to four segments. The lowermost mouthpart is the *labium*, or lower lip. Considerably more complex in structure than the labrum, it is composed of a number of parts. At the base there are two broad sclerites, the *mentum* and *submentum*, the latter connecting the structure to the gula. The central portion of the outer part is known as the *ligula*, on each side is a *palpiger*, which bears the palpus, while between the ligula and the palpiger is a smaller sclerite called the *paraglossa*. (See Plates I, II; these two plates are printed on the endpapers of the book, inside the front and back covers.)

As mentioned previously, the position and character of the eye are often of importance. Normally the eye is always on the side of the head, but its exact location here may vary in different groups. In some cases it may extend well up onto the top of the head and, occasionally, may even meet and touch the one from the opposite side at the center of the vertex, a condition known as "eyes contiguous above." In other cases the eyes are confined to the lateral region, leaving a broad interocular space. Shape and granulation are two characters of the eye often mentioned in descriptions. "Round," "oval," and the like refer, of course, to the outline of the eye against the head; frequently the anterior margin is scooped out or emarginate, usually behind the insertion of the antenna. "Convex" indicates that the surface is more or less rounded; when the convexity is great, the eye is said to be "prominent." "Granulation" refers to the size of the individual facets which make up the compound eye. If these are so small that they are somewhat difficult to distinguish, the eye is said to be "finely granulate"; if they are large enough to be easily apparent, it is "coarsely granulate." Rarely a pair of simple eyes, the *ocelli* (sing. *ocellus*) is present in a few families; these are found on the upper part of the front near the vertex.

The type and locus of attachment of the antennae are much utilized in grouping species into families. In the simplest type, the *filiform* (Figs. 10, 11), the segments are all of about the same thickness or slightly tapering and all of similar, cylindrical shape. *Moniliform* (Fig. 12) differs in having the components spherical, so that distinct constrictions are produced where one segment joins the next, resembling somewhat a minute string of round beads. In the *clavate* type (Figs. 13, 14), the succeeding segments gradually become broader toward the apex, so that the whole resembles a club. *Capitate* (Figs. 15, 16) antennae are similar to this latter type, differing in that only the outer segments are increased in thickness to form a sudden enlargement or *club* at the tip. A form of capitate antennae in which the outer segments are leaflike plates which may be brought closely in contact, forming a transverse or, rarely, rounded club, supported at one side by the stem of the antenna, is known as *lamellate* (Figs. 17, 18). In some cases the antennae are made of rather uniform segments, each of which is more or less triangular and produced toward one side so that a saw-toothed appearance is presented; such antennae are designated as *serrate* (Fig. 20). If the segments are each produced laterally very greatly, the *pectinate* (Fig. 21), or comblike, condition arises. Should the processes be still more elongated, they are known as *flabellate* (Fig. 22) or fan-shaped.

Infrequently the segments are disklike and connected by a stalk passing nearly through their centers; they are then called *perfoliate* (Fig. 19). The antennae are *geniculate* (Fig. 23), or elbowed, when the second segment is attached to the first, or *scape,* in such a way as to make a distinct angle, with the balance of the segments following in the same line as the second. When the antennae are both geniculate and capitate, the segments between the scape and club are together called the *funicle.* Finally, the locus of attachment of the antennae onto the head is in one of these regions: on the gena before the eye or behind the mandibles, on the front, or under the front. Only this last term needs any explanation; the others are self-explanatory. When the antennae are attached under the front (Fig. 322), the front is somewhat hollowed beneath at each side, leaving the side margin unbroken; also, the first antennal segment is usually somewhat curved to fit into the excavation.

The next body division, the *thorax,* is that part which supports the head anteriorly and the abdomen posteriorly and bears also the legs and wings as appendages. It is itself subdivided into three regions, the *prothorax, mesothorax,* and *metathorax,* each bearing a pair of legs and the last two each carrying a pair of wings. Since these subregions are fundamentally much alike, in naming sclerites the same term is used throughout but with a different prefix, pro-, meso-, or meta- as the case may be, depending upon which subdivision is concerned. For example, each subdivision has a sclerite ventrally which is known as the *sternum* (pl. *sterna*); that of the prothorax is designated as the prosternum, of the mesothorax, the mesosternum, etc. Similarly, the tibiae of the front legs are the protibiae, those of the middle legs the mesotibiae, etc. Before a vowel, the meso- and meta- are shortened for the sake of euphony to mes- and met-, as in metepimera. This system is a very convenient one and avoids considerable confusion as well. By using it, one needs to learn the names of the parts of but one subdivision instead of three.

Dorsally only one of these subdivisions is exposed (and usually a very small part of the second), this being the notum of the prothorax, i.e., the *pronotum,* which is greatly enlarged (Plate I). As a whole, the pronotum is probably more diversely modified in shape and in sculpture than any other part of the body. For that reason, it is of much taxonomic value, especially in separating allied species. Figure 24 illustrates some forms of outlines that are frequently encountered. As for the sculpturing, it will be discussed further on in the chapter, as the same terms are applicable to all body regions.

The other dorsal sclerite is usually a small one and is part of the mesothorax. This is the mesoscutellum, referred to throughout the text as the *scutellum* (Plate I), the metascutellar region being concealed. While the scutellum is small, it is often of considerable taxonomic importance. In certain genera, it may be very small or entirely concealed by the elytra, while closely related forms have it exposed and conspicuous. It reaches its greatest development in some of our scarabs, where the tip may nearly attain the apex of the elytra. However, although this sclerite is important, it presents no special difficulty.

In contrast to the simplicity of structure of the dorsal area of the thorax,

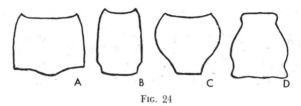

Fᴵɢ. 24

Fig. 24. Pronotal shapes commonly encountered. *A,* oblong, transverse, basal margin broadly lobed at middle. *B,* elongate, constricted at base, basal margin rounded, apical margin emarginate. *C,* cordate, basal margin truncate. *D,* campanuliform, basal margin bisinuate.

the ventral surface (Plate II) is considerably more complex. The one factor which often adds to the complexity is the close association of the meso- and metathorax. The prothorax is *usually* distinctly separated from the others, due to the presence of a hinge joint between it and the mesothorax, which gives it great mobility; but the other two divisions are closely joined —sometimes there is not even a trace of suture between them. However, their limits can be established if it is remembered that the coxae are attached at the apex of the meso- and metathorax and at the base of the prothorax. As for the sclerites, the most important are the *sterna,* found between and expanded somewhat around each of the pairs of coxae. Often they are variously modified by having tubercles, ridges, or lobes on their surface. The other ventral sclerites, collectively referred to as *sidepieces,* are located laterad to the sterna. On all thoracic subdivisions, there are pairs of these sidepieces on each side. The anterior sclerites are the *episterna,* the posterior are the *epimera* (sing. *epimeron*). It should be noted that often in the prothorax all the ventral sclerites, except the sternum, have been fused, so that there are no distinct sidepieces present. While the epimera and episterna are much used in classification, it is their position and shape that are of importance, for they have no special surface structures.

The appendages of the thorax are used frequently in both keys and descriptions for identification. The wings present no special difficulty in identification of the beetles. While two pairs are generally present, both sets or just the lower may be absent, or either pair may be much reduced. The upper pair, the *elytra* (sing. *elytron;* see Plate I), are always sclerotized, although in varying degrees; the hind wings are membranous like those of a fly, but they are only occasionally used in identification. The elytra have several definite regions. The *base* is that portion which is adjacent to the pronotum when the wings are at rest. The line formed by the two internal straight edges of the elytra is the *suture.* On the external (or lateral) side the wing covers may be folded around underneath to a greater or lesser extent; this fold is the *epipleuron* (pl. *epipleura*), or *epipleural fold.* The *humerus* is the point of meeting of the lateral edge and base, usually rounded or angulate. The central portion is the *disk,* and the tip is the *apex.* A few of the families have the elytra abbreviated, exposing the upper

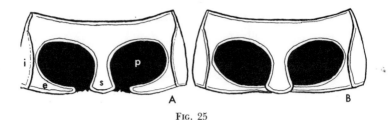

FIG. 25

Fig. 25. Procoxal cavity types. *A*, Procoxal cavities *(p)* open posteriorly, the epimera *(e)* not attaining prosternal process *(s)*; *i*, inflexed sides of pronotum. *B*, Procoxal cavities closed posteriorly by the epimera.

or dorsal side of the abdomen. The Staphylinidae have extremely short elytra, exposing a large portion of the abdomen, but the Histeridae have only two segments exposed.

The modification of the parts of the legs (Fig. 25) is an important factor, too, in the identification of the different groups. The *coxae* (sing. *coxa*), which attach the legs proper to the body, are of several types, particularly the procoxae. They may be prominent, that is, projecting from the body, or not prominent, in which case they are more or less in the same plane as the undersurface; they may be rounded or conical. Often present on the coxa is the *trochantin*, a small plate on the outer side of the coxa and sometimes movable on the coxa (Fig. 234). The adjacent part of the leg, the *trochanter*, is usually small and unmodified and is of little importance. The next section, the *femur* (pl. *femora*), or thigh, is usually cylindrical, but frequently is clubbed or swollen at the apical end, or spindle-shaped. Sometimes, as in a few of the Cerambycidae, the femora and the next part, the *tibia* (pl. *tibiae*), may be greatly elongated. But for the most part the tibiae are not greatly modified; usually they are cylindrical, thin, and slightly enlarged apically. However, in some families, such as the Scarabaeidae and most of the water beetles, they are quite complex. The last segment of the legs, the *tarsus* (pl. *tarsi*), is extremely variable and may even be entirely lacking. If present, they are usually five-segmented, but sometimes they are three- or four-segmented. (In keys, tarsal segments are sometimes expressed as 5–5–5, 3–3–3, 4–5–5, etc., referring to pro-, meso-, and metatarsus, always in that order.) They may be short or elongate, simply cylindrical or broadened apically, entirely glabrous, fringed beneath, or padded with dense patches of setae. On the last tarsal segment are borne the *claws*, which may be variously modified (Fig. 26). These may be simple or divergent; in the latter case the two claws form a distinct angle. Sometimes the claws have become so divergent as to be directly opposite each other, in which case they are said to be "divaricate." The claws themselves may be modified; some bear a tooth at the base; others are split ("bifurcate") for almost their entire length; in some Lamiinae the base of the claw may be rather long before the claw itself begins and is designated as being "appendiculate."

The *abdomen*, the last division of the body, while of importance in taxonomy, has few terms which require explanation. Above, the dorsal

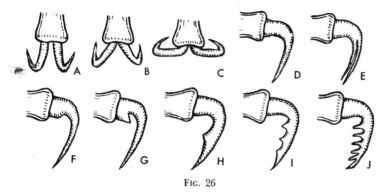

FIG. 26

Fig. 26. Types of tarsal claws. *A* to *C*, from above; *D* to *J*, single claws from the side. *A*, Simple. *B*, Divergent. *C*, Divaricate. *D*, Simple. *E*, Bifid or bifurcate. *F*, Appendiculate. *G, H*, Dentate. *I*, Serrate. *J*, Pectinate.

surface of a segment is known as the *tergite*. These are simply numbered, beginning with the first segment behind the thorax, and only the last two bear distinctive names. The final segment is called the *pygidium* and the preceding one the *propygidium*. On the ventral surface, the *sternites* (Plate II) are also designated by numbers; none of these has a special name. Although the genitalia, which are borne by the abdomen, are of great importance to the advanced student, they need not be considered by the general collector.

Sculpture refers to the various modifications of the surface of the beetle and for the most part can be divided into two kinds, namely, impressions and elevations. The former includes *puncture, fovea, sulcus, stria, striga, ruga, rugose, alutaceous, scabrous,* and *fossa;* the latter includes *carina, tubercle, granule, mucronate, costa, keel, muricate, spine,* and *tooth.* All

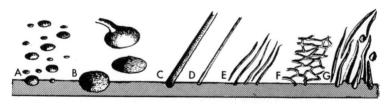

FIG. 27

Fig. 27. Frequently encountered types of impressed sculpturing. *A*, Punctures, the large ones *coarse*, the small ones *fine*. *B*, Foveae. A large fovea which receives a body part, such as a leg or antenna, is called a fossa, as in the topmost figure. *C*, Sulcus. *D*, Stria. Striae differ from sulci in occurring in sets or in bordering the margin of a part, appearing to serve primarily as ornamentation. *E*, Rugae or wrinkles. *F*, An alutaceous surface. *G*, A strigose surface, a combination of elevations and impressions.

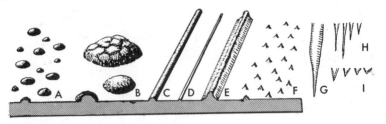

FIG. 28

Fig. 28. Common types of elevated sculpturing. *A*, Granules, coarse and fine. *B*, Tubercles. Very large tubercles are referred to as gibbosities, as in the uppermost figure. When the gibbosity gradually merges with the surrounding surface, it is usually called a tumescence. *C*, Costa. *D*, Carina. *E*, Keel. *F*, Murication. *G*, Mucro. *H*, Spines are more than twice as long as wide. *I*, Teeth are not more than twice as long as wide.

of these terms are defined in the glossary, and some will be found illustrated in Figures 27 and 28.

The attempt was made in the writing of this book to make the format of the verbal descriptions as uniform as possible throughout. In specific characteristics, the shape and appearance are noted first. These are followed in the same sentence by the color, in this sequence: general color above, exception to this, and markings if any; then color beneath, if different from that above. Next the shape and sculpturing of the head and its parts, if important, are given, then the shape and sculpturing of the pronotum, then of the elytra. The underparts and later the legs are described, and finally the size in millimeters (mm.) is stated. In descriptions of families and genera, a somewhat similar form is followed.

BEETLE LARVAE
(Plates III, IV)

Beetles resemble butterflies in being *holometabolic,* i.e., in having a complex life history. Their eggs upon hatching produce young, called *grubs,* which are quite unlike their parents in appearance, being like caterpillars in general body form. As in the case of caterpillars, these grubs increase in size by molting their skins a number of times, and, when full grown, go into a quiescent stage, or *pupa,* before becoming the adult beetle, or *imago.* While, as may be seen from the plates, the larvae differ greatly in appearance from family to family, they may be grouped into several principal types, as outlined by the following scheme of classification:

First of all the larvae are grouped on the basis of the presence or absence of legs on the thorax. All *apodous,* or legless, beetle larvae are classed as the *curculionid* sort, being thick-bodied, crescent-shaped, and having a well-developed head; this type is represented mostly by the curculionids, scolytids, and rhynchophorids, as well as by the later larval stages of mylabrids. On the other hand, those larvae which possess thoracic legs, the *oligopoda* group, are subdivided into *thysanuriform,* which are flattened, very active forms, and *eruciform,* the thick-bodied, caterpillar-like sorts. In turn, the thysanuriform kinds are subdivided, among the beetles, into *caraboid,* those which have strongly developed mandibles, and *triunguloid,* which are minute, very active, and often spiny, and with small mandibles. To the caraboid type belong the larvae of many diverse families, including the tiger and ground beetles, most of the water beetles, and almost all predatory sorts like clerids, staphylinids, histerids, and so forth. The triunguloid sort is represented almost solely by the first-instar (newly hatched) larva of the meloids and rhipiphorids.

The sluggish, usually cylindrical, eruciform larvae are represented in the Coleoptera of our region by two types, in some of which the legs are quite poorly developed or even vestigial. In the *scarabaeoid* forms the body is crescent-shaped and wrinkled and often is covered with hair; larvae of scarabs, lucanids, trogids, and anobiids, in addition to older grubs of meloids, belong in this category. The *cerambycoid* type may be somewhat flattened, as in the buprestids, but are typically rounded, as in the cerambycids and elaterids; they differ from the scarabaeoid sort in not being crescent-shaped and in being much more active.

KEYS AND THEIR USE

Keys are devices that help to identify the groups of beetles, such as families, subfamilies, tribes, genera, and species. They are made up of distinguishing characteristics such as structure, color, shape, and even size of the insect. All of the keys in this book are in couplet form, i.e., there is a choice between two characters. The following is an illustration of a simple, specific key.

1. Elytra black 2
   Elytra bicolored 3
2. Head entirely yellow; elytral punctures large, at least as distant one from another as their own diameters ....a. *scutellaris*
   Occiput of head black; elytral punctures close ....b. *consanguinea*
3. Pronotum entirely yellow; apical half of antennae piceous ......c. *puberula*
   Pronotum with a piceous discal macula; antennae entirely yellowish ....
   ....d. *varians*

To use the key, start with couplet 1 and decide, by examining the specimen, whether the elytra are black or bicolored. If they are black, then proceed to couplet 2, if bicolored to couplet 3. Under each of these a decision would be made between the contrasting characteristics until one is encountered that provides a name for the beetle under examination. Then the specific description may be consulted for the final verification. Similar procedures are used for the family, tribal, and generic keys.

Do not be confused if the name of any one subfamily, genus, or the like appears more than once in the same key. Because of the great breadth of variation that may occur within some groups, it is necessary at times to "key them out" in two, three, or even a half-dozen places. In using keys in which such repetition occurs, the procedure is the same as in those where repetition does not occur.

PLATE III

Beetle Larvae I

1. Family Cicindelidae; genus *Cicindela;* lateral view.
2. Family Carabidae; genus *Calosoma;* dorsal view.
3. Family Gyrinidae; genus *Dineutus;* dorsal view.
4. Family Dytiscidae; genus *Dytiscus;* dorsal view.
5. Family Haliplidae; *Haliplus immaculicollis;* dorsal view.
6. Family Hydrophilidae; genus *Laccobius;* dorsal view.
7. Family Silphidae; genus *Silpha;* dorsal view.
8. Family Staphylinidae; genus *Paederus;* dorsal view.
9. Family Histeridae; genus *Hololepta;* dorsal view.
10. Family Lampyridae; *Photuris pennsylvanicus;* dorsal view. In the genus *Photinus* the body is long and much more slender.
11. Family Lycidae; genus *Eros;* dorsal view.
12. Family Cantharidae; genus *Chauliognathus;* dorsal view.
13. Family Melyridae; *Malachius aeneus;* dorsal view.
14. Family Cleridae; genus *Callimerus;* dorsal view.
15, 16. Family Meloidae; genus *Epicauta.* 15. First-instar larva, often called a "triungulin"; dorsal view. 16. Third-instar larva, of the scarabaeoid type; lateral view.
17. Family Pyrochroidae; *Dendroides cyanipennis;* dorsal view.
18. Family Elateridae; genus *Melanotus;* dorsal view.
19. Family Buprestidae; genus *Chrysobothris;* dorsal view; the larva is legless.
20. Family Buprestidae; genus *Agrilus;* dorsal view; the larva is legless.

MM 0 10 20 30 40 50 60 70

PLATE III 21

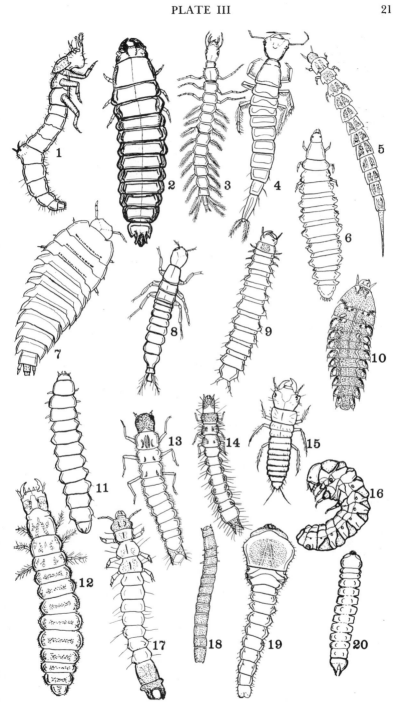

PLATE IV

Beetle Larvae II

1. Family Dermestidae; genus *Attagenus;* dorsal view.
2. Family Ostomatidae; *Tenebroides mauritanicus;* dorsal view.
3. Family Cucujidae; *Cucujus clavipes;* dorsal view.
4. Family Nitidulidae; *Carpophilus lugubris;* dorsal view.
5. Family Erotylidae; genus *Penthe;* dorsal view.
6. Family Coccinellidae; genus *Coccinella;* dorsal view.
7. Family Tenebrionidae; *Meracantha contracta;* dorsal view.
8. Family Melandryidae; genus *Synchroa;* dorsal view.
9. Family Anobiidae; *Lasioderma serricorne;* lateral view.
10. Family Bostrichidae; *Stephanopachys rugosus;* lateral view.
11. Family Scarabaeidae; *Osmoderma eremicola;* lateral view.
12. Family Lucanidae; *Ceruchus piceus;* lateral view.
13. Family Cerambycidae; genus *Prionus;* dorsal view.
14. Family Chrysomelidae; *Plagiodera versicolora;* dorsal view.
15. Family Chrysomelidae; *Cassida rubiginosa;* dorsal view.
16. Family Curculionidae; *Listroderes obliquus;* lateral view.
17. Family Scolytidae; *Hylastinus obscurus;* lateral view.

MM ‖ 0   10   20   30   40   50   60   70

PLATE IV   23

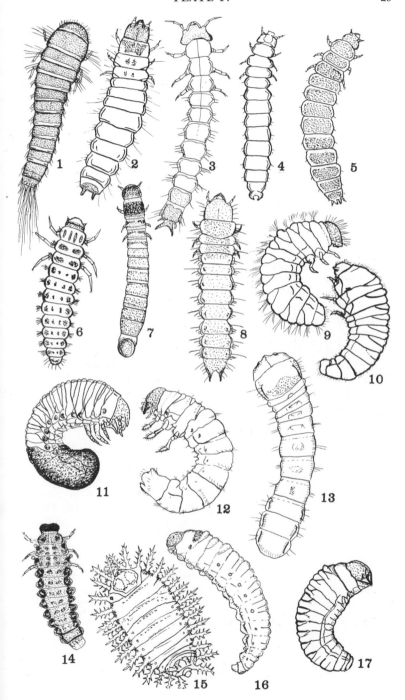

ECOLOGY OF NORTH AMERICAN BEETLES

The relationships that exist between living things and their environment form the body of material included within the science of *ecology*. Environment does not mean just the surroundings and their physical state, such as temperature, relative humidity, and the like, or their chemical composition, but the biological aspects as well. The interplay of the physical, chemical, and biological forces produces a large number and variety of *niches* in nature to which living things may become adapted. Beetles have been able to adapt themselves to a greater number of diverse niches probably than any other single group of living things; in fact, it is difficult to name a niche, with the exception of the strictly marine sorts, that has not been occupied by some species of beetle. To this great measure of adaptability may be attributed the wide diversity of form and the large number of species—one out of every five known species of living thing is a beetle—that characterize this interesting order of insects.

Hence it is apparent that a full study of the environmental adaptations of beetles would involve a study of almost the entire science of ecology and would in itself fill a good-sized book. Obviously only an outline of the main facets of the subject can be presented here; it should be borne in mind that each major niche discussed below may be divided into many finer units. And, in turn, each of these may be subdivided into many even finer ones.

Relations with Water

Aquatic habitats have been classified by ecologists in many ways. Principally two major sorts are recognized, marine and fresh water. Since there are no strictly marine beetles, only the latter needs consideration here. Fresh-water habitats are of two chief types, flowing water or *lotic,* and standing water or *lentic.* In turn each of these is subdivided. The first includes rapidly flowing streams, such as springs and brooks, and slowly flowing streams, such as creeks and rivers. The lentic type is divided into lakes, ponds, swamps, and pools. Many finer divisions of each subdivision are recognized, resulting in a very intricate system of classification. While this system is of immense value in studying the ecology of certain groups of organisms, aquatic beetles as a rule are broadly adaptive, so that it is often possible to find the same species in most of the situations outlined above. Hence the scheme has very little value here, and a far simpler synopsis may be employed.

Surface-dwelling forms. The whirligigs (Gyrinidae) are the only beetles especially adapted for existence on the surface of water. In the first place, they are equipped for rapid locomotion, the middle and hind pairs of legs being broad and paddle-like as well as fringed. Since most members of the family are scavengers, their swimming ability appears to serve primarily as an escape mechanism, as perhaps their erratic movements and ability in diving are also. As a life upon the surface exposes them to attack from above by such predators as birds and snakes as well as from below by fish, their divided eye is an adaptation for service in two directions. During times when fresh waters are frozen over or when air temperatures are too low, the adult gyrinids hibernate in mud or dead vegetable matter at the bottom or edges of ponds and streams.

The strict surface-dwellers are confined largely to lakes and ponds and the slower-moving portions of lotic waters, although a few occur in riffles or even in rapids.

Subsurface water-dwelling forms. This group may well be divided into two major subgroups, the strongly swimming forms and the weakly swimming forms.

Two families of beetles have become adapted for active swimming in water, the predaceous diving beetles (Dytiscidae) and the scavenger water beetles (Hydrophilidae). One outstanding adaptation is found in the modification of the legs for swimming purposes. Among the dytiscids the hind pair of legs has become greatly elongated and flattened, largely due to the elongation and broadening of the tarsi, for the tibiae are often quite reduced in length. In addition, the tarsi, and occasionally the tibiae too, are provided with long fringing hairs, which greatly increase the efficiency of the organs. In use, the legs are employed in an oarlike fashion. The hydrophilids, on the other hand, have both the middle and hind pairs of legs modified for swimming. Here most of the modification is found in the tarsi, which are elongated and slightly flattened, as well as fringed with long hairs; the tibiae and femora do not differ materially from those of terrestrial forms. In use, the legs on opposite sides are used alternately, as in crawling.

In addition to locomotor organs, aquatic forms need provisions for breathing without surfacing too frequently. To this end both families have large cavities or chambers beneath their elytra, enabling them to carry sufficient air for several minutes of complete submersion. In the hydrophilids the beetle surfaces with the body inclined to one side in such a way as to bring the cleft between the head and prothorax into contact with the surface film. The beetle then moves the tip of one antenna into the cleft and raises it, breaking the surface film and permitting air to enter the funnel-like structure formed temporarily by the antenna and the neck cleft. In the dytiscids the posterior end of the body is protruded through the surface film and a fresh supply of air taken under the elytra. In addition to this adaptation, the hydrophilids have their undersurface covered by water-repellent (*hydrofuge*) hairs, which retain a film of air used as an additional source of oxygen. This film, referred to as a "plastron," gives the ventral surface of the submerged insect a silvery appearance.

When the surface of the water freezes over, aquatic forms are likely to be trapped beneath the ice; hence these active-swimming forms have become adapted to low temperatures as well as to their aqueous medium. While some species hibernate beneath dead vegetation or in mud, typically the adults may be seen swimming about beneath the ice. It is of interest to note that the adults of certain dytiscids are known to live and reproduce for two or three summers, and some have been known to survive for five years.

The haliplids and some of the hydrophilids are passively swimming and crawling forms, spending much of their time on the mud and debris of pond bottoms, swimming actively only occasionally. As one might anticipate, their legs are only slightly modified for propulsion through water, being unflattened in form and provided merely with a fringe of long, stiff hairs. In the haliplids all three pairs of legs are thus developed, whereas among the hydrophilids only the middle and hind pairs are. Respiratory and overwintering habits are as discussed in the strongly swimming families.

Members of the families belonging to the subsurface-dwellers are most frequent in quiet pools, ponds, bays, and sluggish streams, in which there are masses of algae and other aquatic vegetation.

Rapid-water-dwelling forms. In swiftly flowing water, a relatively large-bodied and cumbersome form like a beetle would have little chance of maintaining its position in the stream were it to attempt to swim; hence, species adapted to a life under such conditions are equipped for crawling over rocks, logs, and stones. Characteristic of shallow rapids are the members of the families Psephenidae and Dryopidae as well as a number of the Elmidae. These beetles have the tarsi greatly elongated, nearly or quite equaling the tibiae in length, and provided with long, strong claws, with which they are able to cling to the smooth surfaces of stones. No swimming modifications are apparent, but there is a respiratory chamber beneath the elytra as in the haliplids, dytiscids, and hydrophilids. When the beetles are submerged, a film of air also is carried by water-repellent hairs, giving the insects, or at least their ventral surface, a silvery appearance. The food of these beetles seems to consist largely of minute species of algae.

Marl-feeders. Marl, a rather soft deposit of lime largely precipitated through the action of certain algae in lakes, includes within its mass much dead vegetable matter. This organic substance is fed upon by a few species of Elmidae, both as larvae and adults. The only adaptations apparent are those found among the rapid-water species of the same family —hydrofuge hairs, long tarsi, and strong tarsal claws.

Semiaquatic forms. Between dry land and bodies of water, such as ponds, lakes, and rivers, there exists a habitat intermediate between the truly aquatic and terrestrial sorts to which a number of organisms have become adapted. Among the beetles which inhabit the mud can be mentioned the Omophronidae, Limnichidae, and a number of hydrophilids as well as the Heteroceridae. In the first three groups the body is flattened beneath and strongly convex above, so that it may well be that this type of structure is an adaptation to this environment; in the Heteroceridae, however, the situation is completely reversed. Other specializations are not usually in evidence. No swimming or burrowing structures (except for burrowing legs in the heterocerids) are present, and no respiratory specializations for aquatic life have been made; hence, these insects leave their muddy dwelling places during times of high water or when water is washed over the banks.

RELATIONS WITH THE SOIL

Surface-dwelling forms. Several families of beetles have become specialized for a life upon the surface of the ground, chief among these being the Carabidae, Cicindelidae, and many of the Tenebrionidae. For this type of habitat, the legs of these insects are particularly specialized, being long and slender, as a rule, for rapid locomotion, and well provided with spurs, spines, or stiff hairs to provide traction. Some of the carabids and tenebrionids, along with occasional members of a number of other families, conceal themselves during the day beneath rocks or in crevices, emerging at night to feed. Frequently, as might be expected, the bodies of such forms are depressed, permitting entrance into low openings.

The surface of the soil is, of course, far from being uniform in its composition. There are hard clays and soft loams, yielding sands and clinging muds, open grassy sorts and forest-covered soils. To each of these niches some species have become specialized. For example, by examining the descriptions of the tiger beetles of the genus *Cicindela,* one can find that each has a particular habitat where it is most frequently found. *C. dorsalis* is found exclusively along the sandy shores of the oceans, while *C. sexguttata* is found inland along grassy paths. On the other hand, *C. unipunctata* occurs chiefly along woodland trails, while *C. tranquebarica* is commonest on sandy or mud flats twenty or more feet back from running water. Similarly, carabids of the genus *Elaphrus* and of a number of the other genera are characteristic of mud flats and the muddy banks of rivers and lakes. In like fashion, a long list of species which inhabit relatively small niches could be made. As to the adaptations which especially fit them to their environs, very little is known. And the amateur can contribute much to this area of coleopterology by making careful observations and studies of individual species.

One other specialization for this sort of habitat must be pointed out. Some carabids, as well as a few surface-dwelling meloids and tenebrionids, have become so highly adapted to an ambulatory mode of locomotion that the hind pair of wings has been lost. Especially frequently is this wingless condition found among mountain-dwelling and insular species, but it is by no means confined to such forms; for some plains inhabitants and desert-dwellers also are occasionally incapable of flight.

Subterranean forms. Within the soil are to be found a large number of forms which enter the habitat for shelter or for egg-laying purposes, such as the scarabaeids in general, and a few species of carabids that dwell there more or less permanently. Among the temporary occupants of this subterranean province can be named the very numerous species of June beetles (genus *Phyllophaga*), which conceal themselves beneath the soil by day, emerging at night to feed upon the leaves of trees and shrubs. Other scarabs, such as those of the genera *Copris, Geotrupes, Phanaeus,* and *Canthon,* dig burrows in the soil (some, as *Peltotrupes profundus,* as deep as nine feet) and place a mass of dung at the bottom, in which the eggs are laid. Among the permanent inhabitants of this province are particularly certain carabids, species of the genus *Scarites* and closely related genera, whose habits and food requirements are virtually unknown.

Especially essential for a life in the soil, even when the existence there is brief, is a good set of digging organs. Without exception among subterranean beetles, the front legs are specialized for this function. In all cases the tibiae are broad, flat, and provided with stout teeth or spines (the fossorial type), and the femora are robust and well provisioned with strong muscles. In some of the scarabs and lucanids, the middle and hind legs may be modified along similar lines and may play some role in digging.

Cave-dwelling forms. An especially intriguing aspect of the subterranean province is provided by the occasional caves found in many areas and the forms of animal life that occupy them. In the small caves and near the entrance of larger ones are encountered many beetles whose presence there is purely accidental and temporary. For example, surface-dwellers may frequently enter a cave, remain for a relatively brief time, and leave, the visit being entirely fortuitous. Carabids, tenebrionids, staphylinids, histerids and other dung-inhabitants, ladybird beetles, and many others may take such temporary refuge in a cave, but hollow logs, loose bark, or crevices in rocks would be equally suitable for their needs. On the other hand, species may be found, principally in larger caverns, which dwell chiefly or even solely in such a habitat. Among these are a few scavenger forms, such as staphylinids of the genera *Quedius* and *Rheochara,* which feed on bat dung or upon the dead bodies of cave-inhabiting vertebrates. Pselaphids of the genus *Batrisodes* may also belong to this category. Carnivorous species of carabids also are known to be strictly troglodytic and appear to feed especially on the invertebrates that occur in caves. Some such forms, for instance *Trechus,* have the eye reduced in size as compared to surface-dwellers.

RELATIONS WITH PLANTS

It is probably true that beetles have become specialized along more lines in relation with plants than with any other sort of environment. They are found associated with live plants and with dead ones, flowering plants and simpler ones like fungi and mosses, on leaves, on flowers, and on every other part of trees, shrubs, or herbs. As a result, many varied families and species of these insects are to be found adapted to vegetation and vegetable products.

Leaf-dwelling forms. Among leaf-dwellers are permanent residents such as the chrysomelids, temporary residents such as the leaf-eating scarabs, and incidental forms which visit foliage for sun-bathing, such as the buprestids, cerambycids, lampyrids, lycids, cantharids, and lagriids, or to feed on true leaf-inhabitants, as the coccinellids and clerids frequently do. As might be expected, only the chrysomelids, the permanent residents, are primarily adapted for life in this habitat. Living where they do, they are constantly exposed to the attacks of insectivorous birds; hence, many of the adaptations they display seem to be defensive or evasive in nature. For example, some, like the cassidines, are rounded in outline and greatly flattened, probably so as to be as inconspicuous as possible. Others appear to mimic foreign objects and escape notice by this means. *Exema,* for instance, resting on a leaf, looks quite like the droppings of caterpillars. However, many of the leaf beetles are conspicuously colored and of robust form and are hence not easily overlooked by the keen eyes of a bird. To such forms a quick exit provides the only hope of survival. To accomplish a rapid departure from the scene of attack, the halticine chrysomelids, or flea beetles, are provided with powerful metafemora, by means of which they can spring some distance. Others, not so well equipped, merely fold their legs beneath them and fall to the ground, accomplishing their escape in a most effective, but simple, fashion.

Even after they have fallen, leaves continue to serve as shelter and food for many beetles. In the accumulation of dried leaves on a forest floor are to be found representatives of a number of families, including cryptophagids, histerids, mycetophagids, leiodids, etc., which are regular inhabitants of this sort of environment. Others, including coccinellids, nitidulids, tenebrionids, and melandryids, occur here only occasionally or at definite seasons, using the leaf debris as a concealing place in which to hibernate or estivate.

Stem-dwelling forms. On the live stems of herbs are to be found regularly only a few specialized families, particularly languriids and rhynchophorids of the genus *Calendra.* As both of these are elongate in body form, that shape may perhaps be a specialization for this type of habitat. Other families are also found on plant stems in numbers, but their presence is often due to another factor. Coccinellids are concerned with the presence of plant lice and similar soft-bodied stem-dwellers; melyrids and clerids are likewise predators on small plant-eating forms, whether on or off stems. In addition a few families occur on live green stems in order to oviposit. Among these are included those whose larvae are borers, examples being certain species of *Agrilus* of the buprestids and *Hippopsis, Mecas, Tetraopes,* and several other cerambycids.

In living woody stems—the trunks of trees and shrubs—are a number of inhabitants, most of which are adapted to particular subdivisions of this habitat. The outer coat of the stem, the bark, provides food for many adult wood-boring forms, especially the cerambycids. When large numbers of adults, such as *Monochamus,* are present, as occasionally happens in northern forests, almost complete girdling of twigs or even large branches may occur. Others, such as a number of scolytids, spend their whole life cycle within the thick bark of trees. A peculiar adaptation of these scolytids can be mentioned, one that concerns the loss of flight. Young adults are capable of flying long distances and retain this capacity until about the time their young have emerged from the eggs. After that the wing muscles begin to degenerate, so that older beetles are unable to fly, although they remain actively feeding and ovipositing within their burrows in the bark.

Within the wooden interior of the live trunk, many other scolytids are to be found, as well as representatives of the families Bostrichidae and Lyctidae. It will be noted that most of these live-wood-inhabiting types are quite cylindrical in form, with the body of nearly uniform width throughout and of rigid construction. Moreover, in many cases the elytra are strongly declivous at the apex and armed with coarse teeth or tubercles. These features appear certainly to be adaptations for a life within tunnels in tree trunks. In addition to these families which live in this type of environment as adults, there are several others which inhabit it during the larval stage, the adults occurring here only for oviposition or at time of emergence from the pupa. Among these the most important are the buprestids, certain cerambycids, and a few curculionids.

As in the case of leaves, woody stems after death provide a habitat for many kinds of beetles; in fact, a much greater diversity of forms is to be found in fallen logs than in living ones. As might be expected, numbers of scolytids, cerambycids, buprestids, and others which also dwell in live stems occur here, but numerous additional families are particularly adapted for living in dead wood. Beneath the bark especially are various species abundant. When the log has first fallen, of course, the bark is quite tight-fitting, but, with the passing of time, fermentation processes and the action of frost and sunlight gradually cause the bark to loosen. In the narrow confines of the crevice thus provided occur numbers of species with flattened bodies particularly suited for such close quarters. Included among these are most of the cucujids, histerids of certain genera such as *Hololepta* and *Platysoma,* and nitidulids, chiefly of the genus *Epuraea.* As fermentation processes continue and as the wood decays, thicker-bodied sorts, melandryids, alleculids, lathridiids, byrrhids, pyrochroids, rhipicerids, melasids, and elaters occur in numbers and great variety. Many of these same families are also well represented in the decayed wood of the log itself, in company with a few that are strictly confined to this latter situation. Chief among these few are the passalid beetles, which have developed a colonial type of organization; communication between members of a colony is accomplished by means of a stridulating mechanism on the thorax. Several studies of the ecology and succession of forms within logs have been published (e.g., Blackman and Stage [1924] and Moennich [1939]), but many more thoroughgoing investigations of the factors involved need to be made.

Root-dwelling forms. Apparently very few beetles have been able to evolve all the adaptations essential to becoming true root inhabitants, for in this organ of the plant only an occasional form is to be found. Many byrrhids, especially in sandy areas, feed upon the roots of grasses and sedges, but they are really inhabitants of the soil. Only the prionids, several other cerambycids of the genus *Mecas,* and a few curculionids and scolytids seem to have truly conquered this sort of habitat, for they live within the root proper.

Flower-dwelling forms. Next to decaying logs, flowers are probably the richest part of the plant in the number of beetle species. Here are to be found bumblebee-like scarabs of the genera *Trichiotinus, Cotinis,* and *Euphoria,* slender cerambycids, largely of the subfamily Lepturinae, flat-bodied soldier beetles (Cantharidae), and thick-bodied meloids and oedemerids. With these large forms occur numerous small and inconspicuous sorts, which, along with the foregoing, feed largely on pollen or on the petals. Phalacrids and some species of dermestids have quite broad, convex bodies, whereas the mordellids are slender and wedge-shaped. Many of the latter have the tip of the abdomen prolonged into a long style, which perhaps assists in the insect's habit of tumbling from a flower when disturbed. Another peculiar adaptation is found among the anthicids, where the body is often quite antlike in form; some of the less antlike members of this family have a shelflike projection of the pronotum extending over the head, the function of which is not apparent. In addition to the above true flower inhabitants are others which prey upon the true inhabitants, such as clerids, and transients representing most of the two hundred North American families of Coleoptera—even species which normally inhabit dung or carrion may be attracted to such malodorous flowers as the skunk-cabbage bloom.

Miscellaneous plant relations. Among the more prominent minor relations with plants are those between insects and seeds and similar vegetable products. The mylabrids, or seed weevils, are especially noted for their attacks on beans, peas, and lentils. Curculionids of the genus *Apion* live chiefly on whole seeds, while many other families occur in ground seeds, especially in flour and spices. The "drugstore beetles" of the family Anobiidae seem capable of living even on cayenne pepper, in tobacco, and in other highly seasoned materials, as well as in flour. Most other seed-eating families are confined to grain and grain products. The genera *Silvanus* and *Cathartus* of the Cucujidae are only too frequently found in flour bins and baked goods, as are also the Ostomatidae.

Not just the seed plants and their products but the lower plants as well are utilized by various beetles as a habitat. Especially is this the case with the fleshy and woody kinds of mushrooms. Erotylids, many staphylinids and histerids, corylophids, mycetophagids, cryptophagids, and derodontids occur in large numbers within the cap and, occasionally, in the stem of the fleshy species. In addition to these, the Ciidae and a few tenebrionids are found in dried and in woody sorts, such as those which grow upon injured or dying trees or upon stumps.

Relations with Other Animals

Beetles bear many relationships with other animals, which, while diverse in their details, can be grouped in two major divisions, namely, those which affect live animals and those concerned with their by-products, including their dead bodies.

Predatory relations with other live animals. Particularly obvious are the predatory relations beetles bear with other insects and similarly small creatures. Members of many families feed upon prey both as adults and as larvae, while others are predatory only in one stage, usually the larval. A number of the more voracious kinds are not at all specialized in their diets but attack anything of suitable size that comes their way. Such is the case with the tiger beetles on land and the dytiscids in the water, the latter being even more diversified than the former, feeding on snails, tadpoles, worms, small fish, and frogs, as well as insects. In contrast to the vegetable diet of some species, other cantharids are largely predaceous in habit; adults of *Podabrus* and *Cantharis* feed extensively on aphids and other soft-bodied insects, while their larvae, as well as those of *Chauliognathus,* destroy egg masses of locusts as well as adult and larval beetles and moths. Similarly, melyrid and coccinellid adults will feed upon any soft-bodied insect, chiefly aphids, scale insects, and white flies, that they encounter upon the stems and leaves of plants. Correspondingly in the soil, a few elaterid larvae and many forms of carabid adults or larvae prey on worms, grubs, and other insects.

On the other hand, a large number of predatory beetles have diets that are highly specialized. Among the carabids, *Scaphinotus* and its relatives have the mouthparts long and narrow for probing into the shells of snails, upon which they feed exclusively. The species of the genus *Calosoma* subsist almost entirely on caterpillars and readily climb trees in search of their prey, while *Lebia scapularis* is known to attack only the larvae of the elm-leaf beetle (*Galerucella luteola*). Surprisingly enough, most of the silphids, staphylinids, and histerids, which come in large numbers to carrion and dung, are not scavengers at all but thrive on the fly maggots and other scavenging insects. Other members of the families Staphylinidae and Histeridae are very limited in their food habits; members of the rove-beetle genus *Somatium* are known to consume only red-spider mites, while members of the histerid genus *Plegaderus* feed largely on the eggs of bark beetles of the genus *Dendroctonus*. Although most lampyrids as adults and larvae subsist to a large extent on a variety of worms and snails, one species is known to be cannibalistic. The authors have found, if a specimen or two of *Photuris pennsylvanicus* are placed in a large jar along with other species of fireflies and allowed to stand overnight, that by the next morning only this species remains. It can also be observed that the very act of adding one example of this species to a jar of live *Photinus* will stir the latter to a state of high excitement, indicating that the cannibal can be recognized by the others by means of a distinctive odor, perhaps, or, more likely, by the characteristics of its flash. In this fashion, if space permitted, it would be possible to compile a long list of restricted dietary habits, but only a few more distinctive ones will be enumerated. For one, eggs of locusts, or short-horned grasshoppers, form the chief food of the larvae of most meloids and of *Trox suberosus,* while eggs of the dobson fly are fed upon by the anthicid, *Anthicus heroicus.* And as a final example, whereas most clerids prey upon scolytids and other wood-inhabiting beetles, the members of the genus *Cymatodera* show preference for the wasps and their larvae which form galls on leaves and twigs of oak trees.

Parasitic relations with other animals. One of the surprises one receives through studying beetles is the discovery that a number of these usually awkward insects are parasites. True enough, with the exception of *Platypsyllus,* which is an ectoparasite on beavers, it is never the adult that is parasitic; but it is difficult, somehow or other, to visualize a beetle larva living within the body of another creature. Yet such is the case. Indeed, there are no less than five families which contain parasitic species, one family, the Rhipiphoridae, having exclusively such a habit. Wasps of the family Vespidae, such as the hornet, paper wasps, and the like, and other Hymenoptera are used as the host, i.e., are parasitized, by these beetles. Typically the eggs are deposited upon a flower. After hatching, the larvae attach themselves to a wasp when it visits the blossom in search of nectar and are carried to the wasp nest. Here it leaves the mature wasp and enters the body of one of the grubs, usually just beneath the skin of the fourth or fifth segment. As the larva grows, it leaves the body of the grub to secure a position encircling the latter's neck externally, growing to maturity as it consumes its host. Some of the host-parasite relations within this family are highly complex but are only partially known; all species appear highly specific as to the host selected, however.

Certain of the meloids, particularly of the genera *Meloë, Nemognatha, Zonitis,* and related forms, are similarly adapted to a parasitic mode of life involving the Hymenoptera. In this case, however, it is chiefly bees that are attacked, and, in most instances, true parasitism is not involved. For instead of the larva consuming the host, it merely usurps its place in the nest of the bee by eating the egg and then feeding upon the pollen and honey stored in the cell of its rightful owner. The parasitic habit is not so widespread in the three remaining families which have adopted this mode of life. Among the carabids, a number of genera, including *Lebia, Brachinus,* and *Pterostichus,* are parasitic to a greater or lesser extent. *Lebia scapularis,* which feeds solely on elm-beetle pupae, and the various species of *Brachinus,* which feed on the pupae of water beetles, have larvae which are quite normal in appearance and in leg development when newly hatched, the strong legs enabling the young to seek and find a suitable host. Following further development, after the first molt, the older larvae have the legs quite degenerate, small and weak in relation to the size of the body. Feeding is external in all cases. Similar leg reduction in second-instar larvae is found also in staphylinids of the genera *Aleochara* and *Coprochara,* whose larvae parasitize fly pupae, as well as in colydiids of the genus *Bothrideres,* which attack the larvae and pupae of cerambycids and buprestids.

Other relations with live animals. A few beetle families contain species which live in the nests of other insects or of mammals. For example, a large number of Staphylinidae are found in ant nests. Such myrmecophilous forms may vary greatly in their habits, some of them being true guests, others being predators on the young or even on the adults. In some forms, such as *Lomechusa* (Staphylinidae), glands are present which secrete a substance of which the ants are very fond; the larvae of these forms, in spite of the fact that they feed upon the immature stages of the ants, are carefully tended during their development by the hosts. A good many species of this same family of beetles are found in termite nests, i.e., are termitophilous; these seem to be all true guests in habits, not simply predators. The pselaphids as a whole are myrmecophilous and seem to be true guests, while much the same can be said of a number of histerids and of a few small species of silphids.

In mammal nests, such as those of gophers and other burrowing rodents, as well as those of arboreal forms like squirrels, are found members of a small family of beetles known as the Leptinidae. Occasionally these occur in large numbers, as many as one hundred being taken from a single nest, but their role with their host is unknown. It has been suggested that they act as predators upon the fleas and mites that feed on the mammals, but this is still a conjecture. Besides these beetles, a few species of *Trox* live in nests of mammals and birds, apparently feeding on the droppings and on the remains of foods brought into the nests by the occupants.

Relations with animal products and with dead animals. Not all the beetles that are found on dung or on carrion are, as pointed out earlier, feeders upon their habitat but prey upon other forms which live there. Nevertheless, these substances do attract a fair number of beetles which are adapted strictly to them. Most of the silphids feed upon carrion, and some dig burrows close by the carcasses in which they bury a portion of the decaying flesh and oviposit on it. A few of the Staphylinidae, an otherwise predatory family, are strictly carrion-feeders, and perhaps the same can be said of a few histerids. Not all carrion is equally attractive to the various species; some forms show preference for fish, others for other cold-blooded vertebrates, while still others occur only on mammalian or bird remains. Similarly, some species are confined to fresh carrion, while others, such as the dermestids and trogids, are peculiar to the last vestiges of bone and dried skin remaining after the flesh has disintegrated.

Many of the foregoing statements apply equally to the dung inhabitants, but the latter are, as a whole, not so discriminating as to the source or age of their habitation. Like the silphids, many scarabs bury food in burrows for the developing young. But most of the dietary habits of various families of dung beetles have not received thorough study and hence are only sketchily known.

Animal products, like plant products, often receive the unwelcome attentions of sundry beetle species. Animal skins, such as fur rugs and coats, and woolens, including carpets and upholstery as well as wearing apparel, frequently attract dermestids. Even smoked meats, ham, bacon, and the like, are attacked by some members of this same family, particularly the genus *Dermestes,* as are also cheese and lard. Nor are feathers overlooked by them. Silk also is fed upon by a variety of dermestids as well as by the ptinids. Similarly, other insect products, such as beeswax, and the dried bodies of insects, including those in museum collections, are much favored by the larvae and adults of these same two families.

KEY TO FAMILIES

It is often advantageous to use a key backwards, i.e., starting with the family name, then seeing what its key characters are. To aid in the process, the numbers in parentheses with each couplet indicate whence the pair originates. For example, both couplets two and five have, following the numerals, the figure one in parentheses, as both of them are keyed from there.

1. At least hind legs modified for swimming, flattened or at
   least fringed (Figs. 30, 31) 2
   None of the legs modified for swimming 5
2. (1) Eyes divided by lateral margins of the head, making the
   insects appear to have two pairs of eyes (Fig. 29) ......
   ....GYRINIDAE (p. 155)
   Eyes not divided 3
3. (2) Legs much modified for swimming, lengthened and flattened, with large spurs and small claws (Fig. 30); metacoxae normal (Plate II, inside front or back cover) 4
   Legs with only fringes of hair (Fig. 31); metacoxae forming
   large plates (Fig. 32) ....HALIPLIDAE (p. 129)

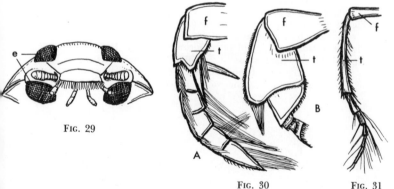

FIG. 29

FIG. 30   FIG. 31

Fig. 29. Head of a gyrinid viewed from the front, with eyes (e) divided
to form two pairs.

Fig. 30. Hind legs modified for swimming. A, Hind leg of a dytiscid
(Cybister) and B, that of a gyrinid (Dineutus). f, portion of
femur; t, tibia.

Fig. 31. Hind leg of Haliplus, only slightly modified for swimming by
the presence of a fringe on the tibia (t) and tarsus, the femur
(f) being weak.

Fig. 32. Metacoxae and abdominal sternites of a haliplid. The meta-coxae (*m*) are greatly expanded, covering at least the first two abdominal sternites.

Fig. 33. Underside of head of a hydrophilid, the labial palpi (*l*) elongate, the antennae (*a*) short and capitate.

Figs. 34–35. Metacoxae and surrounding parts of a carabid, *Scarites* (34) and of a cerambycid (35). The metacoxae (*c*) divide the first abdominal sternite (*1*) so that the second sternite (*2*) projects between them in the former, whereas in the latter the second is far removed from them.

Fig. 36. Head of *Omophron*, the antennal insertion (*i*) below the front (*f*) on the gena, the clypeus (*c*) not prolonged laterally.

Fig. 37. Head of the cicindelid *Tetracha*, the clypeus (*c*) extending laterad of the insertion of the antenna (*i*), which is on the front (*f*).

Fig. 38. Prosternum of *Omophron*, its process (*P*) greatly enlarged and largely covering the mesosternum (*Ms*), attaining the metasternum (*Mt*). *c*, procoxae.

Fig. 39. Head of a curculionid in profile, the head prolonged into a long beak (*b*). *s*, antennal scrobe.

Fig. 40. Head of a scolytid in profile, with a short beak (*b*).

Figs. 41–42. Antennal clubs of curculionids, that of *Attelabus analis* (41) with distinctly separated segments, those of *Cossonus platalea* (42) compactly united.

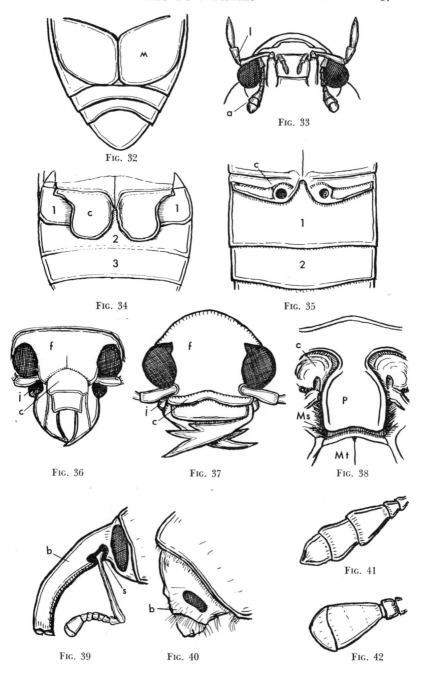

FIG. 32

FIG. 33

FIG. 34

FIG. 35

FIG. 36

FIG. 37

FIG. 38

FIG. 39

FIG. 40

FIG. 41

FIG. 42

4. (3) Labial palpi very elongate, easily mistaken for antennae; antennae capitate, usually concealed in fossae on undersurface of prothorax (Fig. 33) ........HYDROPHILIDAE (p. 158)

Labial palpi normal; antennae filiform, not concealed ....DYTISCIDAE (p. 132)

5. (1) First abdominal sternite divided into two or three parts by metacoxae (Fig. 34) 6

First abdominal sternite not divided (Fig. 35) 8

6. (5) Antennae inserted between eyes and base of mandibles; clypeus not produced laterally beyond bases of antennae (Fig. 36) 7

Antennae inserted on the front above bases of mandibles; clypeus produced laterally beyond bases of antennae (Fig. 37) ................................CICINDELIDAE (p. 49)

7. (6) Scutellum not exposed; prosternum enlarged, concealing mesosternum (Fig. 38) ..........OMOPHRONIDAE (p. 127)

Scutellum exposed; prosternum not covering mesosternum ....CARABIDAE (p. 59)

8. (5) Head below eyes produced into a distinct beak, at the apex of which are the mandibles (Figs. 39, 40); gular sutures confluent on median line or indistinct; palpi usually short, conical, and rigid 9

Head not prolonged into a beak; two gular sutures present (Plate II) 16

9. (8) Beak small, much shorter than wide (Fig. 40); tibiae with a series of teeth externally, or with a curved apical spine; antennae but little longer than head, geniculate, with compact club; palpi rigid; body short, subcylindrical ....SCOLYTIDAE (p. 804)

Beak usually longer than broad, or body form not cylindrical; tibiae never with series of teeth 10

10. (9) Antennae straight, without a distinct club, though outer segments often more or less thickened; body form very slender and elongate ....BRENTIDAE (p. 738)

Antennae straight or elbowed, always with a distinct club .11

11. (10) Palpi flexible; antennal club rarely compact; beak always short and broad; labrum present ..ANTHRIBIDAE (p. 740)

Palpi rigid and labrum not present; antennal club usually compact; beak variable in length, often long and curved downward 12

12. (11) Antennae straight; beak lacking antennal scrobes 14

Antennae more or less completely geniculate (Fig. 39); beak with antennal scrobe (Fig. 39) 13

13. (12) Pygidium exposed .........RHYNCHOPHORIDAE (p. 796)

Pygidium covered ...................CURCULIONIDAE (p. 744)

14. (12) Club composed of completely separated segments (Fig. 41) ..............................CURCULIONIDAE (p. 744)

Club composed of compactly united segments (Fig. 42) 15

15. (14) Length 12 or more millimeters ....BELIDAE (p. 743)
    Length not over 4.5 mm. .............CURCULIONIDAE (p. 744)
16. (8) Several of apical segments of antennae lamellate; meso-
    and metatarsi five-segmented 17
    Antennal segments not lamellate, or tarsal segmentation
    different 20
17. (16) Plates composing antennal club flattened and capable
    of being closely folded together 18
    Plates of club not so, usually not flattened 19
18. (17) Six visible abdominal sternites, or if only five are
    present, mesocoxae are transverse, closed externally (Fig.
    43) ...............................SCARABAEIDAE (p. 505)
    Five visible abdominal sternites; mesocoxae rounded, open
    externally (Fig. 44) ....TROGIDAE (p. 559)
19. (17) Antennae straight; mentum deeply emarginate, the lig-
    ula filling the emargination (Fig. 45) ......PASSALIDAE (p. 573)
    Antennae almost always geniculate; mentum entire (Fig. 46).
    ....LUCANIDAE (p. 566)
20. (16) Elytra truncate, strongly abbreviated, wings capable of
    folding beneath them; more than two dorsal abdominal
    segments and usually the greater part of the dorsal surface
    of abdomen exposed; ventral abdominal segments entirely
    sclerotized, usually all free; prothorax never covering head,
    which is porrect, free, and normal; antennae clavate or fili-
    form 21
    Elytra covering entire abdomen or exposing one or at most
    two dorsal segments; if rarely more strongly abbreviated,
    then they are not truncate, or other characters different
    from above 22
21. (20) Abdomen not flexible, with only five or six visible ventral
    segments ....PSELAPHIDAE (p. 207)
    Abdomen flexible, with seven or eight visible ventral segments
    ...................................STAPHYLINIDAE (p. 182)
22. (20) Tarsal segments 5–5–5 (rarely 4–5–5 or 5–4–4), none of
    the segments rudimentary or minute 23
    Tarsal segments 5–5–4, 4–4–4, or still more reduced, or if
    5–5–5, then one or more segments are minute and not
    easily discernible (Figs. 66–68) 51
23. (22) Tarsal claws very large (Fig. 47); aquatic 24
    Tarsal claws of usual size (Fig. 48) 26
24. (23) Six or seven visible abdominal sternites ....
    ....PSEPHENIDAE (p. 365)
    Five visible abdominal sternites 25
25. (24) Procoxae transverse, with a distinct trochantin; body
    densely clothed with silky pubescence ....DRYOPIDAE (p. 366)
    Procoxae rounded, without trochantin; body only sparsely
    pubescent ....ELMIDAE (p. 367)

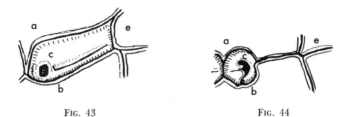

FIG. 43   FIG. 44

Figs. 43–44. Mesocoxae of a scarab, *Diplotaxis* (43), and of *Trox* (44).
    a, mesosternum; *b*, metasternum; *c*, mesocoxa; *e*, mesepi-
    meron.

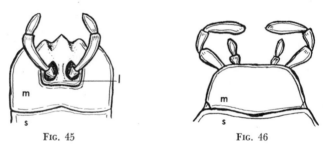

FIG. 45   FIG. 46

Figs. 45–46. Labium of *Popilius*, a passalid (45), and that of *Pseudolu-
    canus* (46). In the first the mentum (*m*) is deeply emar-
    ginate, exposing most of the ligula (*l*), whereas in the
    latter the mentum conceals the ligula. *s*, submentum.

FIG. 47   FIG. 48

Figs. 47–48. A tarsus of *Stenelmis* (47) and of *Laccobius* (48), the tarsal
    claws of the former greatly enlarged.

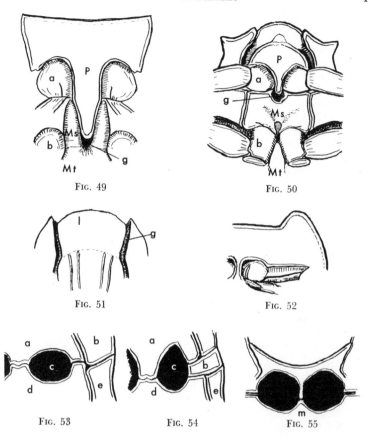

FIG. 49

FIG. 50

FIG. 51

FIG. 52

FIG. 53

FIG. 54

FIG. 55

Figs. 49–50. Portion of underside of the thorax. In *Buprestis* (49), as
in all families which properly key out here, the prosternal
process (*P*) is received in a groove (*g*) in the mesosternum
(*Ms*) which extends nearly to, or even into, the metasternum
(*Mt*). In *Cupes* (50) and in others which occasionally have
the prosternal process (*P*) received in a groove (*g*) in the
mesosternum (*Ms*), the groove is short and in no way even
approaches the metasternum (*Mt*). *a*, procoxa; *b*, mesocoxa.

Fig. 51. Anterior portion of prosternum of the throscid *Drapetes*,
showing the lobe (*l*) which partially conceals the mouthparts.
g, antennal groove.

Fig. 52. The strongly transverse procoxa of the nitidulid *Colopterus*.

Figs. 53–54. Mesocoxal cavity of a cryptophagid, *Anchicera* (53), and of a
cucujid, *Silvanus* (54). In the former the coxal cavity (*c*)
is surrounded by only the mesosternum (*a*) and the metasternum (*d*), whereas in the latter the mesepimeron (*b*)
contacts the cavity as well. *e*, metepisternum.

Fig. 55. Procoxal cavities of *Scaphidium*, invading the mesosternum (*m*).

26. (23) Prosternal process prolonged, fitting into a groove on mesosternum (Fig. 49); usually slender beetles with a free head; legs not usually placed in grooves; antennae filiform, serrate or pectinate, rarely thickened apically; pronotum essentially flat, widened posteriorly 27

     Prosternal process not prolonged to fit into a groove in mesosternum, or if rarely present (Fig. 50), the legs are received in grooves on underside of body, and the general structure different 31

27. (26) Procoxae globular 28

     Procoxae transverse ....BYRRHIDAE   (p. 379)

28. (27) Prosternum widened anteriorly (Fig. 51), covering the mouth; prothorax solidly attached to mesothorax ....

     ....THROSCIDAE   (p. 337)

     Prosternum not widened anteriorly, not covering the mouth (Fig. 49) 29

29. (28) Pronotum not declivous at base, rigidly attached to rest of body ....BUPRESTIDAE   (p. 339)

     Pronotum strongly declivous at base, freely movable 30

30. (29) Posterior margin of next to last ventral abdominal segment with a distinct membrane; labrum visible ....

     ....ELATERIDAE   (p. 307)

     Posterior margin of next to last ventral segment without a membrane; labrum concealed ....MELASIDAE   (p. 335)

31. (26) Antennae distinctly geniculate, clavate; base of pronotum closely applied to elytra; elytra truncate, exposing two dorsal abdominal segments; legs spinose; coxae widely separated; heavily sclerotized beetles ....HISTERIDAE   (p. 219)

     Antennae not geniculate; other characters not the same as above 32

32. (31) Legs received in grooves beneath body; head usually retractile 33

     Legs not received in grooves 34

33. (32) Procoxae transverse, more or less cylindrical ....

     ....BYRRHIDAE   (p. 379)

     Procoxae conical, prominent ....DERMESTIDAE   (p. 369)

34. (32) Antennae clavate or capitate 35

     Antennae neither clavate nor capitate ....CUPESIDAE   (p. 282)

35. (34) Elytra leaving apex of abdomen exposed 36

     Elytra entirely covering abdomen, or if rarely shorter, then the beetles are strongly robust insects with heavily spined legs and thick palpi 42

36. (35) All dorsal abdominal segments connate except the two basal ...........................STAPHYLINIDAE   (p. 182)

     At most only the exposed dorsal abdominal segments are connate 37

37. (36) Procoxae separated, not prominent, and either transverse or globular 38
Procoxae contiguous, prominent, conical or cylindrical ...40
38. (37) Procoxae transverse, with a free trochantin (Fig. 52); short, broad beetles, with a broad pronotum and a distinctly segmented antennal club ....NITIDULIDAE (p. 383)
Procoxae globular, without trochantin; more slender beetles, with a very small antennal club 39
39. (38) Mesocoxal cavities closed externally by sterna (Fig. 53) ................................CRYPTOPHAGIDAE (p. 414)
Mesocoxal cavities open externally (Fig. 54) ....CUCUJIDAE (p. 398)
40. (37) Prothorax closely fitting to the mesothorax so that the procoxae invade the mesosternum (Fig. 55) ....SCAPHIDIIDAE (p. 213)
Procoxae not invading mesoternum 41
41. (40) Procoxal cavities open posteriorly (Fig. 25A); elytra somewhat abbreviated, exposing pygidium ..SILPHIDAE (p. 174)
Procoxal cavities closed posteriorly (Fig. 25B); elytra entire ....LEIODIDAE (p. 178)
42. (35) Tarsi with spongy pubescence beneath or the next to last segment distinctly bilobed, or the last segment with a membranous appendage 43
Tarsi simple, or expanded and with undersurface flat 44
43. (42) Metacoxae flat, not prominent, covered by femora in repose; tarsi with fourth segment very small ..CLERIDAE (p. 272)
Metacoxae conical and prominent, at least internally, not covered by femora; tarsi with fourth segment not reduced 48
44. (42) Head not concealed by prothorax ....EROTYLIDAE (p. 407)
Head concealed or nearly so by prothorax 45
45. (44) Femur joined to apex or near apex of trochanter (Fig. 56) 46
Femur joined to side of trochanter (Fig. 57) 47
46. (45) Antennae inserted on front of head (Fig. 58) ....PTINIDAE (p. 492)
Antennae inserted directly in front of eyes (Fig. 59) ....ANOBIIDAE (p. 495)
47. (45) Procoxae globular; metacoxae contiguous, flat; small, convex, polished beetles ....PHALACRIDAE (p. 430)
Procoxae conical, prominent; metacoxae slightly separated, dilated into a plate which partly protects femora; not polished beetles ....DERMESTIDAE (p. 369)
48. (43) Seven or eight ventral abdominal segments present ..49
Only six ventral abdominal segments present ..MELYRIDAE (p. 265)

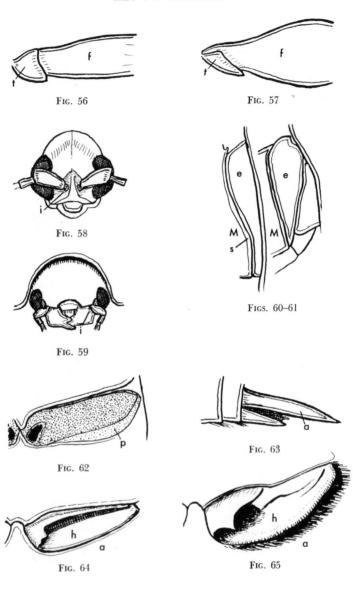

Fig. 56

Fig. 57

Fig. 58

Figs. 60–61

Fig. 59

Fig. 62

Fig. 63

Fig. 64

Fig. 65

Fig. 66

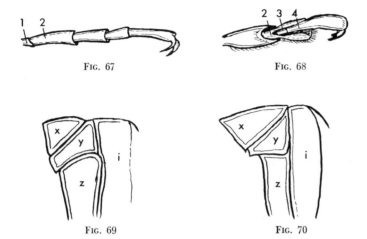

FIG. 67

FIG. 68

FIG. 69

FIG. 70

Figs. 56–57. Trochanter and base of femur in the anobiid *Trypopitus* (56) and in the phalacrid *Olibrus* (57). *f,* femoral base; *t,* trochanter.

Figs. 58–59. The head viewed from above. Head of *Ptinus* (58), the antennal insertion (*i*) on front, between eyes. Head of the anobiid *Xestobium* (59), with the antennal insertion (*i*) under the front, directly anterior to the eye.

Figs. 60–61. Metasternal sidepieces in *Cantharis* (60) and in the lampyrid *Photinus* (61). *e,* metepisternum; *M,* metasternum; *s,* sinuation.

Fig. 62. Metacoxa of *Pentaria,* a mordellid, from which transparent plates (*p*) extend.

Fig. 63. Tip of abdomen of *Mordellistena* viewed from the side. *a,* anal style.

Figs. 64–65. Metacoxa of the anthicid *Notoxus* (64) and of the meloid genus *Epicauta* (65). In the former the hind portion (*h*) of the metacoxa is flat and virtually on the same plane as the abdomen (*a*), whereas in the latter it is rounded and strongly elevated above the abdomen, especially toward the side.

Fig. 66. Tarsus of a cerambycid viewed obliquely from the side, the fourth segment small and nearly entirely hidden in the lobe of the third.

Fig. 67. Protarsus of a bostrichid (*Amphicerus*) viewed from the side, the first segment minute, scarcely visible at base of second.

Fig. 68. Tarsus of *Hippodamia,* a coccinellid, viewed obliquely from above, the third segment minute, concealed in a lobe of the second.

Figs. 69–70. Mesosternal sidepieces of an endomychid, *Aphorista* (69), and of a coccinellid, *Hippodamia* (70). *i,* inflexed margin of elytra; *x,* mesepisternum; *y,* mesepimeron; *z,* metepisternum.

49. (48) Mesocoxae widely separated; elytra with epipleura absent ....LYCIDAE (p. 238)
Mesocoxae contiguous; elytra with epipleura distinct 50
50. (49) Head entirely or largely exposed or at most one-half covered by pronotum; metepisternum sinuate on either side (Fig. 60) ....CANTHARIDAE (p. 256)
Head entirely covered by pronotum or at least more than one-half covered; metepisternum not sinuate on either side (Fig. 61) ....LAMPYRIDAE (p. 248)
51. (22) Tarsi 5–5–4, rarely 4–5–4, or 4–4–3, none of the segments reduced so as to be seen with difficulty 52
Tarsi actually or apparently 4–4–4, 4–3–3, 3–4–4, 3–3–3, or still further reduced; if in fact 5–5–5, either fourth or first segment is so strongly reduced, in comparison to others, as to be readily overlooked 60
52. (51) Procoxal cavities closed posteriorly (Fig. 25B) 53
Procoxal cavities open posteriorly (Fig. 25A) 54
53. (52) Tarsal claws simple (Fig. 26A, D) ..TENEBRIONIDAE (p. 463)
Tarsal claws pectinate (Fig. 26J) ....ALLECULIDAE (p. 456)
54. (52) Head not suddenly and strongly constricted behind eyes 55
Head strongly and suddenly constricted behind eyes into a more or less distinct neck 56
55. (54) Mesocoxae not very prominent; pronotum margined laterally, as broad as elytra at base ...MELANDRYIDAE (p. 480)
Mesocoxae very prominent; pronotum not margined laterally, narrower at base than elytra .....OEDEMERIDAE (p. 283)
56. (54) Pronotum with side margin sharp along edge, base as wide as elytra 57
Pronotum with side margin rounded along edge, narrower at base than elytra 58
57. (56) Metacoxae provided with plates (Fig. 62); abdomen often prolonged into a style or pointed process (Fig. 63) ....MORDELLIDAE (p. 286)
Metacoxae without plates (Fig. 64); abdomen never with a style .............................MELANDRYIDAE (p. 480)
58. (56) Metacoxae not prominent (Fig. 64); tarsal claws simple; antennae filiform and simple ....ANTHICIDAE (p. 303)
Metacoxae large, prominent (Fig. 65) 59
59. (58) Tarsal claws simple; antennae usually pectinate in male, serrate in female ..................PYROCHROIDAE (p. 300)
Tarsal claws cleft or toothed; antennae more or less filiform, rarely moniliform ....MELOIDAE (p. 294)
60. (51) At least one pair of tarsi actually five-segmented, fourth segment minute, third segment nearly always broad and bilobed (Fig. 66) 61
Tarsi not so 67
61. (60) Antennae not distinctly clavate or capitate 62
Antennae distinctly capitate or clavate 64

62. (61) Short, oval beetles, with front prolonged into a short, broad, quadrate beak; elytra short, exposing tip of abdomen; antennae inserted on side margin of front . . . . MYLABRIDAE (p. 730)
Otherwise formed 63

63. (62) Round or depressed, seldom strongly elongate; eyes not surrounding base of antennae; antennae inserted on frontal side margins, which are not prominent; antennae rarely long; if so, the metafemora are thickened for leaping . . . . CHRYSOMELIDAE (p. 658)
Slender, never very broad, shieldlike or circular; bases of antennae usually in part surrounded by eyes; antennae often inserted beneath frontal carinae; metafemora never thickened for leaping . . . . CERAMBYCIDAE (p. 574)

64. (61) Cylindrical; prothorax narrower than base of elytra, not depressed . . . . CLERIDAE (p. 272)
Not as above 65

65. (64) Head without antennal grooves beneath; metacoxae contiguous or approximate 66
Head with antennal grooves beneath; metacoxae widely separated . . . . NITIDULIDAE (p. 383)

66. (65) Procoxal cavities open posteriorly; form extremely slender, tapering . . . . LANGURIIDAE (p. 403)
Procoxal cavities closed posteriorly; form elongate, robust, or very broadly oval . . . . EROTYLIDAE (p. 407)

67. (60) At least one pair of tarsi five-segmented, but first segment minute (Fig. 67) . . . . . . , ... 68
All tarsi with four segments or less 71

68. (67) Metafemur attached to apex of trochanter (Fig. 56) or very near apex 69
Metafemur attached to side of trochanter (Fig. 57) 70

69. (68) First abdominal sternite elongate, much longer than second . . . . LYCTIDAE (p. 503)
First abdominal sternite scarcely longer than second . . . . BOSTRICHIDAE (p. 500)

70. (68) Procoxae transverse; antennae with a distinct club . . . . OSTOMATIDAE (p. 381)
Procoxae globular; antennae at most feebly clavate . . . . CUCUJIDAE (p. 398)

71. (67) Tarsi actually of four segments, third so minute that the tarsi appear to be three-segmented (Fig. 68) 72
Third tarsal segment not minute, tarsi distinctly four-segmented, or actually of three or fewer segments 73

72. (71) Mesepimera distinctly quadrangular (Fig. 69); tarsal claws simple . . . . ENDOMYCHIDAE (p. 426)
Mesepimera irregularly triangular (Fig. 70); tarsal claws usually appendiculate (Fig. 26F) or toothed (Fig. 26G, H) . . . . COCCINELLIDAE (p. 435)

73. (71) Tarsi 4–4–4 74
      Tarsi 3–4–4, 3–3–3, or with fewer segments 75
74. (73) Tarsi not dilated ....COLYDIIDAE (p. 418)
      Tarsi more or less dilated, spongy-pubescent beneath ......
      ....EROTYLIDAE (p. 407)
75. (73) Elytra abbreviated, covering about one-half of abdomen
      ....PSELAPHIDAE (p. 207)
      Elytra covering entire abdomen .......LATHRIDIIDAE (p. 423)

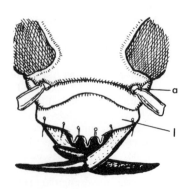

Fig. 71

Fig. 71. Head of *Cicindela formosa* showing antennal insertion (*a*)
   placed on side of front; *l,* labrum.

Family CICINDELIDAE

Tiger Beetles

A rather small family of beetles, having the head large; the eyes prominent; mentum deeply emarginate; antennae eleven-segmented, filiform, and slender, inserted on the front; clypeus produced laterally beyond antennal bases; legs long and slender; tarsi all five-segmented, tarsal claws simple. They are closely related to the Carabidae but differ in having the antennae on the front instead of between the eyes and bases of mandibles and in having the clypeus widened, so that it extends beyond the antennal insertion on each side (Fig. 71).

This group is commonly called "tiger beetles" because of their predatory attacks on other insects. Many of our species are dull-colored above, but all have brilliant metallic colors on the underparts; however, some species are brilliant blue or green on the upper surface. All are slender and graceful, and are great favorites with collectors. From early spring until fall, they may be found along roads, paths, beaches, and mud flats in the hot sunshine. They are active runners and strong flyers, so they are quite difficult to capture. Generally the eggs are laid in holes dug by the females in sandy ground during the summer months. The larvae are elongated, whitish, grublike, and with large curving jaws and live in vertical burrows in the ground, often in the vicinity of a pond or creek, where there is a sandy shore. The larva props itself near the top of the burrow by means of the hump with two hooks on the fifth abdominal segment (Plate III). The jaws are kept open until some unwary insect passes within reach. The prey, once captured, is taken to the bottom of the burrow, which may be a foot or more deep, and devoured.

KEY TO GENERA

Third segment of maxillary palpi longer than fourth ....I. *Tetracha*   (p. 49)
Third segment of maxillary palpi shorter than fourth ......II. *Cicindela*   (p. 50)

Genus I. *TETRACHA* Hope

Large, convex; head large, eyes circular; mandibles each with four teeth; pronotum transverse, sides constricted basally, base much narrower than

49

apex; elytra feebly convex, wider basally than pronotum, deeply, coarsely punctate.

The members of this genus are nocturnal and forage for food at night; they are frequently attracted to lights.

KEY TO SPECIES

Each elytral apex with an arcuate yellow macula, disk medially purplish ......
....a. *carolina*
Elytral apices without yellow macula, disk not purplish ....b. *virginica*

a. *Tetracha carolina* (Linné)   Plate VI, No. 3, p. 57

Oblong-ovate, moderately slender, convex; metallic green, shining; elytra medially purplish bronze, each apex with a large comma-shaped, pale-yellowish macula; antennae, mouthparts, legs, and apex of abdomen pale yellowish. Pronotum entirely smooth except for basal and apical transverse sulci. Elytra moderately densely punctate with irregular-sized punctures which become obsolete apically; apices separately, narrowly rounded. Length 15–17 mm.

b. *Tetracha virginica* (Linné)   Plate VI, No. 1, p. 57

Oblong-ovate, rather robust, convex; dark green, with gold reflex; elytra blackish at middle, sides with a broad, metallic-green stripe; antennae, legs, and last ventral abdominal segment brownish yellow. Pronotum smooth except for basal and apical transverse sulci, medially with a deep, rounded or triangular impression. Elytra coarsely, densely punctate, apical fourth and extreme base impunctate; apices rather broadly, separately rounded. Length 20–24 mm.

This species is found beneath stones, wheat shocks, etc., especially near water.

Genus II. *CICINDELA* Linné

The members of this genus differ from the other tiger beetles in being diurnal in habit.

Generic characters are: head large; eyes prominent; maxillary palpi with third segment shorter than fourth; pronotum variable in form, usually subcylindrical, slightly transverse, narrower than head, anterior sulcus continuous with anterior prosternal sulcus; elytra with sides broadly arcuate or slightly expanded posteriorly, apices usually rounded, sometimes emarginate.

KEY TO SPECIES

1. Elytra blue, green, bronze, or blackish, never whitish or cream-colored......2
   Elytra cream-colored, usually with a few markings ....n. *dorsalis*

2. Abdomen metallic green 3
   Abdomen metallic red ....l. *rufiventris*
3. Elytral markings prolonged along lateral margins to form a more or less
   complete vitta 4
   Elytral markings (if present) not at all prolonged along lateral margin, widely
   separated 7
4. Elytral marginal stripe interrupted at apical fourth ....e. *repanda*
   Elytral marginal stripe continuous to apex from behind middle............5
5. Humeral lunule with apex recurved toward pronotum 6
   Humeral lunule with apex not recurved ....a. *formosa generosa*
6. Elytra each with a rounded macula near scutellum ....o. *marginata*
   Elytra without macula near scutellum ....f. *hirticollis*
7. Elytra with median macula extending across disk in a more or less undulating
   band 8
   Elytra with median macula (if present) confined to margin 11
8. Elytra with humeral lunule complete or only slightly interrupted ....
   ....g. *tranquebarica*
   Elytra with humeral lunule absent, represented at most by two widely separated, small maculae 9
9. Elytral markings confined to posterior half except for occasionally a minute
   macula at humeral angle ....b. *purpurea*
   Elytra with distinct maculae anterior to middle 10
10. Elytra brilliant metallic bronze, margined with metallic green or blue, median
    band wide, with a definite oblique bend posteriorly toward suture
    ....c. *splendida*
    Elytra dull greenish black, only partially margined with metallic green, median
    band narrow, nearly straight, directed toward suture ...d. *duodecimguttata*
11. Elytra without any markings 12
    Elytra with at least one macula laterally 13
12. Entire body blackish with dull-brassy or greenish reflex; elytra distinctly
    punctate ....k. *punctulata*
    Entire body brilliant metallic green or blue; elytra without distinct punctures
    ....i. *scutellaris unicolor*
13. Entirely blackish, above feebly bronzed; elytra with a single macula near
    middle of sides ....m. *unipunctata*
    Entirely brilliant green, blue, or purplish; elytra with at least three maculae
    on sides 14
14. Body above metallic green or blue; elytra without maculae anterior to middle
    .... j. *sexguttata*
    Elytra metallic purple, rarely metallic green, with a humeral lunule or macula
    ....h. *scutellaris lecontei*

a. *Cicindela formosa generosa* Dejean   Plate V, No. 2, p. 52

Oblong-ovate, robust, subconvex; blackish with dull-bronze reflex; white markings wide, prominent, connected on margin, middle band bent backward, then forward, almost reaching suture, a dot near scutellum; abdomen deep metallic green. Pronotum scarcely narrowed posteriorly; disk densely, transversely rugose. Elytra minutely punctate. Length 16–18 mm.

This is the largest of our tiger beetles and is more wary and more difficult to capture than many other species; when disturbed, it often flies for great distances. It is usually found on bare sandy spots and along paths and roads.

PLATE V
Family CICINDELIDAE I

1. *Cicindela purpurea* Olivier (p. 54)

Purplish to coppery, elytra green on suture and sides; 14–16 mm.

2. *C. formosa generosa* Dejean (p. 51)

Blackish; elytral markings whitish; 16–18 mm.

3. *C. duodecimguttata* Dejean (p. 54)

Brownish, elytra dull greenish black, with whitish markings; 12–15 mm.

4. *C. repanda* Dejean (p. 54)

Brownish, coppery-reflexed; elytral markings broken along sides; 12–13 mm.

5. *C. hirticollis* Say (p. 54)

Brown, with bronze sheen; elytral markings continuous on sides; 13–14 mm.

6. *C. tranquebarica* Herbst (p. 55)

Brown, with a bronze sheen; elytral markings white; 13–16 mm.

7. *C. sexguttata* Fabricius (p. 55)

Metallic green or blue; elytral whitish spots variable in number; 10–14 mm.

8. *C. punctulata* Olivier (p. 55)

Blackish or brown; elytra with rows of green spots and sometimes white dots; 11–14 mm.

9. *C. rufiventris* Dejean (p. 58)

Deep brown; elytral spots white; abdomen red; 9–12 mm.

10. *C. marginata* Fabricius (p. 58)

Dull metallic green or bronze; elytral margins whitish; 10–12 mm.

11, 12. *C. dorsalis* Say (p. 58)

Dull metallic green; elytra whitish, with brown markings which vary between the two extremes shown; 13–15 mm.

MM 0 10 20 30 40 50 60 70

PLATE V   53

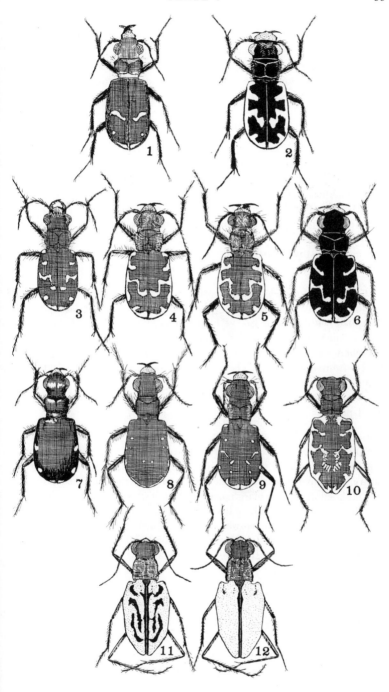

b. *Cicindela purpurea* Olivier   Plate V, No. 1, p. 53

Elongate-ovate, rather robust, subconvex; reddish copper, margins and suture of elytra green; elytral markings consisting of a short median band, a dot near apex, and apex tipped with cream; occasionally there is also a humeral dot; abdomen metallic green. Pronotum strongly transverse; distinctly transversely rugose on disk. Elytra with surface rather finely asperate. Length 14–16 mm.

This species is found especially in meadow pathways and in grass along roads.

c. *Cicindela splendida* Hentz   Plate VI, No. 4, p. 57

Elongate-ovate, rather robust, subconvex; entirely brilliant metallic green or blue; elytra except margins bright metallic bronze, markings consisting of three whitish maculae (one at humerus, one at basal fourth, and another before apex) and two bands (the broad median one recurved, directed obliquely posteriorly toward suture, and a curved one at apex). Pronotum distinctly narrowed posteriorly, surface densely, transversely rugose. Elytra densely, finely asperate. Length 12–14 mm.

d. *Cicindela duodecimguttata* Dejean   Plate V, No. 3, p. 53

Elongate-ovate, robust, subconvex; elytra dull greenish black, partially margined with metallic green; elytra marked with humeral, subhumeral, apical, subapical, and median dots and a short median fascia, white; abdomen metallic green. Pronotum distinctly narrowed posteriorly; disk finely, transversely rugose. Elytra rather coarsely asperate. Length 12–15 mm.

This species inhabits low, moist areas and frequents the margins of small ponds.

e. *Cicindela repanda* Dejean   Plate V, No. 4, p. 53

Elongate-ovate, robust, subconvex; brownish bronze, with more or less coppery reflex; humeral lunule with its tip directed posteriorly or toward suture; median fascia straight to middle of disk, then directed posteriorly and clubbed at suture; marginal white line nearly, but never quite, attaining the apical and humeral lunules; abdomen metallic green. Pronotum subquadrate, distinctly narrowed posteriorly; disk finely, transversely rugose. Elytra with sides parallel in male, suddenly dilated before middle in female; disk finely, sparsely asperate. Length 12–13 mm.

This species is found in open sandy or gravelly places.

f. *Cicindela hirticollis* Say   Plate V, No. 5, p. 53

Oblong-ovate, robust, subconvex; bronze above, undersurface green, densely covered with long, white hairs; elytral white markings as follows: humeral lunule bent forward at apex; marginal line joining humeral lunule, not quite interrupted before the apical lunule; median fascia bent slightly anteriorly, then strongly so posteriorly, with a club near suture.

Prothorax quadrate, densely pubescent, scarcely narrowed posteriorly; disk minutely, irregularly rugose. Elytra dilated before middle in both sexes; disk densely, rather coarsely punctate in female, granulate-punctate in male. Length 13–14 mm.

This species is found along the edges of fresh-water bodies.

g. *Cicindela tranquebarica* Herbst   Plate V, No. 6, p. 53
Elongate-ovate, robust, subconvex; bronze above, dark green beneath; humeral lunule in the form of an oblique band extending almost to suture, the median band rectangularly bent apically and recurved at tip, and an apical lunule also present, these markings all white. Pronotum distinctly narrowed basally; disk finely, irregularly rugose. Elytra finely, rather densely asperate. Length 13–16 mm.

This beetle is common on sandy or muddy flats near running water and also along roads and pathways.

h. *Cicindela scutellaris lecontei* Haldeman   Plate VI, No. 5, p. 57
Elongate-ovate, robust, subconvex; body above, greenish and purplish bronze; elytra brilliant purplish, rarely purplish with green; elytra with an apical lunule, one or two marginal spots, and sometimes a humeral spot or lunule, all whitish; front of head hairy in male, nearly glabrous in female; sides of thorax, pro- and mesocoxae densely clothed with long, white hairs. Pronotum distinctly narrowed posteriorly; disk moderately finely, transversely rugose. Elytra coriaceous, with a very few coarse, scattered punctures. Length 12–13 mm.

This species is usually found in open, rather dry, sandy localities away from water.

i. *Cicindela scutellaris unicolor* Dejean   Plate VI, No. 6, p. 57
Except for color and size this variety is identical with the above variety; entire body metallic green or blue, elytra with a purple reflex, immaculate. Length 10–12 mm.

j. *Cicindela sexguttata* Fabricius   Color Plate C; Plate V, No. 7, p. 53
Elongate-ovate, moderately slender, subconvex; bright metallic green above, often with a bluish cast; elytra each with two white dots and an apical lunule, these occasionally indistinct or even wholly wanting; sometimes there may be from one to three additional dots; body beneath, green, with a few scattered white hairs. Pronotum distinctly narrowed to base; disk rather coarsely, transversely rugose. Elytra densely, rugosely punctate. Length 10–16 mm.

This is probably the most conspicuous species; it frequents pathways in open woods.

k. *Cicindela punctulata* Olivier   Plate V, No. 8, p. 53
Oblong-ovate, slender, subconvex; black, dark brown, or greenish bronze above; greenish beneath; elytra with indistinct, scattered, white dots, these

PLATE VI
Family CICINDELIDAE II

1. *Tetracha virginica* (Linné) (p. 50)

   Deep metallic green, shining; legs and antennae ferruginous; 20–24 mm.

2. *Cicindela unipunctata* Fabricius (p. 58)

   Brown, with a dull bronze, flecked with metallic green; elytral pale spot often absent; 13–15 mm.

3. *Tetracha carolina* (Linné) (p. 50)

   Bright metallic green and red-bronze; elytral maculae and legs pale yellowish; 15–17 mm.

4. *Cicindela splendida* Hentz (p. 54)

   Metallic blue; elytra metallic green or coppery, with whitish markings; 12–14 mm.

5. *C. scutellaris lecontei* Haldeman (p. 55)

   Metallic purple and green; elytral spots creamy white; 12–13 mm.

6. *C. scutellaris unicolor* Dejean (p. 55)

   Metallic blue and green; elytra purplish; 10–12 mm.

Family CARABIDAE I

7. *Aspidoglossa subangulata* Chaudoir (p. 75)

   Black, shining; antennae and legs dull brownish orange; 7.5–8 mm.

8. *Scaphinotus elevatus* (Fabricius) (p. 63)

   Black, with coppery, greenish, or violet reflex; 18–19 mm.

9. *Pasimachus depressus* Fabricius (p. 70)

   Black, shining; elytra with margins often bluish; 24–30 mm.

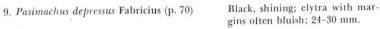

MM 0 10 20 30 40 50 60 70

PLATE VI 57

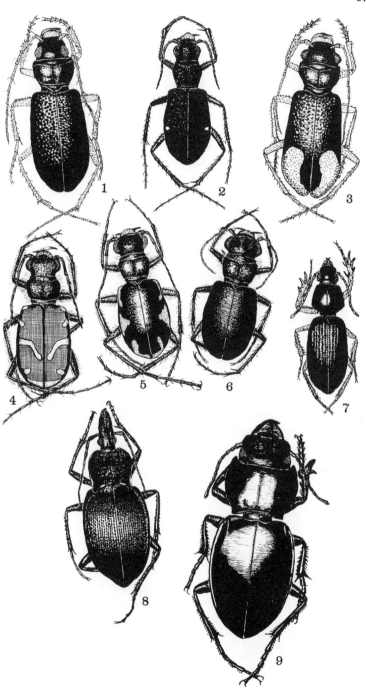

frequently lacking, and a basal row of green punctures along suture. Pronotum narrowed to base; disk finely, irregularly rugose. Elytra densely, rugosely punctate. Length 11–14 mm.

This species occurs along paths and upland roads.

l. *Cicindela rufiventris* Dejean   Plate V, No. 9, p. 53

Elongate-ovate, slender, subconvex; dull, dark brown, varied with metallic green and bronze above; elytral white markings consisting of a humeral, posthumeral, marginal, and two or three discal spots, the first discal spot often united with the marginal to form a short, sinuate median band; in addition there is an apical lunule present; body beneath, bluish green, abdomen red. Head finely striate, not hairy. Pronotum subquadrate, each side with a few white hairs; disk minutely rugose. Elytra densely, minutely alutaceous. Length 9–12 mm.

This species is distinguished at once by its red abdomen. It occurs especially on roads and open paths on the slopes of wooded hills.

m. *Cicindela unipunctata* Fabricius   Plate VI, No. 2, p. 57

Elongate-ovate, rather slender, subconvex; above entirely blackish, feebly bronzed; elytra each with a single whitish macula near middle of sides and with a number of metallic-green punctures; body beneath, metallic green and blue. Pronotum subquadrate, distinctly narrowed to base; disk finely, irregularly rugose. Elytra rather coarsely, rugosely punctate, more finely so posteriorly. Length 14–15 mm.

n. *Cicindela dorsalis* Say   Plate V, Nos. 11, 12, p. 53

Elongate-ovate, robust, subconvex; body above, dull brown with metallic green and bronze; elytra cream-colored, often with several irregular brownish markings; undersurface red, with dense white hair, shining at middle. Pronotum subquadrate, distinctly narrowed anteriorly; margins hairy; disk finely, irregularly rugose. Elytra rather densely, feebly punctate and with a few deep, much coarser punctures especially at base. Length 13–15 mm.

This species is found especially along sandy beaches near large bodies of water.

o. *Cicindela marginata* Fabricius   Plate V, No. 10, p. 53

Elongate-ovate, rather robust, subconvex; above metallic green or bronze; elytra with white marginal band complete from base to apex, humeral lunule recurved basally around to scutellum, median band curved toward base, then acutely recurved toward apex, broken into numerous dots; a macula present near scutellum. Pronotum quadrate; sides subparallel, constricted at apex; disk indistinctly, transversely rugose. Elytra finely, densely asperate, with a number of coarse punctures at base. Length 10–12 mm.

This species is especially common on muddy beaches on the Atlantic seacoast.

Family CARABIDAE

The Ground Beetles

This, one of the largest families of insects, is found throughout the world, and many of its members are very abundant. Most of the species are black or dull brownish in color, but some are yellow, metallic blue, green, or purple. They are for the most part predatory on many of the worst economic pests, such as gypsy moths, cankerworms, cutworms, etc.; however, a few are seed-eaters and can do occasional damage. They are mostly nocturnal in habit and during the day may be found under logs, stones, debris, and loose bark. The larvae are also predaceous and live in burrows in the ground, feeding on soft-bodied larvae of other insects.

Characterized as a family: head narrower than pronotum and directed forward; mentum deeply emarginate; antennae eleven-segmented, filiform, inserted between eyes and base of mandibles, all but basal segments finely pubescent; six abdominal sternites present; legs most usually slender, adapted for running; pro- and mesocoxae globular, metacoxae dilated on inner side; tarsi five-segmented.

KEY TO TRIBES

1. Mesocoxal cavities not entirely closed by meso- and metasternum, mesepimera extending to coxae (Fig. 72) 2
   Mesocoxal cavities entirely closed by meso- and metasternum, mesepimera not extending to coxae (Fig. 73) 6
2. Procoxal cavities open posteriorly (Fig. 74) 3
   Procoxal cavities closed posteriorly (Fig. 75) 5
3. Metacoxae separated; labrum deeply forked ....CYCHRINI (p. 60)
   Metacoxae not separated; labrum not forked 4
4. Mandibles without a bristle-bearing puncture on outer side; length 18 mm. or more ....CARABINI (p. 64)
   Mandibles each with a bristle-bearing puncture on outer side (Fig. 76); length 12 mm. or less ....NEBRIINI (p. 67)
5. Body not pedunculate, bases of elytra and pronotum contiguous; scutellum visible; antennae free at base (Fig. 77) ......ELAPHRINI (p. 67)
   Body pedunculate, the bases of pronotum and elytra well separated; scutellum not visible; antennae arising under a frontal plate (Fig. 78) ....SCARITINI (p. 70)
6. Head with two bristle-bearing punctures above each eye (Fig. 79) 7
   Head with one bristle-bearing puncture above each eye 14

59

60　　　　　　　　　　　　　CARABIDAE

7. Mandibles with a bristle-bearing puncture in scrobe on outer side
　　(Fig. 79) 8
　　Mandibles without a bristle-bearing puncture in scrobe 9
8. Last segment of palpi acuminate (Fig. 79); mesosternal epimera
　　wide; length less than 8 mm. ....BEMBIDIINI　(p. 76)
　　Last segment slender, elongate or subcylindrical; mesosternal
　　epimera narrow ....POGONINI　(p. 83)
9. Margin of elytra interrupted at posterior third and with a distinct
　　internal fold (Fig. 80) ...........................PTEROSTICHINI　(p. 84)
　　Margin of elytra not interrupted and without an internal fold ..10
10. Front of head short (Fig. 81); labrum impressed ....LICININI　(p. 94)
　　Front of head normal (Fig. 82) 11
11. Next to last segment of labial palpi with but two setae 12
　　Next to last segment of labial palpi with a number of setae anteri-
　　orly and always longer than terminal segment ....DRYPTINI　(p. 105)
12. Head elongate, prolonged behind eyes; neck constricted and di-
　　lated into a semiglobular knob ....ODACANTHINI　(p. 104)
　　Head not prolonged behind eyes; neck not semiglobose 13
13. Elytra obliquely sinuate at apex ....PLATYNINI　(p. 98)
　　Elytra truncate at apex ....LEBIINI　(p. 105)
14. Elytra truncate at apex; mandibles with a bristle-bearing puncture
　　in outer groove ....BRACHININI　(p. 107)
　　Elytra entire; mandibles without a bristle-bearing puncture 15
15. Elytral margin more or less interrupted and with an internal fold
　　(Fig. 80); antennae with three basal segments glabrous ....
　　...CHLAENIINI　(p. 108)
　　Elytral margin not interrupted, no internal fold; antennae with two,
　　rarely (Tachycellus) with three, basal segments glabrous ....
　　...HARPALINI　(p. 112)

Tribe CYCHRINI

KEY TO GENERA

Depression at base of labral emargination extending onto the an-
　terior part of clypeus, the base of this emargination bisetose; labial
　palpi with more than two setae ....II. *Sphaeroderus*　(p. 63)
Depression at base of labral emargination entirely anterior to the
　clypeus (Fig. 83), base of this emargination quadrisetose; labial palpi
　bisetose ....I. *Scaphinotus*　(p. 60)

Genus I. *SCAPHINOTUS* Dejean

　Of medium to large size; head elongate, mandibles long, slender, arcuate,
without a bristle-bearing puncture on outer side; labial and maxillary palpi
long, last segment hatchet-shaped and concave, labial bisetose; elytra each
with fourteen to eighteen distinct striae, which are sometimes irregular or
replaced by tubercles; procoxal cavities open posteriorly; metacoxae separated.

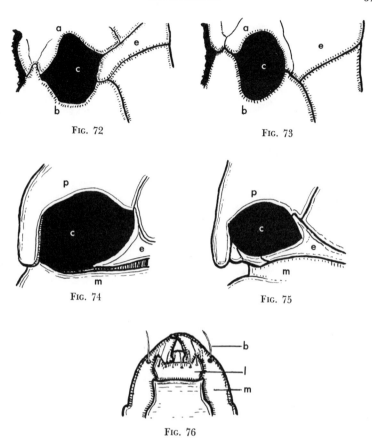

Fig. 72
Fig. 73
Fig. 74
Fig. 75
Fig. 76

Fig. 72. Ventral oblique view of mesocoxa of *Calosoma scrutator,* the
mesocoxal cavity (*c*) bordered by the mesepimeron (*e*) as well
as by the mesosternum (*a*) and metasternum (*b*).

Fig. 73. The same of *Chlaenius aestivus,* the mesocoxal cavity (*c*) bordered only by the mesosternum (*a*) and the metasternum (*b*).
The suture separating the mesosternum from the mesepimeron
(*e*) often is indistinct.

Fig. 74. Procoxal cavity of *Calosoma scrutator* viewed from the side.
The proepimeron (*e*) is short and does not reach the prosternal
process (*p*), so that the cavity (*c*) is open, contacting the mesosternum (*m*).

Fig. 75. Procoxal cavity of *Pasimachus* from the side. The proepimeron
(*e*) reaches behind the procoxal cavity (*c*) and joins an extension
of the prosternum (*p*), so that the cavity is separated from the
mesosternum (*m*).

Fig. 76. Anterior portion of head of *Nebria pallipes* from above, each
mandible (*m*) with a bristle (*b*) arising from a puncture, similar to those on labrum (*l*).

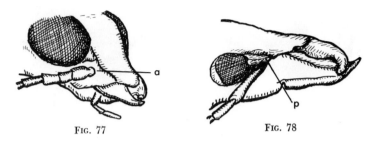

FIG. 77   FIG. 78

Fig. 77. Anterior portion of head of *Elaphrus ruscarius* obliquely from
        the side, with antennal insertion (*a*) not located beneath a
        plate but quite exposed.
Fig. 78. Anterior portion of side of head in *Scarites,* the antennal in-
        sertion concealed under a projecting plate (*p*).

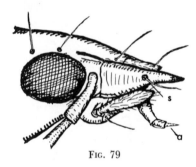

FIG. 79

Fig. 79. Head of *Bembidion* from the side, the mandibles with a setiger-
        ous puncture (*s*), above eye two other similar ones. The maxil-
        lary palpi have the last segment (*a*) acuminate.

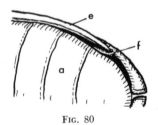

FIG. 80

Fig. 80. Portion of abdomen (*a*) and of an elytron of *Pterostichus*
        viewed obliquely from behind. Elytral margin (*e*) interrupted
        and with an internal fold (*f*) behind its terminus.

Scaphinotus elevatus (Fabricius)   Plate VI, No. 8, p. 57

Ovate, robust; black, with violaceous or cupreous reflex; antennae and legs piceous. Antennae slender, three-fourths as long as body, first segment longer than third. Pronotum subquadrate, side margins and posterior angles reflexed, the latter prolonged over elytra; disk rugose, with distinct median line. Elytral humeral margins strongly reflexed, lateral ones narrowly so; striae punctate; disk coarsely, closely punctate, toward sides becoming rugose. Length 18–19 mm.

These beetles live in moist woods under stones and leaves. Snails are the food of this species, and the head is especially adapted for reaching into the shells.

Genus II. *SPHAERODERUS* Dejean

Moderate-sized, elongate-oval, subdepressed; mandibles rather elongate, almost straight, without a fixed seta in the groove; labrum bifurcate; labial palpi with more than two setae; procoxal cavities open posteriorly; metacoxae separated.

KEY TO SPECIES

Posterior angles of pronotum rectangular; elytral striae interrupted at apex and
    sides ....a. *canadensis*
Posterior angles of pronotum quite obtuse; elytral striae interrupted behind
    middle ....b. *lecontei*

a. *Sphaeroderus canadensis* Chaudoir   Plate VII, No. 1, p. 69

Elongate-oval, subdepressed; violet-brown or black, shining; elytra violaceous. Pronotum subquadrate, evenly arcuate at sides, oblique, almost straight basally; posterior angles almost rectangular; disk with a fine median impressed line and an elongate, feebly punctate, deep fovea each side at base. Elytra finely striate, striae coarsely, sparsely punctate, interrupted at apex and on sides. Length 11–12 mm.

These beetles are usually found beneath stones.

b. *Sphaeroderus lecontei* Dejean   Plate VII, No. 3, p. 69

Elongate-oval, subdepressed; black, shining; elytra violaceous, margin metallic violet. Pronotum subquadrate; sides rounded, straight but oblique basally; disk with a fine median line and a rather broad, punctate fovea each side at base. Elytra finely striate, striae rather closely punctate, interrupted and irregular behind middle. Length 12–14 mm.

This species is found beneath moss, stones, and logs near water and in low-lying woods.

Tribe Carabini

KEY TO GENERA

Genus I. *CARABUS* Linné

Of large or moderate size, elongate-ovate; antennae with third segment cylindrical; mandibles distinctly curved, without a fixed seta in the scrobe; labrum entire, not divided; procoxal cavities open posteriorly; metacoxae contiguous.

KEY TO SPECIES

1. Elytral margin with two to four fine teeth on sides near base; color black, with side margins bright violet .... a. *serratus*
   Elytral margin not serrate; color black, sometimes with blue margins 2
2. Elytra black, with side margins blue, intervals all equally convex ..b. *limbatus*
   Elytra black, bronzed; each with three intervals rather elevated, and broken to form three series of short carinae .... c. *vinctus*

a. *Carabus serratus* Say   Plate VII, No. 2, p. 69

Elongate-oval, comparatively slender; black, shining, with side margins of pronotum and elytra bright violet. Pronotum slightly transverse; sides regularly rounded, base and apex subequal; disk sparsely and finely punctate, coarsely and densely so at sides and base. Elytra finely striate, striae coarsely punctate; intervals convex; three series of very large punctures on each elytron; sides near base with from two to four fine teeth. Length 20–24 mm.

These beetles are found beneath logs and stones in wooded areas.

b. *Carabus limbatus* Say   Plate VII, No. 4, p. 69

Elongate-ovate, rather robust; black, slightly shining, with margins of pronotum and elytra bluish. Pronotum slightly transverse; sides regularly rounded, base and apex subequal; disk rather sparsely and finely punctate, more densely and coarsely so at base. Elytra each with three series of coarse punctures; deeply striate, striae finely, rather closely punctate; intervals convex; sides not serrate. Length 17–26 mm.

These beetles are found beneath logs and stones, especially in moist woodlands.

c. *Carabus vinctus* Weber   Plate VII, No. 6, p. 69

Elongate-oval, rather slender; black, slightly shining, bronzed. Pronotum feebly transverse, sides rounded, base feebly wider than apex; punctate

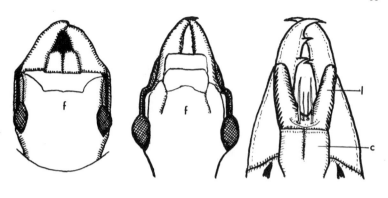

Fig. 81   Fig. 82   Fig. 83

Fig. 81. Head of *Dicaelus* from above, with front (*f*) short.
Fig. 82. Head of *Platynus* from above, with front (*f*) of normal length.
Fig. 83. Anterior portion of head of *Scaphinotus* from above. The emargination of the labrum (*l*) does not penetrate into the clypeus (*c*).

only at basal angles. Elytra striate, striae finely punctate; intervals convex, some more elevated than others and broadly interrupted to form three series of short carinae on each elytron; sides not serrate. Length 20–25 mm.

This species is usually found with *limbatus* but is not quite as common as that species.

Genus II. *CALOSOMA* Weber

Large to very large forms; elongate and oblong-oval in shape, convex; antennae with third segment compressed; mandibles distinctly curved, without a fixed seta in the scrobe; labrum entire; procoxal cavities open posteriorly; metacoxae contiguous.

The members of this genus feed almost entirely on cutworms, caterpillars, and other injurious larvae.

KEY TO SPECIES

1. Elytra bright metallic green, margined with red 2
   Elytra black, with rows of metallic punctures 3
2. Length 25 mm. or more ....a. *scrutator*
   Length 20 mm. or less ....b. *willcoxi*
3. Beneath, black tinged with green; elytral punctures green ....c. *frigidum*
   Beneath, black or blue-black; elytral punctures usually golden, coppery, or
   reddish ....d. *calidum*

a. *Calosoma scrutator* Fabricius   Caterpillar Hunter
                                    Color Plate A; Plate VII, No. 5, p. 69

Elongate-ovate, robust, convex; head, legs, and pronotum deep blue or purple, the pronotum margined with gold, green, or metallic red; elytra metallic green, margined with red or gold; beneath with metallic green, red, and blue reflex. Pronotum strongly transverse, almost entirely smooth; sides sharply curved, base and apex equal in width; posterior angles rounded; disk with a median impressed line. Elytra with numerous fine, punctate striae. Mesotibiae of male arcuate, with a dense patch of hairs on inner surface near apex. Length 25–35 mm.

This very beneficial beetle often climbs trees in search of its favorite food—caterpillars. Hence it is often called the "searcher" or "caterpillar hunter." It comes in large numbers at times to lights and is especially common in spring.

b. *Calosoma willcoxi* LeConte   Plate VII, No. 8, p. 69

Elongate-ovate, robust, convex; head, legs, and pronotum deep blue or purple, the latter margined with gold, green, or red; elytra metallic green or blue-green, margined with green, gold, or red; undersurface with varied metallic colors. Pronotum transverse, disk nearly smooth, with a fine, impressed median line; sides broadly curved, base narrower than apex. Elytra with finely punctate striae. Mesotibiae of male straight; not pubescent at apex. Length 17–20 mm.

This species is similar in color and in habits to *scrutator* but is distinguished by its smaller size and by the base of the pronotum being slightly narrower than the apex.

c. *Calosoma frigidum* Kirby   Plate VII, No. 7, p. 69

Elongate-ovate, moderately robust, convex; black, shining; pronotum and elytra narrowly edged with green, each with three rows of green punctures; undersurface tinged with green. Pronotum transverse; sides rounded; disk sparsely punctate, subrugose. Elytral striae punctate. Length 20–23 mm.

d. *Calosoma calidum* Fabricius   The Fiery Hunter
                                    Plate VII, No. 9, p. 69

Elongate-ovate, robust, convex; black, shining; pronotum and elytra occasionally margined with greenish, the latter each with three rows of bright-yellowish, coppery, or red impressions. Pronotum transverse, sides rounded; disk rugose. Elytral striae deep, finely punctate. Length 21–27 mm.

This species is found especially in meadows and open woodlands. Both the adult and its predaceous black grub, called the "cutworm lion," destroy numbers of cutworms annually.

Tribe ELAPHRINI

Genus *ELAPHRUS* Fabricius

Small, bronzed forms which in general appearance resemble small tiger beetles of the genus *Cicindela*. Head wider than pronotum, eyes prominent; pronotum feebly elongate, usually constricted before base, without bristle-bearing punctures on margin; elytra not striate but with rows of numerous large, shallow foveae.

KEY TO SPECIES

Pronotum sparsely punctate; protarsi of male with four segments dilated ....
....a. *cicatricosus*
Pronotum very densely punctate; protarsi of male with three segments dilated ....b. *ruscarius*

a. *Elaphrus cicatricosus* LeConte   Plate VII, No. 13, p. 69
    Oval, robust, subdepressed; brown-brassy, undersurface sometimes bluish. Pronotum sparsely, rather coarsely punctate; disk deeply impressed at middle and roundly foveate each side. Elytra uniformly, sparsely, and coarsely punctate. Length 6–7.5 mm.
    This species is usually found on sand flats.

b. *Elaphrus ruscarius* Say   Plate VII, No. 10, p. 69
    Oblong-ovate, robust, subdepressed; brown-brassy above, not shining; elytral impressions violet; undersurface metallic green, shining. Pronotum densely, coarsely punctate; disk indistinctly impressed at middle. Elytra densely, coarsely punctate. Length 6 mm.
    This species is especially common in spring on margins of ponds and lakes.

Tribe NEBRIINI

Genus *NEBRIA* Latreille

Of moderate size, elongate-oval; antennae slender, about two-thirds as long as body, segments cylindrical; head with one seta above each eye; mandibles with a fixed seta in the scrobe; elytra with scutellar striae always quite distinct; procoxal cavities open posteriorly.

Nebria pallipes Say   Plate VII, No. 11, p. 69
    Elongate-oval, subdepressed; dark reddish brown to black, shining; legs and antennae pale reddish brown. Pronotum transverse, somewhat cordate, widest anterior to middle, base distinctly narrower than apex; margins dis-

PLATE VII

Family CARABIDAE II

1. *Sphaeroderus canadensis* Chaudoir (p. 63) — Black; elytra with a purple sheen; 11–12 mm.

2. *Carabus serratus* Say (p. 64) — Black; edges of pronotum and elytra blue or violet; 20–24 mm.

3. *Sphaeroderus lecontei* Dejean (p. 63) — Black; elytra with a purple sheen; 12–14 mm.

4. *Carabus limbatus* Say (p. 64) — Black; pronotum and elytra with margins bluish; 17–26 mm.

5. *Calosoma scrutator* Fabricius (p. 66) — Deep blue; pronotum margined with green or gold; elytra green, margined with red; 25–35 mm.

6. *Carabus vinctus* Weber (p. 64) — Black, slightly bronzed; 20–25 mm.

7. *Calosoma frigidum* Kirby (p. 66) — Bluish black; elytra with metallic punctures; 20–23 mm.

8. *C. willcoxi* LeConte (p. 66) — Blue-black; elytra green, margined with red or gold, as is pronotum; 17–20 mm.

9. *C. calidum* Fabricius (p. 66) — Black; elytra with brilliant red, rounded punctures; 21–27 mm.

10. *Elaphrus ruscarius* Say (p. 67) — Brassy; elytral impressions greenish or violet, with dark, elevated centers; 6 mm.

11. *Nebria pallipes* Say (p. 67) — Dark brown to black; antennae and legs deep reddish; 10–12 mm.

12. *Platynus decorus* (Say) (p. 101) — Fuscous; head reflexed with green; pronotum and legs light reddish; 7.5–8.5 mm.

13. *Elaphrus cicatricosus* LeConte (p. 67) — Brown-brassy; elytral impressions greenish, each with two elongate elevations; 7–7.5 mm.

MM 0 10 20 30 40 50 60 70

PLATE VII

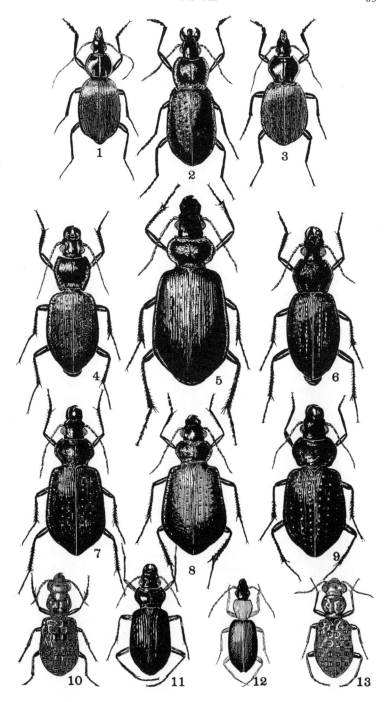

tinctly, strongly reflexed; disk smooth, with a median impressed line. Elytral striae deep, lateral ones punctate; intervals convex, smooth, the third from suture with five large punctures on the external side. Length 10–12 mm.

This species is common beneath stones and logs near water.

Tribe SCARITINI

KEY TO GENERA

1. Basal segment of antennae as long as next three combined; head with bristle-bearing puncture above each eye and at posterior angles of pronotum; medium- or large-sized species, 15 mm. or more in length 2
   Basal segment of antennae subequal in length to second, never as long as next three combined; head with two bristle-bearing punctures above each eye and two at posterior angles of pronotum; species small, less than 10 mm. in length 3
2. Posterior angles of pronotum distinct; elytra with a humeral carina which is variable in length; form broad ....I. *Pasimachus* (p. 70)
   Posterior angles of pronotum lacking; elytra without humeral carina; form narrow ....II. *Scarites* (p. 71)
3. Protarsi not dilated in both sexes 4
   Protarsi dilated in both sexes 5
4. Pronotum subglobose; terminal segment of male palpi dilated and excavated ventrally ....III. *Dyschirius* (p. 72)
   Pronotum more or less quadrate; palpi similar in sexes, not dilated or excavated in male ....IV. *Clivina* (p. 73)
5. Head smooth, without longitudinal grooves or striations; mentum feebly emarginate (Fig. 84) ....V. *Aspidoglossa* (p. 74)
   Head with numerous fine striae or longitudinal grooves; mentum deeply emarginate (Fig. 85) ....VI. *Schizogenius* (p. 75)

Genus I. *PASIMACHUS* Bonelli

Broadly oblong, black species; pronotum usually blue-margined, broad, with distinct posterior angles; elytra rounded or subacute at apex, the humeral carina of variable length; protibiae distinctly widened apically and dentate on outer margin; lacinia obtuse apically, not hooked (Fig. 86).

The species of this genus live under stones, debris, and logs along the borders of cultivated fields; they are extremely predaceous and live on larvae of many kinds of insects, particularly those of the army worm.

Pasimachus depressus Fabricius   Plate VI, No. 9, p. 57
Large, elongate-oblong; black, usually with a blue margin, female dull, male shining. Labrum broadly and feebly trilobed; mandibles feebly or not at all striate. Pronotum transverse, distinctly widened apically, more or

FIG. 84   FIG. 85

Fig. 84. Apical margin of labial mentum of *Aspidoglossa*.
Fig. 85. Apical margin of mentum of *Schizogenius*.

less constricted at base, the posterior angles prominent; disk smooth, with median line distinctly impressed from base to near apex. Elytra smooth, with a short humeral carina; apices together narrowly rounded. Spine of metatibiae slender, acute; metatibiae in male not densely pubescent on inner side; metatarsi long, slender. Length 24–30 mm.

Genus II. *SCARITES* Fabricius

Narrow, oblong, black beetles; body very distinctly pedunculate; lacinia hooked at apex (Fig. 87); posterior angles of pronotum wanting; elytra parallel, rounded at apex, without humeral carinae; protibiae widened, flattened, and dentate on outer margin; antennae with first segment as long as the second, third, and fourth together.

The members of this genus are strictly predaceous and very beneficial.

KEY TO SPECIES

Length 15–20 mm. . . . . .a. *subterraneus*
Length 25–30 mm. . . . . .b. *substriatus*

a. *Scarites subterraneus* Fabricius   Plate VIII, No. 3, p. 79
Elongate-oblong, parallel-sided, slightly convex; black, shining. Head with two deep, parallel lines. Pronotum subquadrate, sides nearly straight, margins fine; apex truncate, base angulate. Elytra distinctly striate, striae

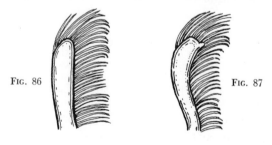

FIG. 86   FIG. 87

Figs. 86–87. Lacinia of *Pasimachus* (86) and of *Scarites* (87), in the latter case bearing a hook at apex.

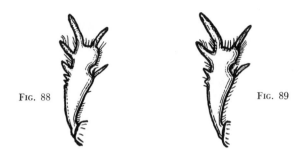

Fig. 88   Fig. 89

Figs. 88–89. Left protibia of *Scarites substriatus* (88) and of *S. sub-terraneus* (89).

impunctate. Protibiae on outer margin with three large teeth preceded by one small one (Fig. 89). Length 15–20 mm.

This species is found most commonly in gardens and along cultivated areas beneath stones, logs, and leaves.

b. *Scarites substriatus* Haldeman   Plate VIII, No. 2, p. 79

Nearly identical with the above but larger, and the sides of the pronotum are broadly arcuate; protibial outer margin with three large teeth preceded by two or three small ones (Fig. 88). Length 25–30 mm.

Genus III. *DYSCHIRIUS* Bonelli

The species of this genus live in burrows in wet, sandy places near fresh water. They may be most easily captured in the evening, at which time they are most active, or they may be aroused during the day by pouring water over their burrows.

Small, black or bronzed, shining forms; pronotum subglobose; head smooth, without longitudinal grooves; antennae with first segment about as long as second.

KEY TO SPECIES

Pronotum broader than long; elytra not punctate apically; third interval with three punctures ....a. *globulosus*
Pronotum not broader than long; elytra indistinctly punctate apically; third interval with two punctures ....b. *sphaericollis*

a. *Dyschirius globulosus* Say   Plate VIII, No. 1, p. 79

Elongate-oval, convex; black or dark reddish brown, strongly shining; legs and antennae light reddish brown. Pronotum ovate, broader than long, disk with median impressed line. Elytral striae attaining base, distinct, coarsely punctate basally but not apically, not present on apical third; third interval with three punctures. Length 2.5–3 mm.

This species is usually found beneath the loose bark of logs in damp woods, as well as in the ground.

b. *Dyschirius sphaericollis* Say   Plate VIII, No. 4, p. 79

Elongate-oval, convex; bronzed black; antennae and legs dark red. Pronotum oval, not broader than long; disk with a median impressed line. Elytra deeply striate; striae entire, punctate indistinctly on apical half; third interval with two punctures. Length 5.5–6 mm.

Genus IV. *CLIVINA* Latreille

These species are similar in habit to those of the preceding genus and often occur with them. They are characterized as small black or reddish-brown forms; head not grooved longitudinally; palpi similar in both sexes; pronotum subquadrate, sides either strongly oblique or rounded toward base, disk with median impressed line; first antennal segment about as long as second; protarsi slender in both sexes.

KEY TO SPECIES

1. Mesotibiae with spur near outer tip (Fig. 90) 2
   Mesotibiae without such a spur 3
2. Profemora with a tooth near apex (Fig. 91); color black ....a. *dentipes*
   Profemora thickened, not dentate; color reddish brown ....b. *impressifrons*
3. Clypeus with a lobe each side (Fig. 93); profemora deeply sinuate near apex
   (Fig. 92); elytra without red spots ....c. *americana*
   Clypeus rounded at sides (Fig. 94); profemora thickened, not sinuate; elytra
   usually with obscure red spots ....d. *bipustulata*

a. *Clivina dentipes* Dejean   Plate VIII, No. 5, p. 79

Elongate, slender; black, shining; legs piceous; antennae and tarsi reddish brown. Head smooth, without an impressed median line. Pronotum quadrate, sides nearly straight, strongly arcuate near base; posterior angles lacking; disk with distinct median impressed line, either side with many fine, transverse striae. Elytral striae finely punctate; intervals convex. Length 7.5–9 mm.

b. *Clivina impressifrons* LeConte   Plate VIII, No. 6, p. 79

Elongate-oblong, convex; reddish brown. Front of head medially deeply impressed. Pronotum slightly elongate, sides broadly sinuate medially; posterior angles broadly rounded; disk with distinct median impressed line and with feeble transverse striations. Elytral striae finely punctate; intervals convex. Length 6–6.5 mm.

These beetles are usually found underneath stones near water and in low, damp fields.

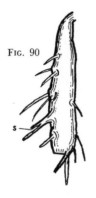

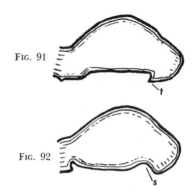

Fig. 90. Right mesotibia of *Clivina dentipes*, with a spur (*s*) on outer side apically.

Fig. 91. Posterior side of the profemur of *Clivina dentipes*, with a tooth (*t*) at apex.

Fig. 92. Posterior side of profemur of *Clivina americana*, with a deep sinuation (*s*) near apex.

c. *Clivina americana* Dejean   Plate VIII, No. 7, p. 79

Elongate-oblong, slender; black; a narrow margin of pronotum and elytra as well as the entire legs reddish brown; antennae pale brown. Front of head with a short median impression. Pronotum quadrate; sides feebly arcuate from base to apex; disk with a median impressed line from near base to apex, either side with numerous irregular, transverse striations. Elytral striae finely, deeply punctate; intervals convex. Length 5 mm.

d. *Clivina bipustulata* (Fabricius)   Plate VIII, No. 8, p. 79

Elongate-oblong, convex; black, usually with two large, indistinct, red spots near base of elytra and two near the apex; legs and antennae reddish brown. Front of head smooth, not impressed medially. Pronotum subquadrate; sides gradually narrowed from base to apex; posterior angles narrowly rounded; median impressed line from base to near apex, sides of disk smooth, without transverse striations. Elytral striae coarsely punctate; intervals feebly convex. Length 6–8 mm.

Genus V. *ASPIDOGLOSSA* Putzeys

Small, elongate-oblong; mentum feebly emarginate; head smooth, without longitudinal grooves; pronotum subglobose, lateral margin with no more than two bristle-bearing punctures; second and fourth intervals of elytra with numerous punctures; protarsi dilated in both sexes.

Only one species comprises this genus. It may be found beneath stones, logs, and debris in moist woods or under stones near water.

Aspidoglossa subangulata Chaudoir   Plate VI, No. 7, p. 57
Elongate-oblong; black, strongly shining; antennae and legs reddish brown; elytra with a reddish spot on apical fourth. Pronotum feebly transverse, sides and base continuously rounded, apex truncate; disk smooth, without a median impressed line. Elytral striae deep, coarsely punctate; second interval with seven or eight, the fourth with five or six dorsal punctures. Length 7.5–8 mm.

Genus VI. *SCHIZOGENIUS* Putzeys

Small, elongate-oblong, slender; blackish or reddish brown; head with several fine, longitudinal grooves, mentum deeply emarginate; pronotum subquadrate, sides feebly arcuate almost to base, thence strongly rounded, disk with a median impressed line and with a long sulcus toward sides; antennae with first segment about as long as second; protarsi rather dilated in both sexes.

In habits, they are similar to the two preceding genera, living in damp places.

KEY TO SPECIES

1. Black or piceous above ....a. *lineolatus*
   Brown above 2
2. Pronotum with posterior angles rounded ....b. *ferrugineus*
   Pronotum with posterior angles dentate ....c. *amphibius*

a. *Schizogenius lineolatus* (Say)   Plate VIII, No. 9, p. 79
Elongate-oblong, subdepressed; black or piceous, shining; beneath, dark reddish brown. Pronotum subquadrate; sides gradually narrowed to apex; disk with a deep, broad, median impressed line and an oblique one either side on basal two-thirds; posterior angles rounded. Elytra subdepressed, deeply striate, striae distinctly punctate. Length 3.5–5 mm.

FIG. 93   FIG. 94

Figs. 93–94. Anterior margin of clypeus of *Clivina americana* (93) and of *C. bipustulata* (94), the sides with a lobe (*l*) in the former.

b. *Schizogenius ferrugineus* Putzeys   Plate VIII, No. 10, p. 79

Elongate-oblong, subdepressed; light yellowish brown to dark brown, shining. Pronotum feebly elongate, sides nearly parallel; disk with a median impressed line distinct but fine, each side with a broad, deeply impressed, arcuate line. Elytra rather convex, deeply striate, striae feebly punctate. Length 3–4 mm.

c. *Schizogenius amphibius* (Haldeman)   Plate VIII, No. 11, p. 79

Elongate-oblong, subdepressed; dark reddish brown, shining; elytra darker. Pronotum feebly elongate; disk with a fine median impressed line and a similar arcuate line each side on basal two-thirds; posterior angles dentate. Elytra subdepressed; striae deep and distinctly punctate. Length 3–4 mm.

Tribe BEMBIDIINI

KEY TO GENERA

Elytra with sutural striae not recurved at apex, scutellar stria present;
   protibiae not obliquely truncate at apex ....I. *Bembidion*   (p. 76)
Elytra with sutural striae recurved at apex, no scutellar stria present;
   protibiae obliquely truncate at apex ....II. *Tachys*   (p. 82)

Genus I. *BEMBIDION* Latreille

Small, oval, depressed beetles; antennae slender, inserted beneath a feeble frontal margin, first two segments glabrous; eyes prominent; pronotum constricted basally; elytra striate, the sutural stria not recurved at apex, a scutellar stria present; protibiae deeply emarginate, apical angle not obliquely truncate; metacoxae contiguous; first two segments of male protarsi dilated, first slightly elongate and nearly quadrate, second triangular, inner angle slightly prolonged.

The adults are most commonly found along the banks of bodies of water and on mud flats.

KEY TO SPECIES

1. Elytra each with two dorsal punctures on third interval 2
   Elytra each with two dorsal punctures on third stria 5
2. Elytral humeri subangulate 3
   Elytral humeri rounded 7
3. Elytra each with two quadrate impressions on third interval each enclosing
   a dorsal puncture 4
   Elytra without quadrate impressions on third interval but with two dorsal
   punctures ....c. *confusum*

4. Elytra with fourth striae sinuate; body slender; pronotum not wider at base than at apex ....a. *inaequale*
   Elytral fourth striae straight; body robust; pronotum wider at base than at apex ....b. *punctatostriatum*
5. Eighth elytral stria distinct from side margin 6
   Eighth elytral stria indistinct from side margin ....f. *picipes*
6. Elytral humeri subangulate, striae entire ....d. *americanum*
   Elytral humeri rounded, first and second striae entire, remaining abbreviated posteriorly ....e. *nigrum*
7. Head with a single stria either side of middle 8
   Head with two striae either side of middle, these often convergent 11
8. Pronotum narrower at base than at apex 9
   Pronotum not narrower at base than at apex 10
9. Form depressed; all striae of elytra entire ....i. *rapidum*
   Form convex; several of elytral striae abbreviated ....j. *versicolor*
10. Pronotal median impression deep, rather broad, except at extreme base and apex, nearly attaining apical margin; elytra dull yellow, with indistinct bands of brownish ....h. *variegatum*
    Pronotal median impression shallow, fine, not attaining base or apex; elytra blackish, with several small, dull-yellow maculae ....g. *patruele*
11. Elytra each with three or four pale, dull-yellowish maculae; pronotal posterior angles obtuse, not projecting (Fig. 95) ....k. *affine*
    Elytra each with two clear, pale-yellow maculae; pronotal posterior angles acute, projecting (Fig. 96) ....l. *quadrimaculatum*

a. *Bembidion inaequale* Say   Plate VIII, No. 12, p. 79

Oval, rather slender, convex; black, brassy-bronzed, shining; antennae piceous, basal segment pale reddish; legs dark green, femora at base and tibiae more or less yellowish. Pronotum subquadrate, sides arcuate from apex to beyond middle, constricted feebly before basal angles, which are subacute; disk with a deep median impressed line, surface finely alutaceous, basal impressions small, deep. Elytral base more than one-half wider than pronotum; striae deep, punctate; intervals flat, alutaceous, third to sixth more or less sinuate, with two quadrate impressed areas around the dorsal punctures. Length 4.5–5.5 mm.

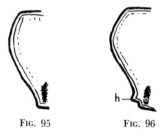

FIG. 95   FIG. 96

Figs. 95–96. Left margin of pronotum of *Bembidion affine* (95) and of *B. quadrimaculatum* (96); in the latter the hind angle (*h*) is acute and projecting, whereas it is merely obtuse in the former.

PLATE VIII
Family CARABIDAE III

1. *Dyschirius globulosus* Say (p. 72) — Black or dark brown; legs yellowish brown; 2.5–3 mm.

2. *Scarites substriatus* Haldeman (p. 72) — Black, shining; 25–30 mm.

3. *S. subterraneus* Fabricius (p. 71) — Black, shining; 15–20 mm.

4. *Dyschirius sphaericollis* Say (p. 73) — Black; elytra fuscous; legs dark reddish; 5.5–6 mm.

5. *Clivina dentipes* Dejean (p. 73) — Black; legs fuscous or dark brown; 7.5–9 mm.

6. *C. impressifrons* LeConte (p. 73) — Reddish brown; 6–6.5 mm.

7. *C. americana* Dejean (p. 74) — Blackish; legs reddish brown; 5 mm.

8. *C. bipustulata* (Fabricius) (p. 74) — Blackish; elytral spots reddish; legs brown; 6–8 mm.

9. *Schizogenius lineolatus* (Say) (p. 75) — Blackish; shining; 3.5–5 mm.

10. *S. ferrugineus* Putzeys (p. 76) — Red-brown; 3–4 mm.

11. *S. amphibius* (Haldeman) (p. 76) — Fuscous; legs dark red-brown; 3–4 mm.

12. *Bembidion inaequale* Say (p. 77) — Black, with a brassy reflex; legs metallic green; 4.5–5.5 mm.

13. *B. punctatostriatum* Say (p. 80) — Black, with a bronze reflex; 6–7.5 mm.

14. *B. americanum* Dejean (p. 80) — Black, with a brassy reflex; 5–6 mm.

15. *B. nigrum* Say (p. 80) — Black, tinged with greenish or bronze; legs red-brown; 3.5–5 mm.

16. *B. picipes* (Kirby) (p. 80) — Black or fuscous; legs brownish yellow; 5–6 mm.

17. *B. affine* Say (p. 82) — Blackish; elytral spots and legs pale brown; 2.5–3.5 mm.

18. *B. versicolor* (LeConte) (p. 81) — Greenish black; elytral spots reddish or yellowish; legs light brown; 2.5–3.5 mm.

19. *B. quadrimaculatum* (Linné) (p. 82) — Fuscous, bronzed; elytra brownish, with yellowish spots; legs yellow-brown; 2.7–3.7 mm.

20. *Agonoderus lecontei* Chaudoir (p. 125) — Brownish yellow; head and elytral spots blackish; 5–7 mm.

21. *Tachys incurvus* (Say) (p. 82) — Dark orange-brown; legs paler; 1.5–2.5 mm.

22. *T. scitulus* LeConte (p. 83) — Brownish yellow; head darker; 2.5–3 mm.

23. *T. inornatus* (Say) (p. 83) — Blackish; legs dark brown; 2–3 mm.

24. *Agonoderus comma* (Fabricius) (p. 126) — Brownish yellow; head and elytral spots blackish; 6–7 mm.

MM | 0 | 10 | 20 | 30 | 40 | 50 | 60 | 70

PLATE VIII 79

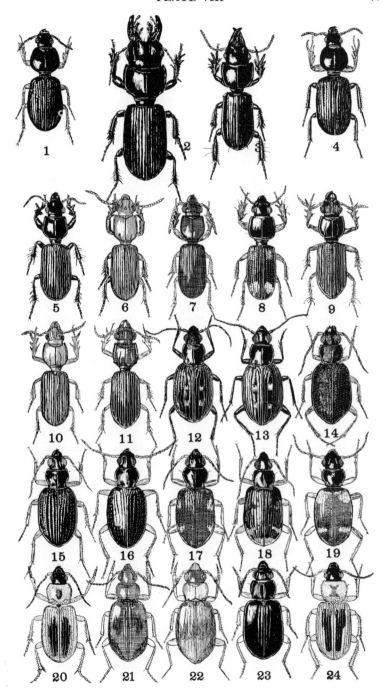

b. *Bembidion punctatostriatum* Say   Plate VIII, No. 13, p. 79

Oval, rather robust, subconvex; black, coppery-bronzed, shining; antennae and legs piceous, bronzed, femora at base and tibiae beneath sometimes yellowish. Pronotum slightly transverse, sides feebly rounded apically, narrower at apex than at base; posterior angles prominent, dentiform; disk feebly rugose, finely alutaceous, median impressed line distinct, basal impressions broad and deep. Elytral striae punctate, fourth stria straight or nearly so; intervals feebly convex, finely alutaceous, third with two quadrate impressed areas around the dorsal punctures. Length 6–7.5 mm.

c. *Bembidion confusum* Hayward   Plate IX, No. 3, p. 91

Elongate-ovate, moderately robust, convex; black, bronzed or coppery, shining; disk of elytra dull brownish yellow, striae metallic green; legs and basal third of antennae pale yellowish. Pronotum with sides arcuate nearly to base; posterior angles prominent, subrectangular, feebly carinate; disk alutaceous, finely rugose basally, basal impressions broad, deep, and bistriate. Elytra about one-half again as wide as pronotum; striae fine and finely punctate; two dorsal punctures on third interval. Length 4.5–6.5 mm.

d. *Bembidion americanum* Dejean   Plate VIII, No. 14, p. 79

Oval, rather robust, subdepressed; black, feebly bronzed, shining; antennae piceous, first and second segments and tibiae dark reddish brown. Pronotum distinctly transverse, sides rounded; apex subtruncate, slightly wider than base; feebly constricted basally; basal angles rectangular; disk finely rugose at base, median line distinct, basal impressions shallow. Elytra feebly striate, striae distinctly punctate to near apex, third with two dorsal punctures, these large and subfoveate in form; intervals flat, finely alutaceous. Length 5–6 mm.

e. *Bembidion nigrum* Say   Plate VIII, No. 15, p. 79

Elongate-oval, slender, subdepressed; black, feebly shining, tinged with greenish or bronze; antennae fuscous, basal segments and legs reddish brown. Pronotum feebly transverse, sides feebly arcuate, sinuate before base, which is slightly narrower than apex; disk nearly smooth, median impressed line distinct, basal impressions broad and deep, bistriate. Elytral humeri broadly rounded; striae deeply, coarsely punctate, not attaining apex, the third with two indistinct dorsal punctures; intervals smooth, subconvex. Length 3.5–5 mm.

f. *Bembidion picipes* (Kirby)   Plate VIII, No. 16, p. 79

Elongate-ovate, rather slender, subdepressed; piceous or black, shining, infrequently bronzed or bluish; antennae piceous or fuscous, basal segment and legs brownish yellow; elytra sometimes with a brownish macula on sides near apex. Pronotum transverse, base narrower than apex; sides arcuate, constricted at base; basal angles rectangular, carinate; disk nearly smooth, median line fine, basal impressions deep. Elytral humeri broadly rounded; striae coarsely punctate, punctures evanescent apically, third stria with two indistinct dorsal punctures, fifth stria merely a groove at apex; intervals smooth, subconvex. Length 5–6 mm.

g. *Bembidion patruele* Dejean   Plate IX, No. 2, p. 91
    Elongate-oval, slender, subconvex; black, somewhat shining; antennae piceous, basal three segments and legs dull yellow; elytra piceous to black, with several small, dull-yellow maculae, two near apex larger and more distinct. Pronotum slightly transverse; sides broadly arcuate, base and apex subequal; basal angles rectangular, carinate; disk alutaceous, median impressed line fine, basal impressions broad and shallow. Elytra with striae irregular, fine, and finely punctate; third interval with two dorsal punctures. Length 3.5–4.7 mm.

h. *Bembidion variegatum* Say   Plate IX, No. 1, p. 91
    Elongate-oval, rather robust, subdepressed; black, somewhat shining; antennae piceous, three basal segments and legs dull yellowish; elytra dull, pale yellow, with irregular dark-brown bands and maculae, a band medially more distinct. Pronotum feebly transverse; sides strongly arcuate; base and apex subequal; basal angles rectangular, carinate; disk alutaceous, with a deep, broad, median impressed line; basal impressions broad and deep. Elytral striae moderately coarse, finely punctate; third interval with two dorsal punctures, anterior much larger than posterior. Length 5–6 mm.

i. *Bembidion rapidum* (LeConte)   Plate IX, No. 4, p. 91
    Elongate-ovate, slightly depressed; black, dark-greenish-bronzed; antennae fuscous, basal segments paler; elytra with apex, a small subapical macula near margin, and rarely a short fascia anterior to middle dull brownish yellow. Head and pronotum alutaceous; pronotal sides curved to beyond middle, thence oblique to base; posterior angles obtuse, carinate; basal impressions small, deep, bistriate. Elytral striae finely punctate to beyond middle; intervals flat. Length 3.7–4.5 mm.

j. *Bembidion versicolor* (LeConte)   Plate VIII, No. 18, p. 79
    Elongate-ovate, slender, subconvex; greenish black, shining, bronzed; elytra yellowish or reddish brown, with three bands of piceous which are usually somewhat connected along suture; antennae piceous, the basal segments and legs reddish brown. Pronotum strongly transverse; base much narrower than apex; posterior angles subacute and slightly projecting; disk smooth except for a number of feebly transverse impressed lines; median impressed line fine but deep; basal impressions deep, sublinear. Elytral striae rather deep, distinctly punctate to behind middle, lateral ones obsolete on apical half; intervals convex, third with two dorsal punctures. Length 2.5–3.5 mm.

k. *Bembidion affine* Say   Plate VIII, No. 17, p. 79

Elongate-oval, rather slender, subconvex; black or piceous, feebly bronzed, shining; elytra with pale-brown spots along the sides, one near humerus, a large triangular one at middle, and a small one at apical fourth, apex also sometimes pale brown; antennae fuscous, basal segments and legs yellowish brown. Pronotum slightly transverse; sides arcuate apically, constricted at base; basal angles rectangular, very finely carinate; disk feebly punctate, with an indistinct median line. Elytra distinctly striate, striae (except first and second) abbreviated apically, coarsely punctate; third interval with two dorsal punctures. Length 2.5–3.5 mm.

l. *Bembidion quadrimaculatum* (Linné)   Plate VIII, No. 19, p. 79

Elongate-oval, subdepressed; head and pronotum bronzed or blackish-bronzed, shining; elytra brown or black, with a triangular subhumeral spot and a smaller one behind middle yellowish; antennae piceous, basal segments and legs dull yellow. Pronotum transverse, base much narrower than apex; posterior angles subacute, projecting; disk smooth, with a fine median line; basal impressions narrow and sublinear. Elytral striae feeble, with distinct punctures, third striae with two dorsal punctures; intervals nearly flat, third with a few minute punctures. Length 2.7–3.7 mm.

Genus II. *TACHYS* Stephens

Small, elongate-oval, convex; antennae slender; eyes rather prominent; pronotum transverse, not constricted basally; elytra glabrous, with or without striae except sutural, which is recurved at apex, scutellar stria wanting; protibiae obliquely truncate at apex.

The species of this genus are usually found in moss, beneath partly decayed logs, and in dead stumps.

KEY TO SPECIES

1. Elytra with only a sutural stria; color dark brown to nearly black, elytra with a yellowish stripe ....a. *incurvus*
   Elytra each with four or five striae 2
2. Brownish yellow; elytra with a dark band behind middle ....b. *scitulus*
   Uniformly black ....c. *inornatus*

a. *Tachys incurvus* (Say)   Plate VIII, No. 21, p. 79

Elongate-ovate, slender, convex; varying from dark reddish brown to nearly black, shining; elytra with a yellowish stripe from humerus nearly to apex, this sometimes interrupted at middle; antennae fuscous, basal segments and legs yellowish. Pronotum feebly transverse, widest before middle, sides rounded apically; basal transverse impression deep, finely punctate; posterior angles rectangular, carinate. Elytra distinctly wider than pronotum, only sutural stria present, although another one is slightly visible. Length 1.5–2.5 mm.

These beetles are usually found beneath stones in open woods.

b. *Tachys scitulus* LeConte   Plate VIII, No. 22, p. 79

Elongate-oval, slender, subdepressed; brownish yellow, feebly shining; head and sometimes pronotum darker; antennae fuscous, basal segment and legs yellowish; elytra with a dark, transverse band behind middle. Pronotum transverse, widest slightly before middle; sides arcuate; apex and base equal in width; posterior angles obtuse. Elytra with four or five fine, distinct striae, these impunctate. Length 2.5–3 mm.

This species is frequently found on mud flats and beneath stones in damp places.

c. *Tachys inornatus* (Say)   Plate VIII, No. 23, p. 79

Elongate-oval, rather robust, subdepressed; black, shining; antennae piceous, basal segments and tibiae and tarsi deep reddish brown. Pronotum feebly transverse, widest before middle; sides rounded apically, oblique basally, feebly sinuate before base; posterior angles rectangular, sometimes carinate; disk finely alutaceous. Elytra with four or five distinct, impunctate striae. Length 2–3 mm.

Tribe POGONINI

Genus *PATROBUS* Dejean

Of medium size, elongate-oval, subconvex; head more or less constricted behind and close to eyes, or transversely impressed; antennae slender, inserted under a feeble frontal ridge; metacoxae contiguous; metatrochanters not acutely pointed; fourth segment of protarsi narrow.

Patrobus longicornis (Say)   Plate X, No. 1, p. 97

Elongate-oval, subconvex; black, shining; beneath piceous; antennae and legs reddish brown, legs paler. Pronotum convex, slightly transverse; sides arcuate to behind middle, thence straight to base; apex with transverse impression and median impressed line deep; basal impressions broad, deep, and punctate; posterior angles rectangular. Elytra deeply striate, the striae punctate; intervals convex, lateral ones more or less flattened. Length 12–14 mm.

This species is found beneath stones and rubbish and along streams and lakes.

Tribe Pterostichini

KEY TO GENERA

1. Elytra without a dorsal puncture 2
   Elytra with at least one dorsal puncture 3
2. Pronotal base strongly wider than apex; elytral humeri rectangular ....X. *Amara*   (p. 92)
   Pronotal base not wider than apex; elytral humeri broadly
   rounded ....I. *Pterostichus*   (p. 85)
3. Metepisterna short, never elongate, usually much shorter than wide
   (Fig. 97) 4
   Metepisterna always distinctly elongate (Fig. 98) 7
4. Elytra with a single dorsal puncture 6
   Elytra with more than one dorsal puncture 5
5. Elytra with two dorsal punctures; pronotal base narrower than
   apex ....IV. *Euferonia*   (p. 86)
   Elytra with three dorsal punctures; pronotal base distinctly wider
   than apex ....V. *Abacidus*   (p. 86)
6. Antennae and protarsi very slender; body small, less than 10 mm.
   in length ....II. *Gastrellarius*   (p. 85)
   Antennae and protarsi robust; body large, more than 12 mm. in
   length ....III. *Eumolops*   (p. 85)
7. Antennae with first two or three basal segments carinate; surface
   usually strongly shining and nearly always with a metallic
   lustre ....VI. *Poecilus*   (p. 87)
   Antennae with first two or three basal segments not carinate; surface strongly shining but not with a metallic lustre 8
8. Pronotum with two basal impressions each side; posterior angles
   subrectangular and slightly projecting ....VII. *Melanius*   (p. 87)
   Pronotum with a single linear basal impression each side; posterior
   angles broadly rounded 9
9. Scutellar stria long, extending to basal fourth ....VIII. *Dysidius*   (p. 89)
   Scutellar stria completely absent ....IX. *Pseudargutor*   (p. 89)

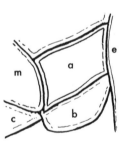

FIG. 97   FIG. 98

Figs. 97–98. Portion of left side of undersurface of *Eumolops* (97) and
of *Poecilus* (98). *a*, metepisternum; *b*, metepimeron;
m, metasternum; *c*, metacoxa; *e*, inflexed portion of elytron.

Genus I. *PTEROSTICHUS* Bonelli

Moderate- or rather large-sized, elongate-ovate, slender, subconvex; next to last segment of labial palpi with two setae; head only feebly constricted behind eyes; elytra without dorsal punctures, margin strongly interrupted posteriorly (Fig. 80); pronotal base not wider than apex; metepisternum subquadrate; protarsi dilated in male.

Pterostichus adoxus (Say)   Plate X, No. 2, p. 97

Elongate-oval, slender, subconvex; black, shining; antennae, legs, and deflexed margin of elytra dark reddish brown. Pronotum slightly elongate, sides arcuate, widest anterior to middle; base narrower than apex; posterior angles rectangular, dentate; disk smooth, with a fine median line and a long, deep impression each side near base. Elytral striae impunctate; intervals subconvex, impunctate. Length 13–15 mm.

This species occurs beneath stones, logs, and the like in woodlands.

Genus II. *GASTRELLARIUS* Casey

Small, elongate-oval, subdepressed; antennae slender, basal segment not carinate; pronotum subquadrate, narrower at base than at apex; elytral sides strongly arcuate, striae entire, scutellar short, each elytron with a single dorsal puncture on third interval; metepisterna subquadrate (Fig. 97).

Gastrellarius honestus (Say)   Plate X, No. 3, p. 97

Elongate-oval, subdepressed; black or piceous, shining; antennae and legs dark reddish brown. Pronotum subquadrate; sides curved, constricted at base and sinuate before posterior angles; disk with a long, deep basal impression each side and with a distinct median line; surface smooth, except between the two basal impressions, where it is sparsely punctate. Elytra wider than pronotum; deeply striate, the striae impunctate; dorsal puncture not very distinct, on apical fourth on third interval from suture. Length 8 mm.

The adults are found beneath logs and stones in wooded areas.

Genus III. *EUMOLOPS* Casey

Moderate-sized, elongate-oval, robust beetles; antennae and protarsi robust; pronotal base narrower than apex, basal impressions bistriate; elytra with a single dorsal puncture, striae with distinct punctures, scutellar stria very short or lacking; metepisterna short (Fig. 97).

Eumolops sodalis (LeConte)   Plate IX, No. 7, p. 91

Elongate-oval, subconvex; dull black; apical half of antennae and tarsi reddish brown. Pronotum with sides strongly arcuate to near base, thence suddenly sinuate; base distinctly narrower than apex; posterior angles distinct but obtuse; disk nearly smooth, median line fine, shallow except near base, where it is suddenly and deeply impressed; basal impressions large and elongate. Elytra deeply striate, the striae rather finely punctate; intervals alutaceous, subconvex. Length 15–17 mm.

Genus IV. *EUFERONIA* Casey

Of medium size, elongate-oval, subdepressed; antennae moderately robust basally, feebly tapering apically; pronotum with base slightly narrower than apex, a broad basal impression either side; elytral striae complete, third interval with two dorsal punctures; metepisterna subquadrate (Fig. 97).

KEY TO SPECIES

Pronotal basal impressions each enclosing a raised portion ....a. *stygica*
Pronotal basal impressions simple ....b. *coracina*

a. *Euferonia stygica* (Say)   Plate X, No. 4, p. 97
Elongate-oval, subdepressed; black, shining; antennae and tarsi piceous. Pronotum subquadrate, sides arcuate, base slightly narrower than apex; posterior angles obtuse, feebly carinate; disk with a fine median line and a broad, rounded impression on each side at base, each of which has a raised portion within it. Elytral striae deep; third interval of each elytron with two large punctures, one at middle and one near apex. Length 14–16 mm.

b. *Euferonia coracina* (Newman)   Plate X, No. 5, p. 97
Elongate-oval, rather robust, subdepressed; piceous to black, shining; antennae and tarsi slightly paler. Pronotum subquadrate; sides arcuate, narrowed posteriorly; basal angles obtuse, feebly carinate; disk with a fine median impressed line and a broad impression each side at base, the latter not containing elevations within. Elytral striae deep; third interval with two dorsal punctures. Length 15–18 mm.

Genus V. *ABACIDUS* LeConte

Of medium size, elongate-ovate, rather robust, subdepressed; basal segments of antennae robust; pronotum quadrate, sides broadly arcuate, base wider than apex, two linear basal impressions each side; elytral striae entire, scutellar distinct, three dorsal punctures present; metepisterna short.

Abacidus permundus (Say)   Plate IX, No. 8, p. 91
Elongate-oval, broad; piceous to black, shining, purplish-bronzed; an-

tennae and legs piceous. Pronotum subquadrate, apex slightly narrower than base; lateral margins narrow anteriorly, wider, depressed, and punctate behind middle; two basal impressions each side, linear, punctate, the outer one shorter. Elytral striae not, or finely, punctate; first dorsal puncture on third stria, the others on the second; intervals convex. Length 12–14 mm.

This species may be found beneath logs in open woods.

Genus VI. *POECILUS* Bonelli

Of moderate size, elongate-oval, subdepressed; basal segments of antennae carinate; pronotum sometimes somewhat narrowed basally, some species with apex narrower than base; elytra each with two to four dorsal punctures, the striae complete; metepisterna distinctly elongate (Fig. 98).

KEY TO SPECIES

Legs with at least femora black; two dorsal elytral punctures ......a. *chalcites*
Entire legs various shades of reddish brown; four dorsal elytral punctures ....
....b. *lucublandus*

a. *Poecilus chalcites* Say   Plate X, No. 6, p. 97
Elongate, oblong-ovate, subdepressed; metallic green, bronzed, or black-green, very shining; legs with at least the femora black, the remaining parts piceous. Pronotum feebly transverse, base and apex subequal; sides arcuate; posterior angles subrectangular; disk with a distinct median impressed line; two linear basal impressions, outer one shorter. Elytra with finely punctate striae; each with two large punctures on third interval; intervals alutaceous. Length 10–14 mm.

This species may be found the year round under rocks and logs.

b. *Poecilus lucublandus* Say   Plate X, No. 7, p. 97
Elongate, oblong-ovate, subdepressed; green or purplish, feebly shining; legs entirely deep or light reddish brown. Pronotum slightly transverse, sides rounded; apex more constricted than base; posterior angles obtuse; disk with a median impressed line and two rather shallow, linear basal impressions each side near base. Elytra usually with impunctate striae; third interval usually with four large punctures, occasionally with only two or three; intervals alutaceous. Length 10–14 mm.

Genus VII. *MELANIUS* Bonelli

Moderate-sized, elongate-oblong, subdepressed; head moderately large, basal segments of antennae not carinate; pronotum narrowed basally, pos-

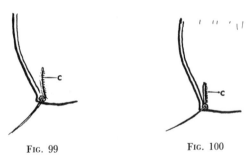

Fɪɢ. 99   Fɪɢ. 100

Figs. 99–100. Left posterior portion of pronotum of *Melaninus ebeninus* (99), with a carina (*c*) near prominent hind angle. In *M. luctuosus* (100) the hind angle is carinate but not prominent.

terior angles carinate (Fig. 99); elytra each with three or four dorsal punctures, the striae complete; metepisterna distinctly elongate.

KEY TO SPECIES

1. Posterior angles of pronotum prominent (Fig. 99) 2
   Posterior angles of pronotum feebly prominent (Fig. 100) 3
2. Basal pronotal impressions impunctate or sparsely so; size 14–16 mm. ......
   ....a. *ebeninus*
   Basal pronotal impressions punctate; size 10–11.5 mm. ....b. *caudicalis*
3. Not longer than 10 mm. ....c. *luctuosus*
   Length 14–15 mm. ....d. *corvinus*

a. *Melanius ebeninus* Dejean   Plate X, No. 8, p. 97

Elongate-oblong, subdepressed; piceous to black, very shining; antennae and legs piceous. Pronotum slightly transverse, distinctly narrowed at base; posterior angles carinate, prominent, rectangular; disk with a median impressed line, a broad basal impression each side with a slight raised area at middle, at most with a few punctures. Elytra finely striate, striae very finely punctate, one dorsal puncture on third stria; intervals subconvex, two dorsal punctures on third interval. Length 14–16 mm.

This species is found beneath logs and stones, especially near water.

b. *Melanius caudicalis* (Say)   Plate X, No. 9, p. 97

Elongate-oblong, slender, subdepressed; black, shining; antennae and legs piceous. Pronotum subquadrate; sides arcuate; base much narrower than apex; posterior angles carinate, prominent, rectangular; disk with a fine median impressed line, a single broad basal impression each side, without an elevated area and distinctly punctate. Elytral striae deep, finely punctate, one dorsal puncture on third stria; intervals subconvex, two dorsal punctures on third interval. Length 10–11.5 mm.

c. *Melanius luctuosus* (Dejean)   Plate X, No. 10, p. 97

Elongate-oblong, slender, subdepressed; fuscous to black, shining; antennae and legs piceous. Pronotum subquadrate; sides arcuate; base slightly narrower than apex; posterior angles carinate, feebly prominent, rectangular; disk with a distinct median line, a broad basal impression each side, strongly punctate. Elytral striae deep, finely punctate, one dorsal puncture on third stria; third interval with two dorsal punctures. Length 8–9 mm.

d. *Melanius corvinus* (Dejean)   Plate X, No. 13, p. 97

Elongate-oblong, rather robust, subdepressed; dark reddish brown to black, shining. Pronotum slightly transverse; sides arcuate, feebly narrowed at base; posterior angles small, feebly prominent or obtuse, carinate; disk with a fine median line, a broad basal impression each side, densely punctate. Elytral striae deep, very finely punctate, one dorsal puncture on third stria; intervals convex, two dorsal punctures on third. Length 13–15 mm.

Genus VIII. *DYSIDIUS* Chaudoir

Of moderate size, elongate-oblong, subdepressed; basal segments of antennae not carinate; pronotum subquadrate, apex equal in width to base; elytra with three dorsal punctures, striae entire, scutellar stria long; metepisternum elongate.

Dysidius mutus (Say)   Plate IX, No. 13, p. 91

Elongate-oblong, rather slender, subdepressed; piceous to black, shining; legs and antennae piceous. Pronotum quadrate; base and apex subequal; sides arcuate; posterior angles subrectangular, feebly prominent; disk with a fine median impressed line, a linear impression each side at base densely punctate. Elytral striae deep, finely punctate, one dorsal puncture on third stria, second and third on second stria; intervals subconvex. Length 10–12.5 mm.

Genus IX. *PSEUDARGUTOR* Casey

Moderately small, elongate-oval, subdepressed; basal segments of antennae not carinate; pronotum feebly elongate, base slightly wider than apex, posterior angles not carinate; elytra each with three dorsal punctures; metepisternum elongate (Fig. 98); metatarsi with basal three or four segments sulcate on outer side.

Pseudargutor erythropus (Dejean)   Plate IX, No. 14, p. 91

Elongate-oval, subdepressed; black, strongly shining; legs and antennae light reddish brown. Pronotum slightly elongate; sides broadly arcuate;

PLATE IX
Family CARABIDAE IV

1. *Bembidion variegatum* Say (p. 81)

Blackish; elytra yellowish, with dark-brown bands; 3.5–4.7 mm.

2. *B. patruele* Dejean (p. 81)

Deep brown or black; elytral spots indistinct, dull yellow; legs yellow-brown; 3.5–4.7 mm.

3. *B. confusum* Hayward (p. 80)

Blackish, elytra red-brown, with green striae; legs yellow-brown; 4.5–6.5 mm.

4. *B. rapidum* (LeConte) (p. 81)

Black; dark-greenish-bronzed; elytral markings brownish yellow; 3.7–4.5 mm.

5. *Amara muscula* (Say) (p. 93)

Blackish, pronotum often paler; legs and antennae reddish brown; 5–5.5 mm.

6. *Calathus gregarius* Dejean (p. 99)

Brown to black, shining; antennae, legs, and pronotal sides orange-brown; 10–11 mm.

7. *Eumolops sodalis* (LeConte) (p. 85)

Black, shining; tarsi reddish brown; 15–17 mm.

8. *Abacidus permundus* (Say) (p. 86)

Blackish, shining; antennae dark brown; 12–14 mm.

9. *Calathus opaculus* LeConte (p. 99)

Dark brown to blackish; elytra not shining; legs, antennae, and pronotal sides orange-brown; 8.5–10 mm.

10. *Amara exarata* (Dejean) (p. 92)

Blackish; antennae and legs red-brown; 8–10 mm.

11. *Rembus laticollis* LeConte (p. 94)

Black; antennae piceous; 13–15 mm.

12. *Amara latior* (Kirby) (p. 92)

Black; legs piceous; antennae reddish brown; 10–10.5 mm.

13. *Dysidius mutus* (Say) (p. 89)

Blackish; antennae and legs piceous; 10–12.5 mm.

14. *Pseudargutor erythropus* (Dejean) (p. 89)

Black, shining; antennae and legs reddish brown; 8–8.5 mm.

MM 0 10 20 30 40 50 60 70

PLATE IX

91

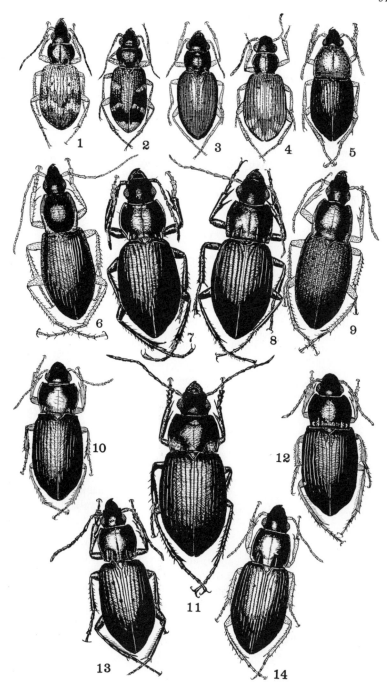

base slightly wider than apex; posterior angles broadly rounded; a single
linear, deep basal impression each side impunctate. Elytral striae deep,
impunctate, scutellar striae absent or very short; intervals convex, three
dorsal punctures on third interval. Length 8–8.5 mm.

This species is usually found under debris near water.

Genus X. *AMARA* Bonelli

Of small or moderate size, oval, robust, subconvex; next to last segment
of labial palpi shorter than apical and with more than two setae anteriorly;
basal two or three segments of antennae carinate; pronotum transverse,
usually narrowed anteriorly, base wider than apex; elytra without dorsal
punctures; metepisternum elongate.

KEY TO SPECIES

1. Pronotum with base and apex subequal; usually cordate 2
   Pronotum much wider at base than at apex, thence gradually narrowed to
   apex 3
2. Scutellar stria very short or obsolete; metasternal sidepieces punctate ....
   ....a. *exarata*
   Scutellar stria long; metasternal sidepieces smooth ....b. *latior*
3. Scutellar stria never more than twice length of scutellum ....c. *muscula*
   Scutellar stria more than four times length of scutellum 4
4. Apical spur of protibiae trifid (Fig. 101) ....g. *angustata*
   Apical spur of protibiae simple 5
5. Basal segments of antennae not carinate 6
   Second and third basal segments of antennae carinate dorsally ....f. *lecontei*
6. Scutellar stria terminating in an ocellate puncture (Fig. 102) ....
   ....d. *impuncticollis*
   Scutellar stria without ocellate puncture ....e. *cupreolata*

a. *Amara exarata* (Dejean)   Plate IX, No. 10, p. 91
   Oblong-oval, robust, strongly convex; piceous to black, shining, antennae
and legs reddish brown. Pronotum subquadrate; two sublinear basal impressions each side punctate; posterior angles small, acute, not distinctly
carinate. Elytral striae deep, closely punctate; intervals flat. Length
8–10 mm.

b. *Amara latior* (Kirby)   Plate IX, No. 12, p. 91
   Oblong-ovate, moderately robust, subconvex; fuscous to black, frequently
bronzed; antennae and tarsi paler. Pronotum transverse; sides broadly
arcuate; posterior angles subrectangular, not distinctly carinate; two sublinear basal impressions each side, the inner one longer, both punctate.
Elytral striae deep, finely punctate, indistinctly so on apical half; intervals
nearly flat. Length 10–10.5 mm.

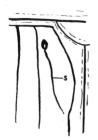

Fig. 101   Fig. 102

Fig. 101. The three-pronged spur (s) of *Amara angustata* and the extreme apex of the left protibia.

Fig. 102. Portion of base of left elytron of *Amara impuncticollis*, the scutellar stria (s) commencing in a large puncture.

c. *Amara muscula* (Say)   Plate IX, No. 5, p. 91

Oblong-ovate; piceous or dark reddish brown, shining; antennae and legs pale reddish brown. Pronotum strongly transverse, distinctly narrowed to apex; posterior angles narrowly rounded; two subobsolete basal impressions finely punctate or smooth. Elytral striae fine, crenately punctate; sutural stria abbreviated; intervals feebly convex; metasternal sidepieces impunctate. Length 5–5.5 mm.

d. *Amara impuncticollis* Say   Plate X, No. 11, p. 97

Oval, robust, convex; fuscous to black, shining, feebly bronzed; tibiae and tarsi dark reddish brown. Pronotum transverse, narrowed anteriorly, impunctate; posterior angles rectangular; basal impression shallow or wanting; disk alutaceous in female, smooth in male. Elytral striae shallow, impunctate, a large puncture present basally at the junction of the sutural and second striae; intervals flat and alutaceous. Length 7–9 mm.

e. *Amara cupreolata* Putzeys   Plate X, No. 12, p. 97

Oval, robust, subconvex; fuscous to black, shining, feebly reflexed with bronze or purple; antennae and legs dark reddish brown. Pronotum transverse, narrowed anteriorly; punctate basally; posterior angles rounded; basal impressions shallow or wanting. Elytral striae finely punctate or impunctate; without a large puncture basally. Length 6–7 mm.

f. *Amara lecontei* Csiki   Plate X, No. 14, p. 97

Oval, robust, subconvex; black, shining, strongly bronzed; bases of antennae, tibiae, and tarsi reddish brown. Second and third segments of antennae carinate. Pronotum strongly transverse, narrowed anteriorly;

posterior angles rectangular; two deep basal impressions each side, inner one sublinear, outer one rounded. Elytral striae fine, shallow, and impunctate; intervals flat, alutaceous. Length 6–7 mm.

g. *Amara angustata* Say   Plate X, No. 15, p. 97
    Oval, robust, subconvex; piceous to black, shining, feebly bronzed; antennae basally and legs reddish yellow. Pronotum transverse, narrowed anteriorly; posterior angles rounded; basal impressions obsolete. Elytra as wide as pronotum; striae deep, fine, impunctate, scutellar stria ending at base in a large puncture; intervals subconvex, alutaceous. Length 6–7.5 mm.

    These beetles may be found around bases of trees and stumps in open woodlands.

Tribe LICININI

KEY TO GENERA

1. Basal three segments of antennae entirely glabrous; size medium to large, 10 mm. or more; at most one dorsal puncture on elytra 2
   Basal two segments of antennae glabrous; size small, not over 7 mm.; third elytral interval with two dorsal punctures ......III. *Badister*   (p. 98)
2. Elytra with one dorsal puncture on third interval; eighth and ninth striae approximate; seventh interval not carinate basally ....I. *Rembus*   (p. 94)
   Elytra without a dorsal puncture; eighth and ninth striae well separated; seventh interval carinate basally ....II. *Dicaelus*   (p. 95)

Genus I. *REMBUS* Latreille

Small to medium-sized; three basal segments of antennae glabrous; elytral eighth and ninth striae approximate; apex of elytra feebly sinuate, seventh interval not carinate basally; metacoxae contiguous; pronotum wider at base than at apex, base feebly overlapping base of elytra.

    The members of this genus are found beneath stones and debris in damp areas.

Rembus laticollis LeConte   Plate IX, No. 11, p. 91
    Broadly ovate, subconvex; black, feebly shining; antennae and tarsi dark brown, basal segments piceous. Pronotum transverse; sides arcuate to behind middle, thence oblique to base; posterior angles rectangular. Elytral striae shallow, not or very feebly punctate; intervals flat. Length 13–15 mm.

Genus II. *DICAELUS* Bonelli

Large, robust, convex; antennae with the basal three segments entirely glabrous; pronotum wider at base than at apex, base prolonged over base of elytra; elytra not sinuate at apex, deeply striate, eighth and ninth striae distant, seventh interval more or less carinate at base, dorsal punctures lacking; metacoxae contiguous, not separated by the apex of the antecoxal piece.

KEY TO SPECIES

1. Pronotum distinctly narrower at apex than at base 2
   Pronotum as wide or wider at apex than at base ....d. *politus*
2. Elytra not uniformly black, but purplish ....b. *purpuratus*
   Elytra black 3
3. Two seta-bearing punctures on pronotal margin near middle ...c. *elongatus*
   One seta-bearing puncture on pronotal margin near middle ....a. *dilatatus*

a. *Dicaelus dilatatus* Say   Plate XI, No. 10, p. 103
   Broadly ovate, very robust; black, very feebly shining; antennae sometimes paler apically. Pronotum transverse; margins slightly reflexed; basal impressions deep and broad; posterior angles narrowly rounded; disk coriaceous. Elytra deeply striate, obsoletely punctate apically; humeral carina extending to apical third. Length 20–25 mm.

b. *Dicaelus purpuratus* Bonelli   Plate XI, No. 12, p. 103
   Elongate-oblong, subdepressed; purplish without a brassy tinge; antennae piceous at base, thence gradually paler to apex; legs black. Pronotum strongly transverse; sides broadly rounded; margins distinctly reflexed; basal impressions deep, broad; posterior angles narrowly rounded; disk transversely coriaceous. Elytral base deeply impressed each side; striae deep, impunctate; intervals strongly convex, alutaceous; humeral carina extending to apical third. Length 20–25 mm.

c. *Dicaelus elongatus* Bonelli   Plate XI, No. 11, p. 103
   Elongate, rather slender, subconvex; black, shining. Pronotum quadrate; margins feebly reflexed; posterior angles broadly rounded; basal impressions deep, sublinear; transverse basal impression shallow. Elytral striae deep, impunctate; humeral carina extending to beyond middle; intervals subconvex, alutaceous, and punctate. Length 15–18 mm.

d. *Dicaelus politus* Dejean   Plate X, No. 16, p. 97
   Elongate-oblong, rather slender, subdepressed; black, shining; antennae dark reddish brown. Pronotum subquadrate; apex and base equal in width; margins scarcely reflexed; posterior angles rounded; basal impres-

PLATE X
Family CARABIDAE V

1. *Patrobus longicornis* (Say) (p. 83) — Black; antennae and legs reddish brown; 12–14 mm.

2. *Pterostichus adoxus* (Say) (p. 85) — Black; legs dark brown; 13–15 mm.

3. *Gastrellarius honestus* (Say) (p. 85) — Chestnut-brown to black; 8 mm.

4. *Euferonia stygica* (Say) (p. 86) — Entirely black; 14–16 mm.

5. *E. coracina* (Newman) (p. 86) — Entirely blackish; 15–18 mm.

6. *Poecilus chalcites* Say (p. 87) — Bronze or green; elytral suture green; 10–14 mm.

7. *P. lucublandus* Say (p. 87) — Green or purplish; legs brown; 10–14 mm.

8. *Melanius ebeninus* Dejean (p. 88) — Entirely black; 14–16 mm.

9. *M. caudicalis* (Say) (p. 88) — Entirely black; 10–11.5 mm.

10. *M. luctuosus* (Dejean) (p. 89) — Entirely blackish; 8–9 mm.

11. *Amara impuncticollis* Say (p. 93) — Blackish, with a brassy reflex; 7–9 mm.

12. *A. cupreolata* Putzeys (p. 93) — Blackish, with a brassy reflex; 6–7 mm.

13. *Melanius corvinus* (Dejean) (p. 89) — Dark brown to black; 13–15 mm.

14. *Amara lecontei* Csiki (p. 93) — Black, with a brassy reflex; 6–7 mm.

15. *A. angustata* Say (p. 94) — Black, with a feeble brassy reflex; 6–7.5 mm.

16. *Dicaelus politus* Dejean (p. 95) — Entirely black; 11–14 mm.

17. *Badister notatus* Haldeman (p. 98) — Black; elytra brown; 4–4.5 mm.

18. *B. pulchellus* LeConte (p. 98) — Dull brownish yellow; elytral spots and head black; 5.5–6.5 mm.

19. *B. micans* LeConte (p. 98) — Head black; remainder piceous; legs yellow-brown; 5.5–6 mm.

20. *Platynus hypolithos* (Say) (p. 100) — Fuscous to black; legs light brown; very slender; 13–15 mm.

21. *P. decens* Say (p. 100) — Black; antennae, legs, and pronotal margin piceous; 12–14 mm.

22. *P. sinuatus* (Dejean) (p. 101) — Dark brown to black; antennae and legs dark brown; 8.5–9.5 mm.

23. *P. melanarius* (Dejean) (p. 101) — Black; 9.5–11 mm.

24. *P. reflexus* LeConte (p. 101) and *P. cincticollis* (Say) (p. 101) — Piceous; legs and antennae paler in *reflexus;* 9.5–11 mm.

25. *P. extensicollis* (Say) (p. 101) — Metallic green or bronze; elytra often purplish; legs light brown; 8–9.5 mm.

MM | 0 10 20 30 40 50 60 70

PLATE X

97

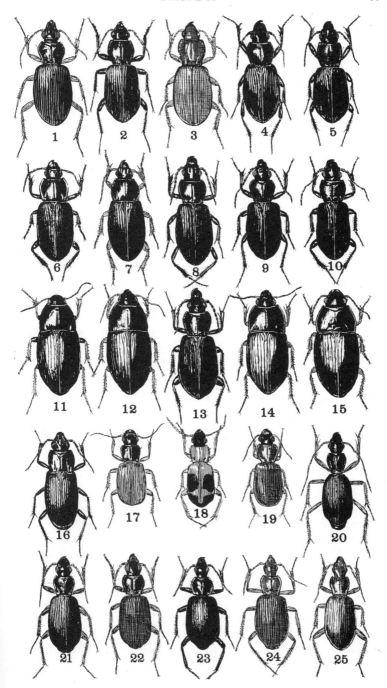

sions narrow, linear. Elytral striae deep, impunctate; humeral carina extending only to basal quarter; intervals convex, impunctate. Length 11–14 mm.

Genus III. *BADISTER* Clairville

Small, elongate-oval, subconvex; antennae with two basal segments entirely glabrous; pronotal base narrower than apex and widely separated from base of elytra; elytral eighth and ninth striae not approximate, third interval with two dorsal punctures, apex not sinuate, seventh interval not carinate basally; metacoxae contiguous, not separated by the apex of the antecoxal piece.

KEY TO SPECIES

1. Elytral striae deep; intervals narrow, convex ....*a. notatus*
   Elytral striae shallow; intervals flat or nearly so 2
2. Elytra maculate ....*b. pulchellus*
   Elytra immaculate ....*c. micans*

a. *Badister notatus* Haldeman   Plate X, No. 17, p. 97
Elongate-oval, slender, subconvex; head and pronotum black, shining; elytra reddish brown, darker apically; antennae and legs reddish yellow. Pronotum obcordate; posterior angles obtuse; basal impressions deep. Elytral striae deep, sparsely punctate; intervals narrow, convex. Length 4–4.5 mm.

b. *Badister pulchellus* LeConte   Plate X, No. 18, p. 97
Elongate-oval, slender, subconvex; dull brownish yellow; head black, elytra with two black, iridescent maculae. Pronotum obcordate, posterior angles broadly rounded; basal impressions broad and shallow. Elytral striae shallow, sparsely punctate; intervals flat or nearly so. Length 5.5–6.5 mm.

c. *Badister micans* LeConte   Plate X, No. 19, p. 97
Elongate-oval, slender, subconvex; piceous, with a bluish lustre; head black; antennal basal segment paler; legs dull yellowish brown. Pronotum transverse; posterior angles narrowly rounded; basal impressions broad and distinct. Elytra shallowly striate; intervals flat. Length 5.5–6 mm.

Tribe PLATYNINI

KEY TO GENERA

Tarsal claws more or less serrate (Fig. 103) ....I. *Calathus* (p. 99)
Tarsal claws not serrate ....II. *Platynus* (p. 99)

Fig. 103   Fig. 104

Fig. 103. Serrate tarsal claws of *Calathus*.
Fig. 104. Pectinate tarsal claws of *Lebia*.

Genus I. *CALATHUS* Bonelli

Small or moderate-sized; antennae slender, inserted under a feeble ridge on front of head, three basal segments glabrous; pronotum with two setigerous punctures each side; elytra margined basally, with dorsal punctures; metacoxae contiguous; tarsi smooth, claws serrate.

The members of this genus are found under stones, logs, and leaves in dry upland woods.

KEY TO SPECIES

Entire upper surface shining; margins of pronotum reflexed ....a. *gregarius*
Head and pronotum shining, elytra dull; pronotal margins depressed, broader
   posteriorly, not reflexed ....b. *opaculus*

a. *Calathus gregarius* Dejean   Plate IX, No. 6, p. 91
    Elongate-ovate, slender, subdepressed; dark reddish brown to piceous, shining; pronotal margins paler; antennae and legs reddish brown. Pronotum feebly elongate; two setigerous punctures each side near margins; side margins slightly reflexed; posterior angles narrowly rounded; basal impressions obsolete. Elytral striae shallow, impunctate; intervals feebly convex, smooth; two dorsal punctures on third interval. Length 10–11 mm.

b. *Calathus opaculus* LeConte   Plate IX, No. 9, p. 91
    Elongate-ovate, moderately robust, subdepressed; head and pronotum reddish brown to piceous, shining; antennae and legs slightly paler; elytra dull piceous or fuscous, opaque. Pronotum subquadrate; side margins broad, depressed; posterior angles narrowly rounded; basal impressions obsolete. Elytral striae fine, impunctate; intervals flat, densely alutaceous; two dorsal punctures on third interval. Length 8.5–10 mm.

Genus II. *PLATYNUS* Say

Of small or medium size, elongate-oval, subconvex; antennae long and slender, pubescent from fourth segment; pronotum widened at or anterior to middle, narrowed toward base and apex, apical angles acute or well defined, two setigerous punctures each side; elytra much wider than pronotum, punctate, eighth stria distant from margin and not deeply impressed; legs more or less long and slender; metacoxae contiguous; claws simple.

KEY TO SPECIES

1. Humeral angles of elytra wanting; metasternal sidepieces short, feebly longer than wide ....a. *hypolithos*
   Humeral angles of elytra broadly rounded; metasternal sidepieces elongate, at least twice as long as wide 2
2. Posterior angles of pronotum not rounded 3
   Posterior angles of pronotum strongly rounded, rarely obtuse or angulate ..8
3. Protarsi without grooves; meso- and metatarsi with grooves on sides 4
   All tarsi with distinct grooves on sides 7
4. Broad species; elytral striae at base deeply impressed, intervals convex 5
   Slender species; elytral striae fine at base; intervals flat or nearly so at base ..6
5. Posterior angles of pronotum obtuse; metasternal sidepieces impunctate ....b. *decens*
   Posterior angles of pronotum rectangular; metasternal sidepieces punctate ....c. *sinuatus*
6. Posterior angles of pronotum almost rounded; elytral intervals alutaceous ....d. *cincticollis*
   Posterior angles of pronotum not rounded; elytral intervals not alutaceous ....e. *reflexus*
7. Pronotum deep green; pronotal basal impressions long and deep ....
   ....f. *extensicollis*
   Pronotum yellow; pronotal basal impressions small, narrow ......g. *decorus*
8. Lateral margins of pronotum wider basally and strongly reflexed 9
   Lateral margins of pronotum narrow, scarcely or not at all reflexed ....
   ....j. *picipennis*
9. Elytral intervals smooth; three dorsal punctures..............h. *melanarius*
   Elytral intervals alutaceous; five or six dorsal punctures ....i. *placidus*

a. *Platynus hypolithos* (Say)   Plate X, No. 20, p. 97
   Elongate-oval, slender, subdepressed; piceous to black, shining; undersurface dark reddish brown or piceous; legs and antennae pale reddish brown. Pronotum one-half longer than wide, constricted basally; margin strongly reflexed; basal impressions deep; median impressed line shallow, indistinct; posterior angles rounded. Elytra deeply striate; intervals convex, alternate ones with an irregular row of coarse punctures along the sides. Length 13–15 mm.

b. *Platynus decens* Say   Plate X, No. 21, p. 97
   Elongate-oval, slender, subdepressed; black; antennae, legs, and margin of pronotum piceous. Pronotum constricted posteriorly; basal impressions elongate, shallow, and punctate; posterior angles obtuse; margins broad, reflexed. Elytral striae deep, obsoletely punctate; intervals convex, finely alutaceous. Length 12–14 mm.

c. *Platynus sinuatus* (Dejean)   Plate X, No. 22, p. 97

Elongate-oval, slender, subdepressed; fuscous to black, shining; antennae, legs, and margin of pronotum piceous. Pronotum elongate, constricted near base; median impressed line shallow; basal impressions broad; margins reflexed; posterior angles rectangular. Elytra deeply striate, finely punctate; intervals convex. Length 10.5–11 mm.

d. *Platynus cincticollis* (Say)   Plate X, No. 24, p. 97

Elongate-oval, slender, subdepressed; piceous. Pronotum constricted at base and apex, more distinctly so at base; margins laterally strongly reflexed; posterior angles obtuse; median impressed line distinct; basal impressions deep, not punctate. Elytra deeply striate, impunctate; intervals basally flat. Length 9.5–11 mm.

e. *Platynus reflexus* LeConte   Plate X, No. 24, p. 97

Elongate-oval, slender, subdepressed; piceous; legs and antennae paler. Pronotum scarcely longer than wide, strongly constricted basally; side margins very strongly reflexed; posterior angles obtuse. Elytra very deeply striate; intervals flattened basally. Length 9.5–11 mm.

This species is found under stones along streams and in caves.

f. *Platynus extensicollis* (Say)   Plate X, No. 25, p. 97

Elongate-oval, slender, subdepressed; head and pronotum greenish or bronzed, shining; elytra greenish or purplish; undersurface piceous; legs and antennae yellowish brown. Pronotum slightly elongate, constricted at base; apical angles acute; basal impressions deep, punctate, with a small blunt tubercle on outer side near acute posterior angles. Elytral striae impunctate; intervals subconvex, finely alutaceous, third with four or five small punctures. Length 8–9.5 mm.

g. *Platynus decorus* (Say)   Plate VII, No. 12, p. 69

Elongate-oval, slender, subdepressed; head green or greenish bronze; entire pronotum, scutellum, legs, and base of antennae reddish yellow; elytra bluish, often green near margins. Pronotum slightly elongate, narrowed at base; posterior angles obtuse; basal impressions and median impressed line distinct. Elytral striae shallow, impunctate; intervals subconvex, finely alutaceous, finely punctate. Length 7.5–8.5 mm.

h. *Platynus melanarius* (Dejean)   Plate X, No. 23, p. 97

Elongate-oval, rather broad, subdepressed; black, shining; tibiae, tarsi, and basal segment of antennae dark reddish brown. Pronotum quadrate; sides broadly arcuate; base and apex subequal; lateral margins wider and more strongly reflexed basally; posterior angles broadly rounded; basal impressions large, with a distinct low tubercle near the angle. Elytral striae distinctly impressed, finely punctate; intervals subconvex, feebly alutaceous; three dorsal punctures, apical one on second stria, other two near third stria. Length 8.5–9.5 mm.

PLATE XI
Family CARABIDAE VI

1. *Lebia viridis* Say (p. 106)

Bright metallic green or purplish blue; legs black; 4.5–5.5 mm.

2. *L. atriventris* Say (p. 106)

Brown-orange; elytra deep purple; 6–7 mm.

3. *L. pumila* Dejean (p. 106)

Piceous, with a brassy reflex; 3–3.5 mm.

4. *L. ornata* Say (p. 107)

Piceous; elytral spots pale yellow; sides of pronotum and legs brown; 4.5–5 mm.

5. *L. grandis* Hentz (p. 106)

Brown-orange; elytra violet or green; 8.5–9.5 mm.

6. *L. scapularis* Dejean (p. 107)

Orange-brown; elytra fuscous, with yellowish stripes; 4.5–5.5 mm.

7. *Brachinus fumans* (Fabricius) (p. 108)

Brown-orange; elytra black-violet; 11.5–12 mm.

8. *B. cordicollis* Dejean (p. 108)

Brown-orange; elytra black-violet; 7.5–9 mm.

9. *Chlaenius tricolor* Dejean (p. 110)

Metallic green; elytra deep blue; antennae and legs orange; 11.5–13 mm.

10. *Dicaelus dilatatus* Say (p. 95)

Black; 20–25 mm.

11. *D. elongatus* Bonelli (p. 95)

Black; 15–18 mm.

12. *D. purpuratus* Bonelli (p. 95)

Black, with a purple sheen; 20–25 mm.

13. *Chlaenius pennsylvanicus* Say (p. 110)

Green; elytra dark green or purple; legs orange-brown; 10–12 mm.

14. *C. nemoralis* Say (p. 110)

Head green or bronze; pronotum bronze; elytra purple; legs yellow-brown; 11–13 mm.

15. *C. cordicollis* Kirby (p. 111)

Above entirely bright violet or green; legs red-brown; 12.5–15 mm.

16. *C. aestivus* Say (p. 111)

Green, with a bronze reflex; elytra black, with bluish tinge; legs orange-brown; 16–17 mm.

MM | 0 | 10 | 20 | 30 | 40 | 50 | 60 | 70

PLATE XI.

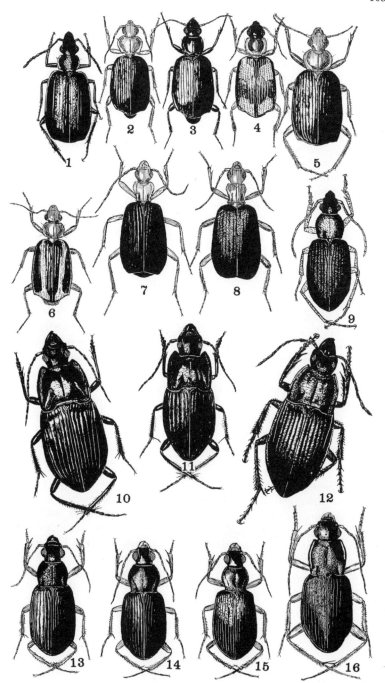

i. *Platynus placidus* (Say)   Plate XII, No. 16, p. 115
Elongate-oval, rather broad, subdepressed; head and pronotum greenish black; elytra bluish or purplish black, subopaque; antennae dark reddish brown basally. Pronotum subquadrate; basal impressions broad and shallow; posterior angles obtuse. Elytral striae fine, impunctate; intervals slightly convex, distinctly alutaceous; five or six dorsal punctures, apical two on second stria, the others on or near the third. Length 7.5–9 mm.

j. *Platynus picipennis* (Kirby)   Plate XII, No. 15, p. 115
Elongate-oblong, very slender, subdepressed; head and pronotum from very dark reddish brown to black; antennae, legs, and elytra brownish yellow. Pronotum as long as wide; lateral margins narrow; posterior angles rounded; basal impressions elongate, shallow. Elytral striae fine, impunctate; intervals nearly flat, the third with four to six dorsal punctures. Length 6–7 mm.

Tribe ODACANTHINI

Genus *COLLIURUS* Latreille

Small, rather slender, subconvex; head elongate, prolonged behind eyes, neck constricted and dilated posteriorly; setigerous punctures of second elytral stria indistinct and rarely more than four in number; antennae slender, first segment nearly as long as next two together, three basal segments glabrous; pronotum scarcely elongate, margin feeble, one or two setigerous punctures on either side; elytral sides narrowly inflexed, apex truncate; metacoxae contiguous; tarsi slender, fourth segment entire or feebly emarginate; claws simple.

These are rather interestingly shaped beetles which have the appearance of ants. They occur beneath logs, stones, and leaves.

Colliurus pennsylvanicus Linné   Plate XIII, No. 4, p. 123
Slender, elongate-oval, subconvex; head and pronotum black; elytra brownish orange, each with two black maculae forming an interrupted transverse band at middle and a small transverse one at apex; antennae fuscous, with three basal segments reddish; legs pale yellowish brown, apex of femora and base of tibiae darker. Pronotum cylindrical, broader at base than at apex. Elytral striae with very large punctures on basal half. Length 7–8 mm.

Tribe DRYPTINI

Genus *GALERITA* Fabricius

Of medium size, rather slender, subconvex; head elongate, strongly constricted at base; mandibles without fixed seta in scrobe; labrum wider than apex of clypeus; first antennal segment elongate; pronotum with lateral margin flattened, narrow but distinct; elytra broadly, obliquely truncate at apex; procoxal cavities with two openings inwardly; mesocoxal cavities entirely closed by sterna.

The members of this genus are often attracted to light and live beneath stones and leaves in open woods.

KEY TO SPECIES

Pronotum feebly longer than wide; posterior angles rectangular, not produced ....a. *janus*
Pronotum strongly elongate, posterior angles distinctly produced .....b. *bicolor*

a. *Galerita janus* Fabricius   Plate XIII, No. 1, p. 123
  Elongate-oval, convex; black, densely clothed with short, pale-yellowish hairs; legs, palpi, pronotum, and base of antennae reddish brown; elytra blue-black. Pronotum slightly elongate; side margins reflexed at the rectangular posterior angles; disk finely, densely rugose. Elytral striae fine, impunctate; intervals flat, finely, transversely rugose. Length 17–22 mm.

b. *Galerita bicolor* Drury   Color Plate C; Plate XIII, No. 3, p. 123
  Elongate-oval, subconvex; black, densely clothed with pale-yellowish hairs; legs, palpi, pronotum, and base of antennae reddish brown; elytra blue-black. Pronotum strongly elongate; side margins feebly reflexed at the slightly produced posterior angles; disk finely, rugosely punctate. Elytral striae fine, impunctate; intervals flat, finely, transversely rugose. Length 17–21 mm.

Tribe LEBIINI

Genus *LEBIA* Latreille

Very small to moderately small, rather broadly oval, subconvex; head constricted into a neck behind eyes; mentum emarginate; mandibles with a distinct scrobe; antennae inserted under a feeble ridge on front of head, at least three basal segments glabrous; pronotum a little wider than head, much narrower than elytra, lateral margins distinct, with a seta each side near basal angle; elytra truncate at apex, margin entire and narrowly inflexed; metacoxae contiguous; tibial spurs always less than one-half length of metatarsus; tarsal claws pectinate (Fig. 104).

KEY TO SPECIES

1. Head and pronotum reddish yellow, elytra entirely dark blue or green 2
   Both head and pronotum not reddish yellow, or if so, elytra not entirely blue 3
2. Elytra deeply striate; antennae pale yellowish; length 8.5–9.5 mm. ...a. *grandis*
   Elytra finely striate; only basal three segments of antennae pale; length 6–7 mm. ....b. *atriventris*
3. Mentum with a distinct tooth (Fig. 105); elytra without pale vittae 4
   Mentum not toothed; elytra with pale-yellow vittae ....f. *scapularis*
4. Elytra either entirely blue, green, or olivaceous 5
   Elytra piceous, with dull-yellow maculae ....e. *ornata*
5. Greenish or bluish; legs black; length 4.5–5.5 mm. ....c. *viridis*
   Olivaceous green; legs piceous, brown, or paler; length 3–3.5 mm. ...d. *pumila*

a. *Lebia grandis* Hentz   Plate XI, No. 5, p. 103

Ovate, rather robust, subconvex; head and pronotum reddish yellow; elytra dark blue or green; underside pale reddish brown, abdomen black. Head finely alutaceous, finely and very sparsely punctate. Pronotum nearly twice as wide as long; margin broad; disk with fine, transverse wrinkles and a distinctly impressed median line; posterior angles obtuse. Elytral striae deep, impunctate; intervals convex, alutaceous. Length 8.5–9.5 mm.

b. *Lebia atriventris* Say   Plate XI, No. 2, p. 103

Ovate, rather robust, subconvex; head and pronotum, legs (except tarsi), and basal segments of antennae reddish yellow; elytra dark purplish blue; palpi, tarsi, and apical two-thirds of antennae piceous. Pronotum nearly twice as wide as long; margins broad; disk transversely alutaceous, finely and sparsely punctate; median impression distinct; posterior angles nearly rectangular. Elytral striae shallow, closely punctate; intervals nearly flat, finely alutaceous. Length 6–7 mm.

c. *Lebia viridis* Say   Plate XI, No. 1, p. 103

Oval, rather robust, subconvex; uniformly green or dark purplish blue, strongly shining; antennae piceous, basal segments greenish; legs black. Head minutely, sparsely punctate. Pronotum strongly transverse; margin narrow except at posterior angles, which are prominent and subrectangular; disk finely, transversely rugose. Elytral striae very fine, sparsely punctate; intervals flat, smooth. Length 4.5–5.5 mm.

This species is frequently found on flowers.

d. *Lebia pumila* Dejean   Plate XI, No. 3, p. 103

Oval, rather slender, subconvex; piceous or dark olive-green above; black beneath; antennae piceous, third segment pale yellow. Pronotum feebly transverse; disk finely alutaceous, median impressed line distinct; lateral

FIG. 105

Fig. 105. Mentum of *Lebia viridis,* with a tooth (*t*) at middle of apical margin.

margins narrow, slightly wider posteriorly; posterior angles rectangular, not prominent. Elytral striae feeble, sparsely punctate; intervals flat, finely alutaceous. Length 3–3.5 mm.

e. *Lebia ornata* Say   Plate XI, No. 4, p. 103
    Oval, rather slender, subconvex; head and pronotum piceous, the latter with pale-yellowish margins; elytra piceous, with narrow margin, each with a large spot on basal half and a smaller one at apex pale yellow; antennae yellowish brown, three basal segments paler; underside and legs yellowish brown. Pronotum strongly transverse; broadly margined; disk finely alutaceous, median impressed line distinct; posterior angles subrectangular. Elytral striae deep, sparsely punctate; intervals convex, finely alutaceous. Length 4.5–5 mm.

f. *Lebia scapularis* Dejean   Plate XI, No. 6, p. 103
    Oval, rather robust, subconvex; head, pronotum, and legs pale reddish yellow; elytra piceous, each with apical and side margins and an irregular median vitta yellow; antennae fuscous, three basal segments paler. Pronotum strongly transverse, broadly margined, lateral margins reflexed near base; posterior angles subrectangular. Elytral striae deep, impunctate; intervals flat, minutely alutaceous. Length 4.5–5.5 mm.
    These beetles are usually found on elder and other plants.

Tribe BRACHININI

Genus *BRACHINUS* Weber

The Bombardier Beetles

Small to medium-sized, rather slender, subconvex; head and pronotum narrow, the former narrowed behind eyes into a neck; two basal segments of antennae glabrous; elytra broadly truncate at apex; mesepimera usually wide; mesocoxal cavities entirely closed by the sterna, so that the mesepimeron does not attain the coxa (Fig. 73); metacoxae separated, the first abdominal sternite visible between them; tarsi slender.

When disturbed these beetles give off an evil-smelling, volatile fluid from the tip of the abdomen with a distinct popping noise.

KEY TO SPECIES

Larger species, 10–15 mm.; pronotal sides on anterior half rounded to apex ....a. *fumans*
Smaller species, not over 9.5 mm.; pronotal sides on anterior third straight ....b. *cordicollis*

a. *Brachinus fumans* (Fabricius) Plate XI, No. 7, p. 103
Ovate, slender, subconvex; head, pronotum, and first two pairs of legs brownish yellow; antennae, abdomen, and often hind legs darker; elytra dull blue. Head distinctly punctate. Pronotum as wide as long, widest at middle, narrowed to apex; disk finely punctate; posterior angles divergent, prominent. Elytral humeri rounded; disk often distinctly costate. Length 11.5–12 mm.

This and the following species are found under stones, logs, and dead leaves.

b. *Brachinus cordicollis* Dejean Plate XI, No. 8, p. 103
Ovate, slender, subconvex; head, pronotum, and first two pairs of legs brownish yellow; antennae, abdomen, and often hind legs darker; elytra blackish blue. Head impunctate. Pronotum as wide as long, narrowed apically, widest at middle; posterior angles acute, divergent; disk sparsely and finely punctate. Elytra slightly widened posteriorly, obsoletely costate. Length 7.5–9 mm.

Tribe CHLAENIINI

KEY TO GENERA

Mentum dentate in center of emargination (Fig. 105) ....I. *Chlaenius* (p. 108)
Mentum not dentate ....II. *Anomoglossus* (p. 112)

Genus I. *CHLAENIUS* Bonelli

Medium-sized or large, elongate-oval or oblong, usually robust, subconvex; antennae inserted beneath a feeble frontal ridge; pronotal lateral setae either slender or wanting; elytra without dorsal punctures, margined at base, sides narrowly inflexed; prosternum not prolonged; metacoxae contiguous; tarsi slender, claws simple; males with first three or four segments of protarsi strongly dilated and with dense, spongy pubescence beneath.

These beetles when disturbed give off an odor that resembles that of leather.

KEY TO SPECIES

1. Third segment of antennae distinctly longer than fourth; mesotibiae of male with a pubescent area at apex (Fig. 106) 2
   Third segment of antennae slightly longer than or equal to fourth; mesotibiae of male without pubescence at apex 5
2. Abdomen smooth at middle, sparsely and finely punctate at sides; entirely purple or green in color ....f. *cordicollis*
   Abdomen sparsely punctate at middle, densely so at sides 3
3. Metepisterna short, outer side shorter than anterior one (Fig. 107); elytra blackish ....g. *aestivus*
   Metepisterna long, outer side longer than anterior one (Fig. 108); elytra green or bluish 4
4. Sides of pronotum not or feebly sinuate near base (Fig. 109); color bright green to blue ....h. *sericeus*
   Sides of pronotum distinctly sinuate near base (Fig. 110); color bluish black or dark blue ....i. *erythropus*
5. Abdomen smooth, glabrous ....a. *tomentosus*
   Abdomen sparsely punctate, entirely pubescent 6
6. Sides of pronotum not sinuate; prosternal process not margined at apex .....
   ....b. *impunctifrons*
   Sides of pronotum at least feebly sinuate (Fig. 110); prosternal process margined at apex (Fig. 111) 7
7. Elytral intervals finely muricate (with numerous fine points) .c. *pennsylvanicus*
   Elytral intervals finely and sparsely punctate, not muricate 8
8. Head and pronotum bright green, varying to blackish blue ....d. *tricolor*
   Head and pronotum coppery bronze ....e. *nemoralis*

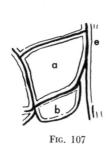
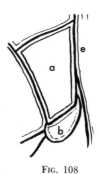

FIG. 106   FIG. 107   FIG. 108

Fig. 106. Anterior apical portion of mesotibia of male *Chlaenius aestivus,* with pubescent area (*a*).

Figs. 107–108. Metepisternum of *Chlaenius aestivus* (107) and of *C. sericeus* (108). *a*, metepisternum; *b*, metepimeron; *e*, deflexed sides of elytron.

a. *Chlaenius tomentosus* (Say) Plate XII, No. 1, p. 115

Broadly elongate-oval, robust; black, shining beneath, subopaque and feebly bronzed above; elytra with very fine, yellowish pubescence; antennae with two basal segments pale. Third antennal segment feebly longer than fourth. Pronotum gradually wider from apex to base; posterior angles rectangular; base as wide as elytra; basal impressions feeble; disk densely punctate at sides and base, middle more coarsely punctate and with irregular smooth spaces. Elytral humeri subangulate; striae moderately deep, punctures coarse; intervals feebly convex, finely, densely punctate. Length 13–15 mm.

This species is frequently found at lights.

b. *Chlaenius impunctifrons* Say Plate XII, No. 2, p. 115

Elongate-oval, robust; body black; head brilliant green; pronotum greenish, subopaque, with yellowish pubescence; elytra blue- or purplish black, opaque, with fine, yellowish pubescence; antennae and legs pale reddish brown. Pronotum slightly transverse; base distinctly wider than apex; sides rounded; posterior angles obtuse; disk densely and finely punctate, median and basal impressions shallow. Elytra with basal margin very feebly subangulate at humeri; striae deep, moderately punctate; intervals flat, densely punctate. Length 13–16 mm.

c. *Chlaenius pennsylvanicus* Say Plate XI, No. 13, p. 103

Elongate-oval, more or less slender, subconvex; head and pronotum bright green, slightly bronzed; antennal basal segments reddish, remaining segments piceous; elytra dark green, with short, brownish pubescence; legs rufotestaceous; undersurface piceous or black. Pronotum slightly transverse; base very little wider than apex; sides rounded, feebly sinuate posteriorly, posterior angles rectangular; basal impressions linear, deep; median line shallow; disk coarsely, sparsely punctate. Elytral striae deep, moderately punctate; intervals flat, densely muricate. Length 10–11.5 mm.

d. *Chlaenius tricolor* Dejean Plate XI, No. 9, p. 103

Elongate-oval, rather robust; head and pronotum green, feebly bronzed; elytra bluish black; antennae and legs orange-brown, entire undersurface piceous. Pronotum subquadrate; sides arcuate and feebly sinuate posteriorly; disk rather coarsely, densely punctate, basal impressions narrow and deep; posterior angles subrectangular. Elytral striae fine, deep, and finely punctate; intervals flat, finely, indistinctly punctate. Length 11.5–13 mm.

e. *Chlaenius nemoralis* Say Plate XI, No. 14, p. 103

Elongate-oval, rather robust, subconvex; head and pronotum coppery bronze (very rarely dull greenish); pronotum more or less subopaque; elytra black, with a bluish or purplish tinge; antennae and legs reddish brown; undersurface black. Pronotum subquadrate; sides rounded, feebly

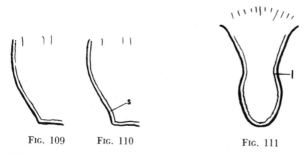

Figs. 109–110. Left hind portions of pronotum of *Chlaenius sericeus* (109) and of *C. erythropus* (110). *s*, sinuation.

Fig. 111. Prosternal process of *Chlaenius tricolor*, with impressed line (*l*) forming a margin.

sinuate posteriorly; base wider than apex; posterior angles rectangular; basal impressions deep; median impressed line shallow; disk alutaceous, finely punctate. Elytral striae coarsely punctate; intervals slightly convex, very finely, sparsely punctate. Length 11–13 mm.

f. *Chlaenius cordicollis* Kirby   Plate XI, No. 15, p. 103

Elongate-oval, slender, subconvex; dark violet-blue or brilliant green; elytra with very short, yellowish pubescence; antennae and legs reddish brown; underside piceous. Pronotum slightly elongate; base as wide as apex; sides arcuate anteriorly, sinuate posteriorly; basal angles slightly obtuse; disk densely punctate at base, basal impressions and median line distinct. Elytral striae rather closely punctate; intervals subconvex, densely and finely punctate. Length 12.5–16 mm.

This species is frequent beneath stones along creeks and rivers.

g. *Chlaenius aestivus* Say   Plate XI, No. 16, p. 103

Elongate-oval, robust, subconvex; head and pronotum green, slightly bronzed; elytra black, with bluish tinge and with short, yellowish pubescence; legs and antennae reddish brown; undersurface piceous. Pronotum subquadrate; sides rounded anteriorly, feebly sinuate posteriorly; base feebly wider than apex; disk coarsely and densely punctate, basal impressions distinct, linear; posterior angles subrectangular. Elytral striae finely punctate; intervals finely, densely, but not distinctly punctate. Length 16–17 mm.

h. *Chlaenius sericeus* Forster   Color Plate D; Plate XII, No. 4, p. 115

Elongate-oval, more or less slender, subconvex; bright green, sometimes with a bluish tinge; elytra with fine, yellowish pubescence; antennae and legs pale brownish yellow; apical segments of antennae darker; undersurface black. Pronotum subquadrate; base wider than apex; posterior angles slightly obtuse, median line and basal impressions not deep; disk coarsely, densely punctate. Elytral striae fine, with small, distant punctures; intervals flat, densely and finely punctate. Length 12.5–17 mm.

This species is common along margins of lakes and streams.

i. *Chlaenius erythropus* Germar   Plate XII, No. 17, p. 115

Elongate-oval, strongly robust, subconvex; piceous; pronotum and elytra tinged with blue; legs and antennae brownish yellow. Pronotum subquadrate; base wider than apex; posterior angles nearly rectangular; basal impressions shallow, elongate; disk densely, rather coarsely punctate. Elytral striae fine, finely punctate; intervals flat, rather finely, densely punctate. Length 21–23 mm.

Genus II. *ANOMOGLOSSUS* Chaudoir

Medium- or large-sized, elongate-oval or oblong; antennae inserted beneath a feeble frontal ridge (Fig. 78), three basal segments glabrous; head not narrowed behind eyes; mentum broad, not dentate in emargination; labrum emarginate at apex; pronotal setae either slender or lacking; elytra without dorsal punctures, basal margin angulate at humerus, sides narrowly inflexed; prosternum prolonged (Fig. 111); metacoxae contiguous; tarsi slender, claws simple.

Anomoglossus emarginatus (Say)   Plate XIII, No. 2, p. 123

Elongate-oval, rather slender, subconvex; head bright green; pronotum green and bronzed; elytra dark blue; antennae and legs pale orange-brown. Pronotum slightly elongate, wider at base than at apex; sides not sinuate near base; posterior angles obtuse; basal impressions arcuate, shallow; disk coarsely, densely punctate. Elytral striae fine, moderately punctate; intervals flat, densely and coarsely punctate. Length 12–14 mm.

These beetles may be found beneath stones and debris in damp areas.

Tribe HARPALINI

KEY TO GENERA

1. Next to last segment of labial palpi bisetose and subequal in length to following segment 7
   Next to last segment of labial palpi plurisetose and longer than the following segment 2
2. First segment of metatarsus as long as the three following combined; prosternum usually with only two setigerous punctures at apex ....III. *Selenophorus* (p. 118)
   First segment of metatarsus not as long as three following combined; prosternum usually with several setigerous punctures at apex ..3

3. Each anterior angle of clypeus with two setigerous punctures (Fig. 112); pro- and mesotarsi of male with dense pads of spongy pubescence beneath 5

Each anterior angle of clypeus without or at most with one setigerous puncture (Fig. 113); protarsi of male never with spongy pubescence beneath, metatarsi often with two rows of scales beneath 4

4. Submentum with its median tooth equal to its lateral lobes (Fig. 114); mesotarsi of male not dilated ....I. *Cratacanthus* (p. 116)

Submentum with its median tooth much shorter than its lateral lobes or, rarely, wanting; mesotarsi of male often dilated 11

5. Basal segment of metatarsi as long as or longer than two following combined 6

Basal segment of metatarsi short, usually not as long as two following combined ....VII. *Anadaptus* (p. 120)

6. Abdomen impunctate, except usual basal punctation 10

Abdomen punctate over entire surface ....VI. *Amphasia* (p. 120)

7. Submentum not dentate 8

Submentum dentate (Fig. 114) 9

8. Second labial palpal segment shorter than third, flattened and subtriangular ....IX. *Stenocellus* (p. 121)

Second labial palpal segment equal or subequal to third, not flattened, slender ....VIII. *Tachycellus* (p. 121)

9. Metatarsi robust basally, tapering to apex ....XI. *Agonoderus* (p. 125)

Metatarsi filiform ....X. *Stenolophus* (p. 124)

10. Terminal spur of protibiae strongly and acutely trifid (Fig. 101) ....IV. *Triplectrus* (p. 119)

Terminal spur of protibiae simple or nearly so, acute, sometimes subangularly swollen near base ....V. *Anisodactylus* (p. 119)

11. Submentum unarmed; body length not over 13 mm. ....V. *Anisodactylus* (p. 119)

Submentum dentate at middle, or if unarmed then body length is more than 20 mm. ....II. *Harpalus* (p. 116)

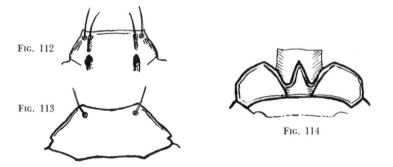

FIG. 112
FIG. 113
FIG. 114

Figs. 112–113. Clypeus of *Anadaptus* (112) and of *Harpalus* (113), the former with two, the latter with a single setigerous puncture each side of apex.

Fig. 114. Submentum of *Cratacanthus,* with a large median tooth.

PLATE XII
Family CARABIDAE VII

1. *Chlaenius tomentosus* (Say) (p. 110) — Black, with a dull violet-bronze reflex; 13–15 mm.

2. *C. impunctifrons* Say (p. 110) — Dull violet; pronotum greenish; head green; 13–15.5 mm.

3. *Harpalus caliginosus* (Fabricius) (p. 117) — Black; 21–25 mm.

4. *Chlaenius sericeus* Forster (p. 111) — Brilliant green; elytra rather opaque; 12.5–17 mm.

5. *Anisodactylus interpunctatus* Kirby (p. 120) — Black; 12–12.5 mm.

6. *Harpalus pennsylvanicus* DeGeer (p. 118) — Black; legs dull brown; 13–15.5 mm.

7. *H. erraticus* Say (p. 117) — Orange-brown; head darker; 14.5–18 mm.

8. *H. compar* LeConte (p. 118) — Black; legs and margins of pronotum orange-brown; 14–16.5 mm.

9. *Anisodactylus harrisii* LeConte (p. 119) — Black; antennae and tarsi dark brown; 11–11.5 mm.

10. *A. nigerrimus* Dejean (p. 120) — Black; 11–12 mm.

11. *Harpalus herbivagus* Say (p. 118) — Black; legs and margins of pronotum orange-brown; 8–10 mm.

12. *H. pleuriticus* Kirby (p. 118) — Black; sides of pronotum and elytra, and legs orange-brown; 7–10 mm.

13. *Amphasia interstitialis* (Say) (p. 120) — Orange-brown; elytra piceous, except on sides and basally; 9.5–10 mm.

14. *Harpalus erythropus* Dejean (p. 117) — Black; legs and margins of pronotum orange-brown; 10.5–12 mm.

15. *Platynus picipennis* (Kirby) (p. 104) — Blackish, shining; elytra and legs brownish yellow; 6–7 mm.

16. *P. placidus* (Say) (p. 104) — Greenish black, shining; elytra bluish black, somewhat opaque; 7.5–9 mm.

17. *Chlaenius erythropus* Germar (p. 112) — Deep blue-black, not shining; legs brown-orange; 21–23 mm.

MM 0 10 20 30 40 50 60 70

PLATE XII   115

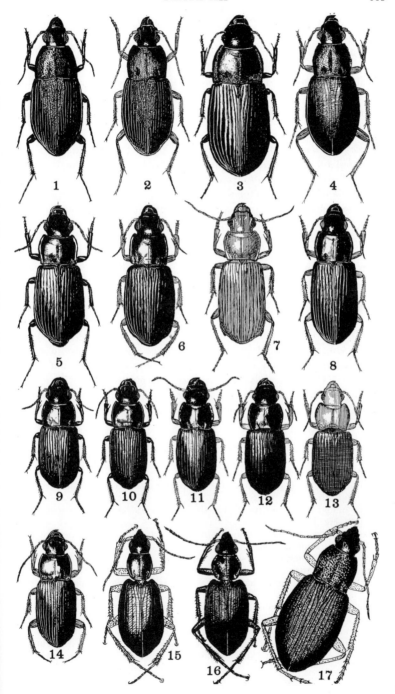

Genus I. *CRATACANTHUS* Dejean

Of medium size, oblong, convex; three basal antennal segments glabrous; submentum dentate medially; pronotum narrower at base than at apex; elytral margins rounded at apex; prosternum with several setigerous punctures at apex; surface of abdomen alutaceous; outer apical angle of protibiae not prolonged; first metatarsal segment short, scarcely longer than second.

Cratacanthus dubius (Beauvois)   Plate XIII, No. 9, p. 123

Oblong, robust, convex; piceous, glabrous; legs and antennae reddish brown. Pronotum strongly transverse; sides broadly arcuate to behind middle, thence strongly sinuate to base; base narrower than apex; basal impressions short, smooth or with a few coarse punctures; posterior angles rectangular. Elytral striae deep, impunctate; intervals feebly convex, smooth. Length 8–10 mm.

This species is usually found around cultivated areas and is frequently attracted to light.

Genus II. *HARPALUS* Latreille

Of large or medium size, oblong; labial palpi with next to last segment bearing several setae and longer than the last segment; anterior clypeal angles lacking setigerous punctures or with only one; pronotum usually transverse; elytral intervals without setigerous punctures or with a single puncture on third stria; protibiae not fossorial, outer angle only slightly prolonged; first segment of metatarsi not as long as the two following combined.

KEY TO SPECIES

1. Elytra without a dorsal puncture on third interval 2
   Elytra with a small dorsal puncture on third interval behind middle and near
   second stria 6
2. Color orange-brown; elytra deeply sinuate at apex, outer angle acute in female (Fig. 115) ....b. *erraticus*
   Black, piceous, or dark reddish brown above; elytra only slightly sinuate, outer
   angle not acute in female 3
3. Legs black; submentum not dentate ....a. *caliginosus*
   Legs and antennae reddish brown; submentum dentate (Fig. 116) 4
4. Pronotum wider at base than at apex; area at basal angles strongly depressed
   ....e. *pennsylvanicus*
   Pronotal base and apex subequal; area at basal angles slightly depressed ...5
5. Length 13.5–16 mm.; seventh and eighth intervals finely punctate ..d. *compar*
   Length 10.5–12 mm.; seventh and eighth intervals impunctate ..c. *erythropus*
6. Posterior angles of pronotum obtusely angulate ....f. *pleuriticus*
   Posterior angles of pronotum very distinctly, broadly rounded ..g. *herbivagus*

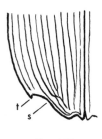
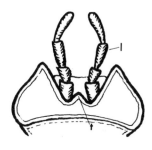

FIG. 115   FIG. 116

Fig. 115. Elytral apex of female *Harpalus erraticus*. In the male the sinus (*s*) is present but not the tooth (*t*).

Fig. 116. Submentum of *Harpalus pennsylvanicus,* with a median tooth (*t*). *l*, labial palpus.

a. *Harpalus caliginosus* (Fabricius)   Plate XII, No. 3, p. 115

Elongate-oblong, robust, subconvex; black, slightly shining; legs piceous; antennae and tarsi reddish brown. Pronotum transverse, as wide as elytra at base, slightly narrower at apex; basal impressions broad, shallow; posterior angles rectangular; disk alutaceous, finely punctate at apex and base. Elytral striae deep; intervals convex, minutely punctate. Length 21–25 mm.

This species is very common about dry fields, occurs in numbers under wheat shocks, and comes readily to light. Annually it destroys large numbers of cutworms.

b. *Harpalus erraticus* Say   Plate XII, No. 7, p. 115

Elongate, subparallel, rather slender; orange-brown; undersurface and legs reddish yellow. Pronotum only feebly transverse; posterior angles obtuse, slightly rounded; disk punctate along margins and minutely alutaceous; basal impressions broad, shallow, closely and finely punctate. Elytra deeply sinuate at apex, outer angle of sinuation acute and dentate in female; deeply striate; intervals convex, minutely alutaceous. Length 14.5–18 mm.

This species is usually in sandy localities and may be attracted to light.

c. *Harpalus erythropus* Dejean   Plate XII, No. 14, p. 115

Elongate-oblong, moderately slender; black, slightly shining; undersurface piceous; legs and antennae yellowish brown. Pronotum subquadrate; slightly narrower than elytra at base; posterior angles obtuse, feebly rounded; disk punctate at base, remainder minutely alutaceous; basal impressions broad, shallow, and finely, densely punctate. Elytra deeply striate; intervals nearly flat, minutely alutaceous. Length 10.5–12 mm.

d. *Harpalus compar* LeConte   Plate XII, No. 8, p. 115

Elongate-oblong, robust; piceous to black, shining; legs and antennae yellowish brown. Pronotum transverse; slightly narrowed basally, not apically; sides only slightly rounded, feebly depressed at basal angles and margins; disk punctate at base and margins; posterior angles obtuse. Elytral striae deep; intervals convex, alutaceous, seventh and eighth intervals finely punctate. Length 14–16.5 mm.

e. *Harpalus pennsylvanicus* DeGeer   Plate XII, No. 6, p. 115

Elongate-oblong, robust, convex; black, shining; antennae and legs pale yellowish; undersurface piceous or reddish brown. Pronotum transverse, as wide as elytra at base; sides arcuate; posterior angles obtuse; margins anterior to basal angles depressed, punctate; basal impressions densely, finely punctate. Elytra deeply striate; intervals convex, minutely alutaceous, fifth to eighth with numerous small punctures in female, very sparsely punctate in male. Length 13–15.5 mm.

This species is often attracted to light and feeds on seeds and caterpillars.

f. *Harpalus pleuriticus* Kirby   Plate XII, No. 12, p. 115

Oblong, robust; black, strongly shining; lateral and anterior margin of front pale, epipleura reddish brown. Pronotum slightly transverse; apex wider than base; posterior angles obtuse; basal impressions linear; disk smooth, near base coarsely punctate. Elytral striae deep, second with a single puncture; intervals convex, smooth. Length 7–10 mm.

g. *Harpalus herbivagus* Say   Plate XII, No. 11, p. 115

Elongate-oblong, robust; black or piceous, shining; lateral margins of pronotum and elytra reddish, translucent; undersurface piceous; antennae and legs yellowish brown. Pronotum transverse; posterior angles rounded; basal impressions shallow, not distinct, sparsely, finely punctate. Elytral striae deep; intervals feebly convex, alutaceous, third with a dorsal puncture. Length 8–10 mm.

Genus III. *SELENOPHORUS* Dejean

Small, oblong or oval, subconvex; labial palpi with next to last segment bearing several setae, longer than the last segment; scutellar stria rather long and distinct; elytral intervals each with three dorsal series of setigerous punctures; protibia not fossorial, outer apical angle not prolonged; first metatarsal segment as long as three following combined.

Selenophorus opalinus LeConte   Plate XIII, No. 8, p. 123

Oblong-oval, robust; black, iridescent; antennae and legs yellowish brown. Pronotum transverse; base as wide as apex; sides slightly arcuate, margins flattened and translucent; basal impressions broad, rather feeble, coarsely punctate; base of disk finely and sparsely punctate. Elytra deeply striate; intervals convex, very minutely and sparsely punctate. Length 9–10 mm.

This species is frequently found beneath bark.

Genus IV. *TRIPLECTRUS* LeConte

Of moderate size, oblong-ovate; mentum not dentate; clypeus with a single setigerous puncture at each outer angle; elytral third interval with one or more dorsal punctures, apices sinuate; metatarsi slender, first segment as long as next two combined, fourth distinctly emarginate at apex.

Triplectrus rusticus (Say)   Plate XIII, No. 11, p. 123

Oblong-oval, robust; brownish black; base of antennae and posterior pronotal angles reddish brown, legs piceous. Pronotum transverse, as broad at base as elytra; sides feebly arcuate; posterior angles obtuse; basal impressions shallow, impunctate. Elytral striae deep; intervals convex, minutely alutaceous, third with one to four dorsal punctures behind middle. Length 9–14 mm.

This species is common in newly plowed fields, particularly in sandy localities.

Genus V. *ANISODACTYLUS* Dejean

Of medium size, oblong-oval, subconvex; next to last segment of labial palpi plurisetose and longer than the last; prosternum with several setigerous punctures at tip; protibia with outer angle not prolonged; protarsi of male with dense, spongy pubescence beneath; first metatarsal segment not as long as three following together.

KEY TO SPECIES

1. Posterior angles of pronotum obtuse; clypeus with two setigerous punctures on each side (Fig. 112) 2
   Posterior angles of pronotum rectangular; clypeus with one setigerous puncture each side (Fig. 113) ....c. *interpunctatus*
2. Antennae and tarsi reddish brown; lateral pronotal margins distinctly depressed ....a. *harrisii*
   Antennae and tarsi black; lateral pronotal margins feebly depressed ....
   ....b. *nigerrimus*

a. *Anisodactylus harrisii* LeConte   Plate XII, No. 9, p. 115

Oblong-oval, moderately robust; black, shining; antennae and tarsi dark reddish brown. Pronotum slightly transverse; basal impressions broad, finely and densely punctate; posterior angles obtuse; median line distinct; base and lateral margins finely punctate, apex more finely punctured, disk smooth. Elytra deeply striate; intervals convex, finely alutaceous, and finely, sparsely punctate. Length 11–11.5 mm.

b. *Anisodactylus nigerrimus* Dejean   Plate XII, No. 10, p. 115
Oblong-oval, robust, subconvex; black, slightly shining. Pronotum transverse; base slightly wider than apex; sides broadly arcuate; basal impressions very shallow, finely, rugosely punctate; lateral margins feebly depressed at middle, not at posterior angles; posterior angles obtuse. Elytral striae deep; intervals convex, finely alutaceous, and finely, sparsely punctate. Length 11–12 mm.

c. *Anisodactylus interpunctatus* Kirby   Plate XII, No. 5, p. 115
Oblong-oval, robust; black, shining, female slightly dull; antennae and legs piceous; basal segment of antennae and a small macula on vertex reddish. Pronotum transverse; base and apex equal in width; sides arcuate, sinuate basally; lateral margins narrowly depressed; posterior angles subrectangular; basal impressions deep, rather coarsely, densely punctate. Elytra deeply striate; intervals convex, finely alutaceous. Length 12–12.5 mm.

Genus VI. *AMPHASIA* Newman

Of medium size, elongate-oval, subconvex; labium emarginate; mentum not dentate; elytral margins sinuate at apex; prosternum usually with several setigerous punctures at apex; abdomen punctured over entire surface; protibiae with outer apical angle not prolonged; first metatarsal segment as long as the three following segments combined.

Amphasia interstitialis (Say)   Plate XII, No. 13, p. 115
Elongate-oval, robust; head, pronotum, antennae, and legs reddish yellow; elytra, meso-, and metathorax piceous; remainder of undersurface reddish yellow. Pronotum transverse; base and apex subequal in width; sides and apex broadly margined; basal impressions shallow, densely punctate; posterior angles broadly rounded. Elytra deeply striate; intervals convex, coarsely and densely punctate. Length 9.5–10 mm.

Genus VII. *ANADAPTUS* Casey

Medium-sized, elongate-oblong; each anterior angle of clypeus with two setigerous punctures; elytra with a dorsal puncture on third interval, apical margin distinctly sinuate; prosternum at apex with a number of setigerous punctures; outer angle of protibiae not prolonged; first segment of metatarsi short, not as long as next two combined.

Anadaptus baltimorensis (Say)　　　　　　　　Plate XIII, No. 10, p. 123

Elongate-oblong, rather slender; piceous, shining; antennae at base, legs, and elytra orange-brown; elytra often with an indistinct piceous area medially. Pronotum distinctly transverse; base narrower than elytra; basal impressions rather shallow and densely, coarsely punctate; lateral margins rather deeply sinuate near basal angles; posterior angles strongly rectangular, finely and sparsely punctate. Elytral striae deep; intervals convex, alutaceous. Length 10.5–11.5 mm.

Genus VIII. *TACHYCELLUS* Morawitz

Small, oblong species; three basal segments of antennae glabrous or nearly so; body glabrous; clypeus with two setigerous punctures each side; elytra striate, with a single dorsal puncture on second stria behind middle, apical margin not or scarcely sinuate; protibial exterior angle not prolonged. First segment of metatarsi short, scarcely longer than second, pro- and mesotarsi of males with two rows of scales ventrally.

Tachycellus badiipennis (Haldeman)　　　　　　Plate XIII, No. 12, p. 123

Elongate-oblong, rather slender; head and pronotum black; antennae and margin of pronotum dull yellow; femora and apices of tibiae often piceous. Pronotum subquadrate; sides arcuate from apex to base; apex and base subequal in width; basal impressions deep, narrow, sparsely punctate; posterior angles broadly rounded. Elytral striae fine; intervals nearly flat, smooth; second stria with one dorsal puncture. Length 5.5–6.5 mm.

Genus IX. *STENOCELLUS* Casey

Small, oblong; mentum with a large tooth; clypeus with two setigerous punctures at each outer angle; elytra obliquely, feebly sinuate at apex, second stria with a dorsal puncture behind middle; metatarsi slender, first segment shorter than next two combined, fourth segment simple.

Stenocellus rupestris (Say)　　　　　　　　　Plate XIII, No. 13, p. 123

Oblong, slender, subconvex; reddish brown, shining; head and elytral disk usually piceous; antennae fuscous, the two basal segments and legs brownish yellow. Pronotum transverse, narrowed behind middle; base slightly narrower than apex; basal impressions broad, shallow, coarsely punctate; posterior angles obtuse. Elytral striae deep; intervals convex,

PLATE XIII
Family CARABIDAE VIII

1. *Galerita janus* Fabricius (p. 105) — Black; pronotum and legs brown-orange; 17–22 mm.

2. *Anomoglossus emarginatus* (Say) (p. 112) — Metallic green and coppery; elytra blue; legs brown-orange; 12–14 mm.

3. *Galerita bicolor* Drury (p. 105) — Black; pronotum and legs brown-orange; 17–21 mm.

4. *Colliurus pennsylvanicus* Linné (p. 104) — Black; elytra brown-orange, maculae black; 7–8 mm.

5. *Stenolophus ochropezus* (Say) (p. 124) — Blackish; pronotum and elytral margins orange-brown; legs brown-orange; 5.5–6 mm.

6. *S. fuliginosus* Dejean (p. 124) — Black; elytra and legs dark brown; pronotal sides narrowly brown; 7–7.5 mm.

7. *S. conjunctus* (Say) (p. 125) — Orange-brown; elytral spots fuscous; 3.5–4.5 mm.

8. *Selenophorus opalinus* LeConte (p. 118) — Blackish; legs and pronotal sides dark brown; 9–10 mm.

9. *Cratacanthus dubius* (Beauvois) (p. 116) — Black, shining; antennae and legs brown-orange; 8–10 mm.

10. *Anadaptus baltimorensis* (Say) (p. 121) — Blackish; antennae, legs, and elytra orangeish, latter often with fuscous spots; 10.5–11.5 mm.

11. *Triplectrus rusticus* (Say) (p. 119) — Blackish; antennae and legs piceous; 9–14 mm.

12. *Tachycellus badiipennis* (Haldeman) (p. 121) — Black; elytra and legs orange-brown, elytral spots blackish; 5.5–6.5 mm.

13. *Stenocellus rupestris* (Say) (p. 121) — Brown-orange, shining; elytral markings black; 4.5–5 mm.

14. *Stenolophus plebejus* Dejean (p. 124) — Blackish; legs, elytra in part, and pronotal margins brownish yellow; 4.5–5 mm.

Family OMOPHRONIDAE

15. *Omophron tessellatum* Say (p. 128) — Pale brownish yellow, marked with metallic green; 6–7 mm.

16. *O. labiatum* (Fabricius) (p. 127) — Dull yellow and shining black or deep brown; 6 mm.

17. *O. americanum* Dejean (p. 128) — Dull yellowish and greenish black; 6–7 mm.

MM 0 10 20 30 40 50 60 70

PLATE XIII

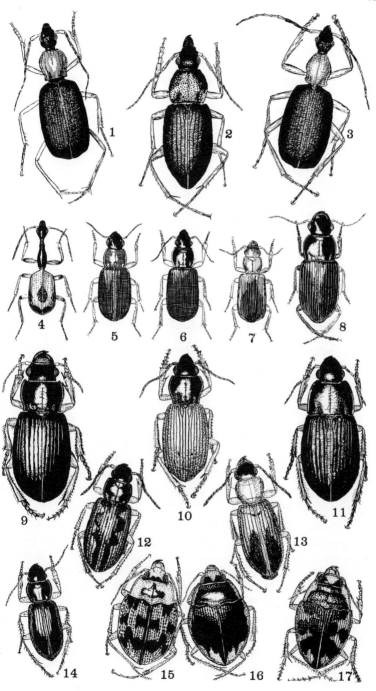

smooth, except for the single dorsal puncture near second stria. Length 4.5–5 mm.

Genus X. *STENOLOPHUS* Dejean

Small, elongate-oblong, subconvex; next to last segment of labial palpi subequal in length to the last segment; antennae with only two glabrous basal segments; posterior angles of pronotum broadly rounded; sides not sinuously narrowed basally; elytral striae impunctate, third interval with a single discal puncture behind middle; prosternum with three or more setigerous punctures at apex; pro- and often mesotarsi of male dilated and with a double row of scales on first four segments; fourth segment of protarsi distinctly bilobed; metatarsi filiform.

KEY TO SPECIES

1. Pronotum across middle slightly narrower than elytra; body robust; pro- and mesotarsi of male dilated 2
   Pronotum across middle distinctly narrower than elytra; body rather slender; protarsi of male moderately dilated, fourth segment deeply bilobed ....a. *ochropezus*
2. Basal impressions of pronotum broad and shallow, coarsely punctate ....b. *fuliginosus*
   Basal impressions of pronotum small, rounded, not or very sparsely punctate 3
3. Pronotal disk distinctly black or piceous, margin reddish brown; length 5 mm. or more ....c. *plebejus*
   Pronotum either uniformly reddish brown or piceous, without distinct black discal spot; length not over 4.5 mm. ....d. *conjunctus*

a. *Stenolophus ochropezus* (Say)   Plate XIII, No. 5, p. 123
   Elongate-oblong, rather slender; black or piceous; elytra frequently iridescent; legs and base of antennae yellowish. Pronotum only slightly transverse; posterior angles obtuse; basal impressions broad and shallow, sparsely punctate. Elytra deeply striate, the sutural stria long; intervals flat, minutely punctate. Length 5.5–6 mm.

b. *Stenolophus fuliginosus* Dejean   Plate XIII, No. 6, p. 123
   Elongate-oval, robust; black, shining; elytra yellowish brown to piceous, slightly iridescent; base of antennae and margin of pronotum dull yellow. Pronotum slightly transverse; posterior angles broad, rounded; basal impressions broad, shallow, coarsely, densely punctate, punctures continuing across base. Elytra deeply striate, sutural stria long; intervals subconvex, minutely punctate. Length 7–7.5 mm.

c. *Stenolophus plebejus* Dejean   Plate XIII, No. 14, p. 123
   Elongate-oblong, rather robust; piceous to black, shining; legs, base of

antennae, and narrow margin of pronotum brownish yellow. Pronotum feebly narrowed basally; basal impressions small, rounded, each with two or three punctures; posterior angles distinctly rounded. Sutural striae of elytra short, oblique, not joining first dorsal; intervals flat, minutely punctate. Length 4.5–5 mm.

d. *Stenolophus conjunctus* (Say)   Plate XIII, No. 7, p. 123
    Elongate-oval, robust; piceous, shining; legs and base of antennae yellowish brown. Pronotum transverse; sides broadly arcuate to base so that the basal angles are lacking; basal impressions shallow, impunctate. Elytra finely, rather deeply striate, sutural stria long; intervals flat, very minutely and densely punctate. Length 3.5–4.5 mm.

This species is especially common in sandy localities.

Genus XI. *AGONODERUS* Dejean

Small, oblong, convex; next to last segment of labial palpi subequal in length to following segment; antennae with only two glabrous basal segments; mentum not dentate; pronotum not sinuously narrowed basally, posterior angles obtuse, usually rounded; elytra without series of punctures along sides of striae, but with a single discal puncture behind middle of elytra; metatarsi robust basally, tapering to apex, first segment shorter than next two combined, fourth segment simple.

The members of this genus are frequently found beneath stones and rubbish about gardens and plowed fields. Moreover, some species come in large numbers to light.

KEY TO SPECIES

Scutellar stria short, about one-eighth the length of elytra ....a. *lecontei*
Scutellar stria long, about one-fifth the length of elytra ....b. *comma*

a. *Agonoderus lecontei* Chaudoir   The Corn-Seed Beetle
                                                     Plate VIII, No. 20, p. 79
    Oblong, moderately slender, convex; head and undersurface black; pronotum and elytra brownish yellow or reddish brown, a large spot on disk of pronotum and a wide, black, oblong elytral spot divided by a sutural stripe of the brownish yellow; antennae reddish brown and legs pale yellowish. Pronotum subquadrate, narrowed basally; posterior angles obtuse; basal impressions and side margins coarsely punctate, the impressions shallow. Elytra deeply striate, scutellar stria short; intervals convex, sparsely, minutely punctate. Length 5–6 mm.

This species is found about lights and is sometimes found in seed corn when the seed is planted in wet soil or under conditions which retard its rapid germination.

b. *Agonoderus comma* (Fabricius)   Plate VIII, No. 24, p. 79

Oblong, moderately robust, convex; head and undersurface black; pronotum and elytra yellowish brown or reddish brown, the former with a large, black spot on disk, the latter with a broad, elongate-oblong spot divided at the suture. Pronotum subquadrate, narrowed posteriorly; basal angles distinctly rounded; basal impressions and side margins coarsely punctate. Elvtra deeply striate, scutellar stria long; intervals convex, sparsely, finely punctate. Length 6–7 mm.

This beetle comes readily to light.

Family OMOPHRONIDAE

These small, very active beetles live along margins of streams, ponds, and lakes in burrows in the wet sand, in openings between roots of plants, or under stones or debris along the water's edge. Collecting them is a simple matter of throwing water over the sand banks so that they leave their burrows, and, since they cannot fly, they are easily captured. They range in size from 5 to 8 millimeters and in color from pale brownish yellow to nearly black or a dark, bronzed green.

The family characters are as follows: head deflexed, narrower than pronotum; antennae filiform, eleven-segmented, and inserted between eyes and base of mandibles, four basal segments glabrous; clypeus not produced laterally over bases of antennae and mandibles, with a bristle-bearing puncture on outer side; pronotum smooth or punctate and immovable because of the structure of prosternum; elytra slightly shortened, leaving only part of the last abdominal segment exposed; prosternum scoop-shaped, entirely covering mesosternum (Fig. 117); hind legs attached so that the coxae divide the first abdominal sternite into three parts and make it not visible its full width; tarsal segments 5–5–5, all visible.

Genus *OMOPHRON* Latreille

This is the only genus according to most authors, and the family characters will serve to distinguish it.

KEY TO SPECIES

1. Broadly ovate, dark brown or nearly black, shining; elytral punctures only at basal end of striae, which are obsolete at apex and indistinct laterally, intervals flat ....a. *labiatum*
   Less broadly ovate, less shining; elytral striae nearly attaining apex, distinct on sides, intervals convex 2
2. Pronotum with only side margin pale ....b. *americanum*
   Pronotum with sides, basal and apical margins pale ....c. *tessellatum*

a. *Omophron labiatum* (Fabricius)   Plate XIII, No. 16, p. 123
   Dark brown or nearly black, shining; margin of front and clypeus pale, labrum silvery white; lateral margin of pronotum and elytra pale, the latter broader at apex and irregular on inner edge; undersurface piceous, with sides and apex of abdomen paler; legs pale. Vertex of head coarsely,

sparsely punctate. Pronotal disk coarsely, irregularly punctate except in a transverse area across middle. Elytral striae moderately deep on basal third, punctate with coarse, distant punctures, punctures effaced beyond middle and striae obsolete apically and laterally. Length 6 mm.

b. *Omophron americanum* Dejean   Plate XIII, No. 17, p. 123

Bronzed or greenish black; head mostly green, front and clypeus pale, labrum silvery white; pronotum and elytra with pale margins, those of the former narrow and suddenly dilated at apex, and with a narrow extension along the base for a short distance. Undersurface reddish brown, paler on sides and apex of abdomen; legs pale. Pronotum coarsely, sparsely punctate, especially on apical and basal thirds. Punctures of elytral striae rather fine and approximated and distinctly visible almost to apex; intervals convex. Length 6–7 mm.

This species sometimes occurs under rubbish at some distance from water.

c. *Omophron tessellatum* Say   Plate XIII, No. 15, p. 123

Pale brownish yellow; head with a green band across base; labrum silvery white; pronotum with a small, subquadrate green spot with narrow processes extending to the basal and apical margins along the median line; elytra with cross-markings of metallic green; undersurface ferrugineous, margins and apex of abdomen paler; legs very pale. Pronotum coarsely punctate near base and apex, more finely and very sparsely at middle and sides. Elytral striae close and fine and with numerous fine punctures to apex; intervals subconvex. Length 6–7 mm.

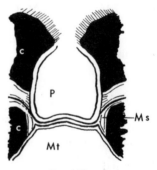

Fig. 117

Fig. 117. Portion of sternum of *Omophron*. The prosternal process (*P*) is greatly enlarged and contacts the metasternum (*Mt*), covering the mesosternum (*Ms*), except on the sides. *c*, coxal cavity.

Family HALIPLIDAE

The Crawling Water Beetles

To this family belong rather small, broadly ovate, convex beetles that live in ponds and lakes. However, instead of swimming actively about as do other aquatic beetles, these crawl leisurely and rather awkwardly along the pond bottom or upon the submerged vegetation. As an adaptation for this type of life, their legs are slender and are not flattened or fringed with hairs for swimming. Both adults and larvae are omnivorous, devouring anything they are able to catch. Plants form the larger portion of their diet, but insects and other small animals are also eaten.

Other characterizations of the family are: antennae glabrous, filiform, ten-segmented, inserted on front before eyes, and metacoxae broadly expanded to form wide plates, which conceal much of undersurface of abdomen.

KEY TO GENERA

Metacoxae greatly expanded, reaching to the base of the last abdominal segment, their lateral margin parallel with the epipleuron, covering its inner portion (Fig. 118); pronotum with two small black dots at base .... II. *Peltodytes* (p. 131)
Metacoxae not so strongly expanded, reaching to the apex of the third abdominal segment, their sides posteriorly diverging from the inner edge of the epipleuron (Fig. 119); pronotum usually without two small black maculae at base .... I. *Haliplus* (p. 129)

Genus I. *HALIPLUS* Latreille

Oval, convex, rather small species, which have the coxae not margined; elytra without trace of fine sutural striae; last segment of palpi smaller than preceding one; metacoxae not margined, attaining apex of third sternite.

KEY TO SPECIES

1. Elytra each with no more than five black dots .... c. *immaculicollis*
   Elytra each with at least seven black maculae 2
2. Pronotum entirely reddish brown, without a trace of black markings ....
   .... a. *fasciatus*
   Pronotum with a median apical black spot .... b. *triopsis*

129

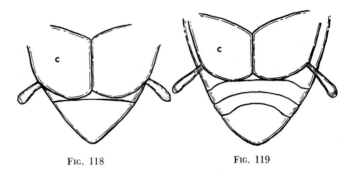

Fig. 118   Fig. 119

Fig. 118. Underside of abdomen of *Peltodytes*. Metacoxae (*c*) enlarged
and covering most of surface.
Fig. 119. Underside of abdomen of *Haliplus*. Metacoxae (*c*) large but
exposing the last three sternites.

a. *Haliplus fasciatus* Aubé   Plate XIV, No. 1, p. 139
Oval, moderately robust, strongly convex; brownish yellow to orange-
brown; elytra with irregular black markings forming three more or less
oblique rows, which are confluent along suture; antennae pale yellow.
Pronotum strongly transverse; entire disk coarsely and deeply punctate.
Elytra with rows of coarse, deep punctures; intervals flat, with rows of
fine, shallow punctures. Length 3–3.5 mm.
This species is usually found in ponds.

b. *Haliplus triopsis* Say   Plate XIV, No. 2, p. 139
Oval, rather slender, strongly convex; pale dull yellow; pronotum with
a transverse black spot at middle of apex; suture, base, apex, and seven
more or less connected spots on each elytron black, middle ones confluent;
apices of all leg segments brownish. Pronotum strongly transverse; disk
moderately coarsely, very densely punctate. Elytra with rows of coarse,
rather shallowly impressed punctures; intervals with rows of fine, feeble
punctures. Length 2.5–3 mm.
This species is found in quiet fresh water.

c. *Haliplus immaculicollis* Harris   Plate XIV, No. 3, p. 139
Oval, robust, distinctly convex; pale dull yellow to brownish yellow;
elytra with base, suture, and apex all black and five more or less rounded
black spots often more or less confluent. Pronotum rather strongly transverse; disk coarsely and sparsely punctate, more densely so along margins.
Elytra with rows of coarse, deep punctures; intervals with scattered coarse
punctures. Length 2.5–3 mm.

Genus II. *PELTODYTES* Regenbar

Small, oval, convex species; last segment of both palpi larger than the preceding one; pronotum marked at base with two black dots; elytra on apical half with a fine stria near suture; metacoxae margined, nearly concealing entire abdomen.

KEY TO SPECIES

Elytra with a large common black macula behind middle ....a. *muticus*
Elytra without a common macula behind middle ....b. *duodecimpunctatus*

a. *Peltodytes muticus* (LeConte)   Plate XIV, No. 5, p. 139
Ovate, robust, convex; dull yellow; elytra each with four small black maculae and with a large common one behind middle; metafemora piceous. Pronotum entirely covered with coarse, rather dense punctures, becoming somewhat finer apically. Elytra each with ten rows of coarse black punctures, much finer on apical half; a fine stria near suture on apical half. Length 3.5–4 mm.

b. *Peltodytes duodecimpunctatus* (Say)   Plate XIV, No. 4, p. 139
Ovate, robust, convex; dull yellow; each elytron with six well-defined black spots on apical two-thirds. Head finely, pronotum rather coarsely and sparsely, punctate. Each elytron with eight rows of large black punctures and two rows of finer, paler ones on sides. Length 3.5–4 mm.
This species is usually found in quiet water.

Family DYTISCIDAE

The Predaceous Diving Beetles

Of the water beetles, this family is one of the most perfectly adapted for aquatic life. Usually shining black or brownish; streamlined form; broadly oval; legs generally fringed and flattened; first abdominal sternite divided into three parts by coxae; metacoxae normal, not platelike.

This group can be confused only with the Hydrophilidae, from which they may be distinguished by their convex undersurface, filiform antennae, short labial palpi, and close-fitting elytra.

They are very active swimmers, preying on other small water life. The larvae (known as "water tigers") of the larger species may at times destroy the fry of game fish.

KEY TO TRIBES

1. Scutellum hidden, or rarely a small tip visible 2
   Scutellum entirely exposed 5
2. Base of prosternum in same plane as its process; pro- and mesotarsi distinctly segmented, fourth segment about as long as third 4
   Base of prosternum not on a plane with its process, which is strongly bent downward; pro- and mesotarsi usually with fourth segment minute and hidden in lobe of third 3
3. Metacoxal process short, flat, almost on a plane with the ventral segments, without lateral lobes so that the base of the trochanter is entirely free (Fig. 120) ....BIDESSINI (p. 134)
   Metacoxal process not on same plane with first sternite but somewhat raised, sides divergent, more or less produced into lobes which cover the bases of the trochanters (Fig. 121) ....HYDROPORINI (p. 136)
4. Metatarsi with two slender claws of equal length; posterior margin of tarsi uniform ...........................HYDROCANTHINI (p. 133)
   Metatarsi with a single thick, straight claw; posterior margin of apical tarsal segments produced into lobes .........LACCOPHILINI (p. 133)
5. Eyes emarginate; first three segments of tarsi in male widened but not forming a round adhesion disk 6
   Eyes not emarginate; first three segments of tarsi in male forming a round or oval adhesion disk 10
6. Metafemora beneath with a more or less thick group of cilia on inner half of inner apical angle; usually these arise from a linear depression (Fig. 122) ....AGABINI (p. 141)
   Metafemora without such cilia 7

132

7. Impressed lines on metacoxae very narrowly separated (almost contiguous with median line) just before diverging posteriorly onto
metacoxal lobes ....COPELATINI   (p. 146)
Metacoxal lines not almost contiguous with median line but each
well separated from it, usually by at least half the width of a
metatrochanter 8
8. Metatarsal claws of same length or virtually so 9
Metatarsal claws obviously unequal, the outer ones only one-third
or two-thirds the length of the inner ....COLYMBETINI   (p. 146)
9. Terminal segment of palpi, especially the labial, notched or
emarginate at apex; pronotum clearly though narrowly mar-
gined laterally ....COPTOTOMINI   (p. 146)
Terminal segment of palpi not emarginate at apex; pronotum with
an exceedingly fine line along lateral edges, but not mar-
gined ....AGABETINI   (p. 143)
10. Posterior margins of first four segments of metatarsi with a coarse
fringe of yellow, flat cilia set along entire length .. THERMONECTINI   (p. 149)
Posterior margins of first four segments of metatarsi without such a
fringe, with cilia only on outer apical angle 11
11. Metatibiae distinctly longer than broad, outer apical spur slender,
not broader than inner ....DYTISCINI   (p. 148)
Metatibiae almost as broad as long, outer apical spur basally strongly
expanded (Fig. 123) ....CYBISTERINI   (p. 153)

Tribe HYDROCANTHINI

Genus *HYDROCANTHUS* Say

Last segment of labial palpi very large, triangular, and compressed;
metafemora short and stout, apical margins strongly ciliated; tibiae short,
smooth; protibiae with a strong spur; metatibiae broad; prosternal process
very broad behind coxae; claws equal.

Hydrocanthus iricolor Say   Plate XIV, No. 6, p. 139
Ovate, convex, attenuate behind; head, pronotum, and underside
reddish yellow; elytra dark reddish brown, polished, iridescent. Elytra with
three irregular dorsal rows of fine punctures visible. Length 4–5 mm.

Tribe LACCOPHILINI

Genus *LACCOPHILUS* Leach

Small, ovate, depressed, very active beetles; pronotum not margined;
scutellum almost concealed; prosternal spine narrow, pointed; metacoxae

expanded into broad processes which are arched in front and almost cover the coxal cavities.

KEY TO SPECIES

Elytra blackish, with one or more greenish-yellow spots ....a. *proximus*
Elytra dull yellow, with a black bar near middle ....b. *fasciatus*

a. *Laccophilus proximus* Say   Plate XIV, No. 8, p. 139
   Ovate; reddish yellow; elytra with margins, four submarginal spots, and three basal lines greenish yellow. Pronotum strongly transverse; disk finely reticulate. Elytra obliquely truncate at apex; finely reticulate, with one or two irregular rows of fine punctures. Length 5.5–6.5 mm.
   This species occurs in pools and flowing water.

b. *Laccophilus fasciatus* Aubé   Plate XIV, No. 9, p. 139
   Ovate, more or less depressed; dull brownish yellow; elytra greenish yellow, with a broad bar near middle blackish. Pronotum and elytra alutaceous, the latter rounded at apex. Length 4.5–5.5 mm.

Tribe BIDESSINI

KEY TO GENERA

Form rounded, convex; prosternal process rhomboidal, acute at apex
....I. *Desmopachria* (p. 134)
Form oblong, depressed; prosternal process oblong ....II. *Bidessus* (p. 136)

Genus I. *DESMOPACHRIA* Babington

Minute, short, and broad species; convex above and beneath; metacoxae greatly developed but coxal cavities exposed and firmly united to ventral segments so that the undersurface of body from the anterior of metasternum to the posterior margin of the third sternite is one rigid piece; prosternal process rhomboidal, acute at apex.

Desmopachria convexa (Aubé)   Plate XIV, No. 10, p. 139
   Rounded, convex; uniformly brownish red, shining. Clypeus with a distinct margin. Elytra finely punctate; tapering, obtuse at apex. Length 1.5–2.5 mm.
   This species is found beneath grass roots along margins of water in stagnant pools; it also comes to lights.

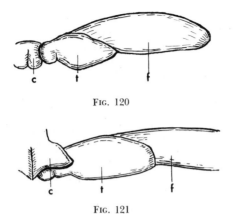

Fig. 120

Fig. 121

Fig. 120. *Bidessus affinis*, hind leg. Metacoxa (*c*) not produced over base of trochanter (*t*) and femur (*f*).

Fig. 121. *Hydroporus undulatus*, hind leg. Metacoxa (*c*) produced over base of trochanter (*t*) and of femur (*f*).

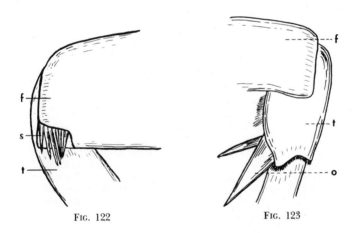

Fig. 122

Fig. 123

Fig. 122. *Agabus gagates*. *f*, metafemur; *s*, setae; *t*, metatibia.

Fig. 123. *Cybister fimbriolatus*. *f*, metafemur; *t*, metatibia; *o*, outer apical spur.

Genus II. *BIDESSUS* Sharp

Very small, oval, depressed beetles; brownish, with paler markings; metacoxae as in preceding genus; pronotum with a basal groove or a longitudinal fold on each side, which is sometimes continued on the elytra.

KEY TO SPECIES

Elytra with a longitudinal basal groove continuing that of pronotum ..b. *affinis*
Elytra without basal groove continuing that of pronotum ....a. *flavicollis*

a. **Bidessus flavicollis** (LeConte)   Plate XIV, No. 11, p. 139
    Oblong-oval, convex; yellowish, subopaque; elytra with three broad bands of dull brown interconnected along suture. Entire surface finely, densely punctate; pronotal basal impressions short. Length 1–1.5 mm.
    The above species is more common in the East.

b. **Bidessus affinis** (Say)   Plate XIV, No. 12, p. 139
    Oblong-oval, shining; head, pronotum, and legs yellowish; elytra and undersurface dark yellowish brown; elytra often with paler margins. Pronotum finely, sparsely punctate, punctures denser at base and apex; basal grooves elongate, extending from before middle to base. Elytra rather coarsely, densely punctate, with a basal groove continuing that of pronotum. Length 1.5–2 mm.
    This species may be distinguished from the preceding by its darker-colored underparts and by its more shining surface.

Tribe HYDROPORINI

KEY TO GENERA

Epipleura with a basal excavation which receives the middle knee; they
    are also apparently obliquely truncate and with an oblique carina
    basally (Fig. 124) ....I. *Hygrotus*   (p. 136)
Epipleura not excavated and without an oblique basal carina (Fig. 125)
    ....II. *Hydroporus*   (p. 137)

Genus I. *HYGROTUS* Stephens

Small, oval or rounded species; brown or pale with black markings, not pubescent; very convex beneath; epipleura of elytra with a basal excavation which receives the apices of mesofemora; epipleura appearing obliquely truncate and with an oblique carina at base.

Fig. 124   Fig. 125

Figs. 124–125. Basal end of epipleuron of *Hygrotus* (124) and of *Hydro-porus* (125) viewed from side, the former with an exca-vation (*e*) to receive middle knee and with an oblique carina (*c*).

KEY TO SPECIES

Elytra without impressed lines ....a. *nubilus*
Elytra usually with a sutural and two or three dorsal impressed lines ....
....b. *impressopunctatus*

a. *Hygrotus nubilus* LeConte   Plate XIV, No. 13, p. 139
    Elongate-oval; head, pronotum, and legs dull yellow; elytra with three or four irregular blackish lines which sometimes expand to form a dark blotch behind middle; beneath, black. Elytra without impressed lines. Length 4–4.5 mm.

b. *Hygrotus impressopunctatus* (Schaller)   Plate XIV, No. 14, p. 139
    Oblong-oval; legs, head, and apical half of pronotum reddish brown; base of pronotum and elytra dark brown. Pronotum and elytra coarsely and deeply punctate, many of the punctures elongate and confluent, each of latter with three impressed lines that extend about to the middle. Length 5–6 mm.
    The coloration and sculpture at once distinguish this species from the preceding.

Genus II. *HYDROPORUS* Clairville

These small and difficult-to-identify beetles are ovate and dark brown; head never margined anteriorly; epipleura not excavated and without basal carina; pronotum margined; prosternum never truncate posteriorly; procoxal processes united as far as apex, which is truncate or slightly produced medially.

PLATE XIV—Aquatic Families I

Family HALIPLIDAE

1. *Haliplus fasciatus* Aubé (p. 130)

Dull orangeish or yellowish, with black markings; 3–3.5 mm.

2. *H. triopsis* Say (p. 130)

Dull orangeish or yellowish, with black markings; 2.5–3 mm.

3. *H. immaculicollis* Harris (p. 130)

Dull orangeish or yellowish, with black markings; 2.5–3 mm.

4. *Peltodytes duodecimpunctatus* (Say) (p. 131)

Dull orangeish or yellowish, with black markings; 3.5–4 mm.

5. *P. muticus* (LeConte) (p. 131)

Dull orangeish or yellowish, with black markings; 3.5–4 mm.

Family DYTISCIDAE I

6. *Hydrocanthus iricolor* Say (p. 133)

Brown-red, elytra darker; 4–5 mm.

7. *Hydroporus consimilis* LeConte (p. 140)

Brownish orange, marked with black; 4–5 mm.

8. *Laccophilus proximus* Say (p. 134)

Dull orangeish; elytra minutely speckled with brown; 4–5 mm.

9. *L. fasciatus* Aubé (p. 134)

Dull orangeish; elytra finely dotted with brown and marked with black; 4.5–5.5 mm.

10. *Desmopachria convexa* (Aubé) (p. 134)

Brownish red; elytra darker; 1.5–2.5 mm.

11. *Bidessus flavicollis* (LeConte) (p. 136)

Yellowish; elytra marked as in either of the two forms illustrated; 1–1.5 mm.

12. *B. affinis* (Say) (p. 136)

Dull yellow, head darker; elytra clouded with brown; 1.5–2 mm.

13. *Hygrotus nubilus* LeConte (p. 137)

Orange; elytra yellow, markings brown; 4–4.5 mm.

14. *H. impressopunctatus* (Schaller) (p. 137)

Dull orangeish; elytra largely brown, with indistinct pale markings; 5–6 mm.

15. *Hydroporus striatopunctatus* Melsheimer (p. 140)

Dull orangeish; elytra paler; markings dark brown; 2.5–3.5 mm.

16. *H. wickhami* Zaitzev (p. 140)

Dull orangeish; elytra paler; markings dark brown; 3–4 mm.

17. *H. undulatus* Say (p. 140)

Brownish red; markings black; 4–4.5 mm.

18. *H. niger* Say (p. 141)

Deep brown, with indistinct pale markings; 4–5 mm.

19. *Copelatus glyphicus* (Say) (p. 146)

Reddish brown; elytra darker, each with ten striae; 5–6 mm.

20. *Agabus confinis* (Gyllenhal) (p. 142)

Black; elytra olive-black, with dull-yellow base and margins; 8.5–9.5 mm.

21. *A. disintegratus* (Crotch) (p. 142)

Dull orange; elytra pale yellow; markings black; 7.5–8.5 mm.

22. *A. seriatus* Say (p. 142)

Shining black; 9–10 mm.

PLATE XIV

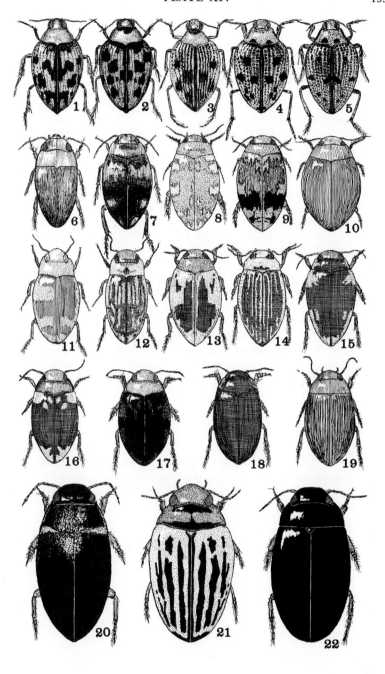

MM

0　　10　　20　　30　　40　　50　　60　　70

KEY TO SPECIES

1. Metacoxal cavities not contiguous ....a. *wickhami*
   Metacoxal cavities contiguous 2
2. At least the sterna black ....e. *niger*
   Beneath, reddish brown 3
3. Elytra coarsely punctate, with two smooth, narrow lines on each ....
   ....d. *striatopunctatus*
   Elytra without smooth lines 4
4. Pronotum finely, indistinctly margined ....c. *consimilis*
   Pronotum broadly, distinctly margined ....b. *undulatus*

a. *Hydroporus wickhami* Zaitzev   Plate XIV, No. 16, p. 139

Elongate-oval, convex, narrowed posteriorly; pale yellow to reddish brown; pronotum with apical half and entire basal margin blackish; elytra with extreme base narrowly black and with two broad, blackish bands connected laterally and along suture. Pronotum minutely, densely punctate. Elytra each with two more or less distinct striae of impressed punctures; entire surface minutely, densely punctate. Length 3–4 mm.

b. *Hydroporus undulatus* Say   Plate XIV, No. 17, p. 139

Elongate-oval, feebly tapering posteriorly; strongly convex; pale yellowish to yellowish brown; pronotum with basal and apical margins narrowly blackish; elytra sometimes entirely blackish, or black area reduced to three irregular bands which are broadly confluent along sides and suture as well as on disk. Pronotum minutely alutaceous, densely and finely punctate. Elytra coarsely, sparsely punctate in male, minutely, densely so in female; both sexes without rows of coarser punctures. Length 4–4.5 mm.

c. *Hydroporus consimilis* LeConte   Plate XIV, No. 7, p. 139

Rather broadly oval, convex, slightly narrowed behind; head, pronotum, undersurface, and legs reddish yellow, the pronotum margined apically and basally with fuscous; elytra blackish, with three irregular, reddish-brown spots, one marginal, extending from humerus for one-third length of elytra, then across nearly to suture, one submedian, and one near apex. Pronotum and elytra densely, finely punctate; elytra more finely so in female; both sexes without rows of coarser punctures. Length 4–5 mm.

d. *Hydroporus striatopunctatus* Melsheimer   Plate XIV, No. 15, p. 139

Elongate-oval, convex, narrowed posteriorly; yellowish; pronotum with apical and basal margin medially piceous; elytra with three piceous bands, median one broad, all narrowly connected along suture. Pronotum finely, rather densely punctate. Elytra each divided into three subequal spaces by two small, impunctate, longitudinal lines; intervals coarsely and sparsely punctate. Length 2.5–3.5 mm.

This species usually lives in running brooks.

e. *Hydroporus niger* Say   Plate XIV, No. 18, p. 139

Elongate-ovate, rather convex, not tapering posteriorly; piceous; head, legs, humeri, and epipleura indistinctly reddish brown. Pronotum and elytra finely but distinctly punctate, denser on elytra; latter without rows of coarse punctures. Length 4–5 mm.

Tribe AGABINI

KEY TO GENERA

1. Metatarsal claws unequal ....III. *Ilybius*   (p. 143)
   Metatarsal claws equal or nearly so 2
2. Lateral lobes of metasternum triangular, sometimes narrow, sometimes wedge-shaped (Fig. 126) ....I. *Agabus*   (p. 141)
   Lateral lobes of metasternum linear, parallel-sided, diverging slightly outward toward apex (Fig. 127) ....II. *Ilybiosoma*   (p. 143)

Genus I. *AGABUS* Leach

Ovate, more or less metallic or black, rarely variegated species; next to last segment of labial palpi normal; pronotum margined; elytra usually minutely reticulate or alutaceous; prosternum often carinate; hind legs rather feebly developed for swimming; claws of metatarsi equal.

The members of this genus can be found beneath stones in wet, grassy places or about roots of plants in marshes and shallow pools.

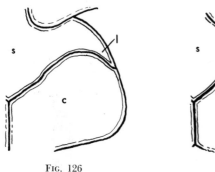
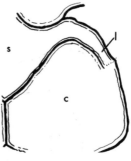

FIG. 126   FIG. 127

Figs. 126–127. Left side of metasternum of *Agabus* (126) and of *Ilybiosoma* (127). *s*, metasternum; *c*, metacoxa; *l*, lateral lobe of metasternum.

KEY TO SPECIES

1. Elytra dull yellow, with black stripes ....b. *disintegratus*
   Elytra black or piceous, sometimes margin pale 2
2. Elytra finely, densely reticulate, only moderately shining; elytral margins
   pale ....c. *confinis*
   Elytra polished, only with rows of scattered punctures; elytra unicolorous ...3
3. Prosternal spine broad, flat (Fig. 128) ....a. *seriatus*
   Prosternal spine narrower, convex (Fig. 129) ....d. *gagates*

a. *Agabus seriatus* (Say)   Plate XIV, No. 22, p. 139

Oblong-ovate, subconvex; black, slightly bronzed, shining; antennae and legs dark reddish brown. Elytra finely reticulate, with two or three dorsal rows of fine, but distinct, punctures. Prosternum with spine carinate. Length 9–10 mm.

b. *Agabus disintegratus* (Crotch)   Plate XIV, No. 21, p. 139

Ovate, subconvex; head and pronotum dull reddish, the latter with apical and basal margins black; elytra dull yellow, with three or four narrow, black stripes; surface smooth. Length 7.5–8.5 mm.

c. *Agabus confinis* (Gyllenhal)   Plate XIV, No. 20, p. 139

Oblong-oval, moderately robust, convex; head, pronotum, and under-surface black; elytra dark brown; antennae, legs, and margin of elytra reddish brown; all femora in part piceous. Elytra finely, densely punctate, with a few coarse punctures intermixed. Length 8.5–9.5 mm.

d. *Agabus gagates* Aubé   Plate XVI, No. 2, p. 151

Ovate, subconvex; piceous, shining; antennae, legs, and sides of pronotum more or less reddish brown. Elytra finely reticulate, with rows of fine, but distinct, punctures. Prosternum with spine carinate. Length 9–10 mm.

FIG. 128   FIG. 129

Figs. 128–129. Prosternal process of *Agabus seriatus* (128) and of *A. gagates* (129).

Genus II. *ILYBIOSOMA* Crotch

Medium-sized species; antennae simple; prosternal process convex; metatibiae and metatarsi very short; first metatarsal segment shorter than the tibial spur and only twice as long as second segment; male with pro- and mesotarsi compressed, narrowly dilated; claws simple.

Ilybiosoma bifarius (Kirby)   Plate XVI, No. 3, p. 151
Oblong-ovate, subconvex; black, shining; head in front, antennae, legs, and thoracic side margins reddish brown. Elytra with numerous minute, longitudinal impressed lines which are transverse behind middle. Length 6–7 mm.

Genus III. *ILYBIUS* Erichson

Oblong, convex; black or metallic; pronotum margined; upper surface finely reticulate, undersurface finely strigose; prosternal spine compressed and acute; metatibiae on inner half of apical angles with a linear group of setae.

Ilybius biguttulus (Germar)   Plate XVI, No. 1, p. 151
Oval, convex, slightly dilated at middle; black above; undersurface and hind legs piceous; antennae and fore- and middle legs reddish brown. Elytra with two small, pale spots on sides, one of which is subapical. Length 10–11 mm.

Tribe AGABETINI

Genus *AGABETES* Crotch

Small, oval, depressed; head more or less flattened; pronotum very short, sides rounded, not margined; prosternal spine with an acute carina; male with protarsal claws very elongate; last abdominal sternite deeply impressed each side.

Agabetes acuductus (Harris)   Plate XV, No. 5, p. 145
Oval, subdepressed; blackish or piceous, slightly shining; head, pronotal side margins, and elytral humeri reddish. Entire surface of elytra and pronotum with many short impressions. Length 7–7.5 mm.
This species is usually found in woodland pools.

PLATE XV
Aquatic Families II
Family DYTISCIDAE II

1. *Dytiscus hybridus* Aubé (p. 148) — Black, with dull-yellowish margins; 26–28 mm.

2. *D. verticalis* Say (p. 149) — Black, margins dull yellowish; 33–35 mm.

3. *D. harrisii* Kirby (p. 149) — Black, with dull-yellowish margins; 38–40 mm.

4. *Graphoderus liberus* (Say) (p. 153) — Orangeish; elytral network black; 11–12 mm.

5. *Agabetes acuductus* (Harris) (p. 143) — Dull orange, marked with fuscous; 7–7.5 mm.

6. *Coptotomus interrogatus* (Fabricius) (p. 146) — Orange-yellow; pronotum with black markings; elytra washed with blackish; 6.5–7.5 mm.

7. *Rhantus binotatus* (Harris) (p. 147) — Dull orangeish; pronotum with two black spots; elytra dull; 11.5–12.5 mm.

8. *Thermonectus basillaris* Harris (p. 153) — Dull orangeish and shining black; 9–10 mm.

9. *Colymbetes sculptilis* Harris (p. 147) — Dull yellow, marked with blackish; 15.5–16.5 mm.

10. *Acilius fraternus* (Harris) (p. 152) — Dull yellowish and black; male without elytral sulci (as in No. 12); 13–15 mm.

11. *Dytiscus fasciventris* Say (p. 148) — Black; margins pale; female often has many fine sulci on elytra; 25–28 mm.

12. *Acilius semisulcatus* Aubé (p. 152) — Dull yellowish and black; head with an M-shaped mark; female sulcate (as in No. 10); 12–14 mm.

MM 0   10   20   30   40   50   60   70

PLATE XV 145

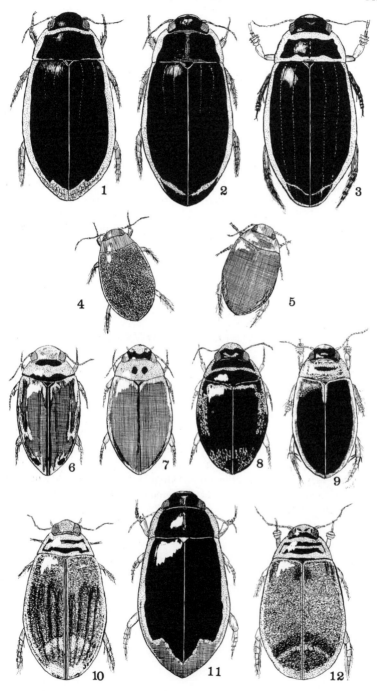

Tribe COPELATINI

Genus *COPELATUS* Erichson

Small, broadly ovate; pronotum finely but distinctly margined laterally; prosternum with an acute carina anteriorly; metafemora not ciliate apically; claws equal in both sexes; male with pro- and mesotarsi dilated, beneath with small, equal disks.

Copelatus glyphicus (Say)   Plate XIV, No. 19, p. 139
    Oblong, ovate, rather slender, subdepressed; dark reddish brown or piceous; antennae and legs paler. Pronotum nearly smooth. Elytra each with ten deeply impressed striae, reaching almost to apex. Length 5–6 mm.
    The above species lives under stones and logs near the edge of brooks or pools.

Tribe COPTOTOMINI

Genus *COPTOTOMUS* Say

Moderate-sized, oval species, with terminal segment of palpi somewhat compressed and notched at apex; prosternum with an elevated carina; side lobes of metasternum narrow, linear; metatarsi with last segment equal to fourth; claws equal, pressed together so as to appear to be single.

Coptotomus interrogatus (Fabricius)   Plate XV, No. 6, p. 145
    Elongate-oval, subconvex; head, pronotum, and beneath reddish brown; vertex black; pronotum black at base and apex; elytra piceous, with numerous, very small, pale-yellowish markings, a short stripe near scutellum and an irregular marginal stripe of the same color. Female with short, indistinct striae at base of elytra. Length 6.5–7.5 mm.

Tribe COLYMBETINI

KEY TO GENERA

Metasternum with a broad, deep groove (Fig. 130); pronotum margined
....I. *Rhantus* (p. 147)
Metasternum with a narrow, indistinct groove (Fig. 131); pronotum not
margined ....II. *Colymbetes* (p. 147)

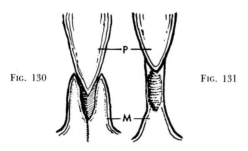

FIG. 130   FIG. 131

Figs. 130–131. Metasternal process (M) of *Rhantus* (130) and of *Colymbetes* (131). In the former there is a deep groove which receives the tip of the prosternal process (P).

Genus I. *RHANTUS* Lacordaire

Medium-sized beetles, usually black; pronotum margined; last segment of metatarsi as short as fourth, claws unequal; male with pro- and mesotarsi compressed, dilated, and with four transverse rows of disks on underside.

Rhantus binotatus (Harris)   Plate XV, No. 7, p. 145
    Subovate, subdepressed; smooth, rather shining; dull yellow; vertex of head black, front with a pair of blackish spots somewhat confluent; pronotum with a pair of transverse black maculae at middle of disk; elytra with entire disk densely covered with black dots and with several series of indistinct black maculae; beneath black, except abdomen, which is banded with dull yellow. Entire upper surface minutely alutaceous; pronotum with a fine median impressed line not attaining apex. Elytra with one or two poorly defined rows of punctures. Length 11.5–12.5 mm.

Genus II. *COLYMBETES* Clairville

Rather large, elongate; sides of pronotum oblique, not margined; scutellum punctate; elytra with very fine, transverse striae; anal segment of male triangularly incised; pro- and mesotarsi with segments two and three covered with small, equal disks.

Colymbetes sculptilis Harris   Plate XV, No. 9, p. 145
    Elongate-oval; rather slender, subdepressed; dull brownish orange; vertex of head and upper portion of front black, with a small, orangeish macula; pronotum medially with an irregular, transverse, blackish fascia; elytra with disk sooty black; body beneath black, apices of abdominal sternites narrowly orange-brown. Head minutely alutaceous. Pronotum finely, irregularly

strigose; all margins finely, densely punctate. Elytra finely, evenly, transversely rugose and each with four series of fine punctures. Length 15.5–16.5 mm.

Tribe DYTISCINI

Genus *DYTISCUS* Linné

Elongate-oval; convex above and beneath; antennae filiform; clypeus with a distinct suture at base; pronotum not margined; elytra of female variable, in some species always smooth, in some deeply grooved, while in others both forms can be found; metatibiae distinctly longer than broad, outer apical spur slender; metatarsi not fringed on outer margin; protarsi of male beneath with two large and numerous small disks.

The largest of the diving beetles belong to this genus. Both adults and larvae are extremely predaceous.

KEY TO SPECIES

1. Pronotum with all margins distinctly and broadly yellow .... d. *harrisii*
   Pronotum with sides yellow, base and apex not or only indistinctly so 2
2. Sternites uniformly black or piceous .... b. *hybridus*
   Sternites reddish brown, with apical margins piceous 3
3. Elytra without a narrow, subapical crossbar of yellow; smaller, 25–28 mm. ...
   ....a. *fasciventris*
   Elytra with a narrow, oblique, subapical crossbar; size larger, 33–35 mm. .....
   ....c. *verticalis*

a. *Dytiscus fasciventris* Say   Plate XV, No. 11, p. 145
Elongate-oval, moderately robust; greenish black; pronotum with only sides yellow, or with a faint trace of yellow at base and apex; elytral margin yellowish, not attaining apex; undersurface and legs pale reddish brown or brownish yellow; metasternum and apical margins of abdominal sternites piceous. Pronotum minutely, indistinctly punctate, at apex with a row of fine punctures. Each elytron of female with ten grooves, extending beyond middle; in both sexes apical third finely and densely punctate, base nearly impunctate. Length 25–28 mm.

b. *Dytiscus hybridus* Aubé   Plate XV, No. 1, p. 145
Elongate-oval, moderately robust; olive-brown; pronotum with apex narrowly yellow and occasionally with a faint yellow line basally; pale-yellow margin of elytra nearly equal in width throughout its length, attaining apex; undersurface, hind legs, and mesotibiae orange-brown, remaining legs and prothorax pale yellowish. Pronotum in male minutely, indistinctly punctate, with a row of fine punctures near apex, in female

distinctly punctate, especially laterally. Elytra each with three rows of fine punctures, rest of surface impunctate in male, in female densely, finely punctate. Length 26–28 mm.

c. *Dytiscus verticalis* Say   Plate XV, No. 2, p. 145

Elongate-oval, moderately slender; olive-brown; pronotum margined only at sides with yellow; elytra with a marginal yellow line narrowed toward apex and a subapical transverse yellow line; undersurface and legs reddish brown, prothorax and pro- and mesofemora dull orange, abdominal sternites with apical margin black or piceous. Pronotum minutely punctate in male, with a row of moderately coarse punctures at base and apex in both sexes; entire disk distinctly, finely punctate in female. Elytra each with three rows of fine punctures in both sexes; intervals with a row of fine, sparse punctures in male, entire surface finely, sparsely punctate in female. Length 33–35 mm.

d. *Dytiscus harrisii* Kirby   Plate XV, No. 3, p. 145

Broadly ovate, robust; olive-brown; pronotum with all margins broadly lined with yellow; marginal line on elytra narrowed only near apex; elytra with a narrow crossbar near apex; undersurface piceous; legs except meso- and metatibiae and metatarsi dull orange; abdominal sternites reddish yellow, margined with piceous. Pronotum and elytra minutely alutaceous; pronotum with a row of punctures at apex and a few each side of middle at base; elytra each with three rows of fine punctures. Length 38–40 mm.

Tribe THERMONECTINI

KEY TO GENERA

1. Mesofemora with setae on posterior margin short, not more than one-third as long as width of femur ....III. *Graphoderus* (p. 153)
   Mesofemora with setae one and one-half to twice as long as width of femur 2
2. Mesofemora with setae on posterior margin equal in length to width of femur; upper surface of body densely, distinctly punctate .....
   ....I. *Acilius* (p. 149)
   Mesofemora with setae one and one-half to twice as long as width of femur; upper surface minutely, indistinctly punctate ....
   ....II. *Thermonectus* (p. 153)

Genus I. *ACILIUS* Leach

Moderately large, subdepressed, slightly obovate; pronotum not margined; metacoxae very large; elytra finely, densely punctate, in female frequently with four broad, longitudinal sulci posteriorly; mesofemora with

PLATE XVI

Aquatic Families III

Family DYTISCIDAE III

1. *Ilybius biguttulus* (Germar) (p. 143) — Black; elytral markings indistinct, pale yellowish; 10–11 mm.

2. *Agabus gagates* Aubé (p. 142) — Black, shining; 9–10 mm.

3. *Ilybiosoma bifarius* (Kirby) (p. 143) — Shining black; head with indistinct reddish marks; 6–7 mm.

4. *Cybister fimbriolatus* (Say) (p. 154) — Black, margins dull yellowish; 30–33 mm.

Family HYDROPHILIDAE I

5. *Tropisternus glaber* (Herbst) (p. 167) — Black, shining; 9.5–11 mm.

6. *T. mixtus* (LeConte) (p. 167) — Shining black; legs pale; 8.5–9 mm.

7. *Helophorus lacustris* LeConte (p. 159) — Brassy-black; elytra brown-orange; 4–5 mm.

8. *H. lineatus* Say (p. 159) — Brassy-black; elytra brown-orange; 3–4 mm.

9. *Hydrochus scabratus* Mulsant (p. 162) — Dull brassy green; 4.5–6 mm.

10. *H. subcupreus* Randall (p. 162) — Metallic gray or dull coppery; elytral punctures small; 3.5–4 mm.

11. *Paracymus subcupreus* (Say) (p. 168) — Piceous; pronotum slightly paler on sides; 1.5–2 mm.

12. *Sphaeridium scarabaeoides* (Linné) (p. 173) — Black; elytra with tips yellowish, basal spot dark red; 5.5–7 mm.

13. *Cercyon haemorrhoidalis* (Fabricius) (p. 173) — Deep red-brown; elytra paler at apex; 2.5–3 mm.

MM 0   10   20   30   40   50   60   70

PLATE XVI   151

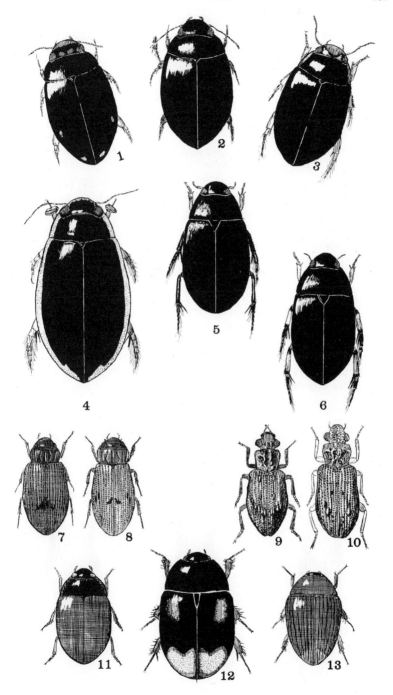

long, conspicuous setae on posterior margin; protarsi of male broadly dilated, with one large or two small disks; mesotarsi simple; metatarsal claws equal; apex of prosternal process broad, gradually tapering and subacute (Fig. 132).

KEY TO SPECIES

Vertex of head with a distinct M-shaped black mark; elytral sulci of female unequal in length, the outer ones longer and reaching nearly to base ....
....a. *semisulcatus*
Vertex of head without an M-shaped mark; elytral sulci of female subequal in length and reaching only to middle ....b. *fraternus*

a. *Acilius semisulcatus* Aubé   Plate XV, No. 12, p. 145
Broadly oval, moderately robust; brownish yellow above; head at base and an M-shaped mark on vertex black; disk of pronotum with two transverse black lines; elytra covered with many black dots except an arcuate area at apex; beneath black, abdomen laterally and at extreme apex yellowish. Pronotum and elytra minutely, densely punctate. Elytral sulci in female unequal in length. Length 12–14 mm.

b. *Acilius fraternus* (Harris)   Plate XV, No. 10, p. 145
Ovate, robust; pale yellowish to yellowish brown; head with vertex indistinctly blackish; pronotum with two transverse fasciae, posterior one sometimes shorter; elytra covered with numerous black dots except for an arcuate area near apex; beneath largely black, as are hind legs; abdominal sternites laterally indistinctly maculate with brownish yellow. Pronotum and elytra very densely punctate. Length 13–15 mm.

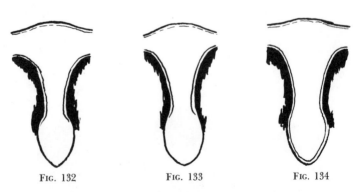

FIG. 132   FIG. 133   FIG. 134

Figs. 132–134. Prosternal process of *Acilius* (132), of *Thermonectus* (133), and of *Graphoderus* (134).

Genus II. *THERMONECTUS* Dejean

Moderate-sized, convex; pronotum not margined; elytra indistinctly, minutely punctate, with one or two rows of coarser punctures, female strigose on basal half; apex of prosternal process broad and obtuse (Fig. 133); mesofemora with long, conspicuous setae on posterior margin; metatarsal claws unequal; protarsi of male beneath with two or three basal disks and with numerous small, unequal ones.

Thermonectus basillaris Harris   Plate XV, No. 8, p. 145
Ovate, moderately slender; black; head anteriorly and a transverse line on vertex dull yellow; pronotum at sides and a narrow bar on disk dull yellow; elytra with margins, a crossbar near base, and some indistinct markings on sides yellowish; beneath reddish brown or piceous; first two pairs of legs dull yellowish, hind ones fuscous. Upper surface minutely, indistinctly punctate; pronotum near apical margin with a few distinct fine punctures; elytra each with three distinct rows of coarser punctures. Length 9–10 mm.

Genus III. *GRAPHODERUS* Dejean

Moderate-sized, convex; pronotum not margined; elytra indistinctly, minutely punctate, each with three rows of coarser punctures; apex of prosternal process broad, slightly dilated and ovate (Fig. 134); mesofemora with a row of short, erect hairs on posterior margin; mesotarsal claws unequal; protarsi of male beneath with two or three basal disks and with numerous small, unequal ones. In the female the elytra may be smooth, or rough with minute tubercles.

Graphoderus liberus (Say)   Plate XV, No. 4, p. 145
Slightly obovate, robust; dull reddish yellow; pronotum sometimes piceous basally; elytra blackish brown, with numerous yellowish, recurved marks, these united along sides to form a yellowish margin; undersurface reddish brown; legs pale brownish yellow. Entire upper surface minutely, indistinctly punctate; pronotum with a series of fine punctures at base and apex; elytra each with three rows of coarser punctures. Length 11–12 mm.

Tribe CYBISTERINI

Genus *CYBISTER* Curtis

Ovate, large species; spiracles very small; hind legs very well adapted for swimming, broad and powerful; metatibiae short and broad; metatarsal claws very unequal, the inner one sometimes lacking; male with protarsal segments one to three dilated into a circular disk bearing four rows of equal-sized cups, and with four or five deep ridges in the hollows behind the metacoxae (used as stridulating organ).

Cybister fimbriolatus (Say)   Plate XVI, No. 4, p. 151

Ovate, more or less wedge-shaped; brown, tinged with green; pronotum and elytra broadly margined with yellow; front and spots on sides of abdominal sternites three to six yellow. Pronotum and elytra of female with numerous fine, short, impressed lines. Length 30–33 mm.

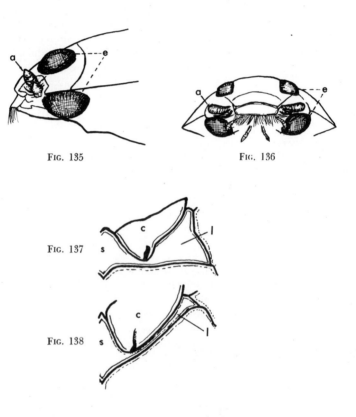

FIG. 135   FIG. 136

FIG. 137

FIG. 138

Figs. 135–136. Head of *Gyrinus,* side view (135), and from the front (136), showing divided eyes (*e*) and antennae (*a*).

Figs. 137–138. Left side of metasternum (*s*) of *Dineutus* (137) and of *Gyrinus* (138). *l,* lateral prolongation; *c,* mesocoxa.

Family GYRINIDAE

The Whirligig Beetles

These beetles derive their common name from their habit of swimming in groups on the surface of ponds and quiet streams, the individuals whirling around and around. When disturbed, they will dive beneath the surface of the water carrying an air bubble on their undersurface. The eyes in this family are divided (Figs. 135, 136), a feature which enables them to see both above and below the water at the same time. Other family characters are: small to moderate size; antennae short, thick, inserted behind mandibles, third segment enlarged, following segments broad and united, forming a spindle-shaped appendage (Fig. 135); front legs long, slender, received in oblique grooves between pro- and mesofemora; middle and hind legs short, broad, strongly flattened; tibiae without spurs; tarsi five-segmented, segments partially flattened and triangular.

KEY TO GENERA

Scutellum concealed; length more than 9.5 mm. ....I. *Dineutus* (p. 155)
Scutellum distinct; length not over 7.5 mm. ....II. *Gyrinus* (p. 156)

Genus I. *DINEUTUS* MacLeay

Medium-sized, broadly oval, subdepressed; labrum rounded and ciliated anteriorly; scutellum concealed; elytra with nine feebly impressed striae, these sometimes indistinct; metasternum with lateral prolongations broadly triangular (Fig. 137); protarsi of male slightly dilated, clothed beneath with dense papillae, forming an elongate, narrow brush.

KEY TO SPECIES

1. Sides of prothorax and elytra with a submarginal bronzed line; 12 mm. or more in length ....a. *ciliatus*
    Sides of prothorax and elytra without submarginal stripe; less than 11 mm. in length 2
2. Undersurface bronzed, brown-yellow ....b. *discolor*
    Undersurface black, usually bronzed 3

3. Sutural angle of elytra of both sexes produced backward; apices of elytra in female feebly separated (Figs. 139, 140) .... c. *americanus*
   Sutural angles of male elytra rounded (Fig. 141), those of female produced, apices widely separated (Fig. 142) .... d. *hornii*

a. *Dineutus ciliatus* Forsberg   Plate XVIII, No. 2, p. 171

Broadly ovate; bronzed black; beneath piceous; sides of pronotum and elytra with bronzed, concave, curved stripe; legs dark brown. Elytra feebly emarginate at apex in both sexes; surface minutely, indistinctly punctate. Length 12–15 mm.

This species is found especially along the Atlantic coast region in ditches and streams, never in ponds.

b. *Dineutus discolor* Aubé   Plate XVIII, No. 5, p. 171

Oblong-oval, narrowed anteriorly; upper surface black, bronzed, shining; beneath brownish to straw-colored. Elytra with side margins and outer apical angle slightly sinuate; sutural angles weakly produced. Length 11.5–13 mm.

c. *Dineutus americanus* (Fabricius)[1]   Plate XVIII, No. 3, p. 171

Oblong-oval, distinctly convex; black, strongly bronzed; beneath black, very shining, abdominal segments often tinged with brown. Elytra of male feebly sinuate near apices, which are but slightly separated at suture, angles but little produced backward; those of female more strongly sinuate both on side margins and near apices, the latter more widely separated at suture, angles distinctly produced. Length 10–12 mm.

This species is more common in small streams than in ponds.

d. *Dineutus hornii* Roberts   Plate XVIII, No. 7, p. 171

Oblong-oval, strongly convex; black, distinctly bronzed; body beneath dark reddish brown, shining; legs and epipleura brownish orange. Elytra of male with sutural angles rounded (Fig. 141); in female acutely produced and widely separated (Fig. 142) and sides strongly sinuate near apex; entire upper surface of both sexes minutely, densely punctate. Length 9.5–11 mm.

Genus II. *GYRINUS* Geoffroy

Small, broadly oval, depressed; each elytron with eleven rows of punctures; scutellum distinct; metasternum with lateral prolongations narrowly triangular, sides subparallel (Fig. 138); last ventral abdominal segment depressed, rounded at apex; protarsi of male dilated, clothed beneath with dense papillae, forming an elongate-ovate brush.

---

[1] This species is usually credited to either Say or Linné, but Fabricius is the actual author of the species, having described it in 1775 in *Systema entomologiae*.

KEY TO SPECIES

1. Under side-margin of prothorax and epipleura brownish yellow ..a. *fraternus*
   Under side-margin of prothorax and epipleura deep reddish brown to black..2
2. Outer rows of elytral punctures only slightly more impressed than inner ones
   ....b. *analis*
   Outer rows of elytral punctures distinctly impressed ....c. *borealis*

a. *Gyrinus fraternus* Couper   Plate XVIII, No. 1, p. 171
Elongate-oval, rather robust; bluish black, shining, without trace of bronze; underparts and epipleura of elytra brownish yellow to yellowish brown. Pronotum with a row of fine punctures on apical margin. Elytra each with eleven rows of fine punctures, marginal one indistinct. Length 5.5–6 mm.

b. *Gyrinus analis* Say   Plate XVIII, No. 6, p. 171
Elongate-ovate, moderately slender; black, feebly bronzed; body beneath piceous to black, epipleura dark reddish brown; legs and last abdominal sternite brownish yellow. Pronotum coriaceous, with a short, transverse row of punctures each side near apical margin. Elytra each with eleven rows of rather fine punctures, uniformly impressed. Length 5–6 mm.

c. *Gyrinus borealis* Aubé   Plate XVIII, No. 4, p. 171
Broadly oval, rather robust; black, strongly shining; margins of elytra bronzed; beneath piceous to black, last abdominal sternite and epipleura dark brown; legs brownish yellow. Pronotum feebly coriaceous with a row of rather coarse punctures along apical margin, narrowly interrupted at middle. Elytra with eleven rows of punctures, inner ones fine, lateral ones coarse, deeply impressed. Length 6.5–7.5 mm.

This, the commonest species of Gyrinidae, is found the year round.

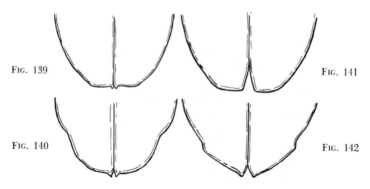

Figs. 139–142. Elytral apices of *Dineutus americanus* (139, 140) and of *D. hornii* (141, 142). In each case the male is shown in the upper figure, the female in the lower.

Family HYDROPHILIDAE

The Water Scavenger Beetles

Most members of this group are wholly aquatic; a few live in dung or moist earth. Color usually black, sometimes with yellow, orange, or red markings along the margins; surface usually smooth, polished, and strongly convex dorsally, flattened ventrally; eyes large; antennae short, six- to nine-segmented, strongly clubbed, inserted under sides of front behind mandibles; labial palpi long, slender, often mistaken for antennae (Fig. 143); metasternum large, frequently carinate and produced into a long spine posteriorly; metacoxae oblique, flat; tarsi five-segmented, first segment often small; pro- and mesotarsi compressed and densely fringed. A number of the smaller species have a slightly different shape, the surface rough and pitted, and crawl on the soil and vegetation beneath the surface of the water rather than swim.

While for the most part members of this family are scavengers, both the larvae and adults of some species are predaceous on small fish and other small aquatic animals.

KEY TO SUBFAMILIES

1. First segment of meso- and metatarsi elongate, longer than second ....SPHAERIDIINAE (p. 172)
   First segment of meso- and metatarsi very short, shorter than second, and often scarcely visible 2
2. Second segment of metatarsi elongate, longer than third; pronotum behind as broad as base of elytra; last tarsal segment shorter than preceding segments united ..............HYDROPHILINAE (p. 162)
   Second segment of metatarsi short, about equal to third; last segment of tarsi as long as or longer than preceding segments together, or that of metatarsi may be shorter 3
3. Last segment of metatarsi shorter than preceding segments united; pronotum posteriorly narrower than base of elytra, and with five longitudinal furrows ........................HELOPHORINAE (p. 159)
   Last segment of metatarsi as long as or longer than preceding united; pronotum not narrowed posteriorly and without longitudinal furrows ....HYDROCHINAE (p. 162)

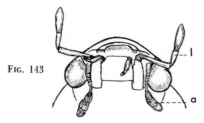

Fig. 143

Fig. 143. Head of a hydrophilid from beneath, showing the short, clavate antennae (*a*) and the long, slender, antenna-like labial palpi (*l*).

Subfamily HELOPHORINAE

Genus *HELOPHORUS* Fabricius

Small, oblong or elongate; antennae nine-segmented; last segment of maxillary palpi longer than one preceding; pronotum rough, with granulate depressions and with five longitudinal grooves, of which the middle one, or those on each side of the middle, are often sinuate; elytra with ten rows of punctures or striae.

KEY TO SPECIES

Pronotum with posterior angles obtuse; not narrowed at base; color piceous-brown ....a. *lacustris*
Pronotum with posterior angles rectangular; slightly narrowed at base; color light brownish yellow, with indistinct fuscous markings ....b. *lineatus*

a, *Helophorus lacustris* LeConte   Plate XVI, No. 7, p. 151
Oblong; piceous-brown, with a slight bronze; head and pronotum tinged with greenish. Pronotum two-thirds wider than long, granulate; sulci narrow, deep, intermediate ones strongly sinuate. Elytral striae deep, punctate. Length 4–5 mm.

This species is frequent in brooks.

b. *Helophorus lineatus* Say   Plate XVI, No. 8, p. 151
Elongate-oblong; light brown, tinged with greenish; elytra often with fuscous mark in the form of an inverted V on the suture behind middle and with two spots on each side. Pronotum with intermediate sulci deep, very strongly curved near middle. Elytral striae with deep, dilated, transverse punctures. Length 3–4 mm.

PLATE XVII

Aquatic Families IV

Family HYDROPHILIDAE II

1. *Enochrus perplexus* (LeConte) (p. 169) — Dark yellow-brown; pronotum lighter on sides; 4–5.5 mm.

2. *E. pygmaeus* Fabricius (p. 169) — Yellow-brown, clouded with blackish; 3.5–4.5 mm.

3. *E. ochraceus* (Melsheimer) (p. 169) — Dark brown and black; paler on sides; 3.5–4 mm.

4. *E. hamiltoni* (Horn) (p. 169) — Dull brownish yellow; markings black; 4.5–5.5 mm.

5. *Anacaena limbata* Fabricius (p. 168) — Dull brownish yellow; head and markings black; 2–2.5 mm.

6. *Hydrobius fuscipes* Linné (p. 167) — Black; elytra feebly paler toward sides; 6.5–8 mm.

7. *H. melaenum* Germar (p. 167) — Nearly hemispherical in form; black; 7–8 mm.

8. *Enochrus cinctus* (Say) (p. 169) — Black; sides of head and pronotum pale, those of elytra less so; 6.5–7 mm.

9. *Tropisternus lateralis* (Fabricius) (p. 167) — Black; sides pale; 8.5–9 mm.

10. *Cymbiodyta fimbriata* (Melsheimer) (p. 169) — Black; elytra and pronotum paler on sides; 4.5–6 mm.
    or *Helocombus bifidus* (LeConte) (p. 172) — Piceous; only elytra paler on sides; 5.5–7 mm.

11. *Cymbiodyta blanchardi* Horn (p. 172) — Deep brown; sides of elytra and pronotum indistinctly paler; 4 mm.

    or *Laccobius agilis* Randall (p. 172) — Blackish, with greenish reflex; margins and entire elytra yellow; 2–3 mm.

12. *Berosus pantherinus* LeConte (p. 165) — Dull yellow, with black and fuscous markings; head black; 3.5–4.5 mm.

13. *B. peregrinus* (Herbst) (p. 165) — Yellow, with brown markings; head black; 3.5–4.5 mm.

14. *B. striatus* (Say) (p. 165) — Dull yellow, with black and fuscous markings; head black; 4–5 mm.

15. *Dibolocelus ovatus* Gemminger and Harold (p. 166) — Shining black; 31–33 mm.

16. *Hydrochara obtusata* (Say) (p. 166) — Shining black; 13–16 mm.

17. *Hydrophilus triangularis* Say (p. 165) — Shining black; 34–37 mm.

MM 0   10   20   30   40   50   60   70

PLATE XVII

161

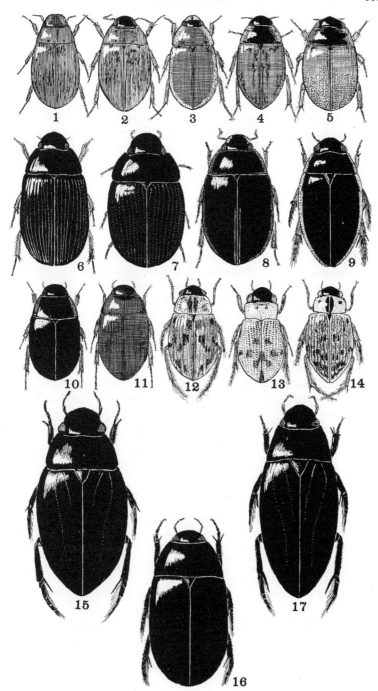

Subfamily HYDROCHINAE

Genus HYDROCHUS Leach

Elongate-oblong species; antennae seven-segmented; last segment of maxillary palpi longer than preceding one; pronotum much narrower than elytra, slightly transverse, disk with small foveae, not furrowed; metatarsal last segment as long as or longer than preceding segments united.

KEY TO SPECIES

Larger, 5.5 mm.; elytral intervals flat and much wider than striae, fourth with large, oblique tubercles ....a. *scabratus*
Smaller, 4 mm.; elytral intervals convex, fourth slightly elevated, but not tubercled ....b. *subcupreus*

a. *Hydrochus scabratus* Mulsant   Plate XVI, No. 9, p. 151
Moderately broadly oval, widened slightly behind middle; gray-brown, with a brassy tinge. Pronotum transverse; sides gradually narrowed apically; disk tubercled. Elytra striate; intervals flat and much wider than striae, fourth interval with three large, oblique tubercles. Length 4.5–6 mm.

b. *Hydrochus subcupreus* Randall   Plate XVI, No. 10, p. 151
Elongate, rather slender; brown, distinctly tinged with brassy; beneath piceous; legs reddish brown, base of tibiae darker. Pronotum subquadrate; disk foveate and coarsely punctate. Elytral intervals convex, wider than striae, fifth slightly elevated, interrupted behind, fourth not tuberculate. Length 3.5–4 mm.

Subfamily HYDROPHILINAE

KEY TO GENERA

1. Meso- and metatibiae fringed on inner side with long swimming hairs; pronotum detached in outline from elytra ......I. *Berosus*   (p. 165)
   Meso- and metatibiae without fringe of swimming hairs; pronotum continuous in outline with elytra 2
2. Meso- and metasternum raised in a common median keel (Fig. 144), produced posteriorly into a spine 3
   Meso- and metasternum not raised to form a common median keel 6
3. Prosternum sulcate; metasternal spine long 4
   Prosternum carinate; metasternal spine short ......IV. *Hydrochara*   (p. 166)
4. Last segment of maxillary palpi shorter than preceding one; body 25 mm. or more long 5

Last segment of maxillary palpi equal to or longer than the preceding one; length not over 12 mm. ....V. *Tropisternus* (p. 166)

5. Prosternal process closed anteriorly, hood-shaped (Fig. 145) ....
....II. *Hydrophilus* (p. 165)

Prosternal process not closed anteriorly, bifurcate (Fig. 146) .....
....III. *Dibolocelus* (p. 166)

6. Maxillary palpi robust and short, little longer or shorter than antennae, last segment as long as, or as a rule longer than, the preceding one 7

Maxillary palpi slenderer, much longer than antennae, last segment as a rule shorter than the one preceding it 10

7. Sutural stria of elytra present; abdomen with five visible ventral segments 8

Sutural stria of elytra absent; abdomen with six visible ventral segments ....XII. *Laccobius* (p. 172)

8. Longer than 5 mm.; elytra striate or rows of punctures very pronounced ....VI. *Hydrobius* (p. 167)

Not over 3 mm. long; elytra confusedly punctate or almost impunctate, never striate 9

9. Meso- and metafemora densely pubescent; upper surface testaceous to piceous, never with a metallic lustre ....VII. *Anacaena* (p. 168)

Meso- and metafemora at most sparsely pubescent at base; above always with a metallic lustre ....VIII. *Paracymus* (p. 168)

10. All tarsi five-segmented ....IX. *Enochrus* (p. 168)

Meso- and metatarsi four-segmented 11

11. Mesosternal carina transverse or elevated medially (Fig. 147); tarsal claws simple ....X. *Cymbiodyta* (p. 169)

Mesosternum with a compressed conical process (Fig. 148); claws broadly toothed at base in male ....XI. *Helocombus* (p. 172)

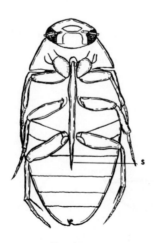

FIG. 144

Fig. 144. Undersurface of *Tropisternus*. s, metasternal spine.

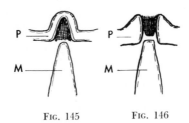

Fig. 145   Fig. 146

Figs. 145–146. Portion of undersurface of *Hydrophilus* (145) and *Dibolocelus* (146), with the mesosternum (*M*) inserting into the prosternal process (*P*).

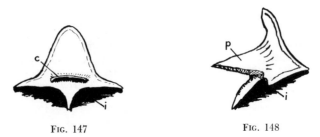

Fig. 147   Fig. 148

Figs. 147–148. Mesosternum of *Cymbiodyta* (147) and of *Helocombus* (148), the latter viewed in profile. *c*, carina; *p*, process; *i*, insertion of mesocoxa.

Fig. 149   Fig. 150

Figs. 149–150. Fifth abdominal sternite of *Berosus peregrinus* (149) and of *B. striatus* (150).

Genus I. *BEROSUS* Leach

Elongate, convex; pale-colored; elytra and pronotum spotted; antennae seven-segmented; scutellum elongate; meso- and metatibiae fringed on inner side with long hairs; posterior margin of fifth abdominal sternite set with short teeth; five visible abdominal segments, sixth retracted.

KEY TO SPECIES

1. Fifth sternite with one tooth at middle of notch (Fig. 149) 2
   Fifth sternite with two teeth at middle of notch (Fig. 150) ....c. *striatus*
2. Elytra with well-defined spots ....a. *pantherinus*
   Elytral spots indistinct ....b. *peregrinus*

a. *Berosus pantherinus* LeConte   Plate XVII, No. 12, p. 161
Elongate-oval, convex; pale, dull yellow; head blackish; pronotum with two black medial spots; each elytron with ten distinct black spots, two near base, four in a transverse band before middle, three forming another band behind middle, and one at apex; abdomen reddish brown. Pronotum finely punctate. Elytral striae coarsely punctate; intervals rather thickly and irregularly punctate. Length 3.5–4.5 mm.

b. *Berosus peregrinus* (Herbst)   Plate XVII, No. 13, p. 161
Elongate-oval, convex; light brownish yellow; head black, slightly bronzed; pronotum with a pair of dark spots near apex medially; elytra each with four or five indistinct, oblong, double spots. Head densely punctate, longitudinally impressed between eyes. Elytral striae more distinctly punctate laterally; intervals finely punctate. Length 3.5–4.5 mm.

c. *Berosus striatus* (Say)   Plate XVII, No. 14, p. 161
Elongate-oval, convex; head black; pronotum and elytra dull greenish yellow, the former with a double fuscous line on disk; elytra with many small, indistinct, black spots. Elytral striae distinct and finely punctate; intervals flat, coarsely punctate. Length 4–5 mm.

Genus II. *HYDROPHILUS* DeGeer

Large, elongate-oval, convex; last segment of maxillary palpi shorter and slightly broader than preceding segments; metasternal spine extending just to about middle of second abdominal segment; prosternal prominence into which the anterior end of the sternal spine fits, closed anteriorly (Fig. 145).

Hydrophilus triangularis Say   Plate XVII, No. 17, p. 161
Elongate-oval, subconvex; above, black, shining, with a slight tinge of olive; beneath, dark brown, abdominal sternites each with a more or less

distinct, triangular, pale-reddish spot laterally; first abdominal sternite wholly pubescent, remaining segments with a broad, smooth space medially. Elytra minutely, densely punctate and with six rows of coarse punctures. Length 34–37 mm.

The adults are often taken at light at night; by day they are found in ponds and streams.

Genus III. *DIBOLOCELUS* Regimbart

Strongly broadly ovate, very convex; last segment of maxillary palpi shorter and not so broad as preceding, which is compressed and broadened; metasternal spine extending to apex of second sternite; prosternal prominence open anteriorly (Fig. 146).

Dibolocelus ovatus Gemminger and Harold   Plate XVII, No. 15, p. 161
Ovate, rather convex; black, tinged with olive; beneath piceous; legs dark reddish brown; abdominal segments pubescent, last three each with an indistinct reddish spot laterally. Elytra minutely and densely punctate and with six rows of coarse punctures. Length 31–33 mm.

Genus IV. *HYDROCHARA* Berthold

Rather large, oval, robust, black or piceous beetles; prosternum entire and raised into a sharp carina; metasternum with spine short; meso- and metatibiae fringed on inner side.

Hydrochara obtusata (Say)   Plate XVII, No. 16, p. 161
Male elongate-oval; female more oblong-oval, strongly obtuse posteriorly; black, shining; beneath dark reddish brown, pubescent. Each elytron with four rows of distinct punctures, outer row double. Metasternal spine not extending beyond metacoxae. Length 13–16 mm.

The adults may be collected from beneath logs and stones near ponds and streams, as well as at electric lights at night.

Genus V. *TROPISTERNUS* Solier

Of moderate size; smooth, oval; usually shining black above; maxillary palpi with last segment equal to or longer than one preceding; metasternal spine long; prosternum sulcate.

The species of this genus are found in lakes and slow-flowing streams.

KEY TO SPECIES

1. Pronotum and elytra narrowly margined with yellow ....c. *lateralis*
   Pronotum and elytra entirely black 2
2. Anterior part of crest on sternum very finely and indistinctly punctate .....
   ....b. *mixtus*
   Anterior part of sternal crest distinctly punctate ....a. *glaber*

a. *Tropisternus glaber* (Herbst)   Plate XVI, No. 5, p. 151
   Elongate-oval, convex; black, feebly bronzed, shining. Elytra finely and equally punctate. Prosternal crest concave and very coarsely punctate anteriorly. Length 9.5–11 mm.
   The adults occur especially beneath rubbish along edges of ponds and lakes.

b. *Tropisternus mixtus* (LeConte)   Plate XVI, No. 6, p. 151
   Elongate-oval, convex; black, more or less bronzed, shining. Elytra irregularly punctate, with coarser and finer punctures intermixed. Length 8.5–9 mm.

c. *Tropisternus lateralis* (Fabricius)   Plate XVII, No. 9, p. 161
   Elongate-oval, convex; bronzy black, shining; pronotum and elytra margined with pale yellow; beneath black to piceous; legs yellow, femora black at base. Elytra finely, very densely punctate, with a few scattered, coarse punctures. Length 8.5–9 mm.

Genus VI. *HYDROBIUS* Leach

Dark-colored, medium-sized, broadly oval or almost circular species; antennae nine-segmented; last segment of maxillary palpi longer than third; elytra with either ten rows of punctures or ten striae.

KEY TO SPECIES

Elytra with well-marked striae; form oblong ....a. *fuscipes*
Elytra with rows of fine punctures; form short, strongly ovate, and very convex
   ....b. *melaenum*

a. *Hydrobius fuscipes* Linné   Plate XVII, No. 6, p. 161
   Oblong, convex; piceous to black, shining; beneath black. Pronotum finely punctate. Elytra striate, the two inner and scutellar striae indistinct basally; intervals flat, not very densely punctate. Length 6.5–8 mm.
   This species is found in ponds and bogs.

b. *Hydrobius melaenum* Germar   Plate XVII, No. 7, p. 161
   Very broadly oval, strongly convex; piceous to black, shining; finely

punctate. Elytra not striate but with rows of distinct punctures; scutellar stria distinct. Length 7–8 mm.

The adults are usually found in fresh running water beneath stones.

Genus VII. *ANACAENA* Thomson

Small, oval, very convex species; above yellow-brown to piceous; meso- and metafemora densely pubescent; prosternum simple, not carinate.

Anacaena limbata Fabricius   Plate XVII, No. 5, p. 161

Oval, very convex; piceous or dark reddish, margins of pronotum and elytra paler. Pronotum very finely punctate, more coarsely so laterally. Elytra more coarsely but less densely punctate than pronotum. Length 2–2.5 mm.

This species is common in brooks; it also occurs in ponds and bogs.

Genus VIII. *PARACYMUS* Thomson

Small, oval, convex; meso- and metafemora at most sparsely pubescent basally; above always more or less metallic, red-brown to piceous.

Paracymus subcupreus (Say)   Plate XVI, No. 11, p. 151

Elongate-oval, convex; piceous above, distinctly bronzed; elytral margins often paler apically; beneath dark reddish piceous. Pronotum and elytra equally, not densely punctate. Length 1.5–2 mm.

This species is found in ponds and bogs.

Genus IX. *ENOCHRUS* Thomson

Small, oblong-oval, piceous or dull brownish yellow; elytra with four rows of coarser punctures, which are sometimes indistinct.

The species of this genus are found especially along edges of ponds and rise to the surface when the water is made turbid.

KEY TO SPECIES

1. Above brownish yellow to pale piceous 3
   Above black or piceous, margins sometimes pale 2
2. Length 6.5–7 mm.; very convex ....d. *cinctus*
   Not over 5.5 mm.; subdepressed ....c. *perplexus*
3. Prosternum distinctly carinate ....a. *pygmaeus*
   Prosternum not carinate 4
4. Smaller, at most 4 mm. ....b. *ochraceus*
   Larger, 4.5–6 mm. ....e. *hamiltoni*

a. *Enochrus pygmaeus* Fabricius   Plate XVII, No. 2, p. 161
Oval, convex; varying from pale yellow to pale piceous, shining; head and beneath piceous. Pronotum and elytra sparsely and indistinctly punctate. Prosternum carinate. Length 3.5–4.5 mm.

b. *Enochrus ochraceus* (Melsheimer)   Plate XVII, No. 3, p. 161
Oval, rather convex; pale piceous or dull brown, shining; head darker, a pale spot before each eye; pronotum and elytra with paler margins. Pronotum and elytra distinctly and rather densely punctate. Length 3.5–4 mm.

c. *Enochrus perplexus* (LeConte)   Plate XVII, No. 1, p. 161
Oblong-oval, rather elongate; piceous to black, shining; pronotum and elytra with a narrow, pale border. Pronotum densely and finely punctate, a distinct marginal line at base. Elytra more coarsely punctate, with feebly indicated rows of coarser punctures. Length 4–5.5 mm.
These beetles are usually found in pools of fresh water.

d. *Enochrus cinctus* (Say)   Plate XVII, No. 8, p. 161
Slightly oblong-oval, convex; black, shining; elytra and pronotum margined with dark reddish brown. Pronotum finely and evenly punctate, the marginal line at base very fine and indistinct; elytra more coarsely and sparsely punctate, with distinct dorsal rows of larger punctures. Length 6.5–7 mm.

e. *Enochrus hamiltoni* (Horn)   Plate XVII, No. 4, p. 161
Oblong-oval, rather convex; blackish or dull brownish yellow; head piceous; pronotum with an irregular, indistinct, discal darker space. Pronotum not very densely punctate. Elytra slightly more coarsely punctate, with faint dorsal rows of larger punctures. Length 4.5–5.5 mm.

Genus X. *CYMBIODYTA* Bedel

Small, oval, brownish or black species, with distinct rows of coarse punctures; maxillary palpi slender, last segment shorter than third; meso- and metatarsi with only four segments.

KEY TO SPECIES

Uniformly piceous or black ....a. *fimbriata*
Brown, pronotum and elytra with paler margins ....b. *blanchardi*

a. *Cymbiodyta fimbriata* (Melsheimer)   Plate XVII, No. 10, p. 161
Oval, convex; uniformly piceous or black. Pronotum transverse, sides rounded to apex. Elytra with rows of distinct punctures. Length 4.5–6 mm.

PLATE XVIII
Aquatic Families V
Family GYRINIDAE

1. *Gyrinus fraternus* Couper (p. 157) — Shining blue-black; 5.5–6.5 mm.

2. *Dineutus ciliatus* Forsberg (p. 156) — Black, with an oily reflex; pronotum and elytra with a dull-brassy vitta; 12–15 mm.

3. *D. americanus* (Fabricius) (p. 156) — Black, with an oily reflex; 10–12 mm.

4. *Gyrinus borealis* Aubé (p. 157) — Black, shining; 6.5–7.5 mm.

5. *Dineutus discolor* Aubé (p. 156) — Black, slightly shining; 11.5–13 mm.

6. *Gyrinus analis* Say (p. 157) — Black, shining; 5–6 mm.

7. *Dineutus hornii* Roberts (p. 156) — Brassy black; 9.5–11 mm.

Family PSEPHENIDAE

8. *Psephenus herricki* DeKay (p. 365) — Fuscous to black; elytra paler; 4–6 mm.

Family DRYOPIDAE

9. *Helichus lithophilus* (Germar) (p. 366) — Reddish brown, densely silky-pubescent; 5–6 mm.

Family ELMIDAE

10. *Stenelmis quadrimaculata* Horn (p. 368) — Reddish brown, largely covered with waxy, whitish pubescence; elytral markings creamy white; 2.7–3.5 mm.

11. *Macronychus glabratus* (Say) (p. 368) — Blackish, shining, with sparse, white pubescence; elytral sides and legs in part densely ashy-pubescent; 3–3.5 mm.

12. *Stenelmis crenata* (Say) (p. 368) — Fuscous, covered with waxy, whitish pubescence; elytral vittae pale yellow; 3–3.5 mm.

MM 0   10   20   30   40   50   60   70

PLATE XVIII 171

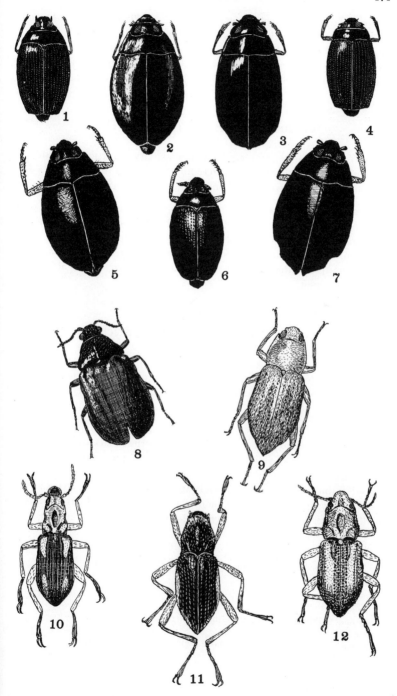

b. *Cymbiodyta blanchardi* Horn   Plate XVII, No. 11, p. 161
  Broadly oval, scarcely narrowed anteriorly, rather convex; dark sooty brown; pronotum and elytra with paler margins; head black, spotted with reddish yellow. Elytra with only outermost row of punctures distinct, remaining rows represented only by a few distant punctures. Length 4 mm.

Genus XI. *HELOCOMBUS* Horn

  Small, oblong-ovate, strongly convex; maxillary palpi long, slender, last segment distinctly shorter than preceding one; pronotum without a basal marginal line; elytra with numerous distinct striae; metasternum not spined.

Helocombus bifidus (LeConte)   Plate XVII, No. 10, p. 161
  Oblong-ovate, strongly convex; piceous, shining; tarsi and narrow margin of elytra paler. Pronotum closely and finely punctate. Elytra deeply striate, striae entire except inner three; intervals laterally convex, broader and flatter on disk, rather densely, finely punctate, rugosely so along sides. Length 5.5–7 mm.

Genus XII. *LACCOBIUS* Erichson

  Very small, broadly oval, subglobose; maxillary palpi rather robust, short, last segment longer than preceding one; pronotal basal marginal line feeble; elytra without striae, but with rows of punctures; metasternum not spined.

Laccobius agilis Randall   Plate XVII, No. 11, p. 161
  Subrotund, convex; head and disk of pronotum blackish with greenish reflex, margins pale yellow; elytra pale yellow, punctures dark brown; undersurface fuscous; legs orangeish brown. Head alutaceous, coarsely, sparsely punctate. Pronotum strongly transverse; as wide as elytra at base; disk coarsely, sparsely punctate, more densely so on sides. Elytral punctures small, close-set in regular rows. Length 2–3 mm.

Subfamily SPHAERIDIINAE

KEY TO GENERA

Antennae eight-segmented; scutellum elongate; eyes usually emarginate ....I. *Sphaeridium* (p. 173)
Antennae of nine or apparently more segments; scutellum equilateral; eyes not emarginate ....II. *Cercyon* (p. 173)

Genus I. *SPHAERIDIUM* Fabricius

Moderate-sized, subglobose, black beetles; elytra not inflexed, epipleura distinct, horizontal, sides not extending below lower surface of body; antennae eight-segmented; scutellum elongate; prosternum carinate medially; last dorsal abdominal segment visible.

The members of this genus are common in manure, rubbish, and decaying vegetable matter and feed on other insect larvae.

Sphaeridium scarabaeoides (Linné) Plate XVI, No. 12, p. 151
Subglobose, convex; black, shining; elytra with a reddish subbasal spot and apical fourth yellowish; beneath piceous; femora with paler maculae. Pronotum and elytra finely and evenly punctate; elytra not striate. Length 5.5–7 mm.

This species, which was introduced from Europe, is particularly common on cow dung in the East.

Genus II. *CERCYON* Leach

Small, black or piceous species; antennae nine-segmented; scutellum equilateral, not elongate; mesocoxae narrowly separated; elytra usually striate; mesosternum elevated between and anterior to mesocoxae; last dorsal segment of abdomen covered.

Cercyon haemorrhoidalis (Fabricius) Plate XVI, No. 13, p. 151
Oval, rather convex; black or piceous; elytra piceous or brownish, apices slightly paler. Pronotum densely punctate. Elytra with ten striae, more distinct at apex; intervals flat, densely punctate. Length 2.5–3 mm.

This species is common in cow dung.

Family SILPHIDAE

The Carrion or Burying Beetles

Usually large, loosely constructed beetles, that have the body black, sometimes ornamented with yellow or red. They vary much in shape, from almost circular to elongate-oblong. Eyes finely granulate; antennae eleven-segmented, but sometimes with nine or ten segments, gradually or suddenly clubbed apically, inserted under margin of front; mesosternum very short; metasternum large, truncate posteriorly; procoxae large, conical, contiguous; mesocoxae contiguous; legs variable, sometimes slender, sometimes adapted for digging; tibiae with large apical spurs; tarsi usually five-segmented.

Decaying animal matter, especially dead birds, mice, and snakes, is the usual habitat of these species, though some occur on decaying fungi. The eggs are deposited in the bodies of small mammals or fragments of decaying flesh, which are then buried by the adults to a depth of from several inches to a foot. Two beetles working together can bury a mouse or other small animal very rapidly.

KEY TO GENERA

Antennae distinctly eleven-segmented, second segment about as long as third, entire antenna either slender or gradually clavate (Fig. 151); elytra not shortened, apices together rounded or prolonged at suture ....II. *Silpha* (p. 176)

Antennae apparently ten-segmented, the second segment being very short, more or less hidden in tip of the first (Fig. 152), last four segments forming a distinct club; elytra short, apices more or less truncate, never dentate or together rounded ....I. *Nicrophorus* (p. 174)

Genus I. *NICROPHORUS* Fabricius

Large, elongate, thick-bodied beetles having elytra ornamented with red spots. Head large, constricted before and behind eyes; antennae apparently ten-segmented, the second segment very minute, appearing as a node at base of third; elytra truncate at apex.

These are often called "sexton beetles" from their supposed habit of burying carrion; the present writers, like Lutz, have never observed them

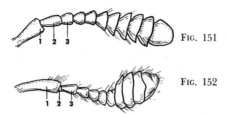

Figs. 151–152. Antenna of *Silpha* (151) and of *Nicrophorus* (152). *1, 2, 3,* first, second, and third segments.

performing this act. Usually they are found on carrion along with members of the genus *Silpha* or at light.

KEY TO SPECIES

1. Pronotum with disk red, not tomentose ....a. *americanus*
   Pronotum with disk black or densely tomentose 2
2. Pronotal disk densely yellowish tomentose ....e. *tomentosus*
   Pronotal disk black, not tomentose......................................3
3. Metatibiae, and often the mesotibiae, curved or bowed 4
   Tibiae all straight ....c. *orbicollis*
4. Pronotum broadly heart-shaped, sides narrowly margined, sinuate at middle; elytra with the basal red band usually reaching suture, its entire side margin red and connected with both bands ....d. *marginatus*
   Pronotum more or less circular, sides broadly margined; elytra with basal red band never reaching suture, the side margins red but not connected to the apical band ....b. *sayi*

a. *Nicrophorus americanus* (Olivier)   Color Plate C; Plate XIX,
                                            No. 11, p. 181
Elongate, robust; black, shining; vertex, disk of pronotum, epipleural fold, and two large, irregular spots on each elytron orange-red. Pronotum wider than long, truncate at apex; disk with a few scattered punctures along margins. Lengths 27–35 mm.

This species is often found at light and on larger decaying animals.

b. *Nicrophorus sayi* Laporte   Plate XIX, No. 14, p. 181
Elongate, robust; black, shining; epipleural fold, a crossbar (prolonged on side to humerus), and a subapical spot on each elytron orange-red; antennal club and often protarsi reddish brown. Pronotum transverse; very finely punctate, margins slightly more coarsely and densely so. Meso- and metatibiae arcuate in both sexes. Length 16–18 mm.

c. *Nicrophorus orbicollis* Say   Plate XIX, No. 13, p. 181
Elongate, robust; piceous to black, shining; elytra with a transverse fascia at basal third and a preapical macula yellowish or red, epipleural fold black; antennal club and sometimes protarsi reddish brown. Pronotum transverse; disk finely, sparsely punctate, sides and basal margins more

densely and coarsely so. Meso- and metatibiae straight in both sexes. Length 20–25 mm.

This species is found on all kinds of carrion.

d. *Nicrophorus marginatus* Fabricius   Plate XIX, No. 12, p. 181
Elongate, robust; black, shining; epipleural fold and two irregular crossbars on elytra orange-red; the two crossbars connected on side margin. Pronotum narrower behind middle; disk nearly smooth. Length 20–27 mm.

This species is found especially on cold-blooded vertebrate carrion.

e. *Nicrophorus tomentosus* Weber   Plate XIX, No. 15, p. 181
Elongate, robust; black, shining; epipleural fold and two crossbars orange-red. Pronotum broader than long, only slightly narrowed posteriorly, densely clothed with silky, yellow hairs. Length 15–20 mm.

This species is found on carrion of all sorts.

Genus II. *SILPHA* Linné

Medium-sized or large, strongly depressed beetles, very broadly ovate or almost round; antennae eleven-segmented, not elongate, last segment oval at apex, flattened; pronotum and elytra with a wide, thin margin; elytra more or less costate, not striate, the side margins reflexed.

KEY TO SPECIES

1. Pronotum transversely oval, almost circular, smooth, shining, uniformly black or piceous; eyes large, prominent; form elongate ....a. *surinamensis*
   Pronotum more or less semicircular, much wider at base than at apex, usually more or less rugose, if smooth, not uniformly colored; eyes moderate; form broadly oval 2
2. Pronotum densely pubescent; elytral intervals with regular, distinct tubercles ....d. *lapponica*
   Pronotum never hairy; elytral intervals smooth or with irregular, transverse, raised lines 3
3. Pronotum uniformly dark, without pale side margins ....b. *inaequalis*
   Pronotum with disk dark, at least with side margins yellowish 4
4. Pronotum with reddish-yellow side margins, base only narrowly the same color; size smaller; elytra with only longitudinal ridges ...c. *noveboracensis*
   Pronotum with sides and base broadly margined with yellow, apex narrowly so; size larger; elytra with longitudinal ridges, the intervals with transverse, irregular elevations ....e. *americana*

a. *Silpha surinamensis* Fabricius   Plate XIX, No. 6, p. 181
Broadly oblong, depressed; black or piceous; elytra with an orange-red crossbar near apex, often broken into spots and sometimes entirely wanting. Pronotum oval, transverse, flattened posteriorly. Elytra slightly wider posteriorly, apex obliquely truncate; disk with three distinct costae. Length 15–25 mm.

b. *Silpha inaequalis* Fabricius   Plate XIX, No. 7, p. 181
Oblong-ovate, depressed; black, not shining. Pronotum twice as wide as long, narrowed apically, basally with a broad, median, truncate lobe. Elytra rounded at apex; disk with three costae, the outer one more distinct and ending in a slight tubercle at apical third. Length 10–14 mm.
This species may be found the year round on carrion.

c. *Silpha noveboracensis* Forster   Plate XIX, No. 10, p. 181
Oblong-ovate, depressed; pronotum piceous, with a wide reddish-yellow margin; elytra brownish to piceous. Pronotum one-half wider than long, truncate at middle of base, sinuate on each side. Elytra rounded at apex; disk with three costae, the outer one more distinct; intervals distinctly punctate. Length 13–14 mm.
Carrion is the usual place to find this species, but they are occasionally found on fungi.

d. *Silpha lapponica* Herbst   Plate XIX, No. 9, p. 181
Broadly oblong-ovate; piceous; pronotum densely covered with yellowish pubescence, but this sometimes almost entirely lacking; disk tuberculate. Elytra with four costae; intervals with regular rows of distinct tubercles. Length 9–13 mm.
This species occurs especially on dead frogs, toads, snakes, and other cold-blooded carrion.

e. *Silpha americana* Linné   Plate XIX, No. 8, p. 181
Broadly ovate, depressed; pronotum yellow, with disk black; elytra brownish, with darker elevations. Pronotum nearly twice as wide as long, narrowed apically, broadly lobed at middle of base; surface densely punctate. Elytra with three indistinct costae, connected by numerous cross-elevations; intervals densely punctate. Length 16–20 mm.
These beetles may be collected from carrion and decaying fungi.

Family LEIODIDAE

The Pill Beetles

Small, oval, very convex forms; eyes finely granulate or absent; antennae of nine to eleven segments, clavate, inserted under the frontal margin at the base of the mandibles (Fig. 153); prothorax without distinct sidepieces; tibiae with large terminal spurs; tarsi variable.

This family of small beetles is very variable in the kinds of antennal clubs and tarsal formula. They occur in decaying fungi and other decaying vegetable matter, ant nests, caves, under stumps, and in logs. Most of the members roll their bodies into a ball when disturbed, hence their common name.

KEY TO GENERA

Head without antennal grooves beneath; tibiae without longitudinal dorsal carina; protarsi five-segmented, meso- and metatarsi four-segmented .... I. *Colenis* (p. 178)
Head with antennal grooves beneath; tibiae with two longitudinal dorsal carinae; pro- and mesotarsi five-segmented, metatarsi four-segmented .... II. *Agathidium* (p. 179)

Genus I. *COLENIS* Erichson

Very small species; labrum emarginate; last segment of maxillary palpi cylindrical; antennae eleven-segmented, club three-segmented, loose, oblong; elytra transversely strigose; protarsi five-segmented, meso- and metatarsi four-segmented; mesosternum carinate between coxae.

Colenis impunctata LeConte Plate XIX, No. 3, p. 181
Very broadly oval, convex; pale reddish brown, shining. Pronotum strongly transverse, sides broadly arcuate, strongly narrowed to apex; apex feebly emarginate; disk smooth; posterior angles subrectangular. Elytral surface finely, transversely strigose. Length 1.5–2 mm.

This species occurs particularly in fungi and does not contract its body into a ball when disturbed.

Genus II. *AGATHIDIUM* Illiger

Very small, black or piceous species that are capable of folding themselves together in the form of a ball; antennae with segments four to eight
small, gradually widened, nine to eleven forming an oblong, loose club;
labrum short, rounded anteriorly; metatarsi with only four segments, pro-
and mesotarsi five-segmented; mesosternum not carinate between coxae.

Agathidium oniscoides Beauvois   Plate XIX, Nos. 4, 5, p. 181
Head and pronotum together, and elytra forming two conjoined spheres;
black or piceous, shining. Pronotum strongly transverse; apical margin
deeply emarginate; anterior and posterior angles rounded. Elytra together
almost circular, impunctate. Length 3.5–4 mm.

This species is completely contractile. They occur beneath bark, especially when fungus is present.

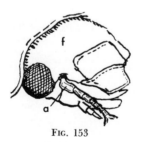

FIG. 153

Fig. 153. Head of *Colenis* in oblique profile, the antenna (*a*) inserted
below sides of front (*f*).

PLATE XIX

Family THROSCIDAE

1. *Throscus chevrolati* Bonvouloir (p. 338) — Reddish brown, densely covered with shaggy, gray pubescence; 2.5–2.8 mm.

2. *Drapetes geminatus* Say (p. 337) — Black; elytral spots reddish; 4 mm.

Family LEIODIDAE

3. *Colenis impunctata* LeConte (p. 178) — Dull orange, shining, with brown markings; 1.5–2 mm.

4. *Agathidium oniscoides* Beauvois (p. 179) — Fuscous, shining; in extended form; 3.5–4 mm.

5. *A. oniscoides* Beauvois (p. 179) — Fuscous, shining; rolled into a ball, as usually found.

Family SILPHIDAE

6. *Silpha surinamensis* Fabricius (p. 176) — Black; elytral markings reddish; 15–25 mm.

7. *S. inaequalis* Fabricius (p. 177) — Dull black; 10–14 mm.

8. *S. americana* Linné (p. 177) — Blackish; pronotum dull yellow, except medially; 16–20 mm.

9. *S. lapponica* Herbst (p. 177) — Dull black; pronotum densely yellow-pubescent; 9–13 mm.

10. *S. noveboracensis* Forster (p. 177) — Brownish; head and pronotum blackish, the latter dull yellowish laterally; 13–14 mm.

11. *Nicrophorus americanus* (Olivier) (p. 175) — Black; pronotal disk and elytral fasciae red; 27–35 mm.

12. *N. marginatus* Fabricius (p. 176) — Black; elytral fasciae red; 20–27 mm.

13. *N. orbicollis* Say (p. 175) — Black; elytral fasciae red; 20–25 mm.

14. *N. sayi* Laporte (p. 175) — Black; elytral fasciae red; 16–18 mm.

15. *N. tomentosus* Weber (p. 176) — Black; elytral fasciae red; 15–20 mm.

MM | 0 | 10 | 20 | 30 | 40 | 50 | 60 | 70

PLATE XIX

181

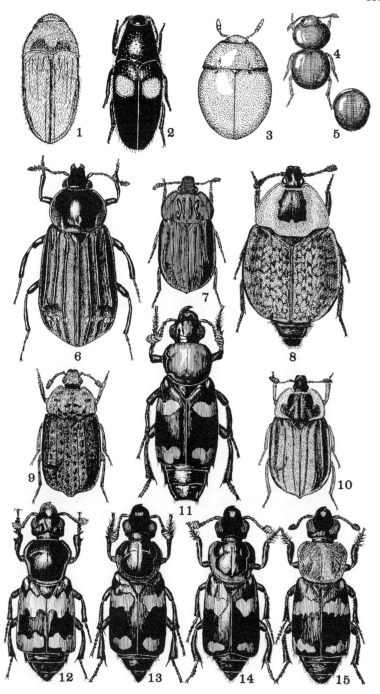

Family STAPHYLINIDAE

The Rove Beetles

This is an extremely large family of very common beetles, difficult to study because the species resemble one another closely. The form is elongate and slender; colors are mostly dull, black predominating, but some are brilliantly ornamented. Other family characters are: antennae clavate or capitate (Figs. 13–16); elytra very short, beneath which the wings are folded, exposing most of the abdomen; tarsal segments variable in number.

The members of this family swarm to carrion or to decaying vegetable matter and occasionally are found on flowers. Frequently the tip of the abdomen is turned upward as they run about on the ground.

KEY TO SUBFAMILIES

1. Metacoxae contiguous or nearly so (Figs. 154, 155) 2
   Metacoxae widely separated, small, globose (Fig. 156) ..STENINAE (p. 184)
2. Metacoxae conical (Fig. 155) ....PAEDERINAE (p. 186)
   Metacoxae transverse or triangular (Fig. 154) 3
3. Metacoxae triangular ........................STAPHYLININAE (p. 192)
   Metacoxae transverse 4
4. Lateral ocelli present (Fig. 157) ....OMALIINAE (p. 182)
   Lateral ocelli absent 5
5. Seven abdominal sternites present 6
   Six abdominal sternites present 7
6. Mesocoxae contiguous ....OXYTELINAE (p. 184)
   Mesocoxae separated ....OXYPORINAE (p. 200)
7. Antennae inserted at sides of head ..............TACHYPORINAE (p. 201)
   Antennae inserted between eyes ................ALEOCHARINAE (p. 204)

Subfamily OMALIINAE

Genus *ANTHOBIUM* Stephens

Small, rather robust, subdepressed; head with an ocellus on each side of front (Fig. 157); last segment of maxillary palpi longer than third; elytra usually reaching nearly to or beyond tip of abdomen; metacoxae transverse, nearly contiguous; tibiae pubescent; tarsi five-segmented, segments of metatarsi short and equal.

Anthobium hornii Fauvel   Plate XX, No. 1, p. 189

Elongate-oval, robust, subdepressed; brownish orange, shining; male with abdomen largely piceous; female with abdomen piceous only at apex. Antennae shorter than head and pronotum together; segments seven to ten transverse, forming a loose club. Pronotum twice as wide as long; sides arcuate; widest at middle; disk finely and sparsely punctate. Elytra more than twice length of pronotum; apices truncate. Length 2–2.5 mm.

This is commonly found on flowers in spring, especially those of maple and spirea.

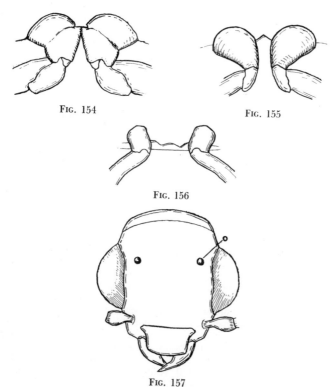

Fig. 154

Fig. 155

Fig. 156

Fig. 157

Figs. 154–156. Metacoxae of various staphylinids. In the Staphylininae (represented by *Staphylinus vulpinus*, 154), triangular and contiguous; in the Paederinae (*Lathrobium armatum*, 155), conical and approximate; and in the Steninae (*Stenus flavicornis*, 156), small, globose, and widely separated.

Fig. 157. The head of an omaliine, viewed from in front. *o*, ocellus.

Subfamily OXYTELINAE

Genus *PLATYSTETHUS* Mannerheim

Small, elongate-oblong, depressed; antennae eleven-segmented; abdomen not margined; pro- and mesotibiae with a single row of spines on outer margin; tarsi three-segmented.

Platystethus americanus Erichson   Plate XX, No. 2, p. 189

Elongate-oblong, depressed; black, shining; elytra piceous to fuscous; tibiae and tarsi paler. Pronotum feebly transverse, sides slightly arcuate; disk finely and sparsely punctate. Elytra slightly wider than pronotum; surface finely punctate. Length 2.5–3.5 mm.

These beetles are usually found in decaying fungi and cow dung.

Subfamily STENINAE

Genus *STENUS* Latreille

Small, rather robust, subconvex; antennae straight, eleven-segmented, inserted between the eyes, last three segments larger than preceding ones; elytra much shorter than abdomen, wider than pronotum at base; abdomen gradually tapering to apex; metacoxae small, globose, widely separated.

KEY TO SPECIES

1. Abdomen above with each segment distinctly and strongly margined later-ally 2
   Abdomen margined at most only on first segment 4
2. Elytra each with a small orange spot behind middle ....a. *bipunctatus*
   Elytra not spotted 3
3. Elytra with several rows of punctures, forming a distinct spiral toward sides of disk; transverse carinae on base of dorsal side of abdominal segments with three cusps each ....b. *juno*
   Elytra with all the punctures uniformly dense over entire disk, without any distinct spiral; abdominal carinae with four cusps each ....c. *colonus*
4. Length 4.5–4.8 mm.; antennae dull yellow ....d. *flavicornis*
   Length 3–3.5 mm.; antennae dark reddish brown ....e. *punctatus*

a. *Stenus bipunctatus* Erichson   Plate XX, No. 3, p. 189

Elongate-ovate, subconvex, rather robust; black, shining, feebly bronzed; elytra each with a small, rounded, orangeish spot behind middle. Head deeply excavated, finely punctate; antennae reaching to middle of pronotum, third segment twice as long as fourth. Prothorax subcylindrical, widest behind middle; pronotum finely and densely punctate, medially narrowly and deeply impressed. Elytra as wide at base as head, feebly elongate, coarsely and evenly punctate. Length 4–4.5 mm.

b. *Stenus juno* (Fabricius)   Plate XX, No. 4, p. 189
Elongate, robust, subconvex; black, shining. Front of head coarsely punctate and deeply grooved on each side. Pronotum slightly elongate, widest at middle; densely and coarsely punctate, especially near base and apical margin; median impressed line indistinct, rather long. Elytra coarsely, densely punctate and channeled. Abdomen narrower at base than elytra; first four tergites deeply impressed at base. Length 4–5 mm.

c. *Stenus colonus* Erichson   Plate XX, No. 7, p. 189
Elongate-ovate, slender; black, more or less shining, sparsely covered with fine, dark-gray pubescence. Head not twice as wide as long; vertex densely, finely, but roughly punctate; antennae short, scarcely longer than width of head, third segment about one-third longer than fourth. Prothorax cylindrical; pronotum widest just behind middle, disk densely, finely, roughly punctate, without a median longitudinal line. Elytra at suture longer than pronotum, slightly wider than head; disk rather coarsely, densely, roughly punctate. Abdomen not as broad as elytra, gradually tapering to apex, finely and rather densely punctate; carinae across base of the basal segments, each bearing four posteriorly directed cusps. Length 3–3.5 mm.

d. *Stenus flavicornis* Erichson   Plate XX, No. 5, p. 189
Elongate, rather slender, subconvex; black, shining, with sparse, grayish pubescence. Front of head finely and densely punctate, grooved on each side; antennae long and slender, third segment almost twice as long as fourth. Pronotum widest before middle, slightly elongate, coarsely and densely punctate. Elytra slightly longer than wide, deeply and sparsely punctate. Abdomen narrower than elytra. Length 4.5–5 mm.

e. *Stenus punctatus* Erichson   Plate XX, No. 6, p. 189
Elongate-ovate, rather robust, subcylindrical; black, shining, rather densely covered with grayish pubescence. Head not excavated, feebly convex between eyes, finely and densely punctate; antennae as long as head is wide, third segment one-third longer than fourth. Pronotum subquadrate, widest at middle; finely, densely punctate. Elytra as wide at base as head, longer at suture, longer than pronotum; deeply, densely, coarsely punctate. Abdomen distinctly narrower than elytra at base, feebly tapering to apex. Length 3–3.5 mm.

Subfamily PAEDERINAE

KEY TO GENERA

1. Fourth segment of metatarsi not lobed beneath 2
   Fourth segment of metatarsi bilobed beneath ....II. *Paederus* (p. 190)
2. Antennae elbowed at apex of long basal segment ..I. *Homoeotarsus* (p. 186)
   Antennae straight or nearly so, basal segments not greatly elongated 3
3. Prosternum shortened between and under procoxae, forming an acute point which does not attain mesosternum (Fig. 158) 4
   Prosternum prolonged behind into a more or less acute point which attains mesosternum, but not much dilated under coxae (Fig. 159)
   ....V. *Sunius* (p. 191)
4. Elytra with a longitudinal fold on the deflexed flank, parallel with side margins (Fig. 160) ....III. *Lathrobium* (p. 190)
   Elytra without lateral fold ....IV. *Lobrathium* (p. 191)

Genus I. *HOMOEOTARSUS* Hochhuth

Large, elongate, parallel; head with neck distinctly constricted abruptly above; mandibles each with three teeth on inner side; gular sutures separated; basal segment of antennae strongly elongate; elytra with a fold or raised line near side margin extending from humeri to outer apical angle; protarsi not dilated, fourth segment of metatarsi not lobed beneath; males usually with last ventral abdominal segment notched at apex and sometimes the second and third segments without a trace of pit or fovea.

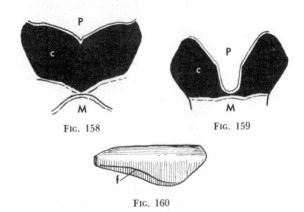

Fig. 158   Fig. 159

Fig. 160

Figs. 158–159. Portion of prosternum and adjacent structures in *Lathrobium* (158) and *Sunius* (159). *P*, prosternum; *c*, procoxal cavities; *M*, mesosternum.

Fig. 160. Elytron of *Lathrobium armatum* viewed from the side. *f*, fold.

KEY TO SPECIES

1. Abdomen bicolorous ....a. *bicolor*
   Abdomen unicolorous 2
2. Elytra black or piceous; posterior angles of head distinct ....b. *pallipes*
   Elytra wholly or in a large part reddish yellow; head obliquely narrowed from eyes to neck, posterior angles entirely lacking ....c. *cribatus*

a. *Homoeotarsus bicolor* (Gravenhorst)   Plate XXII, No. 2, p. 215

Large, elongate, parallel-sided; head black; labrum, antennae, pronotum, elytra, and last two segments of abdomen pale reddish brown; legs pale yellow. Head oblong-oval, coarsely but not densely punctate. Pronotum narrower than head, transverse, sides parallel; disk smooth medially, coarsely, densely punctate at sides. Elytra one-third wider and longer than pronotum; surface irregularly, densely, coarsely punctate. Abdomen slightly narrower than elytra, sparsely and finely punctate. Male with a fold at middle of second ventral abdominal segment, a pit or fovea on third ventral segment, and last segment without a notch at apex; in addition to the pit or fovea on third segment, the latter may or may not be prolonged posteriorly. Length 7.5–10 mm.

This species occurs under stones, debris, and the like and also on fungi, especially in wooded pasture areas.

b. *Homoeotarsus pallipes* (Gravenhorst)   Plate XXII, No. 3, p. 215

Elongate, parallel-sided; piceous or nearly black, shining; antennae dusky; legs dull yellow. Head oval, slightly longer than wide, coarsely, sparsely punctate. Pronotum slightly narrower than head, one-fifth longer than wide; sides feebly arcuate; disk with a distinct smooth medial area, sides coarsely, regularly, rather sparsely punctate. Elytra one-third wider and slightly longer than pronotum, finely, coarsely, and densely punctate. Abdomen as wide as elytra, finely, densely punctate; last ventral of male with a triangular notch at apex, much deeper than wide, third without pit or fovea. Length 8–11 mm.

This species is usually found under stones and debris on sandy banks of streams and ponds.

c. *Homoeotarsus cribatus* (LeConte)   Plate XXII, No. 1, p. 215

Elongate, slender; black, shining; antennae, mouthparts, and elytra reddish yellow, suture of elytra darker on basal third; legs dull yellow. Head elongate-oval, slightly wider than pronotum, with a few coarse punctures behind eyes. Prothorax subcylindrical; pronotum one-fourth longer than wide; sides nearly straight; disk nearly smooth medially, with a row of seven to nine coarse punctures either side of smooth area, and a few laterally. Elytra one-third wider and slightly longer than pronotum, each with nine irregular rows of coarse punctures. Abdomen finely, densely punctate; last ventral abdominal segment of male with a deep, triangular notch at apex. Length 8.5–10 mm.

PLATE XX

Family STAPHYLINIDAE I

1. *Anthobium hornii* Fauvel (p. 183) — Straw-yellow; abdomen blackish, except at apex; 2–2.5 mm.

2. *Platystethus americanus* Erichson (p. 184) — Black; elytra, mandibles, and abdomen fuscous; 2.5–3.5 mm.

3. *Stenus bipunctatus* Erichson (p. 184) — Black; elytral spots dull yellow; 4–4.5 mm.

4. *S. juno* (Fabricius) (p. 185) — Black; elytra with a whorl of punctures; 4–5 mm.

5. *S. flavicornis* Erichson (p. 185) — Black; antennae and legs yellowish, except apices of metafemora; 4.5–5 mm.

6. *S. punctatus* Erichson (p. 185) — Fuscous; abdomen without distinct folds laterally; 3–3.5 mm.

7. *S. colonus* Erichson (p. 185) — Black; 3–3.5 mm.

8. *Lathrobium armatum* Say (p. 190) — Fuscous; elytra slightly paler apically; abdomen ringed with paler; 8–10 mm.

9. *L. simile* LeConte (p. 191) — Dark brown; legs yellow-brown; 7.5–9 mm.

10. *Lobrathium collare* Erichson (p. 191) — Orange-brown; head fuscous; base of elytra and abdomen tinged with blackish; 4.5–6 mm.

11. *Paederus littorarius* Gravenhorst (p. 190) — Dull orange; head, tip of abdomen, and antennae in part black; elytra deep black; 4–5.5 mm.

12. *Sunius confluentus* (Say) (p. 191) — Fuscous; legs yellow-brown; 3–4 mm.

13. *Nudobius cephalus* (Say) (p. 193) — Blackish; elytra and legs brown-orange, former darker obliquely on apices; 6–7.5 mm.

14. *Gyrohypnus hamatus* (Say) (p. 193) — Fuscous; elytra, legs, and tip of abdomen brown-orange; 5–6 mm.

15. *Philonthus fusiformis* Melsheimer (p. 194) — Fuscous; elytra red; legs dull orange; 5–6 mm.

16. *P. longicornis* Stephens (p. 194) — Fuscous; elytra and legs dark brown; 6–8 mm.

17. *P. politus* (Linné) (p. 194) — Black, shining; elytra dark brown; 10–13 mm.

18. *P. lomatus* Erichson (p. 195) — Fuscous; elytra dark brown; 6.5–8 mm.

19. *P. cyanipennis* (Fabricius) (p. 195) — Black, shining; elytra deep metallic green or blue; 12–15 mm.

20. *P. brunneus* (Gravenhorst) (p. 195) — Dark orange-brown; 5–5.5 mm.

MM ┊ 0 ┊ 10 ┊ 20 ┊ 30 ┊ 40 ┊ 50 ┊ 60 ┊ 70

PLATE XX   189

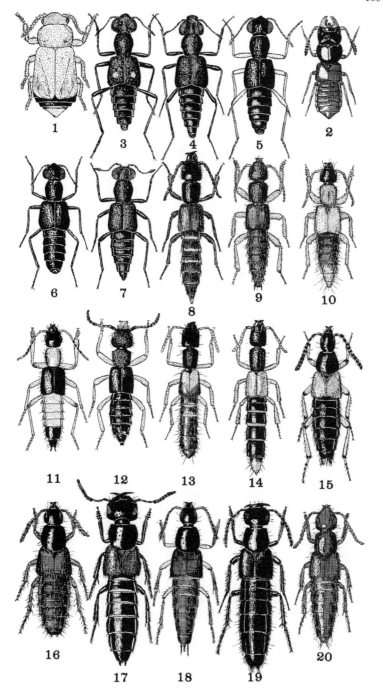

Genus II. *PAEDERUS* Fabricius

Small, slender, convex; head constricted into a neck behind eyes; labrum emarginate at apex; last segment of maxillary palpi obtuse; prosternum abbreviated, ending between and under the procoxae, forming an acute point which does not attain the mesosternum; fourth metatarsal segment bilobed beneath.

Paederus littorarius Gravenhorst   Plate XX, No. 11, p. 189

Elongate-oblong, slender, cónvex; reddish yellow, shining; head black; elytra dark blue; last two segments of abdomen black; antennae piceous at middle, apical segments paler. Head slightly longer than wide, base broadly rounded. Pronotum convex, slightly elongate, feebly narrower than head; sides slightly arcuate; disk finely and sparsely punctate. Elytra slightly wider than pronotum, together wider than long. Abdomen slightly narrower than elytra, sides parallel. Length 4–5.5 mm.

This species is common especially in early spring under stones in damp localities.

Genus III. *LATHROBIUM* Gravenhorst

Small to moderate-sized, elongate-oblong, rather robust; head constricted into a distinct neck; labrum bilobed; fourth segment of maxillary palpi conical, pointed at apex; elytra with a longitudinal fold on the deflexed flanks, parallel with sides (Fig. 160); prosternum abbreviated, ending between and under the procoxae, forming an acute point which does not attain mesosternum.

KEY TO SPECIES

Antennae with middle segments strongly robust, never longer than wide ......
....a. *armatum*
Antennae with middle segments slightly robust, at least one-half longer than wide ....b. *simile*

a. *Lathrobium armatum* Say   Plate XX, No. 8, p. 189

Elongate-oblong, rather robust; black or piceous, slightly shining; antennae, palpi, and legs reddish brown. Head as wide as elytra, sides rounded into base; surface finely and sparsely punctate. Pronotum oblong, nearly as wide as head and elytra; disk coarsely, sparsely punctate, with a narrow, smooth median line. Elytra coarsely, evenly, and sparsely punctate. Abdomen as wide as elytra, sides parallel; finely, rather densely punctate. Length 8–10 mm.

The adults are found under cover in low, moist areas.

b. *Lathrobium simile* LeConte　　　　　　Plate XX, No. 9, p. 189

Elongate-oblong, rather slender; black, shining; elytra and abdomen (except apex, which is reddish brown) piceous; antennae reddish brown, legs paler. Head finely and sparsely punctate. Pronotum feebly elongate, as wide as head; surface coarsely, sparsely punctate. Elytra slightly wider than pronotum, not quite as long as wide. Abdomen equal in width to elytra, very finely and densely punctate; fifth and sixth ventral abdominal segments of male with a deep, narrow, median groove; sixth with a deep, broad notch at apex. Length 7.5–9 mm.

Genus IV. *LOBRATHIUM* Mulsant and Rey

Small, more or less fusiform; head small, constricted into a distinct neck; labrum bilobed; fourth segment of maxillary palpi conical, acute at apex; elytra without lateral fold, seriately punctate; prosternum abbreviated, ending between and under procoxae, forming an acute point which does not reach mesosternum.

Lobrathium collare Erichson　　　　　　Plate XX, No. 10, p. 189

Elongate, slender, subdepressed; head black; pronotum reddish brown; elytra piceous or dark brown; abdomen piceous, paler apically. Head as long as wide; surface coarsely, sparsely punctate. Pronotum slightly elongate, wider than head; sides rounded slightly; disk with median line smooth, this margined on each side by a row of fine punctures; sparsely punctate laterally. Elytra feebly wider than pronotum; surface coarsely punctate, punctures arranged in impressed rows. Abdomen slightly narrower than elytra, densely, finely punctate. Length 4.5–6 mm.

Genus V. *SUNIUS* Stephens

Small, elongate-oblong, rather robust, subconvex; head with neck not greatly constricted; antennae not geniculate, nearly straight, basal segments not much elongated, equal in thickness to those following, third segment distinctly longer than second, outer segments beadlike; labrum feebly dentate; prosternum not carinate; metatarsi with segments one and two subequal in length.

Sunius confluentus (Say)　　　　　　Plate XX, No. 12, p. 189

Elongate-oblong, rather robust, subconvex; dark brown or piceous, feebly shining; legs, base of antennae, and elytra at apex usually lighter brown. Head elongate, posterior angles broadly rounded; surface densely, coarsely, strigosely punctate. Pronotum narrower than head, transverse; disk longitudinally rugose. Elytra slightly wider and one-third longer than pronotum; surface densely, finely, and roughly punctate. Abdomen slightly narrower than elytra, widening gradually apically; densely and finely punctate; sixth ventral segment of male with a small median notch. Length 3–4 mm.

The adults are found on fungi, beneath bark, and in decaying vegetable matter.

Subfamily STAPHYLININAE

KEY TO TRIBES

Bases of antennae subapproximate (Fig. 161); elytra usually overlapping along suture ....Xantholinini (p. 192)
Bases of antennae distant (Fig. 162) ....Staphylinini (p. 193)

Tribe Xantholinini

KEY TO GENERA

Side margin of pronotum rapidly deflexed anteriorly from near middle and united with lower margin before middle (Fig. 163) ...I. *Nudobius* (p. 193)
Side margin of pronotum gradually and feebly deflexed, remaining distant from lower margin (Fig. 164) ....II. *Gyrohypnus* (p. 193)

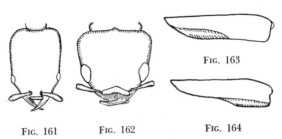

Fig. 161   Fig. 162   Fig. 164
Fig. 163

Figs. 161–162. Head of *Nudobius* (161) and of *Staphylinus* (162), viewed from above.
Figs. 163–164. Pronotum of *Nudobius* (163) and of *Gyrohypnus* (164) viewed from the side.

Genus I. *NUDOBIUS* Thomson

Small, elongate, slender; maxillary palpi with fourth segment long, more robust at base; pronotum sparsely punctate dorsally, lateral margin double, deflexed anteriorly from near middle to unite with lower margin.

Nudobius cephalus (Say)   Plate XX, No. 13, p. 189
    Elongate, slender; black, shining; elytra and legs brownish yellow; antennae and undersurface deep reddish brown to piceous. Head elongate; above sparsely and coarsely punctate, more finely punctate and alutaceous beneath. Pronotum distinctly elongate, as wide as head anteriorly, gradually narrowing to base; sparsely punctate. Elytra as long as and slightly wider than pronotum; surface coarsely and sparsely punctate. Abdomen finely and sparsely punctate. Length 6–7.5 mm.

Genus II. *GYROHYPNUS* Mannerheim

Small, elongate, slender; maxillary palpi with fourth segment much longer than third, acutely conical; pronotum sparsely punctate dorsally, lateral margin double, gradually and feebly deflexed, upper margin not joining lower until apex.

Gyrohypnus hamatus (Say)   Plate XX, No. 14, p. 189
    Elongate, slender; head black, shining; pronotum piceous or reddish brown; antennae, elytra, and legs brownish yellow; abdomen deep brown, apical margins paler. Head feebly oblong, very sparsely, finely punctate. Pronotum slightly elongate; sides parallel, not narrowed posteriorly; disk with rows of fine punctures, some rows shorter, laterally irregular. Elytra one-third longer and slightly wider than pronotum; each with four or five rows of fine punctures. Abdomen finely and sparsely punctate. Length 5–6 mm.

Tribe STAPHYLININI

KEY TO GENERA

1. Fourth segment of maxillary palpi shorter than third 3
   Fourth segment equal to or longer than third 2
2. Ligula emarginate ....II. *Staphylinus* (p. 196)
   Ligula entire ....I. *Philonthus* (p. 194)
3. Pronotum smooth, impunctate, without pubescence except on sides ..
   ....IV. *Creophilus* (p. 200)
   Pronotum punctate, densely pubescent ....III. *Ontholestes* (p. 197)

Genus I. *PHILONTHUS* Curtis

Moderate-sized, elongate, rather slender, subdepressed; ligula entire; maxillary palpi with fourth segment as long as or longer than third, slender, aciculate; antennae distant at base; pronotum at middle of disk with two rows of punctures, lateral margin double; first segment of metatarsi as long as or longer than fifth.

KEY TO SPECIES

1. Protarsi dilated, pubescent beneath 2
   Protarsi not dilated, finely spinose beneath 5
2. The two discal rows of punctures on pronotum each containing three punc-
   tures ....a. *politus*
   Each row containing four punctures ....b. *longicornis*
   Each row containing five punctures 3
3. Elytra brownish red ....c. *fusiformis*
   Elytra not brownish red 4
4. Length 6.5–8 mm.; elytra black or dark brown ....d. *lomatus*
   Length 5–5.5 mm.; elytra dark brown or piceous ....e. *brunneus*
5. Pronotum black; elytra metallic blue or green ....f. *cyanipennis*
   Pronotum orange-yellow; elytra bluish black ....g. *blandus*

a. *Philonthus politus* (Linné)   Plate XX, No. 17, p. 189

Elongate, rather robust; black, shining; elytra bronzed, sparsely pubescent; antennae piceous. Head sparsely punctate behind eyes. Antennal segments five to ten broader than long. Pronotum slightly transverse; sides sinuate behind middle, thence rounded into base; disk sparsely and rather finely punctate. Elytra slightly wider than pronotum, together about as wide as long, sparsely, finely punctate. Abdomen not quite so wide as elytra, coarsely and densely punctate above, more sparsely so beneath; last ventral segment in male with a small triangular notch. Length 10–13 mm.

This species is usually found in fungi.

b. *Philonthus longicornis* Stephens   Plate XX, No. 16, p. 189

Elongate, rather robust; black, shining, sparsely pubescent; antennae piceous. Antennal segments four to ten slightly longer than broad. Head oval, posterior angles punctate. Pronotum slightly elongate, sides nearly straight, slightly narrowed anteriorly; surface rather deeply punctate, punctures coarser basally. Elytra wider than pronotum, together slightly wider than long; surface densely and roughly punctate. Abdomen above finely and densely punctate, more densely so at bases of segments; beneath more densely punctate. Length 6–8 mm.

c. *Philonthus fusiformis* Melsheimer   Plate XX, No. 15, p. 189

Elongate, rather robust; black or piceous, shining; elytra brownish red; antennae (two basal segments paler) and undersurface piceous; legs brownish yellow. Antennae as long as pronotum and head, all segments longer than wide. Pronotum subquadrate. Elytra slightly wider than pronotum, together slightly longer than wide; surface coarsely and densely punctate, sparsely pubescent. Abdomen equal in width to elytra at base, narrowing apically, sparsely and coarsely punctate. Length 5–6 mm.

d. *Philonthus lomatus* Erichson   Plate XX, No. 18, p. 189
   Elongate, rather robust; black or piceous, shining; pronotum and elytra sometimes dark brown, bronzed; undersurface piceous, margins of abdominal segments paler; legs dull yellow. Antennae distinctly longer than head and pronotum. Pronotum elongate, sides arcuate, narrowed apically. Elytra not wider than pronotum, together one-third longer than wide; surface densely and finely punctate. Abdomen as wide as elytra at base, distinctly tapering to apex; finely, rather sparsely punctate. Male with protarsi broadly dilated; last ventral abdominal segment with a triangular notch at apex. Length 6.5–8 mm.

e. *Philonthus brunneus* (Gravenhorst)   Plate XX, No. 20, p. 189
   Elongate, robust; dark brown or piceous, shining; apical margin of abdominal sternites paler; legs and basal segments of antennae brownish yellow. Antennae as long as head and pronotum, segments four to ten as wide as long. Pronotum slightly elongate, feebly narrowed apically. Elytra indistinctly wider than pronotum; surface densely and roughly punctate. Abdomen finely and densely punctate, more coarsely and sparsely so beneath; male with a large oval notch at apex of last segment. Length 5–5.5 mm.
   The adults occur especially on fungi, but are also found beneath damp rubbish and carrion.

f. *Philonthus cyanipennis* (Fabricius)   Plate XX, No. 19, p. 189
   Elongate, robust; black, shining; elytra metallic blue or green; antennae and tarsi piceous. Head quadrate, as wide as or wider than pronotum, coarsely punctate behind eyes. Pronotum slightly elongate; sides rather arcuate, narrowed anteriorly. Elytra wider than pronotum, together broader than long; surface coarsely, rather densely punctate. Abdomen coarsely and sparsely punctate. Length 12–15 mm.
   These beetles are found in fleshy fungi.

g. *Philonthus blandus* (Gravenhorst)   Plate XXI, No. 1, p. 199
   Elongate, slender; bluish black, shining; pronotum, basal half of abdomen, and legs orange-yellow; antennae piceous. Head subquadrate, sparsely punctate behind eyes. Pronotal sides sinuate before base. Elytra wider than pronotum, together longer than wide; surface finely, sparsely punctate. Abdomen equal in width to elytra, very sparsely punctate. Length 5–6 mm.
   This species is usually found in fungi.

Genus II. *STAPHYLINUS* Linné

Moderate to moderately large in size, elongate, robust; head as wide as or wider than pronotum; ligula emarginate; pronotum punctate, pubescent; abdomen more or less tapering; mesocoxae separated, sometimes very narrowly so.

KEY TO SPECIES

1. Head suborbicular, posterior angles rounded ....a. *badipes*
   Head usually subtriangular, suddenly narrowed posteriorly, posterior angles
   obtusely prominent 2
2. Anterior half of abdominal segments beneath densely, finely punctate and
   clothed with golden pubescence 4
   Anterior half of abdominal segments beneath not or but slightly more densely
   punctate than apical half and without golden pubescence 3
3. Head, pronotum, and elytra pale reddish brown ....d. *cinnamopterus*
   Head, pronotum, and elytra blue-violet or coppery ....e. *violaceus*
4. Abdominal segments above with golden pubescence at base and laterally;
   elytra uniformly pale reddish brown ....b. *vulpinus*
   Abdominal segments above with a double row of dark velvety spots medially;
   elytra brown, with elongate, fuscous spots ....c. *maculosus*

a. *Staphylinus badipes* LeConte   Plate XXI, No. 2, p. 199

Elongate, rather robust; black or piceous; antennae and legs reddish brown. Pronotum slightly elongate; disk densely punctate, except for a smooth median line. Head densely punctate; antennae slightly longer than head. Elytra together slightly wider than long; surface densely punctate, with sparse pubescence. Abdomen as wide at base as elytra; segments one to five with a small spot of golden pubescence at middle of anterior margin. Length 10–17 mm.

b. *Staphylinus vulpinus* Nordmann   Plate XXI, No. 7, p. 199

Elongate, robust; head, elytra, and legs light reddish brown, shining; pronotum and antennae dark brown; abdomen piceous, except last segment, which is brown. Antennae slightly longer than head. Pronotum subquadrate; sides feebly arcuate; disk densely punctate; a smooth median line visible only behind middle. Elytra slightly wider than pronotum, densely punctate, sparsely pubescent. Abdomen not as wide at base as elytra; finely punctate. Length 15–18 mm.

This species occurs on carrion and dung, especially near water.

c. *Staphylinus maculosus* Gravenhorst   Plate XXI, No. 6, p. 199

Elongate, robust; dark reddish brown; elytra with fuscous spots; abdomen piceous above, variegated with deep-brown spots; antennae, tibiae, tarsi, and apex of abdomen pale reddish brown; femora piceous, margins paler. Pronotum subquadrate, sides nearly straight; densely punctate except for a short median line behind middle. Elytra densely punctate, sparsely pubescent. Abdomen not as wide at base as elytra, finely punctate. Length 18–25 mm.

The adults are found on carrion, decaying fungi, and dung.

d. *Staphylinus cinnamopterus* Gravenhorst   Plate XXI, No. 4, p. 199
Elongate, rather slender; brownish red, shining; abdomen piceous, except apical margins of segments and entire last segment; antennae, undersurface, and femora piceous. Antennae slightly longer than head. Pronotum subquadrate, sides nearly straight; coarsely and densely punctate, with a smooth median line from base to apex. Elytra slightly wider than pronotum, densely punctate, sparsely pubescent. Abdomen not as wide at base as elytra, more coarsely punctate ventrally than dorsally. Length 12–14 mm.

This species is found on fungi and beneath bark.

e. *Staphylinus violaceus* Gravenhorst   Plate XXI, No. 3, p. 199
Elongate, rather slender; head, pronotum, and elytra deep violet-blue or coppery; antennae piceous; abdomen and legs black. Antennae slightly longer than head. Pronotum subquadrate, sides feebly arcuate; disk, except for smooth median line, coarsely and rather densely punctate. Elytra slightly wider than pronotum, densely and finely punctate, sparsely pubescent. Abdomen not as wide at base as elytra, densely and finely punctate at base, more finely and sparsely so toward apex. Length 12–14 mm.

This species occurs on fungi and carrion and beneath bark and logs.

Genus III. *ONTHOLESTES* Ganglbauer

Moderate-sized, elongate-oblong, robust; antennae slender, attaining middle of pronotum, not subclavate toward apex; lateral marginal lines of prothorax uniting near apex; pronotum punctate, pubescent.

Ontholestes cingulatus (Gravenhorst)   Plate XXI, No. 8, p. 199
Elongate-oblong, robust; dark brown or piceous, densely clothed with yellow, brownish, and blackish pubescence, the black hairs forming irregular spots on head, pronotum, and abdomen; antennae dark, basal segments, tibiae, and tarsi reddish brown; metasternum and apex of abdomen golden. Head wider than pronotum, densely punctate. Pronotum quadrate, widest at apex, sides rounded to base; disk finely, densely punctate. Elytra slightly wider than pronotum and as long, densely, finely granulate. Abdomen narrower than elytra, sparsely, coarsely punctate. Length 13–18 mm.

This species is found on fungi and carrion.

PLATE XXI
Family STAPHYLINIDAE II

1. *Philonthus blandus* (Gravenhorst) (p. 195) — Dull yellow, abdomen darker; head and elytra black; 5–6 mm.

2. *Staphylinus badipes* LeConte (p. 196) — Fuscous; 10–17 mm.

3. *S. violaceus* Gravenhorst (p. 197) — Deep violet-black; 12–14 mm.

4. *S. cinnamopterus* Gravenhorst (p. 197) — Fuscous; elytra and tip of abdomen dull red; 12–14 mm.

5. *Oxyporus femoralis* Gravenhorst (p. 200) — Black; elytral markings dull yellow; 7–8 mm.

6. *Staphylinus maculosus* Gravenhorst (p. 196) — Fuscous; elytra brown; elytral and abdominal markings blackish; 18–25 mm.

7. *S. vulpinus* Nordmann (p. 196) — Fuscous; elytra dull reddish; tomentose patches on abdomen yellowish; 15–18 mm.

8. *Ontholestes cingulatus* (Gravenhorst) (p. 197) — Fuscous, with velvety black markings; next to last abdominal segment golden-yellow-pubescent; 13–18 mm.

9. *Creophilus maxillosus* (Linné) (p. 200) — Black; elytra, abdomen, and pronotum with dull-gray-pubescent markings; 10–20 mm.

10. *Tachyporus jocosus* Say (p. 202) — Dull yellowish; abdomen and sometimes head darker; abdomen here shown telescoped; 3–4 mm.

11. *Coproporus ventriculus* Say (p. 202) — Fuscous, shining; elytra and pronotum tinged with deep red; 2–2.5 mm.

12. *Conosomus crassus* (Gravenhorst) (p. 203) — Fuscous; bases of elytra and pronotum reddish; 3.5–4 mm.

13. *C. imbricatus* Casey (p. 203) — Brownish red; 3.5–4.5 mm.

14. *Gyrophaena vinula* (Erichson) (p. 204) — Pale yellowish; head, outer apices of elytra, and fourth abdominal segment blackish; 1.5–2.5 mm.

15. *Falagria dissecta* Erichson (p. 205) — Piceous or black; elytra and base of abdomen fuscous; 2.2–2.5 mm.

16. *Aleochara lata* Gravenhorst (p. 205) — Black, with fuscous pubescence; 5–7.5 mm.

17. *Baryodma sculptiventris* Casey (p. 206) — Black; elytra tinged with reddish apically toward suture; pubescence fuscous; 3.5–4.5 mm.

18. *B. bimaculata* Gravenhorst (p. 206) — Black; elytra in part piceous, each with a large, pale macula; 4–7 mm.

19. *Bolitobius trinotatus* Erichson (p. 203) — Dull yellowish; each elytron near apex, and fifth abdominal segment, with a dark spot; head black; 3.5–4 mm.

20. *B. cinctus* (Gravenhorst) (p. 204) — Fulvous; head, a broad band on each elytron, and last two abdominal segments black or blue-black; 4.5–6.5 mm.

MM 0 10 20 30 40 50 60 70

PLATE XXI

199

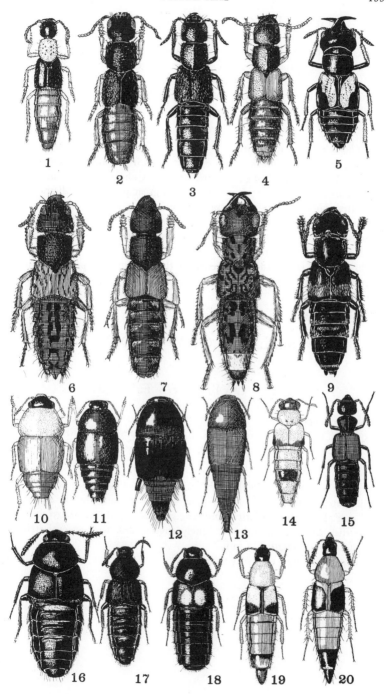

1   2   3   4   5
6   7   8   9
10   11   12   13   14   15
16   17   18   19   20

Genus IV. *CREOPHILUS* Mannerheim

Large, elongate, rather robust; antennae scarcely longer than head, gradually widened apically, last segment longer but narrower than the one preceding, emarginate at apex; maxillary palpi with fourth segment shorter than third; pronotum impunctate, with lateral marginal line not attaining apical margin but terminating at apical third; mesocoxae well separated.

Creophilus maxillosus (Linné)   Plate XXI, No. 9, p. 199

Elongate, robust; black, shining; elytra with a band behind middle composed of coarse, dull-gray hairs; abdomen above with second, third, and usually the fourth segments covered in great part with dull-gray hairs. Pronotum suborbicular, basal margin strongly rounded, apical margin subtruncate; disk without punctures, coarsely setose laterally. Elytra broader than pronotum, very finely and sparsely punctate. Abdomen as wide as elytra. Length 10–21 mm.

This species is recorded as occurring throughout Europe, Asia, Africa, North and Central America, and the West Indies, and may be found on carrion and fungi.

Subfamily OXYPORINAE

Genus *OXYPORUS* Fabricius

Small, elongate, robust; antennae eleven-segmented, inserted under side margins of front; head large, wider than pronotum; eyes small, not prominent; procoxae prominent, conical; mesocoxae separated; abdomen with seven segments.

Oxyporus femoralis Gravenhorst   Plate XXI, No. 5, p. 199

Elongate, robust; black; elytra pale, suture and sides black; tibiae and tarsi pale. Pronotum slightly transverse, sides rounded; base narrower than apex; disk smooth. Elytral sides finely rugose, disk with several striae of fine punctures. Length 7–8 mm.

These beetles feed on fleshy fungi.

Subfamily TACHYPORINAE

KEY TO TRIBES

Side of head not margined beneath eyes; elytra longer than pronotum,
    minutely and irregularly punctate ....TACHYPORINI (p. 201)
Side of head margined beneath eyes; elytra about as long as pronotum,
    smooth or with three or more rows of punctures ....BOLITOBIINI (p. 203)

Tribe TACHYPORINI

KEY TO GENERA

1. Abdomen dorsally with a narrow margin at sides; tibiae with a fringe
     of spines of various sizes at apex 2
   Abdomen above not at all margined at sides; apical fringe of tibiae
     composed of spines which are uniform in size ......IV. *Conosomus* (p. 202)
2. Mesosternum not carinate; maxillary palpi often awl-shaped 3
   Mesosternum carinate; maxillary palpi filiform ......III. *Coproporus* (p. 202)
3. Maxillary palpi filiform; body oblong, somewhat depressed, moder-
     ately tapering; length 3–6 mm. ....I. *Tachinus* (p. 201)
   Maxillary palpi awl-shaped; body short, convex, abruptly tapering;
     length less than 3 mm. ....II. *Tachyporus* (p. 202)

Genus I. *TACHINUS* Gravenhorst

Of moderate size, oblong, depressed; maxillary palpi filiform; mesosternum not carinate; abdomen dorsally with a narrow margin on sides;
tibiae with a fringe of uneven, rather small spines at apex. In males the
protarsi always dilated; last or seventh ventral abdominal segment deeply
divided, forming processes of varying shapes, sixth segment also varied,
sometimes being notched and surface depressed, the depression often
wholly or partially filled with pubescence. In female, protarsi not dilated;
last ventral abdominal segment divided into six long, slender processes;
last dorsal segment trilobed, middle lobe entire, emarginate, and bifid or
trifid at apex.

Tachinus fimbriatus Gravenhorst   Plate XXII, No. 4, p. 215
    Oblong, rather robust, depressed; head and pronotum black, shining;
elytra light reddish brown, apices narrowly piceous; antennae black, four
basal and apical segments paler; abdomen above and legs dark reddish
brown to piceous. Head and pronotum finely alutaceous and minutely
punctate. Elytra together as wide as long; surface minutely alutaceous,
rather coarsely, irregularly punctate, some punctures in distinct rows.
Abdomen shining, sparsely, minutely punctate dorsally, more coarsely so

ventrally; first two ventral segments of both sexes carinate between meta-coxae. Length 7–9 mm.

The female has the last dorsal abdominal segment with the median apical lobe bifid.

Genus II. *TACHYPORUS* Gravenhorst

Small, robust, rather convex; head not margined; antennae inserted at sides of head; mesosternum not carinate; abdomen tapering and margined on sides dorsally, ventrally with six sternites; procoxae conical, prominent; male with protarsi distinctly dilated, last ventral abdominal segment tri-angularly notched and apex of last dorsal segment with posterior margin entire; female with protarsi feebly or not at all dilated, last dorsal ab-dominal segment with four equal, acute teeth.

Tachyporus jocosus Say Plate XXI, No. 10, p. 199

Elongate, robust, subconvex; black, shining; pronotum, elytra, and legs yellowish brown; antennae dull yellow, apical segments dusky. Pronotum distinctly transverse, smooth; posterior angles rounded. Elytra together as long as wide; surface and abdomen punctate, pubescent. Length 3–4 mm.

Genus III. *COPROPORUS* Kraatz

Very small, elongate, convex; head not margined; antennae inserted at sides of head; mesosternum carinate; abdomen tapering, margined lateral-ly above, beneath with six sternites; procoxae conical, prominent; protarsi of male simple.

Coproporus ventriculus Say Plate XXI, No. 11, p. 199

Elongate, robust, convex; black, shining; elytra and abdomen with light-piceous tinge; antennae and legs dark reddish brown. Pronotum strongly transverse, as wide as elytra at base; surface very finely and sparsely punc-tate. Elytra covering more than one-half of abdomen; surface finely punc-tate. Abdomen very finely punctate; last ventral sternite of male with a semicircular notch. Length 2–2.5 mm.

This species occurs beneath bark, particularly that of elm and red oak.

Genus IV. *CONOSOMUS* Motschulsky

Small, elongate-oval, robust, convex; head not margined; antennae in-serted at sides of head; mesosternum carinate; abdomen above not mar-gined laterally, ventrally with six sternites; procoxae conical, prominent.

The abdominal segments of these beetles after death frequently tele-
scope so that the elytra extend to the apex of the abdomen.

KEY TO SPECIES

Mesotibiae each with two terminal spurs; body color dark brown ....a. *imbricatus*
Mesotibiae each with only one terminal spur; body color largely piceous ....
....b. *crassus*

a. *Conosomus imbricatus* Casey   Plate XXI, No. 13, p. 199
    Elongate-oval, robust; dark reddish brown, shining; covered with sparse,
silky pubescence. Pronotum slightly wider than elytra, sides feebly arcuate;
posterior angles acute, subdentiform; surface very finely punctate. Elytra
densely and finely punctate. Length 3.5–4.5 mm.
    This species is usually found on fungi and under decayed leaves.

b. *Conosomus crassus* (Gravenhorst)   Plate XXI, No. 12, p. 199
    Elongate-oval, robust, convex; piceous, with sparse, pale-brown, silky
pubescence; antennae fuscous, apical segment paler; both pronotum and
elytra at base usually with a narrow reddish area; beneath reddish brown;
legs paler. Pronotum slightly wider than elytra; sides arcuate; posterior
angles rounded; disk finely and densely punctate. Elytra together as long
as wide; surface densely and more coarsely punctate than pronotum.
Length 3–5 mm.
    This species occurs beneath bark and on fungi.

Tribe BOLITOBIINI

Genus *BOLITOBIUS* Stephens

    Rather small, elongate-oval; head margined; antennae inserted at sides
of head; maxillary palpi filiform; elytra each with three rows of punctures; abdomen with six ventral segments; procoxae conical, prominent;
meso- and metatibiae fringed at apex with unequal, coarse spinules.

KEY TO SPECIES

Abdomen entirely piceous or yellowish; elytral discal row with numerous punc-
    tures ....a. *trinotatus*
Abdomen bicolored, red, last two segments black; discal row of elytra with few
    punctures ....b. *cinctus*

a. *Bolitobius trinotatus* Erichson   Plate XXI, No. 19, p. 199
    Elongate-oval, subconvex; piceous or dusky yellow; pronotum entirely
pale; elytra with a common triangular spot at base and a larger one near

outer hind angle, black, scutellar spot often lacking. Head oval, not widest at base; maxillary palpi elongate, glabrous. Pronotum slightly narrower at base than elytra; posterior angles obtuse, not broadly rounded. Elytra as wide as long, each with a sutural, discal, and submarginal row of punctures, the discal row with numerous punctures. Length 3.5–4 mm.

The adults are usually associated with decaying fungi.

b. *Bolitobius cinctus* (Gravenhorst)   Plate XXI, No. 20, p. 199

Elongate-oval, rather robust, subconvex; dull reddish yellow; head, two large spots covering most of elytra, last two segments of abdomen, and metasternum black; antennal segments five to ten piceous; legs and remaining segments of antennae dull yellow. Head oval, not widest at base; maxillary palpi elongate, glabrous. Pronotum as wide as base of elytra; posterior angles broadly rounded; disk nearly smooth. Elytra together about as wide as long, with three rows of punctures, discal row with only three or four punctures. Length 4.5–7 mm.

This species is found on fungi, especially those growing about bases of oak stumps.

Subfamily ALEOCHARINAE

KEY TO TRIBES

Tribe BOLITOCHARINI

Genus *GYROPHAENA* Mannerheim

Very small, oblong-ovate, robust; antennae short, inserted between the prominent eyes; third segment of maxillary palpi robust; pronotum distinctly margined; abdomen with six segments; procoxae conical, prominent; metacoxae transverse.

Gyrophaena vinula (Erichson)   Plate XXI, No. 14, p. 199

Oblong-ovate, robust; light brownish yellow; head, elytra at apex, and fourth and fifth segments of abdomen blackish. Pronotum transverse, very feebly and sparsely punctate, with two larger punctures at middle near base. Elytra slightly wider than pronotum; finely and sparsely punctate. Length 1.5–2.5 mm.

This species is found on fleshy fungi.

Tribe ZYRINI

Genus *FALAGRIA* Mannerheim

Small, elongate, rather slender; head with a very narrow neck; antennae inserted between eyes; pronotum quadrate; scutellum distinctly carinate; abdomen six-segmented; procoxae conical, prominent; metacoxae transverse.

Falagria dissecta Erichson   Plate XXI, No. 15, p. 199
Elongate, rather slender; black to piceous, shining, sparsely pubescent; legs brownish yellow. Pronotum subquadrate, slightly transverse; sides strongly rounded apically; disk finely, sparsely punctate, and with a deep median groove. Scutellum bicarinate medially. Elytra distinctly wider than pronotum; finely and sparsely punctate. Abdomen narrower than elytra, sides parallel; densely, finely punctate. Length 2–2.5 mm.

Tribe ALEOCHARINI

KEY TO GENERA

Mesosternum without trace of a carina; body form robust, ovate, not
    parallel ....I. *Aleochara* (p. 205)
Mesosternum with a distinct longitudinal carina medially; body form
    more slender, oblong, parallel-sided ....II. *Baryodma* (p. 206)

Genus I. *ALEOCHARA* Gravenhorst

Small, elongate-oval, robust; head small, distinctly narrower than pronotum; antennae short and robust, inserted between the large eyes; pronotum transverse, posterior angles rounded; mesosternum not carinate; abdomen with six segments, dorsally first three or four segments deeply impressed at base; procoxae conical, prominent; metacoxae transverse.

Aleochara lata Gravenhorst   Plate XXI, No. 16, p. 199
Elongate-ovate, robust; black, shining, covered with sparse, grayish pubescence; tarsi reddish brown. Pronotum transverse; base strongly rounded; sides feebly arcuate, converging apically; disk finely, sparsely punctate. Elytra slightly wider than pronotum; disk coarsely, densely, and roughly punctate. Abdomen as wide at base as elytra, feebly but distinctly narrowed to apex, coarsely, sparsely punctate. Length 5–7 mm.
The adults may be found on carrion and decayed logs.

206 STAPHYLINIDAE

Genus II. *BARYODMA* Thomson

Small, elongate-oblong, rather slender; parallel-sided; head small; antennae short, robust, inserted between eyes; eyes large; pronotum transverse, posterior angles rounded; mesosternum with a distinct longitudinal median carina; abdomen with six segments, dorsally the first three or four deeply impressed at base; procoxae conical, prominent; metacoxae transverse.

KEY TO SPECIES

Elytra each with a pale spot at apex near suture ....b. *bimaculata*
Elytra not spotted ....a. *sculptiventris*

a. *Baryodma sculptiventris* Casey   Plate XXI, No. 17, p. 199
Elongate, oblong-ovate, robust; piceous, shining; abdomen black; legs, basal segments of antennae, and occasionally elytra at apex reddish brown. Pronotum twice width of head, transverse; sides arcuate. Elytra wider than pronotum, finely, densely, and roughly punctate. Abdomen slightly narrower than elytra; sides parallel; basal impressions of first three segments large, deep; surface densely, coarsely punctate. Length 3.5–4.5 mm.

b. *Baryodma bimaculata* Gravenhorst   Plate XXI, No. 18, p. 199
Elongate-oblong, ovate, rather robust; black, shining; elytra paler toward apex; tibiae, tarsi, and ventral abdominal segments with apices reddish brown. Pronotum transverse; sides arcuate; densely, irregularly punctate laterally, at middle with two elongate, feebly punctate foveae. Elytra not as wide as pronotum, densely, coarsely punctate. Abdomen equal in width to elytra, sides parallel; surface densely punctate. Length 4–7 mm.

This species occurs especially in horse dung and fungi.

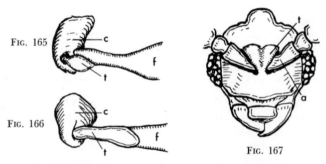

Figs. 165–166. Upper part of middle legs of *Batrisodes* (165) and of *Tmesiphorus* (166). *c*, coxa; *f*, femur; *t*, trochanter.
Fig. 167. Head of *Tyrus* viewed from the front, with the antennae (*a*) inserted under a large tubercle (*t*).

Family PSELAPHIDAE

The Ant-loving Beetles

Of these very small to minute beetles, all are less than 3.5 mm. in length. Some live beneath leaves, stones, or bark, feeding upon mites and other minute animals; others live in ant nests, many exuding a substance from tufts of hairs which is imbibed by the ants, while still others are found in caves. The secondary sexual characters of the males are sometimes very complicated and usually affect the upper surface of the head, clypeus, maxillary palpi, antennae, or abdomen. The family name has been derived from the greatly developed maxillary palpi, which are usually four-segmented and of a variety of interesting forms.

Other family characters are as follows: head with mouthparts projecting forward, equal or nearly equal in width to pronotum; eyes often coarsely granulate; antennae mostly clavate, though sometimes moniliform, with eleven segments as a rule, in some genera with only ten or less; pronotum narrower than elytra, usually with from one to five foveae at base; elytra strongly abbreviated, exposing the abdomen, each usually with two to three foveae at base, apices truncate; prosternal process extremely narrow between procoxae, which are conical, prominent, and contiguous, their cavities open posteriorly; legs long, slender, tarsi two- or three-segmented, inner claw frequently reduced or absent, claws simple, except in a few males of *Batrisodes;* abdomen rigid, sclerotized, usually five segments of dorsal surface exposed by shortened elytra, segments margined rather broadly laterally, except in *Batrisodes* and allies, in which only the first segment is margined.

KEY TO TRIBES

1. All trochanters short, with the femora inserted obliquely upon them (Fig. 165); antennae widely separated at base, inserted on sides of head beneath small tubercles 2
   Mesotrochanters elongate, the femora inserted at their apices and distant from coxae (Fig. 166); antennae usually contiguous at base, inserted on front beneath prominent, contiguous tubercles (Fig. 167) 3
2. First ventral segment of abdomen very short or completely hidden ....BATRISINI (p. 208)
   First ventral segment of abdomen normally long, extending behind mesocoxae ....TYCHINI (p. 209)

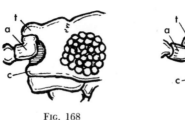

FIG. 168   FIG. 169

Figs. 168–169. Head of *Pilopius* (168) and of *Tyrus* (169) in side view.
a, antenna; *t,* frontal tubercles; *c,* clypeus.

Tribe BATRISINI

Genus *BATRISODES* Reitter

Moderately slender, elongate-cylindrical species; head large, quadrate, with two distinct foveae between eyes more or less connected by a curved sulcus on vertex; antennae with three-segmented club; last segment of maxillary palpi fusiform, more convex on outer side; pronotum as wide as long, with two or three longitudinal grooves and a basal transverse sulcus connecting three foveae; elytra very convex, discal striae confined to basal half, each with three small basal foveae; legs long, femora clavate, metatibiae apically with a fine, slender, terminal spur; tarsal claws unequal.

Most of the pselaphids found in caves in North America are members of this genus.

Batrisodes globosus (LeConte)   Plate XXII, No. 6, p. 215
Very small, elongate, slender; reddish brown, shining, pubescence long, not dense. Head subtriangular, vertex roof-shaped, at middle strongly carinate; foveae deep, rounded, not pubescent, connecting groove deep; margin broad, flat, densely punctate; antennae with first segment large, slightly oblique at apex, second segment obconical, equal in width to third to eighth segments, which are globose and gradually decrease in length, ninth wider, transverse, tenth four times wider than ninth and

with a fovea near base, eleventh narrower than tenth, ovate, acute, oblique-ly impressed from middle on outer side (in female tenth segment a little more robust than ninth). Pronotum slightly wider than long, widest before middle; median sulcus deep, ending in a deep fovea near base and from which a transverse sulcus curves to foveae on sides. Elytra indistinctly, finely punctate, one-half longer than pronotum; each with three small, rounded foveae on base, discal striae short, shallow; humeri tuberculate. Length 1.7–1.8 mm.

This species occurs in numbers in large cone-shaped nests of ants and beneath stones on sloping hillsides, as well as in caves.

Tribe TYCHINI

Genus *TYCHUS* Leach

Very small, elongate, slender; head narrowed anteriorly, more or less triangular, a small spicule or spine in front of each of the two foveae (both foveae and spicules are frequently obsolete); antennae clavate, last segment large, ovate; last segment of maxillary palpi long, hatchet-shaped, the third segment triangular; pronotum slightly transverse, basal foveae small; second segment of metatarsi equal to or longer than third; only one claw present.

Tychus minor LeConte   Plate XXII, No. 5, p. 215
Rather slender; dark reddish brown, shining, pubescence coarse, some-what dense and long, shorter on head and pronotum; antennae and legs paler. Head slightly longer than wide across eyes; eyes very small, semi-circular, foveae very small; antennae slightly longer than head and pro-notum, first segment twice length of second, more robust, second segment longer than wide, subcylindrical, segments three to eight subequal, eighth globular, ninth and tenth wider than long, larger, eleventh nearly twice as wide as ninth, longer than two preceding segments together, acuminate. Pronotum transverse, wider than head, very convex, shining, impunctate; five basal foveae, the middle one the largest. Elytra at base as wide as pronotum, sides divergent posteriorly; apices broadly and transversely truncate; disk with two striae on each elytron, sutural continuous, medial short, attaining only to middle; surface impunctate. First metatarsal seg-ment very short, second and third of equal length. Length 1.5 mm.

This species usually occurs beneath stones on hillsides.

Tribe CTENISTINI

Genus *PILOPIUS* Casey

Minute, robust, convex; head feebly transverse, distinctly narrower than pronotum, with two pubescent foveae; antennae approximate basally, clavate; segments two to four of maxillary palpi with long bristle-like appendages, second segment bent and clavate, the third transversely lunate, fourth segment not angulate and without a spiniform appendage at apex; first four visible dorsal abdominal segments equal in length; tarsi short, slender.

Pilopius lacustris Casey   Plate XXII, No. 7, p. 215
Minute, robust, convex; dark reddish brown; elytra, antennae, and legs paler. Head feebly transverse, distinctly narrower than pronotum. two large foveae on occiput between eyes; eyes coarsely granulate; antennae of male three-fourths length of body, segments cylindrical, nearly equal, in female shorter, with segments seven to ten short, transverse, last segment shorter, oblong-oval. Pronotum transverse; disk with an oblong median fovea at base nearly attaining middle, a smaller one each side. Elytra slightly wider at base than pronotum, thence gradually widening apically; disk of each with a fine, entire sutural and median stria and two basal foveae. Legs long, very slender, tarsi very short, slender. Length 0.72–1.8 mm.

This species is usually found beneath logs and bark and may be swept from stems of bluegrass.

Tribe TYRINI

KEY TO GENERA

1. Antennae moniliform, without a distinct club ....I. *Ceophyllus*   (p. 210)
   Antennae clavate or capitate (Figs. 13–16) 2
2. Last three segments of maxillary palpi with a lateral bristle-like
   appendage (Fig. 170) ....II. *Tmesiphorus*   (p. 211)
   Last segment only with a bristle-like appendage at apex ...III. *Tyrus*   (p. 212)

Genus I. *CEOPHYLLUS* LeConte

Very small; head large, as long as pronotum, convex; antennal tubercles wider than long, contiguous; antennae robust, eleventh segment bluntly pointed; pronotum campanulate; profemora each with three strong spines

Fig. 170

Fig. 170. Maxillary palpus of *Tmesiphorus*, the last three segments with a bristle.

near base; tarsi long and slender; claws equal in length, inner one more robust.

Ceophyllus monilis LeConte   Plate XXII, No. 8, p. 215

Larger, elongate-ovate; reddish brown; impunctate. Head as long and three-fourths as wide as pronotum, convex; antennae robust, male with fifth, sixth, and eighth segments enlarged, in female regularly moniliform, very slightly thickened apically. Pronotum campanulate; disk with fine impressed median line and two foveae near base. Elytra one-half wider at base than pronotum, wider at apical third; disk flat, sutural striae long, others present on basal half only. Legs long, slender; profemora with three spines near base; tarsi long, slender, half length of tibiae, claws equal in length but inner one more robust. Length. 3.3 mm.

This species is always found in ant nests, especially those of *Lasius umbratus* and related forms.

Genus II. *TMESIPHORUS* LeConte

Very small; head (excluding eyes) transverse, with two foveae between eyes; antennae clavate, tubercles longer than wide; maxillary palpi with fourth segment triangular and emarginate, the last three segments with lateral bristle-like appendages (Fig. 170); pronotum slightly transverse; protibiae dilated externally at middle in male, very slightly so in female; abdomen with a short lateral carina either side.

Tmesiphorus costalis LeConte   Plate XXII, No. 9, p. 215

Elongate-oval; dark brown to piceous, shining, clothed with short, fine, appressed, yellowish hair. Head transverse; frontal sulcus branching behind antennal tubercles toward foveae on vertex; eyes prominent; antennae of male more than half body length, second segment cylindrical, shorter and slightly narrower than first, third to seventh globular, eighth to tenth gradually larger, obconical, eleventh equal to ninth and tenth, notched on one side near base; in female shorter, less robust, and without notch on last segment. Pronotum campanulate; laterally with an obtuse tubercle near middle; disk with two shallow apical and two large basal foveae. Elytra each with a broad, deep, long sulcus on basal half; humeri prominent. Abdomen dorsally with a carina on first and second segments. Legs long, slender; protibiae dilated at middle in male, less strongly so in female. Length 3.3 mm.

This species occurs beneath stones and bark and in ant nests.

Genus III. *TYRUS* Aubé

Very small; head (including eyes) slightly transverse or quadrate; antennae clavate, tubercles prominent; maxillary palpi with first segment minute, second long and curved, third short, obovate, fourth with aciculate spine at apex; anterior trochanters very long, clavate, femora inserted at their apex; profemora carinate; third tarsal segment longer than second.

This genus contains some species that are strikingly bicolored in contrast to the more somberly colored genera.

Tyrus humeralis Aubé   Plate XXII, No. 10, p. 215

Small, very robust; body piceous, clothed with fine, short, appressed pubescence; elytra red; antennae, legs, and palpi paler. Head subquadrate; two small foveae between eyes not connected by an impressed line. Antennae of male with first two segments cylindrical; third to seventh rounded, gradually smaller, eighth and ninth larger, globular, tenth obconical, twice as long and thick as ninth, eleventh largest, ovate; female with segments three to nine subequal, tenth larger, eleventh oval. Pronotum campanulate, widest at middle; disk with a median rounded fovea and a narrow transverse sulcus at base, lateral foveae small. Elytra wider than pronotum; disk finely and sparsely punctate. Abdomen but little longer than elytra; margins very broad; a minute tubercle in middle of base. Length 1.6 mm.

The adults may be taken by sifting and from beneath the bark of decayed stumps.

Family SCAPHIDIIDAE

The Shining Fungus Beetles

To this small family belong a number of similarly small, strongly shining, convex species which live in fungi, in and beneath decaying logs and other dead vegetation, and under the bark of dead trees or stumps. With their shortened elytra, shining surface, and broadly oval outline, the adults resemble many of the histerids, but are easily recognized by their strongly tapering or acute anal segment. When disturbed, they usually remain motionless; sometimes, however, they will run with some speed but with a very characteristic, uneven gait. Besides the tapering last abdominal segment and abbreviated elytron, the family is distinguished in having the head with front constricted, prolonged into a short beak (Fig. 171); mentum large, quadrate; antennae filiform or with a loose club, inserted on margin of front; prosternum not prolonged; abdomen with six or seven visible sternites; procoxae large, conical, their cavities widely open behind; tarsi five-segmented, long, and slender.

KEY TO GENERA

1. Scutellum distinct; elytra usually with rows of punctures; antennae with a broad, large, five-segmented club ....I. *Scaphidium* (p. 213)
   Scutellum minute or entirely concealed; elytra either impunctate or with scattered punctures; antennae not or feebly clavate 2
2. Antennae with third segment elongate, cylindrical (Fig. 172); scutellum concealed ....III. *Baeocera* (p. 217)
   Antennae with third segment very short, wedge-shaped or triangular, narrowed to base (Fig. 173); scutellum minute but visible, triangular ....II. *Scaphisoma* (p. 216)

Genus I. *SCAPHIDIUM* Olivier

Small, broadly ovate, subconvex forms; eyes deeply, narrowly emarginate; antennae with a distinct, five-segmented club; pronotum with posterior angles produced, acute, anterior ones obtuse; scutellum comparatively small but apparent; elytra with sides broadly rounded, widest medially, apices broadly arcuately truncate, usually with a basal and one or more

PLATE XXII

Family STAPHYLINIDAE III

1. *Homoeotarsus cribatus* (LeConte) (p. 187)
Blackish, shining; elytra dull reddish; legs and antennae pale yellow; 8.5–10 mm.

2. *H. bicolor* (Gravenhorst) (p. 187)
Reddish orange; head and abdomen in part black; legs pale yellow; 7.5–10 mm.

3. *H. pallipes* (Gravenhorst) (p. 187)
Blackish, shining; legs pale yellow; 8–11 mm.

4. *Tachinus fimbriatus* Gravenhorst (p. 201)
Deep brown to black; elytra dull red; blackish at apex; 7–9 mm.

Family PSELAPHIDAE

5. *Tychus minor* LeConte (p. 209)
Orange-brown, shining; antennal club and legs paler; 1.5 mm.

6. *Batrisodes globosus* (LeConte) (p. 208)
Dark reddish brown, shining; antennal club orange-brown; 1.7–1.8 mm.

7. *Pilopius lacustris* Casey (p. 210)
Orange-brown, shining, with waxy, white markings; 0.72–1.8 mm.

8. *Ceophyllus monilis* LeConte (p. 211)
Orange-brown, shining; 3.3 mm.

9. *Tmesiphorus costalis* LeConte (p. 211)
Dark reddish brown, shining; antennae and legs somewhat paler; 3.3 mm.

10. *Tyrus humeralis* Aubé (p. 212)
Orange-brown, shining; pronotum and head darker; abdomen piceous; 1.6 mm.

Family SCAPHIDIIDAE

11. *Baeocera congener* Casey (p. 218)
Black, shining, becoming piceous on apices of elytra; body beneath, legs, and antennae reddish brown; 2 mm.

12. *B. falsata* Achard (p. 217)
Black, shining; elytra often piceous apically; legs and antennae reddish brown to piceous; 2.7 mm.

13. *Scaphidium quadriguttatum* Say (p. 216)
Dark brown to black, shining; elytral maculae dull reddish; 3.8–4.5 mm.

14. *Scaphisoma suturale* LeConte (p. 216)
Orange-brown, shining; 1.7 mm.

15. *S. convexum* Say (p. 216)
Fuscous, shining; antennae paler; 2.2–2.7 mm.

Family HISTERIDAE I

16. *Plegaderus transversus* Say (p. 224)
Fuscous, slightly shining; 1.3–1.5 mm.

17. *Isolomalus bistriatus* (Erichson) (p. 228)
Dark reddish brown to piceous; antennae and legs reddish brown; 2 mm.

18. *Hister cadaverinus* Hoffmann (p. 229)
Piceous to black, shining; antennae and legs partly reddish brown; 7–8.5 mm.

PLATE XXII

215

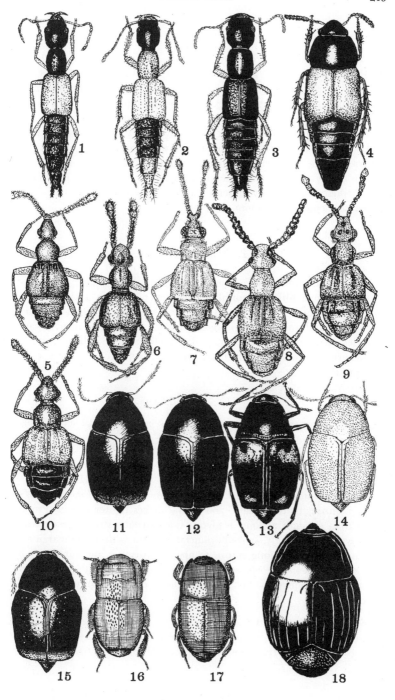

discal rows of coarse punctures; metasternum in male medially with a large, depressed area which is punctate and pubescent.

Scaphidium quadriguttatum Say   Plate XXII, No. 13, p. 215

Oblong-ovate, rather robust, subconvex; black, strongly shining; elytra variable in coloration, usually each with two reddish, transverse maculae, one near base, the other at apex, the maculae, however, may be yellowish or the apical or both may be lacking; tarsi reddish. Pronotum slightly wider across base than long, sides feebly sinuate, strongly tapering to apex; disk smooth except for an undulating row of coarse punctures near base. Elytra with a basal row of coarse punctures, which is continued along suture nearly to apex; disk usually with two or three short rows of punctures, these occasionally absent, surface near apex minutely, sparsely punctate. Length 3.8–4.5 mm.

Genus II. *SCAPHISOMA* Leach

Very small, ovate, convex beetles; eyes not emarginate, elongate-oval, erect; antennae filiform, apical segments not forming a club, third segment much shorter than fourth, tapering to base, triangular; pronotum with posterior angles not produced, acute, front ones nearly wanting, rounded; scutellum minute, triangular; elytra widest at basal third, arcuately narrowed to apices, which are arcuately truncate; disk with scattered, fine punctures.

KEY TO SPECIES

Pronotum more than one-half as long as elytra; body length 2.2 mm. or longer .. ..a. *convexum*
Pronotum just one-half as long as elytra; body length not over 1.7 mm. ....b. *suturale*

a. *Scaphisoma convexum* Say   Plate XXII, No. 15, p. 215

Broadly ovate, robust; dark chestnut-brown to black, moderately shining; antennae, body beneath, and elytral apices lighter brown. Pronotum more than one-half as long as elytra; sides arcuate, strongly narrowed anteriorly; disk minutely, sparsely punctate. Elytra with a fine marginal line at base continuing along suture to apex, between it and suture a row of coarse punctures; disk sparsely, coarsely punctate. Length 2.2–2.7 mm.

Especially frequently this species is taken on fungi growing on oak or other logs.

b. *Scaphisoma suturale* LeConte   Plate XXII, No. 14, p. 215

Rather narrowly ovate, moderately robust; dark chestnut-brown to black, strongly shining; elytra often paler apically. Pronotum strongly transverse,

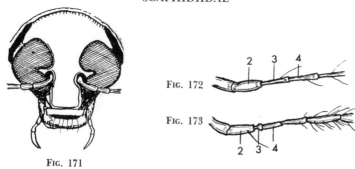

Fig. 171

Fig. 172

Fig. 173

Fig. 171. Head of *Scaphidium* in anterior view, slightly elongated below antennal insertions to form a sort of beak.

Figs. 172–173. Basal portion of antennae of *Baeocera* (172) and of *Scaphisoma* (173) to show the relative proportions of the second, third, and fourth segments.

only one-half as long as elytra, disk minutely, sparsely punctate. Elytra with a rather coarse marginal line at base and continued along suture to apex, without a row of punctures between it and suture; disk densely, coarsely punctate. Length 1.7 mm.

This species is taken largely by sifting dead leaves and other debris, especially that from beech stumps.

Genus III. *BAEOCERA* Erichson

Very small, blackish, ovate forms; eyes shallowly, narrowly emarginate; antennae with last three segments somewhat broadened into a feeble, loose club, third segment elongate, never much shorter than fourth, nearly parallel-sided, cylindrical; pronotum with posterior angles not produced, acute, anterior angles nearly wanting, rounded; scutellum entirely concealed; elytra widest near base but only weakly tapering to apex, which is nearly squarely, broadly truncate, disk without rows of punctures.

KEY TO SPECIES

Elytra sparsely but distinctly punctate; antennae with third segment slender, subequal to fourth; body form robust ....a. *falsata*
Elytra impunctate; antennae with third segment robust, distinctly shorter than fourth; body form less broadly oval ....b. *congener*

a. *Baeocera falsata* Achard   Plate XXII, No. 12, p. 215

Oblong-ovate, robust, strongly convex; black, strongly shining; elytral apices, abdomen, legs, and antennae fuscous. Pronotum strongly transverse, sides narrowed to apex; disk minutely, densely punctate. Elytra about as long as wide, nearly twice as long as pronotum, with a deeply impressed line along base and suture, with a row of coarse punctures between it and suture; disk with a few coarse, scattered punctures. Length 2.7 mm.

As a rule this species is found on fungi of various types.

b. *Baeocera congener* Casey   Plate XXII, No. 11, p. 215

Ovate, only moderately robust, convex; black, strongly shining; antennae and legs pale reddish brown. Pronotum strongly transverse, sides narrowed to apex; disk very finely, rather sparsely punctate. Elytra scarcely longer than wide, twice as long as pronotum; marginal line deep, extending across base and along suture, bordered between it and suture by a row of coarse punctures; disk with a few coarse, scattered punctures. Length 2 mm.

This species may be taken from fungi as well as by sifting debris from rotten logs.

Family HISTERIDAE

The Hister Beetles

These are small to moderate-sized, very hard, compact insects, most of which, with their shining surfaces and short, chunky form, look not unlike so many black pills or seeds. The origin of their name is obscure. On one side, some authorities claim that it is derived from the Latin *histrio* (an actor) because they act as though dead when disturbed, drawing in their head and legs, quite like turtles. But as many insects feign death, a fact with which Linné must certainly have been familiar, other writers claim that the great naturalist would not have used this character as a distinguishing trait of his genus *Hister*. They suggest that he might have had in mind a character of that name, mentioned by the Roman poet Juvenal, who was noteworthy as a low, dirty fellow. And certainly, judging by human standards, some histerids are low and dirty in habits, for many are found in excrement, carrion, and decaying fungi; others, however, live beneath bark of trees, in nests of ants and termites, or in burrows and nests of mammals and birds.

These beetles are predaceous, and those that live in excrement and carrion are undoubtedly of value in keeping down the population of undesirable flies by eating the larvae. Moreover, those forms which live beneath bark feed on the eggs and larvae of scolytids and other injurious wood-borers. By their cylindrical form *Teretrius* and *Teretrisoma* are adapted to following down the burrows of lyctids and scolytids drilled into solid wood. In fact, at least one species, *Plaesius javanicus,* is being employed in biological control work in the West Indies, where it is being used to keep in check certain weevils that attack palm trees.

In addition to their general form, adults are distinguished by their geniculate and capitate antennae, folded into cavities on the underside of pronotum (Figs. 177, 178); five visible abdominal sternites, first one long, last very short; elytra abbreviated and truncate, not attaining apex of abdomen, exposing two tergites, usually striate and punctate; legs short, retractile, tibiae usually compressed, protibiae fossorial, metatibiae often with long spines to provide traction on soft or yielding substances; all tarsi five-segmented.

KEY TO GENERA

1. Head porrect, not covered beneath by prosternum (Plate XXIII,
   Nos. 1, 2) ....I. *Hololepta* (p. 222)
   Head retracted, bent downward 2
2. Antennae inserted under lateral margin of front, the cavity not
   forming an emargination on sides of front 4
   Antennal cavities forming a deep emargination on sides of front
   (Fig. 174) 3
3. Body elongate, cylindrical; prosternum basally emarginate, mesosternum with an anterior process which fits into emargination of
   prosternum (Fig. 175) ....II. *Teretrius* (p. 222)
   Body oval or rounded, often nearly spherical; mesosternum anteriorly emarginate (Fig. 176) ....III. *Plegaderus* (p. 223)
4. Prosternum with an anterior process, often separated by a suture
   (Fig. 177) 6
   Prosternum without an anterior process (Fig. 178) 5
5. Front of head not margined ....IV. *Saprinus* (p. 224)
   Front of head distinctly margined (Fig. 179) ......V. *Pachylopus* (p. 225)
6. Antennal groove lying in middle of deflexed sides of pronotum,
   anterior to the procoxae (Fig. 180) 7
   Antennal groove lying on anterior angle of deflexed sides of pronotum (Fig. 177) 8
7. Prosternum with a lateral stria (Fig. 180) ....VI. *Platylomalus* (p. 227)
   Prosternum without a lateral stria ....VII. *Isolomalus* (p. 228)
8. Middle of anterior margin of mesosternum with a more or less
   prominent point which fits into an emargination in prosternum
   (Fig. 181) ....XI. *Phelister* (p. 237)
   Middle of anterior margin of mesosternum emarginate to receive
   base of usually rounded prosternum (Fig. 182); mesosternum
   rarely truncate (Fig. 185) 9
9. Tarsal groove of protibiae straight, margined only on inner edge
   (Fig. 183) 10
   Tarsal groove sigmoid, deep, sharply margined (Fig. 184) ....
   ....X. *Platysoma* (p. 236)
10. Mesosternum truncate anteriorly (Fig. 185) ....IX. *Atholus* (p. 233)
    Mesosternum emarginate (Fig. 182) ....VIII. *Hister* (p. 228)

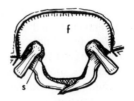

FIG. 174

Fig. 174. Head of *Teretrius*, viewed from the front, with antennal
sockets (s) cut into sides of front (f).

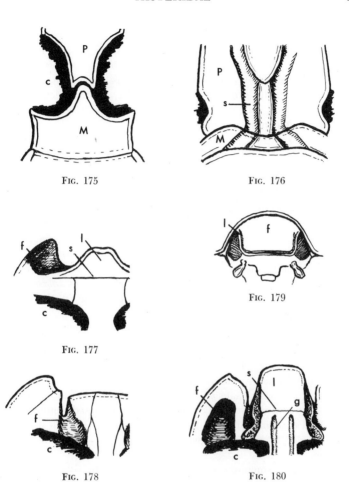

FIG. 175

FIG. 176

FIG. 177

FIG. 179

FIG. 178

FIG. 180

Figs. 175–176. Portion of sternum of *Teretrius* (175) and of *Plegaderus* (176). *P*, portion of prosternum; *c*, procoxal cavities; *M*, mesosternum; *s*, prosternal sulcus.

Figs. 177–178. Anterior portion of prosternum of *Hister* (177) and of *Saprinus pennsylvanicus* (178). *l*, prosternal lobe or process; *f*, antennal fossa; *c*, procoxal cavity; *s*, suture separating lobe from rest of prosternum.

Fig. 179. Upper portion of head of *Pachylopus* viewed from the front. *f*, front; *l*, marginal impressed line.

Fig. 180. Anterior portion of one side of the prosternum of *Platylomalus*. *f*, antennal fossa; *c*, procoxal cavity; *l*, prosternal lobe; *s*, suture; *g*, prosternal stria or groove.

Genus I. *HOLOLEPTA* Paykull

Rather small, oblong, extremely flattened species found under closely fitting bark of trees; head porrect and prominent; front smooth, sometimes striate; mandibles more or less long, usually without teeth; labrum deeply and broadly grooved, apex triangular, strongly deflexed; underside of pronotum with only a slight depression for reception of antennal club; protibiae dentate on inner margin.

KEY TO SPECIES

First dorsal stria of elytra entire, extending nearly to apex .....b..*quadridentata*
First dorsal stria short, not over one-fourth length of elytra ....a. *fossularis*

a. *Hololepta fossularis* Say   Plate XXIII, No. 1, p. 231
Subquadrate, depressed; black, shining. Pronotum transverse, apex broadly emarginate; disk punctate at sides, with an entire marginal stria; male with a deep pit near anterior angles. Elytra with first dorsal stria short, not over one-fourth length of elytra, second shorter, and third abbreviated to a puncture. Propygidium in both sexes with a few coarse punctures laterally; pygidium densely, finely punctate except medially. Length 7–10 mm.

b. *Hololepta quadridentata* (Fabricius)   Plate XXIII, No. 3, p. 231
Oblong, robust, depressed; black, shining. Pronotum transverse; apex broadly emarginate; disk medially with a fine impressed line on basal half, entire surface minutely punctate; entire marginal stria prolonged partially along base; male with a deep pit near anterior angles of pronotum. Elytra with first stria entire, second abbreviated, confined to basal third, third extremely short or lacking. Propygidium in both sexes coarsely punctate except at middle; pygidium densely, finely punctate. Length 7–10 mm.
This species is common in the South, especially the Gulf States.

Genus II. *TERETRIUS* Erichson

Small, elongate, cylindrical; head deeply inserted, the front deflexed and smooth; antennae inserted on front; antennal fossa broad and shallow, situated on underside of the prothorax anterior to coxae; scutellum minute; propygidium transverse, short; prosternal process emarginate at apex receiving mesosternal process; tibiae dentate.

Teretrius americanus (LeConte)   Plate XXIV, No. 1, p. 235
Oblong, cylindrical; piceous, shining; antennae brownish orange except basal segments; sides of elytra and legs dark reddish brown. Pronotum

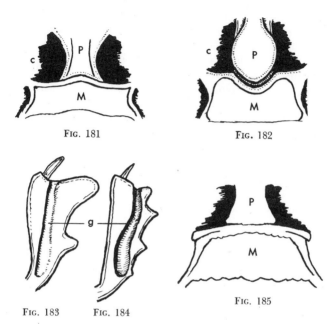

FIG. 181   FIG. 182

FIG. 183   FIG. 184

FIG. 185

Figs. 181–182. Mesosternum of *Phelister* (181) and of *Hister* (182). *M*, mesosternum; *c*, procoxal cavities; *P*, prosternal process.

Figs. 183–184. Upper side of protibia of *Hister arcuatus* (183) and of *Platysoma* (184). *g*, tarsal groove.

Fig. 185. Mesosternum of *Atholus*. *M*, mesosternum; *P*, portion of prosternal process.

slightly longer than wide, widest at apex; entire surface densely, rather finely punctate; marginal line entire, fine. Elytra parallel, convex, densely and distinctly punctate, without striae. Propygidium and pygidium densely, finely punctate in both sexes. Protibiae with five teeth. Length 1.5–2.5 mm.

This species is usually found beneath bark, especially that of pine and soft maple.

Genus III. *PLEGADERUS* Erichson

Small, oblong, subdepressed; head retracted, deflexed; antennae inserted under lateral margin of front; antennal fossa large, deep, and rounded, anterior to procoxae; pronotum on either side with a deep, longitudinal groove and a transverse impression at apical third; prosternum broad, with a deep, longitudinal sulcus either side from anterior lobe convergent to apex of process (Fig. 176); tibiae with many fine teeth.

Plegaderus transversus Say　　　　　　　　Plate XXII, No. 16, p. 215

Oblong-oval, moderately robust, subdepressed; fuscous, moderately shining; antennal club yellowish. Pronotum subquadrate; sides subparallel, feebly narrowing apically; marginal line fine; longitudinal grooves extending from apex to basal third setting off a convex lateral portion; the transverse sulcus shallow; disk anterior to sulcus more densely punctate. Elytra with elongate, confluent punctures and a short, moderately impressed, oblique, humeral stria. Propygidium narrow, strongly transverse, rather coarsely, densely punctate; pygidium uniformly finely, densely punctate. Length 1.3–1.5 mm.

Genus IV. *SAPRINUS* Erichson

Small, oblong-oval species; front of head not margined; antennae inserted under front, fossae broad, shallow, anterior to procoxae; prosternum not produced into a lobe anteriorly; pronotal marginal line fine, entire; elytral striae more or less abbreviated apically, fifth dorsal usually lacking, fourth usually curved at the base to join sutural; elytra usually densely punctate on apical half; propygidium narrow, arcuate, strongly transverse.

KEY TO SPECIES

1. Prosternal striae ascending and ending in a small but distinct pit (Fig. 186); black 2
   Prosternum not anteriorly foveate (Fig. 178); body color green or bronze ....
   ....a. *pennsylvanicus*
2. Pygidium with a deep marginal groove at apex ....b. *assimilis*
   Pygidium not grooved ....c. *conformis*

a. *Saprinus pennsylvanicus* Paykull　　　　　Plate XXIV, No. 5, p. 235

Broadly oval, robust; brilliant metallic green to bronze. Pronotum smooth, with a few punctures along sides and basal margin. Elytra coarsely punctate on apical half between first dorsal stria and suture; first dorsal extending two-thirds to apex, second shorter, third very short, fourth shorter than second, arched at base to join sutural, which is entire; humeral stria strongly oblique, united with first dorsal, not joining internal subhumeral, which is not punctate at apex. Propygidium strongly transverse, slightly arcuate, finely, densely punctate except at extreme base; pygidium about as long as wide, with dense, coarse punctures, finer on apical half. Length 4–5 mm.

This species is found especially along the seashore but may be taken from beneath dung and carrion.

b. *Saprinus assimilis* Paykull　　　　　　　Plate XXIV, No. 7, p. 235

Broadly oval; black, shining. Pronotum impressed near anterior angles, sides coarsely punctate, base with a few punctures and a distinct impression in front of scutellum. Elytra coarsely punctate on apical third; first dorsal stria extending three-quarters to apex, second, third, and fourth gradually shorter and terminating in coarse punctures, fourth joining sutural at base, sutural deeply impressed basally but not attaining apex; humeral stria oblique, indistinct, not joining internal subhumeral, which is punctate at apex. Propygidium strongly transverse, densely, finely punctate, punctures subobsolete on basal third; pygidium slightly longer than wide, densely, coarsely punctate on basal two-thirds, apical third nearly smooth except for a few minute punctures each side, a deep marginal groove each side on apical third extending to apex. Length 4–5.5 mm.

This is especially common on reptile and fish carrion.

c. *Saprinus conformis* LeConte   Plate XXIV, No. 8, p. 235

Broadly oval; black, shining. Pronotum with disk smooth, densely, finely punctate on sides and apical margin, a single row of punctures along base and a single larger one before the scutellum. Elytra with an irregular, triangular patch of coarse punctures on apical third; first dorsal stria extending almost to apex, second, third, and fourth gradually shorter, fourth arched at base to join sutural, which extends two-thirds to apex, continued to apex by punctures; humeral stria fine, internal subhumeral short, subapical. Propygidium strongly transverse, densely, finely punctate on apical two-thirds; pygidium as long as wide, densely, moderately coarsely punctate to middle, thence minutely, densely punctate to apex. Length 3.5–5 mm.

Genus V. *PACHYLOPUS* Erichson

Small, oblong-oval species; front of head distinctly margined; antennae inserted under front, fossae broad, deep, anterior to procoxae; prosternum not produced into a lobe anteriorly; pronotal marginal line rather coarse, entire; elytral striae obsolete apically, fifth usually lacking, fourth curved basally to join sutural; elytra densely punctate, at least on apical half; propygidium broad, moderately transverse, not arcuate.

Fig. 186

Fig. 186. Prosternum of *Saprinus assimilis*, the stria with a fovea (*f*) anteriorly.

KEY TO SPECIES

1. Prosternum compressed, striae entire, converging anteriorly (Fig. 188); metatibiae with two rows of spinules; elytra almost entirely punctate ....
   ....a. *fraternus*
   Prosternum compressed and carinate, its striae short, united anteriorly
   (Fig. 187); metatibiae with three rows of, or with many confused, spines;
   elytra only partially punctate 2
2. Pronotum with a narrow band of coarse punctures along sides and apex ....
   ....b. *patruelis*
   Pronotum smooth except for a narrow band of punctures along base ....
   ....c. *dimidiatipennis*

a. *Pachylopus fraternus* (Say)   Plate XXIV, No. 10, p. 235
   Broadly oval, convex; black, with a bronze tinge, not very shining.
Pronotum rather densely punctate, punctures on sides somewhat strigose;
disk almost smooth in a triangular area on basal third; marginal line coarse,
entire. Elytra entirely punctate except for a shining space near scutellum,
this space extending to fourth dorsal stria; first dorsal stria long, curved at
apex, second, third, and fourth gradually shorter, extending nearly to
middle, fourth joining the entire sutural; humeral subobsolete, nearly
joining internal subhumeral, which extends to apical quarter. Propygidium
broad, slightly transverse, densely punctate on apical two-thirds; pygidium
slightly longer than wide, densely, finely punctate, punctures obsolete on
apical third. Length 3–4 mm.
   This species is found especially along water beneath fish and reptile
carrion on sandy beaches.

b. *Pachylopus patruelis* (LeConte)   Plate XXIV, No. 9, p. 235
   Broadly oval, robust; black, with a bluish-green or slightly bronze lustre,
shining. Pronotum narrowly and coarsely punctate at base, sides, and
apex; disk smooth; marginal line broad, entire. Elytra with sparse, coarse
punctures on apical half, punctures extending beyond middle at suture;
dorsal striae more or less equal, extending to about middle, fourth arched
to join sutural, which is entire; humeral short, not attaining internal subhumeral, which is short and medial. Propygidium broad, densely, rather
finely punctate on entire surface; pygidium about as long as wide, coarsely,
densely punctate, punctures finer apically and with an area nearly smooth
at apical third. Length 3–4 mm.
   This species is usually on carrion.

c. *Pachylopus dimidiatipennis* (LeConte)   Plate XXIV, No. 11, p. 235
   Broadly oval, robust; black, shining; elytra usually black, but occasionally with the sides red. Pronotum smooth, with a narrow space of fine
punctures along base; marginal line broad, entire. Elytra sparsely punctate
apically, punctures extending to middle along suture; first dorsal stria
attaining middle, second and third longer, fourth equal to first, arched at

base, joining the entire sutural; humeral indistinct, not joining internal subhumeral, which is interrupted but extends to apex. Propygidium broad, densely, coarsely punctate, punctures somewhat finer on basal half; pygidium densely, rather coarsely punctate, finer apically. Length 3–4 mm.

This species is also found on carrion.

Genus VI. *PLATYLOMALUS* Cooman

Elongate, oblong, black, strongly depressed; head more or less retracted; mandibles not prominent; scutellum concealed; antennal cavities beneath middle of sides of prothorax, open beneath (Fig. 180), not covered by prosternal lobe, fossa at middle of deflexed sides of pronotum broad, deep; prosternum produced into a lobe anteriorly, not separated by a suture, without a lateral stria; elytral striae reduced in number and abbreviated; propygidium broad, nearly as long as pygidium; protibiae dilated at middle.

Platylomalus aequalis (Say)   Plate XXIV, No. 6, p. 235
Oblong, depressed; black, shining. Pronotum minutely, densely punctate, a single coarse one anterior to scutellum. Elytra entirely without striae, or with traces at base or at middle of two or three dorsals; a humeral stria often present; surface finely, sparsely punctate. Propygidium transverse, uniformly, finely, densely punctate; pygidium minutely punctate in female, coarsely rugose in male. Length 2.5–3 mm.

This species lives beneath bark and logs, especially of cottonwood and poplar.

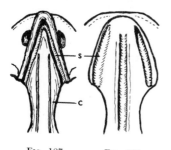

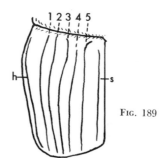

Fig. 189

FIG. 187   FIG. 188

Figs. 187–188. Portion of prosternum of *Pachylopus patruelis* (187) and of *P. fraternus* (188). *c,* carina; *s,* stria.

Fig. 189. Left elytron of *Hister*, viewed slightly obliquely from the side to show subhumeral stria (*h*); the five dorsal striae are numbered in the usual manner of the family. *s,* sutural (or sixth dorsal) stria.

Genus VII. *ISOLOMALUS* Lewis

Very small, elongate-oblong, subdepressed; head more or less retracted; mandibles not prominent; scutellum minute; antennal cavities beneath middle of sides of prothorax, open beneath, not covered by prosternal lobe, fossa at middle of deflexed sides of pronotum broad and deep; prosternum produced into a lobe anteriorly, partially separated by a suture, with a lateral stria (Fig. 177); elytral striae reduced in number and abbreviated; propygidium broad, nearly as long as pygidium.

Isolomalus bistriatus (Erichson)   Plate XXII, No. 17, p. 215

Oblong-oval, subdepressed; dark reddish brown to piceous, shining; antennae and legs reddish brown. Pronotal surface finely, densely punctate; marginal line fine, entire. Elytra more coarsely and sparsely punctate; first and second dorsal striae very short, basal, other striae absent. Propygidium transverse, minutely alutaceous, finely, densely punctate; pygidium coarsely, densely punctate in male, finely, densely so in female. Length 2 mm.

This species is found beneath bark of walnut, elm, and poplar logs and in tree fungi.

Genus VIII. *HISTER* Linné

Small to moderate-sized, broadly oval, convex; pronotum usually with two marginal striae, outer often abbreviated, sometimes absent; elytra rarely punctate, always striate, usually with five dorsals, sometimes six (Fig. 189), striae straight, fourth and sixth often much abbreviated, fifth always so; mesosternum emarginate at middle anteriorly; metatibiae widened at apex, with two rows of spines; protibiae with tarsal groove straight, not distinctly defined externally.

The genus as presented here is apparently composite, at least on the basis of male genitalia; however, until other morphological differences are known, it was thought best not to subdivide it here.

KEY TO SPECIES

1. Sides of pronotum beneath ciliate; elytra with arcuate red spots ...a. *arcuatus*
   Sides of pronotum beneath not ciliate 2
2. Subhumeral stria entire (Fig. 189) 3
   Subhumeral stria abbreviated or absent 8
3. Outer pronotal stria entire 4
   Outer pronotal stria absent or much abbreviated 7
4. Apical tooth of protibiae more prominent than second ....e. *merdarius*
   Apical tooth less prominent than second 5

5. Sutural stria extending from middle to apex of elytra ....b. *interruptus*
   Sutural stria short, only on apical third of elytra 6
6. Elytra with sutural stria longer than fifth ....d. *cadaverinus*
   Elytra with sutural stria shorter than fifth ....c. *immunis*
7. Outer pronotal stria present, usually just a short arc near anterior angles ....
   ....f. *foedatus*
   Outer pronotal stria entirely absent ....g. *cognatus*
8. Protibiae with more than three teeth ....h. *abbreviatus*
   Protibiae tridentate ....i. *depurator*

a. *Hister arcuatus* Say   Plate XXIII, No. 2, p. 231

Broadly oval; black, shining; each elytron with an arcuate, red space medially; meso- and metafemora and antennal club reddish. Pronotum with marginal striae converging at base and between them a confused intermediate stria extending usually beyond middle. Elytral first three dorsal striae entire, fourth short, basal, sutural extending from before middle to apex. Propygidium coarsely, sparsely punctate, with a feeble fovea each side; pygidium sparsely, rather finely punctate, smooth at apex. Length 5–6 mm.

b. *Hister interruptus* Beauvois   Plate XXIII, No. 4, p. 231

Broadly ovate, convex; black, shining; tarsi reddish brown. Pronotum with two entire marginal striae converging but not united at base; surface impunctate. Elytra with first three dorsal striae entire, fourth slightly abbreviated at base, fifth short, apical, sutural extending from middle to apex. Protibiae with five teeth. Mesosternum broadly but very shallowly emarginate apically. Propygidium sparsely, finely punctate; pygidium densely, finely punctate. Length 5.5–7 mm.

c. *Hister immunis* Erichson   Plate XXIII, No. 5, p. 231

Broadly oval, subconvex; piceous to black; legs dark reddish brown. Pronotum with both marginal striae entire, feebly converging to base. Elytra with first three dorsal striae entire, fourth slightly abbreviated at base, fifth and sutural very short, the latter sometimes obsolete; fifth longer than sutural. Propygidium sparsely, finely punctate; pygidium densely, finely punctate. Length 4.5–5.5 mm.

This species is found on carrion and dung, especially the latter.

d. *Hister cadaverinus* Hoffmann   Plate XXII, No. 18, p. 215

Broadly oval, subconvex; piceous to black, shining; antennae and protibiae dark reddish brown. Pronotal outer marginal striae entire, inner one distinctly abbreviated at base; disk minutely punctate, punctures becoming much coarser laterally. Elytra with first three dorsal striae entire, fourth slightly abbreviated at base, fifth confined to apical third, sutural slightly longer than fifth. Propygidium densely, very coarsely punctate; pygidium

PLATE XXIII
Family HISTERIDAE II

1. *Hololepta fossularis* Say (p. 222) Shining black; 7–10 mm.
2. *Hister arcuatus* Say (p. 229) Shining black; elytral maculae red; 5–6 mm.
3. *Hololepta quadridentata* (Fabricius) (p. 222) Shining black; 7–10 mm.
4. *Hister interruptus* Beauvois (p. 229) Shining black; 5.5–7 mm.
5. *H. immunis* Erichson (p. 229) Shining black; 4.5–5.5 mm.
6. *H. merdarius* Hoffmann (p. 232) Shining black; 5.5–7 mm.
7. *H. foedatus* LeConte (p. 232) Shining black; 4–6.5 mm.
8. *H. cognatus* LeConte (p. 232) Shining black; 2.5–3.5 mm.
9. *H. abbreviatus* Fabricius (p. 232) Shining black; 3.5–5.5 mm.
10. *H. depurator* Say (p. 232) Shining black; 5.5–6 mm.
11. *Atholus bimaculatus* (Linné) (p. 233) Shining black; elytral maculae red; 4.5–5.5 mm.
12. *A. sedecimstriatus* (Say) (p. 233) Shining black; 4–5 mm.
13. *A. falli* Bickhardt (p. 236) Shining piceous or black; 3.5–4.5 mm.
14. *A. americanus* Paykull (p. 236) Shining black; 3–4 mm.

MM | 0 | 10 | 20 | 30 | 40 | 50 | 60 | 70

PLATE XXIII

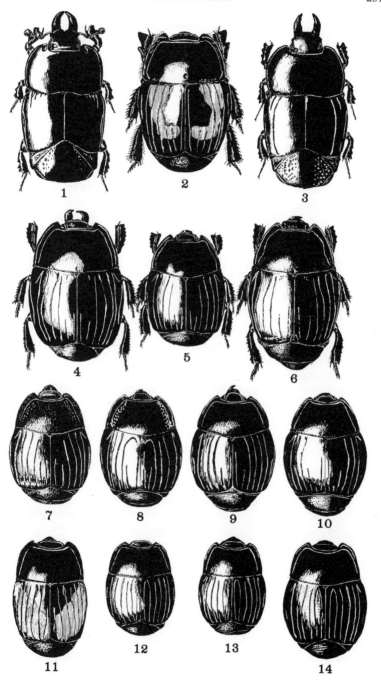

1

2

3

4

5

6

7

8

9

10

11

12

13

14

very densely, rather coarsely punctate. Protibiae with six teeth. Length 7–8.5 mm.

e. *Hister merdarius* Hoffmann   Plate XXIII, No. 6, p. 231

Oblong-oval, subconvex; black, shining. Pronotum with both marginal striae entire, usually united basally; disk sparsely punctate laterally. Elytra with four entire dorsal striae, fourth sometimes abbreviated at base, fifth and sutural extending from behind middle to apex. Propygidium coarsely, sparsely punctate; pygidium coarsely, very densely punctate. Length 5.5–7 mm.

This species is most common in the North Central States.

f. *Hister foedatus* LeConte   Plate XXIII, No. 7, p. 231

Broadly oval, subconvex; piceous to black, shining; antennal club and tarsi dark reddish brown. Pronotum with outer marginal stria very short, only in anterior angle; inner stria usually abbreviated at base; surface minutely punctate, more coarsely so laterally. Elytra with first three dorsal striae entire, fourth slightly abbreviated at base, fifth one-third and sutural one-half length of elytra. Propygidium and pygidium densely, rather coarsely punctate. Protibiae with six or more teeth. Length 4–6.5 mm.

This species is usually on carrion.

g. *Hister cognatus* LeConte   Plate XXIII, No. 8, p. 231

Oblong-oval, subconvex; piceous, shining; antennae and legs dark reddish brown. Pronotal outer marginal stria entire, inner one abbreviated at base, confused by punctures which also extend forward on its inner side. Elytra with first three dorsal striae entire, fourth arcuate, nearly entire, fifth short, apical, sutural variable in length, extending at least from before middle to apex. Propygidium sparsely, coarsely punctate; pygidium finely, densely punctate, extreme apex smooth. Protibiae with five teeth, apical tooth very small. Length 2.5–3.5 mm.

h. *Hister abbreviatus* Fabricius   Plate XXIII, No. 9, p. 231

Broadly oval, convex; black, shining; antennae and legs piceous. Pronotal inner marginal stria nearly entire, outer one extending to middle, sometimes shorter; surface minutely punctate. Elytra with two subhumeral striae, overlapping near middle, inner apical, outer basal; first four dorsal striae entire, fifth short, apical, sutural from before middle to apex. Propygidium sparsely, coarsely punctate; pygidium finely, very densely punctate. Protibiae with four small teeth, apical one bifid. Length 3.5–5.5 mm.

This species is found especially in cold-blooded vertebrate carrion, but also on fungi and dung.

i. *Hister depurator* Say   Plate XXIII, No. 10, p. 231

Broadly oval, convex; black, shining; antennae and spines of legs reddish brown. Pronotal outer marginal stria variable in length, usually attaining middle, inner stria entire. Elytra with first three dorsal striae entire, fourth apical, rarely attaining middle, fifth a trace, sutural from middle to apex. Propygidium coarsely punctate on basal half, punctures very fine and dense on apical portion; pygidium densely, finely punctate. Protibiae tridentate, apical tooth prominent. Length 5.5–6 mm.

This beetle lives especially in fungi and excrement.

Genus IX. *ATHOLUS* Thomson

Small, broadly oval, convex; pronotum usually with one entire marginal stria, the outer marginal, when present, confined to apical half; elytra finely punctate and striate, with five dorsal striae and sutural entire or nearly so, fifth usually joined to sutural at base; mesosternum anteriorly truncate or broadly rounded at middle; metatibiae somewhat dilated apically, with two rows of spines; protibiae with tarsal groove straight, not distinctly defined externally.

KEY TO SPECIES

1. Epipleura narrow, unistriate; elytra each with a large red spot . . . .
. . . . .a. *bimaculatus*
  Epipleura broader, bistriate; elytra entirely black 2
2. Elytra with two subhumeral striae . . . . .b. *sedecimstriatus*
  Elytra without subhumeral striae 3
3. Pronotum smooth; sutural elytral stria abbreviated basally, not joined to fifth at base . . . . .c. *americanus*
  Pronotum distinctly punctate; sutural elytral stria entire, joined to fifth at base . . . . .d. *falli*

a. *Atholus bimaculatus* (Linné)   Plate XXIII, No. 11, p. 231
  Oblong-oval, convex; black, shining; elytra with outer diagonal half orange-red. Pronotum with only one marginal stria, abbreviated at apex; finely punctate on disk; anterior angles with a broad, shallow impression. Elytra with five entire dorsal striae, sutural extending before middle; subhumeral absent. Protibiae tridentate. Length 4.5–5.5 mm.

These beetles are found mostly in cow dung.

b. *Atholus sedecimstriatus* (Say)   Plate XXIII, No. 12, p. 231
  Broadly oval, convex; black, shining; antennae and legs fuscous. Entire upper surface minutely, sparsely punctate. Pronotum with one entire marginal stria, outer one lacking. Elytra with five entire dorsal striae, fifth arching at base and joining sutural; two subhumeral striae present, outer one almost entire, inner one confined to apical half. Propygidium coarsely, rather sparsely punctate; pygidium minutely, sparsely punctate. Protibiae tridentate. Length 4–5 mm.

PLATE XXIV
Family HISTERIDAE III

1. *Teretrius americanus* (LeConte) (p. 222) — Shining black; 1.5–2.5 mm.
2. *Platysoma carolinum* (Paykull) (p. 236) — Piceous to black; 3–4 mm.
3. *P. lecontei* Marseul (p. 237) — Shining black; antennae and legs fuscous; 2.5–3 mm.
4. *Phelister subrotundus* Say (p. 237) — Shining reddish brown to blackish; 2–3 mm.
5. *Saprinus pennsylvanicus* Paykull (p. 224) — Deep metallic green or bronze; 4–5 mm.
6. *Platylomalus aequalis* (Say) (p. 227) — Shining black; 2.5–3 mm.
7. *Saprinus assimilis* Paykull (p. 224) — Shining black; 4–5.5 mm.
8. *S. conformis* LeConte (p. 225) — Shining black; 3.5–5 mm.
9. *Pachylopus patruelis* (LeConte) (p. 226) — Shining black, with a greenish or bronzy sheen; 3–4.5 mm.
10. *P. fraternus* (Say) (p. 226) — Black, with a bronze tinge; 3–4 mm.
11. *P. dimidiatipennis* (LeConte) (p. 226) — Shining black; elytral maculae red, often absent; 3–4 mm.

Family LYCIDAE I

12. *Dictyopterus aurora* (Herbst) (p. 243) — Deep orange; pronotum medially blackish; 6.5–11 mm.
13. *Celetes basalis* LeConte (p. 243) — Dark brown; sides of pronotum and base of elytra yellowish; 6.5–9 mm.
14. *Calochromus perfacetus* (Say) (p. 247) — Black; sides of pronotum orangeish; 6–10.5 mm.

MM 0 10 20 30 40 50 60 70

PLATE XXIV

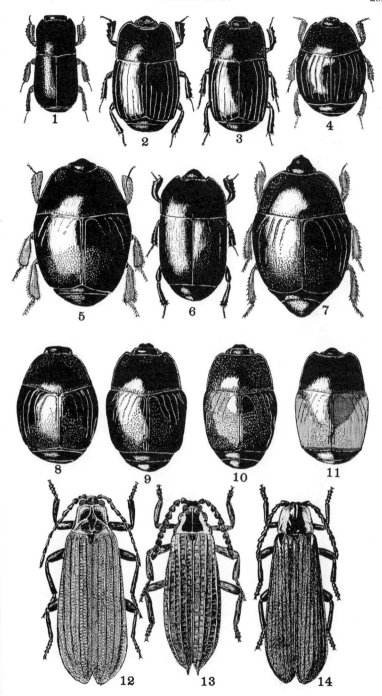

c. *Atholus americanus* Paykull   Plate XXIII, No. 14, p. 231

Broadly oval, slightly convex; black, somewhat shining; antennae and legs piceous. Both pronotum and elytra minutely, sparsely punctate. Pronotal outer marginal stria extremely variable, from a mere arc at anterior angles to almost entire, inner one entire. Elytra with five entire dorsal striae, fifth curved at base and often joining sutural, which is slightly abbreviated basally. Propygidium sparsely, coarsely punctate; pygidium minutely alutaceous with fine, sparse punctures. Protibiae tridentate, apical tooth prominent. Length 3–4 mm.

This species is found in logs and under bark in low, moist woodlands.

d. *Atholus falli* Bickhardt   Plate XXIII, No. 13, p. 231

Broadly oval, subconvex; piceous to black, shining; antennae and legs dark reddish brown. Pronotum and elytra minutely but distinctly punctate, pronotum often with a row of coarse punctures across base. Pronotal outer marginal stria short, confined to apical portion, inner one entire, recurved basally. Elytra with five entire dorsal striae, fifth arcuate basally and joining entire sutural. Propygidium densely, moderately coarsely punctate; pygidium densely, finely punctate. Length 3.5–4.5 mm.

Genus X. *PLATYSOMA* Leach

Small, oblong-ovate, convex or slightly flattened forms; head retracted; antennal cavities beneath sides of front, not covered by prosternal lobe; fossa deep, transverse, beneath anterior angles of prothorax; scutellum small; inner pronotal marginal stria absent; elytra with first three dorsal striae entire, fourth and fifth and sutural abbreviated on apical half, sutural sometimes absent; prosternum produced into a broad lobe anteriorly, not striate; protibiae with a deep, well-defined, sinuous tarsal groove (Fig. 184); meso- and metatibiae armed with two to four teeth or short spines.

KEY TO SPECIES

Pronotum minutely punctate; sutural stria of elytra extending anterior to middle
....a. *carolinum*
Pronotum coarsely punctate laterally; sutural stria confined to extreme apex or absent ....b. *lecontei*

a. *Platysoma carolinum* (Paykull)   Plate XXIV, No. 2, p. 235

Broadly oval, subdepressed; black or piceous, shining; antennae, legs, and abdomen dark reddish brown. Pronotum minutely punctate; outer marginal stria entire. Elytra with first three dorsal striae entire, fourth and fifth apical, nearly attaining the middle, sutural somewhat longer; surface minutely, densely punctate. Propygidium and pygidium coarsely, rather densely punctate, the former nearly smooth basally, the latter nearly smooth apically. Protibiae with five fine teeth; mesotibiae with four, metatibiae with three, short spines. Length 3–4 mm.

b. *Platysoma lecontei* Marseul   Plate XXIV, No. 3, p. 235
Oblong-oval, depressed; black, shining; antennae and legs fuscous. Pronotum minutely punctate, rather coarsely punctate laterally, marginal stria entire. Elytra with three entire dorsal striae, fourth confined to apical half, fifth shorter, sutural usually as long as fifth but often absent. Propygidium coarsely, sparsely punctate, transversely impressed, especially laterally; pygidium coarsely, densely punctate except at extreme apex, where punctures are minute. Protibiae with four teeth; mesotibiae with three spines, metatibiae with two short ones. Length 2.5–3 mm.

This species is found beneath bark of logs and stumps, on fungi, and at sap.

Genus XI. *PHELISTER* Marseul

Small, broadly oval, subconvex; pronotum with only one marginal stria, which is very close to margin; elytra with five dorsal striae and a sutural, usually first five entire, subhumeral stria on apical half; prosternum striate, with a median lobe anteriorly; mesosternum prominent anteriorly; protibiae with tarsal groove straight, not distinct.

Phelister subrotundus Say   Plate XXIV, No. 4, p. 235
Broadly oval, subconvex; dark reddish brown to blackish, shining; antennae and legs reddish brown. Pronotum finely punctate, punctures becoming more coarse laterally, and a row of coarse punctures basally; a small fovea before scutellum; marginal stria distinct but close to margin. Elytra usually with five entire dorsal striae, fifth sometimes confined to apical half, sutural extending anterior to middle; surface finely, densely punctate. Propygidium moderately coarsely and sparsely punctate; pygidium very densely, finely punctate. Protibiae with many fine teeth. Length 2–3 mm.

This species occurs under bark as well as on fungi.

Family LYCIDAE

The Net-winged Beetles

In woodlands, especially where there is sufficient water to support a luxuriant growth of shrubs, these beetles can be found in numbers, resting on the leaves or flying with a slow, mothlike flight. Some of the larger species are prettily colored and have widely expanded elytra; others look somewhat like some of the diurnal fireflies (lampyrids) that fly in the same sort of habitat. Usually, however, in this family the elytra, in addition to being more or less broadened, are covered by an intricate network of raised lines and lack epipleura. The head is often prolonged in front of the eyes into a long, slender beak, barely visible from above; antennae usually quite flattened, with broad segments; mesocoxae widely separated (Fig. 190). This latter characteristic will distinguish this family from their close relatives, the Lampyridae.

While the adults seem to subsist largely on the juices of decomposing vegetable remains, such as decaying wood, they occasionally feed upon small insects.

KEY TO GENERA

1. Head porrect, mouthparts visible from above; scutellum not emarginate ....V. *Calochromus* (p. 246)
   Head deflexed, mouthparts not visible from above; scutellum emarginate at apex 2
2. Antennae and legs only slightly flattened, the former with second segment no shorter than wide; prothoracic spiracles not prominent; procoxae contiguous or nearly so 3
   Antennae and legs strongly flattened, the former with the second segment transverse, very short and inconspicuous, nearly concealed in apex of first segment; prothoracic spiracles usually prominent; procoxae usually well separated 4
3. Pronotum with two more or less distinct longitudinal carinae enclosing a central cell ....III. *Dictyopterus* (p. 243)
   Pronotum without a longitudinal carina ....IV. *Plateros* (p. 243)
4. Elytra strongly widened posteriorly; maxillary palpi with last segment large, strongly transverse; antennae subserrate in both sexes; pronotal apical margin rounded (Fig. 191) ....I. *Calopteron* (p. 239)
   Elytra nearly parallel-sided or feebly widened posteriorly; maxillary palpi with last segment longer than wide; antennae usually flabellate in male (Fig. 22), subserrate in female (Fig. 20); pronotum with apical margin produced into a subtriangular median lobe (Fig. 192) ....II. *Celetes* (p. 242)

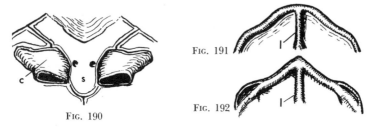

Fig. 190. Mesosternum (*s*) and mesocoxae (*c*) of a lycid (*Calopteron*), the latter widely separated by the former.

Figs. 191–192. Apical margin of pronotum of *Calopteron* (191) and of *Celetes* (192). *l*, anterior portion of longitudinal carina.

Genus I. *CALOPTERON* Guérin

Moderate-sized, subtriangular beetles, with sides diverging posteriorly from apex of pronotum to apical fourth of elytra; head small, when retracted concealed from above by anterior margin of pronotum, antennal prominences elevated, longitudinally impressed; pronotum small, subpentagonal, all sides reflexed; disk with an entire, strongly elevated, median longitudinal carina; scutellum emarginate at apex; elytra each with four discal costae, intervals each with a single row of transverse or subquadrate cells, rows becoming more or less double toward apex; antennae approximate at base, strongly compressed, subserrate in both sexes.

KEY TO SPECIES

1. Elytra with discal costae nearly equally elevated, the dorsal outline of elytra when viewed from the side undulating, with a depression before apical black band and a less distinct one near basal third; elytra bands with a distinct bluish tinge, the premedian band usually absent, if present then it is not produced along suture toward scutellum ....a. *terminale*
   Elytra with first and third discal costae less strongly elevated than other two, dorsal outline of elytra not undulating; elytral bands without a bluish tinge, premedian band when present frequently produced along suture toward scutellum 2
2. Metasternum entirely black; antennae with second segment black, following segments usually not at all paler beneath ....c. *discrepans*
   Metasternum more or less rufous at middle anteriorly; antennae with second segment fulvous or brownish, and several of the following segments usually partly fulvous beneath ....b. *reticulatum*

a. *Calopteron terminale* (Say)   Plate XXV, No. 3, p. 241

Rather narrowly triangular, depressed; black; pronotum with lateral edges dull fulvous; elytra bright fulvous, apical third blue-black, very rarely with a trace of a premedian band. Elytra with discal costae nearly equally elevated, cells less strongly transverse, larger, somewhat irregularly

PLATE XXV
Family LYCIDAE II

1. *Calopteron reticulatum* (Fabricius) (p. 242) — Yellowish, with black or blue-black markings; elytral basal band narrowed laterally; 9.5–18 mm.

2. *C. discrepans* (Newman) (p. 242) — As above, but elytral basal band uniform in width; 9.5–15 mm.

3. *C. terminale* (Say) (p. 239) — Yellowish, with black or blue-black markings; 8.5–16 mm.

4. *Plateros lictor* (Newman) (p. 246) — Black; pronotal margins dull yellow; 3.5–8 mm.

5. *P. canaliculatus* (Say) (p. 246) — Black; pronotal margins orange-yellow; 3.5–7.5 mm.

MM | 0 | 10 | 20 | 30 | 40 | 50 | 60 | 70

PLATE XXV   241

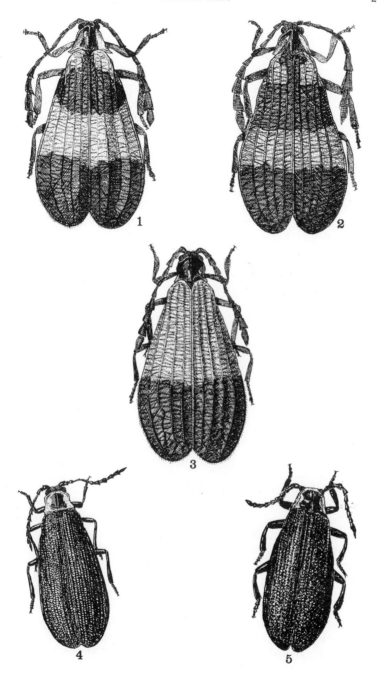

subdivided into double series near apex; elytra when viewed from side undulating, with a broad depression before apical band. Length 8.5–16 mm.

As in the two following members of the genus, the adults are found in moist woods, resting on flowers or foliage.

b. *Calopteron reticulatum* (Fabricius) Plate XXV, No. 1, p. 241

Broadly ovate or subtriangular, depressed; black; pronotum and elytra ochraceous, former with a broad, median black vitta, latter with apical two-fifths black and usually with a premedian black fascia that, as a rule, extends along suture to scutellum; metasternum at middle of base more or less rufous; legs and sides of abdomen sometimes fulvous; antennae with second segment pale, as are the undersurfaces of several succeeding segments. Pronotum more than one-half wider than long. Elytral second and fourth costae more strongly elevated than others; intervals each with a single row of cells, becoming somewhat irregular apically but not definitely dual. Length 9.5–18 mm.

The adults are found mostly on leaves of shrubs, but they also frequent flowers.

c. *Calopteron discrepans* (Newman) Plate XXV, No. 2, p. 241

Broadly ovate or triangular, depressed; black; pronotal margins sometimes narrowly fulvous; elytra with premedian black fascia with anterior margin squarely transverse, so that the fascia is as broad at sides as at suture, sutural extension expanding as it nears base, widest at scutellar region, rarely this extension or the entire fascia may be completely absent; legs with femora rarely fulvous basally; antennae entirely black. Pronotum not quite one-half wider than long. Elytra with second and fourth costae more strongly elevated than others; intervals with a single row of cells, becoming irregular apically but not distinctly dual. Length 9.5–15 mm.

For the most part, adults are to be found in moist woods on leaves of shrubs.

Genus II. *CELETES* Newman

Small, elongate species, with sides subparallel or only feebly widened posteriorly; head small, only partly concealed by pronotum when retracted, eyes largely exposed; antennal prominences rather feebly elevated, longitudinally divided medially; pronotum transverse, subpentagonal, sides broadly reflexed, basally narrowly and abruptly elevated, apex gradually so, disk with an entire median longitudinal carina; scutellum emarginate at apex; elytra each with four discal costae which are sometimes partially abbreviated, each interval with a single row of subquadrate or irregular cells; antennae approximate at base, strongly compressed, half as long as body, flabellate in male (Fig. 22), serrate in female (Fig. 20).

Celetes basalis LeConte   Plate XXIV, No. 13, p. 235

Elongate-oblong, depressed; piceous to black; pronotum on sides and femora basally fulvous; elytra each with a small, subtriangular, fulvous macula on humerus. Pronotum three-fifths again as wide as long, sides widened to base; disk with a moderately prominent carina. Elytra slightly widened posteriorly; disk with second and fourth costae entire, attaining apex, first and third slightly abbreviated apically; intervals with a single row of subquadrate cells, the floors of which are feebly shining. Length 6.5–9 mm.

Frequently this species is found on the foliage of honey locust.

Genus III. *DICTYOPTERUS* Mulsant

Rather small, elongate, subparallel beetles, widened only slightly posteriorly; head deflexed; mouthparts nearly vertical, concealed from above; antennae simple, nearly filiform in male, subdepressed in female, second and third segments together about as long as fourth; antennal insertions approximate, antennal prominence strongly elevated, divided by a longitudinal impression; pronotum small, at least one-half wider than long, base, apex, and sides reflexed, sides more broadly so, disk with two entire longitudinal carinae which are confluent at base and apex and which enclose a rhomboidal cell at center, each side of disk divided by an oblique carina extending from the cell to sides at basal third; scutellum emarginate; elytra each with five or six prominent costae, intervals with a double row of oblong cells.

Dictyopterus aurora (Herbst)   Plate XXIV, No. 12, p. 235

Elongate-oblong, slender, depressed; piceous; pronotum on sides and elytra dull orange-red; scutellum and legs blackish. Front of head not impressed behind antennal prominence; eyes small. Pronotum with discal carinae well defined, widest at base; anterior angles broadly rounded; sides subparallel to basal third, thence expanding to the acute posterior angles. Elytral pubescence short laterally; disks nearly glabrous, each with four prominent costae and ten rows of oblong cells. Antennae in male more than half as long as body, in female shorter. Length 6.5–11 mm.

Especially in early spring the adults may be found on old logs and decaying tree stumps.

Genus IV. *PLATEROS* Bourgeois

Small, oblong-ovate, depressed forms, most easily distinguishable in that the pronotum lacks carinae; head deflexed, with distinct antennal promi-

PLATE XXV–A
Family LAMPYRIDAE I

1. *Pyractomena angulata* (Say) (p. 251)

   Brown and pale yellow; pronotum with two reddish maculae; 8–15 mm.

2. *Photinus pyralis* (Linné) (p. 254)

   Fuscous and pale yellow; pronotum with two smooth, reddish maculae; 10–14 mm.

3. *Ellychnia corrusca* (Linné) (p. 250)

   Black; pronotal vittae yellow, bordered within with reddish; 10–14 mm.

MM 0 10 20 30 40 50 60 70

PLATE XXV–A 245

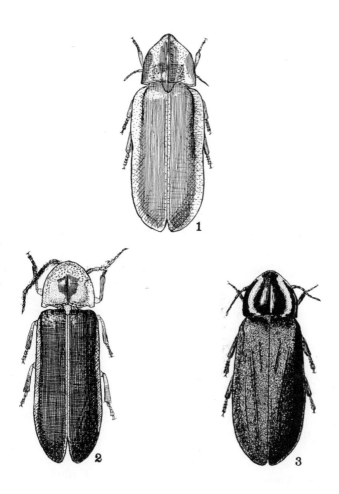

nences; pronotum widest at base, broader than long, all margins reflexed, especially apical one, discal median impression often deep; elytra with four discal costae, intervals with double rows of cells.

KEY TO SPECIES

Eyes small, separated above by about one and one-half times their length; elytral costae evident ....a. *canaliculatus*
Eyes large, separated above by less than their length; elytral costae scarcely distinguishable from the intervals ....b. *lictor*

a. *Plateros canaliculatus* (Say)   Plate XXV, No. 5, p. 241

Elongate, rather robust, depressed; black; pronotum orange-yellow, with a black median area that reaches from base nearly to apex; femora sometimes yellowish at base. Pronotal sides scarcely emarginate; disk entirely minutely alutaceous, anterior lateral impression shallow, posterior one elongate, transverse, median carina lacking. Elytral costae low but evident, inner ones entire or nearly so, outer ones abbreviated apically; entire surface minutely alutaceous, the inner cells regular, subquadrate, the outer ones rather irregular in shape. Length 3.5–7.5 mm.

This species is found in moist woods about old stumps and logs.

b. *Plateros lictor* (Newman)   Plate XXV, No. 4, p. 241

Elongate, rather robust, depressed; black; pronotum variable, usually dull yellow, with a black median macula that attains base but not apex, sometimes nearly entirely black, or with median macula small (especially in southern examples); elytra rarely with humerus fulvous. Pronotal sides broadly emarginate behind middle; disk smooth medially, coarsely rugose laterally, each side with two deep impressions, median carina lacking. Elytral costae not prominent, scarcely distinguishable from the elevated intervals, basal; entire surface minutely alutaceous, cells more or less regular and subquadrate. Length 3.5–8 mm.

This is the most common and widespread member of the genus, its range reaching from the Atlantic to the Pacific coast.

Genus V. *CALOCHROMUS* Guérin

Rather small, flattened beetles; head porrect, eyes small, mouthparts visible from above; antennal prominence very feeble or lacking; antennae slender, feebly compressed, well separated at base, second segment not transverse; pronotum with an oblique elevation each side joining lateral margin near posterior angle, sides not reflexed, median longitudinal impression narrow, striaform, usually entire; elytra punctate or finely rugose, costae feeble or lacking, sides somewhat widened posteriorly.

Calochromus perfacetus (Say)   Plate XXIV, No. 14, p. 235

Oblong-ovate, rather slender, depressed; black, slightly shining; pronotum with sides (and rarely entire disk) fulvous; sparsely pubescent above. Front of head somewhat prolonged before eyes. Pronotum trapezoidal or sub-pentagonal, widest at base, transverse; sides nearly straight. Elytra very finely, densely, rugosely punctate; costae visible but quite feeble. Antennae of male, compressed, subserrate, and distal segments as shining as basal ones Length 6–10.5 mm.

The adults occur on leaves of shrubs and on flowers.

Family LAMPYRIDAE

The Fireflies

The ability to produce light places the lampyrids in an almost unique position among insects. They are singular in the fact that they can produce light, flashing it off and on at will, whereas the other luminescent insects glow continuously. Either or both the adult and larva may possess this power to oxidize a complex organic compound, luciferin, by use of an enzyme, luciferase, in the presence of oxygen, magnesium ions, and adenosin triphosphate, the result of this process being "cold light," without sensible heat. The light-producing organs are on the ventral side of one or several of the posterior abdominal segments, occupying either the entire segment or small areas laterally or medially. As these beetles are mostly nocturnal in habit, this ability to flash their light off and on is employed by the male in finding the female, which usually does not fly actively or may even be completely wingless. Species may be distinguished in flight by the color of the light, number of flashes, and length of flash. The larvae as well as the wingless females are known as "glowworms" and live on the ground or on low herbs and grasses. They are predaceous in both adult and larval stages, feeding on other insects, soft-bodied larvae, snails, and even on each other.

This family may be separated from other families of beetles by the following characters: antennae usually approximate at base; head nearly covered by pronotum; pronotum with margins thin and widely expanded; a distinct epipleuron beneath the edge of each elytron (Plate II); elytra when present soft (not heavily sclerotized), with broad margins; light organs, when not glowing, yellowish or greenish; eight abdominal segments, visible first one entire; mesocoxae contiguous (Fig. 193); metacoxae conical, prominent, not covered by femora in repose; tarsal segments 5–5–5, none of segments rudimentary or reduced.

KEY TO GENERA

1. Head completely covered by pronotum; legs usually short, stout, and compressed 2
   Head visible from above, not completely covered by pronotum; legs usually long, slender, and not compressed; antennae simple ......
   ....VI. *Photuris* (p. 255)

2. Eyes small; light organs feeble or wanting; ventral abdominal segments of male without stigma-like pores 3
   Eyes large (larger in male than female); light organs well developed; male with strongly marked stigma-like pores (Fig. 194) 5
3. Antennae strongly compressed, second segment transverse, minute, about one-fourth as long as third (Fig. 195) ....I. *Lucidota* (p. 249)
   Antennae feebly compressed, second segment longer than wide, at least one-third as long as third (Fig. 196) 4
4. Light organs absent; third antennal segment shorter than fourth; size large, 10 mm. or more ....II. *Ellychnia* (p. 250)
   Light organs present but feeble; third antennal segment as long as or slightly longer than fourth; size small, 5 mm. or less. III. *Pyropyga* (p. 250)
5. Pronotum with a low median carina; light organs of female on sides of ventral segments of abdomen ....IV. *Pyractomena* (p. 251)
   Pronotum not carinate medially, frequently grooved; light organs of female medial on ventral segments of abdomen ......V. *Photinus* (p. 251)

Genus I. *LUCIDOTA* Laporte

Small, oblong, depressed species; head covered by pronotum; antennae broadly compressed, not serrate, gradually narrowed on outer side, second segment short, transverse, last segment elongate, simple; light organs feebly or not at all developed, if present they appear as small yellowish spots on last abdominal sternite of female or last two sternites of male. This genus is composed of diurnal species.

KEY TO SPECIES

Elytra finely granulate, with four or five fine costae which are abbreviated on apical third ....a. *atra*
Elytra coarsely granulate-punctate ....b. *punctata*

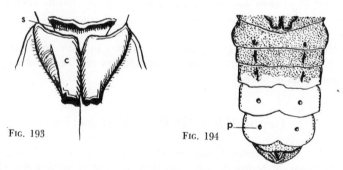

FIG. 193   FIG. 194

Fig. 193. Mesosternum (*s*) and mesocoxae (*c*) of a lampyrid (*Photuris*), the former not visible between the contiguous coxae.
Fig. 194. Abdomen of male *Photinus pyralis* (ventral view). The unstippled portion of the segments indicates the location of the light organs. *p*, stigma-like pores.

a. *Lucidota atra* (Fabricius)   Plate XXVI, No. 6, p. 253

Elongate-oblong, depressed; black; pronotum with sides and apex dull
yellow, a reddish or orange spot between margin and black median space.
Pronotum triangular, apex rounded. Elytra finely granulate, each with four
feeble costae, which are obsolete at apical third. Light organs feebly developed. Length 8–11 mm.

This species is usually found in open woods on leaves and trunks of trees.
When captured, the adult exudes a milky fluid with a strong odor from the
joints of the legs and sides of abdomen.

b. *Lucidota punctata* LeConte   Plate XXVI, No. 1, p. 253

Oblong, rather slender, depressed; black, opaque, with sparse, grayish
pubescence; pronotal disk and basal margin black, remainder of surface
reddish yellow, posterior angles usually dusky. Elytra coarsely granulate-
punctate. Light organs feebly developed. Length 5.5–6 mm.

The adults may be taken by sweeping low herbs.

Genus II. *ELLYCHNIA* Dejean

Moderate-sized, narrow species; head covered by pronotum; last segment
of maxillary palpi triangular, apex acute; abdomen without light organs,
last dorsal segment truncate at apex, not emarginate; fourth tarsal segment
long, lobed; tarsal claws simple.

These species are diurnal.

Ellychnia corrusca (Linné)   Plate XXV–A, No. 3, p. 245

Oblong-oval; black or rusty black; pronotum with disk and side margins
black, a reddish and yellow vitta between disk and side margins. Pronotum
nearly ovate, apex rounded. Elytra finely granulate, thinly covered with
fine, yellowish, prostrate pubescence, each with three or four indistinct
costae. Light organs lacking. Length 10–14 mm.

The adults occur in spring on trunks of trees in open woods, especially
on maple at or near flowing sap; in autumn they may be found on flowers
of goldenrod or asters.

Genus III. *PYROPYGA* Motschulsky

Rather small, narrow forms; antennae moderately wide and compressed,
second segment feebly elongate, one-third as long as third, third segment
as long as or slightly longer than fourth; last dorsal abdominal segment in
both sexes broadly truncate, with rounded angles; light organs feebly developed.

FIG. 195

FIG. 196

Figs. 195–196. Basal segments of antenna of *Lucidota* (195) and of *Ellychnia* (196), the segments appropriately numbered.

Pyropyga decipiens (Harris)   Plate XXVI, No. 5, p. 253

Elongate-oval, subdepressed; black or rusty black; pronotum with wide, pale-reddish-yellow margins. Pronotum apically rounded, base truncate, sides more or less suddenly reflexed; surface scabrose apically, disk obsoletely carinate before basal transverse impression. Elytra confluently, rather finely granulate, with two feeble costae. Length 5–7 mm.

Genus IV. *PYRACTOMENA* Melsheimer

Small, oblong, depressed species; head completely covered by pronotum; antennae narrow, not serrate, second segment feebly elongate, more than one-half as long as third, third segment as long as fourth. Pronotum medially with a low carina, sides broadly reflexed. Light organs well developed in both sexes, in male on fifth and sixth abdominal sternites and marked each side about halfway between middle and side by a large, round pore; in female they are on the sides of the segments and marked by a distinct pore, the middle of the segment piceous.

Pyractomena angulata (Say)   Plate XXV–A, No. 1, p. 245

Elongate-oblong, depressed; blackish brown; pronotum yellowish, with a dark median area and margins, the yellow areas basally tinged with rose; elytral sutural and narrow lateral margins pale yellowish. Pronotum with anterior margin obtusely angulate. Elytra finely granulate, not punctate, each with two or three distinct costae. Abdominal sternites of female dull yellow, spotted with dusky. Length 8–15 mm.

Genus V. *PHOTINUS* Laporte

Elongate, rather slender beetles; antennae slender, feebly compressed, second segment one-half to one-third as long as third; pronotum entirely covering head and not carinate medially, anterior margin obtusely rounded; light organs well developed, largest in male, occupying all the ventral ab-

PLATE XXVI
Family LAMPYRIDAE II

1. *Lucidota punctata* LeConte (p. 250) — Blackish; pronotal margin pale yellow and fuscous, disk with two red maculae; 5.5–6 mm.

2. *Photinus marginellus* LeConte (p. 254) — Light brownish and pale yellow; pronotum with a red macula each side of middle; 6–8 mm.

3, 4. *P. scintillans* (Say) (p. 255) — Brownish and pale yellow; pronotum with a red macula each side of middle; female (No. 4) wingless; 5.5–8 mm.

5. *Pyropyga decipiens* (Harris) (p. 251) — Black; pronotal margins yellow, with an orange macula each side; 5–7 mm.

6. *Lucidota atra* (Fabricius) (p. 250) — Black; pronotum with two reddish maculae on disk, margins yellowish; 8–11 mm.

7. *Photuris pennsylvanica* (DeGeer) (p. 255) — Fuscous and dull yellowish; pronotum with two deep-red maculae; 11–15 mm.

8. *Photinus consanguineus* LeConte (p. 254) — Deep brown, margins pale yellowish; pronotum with two faint reddish maculae; legs gray-brown; 8–12.5 mm.

Family CANTHARIDAE I

9. *Trypherus latipennis* (Germar) (p. 264) — Dark brown, with yellow markings; legs pale yellow; 6–7 mm.

10. *Cantharis fraxini* Say (p. 262) — Black, shining; 4–5 mm.

11. *C. lineola* Fabricius (p. 262) — Blackish; pronotum largely orange-yellow; 4–6.5 mm.

12. *C. bilineatus* Say (p. 264) — Black and dull orangeish; 6–8 mm.

13. *C. nigriceps* LeConte (p. 263) — Black and pale yellowish; 4–6 mm.

14. *Podabrus rugosulus* LeConte (p. 258) — Black; front of head and sides of pronotum dull orangeish; 7–8 mm.

15. *Cantharis impressus* LeConte (p. 264) — Piceous; front dull brownish; pronotal sides yellow; 5–7 mm.

16. *C. dentiger* LeConte (p. 259) — Fuscous; pronotal sides yellow or orange; elytra sides dusky; 8–9 mm.

MM 0 10 20 30 40 50 60 70

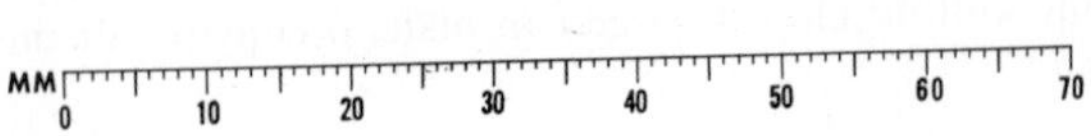

PLATE XXVI

253

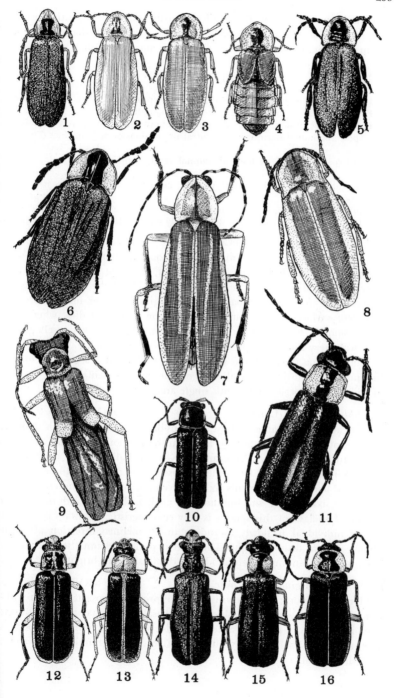

dominal segment behind the third or fourth and with stigmatic pores on the fifth and sixth segments; smaller in female, located medially on the segments, but the stigmatic pores are scarcely or not at all visible.

KEY TO SPECIES

1. Fourth ventral abdominal segment entirely deep brown ......a. *consanguineus*
   Fourth ventral abdominal segment yellowish, at least in part 2
2. Large species (9 mm. or more); disk of pronotum reddish, with a large black spot; abdominal sternites with ventral impressions of male distinct (Fig. 194)
   ....b. *pyralis*
   Small species (8 mm. or less); abdominal ventral impressions of male obsolete
  3
3. Pronotal median blackish spot narrow, tapering basally; female with long elytra and wings ....c. *marginellus*
   Pronotal median blackish spot parallel-sided, usually as broad as roseate area; female without wings, elytra short, widely separated at suture ..d. *scintillans*

a. *Photinus consanguineus* LeConte   Plate XXVI, No. 8, p. 253

Elongate, rather slender; dusky or piceous; pronotum yellowish, with a broad, elongate black spot on basal half, this spot bordered with rose laterally; elytral suture and side margins pale yellow, the latter broadly so. Pronotum convex, with broad lateral margins; anterior margin broadly rounded; surface coarsely punctate except on middle of disk, where it is nearly smooth; median impressed line absent. Elytra finely, densely granulate, with very short, fine pubescence. Length 8–12.5 mm.

The male has the sixth and seventh ventral abdominal segments entirely luminous; female sixth ventral segment luminous in median third or more of width. This species emits both single and double flashes of light.

b. *Photinus pyralis* (Linné)   Plate XXV–A, No. 2, p. 245

Elongate-oblong, rather robust; piceous-brown; pronotum with margins dull yellowish, disk roseate with a median black spot; elytral side margins and suture pale yellow. Pronotum convex, medially with a short longitudinal impressed line. Elytra finely, densely rugose. Length 10–14 mm.

Ventral abdominal segments six and seven are large and luminous in the male; the sixth is pale and luminous on median third of width or more in female. The flash of this species is very characteristic; it always is emitted as the individual is slowly ascending in an inclined direction after an almost vertical drop in flight. The flash is prolonged until it reaches the apex of the ascending sweep, gradually diminishing in brightness.

c. *Photinus marginellus* LeConte   Plate XXVI, No. 2, p. 253

Elongate, slender; dull brownish; disk of pronotum roseate, with or without a narrow brownish spot which tapers basally; antennae and legs dusky. Pronotum broadly rounded anteriorly; disk with finely impressed median line; surface coarsely, densely punctate. Elytra finely granulate, pubescent. Length 6–9 mm.

Sixth and seventh ventral abdominal segments of male large and entirely luminous; female with sixth luminous in median third or more of width. The flash is single and of short duration.

d. *Photinus scintillans* (Say)　　　　　Plate XXVI, Nos. 3, 4, p. 253

Elongate, slender; dusky brown; pronotum roseate, with yellowish margin and a median dark-brown spot which is parallel-sided; elytral suture and side margins pale yellowish. Pronotum broadly rounded at apex, scarcely impressed medially. Elytra finely and indistinctly granulate; those of female not more than one-third the length of the abdomen. Length 5.5–8 mm.

This is one of the most common species in many areas and flies at early dusk, producing a short, yellowish flash at intervals of about five to eight seconds. The male has the sixth and seventh abdominal segments large and entirely luminous; the female has the sixth ventral abdominal segment luminous in median third or more of width.

Genus VI. *PHOTURIS* LeConte

Moderate-sized, elongate, rather slender beetles; eyes large, convex, and widely separated; head not entirely covered by pronotum; antennae slender, filiform, not compressed, second and third segments about equal and together as long as each of the succeeding segments; light organs in both sexes occupy the entire fifth and following segments.

Photuris pennsylvanica (DeGeer)　　　　　Plate XXVI, No. 7, p. 253

Elongate, slender, subdepressed; head and pronotum dull yellowish, disk of latter reddish, with a median blackish vitta; elytra brownish or piceous, suture, narrow side margins, and a narrow, oblique stripe on disk pale yellowish. Pronotum and elytra densely and rather roughly punctate; pronotal anterior margin broadly rounded, median impressed line absent. Length 11–15 mm.

This firefly has a brilliant green light, producing a flash at about two- to three-second intervals after complete darkness. It is a rapid flyer and very cannibalistic.

Family CANTHARIDAE

The Soldier Beetles; Leather-winged Beetles

Small to moderate-sized beetles; head either large and prominent, extending far beyond anterior margin of pronotum, or almost entirely concealed by pronotum; antennae widely separated at base; elytra not heavily sclerotized, epipleura distinct (Plate II); abdomen dorsally sometimes with the tip exposed, without light organs; mesocoxae contiguous (Fig. 193); metacoxae conical, prominent, and at least internally not covered by femora in repose; fourth tarsal segment lobed beneath (Fig. 197).

Many of the adults of this family feed on pollen of goldenrod, milkweed, and hydrangea; others are found on foliage. The larvae are all carnivorous, feeding on other small larvae and insects; they occur mostly beneath bark or rubbish.

KEY TO GENERA

1. Mentum small, quadrate (Fig. 198), often membranous; prosternum normal, fully developed 2
   Mentum very long, wider medially (Fig. 199); prosternum feebly developed, separated by a membrane from surrounding parts .....
   ....I. *Chauliognathus* (p. 256)
2. Elytra entirely covering the wings 3
   Elytra strongly abbreviated; wings exposed; claws appendiculate (Fig. 26F) ....IV. *Trypherus* (p. 264)
3. Pronotum truncate anteriorly; head entirely exposed ....II. *Podabrus* (p. 258)
   Pronotum rounded anteriorly, partly covering head ....III. *Cantharis* (p. 259)

Genus I. *CHAULIOGNATHUS* Hentz

Moderate-sized, rather depressed beetles; head prolonged before and behind eyes; mentum wider medially; maxillae with an extensile, pubescent, threadlike process, the maxillary palpi long and feebly dilated; prosternum small, broadly triangular; claws simple; last ventral segment of male elongate-oval, convex, and more strongly sclerotized than remaining segments, next to last broadly and deeply emarginate.

The mature beetles feed on pollen and nectar of many flowers.

KEY TO SPECIES

Pronotum transverse; head black .... a. *pennsylvanicus*
Pronotum elongate; head yellow, with black spots .... b. *marginatus*

a. *Chauliognathus pennsylvanicus* DeGeer   The Soldier Beetle
Plate XXVII, No. 5, p. 261

Elongate, slender, parallel; head, undersurface, and legs black; pronotum dull orange-yellow, with a broad, black, transverse basal spot on apical third, this sometimes more elongate so as to cover two-thirds or more of the surface. Pronotal margin broad, reflexed. Length 9–12 mm.

The adults are common in autumn on flowers of goldenrod and other allied plants.

b. *Chauliognathus marginatus* Fabricius   Plate XXVII, No. 7, p. 261

Elongate, rather narrow, parallel; dull orangeish yellow; head partially blackish, as are a broad median stripe on pronotum (reaching from base to apex) and a spot on elytra which is very variable in size and rarely wholly lacking; bases of femora and greater part of abdomen yellowish, the remainder blackish. Pronotum narrowly margined on sides. Length 8–11 mm.

This species is abundant on flowers of linden, wild hydrangea, Jersey tea, and other plants.

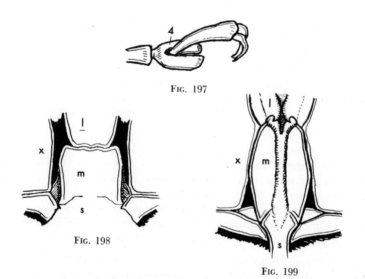

Fig. 197

Fig. 198

Fig. 199

Fig. 197. Portion of tarsus of *Cantharis* viewed obliquely from the side, the fourth segment (*4*) bilobed.
Figs. 198–199. Mentum of *Cantharis* (198) and of *Chauliognathus*. *l*, basal part of ligula; *m*, mentum; *s*, apical part of submentum; *x*, a portion of the swollen base of the maxilla.

Genus II. *PODABRUS* Westwood

Small to moderate-sized species; head prolonged and narrowed behind eyes to form a distinct neck, not covered by pronotum; apical margin of pronotum truncate; seventh ventral segment of male truncate at apex, eighth segment exposed; tarsal claws with a long, acute tooth.

KEY TO SPECIES

1. Head entirely brownish yellow or dull reddish yellow ....d. *tomentosus*
   Head at least partly black 2
2. Pronotum entirely yellowish ....c. *flavicollis*
   Pronotum with median black spot 3
3. Elytra entirely black ....a. *rugosulus*
   Elytra dark brownish, with pale margins ....b. *modestus*

a. *Podabrus rugosulus* LeConte   Plate XXVI, No. 14, p. 253

Elongate; black; anterior portion of head and pronotal sides yellowish. Head coarsely punctate. Pronotum narrowed anteriorly, side margins broad; disk coarsely punctate, with median impressed line distinct and a transverse impression at base and apex. Elytra densely rugose, sides moderately dilated behind middle. Length 7–8 mm.

This species occurs on leaves and flowers of various shrubs.

b. *Podabrus modestus* (Say)   Plate XXVII, No. 1, p. 261

Elongate, parallel; black or grayish black; anterior portion of head, margins of pronotum, and femora nearly entirely yellowish; antennae and tibiae blackish. Pronotum rather transverse, posterior angles rectangular, anterior ones rounded; side margins reflexed; disk finely and sparsely punctate anteriorly, nearly smooth posteriorly, median line distinct on basal half. Elytral side margins feebly dilated behind middle; disk densely, finely rugose. Length 9–13 mm.

c. *Podabrus flavicollis* LeConte   Plate XXVII, No. 2, p. 261

Elongate, parallel; black; a transverse band across front of head, entire prothorax, side margins and suture of elytra, and scutellum all yellowish. Pronotum strongly transverse; basal angles dentate, apical ones rounded; side margins broad, not reflexed; disk moderately coarsely punctate; median impressed line distinct on basal half. Elytral sides scarcely dilated behind middle; disk rather coarsely rugose. Length 9–11 mm.

d. *Podabrus tomentosus* (Say)   Plate XXVII, No. 3, p. 261

Elongate, slender, parallel; head, prothorax, two basal segments of antennae, abdomen in large part, and femora dull reddish yellow; remainder of antennae, tibiae, and tarsi blackish; elytra black, with fine, grayish pubescence. Pronotum quadrate; side margins narrowly expanded, feebly reflexed; posterior angles subacute, anterior ones rounded; disk finely, sparsely punctate, median impressed line distinct. Elytral sides expanded only before apex; disk rather coarsely rugose, covered with fine pubescence. Length 9–12 mm.

Very abundantly sometimes, this species may be found on the giant ragweed, usually along the borders of streams.

Genus III. *CANTHARIS* Linné

Small to medium-sized, soft-bodied beetles; head partly concealed, short and broad; last segment of maxillary palpi dilated, hatchet-shaped; pronotal anterior margin truncate, sides not notched, posterior angles rounded; elytra entirely covering the wings; tarsal claws simple, cleft, or toothed, sometimes the inner and outer claws not alike.

Most of the species of this genus occur on foliage of low herbs and shrubs, especially in moist places.

KEY TO SPECIES

1. Pronotum entirely black ....c. *fraxini*
   Pronotum at least in part yellowish or reddish yellow 2
2. Pronotum with two black maculae or vittae; tibiae and tarsi black ....
   ....k. *bilineatus*
   Pronotum immaculate or with a single macula; tibiae and tarsi variable
  3
3. Legs entirely black 4
   Legs not entirely black 7
4. Pronotal black spot large, much wider at base than at apex; body size 8–11
   mm. 5
   Pronotal black spot elongate, not widened basally; body size 5–7 mm. 6
5. Elytral side margin narrowly pale yellowish ....a. *dentiger*
   Elytra entirely black ....d. *carolinus*
6. Tarsal claws alike 9
   Tarsal claws unlike, outer claw of all tarsi toothed at base, entire at tip,
   the inner claw simple (Fig. 200) ....j. *impressus*
7. Pronotum with a black macula medially 10
   Pronotum without a black macula medially 8
8. Elytra without pale margins; head entirely yellowish ....i. *rotundicollis*
   Elytra with pale margins; head at least partially black ....h. *nigriceps*
9. Tarsal claws appendiculate at base (Fig. 26F); elytral lateral margins usually
   yellowish ....b. *excavatus*
   Tarsal claws cleft or dentate; elytra entirely black ....e. *lineola*
10. Legs piceous, tarsi and tibiae in part very dull yellow; elytral lateral margins
    (and rarely sutural) whitish ....f. *rectus*
    Legs bright yellow; elytral lateral and sutural margins yellow ....g. *scitulus*

a. *Cantharis dentiger* LeConte   Plate XXVI, No. 16, p. 253
   Elongate-oblong, rather robust; grayish black, clothed with fine, grayish pubescence; pronotum yellowish, medially with a large, transverse, blackish spot which is expanded basally; genae, mouthparts, side margins of ab-

PLATE XXVII
Family CANTHARIDAE II

1. *Podabrus modestus* (Say) (p. 258) — Dusky yellow-brown and blackish; 9–13 mm.

2. *P. flavicollis* LeConte (p. 258) — Blackish and dull yellow; 9–11 mm.

3. *P. tomentosus* (Say) (p. 258) — Bright or dull orange and black; 9–12 mm.

4. *Cantharis carolinus* Fabricius (p. 262) — Black; pronotal sides orangeish; 9–11 mm.

5. *Chauliognathus pennsylvanicus* DeGeer (p. 257) — Dull yellow and black; pronotum transverse; 9–12 mm.

6. *Cantharis rotundicollis* Say (p. 263) — Brownish yellow; elytra largely brown-gray; 12–14 mm.

7. *Chauliognathus marginatus* Fabricius (p. 257) — Dull yellow and black; pronotum as long as wide; 8–11 mm.

8. *Cantharis excavatus* LeConte (p. 262) — Blackish; pronotal sides and legs in part dull yellow; 5–6 mm.

9. *C. scitulus* Say (p. 263) — Blackish and clear yellow; pronotal dark marking variable, sometimes absent; 4–6 mm.

10. *C. rectus* Melsheimer (p. 262) — Fuscous; head with front and pronotum laterally yellow, remainder of head black; 4.5–6 mm.

Family CUPESIDAE

11. *Cupes concolor* Westwood (p. 282) — Dark brown, covered with brown and whitish scales; 7–11 mm.

Family LATHRIDIIDAE

12. *Lathridius liratus* LeConte (p. 424) — Reddish brown; 2–2.2 mm.

13. *Corticaria serrata* (Paykull) (p. 424) — Dark reddish brown; 2–2.2 mm.

14. *C. elongata* Gyllenhal (p. 424) — Reddish brown to deep brown; 1.4–1.8 mm.

15. *Melanophthalma distinguenda* Comstock (p. 425) — Reddish brown; 1.5–1.8 mm.

16. *M. cavicollis* Mannerheim (p. 425) — Dark yellowish brown; 1.2–1.5 mm.

MM 0 10 20 30 40 50 60 70

PLATE XXVII   261

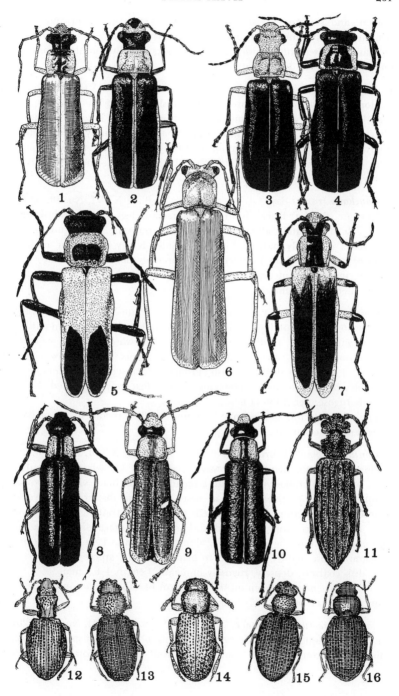

domen, and sometimes elytral margins dull yellowish. Head and elytra
densely, roughly punctate. Pronotum more sparsely and coarsely punctate;
median impressed line distinct; anterior angles broadly rounded; posterior
ones narrowly rounded. Length 8–9 mm.

b. *Cantharis excavatus* LeConte   Plate XXVII, No. 8, p. 261
Elongate, slender; black; pronotum reddish yellow, with a narrow, median, black vitta, which is sometimes wanting; narrow lateral margins of
elytra, tibiae, tarsi, and basal third of antennae usually dull yellowish. Head
finely, densely punctate. Pronotum about as long as wide, nearly smooth;
sides straight, excavated at middle; median impressed line deep. Elytra
feebly, rugosely punctate. Length 5–6 mm.

c. *Cantharis fraxini* Say   Plate XXVI, No. 10, p. 253
Elongate, slender; black, shining; antennae and legs sometimes brownish
black. Head minutely alutaceous and finely punctate. Pronotum feebly
transverse, gradually narrowed apically; sides feebly sinuate at middle;
anterior angles broadly rounded, posterior ones obtusely angulate; disk
uneven, nearly impunctate; median impressed line absent. Elytra coarsely
rugose. Length 4–5 mm.

d. *Cantharis carolinus* Fabricius   Plate XXVII, No. 4, p. 261
Elongate, robust, subdepressed; black, finely pubescent; pronotum reddish
yellow, with a large, median, shining, black spot which is much widened
basally; mouthparts, three basal antennal segments, and narrow lateral
margin of abdomen dull yellowish. Pronotum transverse, anterior angles
and sides broadly rounded; posterior angles subacutely angulated. Elytra
coarsely rugose. Length 9–11 mm.
The adults of this species may be found on flowers and leaves of hawthorn and other shrubs.

e. *Cantharis lineola* Fabricius   Plate XXVI, No. 11, p. 253
Elongate-oblong, slender, depressed; black, very sparsely grayish-pubescent; pronotum orange-yellow, with a broad, median, black vitta, narrowed
behind middle and re-expanded at base. Pronotum distinctly transverse,
anterior and posterior angles rounded; sides nearly straight, narrowing to
apex, the margins strongly reflexed; disk minutely alutaceous, with median
impressed line wanting or obsolete, along base with a deep transverse impression. Elytra slightly expanded to behind middle, apices broadly truncate; disk coarsely, densely, rugosely punctate. Length 4–6.5 mm.
This species may be taken on the flowers of blackberry and on foliage of
many shrubs and herbs.

f. *Cantharis rectus* Melsheimer   ·   Plate XXVII, No. 10, p. 261
Elongate-oblong, slender, depressed; piceous to black, with sparse, grayish
pubescence; pronotum and front of head dull orange-yellow, the former

with a broad, black, median vitta of nearly uniform width throughout; coxae, tibiae in part, and tarsi indistinctly yellowish; elytral lateral margins (and sometimes sutural as well) whitish. Pronotum distinctly transverse, anterior angles rounded, posterior ones subrectangular; sides sinuate medially, narrowing to apex, margins scarcely reflexed; disk minutely alutaceous, without distinct median impressed line, basal transverse impression shallow. Elytra scarcely expanded posteriorly; disk coarsely, rugosely punctate. Length 4.5–6 mm.

g. *Cantharis scitulus* Say   Plate XXVII, No. 9, p. 261
Elongate, slender; piceous or grayish black; pronotum with an elongate, blackish spot, irregular in outline; elytra with broad marginal and sutural stripes of pale yellow, the sutural one usually wider basally. Pronotum transverse, broadly concave on each side; margins narrow, slightly reflexed; anterior angles narrowly rounded, posterior ones obtusely angulate; disk impunctate. Elytra feebly, moderately coarsely rugose. Length 4–6 mm.

h. *Cantharis nigriceps* LeConte   Plate XXVI, No. 13, p. 253
Elongate, slender; black or piceous; front of head, pronotal margins, and legs dull yellow; elytra with narrow sutural and lateral margins pale yellowish. Pronotum as long as wide, sides nearly straight, margins feebly reflexed; anterior angles broadly rounded, posterior ones subacutely angulate; disk uneven, impunctate. Elytra coarsely but not deeply rugose. Length 4–6 mm.

i. *Cantharis rotundicollis* Say   Plate XXVII, No. 6, p. 261
Elongate, moderately slender; dull reddish yellow, shining; pronotum immaculate; elytra entirely dark gray, subopaque. Pronotum about as long as wide, slightly widened apically; sides nearly straight; anterior angles broadly rounded, posterior ones rectangular; disk with a median impressed line basally, surface impunctate. Elytra moderately granulate. Length 12–14 mm.

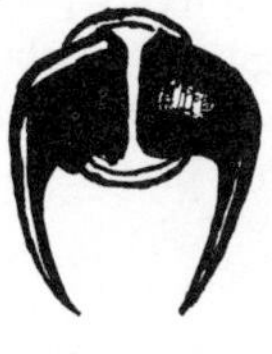

Fig. 200

Fig. 200. Tarsal claws of *Cantharis impressus,* the outer claw dentate at base, the inner one simple.

j. *Cantharis impressus* LeConte   Plate XXVI, No. 15, p. 253

Elongate, rather slender; black, shining; mouth and pronotum yellowish, the latter with a broad, black, dorsal stripe which sometimes is broadened along basal and apical margins. Pronotum quadrate in male, transverse in female; disk impunctate, medially with a deeply impressed line and a transverse impression each side; anterior angles broadly rounded, posterior ones rectangular in males and rounded in females. Elytra coarsely, rather deeply rugose. Length 5–7 mm.

This species is common on foliage of alder and other shrubs along borders of marshes.

k. *Cantharis bilineatus* Say   Plate XXVI, No. 12, p. 253

Oblong, robust; dull reddish yellow; occiput of head, elytra, two oblong spots on pronotum, antennae except basal segment, tibiae, tarsi, and apex of femora black. Pronotum slightly transverse; strongly narrowed anteriorly; sides nearly straight; anterior angles rounded, posterior ones subangulate; disk with a distinct median impressed line, surface rather coarsely punctate. Elytra coarsely, rugosely punctate. Length 6–8 mm.

This species is especially abundant on flowers of red haw.

Genus IV. *TRYPHERUS* LeConte

A rather small species; last segment of maxillary palpi elongate, hatchet-shaped; mandibles toothed; eyes large and prominent in male; wings long and covering abdomen, elytra abbreviated; mesofemora more robust in male than in female; claws appendiculate.

Only one species belongs to this genus.

Trypherus latipennis (Germar)   Plate XXVI, No. 9, p. 253

Elongate, slender; piceous above, dull yellow on undersurface; antennae blackish; margins of pronotum and tips of elytra dull yellow. Antennae slender, one-half as long as body; third segment equal to second and slightly shorter than fourth. Pronotum feebly transverse; anterior margin broadly arcuate, basal margin truncate. Elytra nearly twice as long as pronotum, rugosely punctate; apices separately, broadly rounded; female with last dorsal abdominal segment trilobed at apex. Length 6–7 mm.

T. latipennis is frequently found on catnip and flowers of red haw, as well as on foliage of various other plants.

Family MELYRIDAE

The Soft-winged Flower Beetles

These are small, soft-winged forms which resemble the Lampyridae but are not as elongate in form. Other family characters are: antennae eleven-segmented (in *Collops* the antennae only appear to be ten-segmented; the second segment is very small and concealed), inserted on the front of head at sides, usually before eyes, frequently serrate and in males knotted or with segments dilated and dentate; head exserted, prolonged into a short, broad beak (Fig. 204); mentum small, quadrate, corneous; elytra usually entire, more or less truncate at apex, widened behind middle; prosternum short, not extending between procoxae (Fig. 201); procoxae contiguous, conical, with distinct trochantins (Fig. 201); procoxal cavities large, open posteriorly (Fig. 25A); tarsi filiform, five-segmented, fourth segment not bilobed, claws usually with a large membranous lobe inserted between them (Fig. 202).

Both larvae and adults are predaceous, feeding on insect eggs, larvae, and soft-bodied adults; the adults, however, are often found on flowers and herbs, the larvae under bark in tree trunks or on dead animals. In a number of species the adults can protrude many soft, orange-colored sacs from the sides of the abdomen, supposedly scent organs for defense.

KEY TO GENERA

1. Antennae distinctly of eleven segments 2
   Antennae apparently ten-segmented (Fig. 203) ....I. *Collops* (p. 265)
2. Antennae inserted on front of head nearly between eyes (Fig. 204)
   ....II. *Malachius* (p. 268)
   Antennae inserted at anterior edge of front near the sides (Fig. 205)
  3
3. Labrum as long as clypeus, on same plane (Fig. 205); protarsi of male with second segment prolonged over third (Fig. 206) ....IV. *Attalus* (p. 269)
   Labrum much shorter and strongly deflexed; male protarsi simple
   ....III. *Pseudebaeus* (p. 268)

Genus I. *COLLOPS* Erichson

Rather small, oblong-ovate; antennae apparently with only ten segments, second very small and concealed, third (apparently the second) of male enlarged, at base an odd, slender, jointed appendage, tipped with a brush of stiff hairs, usually concealed in a cavity on the upper surface of the segment (Fig. 203); sides of body with extensible sacs, anterior pair projecting from suture between pronotum and prosternum near anterior angles; last segment of tarsi with two membranous appendages beneath claws, which are simple and divaricate (Fig. 202).

KEY TO SPECIES

1. Elytra uniformly deep blue 2
   Elytra at least margined with yellow or reddish yellow 3
2. Pronotum uniformly reddish yellow .... a. *tricolor*
   Pronotum with a quadrate black macula on disk .... b. *nigriceps*
3. Elytra deep blue, with wide marginal bands of yellowish at sides and suture, these usually widened before middle .... c. *vittatus*
   Elytra reddish yellow, each with two blue maculae, one quadrate, small, on base, and the other a large one occupying apical half .... d. *quadrimaculatus*

a. *Collops tricolor* (Say)   Plate XXVIII, No. 1, p. 271

Oblong-ovate, widened behind middle; head, legs, and sterna black; antennae dark reddish brown; pronotum and abdomen reddish yellow; elytra blue or bluish black. Pronotum distinctly transverse, sides broadly rounded; surface very sparsely, finely punctate, with sparse, erect hairs. Elytra densely, rather finely punctate and with sparse, erect hairs. Length 4–5 mm.

b. *Collops nigriceps* (Say)   Plate XXVIII, No. 2, p. 271

Elongate-oblong, slightly widened posteriorly; head black, as is the undersurface, except abdominal sternites, which are yellowish brown; front of head, antennae, and femora yellowish; pronotum dull yellow, with a large blackish macula at middle; elytra bluish to bluish black. Pronotum strongly transverse; sides strongly rounded basally, feebly so apically; disk sparsely, minutely punctate, with sparse, erect hairs. Elytra densely, coarsely punctate, with sparse, erect hairs. Length 6–8 mm.

These are found on flowers and herbs.

c. *Collops vittatus* (Say)   Plate XXVIII, No. 3, p. 271

Elongate-oval; black; pronotum, elytra at sides and suture, and body beneath reddish yellow; pronotum sometimes with a median black macula; elytra each with a broad stripe of blue on disk. Pronotum pubescent; surface densely, rather finely punctate. Elytra coarsely, densely punctate, with sparse, erect hairs. Length 4–5 mm.

d. *Collops quadrimaculatus* (Fabricius)   Plate XXVIII, No. 4, p. 271

Oblong-ovate, wider posteriorly; head and abdomen black; pronotum and elytra reddish yellow, latter each with a large basal and preapical macula, blue or bluish black; tibiae, tarsi, and antennae apically, dusky or piceous. Pronotum minutely alutaceous and with very sparse, coarse

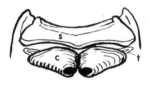

Fig. 201.

Fig. 202.

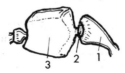

Fig. 203.

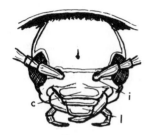

Fig. 204.

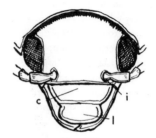

Fig. 205.

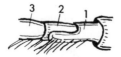

Fig. 206.

Fig. 201. Prosternum (s) and procoxae (c) of *Collops*, showing the typical condition in this family. *t*, trochantin.

Fig. 202. Tarsal claws of *Malachius* viewed from the tip, with membranous lobes (*l*) between them.

Fig. 203. Antennal basal segments of a male *Collops*, from beneath. The second segment (2) is concealed in the tip of the first (1), so that the antennae appear to be 10-segmented. In the female the third segment is not enlarged as here (3) in the male.

Figs. 204–205. Heads of melyrids viewed from the front. *Malachius* (204) with antennae inserted between eyes and *Attalus* (205) with the insertion (*i*) below level of eyes. *c*, clypeus; *l*, labrum.

Fig. 206. Tarsus of male *Attalus*, only the basal segments of which are shown, the first segment prolonged along the second.

punctures; pubescence sparse and erect. Elytra minutely alutaceous, with dense, coarse, rather shallow punctures which become much finer apically; pubescence sparse and erect. Length 4–6 mm.

This species may be collected by sweeping and beating herbs and grasses, especially in damp areas.

Genus II. *MALACHIUS* Fabricius

Of moderate size, elongate-oblong, slightly convex; pronotum subquadrate, feebly transverse; antennae inserted on front nearly between eyes, distinctly eleven-segmented; sides of body with extensible sacs, anterior pair projecting from suture between pronotum and prosternum near anterior angles; last segment of tarsi with two membranous appendages beneath claws, which are simple.

Malachius aeneus (Linné)   Plate XXVIII, No. 8, p. 271

Broadly oblong; metallic green, shining; elytra brownish red or brownorange, with the extreme base and a vitta along suture for three-quarters its length metallic green; pronotum with anterior angles reddish. Pronotum with an indistinct median impressed line; disk minutely alutaceous, along lateral and apical margins sparsely and finely asperate. Elytra sparsely, transversely rugose and densely alutaceous. Length 6–7 mm.

As a whole, this species resembles a scarab in coloration and form.

Genus III. *PSEUDEBAEUS* Horn

Very small, oval, convex species; antennae distinctly eleven-segmented, inserted at anterior edge of front near sides; pronotum distinctly transverse; elytra broadened posteriorly; sides of body with extensible sacs, anterior pair projecting from suture between pronotum and prosternum near anterior angles; all tarsi slender, simple, last segment not elongate and with a pair of membranous appendages beneath claws, which are simple and divaricate. Elytra of males produced at apex and bearing a hooklike appendage.

Pseudebaeus oblitus (LeConte)   Plate XXVIII, No. 5, p. 271

Oblong-ovate, widened posteriorly; piceous to bluish black, shining; legs and antennae pale yellowish, apex of latter darker. Pronotum densely, finely punctate. Elytra very finely, sparsely punctate and densely alutaceous. Length 1.5–2 mm.

Genus IV. *ATTALUS* Erichson

Small, oblong, feebly widened posteriorly, subconvex; antennae distinctly eleven-segmented; pronotum slightly transverse; elytra similar in both sexes; sides of body with extensible sacs, anterior pair projecting from suture between pronotum and prosternum near anterior angles; tarsi simple, five-segmented, second segment of protarsi in male prolonged over third and grooved beneath (Fig. 206).

KEY TO SPECIES

1. Body above entirely black or nearly so, apical margins of elytra in male bordered narrowly with yellow; female wholly black ....a. *terminalis*
   Black, either head or pronotum with yellow 2
2. Head black, front pale yellow; pronotum dull yellow, rarely with a black vitta; elytra black, tinged bluish ....b. *otiosus*
   Head dull yellow, occiput black; pronotum dull yellow, with a broad median vitta; elytra dull yellow, with suture at base and side margins usually black
   ....c. *scincetus*

a. *Attalus terminalis* (Erichson)   Plate XXVIII, No. 6, p. 271
   Oblong, depressed, widened posteriorly; black, shining, sparsely pubescent; male with apices of elytra and a marginal vitta laterally pale yellow, legs largely dull yellow. Pronotum slightly transverse, nearly circular in outline; disk sparsely, finely punctate. Elytra feebly, transversely rugose and coarsely, rather densely punctate. Length 2–3 mm.

b. *Attalus otiosus* (Say)   Plate XXVIII, No. 7, p. 271
   Oblong-ovate, strongly widened posteriorly, subdepressed; head black, front pale yellow; pronotum dull yellow, rarely with a black median vitta; elytra sooty, with a bluish tinge; legs dull yellowish brown. Pronotum distinctly transverse; apex and base broadly rounded; disk finely, irregularly strigose. Elytra densely alutaceous and coarsely, shallowly punctate. Length 2.5–3 mm.

c. *Attalus scincetus* (Say)   Plate XXVIII, No. 9, p. 271
   Oblong, feebly widened posteriorly, subdepressed; dull yellow; occiput, a broad median vitta on pronotum, scutellum, and sutural vitta on basal half of elytra blackish; antennae, legs, and body beneath yellowish. Pronotum slightly transverse; basal margin straight medially, apical margin narrowly rounded; disk finely, sparsely punctate. Elytra densely alutaceous, coarsely and rather sparsely punctate. Length 2.5–3 mm.

   The adults are found on flowers of dogwood, red and black haw, wild rose, and viburnum.

PLATE XXVIII

Family MELYRIDAE

1. *Collops tricolor* (Say) (p. 266)
Deep metallic green; pronotum dull orange; 4–5 mm.

2. *C. nigriceps* (Say) (p. 266)
Black; pronotum edged with dull orange; elytra deep green; 6–8 mm.

3. *C. vittatus* (Say) (p. 266)
Dull orange; head black; elytral vittae deep green; 4–5 mm.

4. *C. quadrimaculatus* (Fabricius) (p. 266)
Dull yellowish; head black; elytral maculae deep bluish; 4–6 mm.

5. *Pseudebaeus oblitus* (LeConte) (p. 268)
Piceous; legs and antennae pale; 1.5–2 mm.

6. *Attalus terminalis* (Erichson) (p. 269)
Black; elytral tips pale yellowish in male, in female entirely black; 2–3 mm.

7. *A. otiosus* (Say) (p. 269)
Black; front of head, part of pronotum, and most of legs pale yellowish; 2.5–3 mm.

8. *Malachius aeneus* (Linné) (p. 268)
Deep metallic green; pronotal anterior angles, front of head, and much of elytra dull orangeish; 6–7 mm.

9. *Attalus scincetus* (Say) (p. 269)
Pale yellowish; pronotum (except at base) and head black; 2.5 mm.

Family CLERIDAE I

10. *Phyllobaenus humeralis* (Say) (p. 274)
Piceous and blackish blue; elytral band silvery white; 3.5–5.5 mm.

11. *Enoclerus nigripes* (Say) (p. 278)
Dull red; elytra black on apical two-thirds, bands whitish; legs black; 5–7 mm.

12. *Phyllobaenus verticalis* (Say) (p. 274)
Pronotum, scutellum, and tips of elytra black; head and front part of pronotum dull orange, remainder very pale yellowish; 3.5–5 mm.

13. *Thanasimus dubius* Fabricius (p. 278)
Dull orange; elytra largely black, except at base; bands whitish; 7–9 mm.

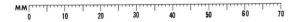

PLATE XXVIII 271

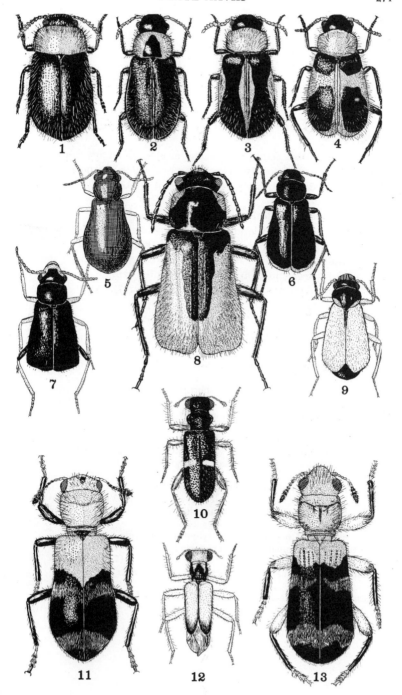

Family CLERIDAE

The Checkered Flower Beetles

Brightly colored, active, predaceous beetles, found on trunks of trees, timber, flowers, and foliage. The larvae live within the burrows of wood-borers or under bark and are very useful in keeping these and bark beetles in check.

Following are the distinguishing family characteristics: antennae capitate or clavate, ten- or eleven-segmented, usually serrate, inserted at sides of front; elytra usually entire or nearly so, rather soft; procoxae prominent, usually contiguous, cavities open posteriorly (Fig. 25A); metacoxae flat; tarsi five-segmented, first and fourth often minute, segments one to four with membranous appendages beneath (Fig. 207).

KEY TO GENERA

Fig. 207   Fig. 208

Figs. 207–208. Tarsus of *Thanasimus* (207) and of *Necrobia* (208). In
the latter the fourth segment is greatly reduced. *l,* membranous lobes, characteristic of the entire family.

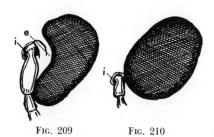

Fig. 209   Fig. 210

Figs. 209–210. Eye of *Thanasimus* (209) and of *Phyllobaenus* (210).
e, emargination; *i,* antennal insertion.

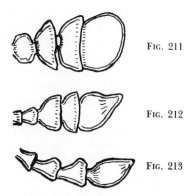

Fig. 211

Fig. 212

Fig. 213

Figs. 211–213. Antennal clubs of three melyrids. *Necrobia* (211); *Enoclerus* (212); and *Thanasimus* (213).

Genus I. *PHYLLOBAENUS* Dejean

Small, elongate, convex; eyes entire, finely granulate; maxillary palpi cylindrical, last segment feebly tapering apically; labial palpi elongate, last segment strongly dilated; antennae nearly filiform, club abruptly formed, compact, subglobose, two-segmented, apical segment very small; tarsi apparently four-segmented, rather slender, short; claws broadly dentate basally.

KEY TO SPECIES

1. Elytra dark blue, humeri usually red; pronotum one-third wider than long, constricted near base and apex ....a. *humeralis*
   Elvtra black or dull yellow; pronotum as long as wide 2
2. Head pale yellowish, usually with a black, oblong macula on vertex; elytra coarsely but not densely punctate ....b. *verticalis*
   Head black; elytra coarsely and densely punctate, punctures often confluent ....c. *pallipennis*

a. *Phyllobaenus humeralis* (Say)   Plate XXVIII, No. 10, p. 271
   Elongate, moderately slender, convex; violaceous or bluish black; elytra dark blue, humeri usually reddish orange; antennae and legs usually mostly reddish. Pronotum wider than long, sides moderately tuberculate, constricted anteriorly and posteriorly. Elytra widest at apical third, covering abdomen; sides subparallel; surface densely, coarsely punctate. Length 3.5–5.5 mm.

b. *Phyllobaenus verticalis* (Say)   Plate XXVIII, No. 12, p. 271
   Elongate, moderately convex; black; head all or in part pale yellow, usually with a black macula on vertex; antennae and legs pale yellowish; pronotum brownish yellow, often with a white vitta or macula on each side; elytra at base dull yellow, sometimes entirely black or occasionally entirely pale, with black apices. Pronotum cylindrical, transverse; disk irregularly, coarsely punctate. Elytra narrowed to apex, two-thirds the length of the abdomen; disk coarsely, densely punctate. Length 3.5–5 mm.
   These beetles have been recorded as breeding in bittersweet infested with cerambycid larvae, wild grape and blackberry infested with buprestid larvae, and hickory also infested with wood-borers. The adults are found on flowers and foliage as well as on timber.

c. *Phyllobaenus pallipennis* (Say)   Plate XXIX, No. 4, p. 277
   Elongate, subdepressed; black, slightly bronzed; mouthparts, antennae. elytra, and legs brownish yellow, elytra with sides, apex, suture, and a median fascia brownish or black, these markings frequently fine. Pronotum feebly transverse, widest at middle, constricted apically and basally; disk

with a transverse depression just behind apex and at base; surface sparsely, irregularly punctate. Elytra shorter than abdomen, widest at base; each tumid near apex; surface coarsely, densely, confluently punctate. Length 3.5–5 mm.

Genus II. *ZENODOSUS* Wolcott

Small, oblong-ovate, subdepressed; eyes entire, finely granulate; maxillary palpi compressed, last segment tapering on apical half; labial palpi triangular, last segment dilated apically; antennae robust, club loose, gradually formed, three-segmented; tarsi slender, apparently four-segmented, last segment as long as preceding combined; claws simple.

Zenodosus sanguineus (Say)   Plate XXIX, No. 8, p. 277

Elongate, rather slender, subdepressed; head, pronotum, and undersurface fuscous; apical segments of antennae, legs, and abdomen usually dull red; elytra bright orange-red, feebly shining. Head and pronotum densely, confluently punctate. Elytral sides subparallel, feebly widened behind middle; surface coarsely, densely, and rather deeply punctate. Length 4.5–6.5 mm.

The adults of this species occur beneath bark and moss.

Genus III. *PLACOPTERUS* Wolcott

Small, oblong-ovate, subconvex; eyes deeply emarginate anteriorly, finely granulate; last segment of maxillary palpi elongate, cylindrical, feebly tapering apically; labial palpi with all segments elongate, last one longer, dilated, triangular; antennal segments submoniliform, last three segments forming a rather compact club, last segment subtriangular, compressed apically; tarsi with apparently four segments, claws broadly dentate.

Placopterus thoracicus (Olivier)   Plate XXIX, No. 3, p. 277

Oblong-ovate, subconvex, slightly widened posteriorly; black, frequently tinged with bluish or violet; pronotum and occasionally front of head reddish yellow, former with a large, black macula on basal half of disk. Pronotum much wider than head, widest at middle, constricted basally; disk with a transverse, rounded depression behind apex and before base; surface with scattered, fine punctures. Elytra rather coarsely and very densely punctate, with obsolete costae. Length 5–7 mm.

The larvae are recorded as predators on bark beetles and borers of small branches of deciduous trees; the adults are found especially on foliage in damp meadows.

PLATE XXIX
Family CLERIDAE II

1. *Phlogistosternus dislocatus* (Say) (p. 280)   Black; legs and elytral markings dull yellowish; 3.5–6 mm.

2. *Trichodes nutalli* (Kirby) (p. 279)   Deep metallic blue; elytral fasciae yellow; 8–11 mm.

3. *Placopterus thoracicus* (Olivier) (p. 275)   Black; pronotum partly reddish; 5–7 mm.

4. *Phyllobaenus pallipennis* (Say) (p. 274)   Black; legs and elytra pale yellow, the latter with blackish markings; 3.5–5 mm.

5. *Necrobia rufipes* DeGeer (p. 280)   Black, reflexed with green or blue; legs and antennal base reddish; 3.5–6 mm.

6. *N. ruficollis* (Fabricius) (p. 280)   Black and reddish, with a dull-blue reflex; 4–5 mm.

7. *N. violacea* (Linné) (p. 281)   Black, with a bright blue or violet sheen; 3–4.5 mm.

8. *Zenodosus sanguineus* (Say) (p. 275)   Dark reddish brown; elytra orange-red; 4.5–6.5 mm.

9. *Enoclerus rosmarus* (Say) (p. 279)   Yellowish brown; legs dark brown; elytral markings whitish and black; 4–7 mm.

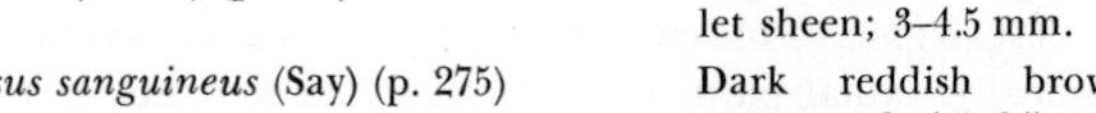

MM ‖‖‖‖‖‖‖‖‖‖‖‖‖‖‖‖‖‖‖‖‖‖‖‖‖‖‖‖‖‖‖‖‖‖‖‖
0   10   20   30   40   50   60   70

PLATE XXIX 277

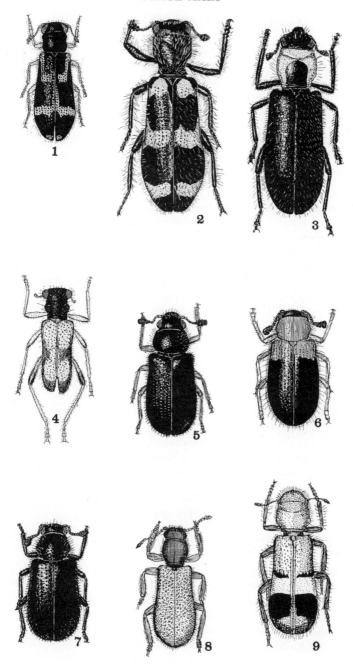

Genus IV. *THANASIMUS* Latreille

Small to moderate-sized, elongate, subdepressed; eyes emarginate on anterior margin (Fig. 209), finely granulate; antennal club loosely three-segmented, very gradually clavate, last segment not truncate at apex; maxillary palpi filiform, last segment slender, tapering to apex; labial palpi with segments slightly elongate, last segment compressed, expanded at basal third, elongate-triangular in shape; pronotum with a deep, transverse, subapical sulcus joined by a median impressed line; tarsi slender, elongate, apparently four-segmented; third and fourth segments of metatarsi not distinctly dilated; claws with a broad tooth.

Thanasimus dubius Fabricius   Plate XXVIII, No. 13, p. 271

Elongate, slender, subdepressed, broader posteriorly; reddish brown; apical four-fifths of elytra black, with two sinuate fasciae of white pubescence; antennae and legs varying from red to black. Pronotum slightly transverse, constricted at base and apex; disk with a deep, transverse, subapical sulcus connected by a median line; surface densely, finely punctate. Elytra widest at apical fourth; surface coarsely punctate basally, denser and finer on apical fourth. Length 7–9 mm.

This species is found on both flowers and herbage; both larvae and adults are predators on bark beetles in dead and dying spruce, pine, and elm trees.

Genus V. *ENOCLERUS* Gahan

Moderate-sized, elongate, convex; eyes distinctly emarginate on anterior margin, finely granulate; maxillary palpi slender; labial palpi dilated; antennal club three-segmented, rather abruptly enlarged, conical; pronotum with a shallow, subapical groove, without a median line joining it; tarsi apparently four-segmented; third and fourth segments of metatarsi dilated; claws broadly dentate.

KEY TO SPECIES

Abdomen reddish brown ....a. *nigripes*
Abdomen black ....b. *rosmarus*

a. *Enoclerus nigripes* (Say)   Plate XXVIII, No. 11, p. 271

Elongate, moderately robust; dull reddish brown; apical three-fifths of elytra black; antennae, legs, and meso- and metasterna dark brown to black; elytra with a narrow fascia near middle and an apical macula or fascia whitish. Pronotum subquadrate, strongly constricted basally; disk with a feeble, transverse, subapical and basal impression; surface finely, densely punctate. Elytra widest at apical third; surface coarsely, densely punctate at base. Length 5–7 mm.

One of the commonest clerids, it has been recorded as a predator on larvae and adults of Scolytidae and *Pissodes* in pine, spruce, and juniper and on other borers in hardwoods. The adults are usually found on these trees during late spring and early summer.

b. *Enoclerus rosmarus* (Say)   Plate XXIX, No. 9, p. 277
Elongate, convex, robust, slightly wider posteriorly; brownish orange, subopaque; elytra with a narrow fascia anterior to middle and a broader one on apical third black, the two separated by a curved, whitish fascia, apex usually yellowish white; tibiae and apical segments of antennae fuscous; abdomen fuscous to black, shining. Pronotum campanulate, densely, finely punctate. Elytra with irregular rows of coarse, dense punctures; intervals subcostate, these more distinct basally; the whitish band and apex with dense, whitish hairs. Length 4–7 mm.

The adults occur on greater horseweed in particular.

Genus VI. *TRICHODES* Herbst

Moderate-sized, elongate; eyes deeply emarginate on anterior margin, finely granulate; antennal club triangular, three-segmented, last segment truncate at apex; maxillary palpi subcylindrical, last segment longer and slightly wider than preceding; labial palpi strongly dilated; tarsi apparently four-segmented.

The generic name means "shaggy" and indicates the hairiness of the species.

Trichodes nutalli (Kirby)   Color Plate D; Plate XXIX, No. 2, p. 277
Elongate, subcylindrical; dark blue, sometimes purplish or greenish blue; antennae and mouthparts brown; elytra blue-black, with three fascia, broken at suture, and the margin from humerus to middle, reddish yellow, the prominence on humeri blue. Pronotum campanulate, with a transverse, subapical and basal depression; disk sparsely, coarsely, irregularly punctate. Elytra widest at apical third; surface coarsely and irregularly punctate. Length 8–11 mm.

The adults are found on flowers and foliage; the larvae are recorded as being predators in nests of bees and wasps.

Genus VII. *PHLOGISTOSTERNUS* Wolcott

Small, elongate; eyes emarginate on anterior margin; antennae ten-segmented, seventh very small, eight to ten much larger, depressed, last segment oval, club shorter than funicle; tarsi slender, short, fourth segment rudimentary; claws strongly dentate basally.

Phlogistosternus dislocatus (Say)   Plate XXIX, No. 1, p. 277

Elongate, subcylindrical; dark brown to black; mouthparts, antennae, and legs yellowish brown; elytra variable, each usually with an oblique, pale-yellow vitta which extends from humerus to suture before middle, then along suture to just behind middle, where it usually connects with a narrow, yellow fascia; frequently there is also a small yellow spot near apex. Pronotum subcylindrical, widest near base; sides sinuate; disk rather densely and finely punctate, a depression each side near base. Elytra with rows of densely placed, coarse, quadrate punctures; widest at apical third. Length 3.5–6 mm.

These are found on dead branches of ash, *Rhus,* butternut, hickory, and blackberry canes and also on flowering shrubs.

Genus VIII. *NECROBIA* Olivier

Small, ovate; eyes entire (Fig. 210), coarsely granulate; antennae eleven-segmented, club small, compact, and three-segmented (Fig. 211); last segment of maxillary palpi oval, truncate apically; tarsi more or less broad and short, fourth segment very small; claws dentate basally.

KEY TO SPECIES

1. Upper surface bicolored ....a. *ruficollis*
   Upper surface unicolored 2
2. Antennae with basal segment brown; legs brown ....b. *rufipes*
   Antennae entirely black; legs bluish black ....c. *violacea*

a. *Necrobia ruficollis* (Fabricius)   Red-shouldered Ham Beetle
                                                      Plate XXIX, No. 6, p. 277

Oblong-ovate, robust; front of head and apical three-fourths of elytra metallic blue; base and ventral surface of head, pronotum, base of elytra, meso- and metasternum, and legs brownish red. Head and pronotum densely punctate on sides. Elytra with rows of fine, distinct punctures, these gradually finer posteriorly but visible almost to apex. Length 4–5 mm.

This species is found in the same habitat as *rufipes*.

b. *Necrobia rufipes* DeGeer   Red-legged Ham Beetle
                                                      Plate XXIX, No. 5, p. 277

Elongate-oblong, subconvex; metallic blue or green, shining; antennae dark brown, basal segments and legs reddish brown. Head and pronotum finely, rather densely punctate. Elytra widest behind middle; surface with rows of widely separated punctures; intervals finely, densely punctate. Length 3.5–6 mm.

This species occurs on drying carrion and bones, fish, cheese, and ham; it is also predaceous.

c. *Necrobia violacea* (Linné) The Violet Ham Beetle
Plate XXIX, No. 7, p. 277

Elongate, oval, robust; metallic dark blue or green; antennae black, legs bluish black. Head and pronotum finely, densely punctate. Elytra widest behind middle; surface with rows of rather coarse punctures, the punctures becoming indistinct behind middle; intervals minutely, densely punctate. Length 3–4.5 mm.

This is a cosmopolitan species which frequents dried skins of dead animals and dried fish; it is also predaceous on dermestid larvae.

Family CUPESIDAE

This is one of the smaller and less well-known families of beetles, of whose species only one is widely distributed. They are small, flattened forms covered with scales and have the elytra entire, disk with rows of large, square punctures, intervals carinate. Head tuberculate, suddenly constricted behind, forming a distinct neck; pronotum small, quadrate, side margins distinct; prosternum prolonged and fitting into a groove in the mesosternum much as in the Elateridae or click beetles (Fig. 50); procoxae small, not prominent, the cavities transverse, open behind; mesosternum with sidepieces excavated for retraction of the middle legs (Fig. 50); metacoxae transverse, flattened, sulcate posteriorly, receiving the tibiae when retracted; tibiae without terminal spurs, tarsi five-segmented and with spongy pads beneath, claws simple.

The adults are found mostly beneath bark and about old frame or log houses; the larvae live mostly in dead or decaying wood.

Genus *CUPES* Fabricius

Small, subdepressed beetles with the antennae subapproximate at base, more than half as long as the beetle itself; eyes strongly convex; sides of prothorax excavated for reception of front legs.

Cupes concolor Westwood   Plate XXVII, No. 11, p. 261

Elongate, slender, subdepressed; pale brownish or ashy gray, densely covered with small scales; elytra with darker-brown, oblong patches, which form three indistinct, undulating bands. Antennae nearly as long as body. Head with four feebly separated tubercles. Pronotum wider than long, about one-half as wide as elytra at base; disk with a median longitudinal carina and a deep impression each side; side margins abbreviated near the front and hind angles. Elytra with rows of large, quadrate punctures; intervals convex, alternate ones raised. Length 7–11 mm.

Family OEDEMERIDAE

The Oedemerid Beetles

Small or medium-sized, slender, more or less cylindrical; elytra soft in texture, smooth or with fine punctures and silky hair; front of head oblique, prolonged (Fig. 214); antennae long and slender, eleven- to twelve-segmented, filiform; palpi four-segmented, last segment dilated; pronotum narrower than elytra at base; procoxae large, conical, contiguous (Fig. 215), cavities open posteriorly (Fig. 25A); mesocoxae prominent; tarsi with next to last segment dilated and with a dense brush of hairs beneath, pro- and mesotarsi five-segmented, metatarsi four-segmented; tarsal claws usually simple, rarely dentate basally.

The adults of this small family are usually found on flowers or foliage near water; their larvae live in decaying wood.

KEY TO GENERA

1. Protibiae with a single spur (Fig. 216); antennae of male twelve-segmented .... I. *Nacerda* (p. 283)
   Protibiae with two spurs (Fig. 217); antennae of both sexes eleven-segmented 2
2. Right mandible bifid, left one entire .... II. *Alloxacis* (p. 284)
   Both mandibles bifid .... III. *Asclera* (p. 284)

Genus I. *NACERDA* Stephens

Moderate-sized; elongate, subcylindrical; fourth segment of maxillary palpi elongate, triangular; antennae one-half length of body, twelve-segmented in male, eleven-segmented in female; pronotum distinctly constricted at base; protibiae with a single spur.

Nacerda melanura (Linné)   Plate XXXVI, No. 10, p. 361
Elongate-slender, parallel, more or less depressed; dull yellow above; elytra at apex deep purple; legs and undersurface largely piceous. Pronotum widened before middle, narrowed posteriorly; surface rather coarsely and densely punctate. Elytra each with four narrow, slightly elevated lines; disk finely and densely punctate. Length 8–12 mm.

This species is common in woodsheds, cellars, and lumberyards. Originally European, it has been spread by commerce over the world.

Genus II. *ALLOXACIS* Horn

Of moderate size; elongate, pale forms, which resemble Cerambycidae; right mandible bifid, the left entire; maxillary palpi filiform, last segment tapering to apex; antennae eleven-segmented in both sexes; pronotum slightly elongate, widest before middle, gradually tapering to base; elytral costae subobsolete; protibiae with two spurs; tarsal claws broadly dentate basally.

Alloxacis dorsalis (Melsheimer)　　　　　　　Plate XXXVI, No. 11, p. 361

Elongate, slender, subcylindrical; pale yellowish white to dull yellow; pronotum with a longitudinal, dark median vitta and another on side margins; each elytron with two dark, longitudinal vittae uniting near apex, these often broken or entirely lacking. Pronotum with two foveae each side on anterior half; surface densely, finely punctate. Elytra alutaceous, very densely, finely punctate. Length 10–13 mm.

This species is common under or in wet boards, timber, etc.

Genus III. *ASCLERA* Stephens

Elongate, slender, blackish forms; both mandibles bifid; last segment of maxillary palpi triangular; antennae eleven-segmented in both sexes; elytra distinctly costate; protibiae with two spurs; tarsal claws dentate basally.

Asclera ruficollis (Say)　　　　　　　　　　Plate XXXVI, No. 9, p. 361

Elongate, slender; black, not shining; pronotum entirely red. Pronotum broader than long; sides narrowed anteriorly, oblique posteriorly; disk smooth, except for a row of coarse basal punctures and three foveae, one each side of middle, the other before scutellum. Elytra each with three distinct costae; intervals densely and minutely granulate-punctate. Length 5–6.5 mm.

This species is common on willow catkins in early spring, as it is also on the flowers of dogtooth violet, wild plum, black haw, and the like.

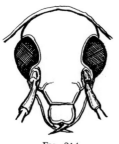

Fig. 214

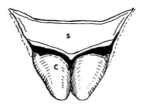

Fig. 215

Fig. 216 Fig. 217

Fig. 214. Head of an oedemerid (*Alloxacis*) viewed from the front.

Fig. 215. Underside of prothorax of *Alloxacis*. *c*, procoxae; *s*, prosternum.

Figs. 216–217. Tip of protibia of *Nacerda* (216) and of *Alloxacis* (217), viewed on inner surface; the former has only a single spur present. A portion of the first tarsal segment is shown.

Family MORDELLIDAE

The Tumbling Flower Beetles

The arched, wedge-shaped, or fusiform body, usually ending in a conical process (Fig. 218), the long, flattened, spiny hind legs, and their habit of jumping and tumbling off the flowers on which they occur in crowds readily distinguish these beetles.

Other family characters are as follows: small; body densely clothed with silky hairs, usually black, sometimes brown, often spotted or banded with yellow or silver; maxillary palpi four-segmented; head vertical, held close to prosternum in repose, suddenly constricted behind eyes; antennae eleven-segmented, slender, slightly thickened apically, inserted at sides of front before eyes; pronotum strongly narrowed anteriorly, as wide as elytra at base, with a distinct marginal line; elytra narrowed and pointed at apex, but exposing the pygidium; front legs short, hind ones generally long; procoxae large, conical, contiguous (Fig. 219), without trochantins, cavities open posteriorly (Fig. 25A); tibiae often dilated, spurs large; metacoxae flat, contiguous, usually very large; metatarsi long, compressed; pro- and mesotarsi five-segmented, metatarsi four-segmented; claws either simple (Fig. 26A, D) or cleft (Fig. 26E) to base, basal part usually pectinate (Fig. 220).

KEY TO GENERA

1. Abdomen with last segment prolonged, conical (Fig. 218); claws cleft and pectinate (Fig. 220); metafemora very robust 3
   Abdomen without anal prolongation; tarsal claws not cleft; metafemora moderate 2
2. Pro- and mesotarsi with third and fourth segments equal ....
   ....IV. *Pentaria*   (p. 292)
   Pro- and mesotarsi with fourth segment very small ....
   ....V. *Anaspis*   (p. 292)
3. Metatibiae with a small, subapical ridge (Fig. 221); eyes finely granulate 4
   Metatibiae and tarsi with oblique ridges on outer face (Fig. 222); eyes coarsely granulate ....III. *Mordellistena*   (p. 291)
4. Scutellum usually emarginate posteriorly; anal style short, obtuse; length over 10 mm. ....I. *Tomoxia*   (p. 287)
   Scutellum triangular; anal style long and slender, length less than 7 mm. ....II. *Mordella*   (p. 290)

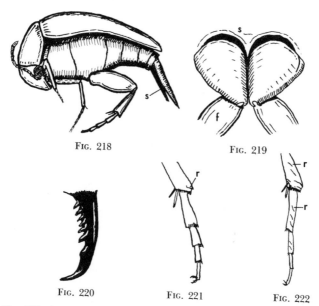

Fig. 218.   Fig. 219.

Fig. 220.   Fig. 221.   Fig. 222.

Fig. 218. Adult mordellid viewed from the side, showing the characteristic arched form and the anal style (s) found on many members.

Fig. 219. Procoxae viewed obliquely anteriorly, with a portion of the
profemur (f) and of the prosternum (s).

Fig. 220. A tarsal claw of *Mordellistena*.

Figs. 221–222. Apex of metafemur and entire metatarsus of *Mordella*
(221) and of *Mordellistena* (222). r, ridge.

Genus I. *TOMOXIA* Costa

Body more or less wedge-shaped; covered with fine pubescence and
finely punctate; antennae serrate; last segment of maxillary palpi more
or less elongate and triangular, robust, apical face concave; scutellum
emarginate posteriorly; pygidium prolonged into a style; sixth ventral
abdominal segment not visible; metafemora robust and flat.

Tomoxia bidentata (Say)   Plate XXX, No. 3, p. 297
Robust, wedge-shaped; brown; pronotum with four ashy-gray stripes
radiating from middle of front margin, anterior and side margins ashy
gray; each elytron with three or four stripes basally, an interrupted band
behind middle, and apex ashy gray, at base with a large, rhomboidal,
brown spot. Length 10–13 mm.

This species is found on dead trees, especially oak and hickory.

PLATE XXIX–A

Family MORDELLIDAE I

1. *Mordellistena pustulata* (Melsheimer) (p. 292)

    Black, with silvery-gray maculae; 2–3 mm.

2. *Mordella melaena* Germar (p. 290)

    Black; 5–7 mm.

3. *M. octopunctata* Fabricius (p. 290)

    Black, with yellowish maculae; 6–7 mm.

4. *M. atrata* Melsheimer (p. 290)

    Black; 3–6 mm.

5. *Mordellistena trifasciata* (Say) (p. 291)

    Black and dull yellowish, the markings variable in form; 2.3–2.8 mm.

6. *Mordella marginata* Melsheimer (p. 290)

    Black, with markings of silvery pubescence; 3–4.5 mm.

7. *Anaspis flavipennis* Haldeman (p. 293)

    Black and brownish yellow; 3–4 mm.

8. *A. rufa* Say (p. 293)

    Dull reddish orange, with piceous markings; 3–4 mm.

9. *Mordellistena scapularis* (Say) (p. 291)

    Black, with reddish-orange maculae; 3.5–5 mm.

10. *M. comata* LeConte (p. 291)

    Black and reddish; 2.8–3.2 mm.

MM 0   10   20   30   40   50   60   70

PLATE XXIX–A

289

Genus II. *MORDELLA* Linné

Moderate-sized, wedge-shaped; covered with pubescence and finely punctate; last segment of maxillary palpi elongate, triangularly and obliquely truncate; scutellum triangular; anal style long and slender; metafemora robust and flat.

KEY TO SPECIES

1. Elytra without conspicuous markings 2
   Elytra with distinct yellow or gray spots 3
2. Deep black, finely pubescent; base of pronotum broadly rounded at middle
   ....a. *melaena*
   Dull black, pubescence brownish; base of pronotum much less rounded
   ....b. *atrata*
3. Elytra each with four yellowish spots ....c. *octopunctata*
   Elytra each with small, silvery, more or less confluent spots ....d. *marginata*

a. *Mordella melaena* Germar   Plate XXIX–A, No. 2, p. 289

Deep, velvety black; base of elytra and body beneath at sides with the pubescence more or less iridescent; base of pygidium with silvery-gray pubescence. Length 5–7 mm.

This species frequents wild-rose blossoms.

b. *Mordella atrata* Melsheimer   Plate XXIX–A, No. 4, p. 289

Dull black, with brownish pubescence; scutellum sometimes ashy gray; meso- and metasternum at sides and apical margins of abdominal sternites more or less ashy or silvery gray. Length 3–6 mm.

This species is found especially on goldenrod, also on other Compositae.

c. *Mordella octopunctata* Fabricius   Plate XXIX–A, No. 3, p. 289

Dark-grayish pubescent; pronotum with a network of grayish-yellow hairs; each elytron with four yellowish spots of pubescence, the basal one broadly curved, partly enclosing a round, black spot, a subhumeral spot narrow and oblique; underparts spotted with ashy gray. Length 6–7 mm.

d. *Mordella marginata* Melsheimer   Plate XXIX–A, No. 6, p. 289

Dark gray; pronotum having the margins, a narrow stripe each side of middle, and a short stripe each side near posterior angles silvery or ashy gray; elytra with small silvery spots, which are more or less confluent, varying in size and disposition; beneath varied with silvery and black. Length 3–4.5 mm.

The adults of this species may be taken from flowers of wild hydrangea, dogwood, and Jersey tea.

Genus III. *MORDELLISTENA* Costa

Small, more or less slender, linear or wedge-shaped; scutellum subtriangular, rounded; anal style long and slender; metatibiae with a subapical, short, transverse ridge (Fig. 222) and with from one to five oblique
ridges on outer face; metatarsi with from one to three ridges on second
and third segments.

KEY TO SPECIES

1. Metatibiae with two oblique ridges on outer face 2
   Metatibiae with three or more short, oblique, parallel ridges 6
2. Metatibial ridges equal in length 3
   Metatibial ridges unequal, upper one extending almost across outer face of
     tibiae ....*e. andreae*
3. First segment of metatarsi with two oblique ridges ....*a. trifasciata*
   First segment of metatarsi with three oblique ridges 4
4. Elytra black, with reddish-orange humeral spot; head black ....*b. scapularis*
   Elytra without distinct humeral spot 5
5. Head wholly or partly reddish; pronotum brick-red, usually with an oblong
     black spot basally ....*c. comata*
   Head and pronotum black; pubescence brownish gray ....*d. aspersa*
6. Metatibiae with three ridges on outer face (Fig. 222) 7
   Metatibiae with four or more ridges on outer face ....*h. pubescens*
7. First segment of metatarsi with three ridges (Fig. 222) ....*f. pustulata*
   First segment of metatarsi with four ridges ....*g. marginalis*

a. *Mordellistena trifasciata* (Say)   Plate XXIX–A, No. 5, p. 289
   Body narrow, nearly parallel; black; pronotum with margin at base and
sides dull yellow; head dull yellow; legs and abdomen tinged with yellow;
elytra with two transverse, yellowish bands. Length 2.3–2.8 mm.

b. *Mordellistena scapularis* (Say)   Plate XXIX–A, No. 9, p. 289
   Slender, elongate-oblong, sides subparallel; head and pronotum black;
elytra black, with a reddish-orange humeral spot; beneath black, apex of
abdomen bright reddish. Length 3.5–5 mm.

c. *Mordellistena comata* LeConte   Plate XXIX–A, No. 10, p. 289
   Slender, elongate-oblong, only slightly wedge-shaped; black; head wholly,
or at least in part, reddish; pronotum brick-red, usually with an oblong
black spot near base; front and middle legs in part dull yellow. Length
2.8–3.2 mm.

d. *Mordellistena aspersa* (Melsheimer)   Plate XXX, No. 1, p. 297
   Slender, sublinear; black, with brownish-gray pubescence rather dense
and evenly distributed. Length 2–3 mm.

e. *Mordellistena andreae* LeConte Plate **XXX**, No. 2, p. 297

Elongate, sublinear; yellow; pronotum sometimes black at base; elytra with base, apex, suture, and a large marginal spot black; forelegs yellow; metatibiae and tarsi dull yellow. Length 2.5–3 mm.

f. *Mordellistena pustulata* (Melsheimer) Plate **XXIX–A**, No. 1, p. 289

Elongate-ovate, sides subparallel, subconvex; black, covered with blackish pubescence and with fine, silvery-gray pubescence forming numerous irregular maculae on elytra. Entire upper surface minutely alutaceous and finely, sparsely asperate. Length 2–3 mm.

g. *Mordellistena marginalis* (Say) Plate **XXX**, No. 4, p. 297

Rather robust, wedge-shaped; black; head and pronotum reddish yellow, head usually spotted with black; pronotum either with base entirely black or with an oblong spot at middle of base and another smaller one on each posterior angle. Length 3–4 mm.

The adults may be taken by sweeping flowering herbs.

h. *Mordellistena pubescens* Fabricius Plate **XXX**, No. 5, p. 297

Rather robust, wedge-shaped; black, with brownish pubescence; pronotum either entirely black or reddish yellow, with a black discal spot; elytra with a spot on humerus and two crossbands yellowish. Length 2.5–3 mm.

This species may be taken by sweeping flowering herbs.

Genus IV. *PENTARIA* Mulsant

Small, fusiform; eyes oval, narrowly emarginate; last dorsal abdominal segment not prolonged into a style; sixth ventral abdominal segment not visible; metafemora not or but feebly dilated; fourth metatarsal segment distinct, slightly shorter than third; claws simple.

Pentaria trifasciatus (Melsheimer) Plate **XXX**, No. 6, p. 297

Elongate-oblong, subdepressed; head, pronotum, legs, and base of antennae dull reddish yellow; elytra yellow, with base, apex, and a broad band behind middle dark brown, basal band sometimes lacking; abdomen and sometimes entire undersurface fuscous. Entire upper surface finely rugose, covered with short, prostrate hairs. Length 3–4 mm.

Genus V. *ANASPIS* Geoffroy

Small, elongate, slender; abdomen not prolonged into a style; fourth segment of pro- and mesotarsi small, almost concealed within the third, which is feebly lobed; claws not cleft, simple; male with two slender appendages between fourth and fifth ventral abdominal segments.

KEY TO SPECIES

Pronotum black ....a. *flavipennis*
Pronotum dull reddish yellow ....b. *rufa*

a. *Anaspis flavipennis* Haldeman   Plate XXIX–A, No. 7, p. 289
Elongate, slender; black; elytra pale brownish yellow; tibiae, tarsi, and mouthparts brownish yellow. Length 3–4 mm.

The adults are found on flowers of haw, viburnum, and huckleberry.

b. *Anaspis rufa* Say   Plate XXIX—A, No. 8, p. 289
Elongate, slender; head yellowish or piceous to a greater or lesser extent; elytra dull reddish yellow; antennae and abdomen fuscous or yellow. Length 3–4 mm.

This species is found on sour-gum, spiraea, maple, and other blossoms.

Family MELOIDAE

The Oil or Blister Beetles

Moderate to large in size; elongate, slender, usually subcylindrical; body and elytra soft in texture; head and elytra wider than pronotum; head constricted far behind eyes into a neck; antennae eleven-segmented, inserted at sides of front; elytra sometimes shortened, when short never truncate apically; legs long; pro- and mesocoxae large, conical, contiguous (Fig. 223); procoxal cavities open posteriorly (Fig. 25A); pro- and mesotarsi five-segmented, metatarsi four-segmented; tarsal claws each usually with a long appendage beneath it (Fig. 224).

The adults at times are very destructive to flowers and foliage; the so-called "old-fashioned potato bug" is a good example of one of the more destructive members of the family and does a great amount of damage to crops. However, many of the larvae feed voraciously upon grasshopper eggs and doubtless are of great value in the control of these pests. In Europe, the adults of one species were used in poultices to raise blisters, whence the common name of this family; some of the United States species also cause blisters when they touch the skin.

KEY TO GENERA

1. Profemora with a silky pubescent patch beneath at apex; antennae
filiform or setaceous ....I. *Epicauta* (p. 295)
Profemora without a silky patch beneath 2
2. Fully winged; elytra long ....II. *Pomphopoea* (p. 298)
Wingless; elytra shortened and overlapping at suture .....III. *Meloë* (p. 299)

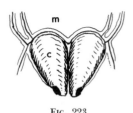

FIG. 223   FIG. 224

Fig. 223. Mesocoxae of a meloid, *Epicauta vittata*. The coxae (*c*) are not separated by the mesosternum (*m*).

Fig. 224. A tarsal claw of *Epicauta*, viewed from the side. *a*, appendage.

294

Genus I. *EPICAUTA* Redtenbacher

Medium-sized to large, elongate, subcylindrical; first antennal segment usually shorter, rarely equal to, and never longer than, third, second segment much shorter than third, third to fifth not elongate, though third may be longest of the segments; elytra without costae; wings nearly always present; metasternum elongate; profemora with patches of silky pubescence beneath near apex; next to last segment of tarsi cylindrical.

KEY TO SPECIES

1. Elytra, head, and pronotum dull clay-yellow, each elytron with two black vittae ....a. *vittata*
   Body above black or grayish 2
2. Elytra uniformly colored, not margined 3
   Elytra black, clothed with grayish hairs, margined externally and at suture with gray ....b. *pestifera*
3. Elytra uniformly black-pubescent ....c. *pensylvanica*
   Elytra uniformly gray-pubescent ....d. *fabricii*

a. *Epicauta vittata* (Fabricius)   Plate XXX, No. 7, p. 297
Elongate, slender, subcylindrical; upper surface dull yellow, body beneath and legs black, head and pronotum with two fuscous vittae; elytra each with two vittae of same color, wider than yellow areas. Entire upper surface finely, densely alutaceous; head and pronotum finely, rather densely punctate; elytra densely, finely granulate. Length 12–18 mm.

This species sometimes damages soybean foliage.

b. *Epicauta pestifera* Werner   Plate XXX, No. 8, p. 297
Elongate, robust; black; head and pronotum densely clothed with gray pubescence and each with two black maculae; elytra with only sutural and lateral margins gray-pubescent; body beneath and legs except tarsi with long, gray pubescence. Pronotum finely, densely punctate, medially at base with a rounded, shallow impression. Elytra densely, finely granulate. Length 6–17 mm.

This is the "old-fashioned" potato beetle that is very destructive to crops; it is found especially on wild flowers, tomatoes, potatoes, clematis, eggplant, and pigweed.

c. *Epicauta pensylvanica* (DeGeer)   The Goldenrod Beetle
                                                   Plate XXX, No. 9, p. 297
Elongate, slender; uniformly dull black, sparsely clothed with black pubescence. Entire surface finely and densely punctate. Pronotum quadrate; anterior angles rounded; median impressed line distinct, basal impression shallow. Scutellum very small. Protibiae with two spiniform spurs in both sexes, inner one longer and more robust, especially in male. Length 7–15 mm.

PLATE XXX

Family MORDELLIDAE II

1. *Mordellistena aspersa* (Melsheimer) (p. 291)

Black, shining; 2–3 mm.

2. *M. andreae* LeConte (p. 292)

Yellow, with blackish markings; 2.5–3 mm.

3. *Tomoxia bidentata* (Say) (p. 287)

Fuscous, with ashy-gray pubescent markings; 10–13 mm.

4. *Mordellistena marginalis* (Say) (p. 292)

Black and reddish yellow; 3–4 mm.

5. *M. pubescens* Fabricius (p. 292)

Black and reddish yellow; 2.5–3 mm.

6. *Pentaria trifasciatus* (Melsheimer) (p. 292)

Reddish yellow, with dark-brown markings which vary in extent; 3–4 mm.

Family MELOIDAE

7. *Epicauta vittata* (Fabricius) (p. 295)

Dull yellow, with blackish vittae; 12–18 mm.

8. *E. pestifera* Werner (p. 295)

Black, with ashy-gray markings; 12–17 mm.

9. *E. pensylvanica* (DeGeer) (p. 295)

Black; 7–15 mm.

10. *E. fabricii* (LeConte) (p. 298)

Black, densely ashy-gray-pubescent; 8–15 mm.

11. *Pomphopoea sayi* LeConte (p. 298)

Bright metallic green, shining; antennae black; legs brownish orange and black; 13–19 mm.

12. *Meloë angusticollis* Say (p. 299)

Dark blue and black; elytra violet; 12–15 mm.

13. *Pomphopoea aenea* Say (p. 298)

Dull metallic green; antennae piceous; legs largely bright yellow; 10–16 mm.

MM 0 10 20 30 40 50 60 70

PLATE XXX

297

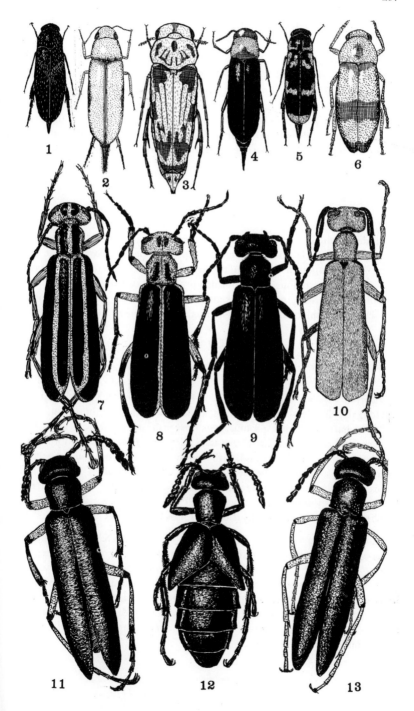

This species occurs most frequently on flowers of goldenrod, although it is sometimes found on flowers of thoroughwort and ironweed.

d. *Epicauta fabricii* (LeConte)   Plate XXX, No. 10, p. 297

Elongate, subcylindrical; black or fuscous, covered with dense, grayish hairs; elytra with dark humeral and scutellar maculae. Male with second segment of antennae longer than third and fourth combined and nearly twice as broad; female with second segment not quite equal to third and fourth together. Pronotum slightly elongate; disk usually with a distinct, glabrous, impressed median line; basal impression small, deep, variable in form. Length 8–15 mm.

Genus II. *POMPHOPOEA* LeConte

Moderate-sized, elongate, slender, subcylindrical; antennae submoniliform; eyes small; labrum prolonged, deeply, bilobedly emarginate at apex (Fig. 225); pronotum campanulate, disk flat; elytra extremely elongate, about five times as long as pronotum; profemora of male without patches of pubescence; tibiae more or less arcuate; tarsi slender, pro- and mesotarsi five-segmented, metatarsi four-segmented, last segment as long as first.

KEY TO SPECIES

Tarsi orange-yellow; body above black with a brassy tinge ....b. *aenea*
Tarsi piceous; body above dark metallic green ....a. *sayi*

a. *Pomphopoea sayi* LeConte   Color Plate B; Plate XXX, No. 11, p. 297

Elongate, slender, subcylindrical; uniformly dark metallic green, without long hairs; antennae piceous; legs brownish orange, femora and tibiae at base and apex black-annulate, tarsi piceous. Head and pronotum minutely, densely alutaceous and with widely scattered, fine punctures; pronotum with a feeble impression medially at base, median longitudinal, impressed line absent. Elytra rather coarsely, densely rugose and with dense, fine punctures interspersed. Length 13–19 mm.

The adult sometimes is injurious to blossoms of fruit trees.

b. *Pomphopoea aenea* Say   Plate XXX, No. 13, p. 297

Elongate, slender, subcylindrical; black, with a strong brassy reflex; antennae and tarsal claws piceous; legs bright orange-yellow, femora and tibiae apically sometimes narrowly annulate with blackish. Head and pronotum minutely alutaceous, sparsely, coarsely punctate; pronotum with a deep, transverse impression at base, median longitudinal line fine, rarely absent. Elytra coarsely, densely rugose, without distinct punctures. Length 10–16 mm.

Genus III. *MELOË* Linné

Large; irregular in outline; bluish, purplish, or black species; head broader than pronotum; antennae of male dilated medially; elytra short, overlapping at suture, divergent apically, exposing most of the abdomen; wings absent; legs rather short, tibial spurs long, outer and sometimes inner one expanded and concave at apex (Fig. 226); tarsal claws cleft, upper and lower parts equal (Fig. 224).

Especially in spring or late autumn the adults may be found on the ground or on low herbs.

Meloë angusticollis Say Plate XXX, No. 12, p. 297

Head and pronotum dark blue; elytra and underparts violaceous. Head finely, deeply, and sparsely punctate. Pronotum narrower than head, nearly one-half longer than wide; sparsely punctate, in male with two small impressions on each side of middle. Elytra finely, shallowly rugose. Length 12–15 mm.

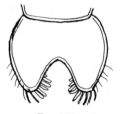

Fig. 225.   Fig. 226.

Fig. 225. Labrum of *Pomphopoea.*
Fig. 226. Tibial spurs of *Meloë angusticollis,* the inner one simple, the outer one strongly expanded and concave at apex.

Family PYROCHROIDAE

The Fire-colored Beetles

This is a small family of moderate-sized, flattened beetles with soft elytra, which are usually black or deep blue, contrasting with the red or yellowish pronotum. Other distinguishing family characters are: head feebly inclined, constricted behind eyes into a distinct neck (Fig. 228); eyes emarginate, coarsely granulate, and sometimes very large; antennae eleven-segmented, inserted at the sides of the front just anterior to eyes, serrate or subpectinate in female, usually flabellate in male; elytra wider than pronotum at base and abdomen, epipleura present only at base; abdomen with five free ventral segments, fifth emarginate at apex, exposing a sixth segment in male; procoxae large, conical, contiguous, cavities widely open posteriorly (Fig. 25A); mesocoxae with distinct trochantins (Fig. 227); tarsi with next to last segment dilated; claws simple.

These beetles are found about dead or decaying trees and come frequently to light.

KEY TO GENERA

1. Eyes very large, dorsally contiguous in male, approximate in female (Fig. 228) ....III. *Dendroides* (p. 302)
   Eyes moderate in size, in both sexes separated by a space at least as wide as one of them 2
2. Last segment of maxillary palpi broad and quadrate, eyes occupying almost entire side of head behind antennae, genae behind them very much reduced; length of body 15–17 mm. .....I. *Neopyrochroa* (p. 300)
   Last segment of maxillary palpi oval; eyes smaller, leaving distinct genae between them and the neck; length of body 6–8 mm. ......
   ....II. *Schizotus* (p. 301)

Genus I. *NEOPYROCHROA* Blair

Large, elongate-oblong, strongly flattened; last segment of maxillary palpi curved and acuminate at apex; antennae subpectinate in female, pectinate or flabellate in male; eyes large, but distinctly separated dorsally, occupying the greater part of the sides of the head; pronotum nearly circular, just feebly transverse; elytra very elongate, slightly widened posteriorly.

Neopyrochroa flabellata (Fabricius)   Plate XLI, No. 8, p. 417

Elongate, depressed; reddish yellow; antennae except two basal segments piceous; elytra black, with sparse, short pubescence. Pronotum distinctly transverse, wider than head, sides and angles rounded; disk smooth, with a broad, median impression basally. Elytra wider behind middle; surface finely granulate-punctate. Male with head broadly concave between eyes. Length 15–17 mm.

The adults occur on foliage in open woodlands and sometimes beneath bark scales.

Genus II. *SCHIZOTUS* Newman

Head porrect, strongly triangular, rounded posteriorly; last segment of maxillary palpi long, oval, apex rounded; antennae subpectinate in female and flabellate in male; pronotum broad, behind each eye with a large fovea; eyes distinct, smaller; elytra broader than pronotum, linear, not widened posteriorly.

Schizotus cervicalis Newman   Plate XLI, No. 6, p. 417

Elongate, subovate, depressed; blackish to piceous, covered with fine, yellowish hairs; front of head, pronotum, and a very narrow sutural and marginal line of elytra dull reddish. Pronotum one-half wider than long; sides and angles rounded; disk with a broad median groove, finely and densely punctate. Elytra very feebly or not at all widened posteriorly; densely granulate-punctate. Length 6–8 mm.

Head of male with a deep fovea each side at base.

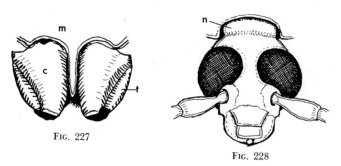

Fig. 227.

Fig. 228.

Fig. 227. Mesocoxae of *Dendroides*. The coxae (*c*) are narrowly separated by the mesosternum (*m*) and are provided with a trochantin (*t*).

Fig. 228. Head of female *Dendroides cyanipennis*, viewed obliquely from above; the eyes are approximate above in this sex, and in actual contact in the male. *n*, neck.

Genus III. *DENDROIDES* Latreille

Elongate, more or less parallel, subdepressed; very soft, fragile forms; last segment of maxillary palpi rounded at apex; eyes very large, contiguous in male, approximate in female; antennae flabellate in male, subpectinate in female; pronotum slightly elongate, sides rounded, narrower at apex than at base; elytra widened posteriorly.

KEY TO SPECIES

Head and elytra piceous, pronotum reddish yellow ....a. *cyanipennis*
Entire upper surface pale yellowish ....b. *concolor*

a. *Dendroides cyanipennis* Latreille   Plate XLI, No. 7, p. 417

Elongate, slender, rather parallel; reddish yellow; head and elytra piceous. Pronotum about as wide as long, widest at middle; disk with a median impression on basal half, surface coarsely, moderately densely punctate. Elytra parallel in male, slightly widened posteriorly in female; disk coarsely, very densely punctate, with three subobsolete costae on apical half. Length 9–13 mm.

This species is usually found beneath bark.

b. *Dendroides concolor* Newman   Plate XLI, No. 9, p. 417

Elongate, slender, parallel; uniformly pale brownish yellow. Pronotum distinctly longer than wide; a median impression at base; surface very sparsely, minutely punctate. Elytral sides subparallel; disks coarsely, rather densely punctate and each with three indistinct costae for its entire length. Length 11–13 mm.

This species is found beneath bark, especially that of pine.

Family ANTHICIDAE

The Antlike Flower Beetles

Some of the adults of the species in this family resemble ants in body form and in being able to run about rapidly; others are somewhat different in body form and bear a prominent horn on the front of the pronotum. The adults are found in spring and summer on flowers and foliage of various trees and shrubs as well as under logs, stones, and rubbish, usually in moist or sandy places. The larvae, some of which are predaceous, live in decaying vegetable matter and fruit.

The family characters are as follows: small to medium-sized; head deflexed, constricted behind eyes into a distinct, slender neck; antennae subfiliform or moniliform, eleven-segmented, inserted before eyes on front of head; pronotum narrower than elytra; elytra rounded at apex and covering abdomen; procoxae conical, prominent, contiguous, cavities confluent (Fig. 158) and open posteriorly; mesocoxae with distinct trochantins; metacoxae transverse; next to last segment of tarsi usually emarginate (Fig. 229); tarsal claws simple; abdomen usually with five free ventral segments, rarely four or six.

KEY TO GENERA

1. Pronotum near apex prolonged into a hornlike process (Fig. 230)
....I. *Notoxus* (p. 303)
Pronotum not prolonged over head 2
2. Pronotum strongly constricted near basal third and then broadened, forming two lobes, the anterior one larger (Fig. 231) ....
....II. *Tomoderus* (p. 305)
Pronotum gradually narrowed to base (Fig. 232) ....III. *Anthicus* (p. 306)

Genus I. *NOTOXUS* Geoffroy

Small, elongate-ovate, subconvex; mandibles emarginate at apex; antennae filiform, apical segments feebly widened, last segment entire; pronotum with a hornlike projection over head; mesocoxae contiguous; five ventral abdominal segments in both sexes; femora subcylindrical, feebly widened at apical third; tarsi short, next to last segment feebly dilated.

KEY TO SPECIES

1. Elytra uniformly purplish black ....a. *murinipennis*
   Elytra more or less variegated 2
2. Elytra black or piceous, with pale markings 3
   Elytra pale, with a single black fascia behind middle which is produced forward along suture for a short distance ....d. *monodon*
3. Elytra each with two large, oblique maculae of pale pinkish; apices truncate in female ....b. *talpa*
   Elytra with two pale-yellowish or pinkish fasciae, one before and one behind middle, both interrupted at suture; apices rounded in both sexes ......
   ....c. *bifasciatus*

a. *Notoxus murinipennis* LeConte   Plate XXXVI, No. 12, p. 361

   Elongate-ovate, rather slender; head and apical half of antennae fuscous; pronotum, legs, and undersurface reddish yellow; elytra purplish black, clothed with fine, recumbent, grayish pubescence. Pronotum oval, slightly transverse; horn broad, obtuse at apex, sides coarsely dentate, crest margined and finely serrate. Elytral apices together rounded in both sexes; disk finely but not densely punctate. Length 3.5 mm.

b. *Notoxus talpa* LaFerté-Sénectère   Plate XXXVI, No. 13, p. 361

   Elongate-ovate, moderately slender; pronotum, antennae, and legs dull reddish brown; head, elytra, and undersurface piceous, elytra each with a large, oblique, pinkish macula extending from humerus to middle of suture, and another of same color, irregular in shape, slightly narrower, on apical third. Pronotum oval, distinctly transverse; horn broadly margined and serrate, the crest abruptly and strongly elevated, distinctly margined, and feebly crenulate. Elytra in male with apices separately rounded, disk obliquely impressed behind humeri; in female apices truncate, disk scarcely impressed; disk finely but not densely punctate. Length 3.5–4 mm.

   This species is more frequent on foliage of hazel and oak along lakes and marshes.

c. *Notoxus bifasciatus* LeConte   Plate XXXVI, No. 16, p. 361

   Elongate-ovate, slender; piceous, shining; pronotum and legs usually reddish brown; elytra with two pale-yellowish or pinkish fasciae, one before and one behind middle, interrupted at suture; finely, sparsely pubescent. Pronotum globose, slightly wider than long; horn moderate in length, distinctly margined, sides feebly serrate, crest abruptly elevated and margined, not serrate. Elytral apices together rounded in both sexes; disk finely, sparsely punctate. Length 3–3.8 mm.

   The adults occur especially on flowers of dogwood and wild cherry.

d. *Notoxus monodon* Fabricius   Plate XXXVI, No. 17, p. 361

   Elongate, slender; dull brownish yellow; elytra with a fascia behind middle, two basal maculae, and often a subhumeral and apical macula on each, piceous; head and sides of pronotum frequently piceous. Pronotum oval, slightly wider than long; disk sparsely, finely punctate; horn broad, margined, and serrate on sides, crest in large specimens distinctly elevated and granulate. Elytral apices rounded together in both sexes; disk coarsely, densely punctate, with rows of erect hairs interspersed with dense, recumbent, grayish pubescence. Length 2.5–4 mm.

This species occurs on foliage and beneath stones and debris in sandy localities.

Genus II. *TOMODERUS* LaFerté-Sénectère

Small, ovate, robust, convex; antennae robust, moniliform, thickened and subperfoliate at apices; eyes small, coarsely faceted; pronotum strongly constricted behind middle; elytral sides strongly, broadly rounded; sides of metasternum dilated; procoxal cavities widely open posteriorly; femora robust, clavate; next to last tarsal segment bilobed.

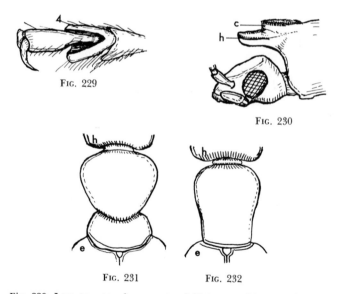

Fig. 229. Last two tarsal segments of *Notoxus*, with a portion of the third; the fourth segment (*4*) is emarginate at its apex.

Fig. 230. *Notoxus bifasciatus*. Head and anterior portion of prothorax in profile. *c*, crest; *h*, horn or anterior process of pronotum.

Figs. 231–232. Pronotum of *Tomoderus* (231) and of *Anthicus* (232), that of the former strongly constricted before base, that of the latter gradually narrowed to base. *e*, elytron; *h*, head.

Tomoderus constrictus (Say)   Plate XXXVI, No. 14, p. 361

Ovate, robust; dark reddish brown to piceous, shining; sparsely pubescent; most of basal half of elytra reddish brown, antennae dark reddish brown, legs slightly paler. Pronotum elongate, strongly constricted behind middle, the anterior lobe subglobose, larger, smooth or nearly so. Elytral apices separately rounded; disk finely, irregularly punctate on apical half, coarser and in more or less distinct rows on pale portion of base. Length 2.5–3 mm.

Genus III. *ANTHICUS* Paykull

Small, oblong-ovate, subconvex; last segment of maxillary palpi moderate in size and hatchet-shaped; antennae filiform, apical segments more or less moniliform, short, gradually thickened apically, last segment entire; pronotum not constricted, evenly convex; sides gradually converging basally; sides of metasternum not dilated but straight and slightly oblique; procoxal cavities open posteriorly; next to last tarsal segment bilobed.

Anthicus cervinus LaFerté-Sénectère   Plate XXXVI, No. 15, p. 361

Oblong-ovate, slender, subconvex; reddish brown, feebly shining, sparsely and finely pubescent; antennae and legs dull yellow; elytra with two piceous fasciae on apical half enclosing a rounded, pale-yellow macula on apical third. Head broad, subtruncate basally, coarsely, sparsely punctate, smoother medially. Pronotum elongate, sides gradually converging basally; disk finely, densely punctate. Elytral apices together rounded; disk finely, densely punctate. Length 2.4–2.7 mm.

This species occurs beneath rubbish and stones in sandy areas.

Family ELATERIDAE

The Click Beetles

If, by accident or through human agency, one of these beetles finds itself upon its back, it has a very singular method of righting itself. The body is bent upward on a loose hinge between the pro- and mesothorax. Then, with a sudden snap, it bends itself in the opposite direction with such force that the whole insect is tossed several inches into the air, turning over and over as it goes. Occasionally several trials are necessary, but it is amazing how frequently the insect will land upon its feet the first time. It is the small and medium-sized species that can "leap" the highest, not infrequently to a height of eight or ten inches; the big ones, such as *Alaus ocellatus*, are often scarcely able to leap more than an inch or two. The "clicking" device is simple enough. Primarily it consists of a long spine on the posterior end of the prosternum which fits into a groove on the mesosternum. In action this spine is inserted into the groove by the raising of the prothorax; its sudden release then causes the springing action —quite comparable to the snapping of our fingers. Other common names given to this group are "spring beetles," "snapping bugs," and "skipjacks."

The adults are often black or dull brown, others are more brilliantly colored, and still others, represented in the South, have luminous maculae as well as some larvae that are luminous. They occur on flowers and herbs and on the leaves of trees and shrubs; often, too, they are found in decaying logs, and many forms come to light. Many species can be found the year round because they live in protected habitats. The food habits of the adults are apparently not very well known; some species are known to be predaceous. However, the larvae, known as "wireworms" (Plate III; No. 18) because of their slender form and hard covering, are frequently very destructive to crops. They live in the soil for several years before they emerge as adults, in the meantime damaging large quantities of corn and grain by eating the seed before it has sprouted. They also damage potatoes and other root crops by boring holes in them and weaken other plants by feeding upon the roots.

Other family characters which distinguish them are: antennae eleven-segmented, more or less serrate (Fig. 20), widely separated, inserted in pits before eyes and under margin of front (Fig. 233); mandibles short, retracted

(Fig. 233); prosternum bears a process as described above (Fig. 234); legs slender, tarsi five-segmented, procoxae small, rounded, without trochantins, cavities open posteriorly; mesocoxae with a small but distinct trochantin (Fig. 234); metacoxae transverse, oblique, contiguous (Figs. 236, 237).

KEY TO GENERA

1. Antennae in repose received in deep grooves on underside of prothorax (Fig. 235) ....I. *Lepidotus* (p. 310)
   Antennae not received in grooves on prosternum 2
2. Meso- and metasternum united, without visible suture ...II. *Alaus* (p. 312)
   Mesosternal suture distinct (Fig. 234) 3
3. Metacoxal plates abruptly dilated near middle, outer portion much narrower than inner (Fig. 236) 4
   Metacoxal plates gradually, sometimes scarcely, dilated on inner side (Fig. 237) 8
4. Margin of front of head elevated behind labrum 5
   Margin of front of head not elevated behind labrum ....
   ....VIII. *Ctenicera* (p. 319)
5. Prosternal spine truncate at apex, fitting like a wedge into notch of mesosternum; scutellum cordate ....XVI. *Cardiophorus* (p. 333)
   Prosternal spine acute at apex; scutellum oval 6
6. Prosternum very broad, sutures single, convex on outer side (Fig. 238) ....X. *Hypolithus* (p. 325)
   Prosternum of moderate width, sutures double, either straight or curved on outer side (Fig. 234) 7
7. One or more of tarsal segments lobed beneath (Fig. 239) ....
   ....III. *Conoderus* (p. 312)
   Tarsal segments not lobed beneath (Fig. 240) 15
8. Front, or clypeus, convex, its edge higher than labrum (Fig. 241); mouth inferior and resting against prosternum in repose (Fig. 241) 9
   Front flattened; mouth horizontal or anterior (Fig. 242) 10
9. Side margins of pronotum bent downward anteriorly (Fig. 243) ....XIII. *Agriotes* (p. 326)
   Side margins of pronotum straight ....XII. *Dalopius* (p. 326)
10. Front margined laterally 11
    Front not margined laterally, usually slightly concave 14
11. Tarsal claws with comblike teeth (Fig. 26J) ....XV. *Melanotus* (p. 332)
    Tarsal claws simple (Fig. 26D) 12
12. First segment of metatarsi scarcely longer than second (Fig. 244) ....V. *Limonius* (p. 317)
    First segment of metatarsi elongate (Fig. 245) 13
13. Prosternal lobe very short (Fig. 246) ....VII. *Denticollis* (p. 319)
    Prosternal lobe long (Fig. 247) ....VI. *Athous* (p. 318)
14. Sides of mesosternal cavity not protuberant (Fig. 248); color rarely uniformly black ....IX. *Hemicrepidius* (p. 324)
    Sides of mesosternal cavity protuberant (Fig. 249); color uniformly black ....XI. *Melanactes* (p. 326)
15. Prosternal sutures excavated anteriorly (Fig. 250) ...XIV. *Ampedus* (p. 328)
    Prosternal sutures not excavated anteriorly ....IV. *Aeolus* (p. 316)

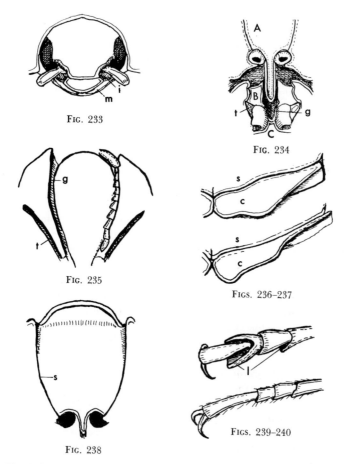

FIG. 233

FIG. 234

FIG. 235

FIGS. 236–237

FIG. 238

FIGS. 239–240

Fig. 233. Head of an elater, *Lepidotus,* viewed obliquely from the front. *i,* antennal insertion; *m,* mandible.

Fig. 234. Central region of underside of thorax. Prosternum (*A*) bears a long process which fits into a groove (*g*) in the mesosternum (*B*). *C,* metasternum; *t,* trochantin of mesocoxae.

Fig. 235. Prothorax of *Lepidotus;* anterior part viewed from beneath. *g,* antennal groove (on the right the antenna is shown in position in the groove); *t,* tarsal groove.

Figs. 236–237. Metacoxa of *Conoderus* (236) and of *Athous* (237); the coxa (*c*) of the former is strongly expanded at its middle, that of the latter only weakly so, the inner portion being widest. *s,* metasternum.

Fig. 238. Prosternum of *Hypolithus. s,* suture.

Figs. 239–240. Tarsus of *Conoderus lividus* (239) and of *Ampedus* (240); only the last four segments are shown. *l,* lobes.

Genus I. *LEPIDOTUS* Stephens

Moderate-sized, elongate, subdepressed; antennal grooves distinct near prosternal sutures, abbreviated posteriorly (Fig. 235); third and fourth segments of antennae equal, much smaller than following segments; prothorax beneath with deep grooves which receive profemora and, in addition, a smaller groove to receive the tarsi (Fig. 235); prosternum lobed anteriorly (Fig. 241).

KEY TO SPECIES

1. Protarsi in repose received in grooves on underside of prothorax (Fig. 235) ..2
   Tarsal grooves entirely absent ....a. *obtectus*
2. Tarsal grooves deep, oblique, distinctly limited, uniting posteriorly with the antennal grooves (Fig. 235) ....b. *marmoratus*
   Tarsal grooves feebly impressed, neither distinctly limited nor joining antennal grooves ....c. *discoideus*

a. *Lepidotus obtectus* (Say) Plate XXXII, No. 1, p. 323

Elongate-oblong, subdepressed; dark reddish brown to piceous, with scattered, pale scales. Pronotum oblong, sides gradually curved from base to apex, with rather broad, flattened margins; disk deeply and broadly grooved at middle. Elytra with two indistinct raised lines basally, one extending beyond middle. Length 14–16 mm.

This species is usually found under bark.

b. *Lepidotus marmoratus* (Fabricius) Plate XXXI, No. 16, p. 315

Elongate, robust, strongly depressed; dark reddish brown, subopaque; sparsely covered with dull-yellow and black scales, those on elytra forming irregular maculae. Pronotum subquadrate; disk subconvex, with a deep median sulcus; sides nearly straight; posterior angles short, acute, strongly divergent; surface densely, coarsely punctate. Elytra gradually, feebly narrowed from base to apex; surface densely, rather coarsely punctate. Length 15–17.5 mm.

This species is frequently gregarious and may be found under bark of logs in moist woods.

c. *Lepidotus discoideus* (Weber) Plate XXXII, No. 2, p. 323

Elongate-oblong, subdepressed; black, more or less shining; head and margins of pronotum thickly covered with golden scales. Pronotum oblong, sides nearly straight, curved near apex; disk with a rather deep median groove; surface densely and coarsely punctate. Elytra densely covered with coarse punctures. Tarsal groove long, shallow, parallel to antennal groove. Length 8–11 mm.

This species is found under bark, in dead logs, etc.

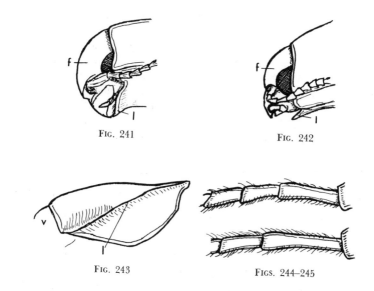

FIG. 241   FIG. 242

FIG. 243   FIGS. 244–245

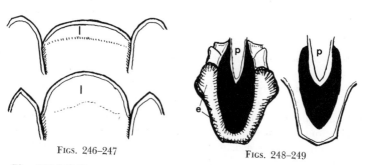

FIGS. 246–247   FIGS. 248–249

Figs. 241–242 Head (in profile) of *Dalopius* (241) and of *Ampedus* (242).
In the former the mouth is close to the prosternal lobe
(*l*), whereas it is well separated from the lobe in the
latter. *f*, front.

Fig. 243. Pronotum of *Agriotes* in profile. *l*, lateral margin; *v*, vertex of
head.

Figs. 244–245. Basal segments of metatarsus in *Limonius* (244) and in
Denticollis (245).

Figs. 246–247. Anterior portion of prosternum of *Denticollis* (246) and
of *Athous* (247). *l*, lobe.

Figs. 248–249. Mesosternum of *Hemicrepidius* (248) and of *Melanactes*
(249). *e*, elevated portion; *p*, prosternal process.

Genus II. *ALAUS* Eschscholtz

Medium-sized to large, elongate, rather robust beetles, distinguished at once by the presence of two large, velvety black spots on pronotal disk; prothorax beneath without antennal grooves; scutellum oval; elytra strongly margined; metacoxal plates gradually dilated on inner side and strongly toothed at insertion of femora (Fig. 236); tarsi not lobed but very pubescent beneath, claws with one or more bristles at base.

The larvae and adults are both frequently predaceous.

KEY TO SPECIES

Eyelike maculae large, rounded, surrounded by a distinct ring of pale scales .. ..a. *oculatus*
Eyelike maculae narrow, elliptical, margin of pale scales indistinct ..b. *myops*

a. *Alaus oculatus* (Linné)   The Eyed Elater
                                                 Plate XXXII, No. 6, p. 323

Elongate, subconvex; black, shining, with many small, irregular maculae of silvery scales; pronotum with eyespots large, almost circular, surrounded by a ring of gray scales. Elytra distinctly striate; intervals convex, finely and sparsely punctate. Length 25–45 mm.

The adults are common in decaying logs in open wooded areas or orchards and occur nearly throughout the year, but are most frequent in spring.

b. *Alaus myops* (Fabricius)   The Blind Elater
                                                 Plate XXXII, No. 9, p. 323

Elongate, subconvex, reddish brown to black, feebly shining, with sparse, irregular, grayish pubescence; pronotal eyespots smaller than in *oculatus*, elliptical, only indistinctly margined with grayish scales. Pronotum elongate, convex, slightly wider anteriorly. Elytra finely, distinctly striate; intervals flattened, densely and finely granulate-punctate. Length 24–38 mm.

The adults are usually found beneath the bark of dead pine trees and are more common in the southern states.

Genus III. *CONODERUS* Eschscholtz

Elongate-oblong, robust; first antennal segment rather elongate; metacoxal plates strongly expanded internally, angles rounded; femora dentate basally; fourth tarsal segment broadly lobed; claws not pectinate.

Most of the species of this genus are bicolored.

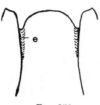

FIG. 250   FIG. 251

Fig. 250. Prosternum of *Ampedus* (anterior portion only). *e,* excavated part of suture.

Fig. 251. Apical segments of tarsus of *Conoderus vespertinus. l,* lamellate lobe.

KEY TO SPECIES

1. Lobe of fourth tarsal segment very broad (Fig. 239); length 10 mm. or more ....a. *lividus*
   Lobe of fourth tarsal segment narrow (Fig. 251); length less than 10 mm. ..2
2. Fourth tarsal segment strongly lamellate beneath, lamellae visible from above (Fig. 251); usually more than 7 mm. long ....b. *vespertinus*
   Fourth tarsal segment with lamellae but not visible from above; usually less than 7 mm. in length 3
3. Species 5 mm. or more in length ....c. *auritus*
   Species 4 mm. or less in length ....d. *bellus*

a. *Conoderus lividus* (DeGeer)   Plate XXXI, No. 12, p. 315

Elongate, subconvex; dull brown, antennae reddish brown, legs yellowish; densely covered with short, prostrate, grayish pubescence. Pronotum slightly elongate, widest at middle, tapering to apex; posterior angles prominent, divergent, and carinate; sides sinuate before base; disk densely, coarsely punctate, the punctures varying in size. Elytral striae deep, with close-set oblong punctures; intervals flat, minutely asperate. Length 11–17 mm.

This species may be beaten from trees and shrubs, especially walnut and hickory.

b. *Conoderus vespertinus* (Fabricius)   Plate XXXII, No. 3, p. 323

Elongate, slender, subconvex; color variable, above usually dark reddish brown to piceous; head with black macula; pronotum yellow medially and laterally; elytra with a broad stripe, extending from humerus to beyond middle, and an apical macula yellow, these markings sometimes reduced to a few small, yellowish maculae on apex and humeri of elytra; scutellum always yellowish, as is the undersurface. Pronotum slightly elongate; sides feebly arcuate, sinuate basally, narrowed apically; posterior

PLATE XXXI

Family PHALACRIDAE

1. *Phalacrus politus* (Melsheimer) (p. 432) — Black, shining; legs and antennae fuscous; 1.5–2.2 mm.

2. *Olibrus semistriatus* LeConte (p. 432) — Dark reddish brown, shining; 1.7–2.3 mm.

3. *Stilbus apicalis* (Melsheimer) (p. 434) — Deep reddish brown, very shining; elytral apices light brown; 1.5–1.8 mm.

4. *S. nitidus* (Melsheimer) (p. 434) — Brownish orange, shining; 1.2–1.4 mm.

5. *Acylomus ergoti* Casey (p. 433) — Reddish brown, shining; antennae and legs yellowish; 1.6–1.8 mm.

Family ENDOMYCHIDAE

6. *Lycoperdina ferruginea* LeConte (p. 428) — Blackish and reddish brown; 4.5–6 mm.

7. *Aphorista vittata* (Fabricius) (p. 428) — Dull orange to reddish; elytral vittae black; 5.5–6.2 mm.

8. *Endomychus biguttatus* Say (p. 429) — Brownish orange and black; 3.5–5 mm.

9. *Mycetina perpulchra* (Newman) (p. 429) — Black and dull orange; 3.5–4 mm.

Family MELASIDAE

10. *Microrhagus pectinatus* LeConte (p. 336) — Fuscous to piceous, shining; 4.5–5 mm.

11. *Melasis pectinicornis* Melsheimer (p. 335) — Blackish; 6–8 mm.

Family ELATERIDAE I

12. *Conoderus lividus* (DeGeer) (p. 313) — Reddish brown, covered with grayish pubescence; 11–17 mm.

13. *Aeolus dorsalis* (Say) (p. 317) — Reddish brown; elytra and legs often yellowish; 4–4.5 mm.

14. *Ampedus sanguinipennis* (Say) (p. 329) — Black; elytra red; 7–8.5 mm.

15. *Hypolithus obliquatulus* (Melsheimer) (p. 325) — Dull reddish to piceous; elytral markings yellow; 2.3–4 mm.

16. *Lepidotus marmoratus* (Fabricius) (p. 310) — Dark reddish brown, marked with whitish and black scales; 15–17.5 mm.

MM 0 10 20 30 40 50 60 70

PLATE XXXI

315

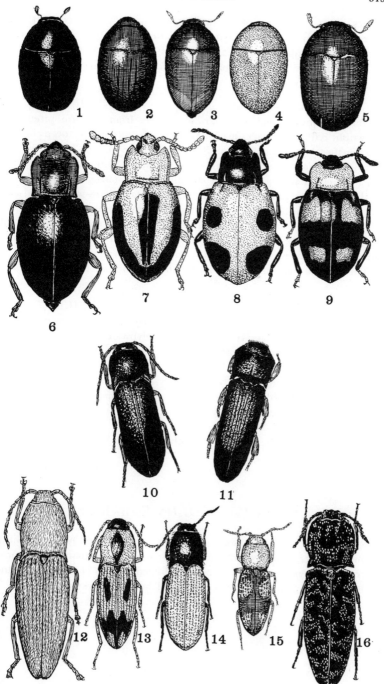

angles acute, feebly carinate near lateral edge, slightly divergent; disk coarsely, closely punctate. Elytral striae indistinctly punctate; intervals nearly flat, indistinctly punctate. Length 7–10 mm.

The adults are found on mullein and foliage; the larvae are injurious to tobacco and truck crops.

c. *Conoderus auritus* (Herbst)   Plate XXXII, No. 4, p. 323

Oblong, robust; color very variable above, from uniform piceous to brownish red with black markings; beneath piceous or deep brown; usually three types occur: (1) uniform piceous or piceous with a median vitta on pronotum; (2) brownish red, pronotum with two small, black maculae, elytra with a macula at scutellum and a fascia near apex black; (3) brownish red, pronotum with two black vittae, elytra with sutural and side margins and apex black. Pronotum convex, feebly elongate; sides slightly arcuate; posterior angles nearly parallel or feebly divergent, carinate; disk densely and rather coarsely punctate. Elytral striae punctate; intervals subconvex, finely, roughly punctate. Length 5–7 mm.

This species may usually be found the year round beneath logs and dead leaves, and in mullein leaves.

d. *Conoderus bellus* (Say)   Plate XXXII, No. 5, p. 323

Oblong, subconvex; black, sparsely yellow-pubescent; pronotum with a median line and posterior angles reddish; elytra dull red, each with two or three black lines, these sometimes connected at middle and near apex by two narrow and sinuous black fasciae; antennae and legs yellowish. Pronotum slightly longer than wide, convex, narrowed apically; sides feebly arcuate on apical half; posterior angles short, obtuse, parallel, carinate; disk sparsely and rather coarsely punctate. Elytra tapering to apex; striae punctate. Length 3.5–4.5 mm.

This species may be found under debris and the like in moist areas; it also comes readily to light.

Genus IV. *AEOLUS* Eschscholtz

Rather small, elongate-oblong, subconvex; antennae feebly serrate, third segment longer than second, the two together longer than fourth; prosternal sutures not excavated anteriorly; dilated portion of metacoxae truncate posteriorly; tarsal segments not lobed beneath; claws simple.

Aeolus dorsalis (Say) Plate XXXI, No. 13, p. 315

Elongate-oblong, subconvex; reddish brown; elytra and legs dull yellowish; head, median diamond-shaped macula or vitta on pronotum, scutellum, macula before middle on each elytron and subapical fascia, black; covered with sparse, yellow pubescence. Pronotum feebly elongate; posterior angles slightly divergent, carinate; sides sinuate in front of posterior angles; disk coarsely punctate, interspaces shining. Elytral striae very coarsely punctate; intervals convex, very finely punctate. Length 4–4.5 mm.

Genus V. *LIMONIUS* Eschscholtz

Small or moderate-sized, rather slender, elongate beetles; front distinctly margined and elevated above labrum (Fig. 241); prosternal groove opened anteriorly (Fig. 252); tarsal segments gradually shorter beginning with first, without lobes; tarsal claws simple.

KEY TO SPECIES

1. Color brown or gray-brown; size 10 mm. or more in length 2
   Color black; size less than 6 mm. 3
2. Antennae much paler than body, third segment distinctly longer than second; pronotal median impressed line indistinct; 10–14 mm. ....a. *griseus*
   Antennae about same color as body; third segment at most feebly longer than second; pronotal median impressed line distinct; 13–18 mm. ....
   ....b. *interstitialis*
3. Pronotal posterior angles same in color as disk and sides; antennae with second and third segments together longer than fourth ....c. *quercinus*
   Pronotal posterior angles pale reddish yellow; antennae with second and third segments together distinctly shorter than fourth ....d. *basillaris*

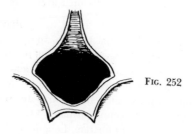

Fig. 252

Fig. 252. Mesosternum of *Limonius*, the cavity for the reception of the prosternal spine without sharp limits anteriorly.

a. *Limonius griseus* Beauvois   Plate XXXII, No. 23, p. 323

Elongate, rather slender; grayish or dark brown; densely clothed with grayish-yellow pubescence on head and pronotum, on elytra more sparsely so; epipleura, apical and side margins of pronotum, and frequently elytral side margins dark reddish. Antennal third segment nearly one-third longer than second, the two together longer but narrower than fourth. Pronotum slightly elongate, narrowed apically. Elytra striate, striae rather coarsely punctate; intervals flat, each with three series of small punctures. Length 10–14 mm.

This species is found on rhubarb flowers, weeds, etc.

b. *Limonius interstitialis* (Melsheimer)   Plate XXXII, No. 24, p. 323

Elongate, rather robust; blackish brown, feebly bronzed, with sparse, yellowish pubescence, denser on head. Antennal third segment scarcely one-fourth longer than second, together slightly shorter than fourth. Pronotum quadrate, sides feebly arcuate before middle; posterior angles acute, strongly carinate; disk rather densely and coarsely punctate, a median impressed line basally. Elytral striae finely punctate; intervals subconvex, rather coarsely punctate. Length 13–18 mm.

These beetles are found on foliage and beneath stones and debris.

c. *Limonius quercinus* (Say)   Plate XXXII, No. 18, p. 323

Elongate-oblong, slender; black, with sparse, gray pubescence; antennae piceous, three basal segments reddish; legs reddish yellow. Clypeus broadly emarginate. Second and third antennal segments together never longer than fourth. Pronotum slightly elongate, convex; sides feebly arcuate; posterior angles short, acute, indistinctly carinate; disk finely and densely punctate. Elytral striae deeply punctate; intervals finely and sparsely punctate. Length 4.5–6 mm.

The adults are found especially on leaves of oak and hazel.

d. *Limonius basillaris* (Say)   Plate XXXII, No. 19, p. 323

Elongate-oblong, slender; black, with sparse, grayish pubescence; posterior angles of pronotum always, lobes of prosternum, and legs reddish yellow. Clypeus broadly emarginate. Second and third antennal segments short, combined length not equaling that of fourth. Pronotum slightly elongate, strongly convex, sides feebly arcuate; posterior angles more obtuse than in *quercinus*, feebly carinate. Elytral striae deeply punctate; intervals finely and sparsely punctate. Length 4–5.5 mm.

These are found on oaks.

Genus VI. *ATHOUS* Eschscholtz

Small or moderate-sized, rather slender beetles; front distinctly margined and elevated behind labrum (Fig. 242); prosternal grooves single, closed anteriorly, lobe long (Fig. 247); first segment of metatarsi elongate, as long as second and third together; tarsal claws simple.

Athous cucullatus (Say)   Plate XXXIII, No. 1, p. 331

Elongate, slender; dark reddish brown or dark brown; antennae and legs slightly paler, with sparse, yellowish pubescence. Clypeus feebly rounded, with a large, triangular impression. Antennae elongate, second segment about one-third as long as third, latter as long as fourth or longer. Pronotum longer than wide, in male sides straight, in female broadly rounded before middle; posterior angles rounded, distinctly carinate; disk densely and coarsely punctate. Elytral striae feebly, sparsely punctate; intervals subconvex, finely, transversely rugose and finely, sparsely punctate. Second and third tarsal segments lobed beneath. Length 10–12 mm.

The larvae of this species are predaceous.

Genus VII. *DENTICOLLIS* Piller and Mitterpacher

Of moderate size, elongate-oblong; front margined anteriorly; antennae eleven-segmented; posterior angles of pronotum not carinate, pronotal sides yellow and translucent; elytra wider than pronotum; prosternal lobe short (Fig. 246); six abdominal sternites at least in male; metatarsi with first segment elongate; tarsal claws simple.

Because of the shape of the elytra and the yellow, translucent margins of the pronotum the members of this genus resemble the Lampyridae.

Denticollis denticornis (Kirby)   Plate XXXIII, No. 2, p. 331

Elongate-oblong, subdepressed; dark brown, subopaque; head (except front and apex), pronotal median line and lateral and apical margins, and elytra with humerus and side margins yellow or reddish; surface covered with long, yellow pubescence. Antennae serrate, second segment globular, third much larger, similar to fourth. Pronotum transverse, sides expanded into an irregular, flattened, translucent margin; posterior angles distinct, acute, divergent; disk very coarsely, densely punctate. Elytra strongly, transversely rugose, striae confused. Length 11–13 mm.

This species may be collected on weeds in damp localities.

Genus VIII. *CTENICERA* Latreille

Elongate, slender, subdepressed; front of head somewhat flattened; clypeal elevated margin interrupted or absent at middle; prosternum with a long lobe (Fig. 247); mesosternal groove bent inward; metacoxal plates less suddenly dilated on inner side, strongly dentate at insertion of femora (Fig. 253); tarsal segments not lobed, pubescent beneath; claws simple.

KEY TO SPECIES

1. Segments three and four of antennae subequal, or third rarely slightly longer
   than fourth 2
   Third segment of antennae distinctly shorter and narrower than fourth; form
   elongate, parallel; uniformly chestnut-brown, shining ....d. *sulcicollis*
2. Antennae serrate; segments four to ten more or less triangular 3
   Antennae not distinctly serrate; segments three to ten usually subcylindrical;
   elytra uniformly dull reddish brown; length 15 mm. or more ....a. *pyrrhos*
3. Third antennal segment triangular, not much narrower than fourth; body
   not strongly robust 4
   Third antennal segment cylindrical, distinctly narrower than fourth; body
   robust 5
4. Color above not uniformly brown or piceous; elytra dull yellow, without spots;
   pronotum black ....c. *tarsalis*
   Color above uniformly dull brown or piceous; elongate, slender, subcylindrical;
   length 11–12.5 mm. ....b. *cylindriformis*
5. Color black, shining; length 15–23 mm. ....e. *aethiops*
   Color not black, length 8–12 mm. 6
6. Elytra dull yellow, with two undulated, darker fascia; form subdepressed ..
   ....g. *hieroglyphica*
   Uniformly bronzed piceous; form convex ....f. *inflata*

a. **Ctenicera pyrrhos** (Herbst)   Plate XXXIII, No. 3, p. 331
   Elongate, slender, subdepressed; dark reddish brown, finely and sparsely
pale-yellow-pubescent. Third segment of antennae equal to fourth and
nearly three times as long as second. Pronotum distinctly elongate, subconvex; sides nearly straight; disk coarsely and densely punctate on sides,
more sparsely so medially; anterior angles distinct; posterior angles strongly
divergent, finely carinate. Elytral striae deep, coarsely punctate; intervals
nearly flat, finely and closely punctate. Length 18–23 mm.
   This species is usually found on walnut, hickory, and other trees.

b. **Ctenicera cylindriformis** (Herbst)   Plate XXXIII, No. 4, p. 331
   Elongate, slender, subcylindrical; blackish brown or piceous, faintly
bronzed, shining; antennae, anterior and posterior margins of pronotum,
legs, and sutural vitta of elytra reddish; surface sparsely gray-pubescent.
Third antennal segment three times as long as second. Pronotum of male
distinctly elongate, sides nearly straight; disk densely and coarsely punctate on sides, more sparsely so medially, median impressed line at base;

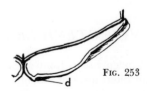

Fig. 253. Metacoxa of *Ctenicera*. d, dentation at insertion of femur.

posterior angles rather strongly divergent, feebly carinate. Pronotum of female quadrate; posterior angles feebly divergent, feebly carinate, canaliculate basally, sparsely punctate. Elytral striae finely, distantly punctate; intervals flat, finely and densely punctate; sides parallel to apical fourth, thence rounded to apices. Length 11.5–19 mm.

These beetles are found on vegetation, usually close to the ground, or under stones in fields.

c. *Ctenicera tarsalis* (Melsheimer)   Plate XXXIII, No. 5, p. 331

Elongate, rather slender, subdepressed; black, shining, sparsely pubescent; elytra dull yellow, suture and lateral margins narrowly edged with black. Antennae with second segment very small, third as wide as and slightly longer than fourth. Pronotum elongate, narrowed anteriorly; disk densely and rather coarsely punctate laterally, more sparsely so medially; posterior angles obtuse, parallel, not carinate. Elytral striae strongly impressed, coarsely punctate; intervals subconvex, finely, densely punctate. Length 9–12 mm.

This is a common species and is found on blossoms of fruit trees, mustard, and rhubarb.

d. *Ctenicera sulcicollis* (Say)   Plate XXXIII, No. 6, p. 331

Elongate, slender, subconvex; reddish brown, shining, with very sparse, inconspicuous, brown pubescence. Third antennal segment twice as long as second, shorter and slightly narrower than fourth. Pronotum slightly elongate, widest at apex; surface rather coarsely and densely punctate, deeply canaliculate the entire length; median line entire and deeply impressed; posterior angles acute, slightly divergent, carinate. Elytral striae deep, punctate; intervals subconvex, alutaceous, finely and densely punctate. Length 14–18 mm.

e. *Ctenicera aethiops* (Herbst)   Plate XXXIII, No. 7, p. 331

Elongate, rather broad, subdepressed; black, shining; antennae and legs brown; surface very sparsely pubescent. Third antennal segment twice as long as second and slightly shorter and distinctly narrower than fourth. Pronotum feebly elongate, narrowed apically; sides slightly arcuate; disk finely, sparsely punctate medially, more coarsely and densely so laterally; median impressed line indistinct; anterior angles rounded, posterior angles slightly divergent, distinctly carinate. Elytral striae strongly impressed, finer and shallow apically, finely and densely punctate; intervals subconvex, closely and coarsely punctate. Length 15–25 mm.

This species is found beneath stones and rubbish, as well as on Virginia creeper.

f. *Ctenicera inflata* (Say)   Plate XXXIII, No. 9, p. 331

Elongate-oblong, very robust, convex; bronzed black; legs and epipleura sometimes reddish; surface covered with dense, prostrate, yellowish pubes-

PLATE XXXII
Family ELATERIDAE II

1. *Lepidotus obtectus* (Say) (p. 310)

   Dull fuscous, with gray scales; 14–16 mm.

2. *L. discoideus* (Weber) (p. 310)

   Dull black; sides of pronotum orangeish; 8–11 mm.

3. *Conoderus vespertinus* (Fabricius) (p. 313)

   Yellow, with brown markings; 7–10 mm.

4. *C. auritus* (Herbst) (p. 316)

   Dull orange, with black markings; 5–7 mm.

5. *C. bellus* (Say) (p. 316)

   Dull orange, with black markings; 3.5–4.5 mm.

6. *Alaus oculatus* (Linné) (p. 312)

   Shining black, with whitish scales; 25–45 mm.

7. *Melanactes piceus* (DeGeer) (p. 326)

   Polished black; 23–32 mm.

8. *Hemicrepidius memnonius* (Herbst) (p. 325)

   Brown, shining; 12–22 mm.

9. *Alaus myops* (Fabricius) (p. 312)

   Covered with brown and gray scales; 24–38 mm.

10. *Ampedus nigricollis* (Herbst) (p. 328)

    Black; elytra dull yellow; 8–12 mm.

11. *A. linteus* (Say) (p. 328)

    Black; elytra dull yellow, with black markings; 7.5–11 mm.

12. *A. rubricus* (Say) (p. 329)

    Black; base of pronotum reddish; 7–9 mm.

13. *A. collaris* (Say) (p. 329)

    Black; pronotum entirely reddish; 8–9 mm.

14. *A. pedalis* (Germar) (p. 329)

    Black; 6–8 mm.

15. *Cardiophorus cardisce* (Say) (p. 333)

    Dull black; elytral markings dull orange; 5.5–8 mm.

16. *C. convexus* (Say) (p. 334)

    Black; 8–10 mm.

17. *C. gagates* Erichson (p. 334)

    Black; 5–8 mm.

18. *Limonius quercinus* (Say) (p. 318)

    Black; elytra piceous; 4.5–6 mm.

19. *L. basillaris* (Say) (p. 318)

    Black; pronotal hind angles and base of elytra pale; 4–5.5 mm.

20. *Melanotus castanipes* (Paykull) (p. 332)

    Red-brown; 15–21 mm.

21. *M. communis* (Gyllenhal) (p. 332)

    Red-brown; 11–15 mm.

22. *M. fissilis* (Say) (p. 333)

    Fuscous; 13–17 mm.

23. *Limonius griseus* Beauvois (p. 318)

    Fuscous, with mats of whitish hairs; 10–14 mm.

24. *L. interstitialis* (Melsheimer) (p. 318)

    Rather dark brown; 13–18 mm.

MM | 0 | 10 | 20 | 30 | 40 | 50 | 60 | 70

PLATE XXXII

323

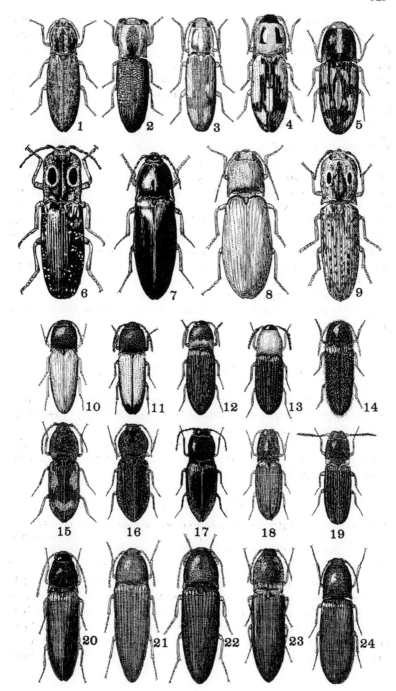

cence. Third antennal segment more than twice as long as second, slightly longer and more slender than fourth. Pronotum subquadrate; sides arcuate; disk coarsely, densely punctate, median impressed line on basal half; anterior angles rounded; posterior angles short, feebly divergent, carinate. Elytral striae strongly impressed, finely punctate; intervals subconvex in male, flat in female, finely rugose and densely, finely punctate. Length 8–12 mm.

This species is found on foliage in open woods.

g. *Ctenicera hieroglyphica* (Say) Plate XXXIII, No. 8, p. 331

Elongate-oblong, robust; head and pronotum black, posterior angles of latter yellow; surface covered with sparse, grayish-yellow pubescence; elytra dull yellow, marked with two fasciae and a narrow vitta, dark brown, first fascia undulated, extending obliquely from humerus to suture, another similar but broader fascia behind middle, which is extended by a sutural spur nearly to apex. Pronotum feebly elongate; sides broadly arcuate; disk coarsely and densely punctate; a feeble median impressed line on basal half; anterior angles rounded; posterior angles short, feebly divergent, indistinctly carinate. Elytral striae coarsely punctate; intervals subdepressed, densely punctate. Length 11–13 mm.

The adults of this species are predaceous and may be found on the foliage of shrubs and trees.

Genus IX. *HEMICREPIDIUS* Germar

Elongate, slender, subdepressed; clypeus more or less flattened, not margined anteriorly; prosternum with a long lobe (Fig. 247); mesosternal groove inclined, not bent inwardly at a right angle; tarsi broadened or lobed, first segment as long as next two together, second and third with a prominent lobe (Fig. 254), fourth small and narrowed, received upon the third, fifth elongate; claws simple.

KEY TO SPECIES

Pronotal posterior angles not divergent; prosternal spine curved (Fig. 255) . . . .
. . . . .b. *memnonius*
Pronotal posterior angles divergent; prosternal spine straight (Fig. 256) . . . . . .
. . . . .a. *decoloratus*

a. *Hemicrepidius decoloratus* (Say) Plate XXXIII, No. 10, p. 331

Elongate-ovate, robust; piceous or black, shining; yellow-pubescent; elytra often dark reddish brown, sometimes base of pronotum reddish; antennae and legs often paler. Pronotum elongate, sides nearly straight in male, arcuate in female; disk rather sparsely and finely punctate; posterior angles carinate, distinctly divergent. Elytral striae closely, rather finely punctate; intervals convex, minutely punctate. Prosternal spine straight or nearly so. Length 9–15 mm.

The adults are usually found on leaves, particularly those of asparagus.

b. *Hemicrepidius memnonius* (Herbst)   Plate XXXII, No. 8, p. 323

Elongate-ovate, robust; varying from piceous to pale brown, antennae and legs somewhat paler; surface sparsely yellow-pubescent, velvety in appearance. Pronotum subquadrate, with sides nearly straight in male, transverse with sides arcuate in female; disk rather densely and coarsely punctate; posterior angles strongly carinate, not divergent. Elytral striae coarsely, shallowly punctate; intervals subconvex, rather densely punctate. Prosternal spine curved. Length 12–22 mm.

This species may be found throughout the year as it hibernates as an adult beneath stones, etc., in dry places.

Genus X. *HYPOLITHUS* Eschscholtz

Small, oblong-ovate, convex; margin of front elevated behind labrum; prosternum broad, sutures single and convex on outer side; epimera of mesothorax do not attain mesocoxae, and the latter are closed only by the meso- and metasternum (Fig. 44); tarsal segments beneath with stiff hairs; claws simple.

Hypolithus obliquatulus (Melsheimer)   Plate XXXI, No. 15, p. 315

Oblong, feebly convex; dark orangeish brown to piceous; each elytron with a median fascia of yellow not attaining suture and with an oval apical macula of same color; antennae and legs yellowish; surface covered with yellowish pubescence. Pronotum transverse, widest at middle; sides arcuate; posterior angles acute, divergent, and carinate; disk finely, sparsely punctate. Elytral punctation finer and sparser than on pronotum, without striae. Length 2.3–4 mm.

This species is found in sandy localities beneath logs and stones and may be taken by sifting.

FIG. 254

Fig. 254. Tarsus of *Hemicrepidius.*

Genus XI. *MELANACTES* LeConte

Large, smooth, shining; antennae serrate, third segment usually slightly longer than fourth; pronotum with posterior angles prominent, strongly carinate; mesosternal groove horizontal, directed forward, the sides of the groove raised and swollen, protuberant (Fig. 249); tarsal segments simple, beneath with a dense brush of hair.

Melanactes piceus (DeGeer)   Plate XXXII, No. 7, p. 323

Elongate, subdepressed; black, smooth, shining; antennae and tarsi piceous. Pronotum slightly elongate, narrowed at base and apex; sides strongly margined; disk very finely and sparsely punctate; sides more densely so. Elytra not striate but with rows of punctures; intervals smooth, very sparsely and minutely punctate. Length 23–32 mm.

The adults are found beneath stones and rubbish in dry localities.

Genus XII. *DALOPIUS* Eschscholtz

Rather small, elongate-oblong, subdepressed; front convex, bent downward at nearly a right angle, not margined behind labrum; antennae slender, subserrate; pronotum with lateral margin straight as viewed from the side, not bent downward anteriorly (Fig. 241); prosternum lobed anteriorly, its sutures double; metacoxal plates only slightly broader medially (Fig. 237); tarsal claws simple.

Dalopius lateralis Eschscholtz   Plate XXXIII, No. 11, p. 331

Elongate, slender, subconvex; piceous or fuscous, with conspicuous yellowish pubescence; apex and posterior angles of pronotum, elytral subhumeral vitta, legs, and basal segments of antennae all yellowish. Pronotum subquadrate, sides parallel to apical fourth, thence rounded to apex; posterior angles acute, prominent, parallel, and carinate; disk rather finely, densely punctate, an indistinct median impressed line basally. Elytral striae distinctly pnctate; intervals flat, finely, densely, and rugosely punctate. Length 5–8 mm.

This species may be beaten from foliage of trees and flowers.

Genus XIII. *AGRIOTES* Eschscholtz

Of moderate size, oblong; front very convex, bent downward at nearly a right angle, not margined behind labrum; antennae slender, subserrate; pronotum with lateral margin bent downward apically, directed toward the lower margin of eye (Fig. 243); prosternum lobed anteriorly, its sutures double (Figs. 246, 248); metacoxal plates but slightly broader medially, dentate above the insertion of femora (Fig. 253); tarsal claws simple.

KEY TO SPECIES

Pronotum broader than long, punctures very coarse and contiguous ..a. *mancus*
Pronotum longer than broad, punctures umbilicate at middle (Fig. 257) ......
....b. *oblongicollis*

a. *Agriotes mancus* (Say)   Plate XXXIII, No. 12, p. 331
    Elongate-oblong, subconvex; yellowish brown; antennae and legs slightly paler; surface covered with sparse, short, yellowish pubescence; head and pronotum often fuscous. Antennae feebly serrate; second, third, and fourth segments subequal, fourth slightly wider. Pronotum slightly transverse, sides regularly arcuate; posterior angles short, carinate, feebly divergent; disk with a feeble median impressed line basally, coarsely and closely punctate. Elytral striae with large, deep punctures; intervals subdepressed, transversely, finely rugose and minutely punctate. Length 7–9 mm.

    The so-called "wheat wireworm" is the larva of this species, and does considerable damage to wheat, potatoes, and other crops.

b. *Agriotes oblongicollis* (Melsheimer)   Plate XXXIII, No. 13, p. 331
    Elongate-oblong, slender, convex; dark reddish brown, antennae and legs slightly paler; surface covered with yellowish pubescence. Antennal second and third segments subequal, together equal to fourth. Pronotum elongate; sides almost straight to near apex, then arcuate; posterior angles carinate, slightly divergent; disk coarsely and densely punctate, punctures umbilicate. Elytral striae deep, with oblong punctures; intervals transversely rugose and minutely punctate. Length 6–9 mm.

    In spring the adults are found especially on red haw, but later in the season they occur on foliage of other plants.

FIGS. 255–256   FIG. 257

Figs. 255–256. Prosternal spine of *Hemicrepidius memnonius* (255) and of *H. decoloratus* (256) in profile. *c,* procoxa.
Fig. 257. A group of umbilicate punctures from the pronotum of *Agriotes oblongicollis.*

Genus XIV. *AMPEDUS* Dejean

Medium or small in size, more or less wedge-shaped; pubescent; front convex, margin elevated behind labrum; antennae serrate or pectinate, third segment feebly wider than second, as long as fourth; pronotum narrowed anteriorly; posterior angles elongate, distinctly carinate; scutellum rounded; prosternal sutures double and excavated anteriorly (Fig. 250); tarsi as long as tibiae, segments one to four gradually shorter, fifth long, ciliate beneath, simple; claws simple.

The larvae of this genus feed on decaying wood; the adults usually are on flowers or under bark.

KEY TO SPECIES

1. Elytra and pronotum of one color ....f. *pedalis*
   Bicolored 2
2. Pronotum not black 3
   Pronotum entirely black 4
3. Pronotum entirely red ....d. *collaris*
   Pronotum bicolored ....c. *rubricus*
4. Legs pale-colored ....a. *nigricollis*
   Legs black or piceous 5
5. Elytra unicolorous ....e. *sanguinipennis*
   Elytra bicolored ....b. *linteus*

a. *Ampedus nigricollis* (Herbst)   Plate XXXII, No. 10, p. 323

Oblong, subdepressed; black; sparsely yellow-pubescent; elytra dull yellow; legs reddish; antennae pale reddish brown. Antennae strongly pectinate (Fig. 21); second segment globular; third triangular, twice as long as second, as long but not as wide as fourth; fourth and remaining segments about as long as wide. Pronotum elongate, gradually narrowed from base to apex; posterior angles acute, feebly divergent, carinate; surface coarsely, densely punctate, the punctures closer and umbilicate (Fig. 257) laterally. Elytral striae feebly impressed, with large punctures; intervals convex, each with a double row of setigerous punctures. Length 8–12 mm.

This species occurs beneath bark and in decayed willow, ironwood, and other logs in moist woodlands.

b. *Ampedus linteus* (Say)   Plate XXXII, No. 11, p. 323

Oblong, subdepressed; black; sparsely pubescent with yellowish hairs; elytra grayish yellow, except suture and apex, which are black; antennae and legs piceous or somewhat paler. Antennae serrate, more strongly so in male; second segment globular, not as wide as fourth in female; remaining segments as long as wide. Pronotum elongate in male, nearly quadrate in female; posterior angles acute, carinate; disk roughly, coarsely, and umbilicately punctate. Elytral striae feeble, coarsely punctate; intervals subconvex, minutely punctate. Length 7.5–11 mm.

The adults live beneath bark of oak and other logs in dry, sandy localities.

c. *Ampedus rubricus* (Say)   Plate XXXII, No. 12, p. 323

Oblong, subconvex; black, with sparse, yellow hairs; basal third to one-half of pronotum and sides of prosternum red; antennae and legs piceous, except three basal segments of antennae and tarsi, which are lighter. Antennae serrate, third segment half again as long as second and nearly as long as fourth; fourth triangular; remaining segments as long as broad. Pronotum slightly transverse; sides feebly arcuate; posterior angles acute, slightly divergent, and sinuate; disk coarsely, sparsely punctate, punctures denser laterally. Elytral striae deep, rather coarsely punctate; intervals feebly convex, slightly rugose, and very finely, sparsely punctate. Length 7–9 mm.

This species is found on flowers and foliage of viburnum and other shrubs.

d. *Ampedus collaris* (Say)   Plate XXXII, No. 13, p. 323

Oblong, rather slender, subconvex; black, shining; covered with sparse, yellow pubescence; prothorax above and its sides beneath bright red; antennae and legs piceous, tarsi paler. Antennae serrate; middle segments as long as wide, second and third subequal, latter shorter than fourth. Pronotum slightly elongate; sides feebly arcuate apically; posterior angles acute, feebly divergent; disk finely and sparsely punctate. Elytral striae feeble, deeply and coarsely punctate; intervals finely rugose, sparsely and very finely punctate. Length 8–9 mm.

This species is found on foliage in the summer, in spring beneath stones and logs.

e. *Ampedus sanguinipennis* (Say)   Plate XXXI, No. 14, p. 315

Elongate-oblong, subconvex; black, brown-pubescent; elytra brick-red; basal segments of antennae and tarsi piceous. Antennae serrate; second segment globular, third one-half again as long as second, longer than fourth; fourth triangular and slightly longer than wide. Pronotum as broad basally as long; sides converging from base to apex; posterior angles short, acute; disk coarsely, sparsely punctate, not becoming denser laterally. Elytral striae feebly impressed with coarse, deep punctures; intervals rather flat, minutely punctate. Length 7–8.5 mm.

This is an easily recognized species which lives beneath loose bark in moist woodlands.

f. *Ampedus pedalis* (Germar)   Plate XXXII, No. 14, p. 323

Elongate-oblong, convex; black, shining, covered with sparse, brown

PLATE XXXIII
Family ELATERIDAE III

1. *Athous cucullatus* (Say) (p. 319) — Dark yellow-brown; 10–12 mm.

2. *Denticollis denticornis* (Kirby) (p. 319) — Dark brown, much of head and pronotum and sides of elytra dull yellow; 11–13 mm.

3. *Ctenicera pyrrhos* (Herbst) (p. 320) — Dark tan; elytra somewhat paler; 18–23 mm.

4. *C. cylindriformis* (Herbst) (p. 320) — Blackish; elytra dark brown; 11.5–19 mm.

5. *C. tarsalis* (Melsheimer) (p. 321) — Black; elytra light tan, with black markings; legs yellowish; 10–11 mm.

6. *C. sulcicollis* (Say) (p. 321) — Dark brown; 14–18 mm.

7. *C. aethiops* (Herbst) (p. 321) — Black; 15–25 mm.

8. *C. hieroglyphica* (Say) (p. 324) — Dark brown; posterior angles of pronotum and legs dull yellow; elytra yellowish, with dark markings; 11–13 mm.

9. *C. inflata* (Say) (p. 321) — Black; 8.5–11 mm.

10. *Hemicrepidius decoloratus* (Say) (p. 324) — Dark brown; 9–15 mm.

11. *Dalopius lateralis* Eschscholtz (p. 326) — Dark brown; elytra yellowish, with black markings; 5–8 mm.

12. *Agriotes mancus* (Say) (p. 327) — Dark brown; pronotal posterior angles and elytral sides dull yellow; 7–9 mm.

13. *A. oblongicollis* (Melsheimer) (p. 327) — Dark yellowish brown; 6–9 mm.

Family BUPRESTIDAE I

14. *Acmaeodera tubulus* (Fabricius) (p. 340) — Black; elytral spots orange; 5–7.5 mm.

15. *A. pulchella* (Herbst) (p. 340) — Black; elytral markings orange; 6–12 mm.

16. *Melanophila aeneola* Melsheimer (p. 348) — Black; dull-green or purplish reflex; 5–6.5 mm.

17. *Buprestis fasciata* Fabricius (p. 348) — Brilliant metallic green; elytral markings yellowish; 12–18 mm.

18. *Melanophila fulvoguttata* (Harris) (p. 349) — Black, with dull-green or coppery reflex; elytral spots tan; 9–12 mm.

19. *M. acuminata* (DeGeer) (p. 349) — Black, with a feeble metallic sheen; 7.5–11 mm.

MM 0 10 20 30 40 50 60 70

PLATE XXXIII

331

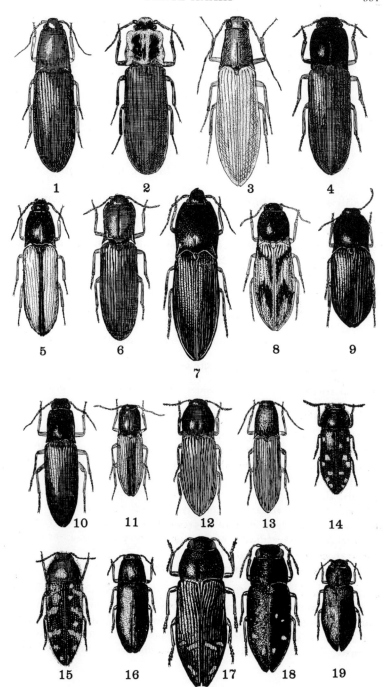

pubescence; legs and antennae dark brown, tarsi paler. Antennae feebly serrate; second and third segments subequal, together slightly longer than fourth, which is twice as wide as long at apex. Pronotum feebly transverse, convex; sides feebly arcuate, converging apically; posterior angles acute, straight, obliquely carinate; disk finely and sparsely punctate. Elytral striae shallow, coarsely, deeply punctate; intervals flat, transversely rugose, and minutely punctate. Length 6–8 mm.

This species may be beaten from vegetation, especially tamarack.

Genus XV. *MELANOTUS* Eschscholtz

Small or moderate-sized; dull brown or black; margin of front elevated behind labrum; antennae serrate, in male segments pilose, first segment broad; prosternum lobed anteriorly (Fig. 246), sutures double and concave externally; metacoxal plates dilated internally, toothed above insertion of femora (Fig. 253); tarsi not lobed; claws pectinate (Fig. 26J).

The larvae of some of the species of this genus are among the most destructive of the "wireworms."

KEY TO SPECIES

1. Antennae with second and third segments subequal, together shorter than
   fourth ....a. *castanipes*
   Antennae with third segment twice as long as second, together as long as or
   longer than fourth 2
2. Color reddish brown; median impressed line on basal half of pronotum ....
   ....b. *communis*
   Color dark brown or piceous; no median line on pronotum ....c. *fissilis*

a. *Melanotus castanipes* (Paykull)   Plate XXXII, No. 20, p. 323

Elongate-ovate; dark reddish brown, covered with sparse pubescence. Antennae with second and third segments subequal, the two together slightly shorter than fourth. Pronotum subquadrate, narrower apically than basally; sides feebly arcuate; posterior angles elongate, acute, each with a distinct, oblique carina; disk coarsely and rather densely punctate, more densely so laterally, a median impressed line on basal half. Elytra with parallel sides; disk with rows of punctures, these each with a row of smaller punctures either side. Length 15–21 mm.

The adults are usually found beneath the loose bark of pine.

b. *Melanotus communis* (Gyllenhal)   Plate XXXII, No. 21, p. 323

Elongate-ovate, slender; reddish brown, slightly pubescent. Antennae with third segment rarely much shorter than fourth. Pronotum subquadrate, sides arcuate, narrowed apically; posterior angles elongate, acute, carinate; disk rather finely punctate, a feeble median impressed line on basal half. Elytra gradually tapering to apex; striae punctate; intervals flat, finely punctate. Length 11–15 mm.

This is probably the most common elater and is abundant under bark of pine logs in winter. The larva does much damage to corn and potatoes.

c. *Melanotus fissilis* (Say)   Plate XXXII, No. 22, p. 323

Elongate-ovate, rather robust; dark brown to piceous, sparsely pubescent. Antennal third segment as least twice as long as second. Pronotum subquadrate; sides arcuate, narrowed apically; posterior angles elongate, acute, each carinate; disk without a median impressed line, coarsely punctate. Elytra gradually narrowed to apex, striae with crenate punctures; intervals flat, sparsely punctate, and transversely rugose. Length 13–17 mm.

The adults may be found beneath loose bark, mullein leaves, and rubbish.

Genus XVI. *CARDIOPHORUS* Eschscholtz

Small, convex; antennae in male with segments three to ten broader in middle than in female; scutellum cordate, emarginate at base; marginal line on side of prothorax becomes inferior and invisible from above; prosternal process short, truncate; mesosternal groove horizontal, anteriorly suddenly bent inward at right angles; tarsi simple; claws simple or dentate.

The heart-shaped scutellum distinguishes the species of this genus from the others.

KEY TO SPECIES

1. Pronotum with posterior angles obliquely truncate; elytra each usually with two yellow maculae; posterior margin of sidepieces of posternum straight . . . . a. *cardisce*
   Pronotum with posterior angles produced and carinate; elytra without maculae; posterior margins of sidepieces of prosternum with a deep notch next to the outer angle 2
2. Sides of mesosternal cavity prominent and nearly vertical anteriorly; upper surface densely covered with short, prostrate, yellowish hairs; legs reddish yellow . . . . b. *convexus*
   Sides of mesosternal cavity not prominent, oblique anteriorly; prosternal process margined behind coxae; pubescence of upper surface sparse; legs wholly black . . . . c. *gagates*

a. *Cardiophorus cardisce* (Say)   Plate XXXII, No. 15, p. 323

Elongate, convex; black, with rather dense, short, yellowish pubescence; elytra each with two yellow maculae, one before middle, other near apex, both varying greatly in size and form and sometimes entirely lacking. Pronotum strongly convex, slightly elongate in male, subquadrate in female; posterior angles parallel; surface finely, densely punctate. Elytra with coarsely punctate striae; intervals subconvex, finely, densely punctate. Body beneath, smooth, shining, finely punctate. Length 5.5–8 mm.

b. *Cardiophorus convexus* (Say)   Plate XXXII, No. 16, p. 323

Elongate, subconvex; black, shining; basal segments of antennae, posterior angles of pronotum, and legs reddish, elytra sometimes piceous; pubescence dense and yellow in fresh specimens. Pronotum slightly longer than wide, broadest at middle, narrowed apically, base tridentate at middle, with a short groove at each side; posterior angles parallel; disk finely and densely punctate. Elytra broader than pronotum, tapering from humerus to apex; striae strongly punctate; intervals subconvex, densely, finely punctate. Undersurface with fine, brownish pubescence, densely punctate. Length 8–10 mm.

The adults are found on foliage and beneath stones in fields.

c. *Cardiophorus gagates* Erichson   Plate XXXII, No. 17, p. 323

Oblong, robust, convex; black, shining, with fine, sparse, grayish-yellow pubescence. Pronotum strongly convex, slightly elongate; base tridentate at middle, with a short groove each side; posterior angles parallel; disk densely and finely punctate. Elytral striae deeply, distantly punctate; intervals flat, finely and densely punctate. Length 5–8 mm.

FIG. 258

FIG. 259

Figs. 258–259. Last segment of maxillary palpus in *Melasis* (258) and in *Microrhagus* (259).

Family MELASIDAE

The Cross-Wood Borers

The beetles belonging to this small family, which was once a part of the family Elateridae, are very active, but most of them do not have the structure to enable them to spring like the click beetles. They also resemble the Buprestidae both in form and habits, in that their bodies are widened anteriorly and they usually occur in wood which is just beginning to decay. Other characters which will help in identifying them are: head convex, deflexed, and resting against the sternum in repose; labrum absent or only slightly visible; prosternum movable but less so than in the Elateridae, without a lobe anteriorly; antennae inserted on front at the inner extremity of transverse grooves, often pectinate, especially in the males.

This family and the following receive their name of "cross-wood borers" from burrows the larvae make across the grain of the wood.

KEY TO GENERA

Last segment of maxillary palpi acute (Fig. 258); bases of antennae
  moderately distant ....I. *Melasis* (p. 335)
Last segment of maxillary palpi dilated (Fig. 259); bases of antennae
  subapproximate ....II. *Microrhagus* (p. 336)

Genus I. *MELASIS* Olivier

Elongate, cylindrical beetles, with the antennae strongly pectinate in male, more feebly so in female; labrum concealed, last segment of maxillary palpi acute; prosternal sutures widely separated and parallel; no antennal grooves on prosternum; metacoxal plates very broad on inner side, narrow externally; last abdominal sternite prolonged, with a slight elevation before apex.

Melasis pectinicornis Melsheimer   Plate XXXI, No. 11, p. 315
    Elongate, subcylindrical; piceous or black, opaque; sparsely clothed with grayish pubescence; antennae reddish brown, scarcely attaining middle of pronotum. Pronotum broader than long, slightly narrowed basally; sides deeply sinuate before posterior angles, which are acute and divergent in

female; disk with a distinct median impressed line, coarsely punctate and granulate. Elytra feebly attenuate behind middle, apices acute; disk with deep, punctate striae; intervals feebly convex, granulate and rugose. Length 6–8 mm.

This species breeds beneath bark of hardwoods and pine.

Genus II. *MICRORHAGUS* Eschscholtz

Small, elongate beetles, with the last segment of the maxillary palpi dilated; antennae at least half as long as body, second segment small, third subequal to fourth and fifth together, fourth to tenth serrate, sometimes pectinate in male; antennal grooves entire, near the middle of prosternum.

The adults may be found on the surface of dead timber on sunny days or in crevices on cloudy ones.

Microrhagus pectinatus LeConte   Plate XXXI, No. 10, p. 315

Elongate-oblong, slightly narrowed behind middle; piceous, moderately shining; legs brownish, tibiae and tarsi paler. Antennae two-thirds the length of body and pectinate in male; one-half body length and acutely serrate in female. Pronotum wider than long, sides parallel, apex rounded, posterior angles finely carinate; disk coarsely but not densely punctate. Elytra equal in width at base to pronotum; obsoletely striate, densely, coarsely punctate. Antennal grooves slightly wider posteriorly, outer carina entire, extending to posterior angles of prosternum. Length 4.5–5 mm.

These beetles are found in decayed logs, particularly those of elm.

Family THROSCIDAE

The Pseudo Click Beetles

In this family of small, oblong, black or brownish forms are found strong resemblances to the Elateridae in shape and in the prosternal spine. Since the spine is firmly attached to the mesosternum, the power of leaping or snapping possessed by the Elateridae is not present. They also resemble the Buprestidae, but the abdominal sternites are all free, not fused as in that family, and the long, pointed basal angles of the pronotum curve around the humeral angles of the elytra. Other characters are as follows: antennae eleven-segmented, inserted on the front of head and in repose received in grooves along inner margins of inflexed portion of prosternum; head retracted to eyes in pronotum; mouthparts in repose covered by an anterior rounded lobe of the prosternum; elytra covering entire abdomen dorsally; pro- and mesocoxae small, rounded, without trochantins, cavities of former closed posteriorly by mesosternum; metacoxae transverse, dilated into a plate partly covering femora; tarsi short, five-segmented, segments one to four with long, membranous lobes beneath; claws simple.

The habits of the larvae are not as well known as those of the adults, which are usually found on flowers.

KEY TO GENERA

Antennae serrate; antennal grooves on prosternum short, straight; no
   tarsal grooves on metasternum ....I. *Drapetes*   (p. 337)
Antennae terminating in a three-segmented club; antennal grooves on
   prosternum long and curved; tarsal grooves present on metasternum
   ....II. *Throscus*   (p. 338)

Genus I. *DRAPETES* Dejean

Members of this genus are brightly colored with red and black (except *D. nitidus* Melsheimer, which is entirely black). Antennae are alike in both sexes, serrate, never clubbed.

Drapetes geminatus Say   Plate XIX, No. 2, p. 181
   Oblong, convex; black, shining, sparsely pubescent; elytra with a broad, subbasal red fascia, this sometimes interrupted at suture or reduced to a

337

rounded macula on each elytron. Pronotum as wide at base as long, gradually narrowing to apex; disk sparsely and rather coarsely punctate; carina of posterior angles extending two-thirds to apex. Elytra slightly wider than pronotum, not striate, finely, irregularly punctate. Length 4 mm.

The adults occur especially on flowers of milkweed, and the larvae are usually in dead hickory.

Genus II. *THROSCUS* Latreille

The antennae in this genus vary between the sexes; in the male the club is one and one-half times the length of and three times as broad as all the preceding segments combined, in the female it is very little longer than the six preceding segments and not more than twice as wide; eyes of male larger and less separated in front.

The members of this genus are dull and uniform in color.

Throscus chevrolati Bonvouloir   Plate XIX, No. 1, p. 181

Oblong, convex; reddish brown, uniformly densely clothed with coarse, yellowish pubescence. Clypeus with two distinct, parallel carinae. Eyes obliquely impressed. Pronotum nearly twice as wide as long, strongly narrowed apically, widest before posterior angles, which are prolonged and indistinctly carinate; disk rather finely and sparsely punctate, basal region not depressed. Elytra slightly narrower than pronotum, narrowed behind middle; disk with distinctly impressed and punctate striae; intervals each with two rows of fine punctures. Length 2.5–2.8 mm.

Family BUPRESTIDAE

The Metallic Wood-boring Beetles

These are usually metallic or otherwise brightly colored beetles, which vary greatly in shape and size; the larger species are mostly elliptical and somewhat flattened, whereas the smaller ones are either elongate-cylindrical or broadly ovate. Other family characteristics which distinguish them are as follows: body very heavily sclerotized; antennae eleven-segmented, short, rather slender, finely serrate (Fig. 20), distal segments with pores (Fig. 260); head retracted into prothorax to eyes; prothorax rigidly attached to remainder of body, so that these beetles, unlike the Elateridae, are incapable of leaping; elytra covering abdomen or leaving one segment exposed; abdomen with five ventral segments, first and second united, the others free; mesosternum divided into two sections (Fig. 261); metacoxae expanded into a plate partially covering the femora (Fig. 262); tarsi five-segmented.

The adults are fond of basking in the sun on flowers, tree trunks or limbs, and leaves and, when disturbed, readily take flight or feign death and drop to the ground. The larvae, known as "flat-headed borers" or "hammerheads" (Plate III, Nos. 19, 20), are very destructive to orchard and forest trees. Some larvae take years to develop into adults; in one instance in the authors' experience it required about eight and a half years.

KEY TO TRIBES

1. Metacoxal plates distinctly dilated internally, cut off externally by a prolongation of the abdomen (Fig. 262); anterior margin straight, posterior oblique 2
   Metacoxal plates scarcely dilated internally 4
2. Prosternum obtusely angulated behind coxae (Fig. 261); metepimera triangular, uncovered (Fig. 262); front not contracted by insertion of antennae 3
   Prosternum acutely angulated behind coxae (Fig. 263); metepimera partly covered by abdomen (Fig. 264); front contracted by insertion of antennae (Fig. 265) ....................CHRYSOBOTHRINI (p. 350)
3. Meso- and metasternum closely united ............CHALCOPHORINI (p. 342)
   Meso- and metasternum separated by a suture (Fig. 261) ..BUPRESTINI (p. 343)
4. Front not narrowed by insertion of antennae; pronotum truncate at base ....POLYCESTINI (p. 340)
   Front narrowed by insertion of antennae (Fig. 265); pronotum lobed at base (Fig. 266) ....AGRILINI (p. 354)

Tribe POLYCESTINI

Genus *ACMAEODERA* Eschscholtz

Small or medium-sized beetles; elongate-ovate, convex; front not narrowed by insertion of antennae; antennae short, serrate from fifth segment, not foveate, but with pores on lower surface; pronotum truncate at base; scutellum indistinct; metepimera partially covered by abdomen; tarsal claws dentate (Fig. 26G, H); metatarsi with first segment elongate.

KEY TO SPECIES

Pronotum with orange or yellow near posterior angles ....a. *pulchella*
Pronotum not maculate at all ....b. *tubulus*

a. *Acmaeodera pulchella* (Herbst)   Plate XXXIII, No. 15, p. 331

Elongate-ovate, convex; deep brown, shining, slightly bronzed; pronotum with a macula of orange or yellow near posterior angles; elytra black, reflexed with metallic colors and with variable orange-yellow markings, usually a broad marginal and a narrow discal vitta at base, two transverse subapical fasciae and a macula at apex; however, the basal vittae may be broken up so that narrow, transverse fasciae are formed. Pronotum strongly transverse; base and apex truncate; disk with a basal fovea each side, densely and coarsely punctate. Elytral lateral margins serrate; disk with finely punctate striae; intervals flat, each with a single row of punctures bearing short, brownish hairs. Length 5.5–12 mm.

The adults frequent flowers, especially those of Jersey tea.

b. *Acmaeodera tubulus* (Fabricius)   Plate XXXIII, No. 14, p. 331

Elongate-ovate, subcylindrical, convex; black, shining, bronzed, covered with sparse, white, erect pubescence; elytra with irregular maculae of yellow or orange. Pronotum strongly transverse; disk with three foveae at base; surface densely punctate. Elytral striae deeply, rather coarsely punctate; sides serrate on apical third. Length 5–7.5 mm.

The adults are on flowers such as wild cranesbill and red haw, and on foliage; the larvae are usually in hickory, white oak, and redbud.

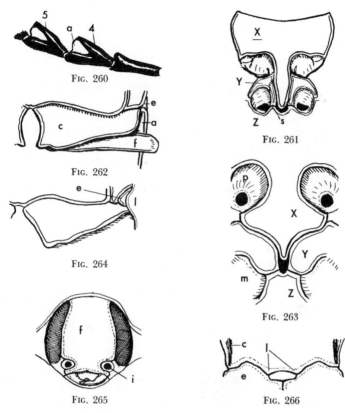

Fig. 260. Several segments of the antenna of *Buprestis*. On the posterior surface of the segments beyond the third, poriferous areas (*a*) are present.

Fig. 261. Undersurface of the thorax in *Buprestis*. The prosternum (*X*) bears a process projecting into a groove in the mesosternum (*Y*) which divides the latter into two portions. *s,* suture; *Z*, metasternum.

Fig. 262. Metacoxa of *Buprestis*, broadened mesially into a plate which conceals much of the femur (*f*). The abdomen (*a*) extends laterad to the coxa (*c*). *e*, metepimeron.

Fig. 263. Prosternal process with portions of the mesosternum and metasternum of *Chrysobothris*. *m*, mesocoxa; *p*, procoxa; *X*, prosternal process; *Y*, mesosternum; *Z*, metasternum.

Fig. 264. Metacoxa of *Chrysobothris*, with metepimeron (*e*) partly covered by a lobe (*l*) of the abdomen.

Fig. 265. Head of *Chrysobothris* viewed from the front, the front (*f*) constricted by the antennal insertions (*i*).

Fig. 266. Pronotal base of *Agrilus*, with a lobe (*l*) before scutellum and a carina (*c*) in posterior angles. *e*, elytron.

Tribe CHALCOPHORINI

Genus *CHALCOPHORA* Solier

Large, elongate-oval, robust; front not narrowed by insertion of antennae; mentum broadly emarginate (Fig. 267) anteriorly; antennae rather robust, nearly as long as head and pronotum together, first segment rather elongate, clavate apically, second segment very short, globular, third slightly shorter than first, more slender and cylindrical, remaining segments longer than wide, obtusely dentate on inner side, with setigerous pores (densely, minutely punctate areas) on both sides, but not distinctly foveate; prosternal process grooved; metatarsi with first segment as long as next two together; males with a distinct sixth ventral abdominal segment.

KEY TO SPECIES

Elytral sutural stria only on apical half; color black, slightly bronzed . . . .
. . . . .a. *virginiensis*
Elytral sutural stria entire; color brassy or cupreous . . . . .b. *liberta*

a. *Chalcophora virginiensis* (Drury)   The Larger Flat-headed Pine Borer
Plate XXXIV, No. 1, p. 347

Elongate-ovate, robust; black, shining, slightly bronzed; undersurface brassy; impressions of pronotum and elytra often brassy. Pronotum transverse, roughly sculptured; sides rounded anteriorly, subparallel basally; disk with a median impression and two each side near basal and apical angles. Elytra with sides parallel, converging apically, slightly serrate toward apex; roughly sculptured, with irregular, smooth, connected costae, separated by irregular, punctate striae; sutural stria only on apical half. Length 20–30 mm.

This species is common in pine areas.

b. *Chalcophora liberta* (Germar)   The Smaller Flat-headed Pine Borer
Plate XXXIV, No. 2, p. 347

Elongate-ovate, robust; cupreous or brassy, shining; antennae, legs, and raised lines on pronotum and elytra dark brown. Pronotum transverse; sides rounded apically, subparallel basally; disk with a median impression and two others each side; surface coarsely, irregularly punctate. Elytral sides parallel, converging apically, not serrate; roughly sculptured, with four irregular, smooth, connected costae, separated by irregular, punctate striae; sutural stria entire. Length 19–24 mm.

The adults are found mostly at the tip of limbs of pines, clinging to the needles with the head inward, eating the young buds. The larvae live in the decaying wood of pines.

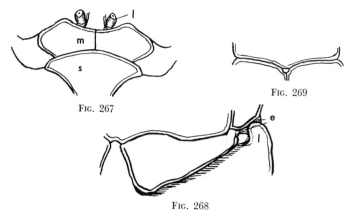

Fig. 267. Mentum of *Chalcophora*. *l*, labial palpus; *m*, mentum; *s*, submentum.

Fig. 268. Metacoxa of *Melanophila*. *l*, lobe of abdomen which partially covers the metepimeron (*e*).

Fig. 269. Pronotal base of *Melanophila*.

Tribe BUPRESTINI

KEY TO GENERA

1. Metepimera triangular, uncovered (Fig. 262); prosternum obtusely angled behind coxae (Fig. 261) 3
   Metepimera partly covered by abdomen (Fig. 268); prosternum acutely angled behind coxae (Fig. 263) 2
2. Mentum coriaceous anteriorly; pronotum sinuate basally (Fig. 269) ....III. *Melanophila* (p. 348)
   Mentum entirely corneous ....IV. *Anthaxia* (p. 349)
3. Elytra regularly sculptured ....II. *Buprestis* (p. 345)
   Elytra with irregularly placed, impressed, densely punctate areas ....I. *Dicerca* (p. 343)

Genus I. *DICERCA* Eschscholtz

Moderate-sized beetles, elongate-ovate, robust; front not narrowed by insertion of antennae; mentum entirely corneous; antennae slender, extending to about middle of pronotum, first segment short, clavate, second and third subequal in length, shorter and more slender than first, fourth longer than third, feebly triangular, remaining segments triangular, dentate on inner side, each with a fovea (enclosing the sensory pores) on lower side near apex; metatarsi with first segment equal to second in length; elytra irregularly sculptured, apices more or less prolonged.

FIG. 270 FIG. 271 FIG. 272

Figs. 270–272. Elytral apices of *Dicerca lurida* (270), *D. divaricata* (271), and *D. punctulata* (272).

KEY TO SPECIES

1. Apices of elytra not dentate 2
   Apices of elytra bidentate (Fig. 270) 3
2. Apices of elytra distinctly prolonged (Fig. 271) ....a. *divaricata*
   Apices of elytra feebly prolonged (Fig. 272) ....b. *punctulata*
3. Smooth median space of pronotum impressed and roughly punctate medially
   ....d. *tuberculata*
   Smooth median space of pronotum very sparsely punctate ....c. *lurida*

a. *Dicerca divaricata* (Say)   Plate XXXIV, No. 3, p. 347

Elongate-ovate, robust, convex; brown or gray, with a coppery, brassy, or greenish bronze; undersurface cupreous, shining. Pronotum strongly transverse, widest near middle; sides feebly angulated at middle; median impressed line shallow, often interrupted, deep basally; sides of disk roughly and coarsely punctate. Elytral apices distinctly prolonged and usually slightly divergent; surface substriate, coarsely punctate, and with scattered, smooth, raised spaces. Length 16–21 mm.

The adults sun on limbs of trees in which they breed; the host trees include apple, peach, pear, cherry, birch, ironwood, black ash, sugar maple, and others.

b. *Dicerca punctulata* (Schönherr)   Plate XXXIV, No. 4, p. 347

Elongate-ovate, robust, convex; grayish brown, feebly shining; pronotum and elytra with smooth, deep-brown streaks and spaces, shining. Pronotum transverse; sides slightly sinuate behind middle, widest before middle, curving distinctly thence to apex; densely, rather coarsely, regularly punctate, except for four smooth, longitudinal, raised spaces on disk, the two center ones broader. Elytra slightly prolonged and feebly divergent at apex; densely, rather coarsely punctate, with only a few scattered, smooth, raised lines and with several rows of much coarser punctures. Length 12–15 mm.

The adults may be captured by beating pitch pine trees, in which they breed.

c. *Dicerca lurida* (Fabricius)   Plate XXXIV, No. 5, p. 347

Elongate-ovate, robust, convex; dark brown, with coppery and greenish bronze, shining; above, along sides, covered with gray pubescence; undersurface cupreous. Pronotum transverse; sides arcuate behind middle, feebly curved to apex, which is not much narrower than base; disk irregularly, densely punctate, with a broad, sparsely punctate, longitudinal space at middle and an indistinct one laterally. Elytral apices feebly prolonged, each bidentate; striae punctate; intervals coarsely punctate; entire surface, especially laterally, with scattered, impressed, densely punctate and pubescent areas. Length 14–19 mm.

The adults occur on trunks and limbs of hickory and alder, in which they also breed.

d. *Dicerca tuberculata* (Castelnau) Plate XXXIV, No. 6, p. 347

Elongate-ovate, robust, convex; dark brown, brassy- and greenish-bronzed, shining; undersurface cupreous. Pronotum transverse; sides angulated before middle; disk with four smooth, elevated spaces, the two at middle broad, separated by a roughly punctate, impressed space, the other two more lateral, short; remainder of surface densely punctate. Elytra punctate-striate, densely punctate, with numerous subtuberculate, smooth, raised spaces; apices feebly prolonged, divergent, each bidentate. Length 13–18 mm.

The adults frequent blossoms of crab apple and other fruit trees and breed in hemlock, pine, and arborvitae.

Genus II. *BUPRESTIS* Linné

Of moderate size, elongate-ovate, robust; front not narrowed by insertion of antennae; mentum with front margin membranous; antennae long and slender, nearly attaining base of pronotum, first segment elongate, more or less clavate, third at least twice as long as second, remaining segments elongate, triangular, dentate internally, foveate beneath at apices; scutellum small, rounded; metatarsi with first segment longer than second; pronotum sinuate basally; elytra narrowed posteriorly, regularly sculptured or smooth; metepimera entirely uncovered.

KEY TO SPECIES

1. Elytra brassy black, immaculate ....b. *maculativentris*
   Elytra with distinct maculae 2
2. Elytra green with yellow markings ....c. *fasciata*
   Elytra brassy black, each with four often more or less connected yellow
   maculae ....a. *lineata*

a. *Buprestis lineata* Fabricius Plate XXXVI, No. 1, p. 361

Elongate-ovate, rather robust, subdepressed; above, black with a brassy tinge; elytra each with four yellowish maculae, these sometimes united to form two broad vittae; undersurface dull orange, head and anterior mar-

PLATE XXXIV
Family BUPRESTIDAE II

1. *Chalcophora virginiensis* (Drury) (p. 342) — Black, with brassy reflex; 20–30 mm.

2. *C. liberta* (Germar) (p. 342) — Black, with brassy reflex; 19–24 mm.

3. *Dicerca divaricata* (Say) (p. 344) — Brassy; 16–20 mm.

4. *D. punctulata* (Schönherr) (p. 344) — Black, with grayish pubescence; 12–15 mm.

5. *D. lurida* (Fabricius) (p. 344) — Brassy black, with grayish pubescence; 15–18 mm.

6. *D. tuberculata* (Castelnau) (p. 345) — Black, with grayish pubescence; 13–18 mm.

7. *Buprestis maculativentris* Say (p. 348) — Black, with metallic-green reflex; 17–20 mm.

8. *Anthaxia viridifrons* Gory (p. 349) — Black, with blue reflex; sides of pronotum coppery and green; front of head brilliant green; 4–6 mm.

9. *A. viridicornis* (Say) (p. 350) — Dull black, with feeble bluish reflex; sides of pronotum dull coppery; 5–6.5 mm.

10. *A. quercata* (Fabricius) (p. 350) — Black, with blue reflex; 4–6 mm.

11. *Chrysobothris sexsignata* (Say) (p. 352) — Black, with blue reflex; elytra each with three impressed metallic marks; 7–11 mm.

12. *C. scitula* Gory (p. 352) — Black, with bright-blue reflex; elytra with a purple reflex and metallic-blue spots; 6–7.5 mm.

13. *C. dentipes* (Germar) (p. 352) — Black and dull grayish; 10–16 mm.

14. *C. floricola* Gory (p. 353) — Metallic black and dull grayish; 8.5–12 mm.

15. *C. pusilla* Castelnau and Gory (p. 352) — Coppery black; elytra with impressed maculae; 5–7.5 mm.

MM 0 10 20 30 40 50 60 70

PLATE XXXIV

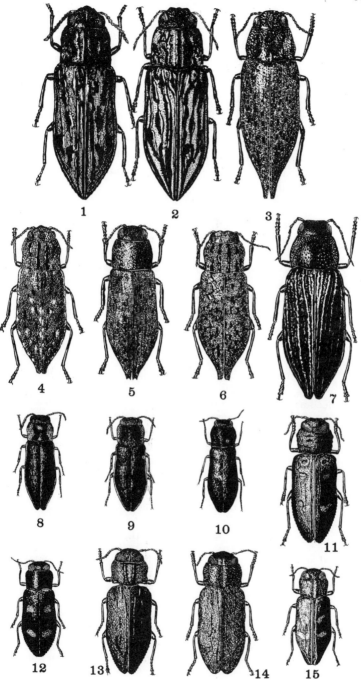

gin of prosternum dull yellowish. Pronotum strongly narrowed from base
to apex; disk sparsely, irregularly, and coarsely punctate. Elytral striae
finely punctate; intervals convex, sparsely and coarsely punctate; apices
each bidentate. Length 11–15 mm.

b. *Buprestis maculativentris* Say   Plate XXXIV, No. 7, p. 347

Elongate-ovate, robust, subconvex; black, feebly brassy- or greenish-
bronzed; portions of head, sometimes anterior angles of pronotum, and
abdominal sternites with lateral spots of yellow, frequently confined to a
single sternite. Pronotum transverse, sides feebly curved to apex, which is
narrower than base; disk coarsely, rather densely, and unevenly punctate.
Elytral striae finely punctate; intervals subconvex, coarsely punctate.
Length 17–20 mm.

The adults occur on and breed in balsam and spruce.

c. *Buprestis fasciata* Fabricius   Plate XXXIII, No. 17, p. 331

Elongate-ovate, robust; metallic green or blue, shining; elytra in female
each with two yellow maculae near apex, margined with black; in male
each with three yellow maculae. Pronotum transverse, with a feeble median
impressed line; surface moderately, sparsely punctate. Elytral striae finely
punctate; intervals subconvex, finely punctate. Length 12–18 mm.

The larvae live in pine, maple, and poplar; the adults sun themselves
on limbs of the infested trees.

Genus III. *MELANOPHILA* Eschscholtz

Rather small or moderate in size, elongate-ovate, subdepressed; front not
narrowed by insertion of antennae; mentum with front margin coriaceous;
antennae with first segment elongate, more or less clavate, third slightly
longer than second, shorter than first; following segments triangular, dentate internally, with a fovea (bearing sensory pores) beneath at apices;
pronotum sinuate at base; elytra regularly sculptured or smooth; metepimeron partially covered by a lateral prolongation of abdomen (Fig. 268);
metatarsi with first segment longer than second.

KEY TO SPECIES

1. Elytral apices rounded 2
   Elytral apices acute .... c. *acuminata*
2. Elytra usually with yellow maculae .... b. *fulvoguttata*
   Elytra without yellow maculae .... a. *aeneola*

a. *Melanophila aeneola* Melsheimer   Plate XXXIII, No. 16, p. 331

Elongate-ovate, moderately subdepressed; black, with a brassy, greenish,
or purple bronze. Head and pronotum finely reticulate, the latter slightly
transverse, sides nearly straight, apex slightly narrower than base. Elytra

densely, rather finely, rugosely punctate; apices rounded. Length 5–6.5 mm.
The adults may be beaten from pine, in which the larvae live.

b. *Melanophila fulvoguttata* (Harris) The Spotted Buprestid
Plate XXXIII, No. 18, p. 331

Elongate-ovate, robust, subconvex; black, shining, brassy-reflexed; elytra
each with three or four small, orange-yellow maculae arranged in a longitudinal arc on apical half, sometimes much reduced in size or, rarely, lacking. Head densely, deeply, rather coarsely punctate. Pronotum rugosely
punctate, transverse; sides feebly but regularly curved; apex narrower than
base. Elytra rugose, with coarse punctures; apices rounded. Length 9–12
mm.

The adults are very common on cut pine logs and also occur on limbs
of spruce and hemlock. This species breeds in various conifers; the larvae
are bark- and wood-borers.

c. *Melanophila acuminata* (DeGeer) Plate XXXIII, No. 19, p. 331

Elongate-ovate, subdepressed; piceous, feebly shining. Head densely and
finely punctate. Pronotum transverse, widest before middle; base and apex
subequal; disk reticulately punctate. Elytra densely, coarsely scabrous, with
a broad, rather deep impression at base; apices acuminate. Length 7.5–11
mm.

Genus IV. *ANTHAXIA* Eschscholtz

Small, oblong-ovate, subdepressed; front not narrowed by insertion of
antennae; mentum entirely corneous; antennae with segments four to
eleven with foveae at apices beneath; pronotum truncate basally; mesosternum narrowly divided from metasternum by a distinct suture (Fig. 263).

KEY TO SPECIES

1. Tarsal claws simple or slightly broader at base; piceous, bronzed 2
   Tarsal claws dentate at base; green, blue, or purple ....c. *quercata*
2. Pronotum with sides broadly and brightly bronzed ....b. *viridicornis*
   Pronotum uniformly colored, or sides narrowly green ....a. *viridifrons*

a. *Anthaxia viridifrons* Gory The Hickory Twig-Borer
Plate XXXIV, No. 8, p. 347

Oblong-ovate, subdepressed; piceous, dully bronzed; head and narrow
side margins of pronotum sometimes green. Pronotum transverse, sides
arcuate; surface reticulately punctate and usually with two broad, shallow
impressions each side. Elytra gradually tapering at apical third; apices obtuse; surface distinctly rugose. Length 4–6 mm.

The adults may be collected from vegetation and come to light; the
larvae occur in American elm and hickory.

b. *Anthaxia viridicornis* (Say)   Plate XXXIV, No. 9, p. 347

Oblong-ovate, subdepressed; piceous, purplish-bronzed; entire front of head and pronotum broadly on sides bright cupreous; undersurface bluish, shining. Pronotum strongly transverse, sides feebly arcuate; disk regularly, reticulately punctate, a transverse impression each side. Elytra finely rugose; apices obtuse. Length 5–6.5 mm.

This species is rather scarce in the eastern states, but is frequent in the central ones. The adults may be found on foliage, and the larvae live in willow, hickory, and elm.

c. *Anthaxia quercata* (Fabricius)   Plate XXXIV, No. 10, p. 347

Oblong-ovate, subdepressed; usually bluish or purple, shining; occasionally green, with pronotum at middle and elytra each with a median vitta, brown. Pronotum strongly transverse; disk deeply impressed each side. Elytra smoother apically than at base; apices obtuse. Length 4–6 mm.

The adults are common on oak leaves and breed in chestnut, redbud, white pine, and American larch.

Tribe CHRYSOBOTHRINI

KEY TO GENERA

Third tarsal segment truncate (Fig. 273); first metatarsal segment elongate ....I. *Chrysobothris* (p. 350)
Third tarsal segment prolonged on each side into a long spine, which extends beyond fourth segment (Fig. 274); first and second metatarsal segments subequal ....II. *Actenodes* (p. 353)

Genus I. *CHRYSOBOTHRIS* Eschscholtz

A genus containing many species, some of which are small, some large, but the majority are moderate in size; body elongate-oval, subdepressed, robust; front narrowed by insertion of antennae; mentum membranous apically; antennae with scape elongate, clavate, second segment short, globular, third elongate, subclavate, remaining segments short, triangular, with a fovea on interior margin of the segments; scutellum large, acuminate; prosternum acutely angulate behind coxae and acute at apex (Fig. 263); profemora strongly dentate; metatarsi with first segment as long as or longer than next three together; tarsi with third segment not armed with two long spines.

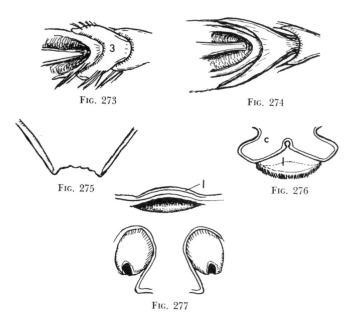

FIG. 273   FIG. 274

FIG. 275   FIG. 276

FIG. 277

Figs. 273–274. Third tarsal segment of *Chrysobothris* (273) and of
Actenodes (274), with portions of adjacent segments.
Fig. 275. Apex of last abdominal sternite in *Chrysobothris femorata*.
Fig. 276. Clypeus (*c*) of *Chrysobothris femorata*. *l*, labrum.
Fig. 277. Prosternum of *Chrysobothris floricola*. *l*, lobe.

KEY TO SPECIES

1. Last abdominal sternite dentate laterally (Fig. 275) 3
   Last abdominal sternite not dentate laterally 2
2. Color bronze, with coppery markings on elytra; elytra costate ..a. *sexsignata*
   Color purple; elytra without costae ....b. *scitula*
3. Clypeus acutely and deeply notched, the lobes forming semicircles in outline
   (Fig. 276); male with protibiae curved as usual, and with numerous fine
   teeth on inner edge ....f. *femorata*
   Clypeus not as above; male with protibiae curved, with at most one tooth on
   inner edge 4
4. Male with protibiae and metatibiae curved; female with protibiae curved,
   metatibiae straight ....g. *scabripennis*
   Male with only protibiae curved; female with all tibiae straight 5
5. Prosternum distinctly lobed anteriorly (Fig. 277) 6
   Prosternum not lobed anteriorly ....d. *dentipes*
6. Clypeus truncate medially ....e. *floricola*
   Clypeus with a broad, triangular emargination at middle ....c. *pusilla*

a. *Chrysobothris sexsignata* (Say) Plate XXXIV, No. 11, p. 347

Elongate-ovate, subdepressed; piceous, feebly bronzed, shining; elytra each with three impressed metallic spots, at base, at middle, and at apical third; undersurface green, laterally bronzed. Clypeus triangularly emarginate at middle. Pronotum strongly transverse; posterior angles obtuse; disk densely and coarsely punctate, transversely strigose, frequently indistinctly impressed at base and on each side near apex. Elytra feebly costate, lateral one more distinct, entire; disk densely and coarsely punctate, with a shallow impression at apical third and a larger one anterior to middle, basal fovea deep; apices obtuse. Length 7–11 mm.

The larvae live in dead branches of hickory, oak, beech, birch, ash, and hemlock.

b. *Chrysobothris scitula* Gory Plate XXXIV, No. 12, p. 347

Elongate-ovate, moderately convex; usually purplish-bronzed, shining; elytra medially faintly piceous, laterally purple, each with three bright blue or green impressed maculae, one at middle, one at base, third near apex. Clypeus finely, triangularly emarginate at middle. Pronotum transverse, not impressed; densely and coarsely punctate, transversely strigose laterally. Elytral lateral margins serrate; disk coarsely, rather densely punctate, not costate; apices obtusely rounded; each elytron with a basal and two discal foveae. Length 6–7.5 mm.

The larvae live in alder, white birch, and oak.

c. *Chrysobothris pusilla* Castelnau and Gory Plate XXXIV, No. 15, p. 347

Elongate-ovate, subconvex; uniformly coppery bronze. Clypeus with a broad, triangular emargination at middle, truncate each side. Pronotum strongly transverse, sides more or less parallel, feebly curved; disk coarsely punctate, with a feeble median impressed line. Elytra feebly costate, with three irregular, broad foveae, one at base, one at middle, and one at apical third; surface coarsely, not densely punctate; apices obtuse. Prosternum with a short, but distinct, lobe anteriorly; last ventral abdominal segment serrulate. Length 5–7.5 mm.

The adults are found on hard pine and breed in pine, hemlock, and spruce.

d. *Chrysobothris dentipes* (Germar) Plate XXXIV, No. 13, p. 347

Elongate-ovate, subdepressed; piceous, bronzed, shining. Clypeus broadly, triangularly emarginate at middle, rounded each side. Pronotum strongly transverse; disk with a distinct median impressed line; surface densely, coarsely, irregularly punctate, with irregular, smooth, raised spaces, entire surface transversely strigose. Elytra coarsely and densely punctate, with irregular, smooth, raised areas and lines; lateral margins serrate. Length 10–16 mm.

The larvae are found in white pine and tamarack.

e. *Chrysobothris floricola* Gory   Plate XXXIV, No. 14, p. 347

Elongate, more or less oblong, subdepressed; dark bronze, slightly tinged with coppery. Clypeus truncate medially. Pronotum transverse, sides narrowed posteriorly and anteriorly; disk with median impressed line distinct, an irregular impression each side, coarsely, densely punctate, more sparsely so medially. Elytra narrowed from behind middle to apex, sides somewhat serrate; apices rounded; disk densely punctate, more sparsely so basally, feebly costate, external costae rather distinct; basal and medial impressions shallow, apical one distinct, double. Prosternum usually distinctly lobed anteriorly. Protibiae of male unidentate beyond middle. Length 8.5–12 mm.

The adults occur on pine branches and young needles and breed in pines.

f. *Chrysobothris femorata* (Olivier)   The Flat-headed Apple-Tree Borer
                                                Plate XXXV, No. 2, p. 357

Elongate-oblong, subdepressed; dark bronze, sometimes with brassy or cupreous tinge. Clypeus acutely and deeply emarginate medially, lobes each side semicircular. Pronotum strongly transverse, widest near apex; disk densely and coarsely punctate, more sparsely so near middle, median impressed line indistinct, with several impressions laterally and a deep one each side at apex. Elytra gradually narrowed from behind middle to apex; sides serrate; apices obtuse; sculpturing very variable, usually with two lateral costae which are distinct apically; basal impression usually obsolete; coarsely and densely punctate. Male with numerous fine teeth on protibiae internally. Length 7–16 mm.

This beetle breeds in many hardwood trees; it sometimes is very injurious, often to apple and other orchard trees. The adults are usually found on trunks of trees.

g. *Chrysobothris scabripennis* Castelnau   Plate XXXV, No. 1, p. 357

Elongate-oblong, subdepressed; black, reflexed with brassy or green; beneath coppery. Clypeus broadly emarginate medially, rounded each side. Pronotum strongly transverse, narrowed at base and apex, sides nearly parallel medially; disk with median impression densely punctate, bordered each side by an irregular, smooth callus; surface laterally irregularly, densely punctate. Elytral sides parallel basally, arcuate apically; apices each broadly, obtusely rounded; lateral margins serrulate; disk of each elytron with four costae, interrupted by converging lines and by shining, depressed, densely punctate areas. Length 8.5–10.5 mm.

The adults are borers in dead white pine, hemlock, and spruce.

Genus II. *ACTENODES* Lacordaire

Of moderate size, elongate-ovate, robust, subdepressed; front narrowed by insertion of antennae (Fig. 265); antennae dentate from fourth segment to apex, these segments with foveae beneath near apex; scutellum small; profemora usually dentate; metatarsi with first segment as short as second; tarsi with third segment having two long spines, which extend beyond fourth (Fig. 274).

Actenodes acornis (Say) Plate XXXV, No. 3, p. 357

Elongate-ovate, robust, subdepressed; black, tinged with bronze or green; undersurface cupreous. Eyes prominent, nearly united on vertex. Clypeus very broadly and feebly emarginate at middle. Pronotum strongly transverse; posterior angles dentate; disk densely and coarsely punctate, strigose, transversely impressed before base. Elytra with a feeble, irregular impression, not costate; disk densely, transversely strigose; sides serrate. Length 10–13 mm.

The adults are found on vegetation and foliage and breed in the dead wood of red maple, beech, birch, black oak, and hickory.

Tribe Agrilini

KEY TO GENERA

1. Antennae free .... I. *Agrilus* (p. 354)
   Antennae received in grooves 2
2. Scutellum small; tibiae linear 3
   Scutellum large .... II. *Pachyschelus* (p. 359)
3. Body elongate .... IV. *Taphrocerus* (p. 363)
   Body ovate .... III. *Brachys* (p. 362)

Genus I. *AGRILUS* Stephens

Small, elongate-oblong, slender, subcylindrical; front narrowed by insertion of antennae (Fig. 265); antennae not received in grooves on underside of prothorax, serrate from fourth or fifth segment, segments foveate beneath at apices; pronotum sinuate at base; scutellum transverse and acuminate; prosternum acuminate posteriorly (Fig. 278); mesocoxae not more widely separated than procoxae; femora not serrate on inner edge.

KEY TO SPECIES

1. Elytra with a vitta or maculae 2
   Elytra immaculate 3
2. Elytra each with a fine, bronze vitta .... a. *bilineatus*
   Elytra each with a white vitta interrupted apically, sometimes reduced to a very small macula at apex .... h. *obsoletoguttatus*
3. Pronotum a contrasting color to elytra 4
   Pronotum and elytra similarly colored 5

4. Pygidium carinate, carina prolonged as a short spine visible between apices of elytra (Fig. 279) ....c. *ruficollis*
   Pygidium not carinate nor spined ....e. *arcuatus*
5. Size smaller, 3–5 mm. 6
   Size larger, 5–13 mm. 7
6. Pronotum with a distinct median impressed line, at least basally; antennae serrate from fifth segment ....d. *egenus*
   Pronotum without median impressed line; antennae serrate from fourth segment ....f. *otiosus*
7. Pygidium carinate, carina prolonged as a short spine visible between elytral apices (Fig. 279) ....b. *anxius*
   Pygidium not carinate or spined ....g. *politus*

a. *Agrilus bilineatus* (Weber) The Two-lined Chestnut Borer
Plate XXXV, No. 4, p. 357

Elongate, subcylindrical; black, subopaque, sometimes tinged with blue or green; a narrow line of brown-yellow, or bronze, along lateral edges of pronotum and sinuately over disk of elytra to extreme apex; undersurface greenish black, feebly shining. Pronotum transverse, narrower at base; sides feebly rounded and feebly sinuate near base; posterior angles rectangular; disk finely, transversely strigose, feebly impressed medially and on each side. Scutellum transversely carinate. Elytral sides broadly sinuate basally; apices rounded, finely serrate; surface densely granulate. Prosternal lobe truncate anteriorly. Length 5–9.5 mm.

This beetle attacks various dead and dying oaks and chestnut.

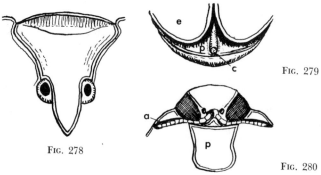

Fig. 278. Prosternum of *Agrilus*.
Fig. 279. Posterior end of body of *Agrilus ruficollis*, viewed obliquely from behind. *c*, carina; *e*, elytral apex; *p*, pygidium.
Fig. 280. Head and portion of prothorax of *Pachyschelus*, viewed from beneath. *a*, antennal groove; *p*, prosternum.

PLATE XXXV

Family BUPRESTIDAE III

1. *Chrysobothris scabripennis* Castelnau (p. 353)

   Black, with green and brassy reflexes; 8.5–10.5 mm.

2. *C. femorata* (Olivier) (p. 353)

   Black, with a coppery reflex; 7–16 mm.

3. *Actenodes acornis* (Say) (p. 354)

   Black, with green and bronze reflexes; 10–13 mm.

4. *Agrilus bilineatus* (Weber) (p. 355)

   Green-black, with indistinct brassy lines; 5–9.5 mm.

5. *A. ruficollis* (Fabricius) (p. 358)

   Blue-black, pronotum metallic red; 4–7 mm.

6. *A. arcuatus* (Say) ♀ (p. 358)

   Blue-black, head and pronotum coppery; 5–9 mm.

7. *A. arcuatus* (Say) ♂ (p. 358)

   Black, with brassy and green reflexes; 5–9 mm.

8. *A. politus* (Say) (p. 359)

   Metallic green, with blue and bronze reflexes; 5–8.5 mm.

9. *A. obsoletoguttatus* Gory (p. 359)

   Brassy black; pronotum indistinctly margined with dull pubescence; 5–8 mm.

10. *Pachyschelus purpureus* (Say) (p. 362)

    Black; elytra blue-black, with an indistinct preapical whitish band; 3–3.5 mm.

11. *Agrilus egenus* Gory (p. 358)

    Black; male with a small, whitish spot on side of pronotum; 3.5–5 mm.

12. *Pachyschelus laevigatus* (Say) (p. 362)

    Black; 2.5–3 mm.

13. *Agrilus otiosus* Say (p. 359)

    Black; 3.5–5 mm.

14. *Brachys aerosus* Melsheimer (p. 362)

    Blue-black, with brassy reflex and fulvous markings; 4–4.5 mm.

15. *B. ovatus* (Weber) (p. 363)

    Bluish black, with blue reflex and brassy markings; 5–7 mm.

16. *Agrilus anxius* Gory (p. 358)

    Olive-black, sometimes tinged with coppery; 6–13 mm.

17. *Brachys aeruginosus* Gory (p. 363)

    Bluish black; markings largely white, with sparse, fulvous pubescence intermixed; 3–4 mm.

18. *Taphrocerus gracilis* (Say) (p. 363)

    Black, reflexed with green and bronze; 3–5 mm.

MM 0 10 20 30 40 50 60 70

PLATE XXXV

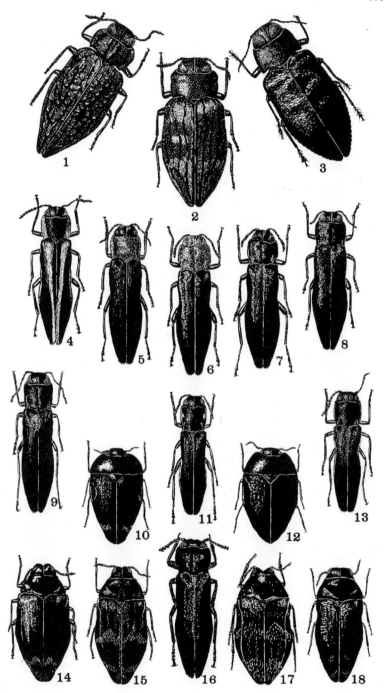

b. *Agrilus anxius* Gory   The Bronze Birch Borer
                                                     Plate XXXV, No. 16, p. 357

Elongate, subcylindrical; olive-black, sometimes with coppery tinge, sub-opaque; undersurface more greenish and more shining. Pronotum slightly transverse, base narrower than apex, widest at middle; sides broadly arcuate, feebly sinuate at base; posterior angles somewhat acute, a distinct carina before humerus each side, and a feeble impression at middle and laterally; surface finely, transversely strigose. Scutellum transversely carinate. Elytra slightly broader behind middle; disk strigosely punctate, becoming densely granulate apically; apices each rounded, finely serrate. Prosternal lobe distinctly emarginate at middle. Pygidium with a strong carina (Fig. 279). Length 6–13 mm.

These beetles are found on various species of birch, willow, and poplar.

c. *Agrilus ruficollis* (Fabricius)   Plate XXXV, No. 5, p. 357

Elongate, subcylindrical; black or bluish black, feebly shining; head and pronotum bright coppery. Pronotum slightly transverse, apex slightly wider than base; sides feebly rounded; posterior angles rectangular, not carinate; disk feebly impressed each side and more deeply so at middle, finely, densely, transversely strigose. Scutellum transversely carinate. Elytra feebly wider behind middle, each apex rounded and finely serrate; disk deeply impressed basally, densely, finely granulate. Prosternum with lobe obtusely rounded anteriorly. Pygidium strongly carinate. Length 4–7 mm.

Considerable damage is done to living blackberry, raspberry, and dewberry bushes by these beetles' boring in their stems and causing a gall.

d. *Agrilus egenus* Gory   Plate XXXV, No. 11, p. 357

Elongate, subcylindrical; black, feebly shining, brownish- or greenish-bronzed; head sometimes light green. Antennae serrate from fifth (inclusive) segment, not from fourth. Pronotum slightly transverse, sides subparallel, feebly rounded basally; carinate near posterior angles; disk impressed each side, finely punctate and transversely strigose. Scutellum transversely carinate. Elytra slightly wider behind middle; apices each rounded, finely serrate; disk feebly but broadly impressed along suture, deeply so basally, densely, imbricately granulate. Prosternum emarginate. Pygidium not carinate. Length 3.5–5 mm.

The adults are found on woodbine, locust, and hickory, in which plants the larvae live.

e. *Agrilus arcuatus* (Say)   Plate XXXV, Nos. 6, 7, p. 357

Elongate, subcylindrical; brown; head and pronotum cupreous or brassy; elytra black or blue. Pronotum transverse, not narrowed basally, sides regularly rounded; apex and base subequal, widest at middle; disk bi-impressed medially, obliquely impressed each side, slightly arcuately carinate near posterior angles, finely punctate and transversely strigose. Scutellum feebly, transversely carinate. Elytra widened behind middle; apices each rounded, finely serrate; disk densely granulate, deeply impressed basally. Prosternal lobe broadly emarginate. Pygidium without carina. Length 5–9 mm.

This beetle occurs in beech, hickory, white oak, and hazel.

f. *Agrilus otiosus* Say   Plate XXXV, No. 13, p. 357

Elongate, slender, subcylindrical; dark green, shining, bronzed; pronotum with sides and head bluish; elytra piceous, tinged with bronze or greenish. Pronotum feebly transverse; posterior angles indistinctly carinate in male, distinctly so in female; disk obliquely impressed each side, two impressions on median line, transversely strigose and finely punctate. Scutellum transversely carinate. Elytra slightly wider behind middle; apices rounded, finely serrate; disk granulate and distinctly impressed basally, with a feeble costa extending from humerus to behind middle. Prosternal lobe obtuse, feebly emarginate. Pygidium indistinctly carinate. Length 3.5–5 mm.

The larvae are found especially in dead hickory.

g. *Agrilus politus* (Say)   Plate XXXV, No. 8, p. 357

Elongate, rather robust, subcylindrical; bronze or brassy, shining, sometimes greenish. Pronotum transverse, posterior angles feebly carinate; disk with feebly impressed median line, impression interrupted before middle, transversely, rather coarsely strigose and punctate. Scutellum transversely carinate. Elytra wider behind middle; apices rounded, finely serrate; disk imbricately granulate, feebly impressed basally. Prosternal lobe truncate. Pygidium not carinate. Length 5–8.5 mm.

This beetle breeds in living maples, willows, and hazelnuts.

h. *Agrilus obsoletoguttatus* Gory   Plate XXXV, No. 9, p. 357

Elongate, slender, subcylindrical; olive-brown to black, bronzed, feebly shining; head bluish green; male aëneous or cupreous; elytra of female each with three, sometimes four, pubescent, pale-yellowish maculae, middle one often elongate. Pronotum feebly transverse, slightly narrower at base; posterior angles distinctly carinate; disk feebly impressed on each side, distinctly so medially at apex, transversely strigose and punctate. Elytra very feebly widened behind middle; apices rounded, finely serrate; disk imbricately granulate, foveate at base, and with a feeble costa extending behind middle. Prosternal lobe emarginate. Pygidium without a carina. Length 5–8 mm.

The larvae attack dead beech, oaks, ironwood, blue beech, birch, and hickory.

Genus II. *PACHYSCHELUS* Solier

Small, broadly ovate, almost triangular, subconvex; antennae received in grooves on underside of prothorax (Fig. 280); front narrowed by inser-

PLATE XXXVI

Family BUPRESTIDAE IV

1. *Buprestis lineata* Fabricius (p. 345)

Black, with a brassy sheen; elytral stripes yellow, often more extensive, sometimes reduced and broken into two maculae; 11–15 mm.

Family COLYDIIDAE

2. *Aulonium parallelopipedum* Say (p. 420)

Dark brown to blackish, shining; 4.5–6 mm.

3. *Coxelus guttulatus* LeConte (p. 419)

Blackish, not shining; elytra with dull-whitish patches; 4–5 mm.

4. *Colydium lineola* Say (p. 420)

Black, shining; legs orangeish; 4–6.5 mm.

5. *Bitoma quadriguttata* Say (p. 419)

Dark reddish brown to blackish; elytral spots indistinct, pale reddish; 2.5–3 mm.

6. *Bothrideres geminatus* (Say) (p. 421)

Fuscous, shining; 3–4.5 mm.

7. *Cerylon castaneum* Say (p. 421)

Bright orange-brown, shining; 2–3 mm.

8. *Philothermus glabriculus* LeConte (p. 422)

Reddish brown, shining; 2–3 mm.

Family OEDEMERIDAE

9. *Asclera ruficollis* (Say) (p. 284)

Piceous; pronotum dull red; 5–6.5 mm.

10. *Nacerda melanura* (Linné) (p. 283)

Yellowish white; elytral apex black; legs in part blackish; 8–12 mm.

11. *Alloxacis dorsalis* (Melsheimer) (p. 284)

Pale brownish yellow, with brown markings; elytral inner vitta often shortened; 10–13 mm.

Family ANTHICIDAE

12. *Notoxus murinipennis* LeConte (p. 304)

Piceous and light yellowish brown; 3.5 mm.

13. *N. talpa* LaFerté-Sénectère (p. 304)

Piceous and reddish brown; elytral markings yellowish; 3.5–4 mm.

14. *Tomoderus constrictus* (Say) (p. 306)

Dark brown to blackish; elytra in part deep red; 2.5–3 mm.

15. *Anthicus cervinus* Laferté-Sénectère (p. 306)

Reddish brown; elytra and legs brownish yellow, the markings dark brown to blackish; 2.4–2.7 mm.

16. *Notoxus bifasciatus* LeConte (p. 304)

Black and reddish brown; elytral bands pale reddish; 3–3.8 mm.

17. *N. monodon* Fabricius (p. 304)

Dull reddish, with black markings; 2.5–4 mm.

MM 0 10 20 30 40 50 60 70

PLATE XXXVI

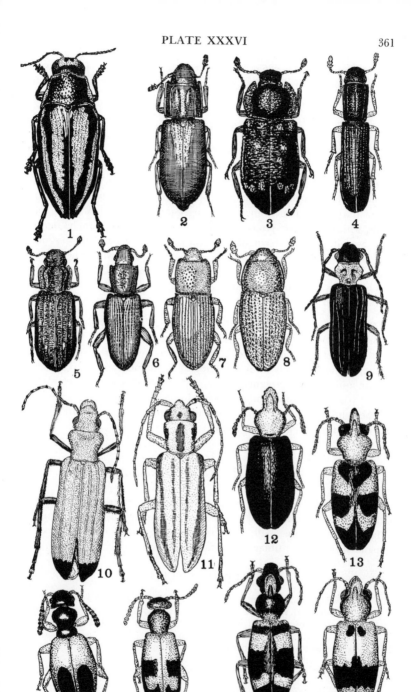

tion of antennae (Fig. 265); scutellum large; prosternum very broad, sub-truncate posteriorly (Fig. 280); metacoxae not expanded internally; tibiae dilated.

KEY TO SPECIES

Elytra purple or blue, remainder of body black ....a. *purpureus*
Body, including elytra, black ....b. *laevigatus*

a. *Pachyschelus purpureus* (Say)   Plate XXXV, No. 10, p. 357
    Broadly oval, strongly attenuate posteriorly, subconvex; black, shining; elytra purple or blue. Pronotum strongly transverse; disk without impressions, with sparse, fine punctures, more numerous at basal angles and laterally. Scutellum large, triangular. Elytra each with a basal impression and one behind humerus; sides serrate posteriorly; disk with rows of coarse punctures becoming rather obsolete apically. Length 3–3.5 mm.
    The adults are usually found on vegetation and foliage; the larvae mine in bush clover.

b. *Pachyschelus laevigatus* (Say)   Plate XXXV, No. 12, p. 357
    Broadly ovate, strongly attenuate posteriorly, subconvex; black, shining. Pronotum strongly transverse; disk impressed each side, sparsely, finely punctate, more densely so at basal angles. Scutellum large. Elytral margins serrate apically; disk irregularly, coarsely, obsoletely punctate; each elytron with a basal depression and one behind humerus. Length 2.5–3 mm.
    The adults occur on foliage of various trees; the larvae are found in leaves of bush clover and tick trefoil.

Genus III. *BRACHYS* Solier

    Small, broadly oval, subdepressed; antennae received in grooves on underside of prothorax (Fig. 280); front narrowed by insertion of antennae (Fig. 265); scutellum small; prosternum obtuse posteriorly; metacoxae not expanded internally; tibiae linear, not dilated.

KEY TO SPECIES

1. Larger, 5–6.5 mm.; last ventral abdominal sternite with apex rounded in male, emarginate and fimbriate in female ....c. *ovatus*
   Smaller, not over 4.5 mm.; last abdominal sternite rounded at apex in both sexes 2
2. Pubescence of elytra more dense on apical third, mostly fulvous, or brilliant cupreous ....a. *aerosus*
   Pubescence of elytra more dense at middle, mostly white ......b. *aeruginosus*

a. *Brachys aerosus* Melsheimer   Plate XXXV, No. 14, p. 357
    Broadly ovate, subdepressed; black or blue-black, feebly shining; covered

irregularly with fulvous pubescence, on elytra forming three irregular fasciae, that on apex most distinct. Pronotum strongly transverse, convex, basally broadly impressed each side, coarsely, not densely punctate. Elytra rather seriately punctate, especially at base, more confused apically; strongly, sinuately carinate from humerus to apex. Last abdominal sternite rounded and without dense pubescence. Length 4–4.5 mm.

The adults are found on foliage of oaks, hickory, and elm; the larva is a leaf-miner in oak.

b. *Brachys aeruginosus* Gory   Plate XXXV, No. 17, p. 357
     Broadly ovate, subdepressed; black or blue-black, shining; elytra with three white and fulvous-pubescent fasciae, the white predominating, the median fascia of denser pubescence than the others. Pronotum strongly transverse, convex; basally broadly impressed each side; disk minutely, densely alutaceous and with coarse, sparse punctures. Elytra strongly, sinuately carinate from humerus to apex; disk subseriately, coarsely, rugosely punctate, the rows more distinct basally. Abdomen with last sternite rounded at apex, not fimbriate. Length 3.5–4 mm.

The adult occurs on the foliage of many species of forest trees.

c. *Brachys ovatus* (Weber)   Plate XXXV, No. 15, p. 357
     Broadly ovate, subdepressed; black or blue-black, feebly shining; covered irregularly with white and golden pubescence, that on elytra arranged in three irregular fasciae, these margined with white pubescence. Pronotum strongly transverse, convex, broadly, obliquely impressed at base each side; sparsely, coarsely punctate, especially basally. Elytra from humerus to apex strongly carinate; disk with rows of rather coarse punctures. Last abdominal sternite emarginate and fimbriate in female, rounded and not pubescent in male. Length 5–7 mm.

Both the adult and larva are found on oak; the adult occurs on the leaves, and the larva mines in the leaves.

Genus IV. *TAPHROCERUS* Solier

Small, elongate-ovate, subdepressed; antennae received in grooves on underside of prothorax (Fig. 280); front narrowed by insertion of antennae; scutellum small; prosternum narrow, acuminate posteriorly; metacoxae not expanded internally; tibiae linear, sulcate for reception of tarsi; legs retractile; tarsi short.

Taphrocerus gracilis (Say)   Plate XXXV, No. 18, p. 357
     Elongate-ovate, subdepressed; black, shining, feebly bronzed; elytra usually with indistinct maculae of whitish pubescence, especially on basal half. Pronotum transverse; basal angles broadly depressed; side margins deflexed anteriorly; disk finely, densely punctate. Scutellum not carinate. Ely-

tral sides sinuate; apices rounded, serrate; disk impressed at base, seriately, coarsely punctate, obsoletely so apically. Length 3–5 mm.

The adults may be swept from grasses and low herbs in moist areas.

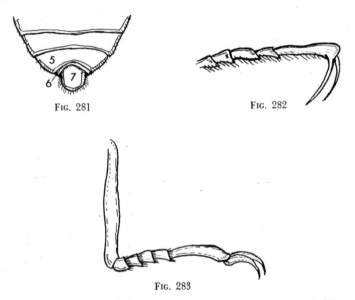

FIG. 281

FIG. 282

FIG. 283

Fig. 281. Abdominal apex of male *Psephenus* in ventral view. *5, 6, 7,* fifth to seventh abdominal sternites.

Fig. 282. Tarsus of a dryopid.

Fig. 283. Tibia and tarsus of an elmid to show relative lengths of the structures.

Family PSEPHENIDAE

The Long-toed Water Beetles

Head free, not retractile; labrum broad, entirely covering mandibles; maxillary palpi elongate, last segment broad, hatchet-shaped; antennae widely separated, serrate, eleven-segmented, longer than head and pronotum; prosternum carinate, prolonged behind into an acute point which fits into a narrow groove extending the full length of the mesosternum; abdomen of male with seven ventral segments, first and second united, fifth broadly emarginate, sixth deeply bilobed, visible only around the notch of the fifth (Fig. 281), seventh rounded, entire, filling the notch of the sixth, female with the segment corresponding to the sixth in male absent.

The larva is called the "water penny" and is a strongly flattened, broadly oval form, found on the underside of stones in rapidly flowing water. The adults are usually found during the day on stones in midstream which just break the surface of the water of creeks. The eggs are laid on the underside of stones in the swiftest water.

Genus *PSEPHENUS* Haldeman

Ovate, depressed, black beetles; densely covered with fine, silky hairs; elytra weakly costate; tarsal claws simple, large, without a basal membranous appendage.

Psephenus herricki DeKay   Plate XVIII, No. 8, p. 171

Rather elongate-ovate, depressed; dull black or fuscous, very finely pubescent; head and pronotum usually darker than elytra, always quite black in the female. Pronotum with sides arcuate posteriorly, strongly narrowed anteriorly, the base twice as broad as apex; disk finely punctate; basal margin bisinuate, distinctly lobed at middle; hind angles rather obtuse. Elytra finely, densely punctate; disk with three broad, not very prominent costae. Length 4–6 mm.

Family DRYOPIDAE

The Hairy Water Beetles

In this small family of beetles both adults and larvae have interesting habits. The adults are found clinging either to the upper surface of partially submerged stones or debris or to the underside, completely under water. Because of their densely pubescent bodies, they are surrounded by an air pocket, which supplies the necessary air while they are submerged. The flattened larvae live on the underside of stones, plants, etc., in rather swift-running water and feed on decaying vegetable matter. The adults may be separated from other closely allied families by the head being retractile; antennae short, six- or eleven-segmented, the segments mostly broader than long; only five abdominal sternites visible; tarsi of five segments, and metatarsi long and with very long claws (Fig. 282).

Genus *HELICHUS* Erichson

Small, oblong, compact species, usually covered with short pubescence; head retractile and, when bent downward, protected beneath by a lobe of the prosternum; antennae widely separated at base, short, segments four to eleven distinctly lamellate (Fig. 17); prosternal spine broad; pronotum convex, with apical angles prominent; elytra fitting very tightly to sternites, last one possessing a groove into which the elytral apices fit; prosternum long, process broad, matching a groove in mesosternum; metatarsi five-segmented, last segment nearly as long as four preceding; claws large.

Helichus lithophilus (Germar)   Plate XVIII, No. 9, p. 171
Oblong, subconvex; dark reddish brown, entire body densely covered with fine, silky pubescence which gives the insect a bronzy sheen; last abdominal sternite pale reddish. Pronotum transverse, narrowed anteriorly; anterior and posterior angles acute; basal margin bisinuate; disk convex, densely, finely punctate. Elytra with sides strongly tapering behind middle; disks coarsely, sparsely punctate and each with four rows of punctures; apices acute. Abdomen with last sternite nearly glabrous. Length 5–6 mm.

Family ELMIDAE

The Marl Water Beetles

In this family both the larva and adult are generally aquatic, or at least semiaquatic, spending most of the life-cycle beneath water. Many forms are to be found clinging to stones or beneath rocks in swiftly flowing streams; others are found associated with marl deposits in lakes, whence the common name of the family. Like the other beetles of similar habits, the dryopids and psephenids, the adults of this family have extremely long tarsi, which are as long as the tibiae (Fig. 283), and long, robust tarsal claws. The Elmidae can, however, be distinguished by the eyes being free of hair; antennae slender, filiform, inserted on front near eyes; procoxae round, trochantin not visible; meso- and metacoxae widely separated, the latter not dilated. Unlike those of dryopids and psephenids, the larvae of the Elmidae are long and slender, only occasionally being flattened in the thoracic region.

KEY TO GENERA

Antennae with eleven segments ....I. *Stenelmis* (p. 367)
Antennae with only seven segments ....II. *Macronychus* (p. 368)

Genus I. *STENELMIS* Dufour

Very small, elongate, subcylindrical; head retractile, protected beneath by a prosternal lobe; antennae eleven-segmented, segments gradually broader from base to apex, the first one or two broader and more rounded than following ones; pronotum quadrate or slightly elongate, apical angles prominent, usually with tubercles; elytra punctate-striate, third and sixth intervals more or less elevated or carinate.

KEY TO SPECIES

Tarsi with last segment distinctly longer than preceding four segments combined; tarsal claws robust ....b. *quadrimaculata*
Tarsi with last segment not longer than preceding four segments together; tarsal claws comparatively slender ....a. *crenata*

367

a. *Stenelmis crenata* (Say)   Plate XVIII, No. 12, p. 171

Oblong-ovate, robust, widened posteriorly, subconvex; fuscous to black; margins of pronotum, body beneath, and legs reddish brown; elytra each with two dull-reddish maculae, which sometimes unite to form a vitta, always located on the sutural side of the sixth interval. Pronotum widest behind middle, thence arcuately narrowed to base, which is wider than apex; median impressed line deep, widest before middle, tapering behind; each side with two tubercles, the basal one elongate, narrowed posteriorly, anterior tubercle prominent, slightly longer than wide; disk finely and sparsely granulate. Elytra with a number of striae of coarse punctures, first stria complete, extending to apex; third interval distinctly elevated on basal sixth. Length 3–3.5 mm.

b. *Stenelmis quadrimaculata* Horn   Plate XVIII, No. 10, p. 171

Elongate, cylindrical, subconvex; piceous to black; pronotum often largely dull-yellowish gray; elytra each with an oblong yellow macula behind humerus and a more elongate one on apical third; body beneath and antennae dull-reddish brown. Pronotum with sides subparallel on basal half, gradually rounded to apex, which is distinctly narrower than base; median sulcus deep, slightly narrowed posteriorly; lateral tubercles oblong, oblique, separated from one another by an oblique depression; disk sparsely, finely granulate. Elytra with a number of striae of coarse punctures, the first one entire, attaining apex; third interval elevated near base, fifth carinate its entire length; disk with deep punctures, which become finer apically. Length 2.7–3.5 mm.

Genus II. *MACRONYCHUS* Müller

Very small, oblong-ovate, subconvex forms; head retractile, protected beneath by a prosternal lobe; antennae seven-segmented, the first two segments cylindrical, nearly fused together, third and seventh elongate, tapering to base, the fourth to sixth short, transverse; pronotum subquadrate, slightly narrower apically, apical angles obtuse, disk usually gibbous at base of sides; elytra with a number of rows of coarse punctures, the ninth interval carinate.

Macronychus glabratus (Say)   Plate XVIII, No. 11, p. 171

Oblong-ovate, moderately robust, subconvex; blackish; antennae and legs piceous. Head with front densely tomentose. Pronotum with apical margin broadly and deeply sinuate each side behind eye; a small gibbosity on each side of middle at base, feebly elevated; median impressed line lacking. Elytra not striate, but with rows of coarse punctures; seventh interval carinate. Metasternum with a deep, oval impression each side occupying most of sides between meso- and metacoxae. Length 3–3.5 mm.

Family DERMESTIDAE

The Carpet Beetles or Buffalo Bugs

A family, rather uninteresting in form, habits, and color, that consists of small, oblong, chunky beetles which live in skins, furs, woolen materials, and dried animal matter. The adults are occasionally found on flowers as well. While uninteresting, they often forcibly command the entomologist's attention by devouring his insect collection. Most of the larvae are brown, active grubs, clothed with long hairs.

Other distinguishing characters of this family are: body partly covered with colored maculae composed of flattened hairs or scales; head small, deflexed, retractile up to eyes, one median ocellus usually present (Fig. 284); antennae short, usually eleven-segmented but sometimes nine- or ten-segmented, clavate, usually fitting into an excavation on underside of prothorax; five abdominal sternites present; legs short and weak, capable of folding tightly against the body; procoxae long, conical or oblique, open posteriorly (Fig. 25A), except in *Byturus* it is closed posteriorly (Fig. 25B); mesocoxae oval, oblique; metacoxae slightly separated, dilated into plates which are grooved to receive femora (Fig. 285); tibiae with distinct spines; tarsi five-segmented, claws simple or dentate (Fig. 26G, H).

KEY TO GENERA

1. Head without an ocellus on front 2
   Head with an ocellus on front (Fig. 284) 3
2. Procoxal cavities closed posteriorly (Fig. 25B) ....I. *Byturus*   (p. 370)
   Procoxal cavities open posteriorly (Fig. 25A) ....II. *Dermestes*   (p. 370)
3. Metacoxal plates extending laterally half way across the parapleura
   (Fig. 285) 4
   Metacoxal plates extending laterally to and abutting against the inner boundary of the parapleura (Fig. 286) ....VI. *Anthrenus*   (p. 376)
4. Basal segment of metatarsi much shorter than second (Fig. 287)
   ....III. *Attagenus*   (p. 372)
   Basal segment of metatarsi elongate, generally but little shorter than second and third together (Fig. 288) 5
5. Antennae robust, subserrate, club six- to eight-segmented in male, four-segmented in female; mandibles and labrum not covered by prosternum in repose ....IV. *Trogoderma*   (p. 373)
   Antennae with a large, oval, and compactly two-segmented club closely fitting in repose in a deep fossa on underside of prothorax (Fig. 289); mandibles but not labrum covered in repose by prosternum ....V. *Cryptorhopalum*   (p. 376)

Genus I. *BYTURUS* Latreille

Small, oblong-ovate, convex; head large, front as wide as long; eyes prominent, coarsely faceted; antennae eleven-segmented, club three-segmented, not received in pit or grooves; scutellum large, quadrate; procoxal cavities closed posteriorly (Fig. 25B); tarsi with five distinct segments, second and third with membranous lobe beneath (Fig. 290); claws strongly dentate basally (Fig. 290).

Byturus rubi Barber   Plate XXXVII, No. 12, p. 375

Oblong-ovate, convex; dull brownish yellow; head and pro-, meso-, and metasternum dark brown; above densely clothed with pale-yellowish, silky pubescence, hairs on undersurface whitish. Pronotum strongly transverse; sides regularly arcuate; margins broadly depressed; base wider than apex; disk coarsely, densely punctate. Elytra coarsely, densely punctate, with traces of numerous elevated lines. Length 3.7–4.5 mm.

The "raspberry fruit worm," a small white grub which infests the fruit of blackberries and raspberries, is the larva of this beetle; the adults occur on flowers of both blackberry and raspberry.

Genus II. *DERMESTES* Linné

Small, elongate-oblong; body clothed with short hairs; head capable of being retracted within prothorax, without ocelli; antennae eleven-segmented, club three-segmented; epipleura strongly defined, wide, and inflexed toward base; procoxae contiguous (Fig. 291); prosternum not visible between procoxae (Fig. 291); mesosternum between coxae moderately wide, not sulcate.

KEY TO SPECIES

1. Abdomen thickly covered with long, whitish pubescence and with a row of black maculae on each side; anterior portions of side margins of pronotum not visible from above 2
   Abdomen without whitish pubescence or rows of black maculae; side margins of pronotum entirely visible from above; basal two-fifths of each elytron grayish yellow, enclosing three black maculae .... c. *lardarius*
2. Pubescence of pronotum densely covering entire surface, variegated with small maculae of black, gray, and reddish brown .... a. *caninus*
   Pubescence of pronotum gray and limited to the margins, disk with a large, triangular, nearly smooth area, black .... b. *vulpinus*

a. *Dermestes caninus* Germar   Plate XXXVII, No. 1, p. 375

Elongate-oblong; black; pronotum with a dense yellow and white pubescence; scutellum densely covered with long, yellow hairs; elytra with gray and black pubescence rather dense on basal half, sometimes covering al-

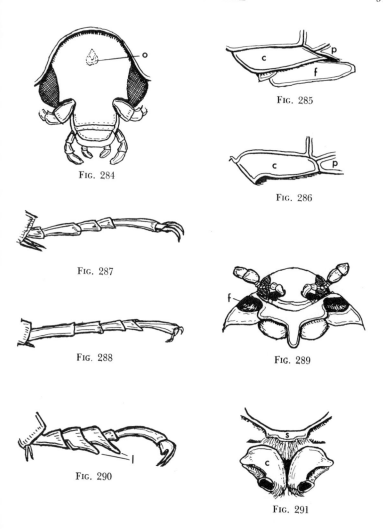

Fig. 284. Head of *Attagenus piceus. o,* ocellus.

Figs. 285–286. Metacoxa of *Cryptorhopalum* (285) and of *Anthrenus* (286). *c,* metacoxa; *f,* metafemur; *p,* parapleuron.

Figs. 287–288. Metatarsus of *Attagenus* (287) and of *Trogoderma* (288).

Fig. 289. Head and prothorax of *Cryptorhopalum* viewed from beneath. *f,* antennal fossa.

Fig. 290. Metatarsus of *Byturus* from the side. *l,* membranous lobe.

Fig. 291. Procoxae of *Dermestes. c,* procoxa; *s,* prosternum.

most entire surface of elytra; undersurface clothed with short, gray pubescence; meso- and metatibiae with rings of gray pubescence. Male with a median pit on third and fourth ventral abdominal segments, from which arises a tuft of erect, brown hairs. Length 7–8.2 mm.

On dead animals, when only the bones and skin remain, this species can usually be found in numbers. This beetle has been put to good use by vertebrate morphologists for cleaning off the bony skeletons of specimens.

b. *Dermestes vulpinus* Fabricius   Plate XXXVII, No. 2, p. 375

Elongate-oblong; piceous, sparsely clothed with black and yellowish hairs; last ventral abdominal segment brown, with two white maculae basally; fourth ventral segment of male with a median pit bearing a tuft of brown hairs. Pronotum and elytra rather finely and densely punctate. Length 6–9 mm.

Improperly cured meat is often infested by this species.

c. *Dermestes lardarius* Linné   The Larder Beetle
                                           Plate XXXVII, No. 3, p. 375

Elongate-oblong; black or piceous; each elytron with basal half densely covered with coarse, yellowish hairs, with the exception of a macula at humerus and a transverse row of three maculae, the two end maculae of rows placed slightly nearer base, glabrous; apical half with very fine, sparse hairs; undersurface and legs black, with fine, sparse, yellowish pubescence. Pronotum and elytra finely and densely punctate. Length 6–7.5 mm.

Widely spread by commerce, this species is a commercial as well as household pest in stored ham and bacon.

Genus III. *ATTAGENUS* Latreille

Rather small, oblong, convex; antennae eleven-segmented, two basal segments of male's club short and transverse, last segment greatly elongate and acuminate at apex; mesosternum between coxae longer than wide, not sulcate; procoxae narrowly separated; metacoxal plates greatly elongate internally (Fig. 292).

Attagenus piceus Olivier   The Black Carpet Beetle
                                           Plate XXXVII, Nos. 4, 5, p. 375

Oblong, convex; head and pronotum black; elytra reddish brown, piceous, or black, clothed with short, sparse pubescence. Pronotum coarsely punctate, base bisinuate, with a slight impression before scutellum. Elytra finely and densely punctate. Length 3.5–5 mm.

A common museum and household pest. The larva often causes much damage to rugs, carpets, upholstery, and other woolen materials, also silks and feathers.

Genus IV. *TROGODERMA* Latreille

Very small, oblong-ovate; antennae robust, claviform, and usually serrate in male, with second segment small; in female generally very small and with a narrow, four-segmented club; mesosternum very short and wide between coxae and completely divided longitudinally by a deep, broad sulcus; procoxae rather narrowly separated; metacoxal plates short, gradually and feebly rectilinearly longer internally (Fig. 293); profemora retractile.

KEY TO SPECIES

Eyes entire, inner frontal margin not emarginate; antennae of male serrate (Fig. 294), third and fourth segments equal in length ....a. *ornata*
Eyes feebly emarginate at about the middle of their anterior margin; male antennae compact, not serrate ....b. *versicolor*

a. *Trogoderma ornata* Say   Plate XXXVII, No. 6, p. 375
Oblong-ovate, subconvex; black, shining, irregularly covered with yellowish pubescence; elytra black, with a broad, red macula basally and with scattered, interconnecting, red maculae apically. Pronotum transverse, widest slightly before basal angles; sides regularly arcuate; disk densely, strongly punctate. Elytral sides gradually tapering to apex; surface with irregular pubescent areas and finely, densely punctate. Prosternum long, broad at apex, subcarinate. The club of male antennae is pectinate. Length 2–2.5 mm.

This is usually a household pest but occasionally occurs in museums.

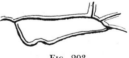

FIG. 292   FIG. 293

FIG. 294

Fig. 292. Metacoxa of *Attagenus,* prolonged on its inner edge.
Fig. 293. Metacoxa of *Trogoderma.*
Fig. 294. Antennal club of male *Trogoderma ornata,* the segments loosely arranged and serrate.

PLATE XXXVII

Family DERMESTIDAE

1. *Dermestes caninus* Germar (p. 370) — Black; marked with yellow, white, and black pubescence; 7–8.2 mm.

2. *D. vulpinus* Fabricius (p. 372) — Blackish, with yellow and black hairs; 6–9 mm.

3. *D. lardarius* Linné (p. 372) — Blackish; elytral fascia dull yellowish; 6–7.5 mm.

4, 5. *Attagenus piceus* Olivier (p. 372) — Black; elytra variable, dark brown to blackish, with short pubescence; 3.5–5 mm.

6. *Trogoderma ornata* Say (p. 373) — Black, with yellowish pubescence; elytral maculae reddish; 2–2.5 mm.

7. *T. versicolor* Creutzer (p. 376) — Black, with grayish pubescence; elytral fasciae reddish, overlaid with gray pubescence; 2–3.5 mm.

8. *Cryptorhopalum haemorrhoidale* LeConte (p. 376) — Black and dark brown or piceous; elytral fasciae dull yellow; 2–2.5 mm.

9. *C. picicorne* LeConte (p. 376) — Blackish, with sparse, yellowish pubescence; 2–3 mm.

10. *Anthrenus verbasci* (Linné) (p. 377) — Black; pronotum with sparse, white scales; elytra marked with white and yellow; 2–3 mm.

11. *A. scrophulariae* (Linné) (p. 377) — Black; pronotal markings of white scales; elytral markings white, those along suture and at apex red; 2.2–3.5 mm.

12. *Byturus rubi* Barber (p. 370) — Dull brownish yellow, covered with white hairs; head dark brown; 3.7–4.5 mm.

13. *Thylodrias contractus* Motschulsky (p. 378) — Dull brownish yellow; elytra and legs paler yellow; 2.5–3 mm.

MM 0 10 20 30 40 50 60 70

PLATE XXXVII

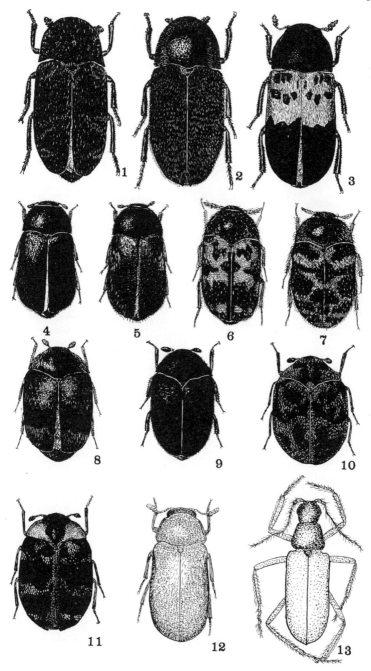

1

2

3

4

5

6

7

8

9

10

11

12

13

b. *Trogoderma versicolor* Creutzer   Plate XXXVII, No. 7, p. 375

Oblong-ovate; black; pronotum with lines of gray hairs; elytra with four sinuous, more or less confluent reddish bands covered with gray pubescence, the subapical band enclosing a small blackish macula at suture. Pronotum strongly transverse; disk finely, sparsely punctate, more densely so in female. Elytra more coarsely and densely punctate; sides subparallel. Prosternum elongate, gradually tapering to apex, with a strong median carina. Segments of antennal club in male simple. Length 2–3.5 mm.

Genus V. *CRYPTORHOPALUM* Guérin

Small, oval, subconvex; antennal club two-segmented, close-fitting in repose within a deep fossa on underside of prothorax; prosternum covering all mouthparts except labrum, its process with a broad apex widely dividing the mesosternum; procoxae more widely separated; metacoxal plates short, with posterior margin transverse (Fig. 285).

KEY TO SPECIES

Uniformly black or piceous ....b. *picicorne*
Body black, elytra and pronotum deep brown, elytra at apex yellow ....
....a. *haemorrhoidale*

a. *Cryptorhopalum haemorrhoidale* LeConte   Plate XXXVII, No. 8, p. 375

Oval, subconvex; black, shining; pronotum and elytra deep reddish brown or piceous, latter dull yellow on apical third and with two fasciae of yellowish pubescence; long, sparse, yellow pubescence underneath. Head coarsely, densely punctate; pronotum more finely punctate. Segments of club of male antennae subequal, oval, together twice as long as preceding segments combined. Length 2–2.5 mm.

The adults frequent flowers, especially the panicled dogwood, *Cornus candidissima*.

b. *Cryptorhopalum picicorne* LeConte   Plate XXXVII, No. 9, p. 375

Ovate, subconvex; black or piceous, with sparse, yellowish pubescence; antennae dark reddish brown. Pronotum finely and densely punctate, the lobe at the middle of base narrow and truncate; posterior angles acute. Elytra coarsely and densely punctate. Length 2–3 mm.

Genus VI. *ANTHRENUS* Fabricius

Small, compact, slightly convex; body clothed with scales; pronotum broad at base, narrow at apex, lateral margins bent under the body and divided by a deep groove for the reception of antennal club (Fig. 295);

scutellum minute; prosternum visible between coxae (Fig. 295), projecting anteriorly and covering all mouthparts except labrum; metacoxal plate extending laterally to the inner side of sternal sidepiece; legs all very strongly retractile.

KEY TO SPECIES

Eyes emarginate (Fig. 209); scales of surface coarse, large, triangular, as wide as long; antennal club oval; white scales on elytra in two or three narrow, sinuous fasciae or maculae, these usually connected with projections from a vitta of orange scales along suture ....a. *scrophulariae*
Eyes entire; scales fine, elongate, three times as long as wide; antennal club elongate ....b. *verbasci*

a. *Anthrenus scrophulariae* (Linné) The Carpet Beetle
Plate XXXVII, No. 11, p. 375

Ovate, slightly convex; pronotum with sides covered with white scales, disk free from scales; elytra with a sutural vitta and an apical macula of brick-red or dull yellow, the vitta with three equidistant, lateral projections; two narrow, sinuous, white fasciae extending from the first two projections of sutural vitta to edge of elytra; body beneath black, covered with yellowish and white scales. Pronotum very strongly transverse, two and one-half times as wide as long; median lobe strongly produced, nearly concealing scutellum; disk finely, densely punctate, punctation usually concealed by scales. Elytra finely, densely punctate. Length 2.2–3.5 mm.

The adults are found on flowers; the larvae, known as "buffalo bugs" or "moths," are destructive to carpets, woolen materials, feathers, and fur; also a museum pest.

b. *Anthrenus verbasci* (Linné) The Varied Carpet Beetle
Plate XXXVII, No. 10, p. 375

Broadly oblong-ovate, slightly convex; pronotum black, with sparse, yellow scales on disk, sides more densely clothed with white scales; elytra black, with a large basal ring and two transverse, zigzag fasciae of white scales bordered with yellow scales and a small apical fascia of white scales bordered with yellow; undersurface clothed with pale-yellow scales. Pronotum strongly transverse, about twice as wide as long; median lobe subtriangular; disk minutely punctate. Elytra finely, densely punctate. Length 2–3 mm.

The adults are found especially on flowers of wheat or corn cockle and also of spiraea; the larvae are also a museum pest.

Incertae Sedis

While the following genus is ordinarily placed in the Dermestidae, its structural characteristics are so atypical that it probably should be placed in a separate family. Its prominent head, long legs, and filiform antennae make it distinct from the general shape of the dermestids. The only feature which is dermestoid is its habit of attacking dried insect specimens, and for this reason it has been included here.

Genus *THYLODRIAS* Motschulsky

Small, elongate-oblong, subdepressed; head as long as pronotum; eyes prominent, coarsely faceted; antennae long, filiform, eleven-segmented, not clavate or fitting into any groove or pit; elytra soft, parallel-sided; wingless; procoxal cavities widely open posteriorly; metacoxae prominent, conical; legs long, slender; tarsi filiform, not lobed beneath, five-segmented, first segment elongate; claws simple.

Thylodrias contractus Motschulsky   Plate XXXVII, No. 13, p. 375

Elongate-oblong, slender, subdepressed; dull yellowish brown, rather densely covered with silky, whitish pubescence; elytra, antennae, and legs pale brownish yellow. Pronotum distinctly transverse, strongly constricted apically; disk finely, densely punctate, behind middle with an arcuate transverse impressed line. Scutellum large, triangular. Elytra with sides nearly parallel; apices together rounded; entire disk coarsely, rather densely punctate. Length 2.5–3 mm.

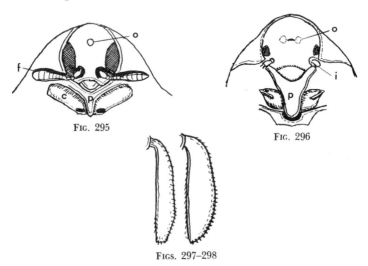

FIG. 295

FIG. 296

FIGS. 297–298

Fig. 295. Head and prothorax of *Anthrenus*, viewed from beneath. *c*, procoxa; *f*, antennal fossa; *o*, ocellus; *p*, prosternum.

Fig. 296. Head and prothorax of *Byrrhus* viewed from below. *i*, antennal insertions; *o*, ocellus-like spots; *p*, prosternum.

Figs. 297–298. Tibia of *Cytilus* (297) and of *Byrrhus* (298).

Family BYRRHIDAE

The Pill Beetles

Small, very convex forms, usually black, with short pubescence, which imparts a silky sheen; head retracted, beneath more or less protected by the prosternum (Fig. 296); antennae eleven-segmented, apical segments forming an elongate club, rarely almost filiform, inserted beneath sides of head (Fig. 296); legs short, robust, and arranged so that they can be folded so closely to the body as to be invisible; prosternum short, truncate apically, process slightly prolonged and fitting into the apical margin of mesosternum (Fig. 296); procoxal cavities open posteriorly (Fig. 25A); metacoxae broad, extending to lower edge of elytra and frequently covering metafemora; tarsi five-segmented, last segment nearly as long as preceding ones combined.

These slow-moving, very hard-bodied beetles are found beneath logs, in crevices, in roots of grasses, and in sand along lakes and streams of water. When disturbed, they retract their antennae and legs, forming a compact ball, whence their common name, the "pill beetles."

KEY TO GENERA

Tibiae more slender, nearly straight, apex obliquely truncate externally (Fig. 297); vertex of head unmodified ....I. *Cytilus* (p. 379)
Tibiae broader, more flattened, evenly rounded externally throughout their length (Fig. 298); vertex generally with a short, transverse line at middle, immediately behind which are two small, pale, ocelli-like spots (Fig. 296) ....II. *Byrrhus* (p. 380)

Genus I. *CYTILUS* Erichson

Head vertical or bent downward, retracted; mentum small, quadrate; labrum distinct, fitting close to the front; epistoma not distinct; antennae eleven-segmented; tibiae feebly expanded, distinctly narrower than femora; only protarsi retractile; body covered with a fine, easily removed pubescence, forming varied patterns.

Cytilus alternatus (Say)   Plate XLV, No. 2, p. 459
Subovate, narrowed anteriorly, strongly convex; bronzy black, shining, with a dense, fine pubescence; pubescence on head and pronotum nearly

uniformly bronze; elytra with the four or five inner intervals, some of which are narrow and uniformly metallic green, alternate ones wider, slightly elevated, and green varied with black. Pronotal disk finely, densely punctate; median impressed line subobsolete. Elytra minutely alutaceous, with numerous fine striae, which are sparsely, finely punctate. Length 4.5–5.5 mm.

These beetles are usually found among grass roots.

Genus II. *BYRRHUS* Linné

Head vertical or bent downward, retracted; mentum small, quadrate; labrum distinct, fitting close to front (Fig. 296); epistoma not distinct (Fig. 296); antennae eleven-segmented; tibiae strongly expanded, subequal in width to femora; all tarsi retractile; body covered with fine, easily removed pubescence.

Byrrhus americanus LeConte   Plate XLV, No. 1, p. 459

Ovate, very convex, narrowed anteriorly; black, with fine, dense, grayish pubescence; pronotum with indistinct gray markings; elytra each with three or four narrow, interrupted black lines and a double, narrow, sinuous gray fascia at middle. Pronotum finely, very densely punctate; median impressed line obsolete or lacking. Elytra minutely, densely asperate; striae very fine, often with finely beaded edges and with fine, very widely separated punctures. Length 8.5–9.5 mm.

FIGS. 299–300

Figs. 299–300. Protibia of *Airora* (299) and of *Tenebroides* (300), the former with coarse spines.

Family OSTOMATIDAE

The Grain and Bark-gnawing Beetles

Small or moderate-sized, oblong, subdepressed beetles; maxillae two-lobed; antennae short, eleven-segmented, inserted under sides of front, last three segments expanded, forming a loose club; abdomen with five visible sternites; all coxae transverse, pro- and mesocoxae separated, metacoxae contiguous; tarsi five-segmented, first segment very short, second slightly longer, fourth strongly elongate; claws simple.

These beetles are found primarily under bark, where they possibly feed on fungi. A few species occur in granaries, where they feed upon the larvae of grain-eating insects; at least one form is a pest in flour and cereal products.

KEY TO GENERA

Tibiae with spines (Fig. 299) ....I. *Airora* (p. 381)
Tibiae without spines (Fig. 300) ....II. *Tenebroides* (p. 382)

Genus I. *AIRORA* Reitter

Small to moderate-sized, elongate, cylindrical; head large; eyes transverse, not prominent; antennae short, extending backward, scarcely attaining apex of pronotum; pronotum elongate; elytra parallel-sided; all tibiae with distinct spines externally; anterior margin of prosternum separated from anterior margin of pronotum by the more or less projecting apical angles.

Airora cylindrica (Serville)   Plate XLIV, No. 3, p. 453
    Elongate, cylindrical, slender, convex; dark reddish brown or piceous. Pronotum longer than wide, slightly narrowed from apex to base; posterior angles obtuse; disk finely, sparsely punctate. Elytral base separated from pronotal base; sides subparallel; apices together rounded; striae finely, serrately punctate; intervals minutely punctate. Length 5–14 mm.

    The adults are found beneath bark of hickory, elm, and other hardwoods. The males are much smaller than the females.

Genus II. *TENEBROIDES* Piller and Mitterpacher

Oblong, subdepressed forms; head large; eyes transverse, not prominent; pronotum transverse, broadly emarginate at apex, sides arcuately narrowed posteriorly; elytra with basal marginal beading distinct near humeri but obliterated near scutellum; meso- and metatibiae without spines; antennae attaining middle of pronotum, sometimes feebly clavate.

KEY TO SPECIES

Antennae with first two segments of club strongly transverse, at least half again as wide as long, last segment of club only slightly longer than wide ....a. *mauritanicus*
Antennae with first two segments at least slightly elongate, usually distinctly longer than wide, last segment of club strongly elongate ......b. *americanus*

a. *Tenebroides mauritanicus* (Linné)   The "Cadelle"
                                                   Plate XLIV, No. 5, p. 453

Elongate-oblong, subdepressed; deep brown to black, shining. Head and pronotum not alutaceous, densely, rather coarsely punctate; pronotum half again as long as wide. Elytra with rather deeply impressed striae; intervals each with two rows of punctures, surface feebly rugose. Length 6–11 mm.

Both adult and larva occur in grains, flour, and seeds, but feed on other insects as well. The adult appears like a small edition of the mealworm (*Tenebrio molitor*).

b. *Tenebroides americanus* (Kirby)   Plate XLIV, No. 4, p. 453
Oblong-ovate, subdepressed; fuscous to piceous, shining; body beneath and legs dark reddish brown. Head and pronotum densely and finely alutaceous, rather finely, sparsely punctate; the latter two-thirds again as wide as long, lateral margins reflexed, sides sinuate basally, posterior angles acute. Elytra ovate; striae shallow, moderately finely punctate; intervals subconvex, densely rugose, each with two rows of fine punctures. Length 9–11 mm.

Family NITIDULIDAE

The Sap-feeding Beetles

More or less flattened, rather small beetles, black or sometimes brightly colored or marked; oblong, nearly as broad as long; antennae short, eleven-segmented, with a round or oval, two- or three-segmented club, inserted beneath margin of front (Fig. 301); pronotal margins usually expanded and thin, base closely uniting with or covering base of elytra; elytra usually short, truncate at apices, and exposing part of the abdomen but sometimes rounded and covering entirely or nearly so the tip of the abdomen; five abdominal sternites present; legs short and robust, more or less retractile; tarsi often dilated and pubescent beneath, last segment elongate.

For the most part the adults of this family feed on sap of freshly cut trees or on decaying fruit or melons, although there are some which are found on flowers, probably feeding on pollen and nectar, and a few which are attracted to fungi. Still others may be found under bark of decaying logs or are pests in corn or in stored rice products, and some live and breed on or near dried or fresh carcasses. Larvae of some genera are thought to be predaceous on Scolytidae.

KEY TO SUBFAMILIES

1. Labrum free, more or less visible (Fig. 301) 2
   Labrum continuous with the clypeus, not distinct (Fig. 302) ......
   ....CRYPTARCHINAE (p. 396)
2. Maxillae with two lobes; antennae feebly capitate (Fig. 303) ......
   ....CATERETINAE (p. 383)
   Maxillae with one lobe; antennae distinctly capitate (Fig. 304) ..3
3. Abdomen with two segments exposed above ....CARPOPHILINAE (p. 386)
   Abdomen covered above, or at most pygidium exposed ....
   ....NITIDULINAE (p. 390)

Subfamily CATERETINAE

KEY TO GENERA

1. Claws distinctly toothed at base (Fig. 26G) ....III. *Brachypterus* (p. 384)
   Claws simple or nearly so (Fig. 26D) 2
2. Color brown ....I. *Cateretes* (p. 384)
   Color metallic green or blue above; abdomen reddish ....
   ....II. *Boreades* (p. 384)

Genus I. *CATERETES* Herbst

Small, oval, subconvex species, brown in color; antennae eleven-segmented, club two-segmented, elongate, loose; maxillae with two lobes; pronotum about twice as wide as long, slightly narrower than elytra at base; elytra margined laterally; epipleura distinct; tarsi five-segmented, claws simple.

Cateretes pennatus (Murray)   Plate XXXVIII, No. 1, p. 389

Oval, subconvex; varying from yellowish brown to dark brown; slightly shining; sparsely pubescent. Pronotum strongly transverse; apex feebly emarginate; sides arcuate and posterior angles obtuse in male, sides sinuate posteriorly and posterior angles distinct in female; disk densely punctate. Elytra with apices rounded at extreme apex, narrowly truncate, leaving the pygidium exposed; surface coarsely, not densely punctate. Length 2.3–2.5 mm.

The adults may be found on elder and wild-hydrangea flowers.

Genus II. *BOREADES* Parsons

Small, oval, convex; metallic above; antennae eleven-segmented, with a loose, three-segmented club; maxillae with two lobes; pronotum slightly transverse, short, one-third wider than long, sides arcuate; tarsi five-segmented; claws simple or nearly so.

Boreades abdominalis (Erichson)   Plate XXXVIII, No. 2, p. 389

Oval, convex; metallic blue or greenish, shining; abdomen and legs reddish; antennae reddish brown, club piceous. Pronotum convex, slightly transverse; apex slightly narrower than base; posterior angles rectangular; disk rather coarsely but not densely punctate. Elytra feebly elongate; apices separately, broadly rounded, exposing pygidium and part of propygidium; disk coarsely and densely punctate. Length 2–2.5 mm.

The adults frequent various flowers, those of bloodroot and elder especially; they are also found on foliage of trees and shrubs in low areas.

Genus III. *BRACHYPTERUS* Kugelann

Small, oblong-ovate; antennae eleven-segmented, with a feeble, three-segmented club; pronotum distinctly transverse; elytra with distinct epipleura; prosternum elevated at tip; tarsi five-segmented, claws distinctly toothed at base.

Brachypterus urticae (Fabricius)   Plate XXXVIII, No. 3, p. 389

Oblong-ovate, convex; piceous, shining, feebly bronzed; very sparsely pubescent; antennae and legs reddish brown. Pronotum strongly transverse, almost twice as wide as long, convex; sides arcuate, feebly sinuate near posterior angles; disk coarsely and densely punctate. Elytra obliquely truncate at apex, exposing pygidium; disk more coarsely but less densely punctate than pronotum. Length 2 mm.

This species is usually found on flowers of nettle and elder.

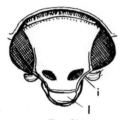

FIG. 301

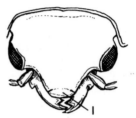

FIG. 302

FIGS. 303–304

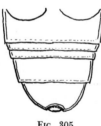

FIG. 305

FIG. 306

FIG. 307

Figs. 301–302. Head of *Conotelus* (301) and of *Glischrochilus* (302) from above. *i*, antennal insertion; *l*, labrum.

Figs. 303–304. Antenna of *Cataretes* (303) and of *Nitidula* (304).

Figs. 305–307. Abdominal sternites of *Carpophilus* (305), *Colopterus* (306), and *Conotelus* (307).

Subfamily CARPOPHILINAE

KEY TO GENERA

Second and third ventral abdominal segments short, first, fourth, and
fifth longer (Fig. 305) ....III. *Carpophilus* (p. 387)
First through fourth ventral abdominal segments short, fifth nearly
as long as preceding combined (Fig. 306) ....I. *Colopterus* (p. 386)
First and second ventral abdominal segments short, third and fourth
longer, fifth longest (Fig. 307) ....II. *Conotelus* (p. 386)

Genus I. *COLOPTERUS* Erichson

Small, oblong-ovate, rather robust, depressed; antennae eleven-segmented,
club three-segmented, rounded, compact; maxillae with one lobe; pronotum
about twice as wide as long; elytra exposing at least two abdominal segments; abdominal sternites one to four short, fifth nearly as long as
others combined, in male last sternite emarginate, exposing a small additional segment.

Colopterus truncatus (Randall)　　　　　　Plate XXXVIII, No. 4, p. 389
Oblong-ovate, strongly depressed; reddish brown, shining; head usually
piceous. Pronotum distinctly transverse; apex about one-half width of
base; disk convex, rather densely punctate. Elytral apices broadly truncate,
exposing pygidium and propygidium; disk rather densely punctate. Length
2–2.5 mm.
This species comes to sap in the spring and is found on flowers in the
summer.

Genus II. *CONOTELUS* Erichson

Elongate, in general form resembling very much one of the small Staphylinidae; antennae eleven-segmented, distinctly clubbed; pronotum slightly
transverse; elytra exposing three dorsal abdominal segments; first and second abdominal sternites short, third and fourth equal and longer, fifth
longer than preceding two combined, conical, and somewhat flattened
(Fig. 307); in males the terminal dorsal abdominal segment is truncate and
feebly emarginate, exposing a small additional segment.

Conotelus obscurus Erichson　　　　　　　Plate XXXIX, No. 3, p. 395
Elongate, slender, subdepressed; piceous or black, opaque; legs and antennae brownish yellow, club of latter piceous. Pronotum slightly transverse, feebly narrowed apically; disk sparsely punctate, finely rugose; posterior angles obtusely rounded. Elytra about twice as long as wide; apices

broadly, separately rounded, exposing last three dorsal abdominal segments; disk finely granulate, with irregular rows of indistinct punctures. Length 3.5–4 mm.

Especially abundant in spring on dandelion and dogwood flowers, this species is also found on hollyhocks.

Genus III. *CARPOPHILUS* Stephens

Small, oblong-ovate, convex; antennae eleven-segmented, club oval, flattened; maxillae with one lobe; labrum bilobed; elytra exposing two dorsal segments of abdomen; second and third abdominal sternites short; tarsi five-segmented, dilated; claws simple.

KEY TO SPECIES

Pronotum distinctly narrower at apex than at base; body length 3.5–4 mm. ..
. . . . .a. *niger*
Pronotal apex as wide as base; body length 2–3 mm. . . . . .b. *brachypterus*

a. *Carpophilus niger* (Say) Plate XXXVIII, No. 6, p. 389
Oblong-ovate, convex; deep brown or piceous; sparsely pubescent; legs, antennal scape, and sternites reddish brown. Pronotum distinctly transverse; sides uniformly arcuate; apex narrower than base; posterior angles rectangular; disk densely punctate. Elytral humeri prominent; apices broadly, obliquely truncate, exposing propygidium and pygidium; disk densely punctate. Length 3.5–4.2 mm.

This species is found on flowers, at sap, and sometimes beneath bark of decaying logs.

b. *Carpophilus brachypterus* (Say) Plate XXXVIII, No. 5, p. 389
Oblong-ovate, subdepressed; piceous, slightly shining, finely and sparsely pubescent; legs and antennae reddish brown. Pronotum strongly transverse, nearly twice as wide as long; apex and base equal in width; sides moderately arcuate; disk rather coarsely but not densely punctate, laterally more densely and finely so. Elytral apices broadly truncate, exposing propygidium and pygidium; disk more finely punctate than pronotum. Length 2–3 mm.

This species occurs at sap and on flowers of cherry, black haw, and other shrubs.

PLATE XXXVIII

Family NITIDULIDAE I

1. *Cateretes pennatus* (Murray) (p. 384) — Dull yellow to dark brown; 2.3–2.5 mm.

2. *Boreades abdominalis* (Erichson) (p. 384) — Fuscous to blackish, with green reflex; abdomen yellowish brown; 2–2.5 mm.

3. *Brachypterus urticae* (Fabricius) (p. 385) — Piceous to black; legs and antennae reddish brown; 2 mm.

4. *Colopterus truncatus* (Randall) (p. 386) — Various shades of dull yellow and brown; 2–2.5 mm.

5. *Carpophilus brachypterus* (Say) (p. 387) — Fuscous to blackish; 2–3 mm.

6. *C. niger* (Say) (p. 387) — Deep brown to blackish; 3.5–4.2 mm.

7. *Phenolia grossa* (Fabricius) (p. 393) — Dull brown, with indistinct dull-yellowish markings; 6.5–8 mm.

8. *Prometopia sexmaculata* (Say) (p. 393) — Piceous, with dull-yellow margins and markings; 5–6 mm.

9. *Nitidula ziczac* Say (p. 391) — Dark brown to blackish; elytral spots dull yellow; 3–4 mm.

10. *N. bipunctata* (Linné) (p. 390) — Dark brown; elytral spot dull yellow; 4.5–6 mm.

11. *Glischrochilus fasciatus* (Olivier) (p. 397) — Black; elytra with orange bands; 4–7 mm.

12. *G. quadrisignatus* (Say) (p. 397) — Black; elytra with orange bands; 4.5–6 mm.

13. *G. sanguinolentus* (Olivier) (p. 397) — Black; elytra at base bright orange-red; 4–6 mm.

14. *Cryptarcha ampla* Erichson (p. 396) — Dull brown to blackish; 6–7 mm.

MM 0 10 20 30 40 50 60 70

PLATE XXXVIII

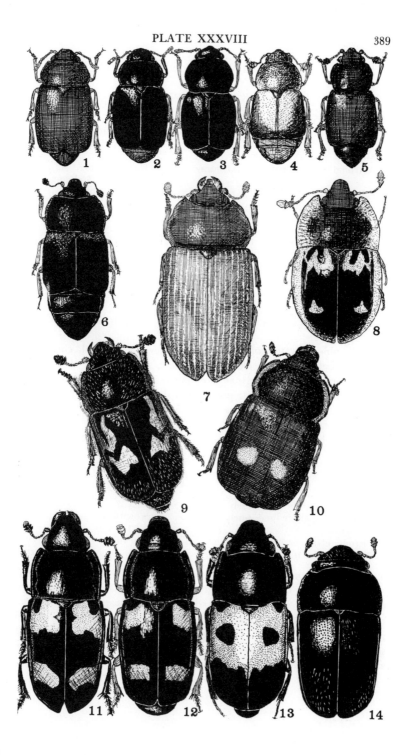

1

2

3

4

5

6

7

8

9

10

11

12

13

14

Subfamily NITIDULINAE

KEY TO GENERA

1. All tarsi very distinctly dilated (Fig. 308) 2
   Tarsi (except protarsi sometimes) not dilated or but feebly so (Fig. 309) 4
2. Antennal grooves strongly convergent (Fig. 310) 3
   Antennal grooves parallel, extending directly backward (Fig. 312) ....IV. *Stelidota*   (p. 392)
3. Labrum bilobed (Fig. 311); males with a sixth dorsal abdominal segment ....III. *Epuraea*   (p. 392)
   Labrum feebly emarginate; males without a sixth dorsal segment ....I. *Nitidula*   (p. 390)
4. Mentum broad, covering base of maxillae (Fig. 312). . V. *Prometopia*   (p. 393)
   Mentum not covering the maxillae 5
5. Apex of mandibles slightly bifid (Fig. 302) ....VI. *Phenolia*   (p. 393)
   Apex of mandibles not bifid ....II. *Omosita*   (p. 392)

Genus I. *NITIDULA* Fabricius

Small, oblong-ovate, convex; antennae eleven-segmented, club distinct, three-segmented; labrum feebly emarginate, not bilobed; elytra without costae or rows of punctures, at most partly exposing pygidium; antennal grooves strongly convergent; prosternum depressed behind procoxae, not prolonged; abdominal sternites two to five equal, first slightly longer; all tarsi distinctly dilated.

The members of this genus are usually found on carrion or dried skin and bones.

KEY TO SPECIES

1. Pronotum coarsely and densely punctate 2
   Pronotum sparsely and finely punctate; elytra with irregular, dull-yellow maculae ....c. *ziczac*
2. Piceous; elytra each with a round, red macula on disk ....a. *bipunctata*
   Piceous; elytra not maculate ....b. *rufipes*

a. *Nitidula bipunctata* (Linné)   Plate XXXVIII, No. 10, p. 389

Broadly oblong-ovate, subconvex; piceous, feebly shining, finely pubescent; elytra each with a round, reddish macula near middle. Pronotum transverse, narrowed to apex; lateral margins somewhat flattened; posterior angles nearly rectangular. Elytra together longer than wide; apices broadly, separately rounded, exposing part of the pygidium; disk rather sparsely and finely punctate. Length 4.5–6 mm.

The habitat of this species is bones and skins of dried carcasses.

b. *Nitidula rufipes* (Linné) Plate XXXIX, No. 1, p. 395

Oblong-ovate, subconvex; piceous, subopaque; pubescent; antennae (except club) and legs reddish brown. Pronotum distinctly transverse; base only slightly wider than apex; side margins narrowly flattened; disk densely and rather coarsely punctate. Elytra coarsely and densely punctate; apices each broadly rounded, exposing part of the pygidium. Length 3.5–4 mm.

This species occurs on flowers and also with the preceding species.

c. *Nitidula ziczac* Say Plate XXXVIII, No. 9, p. 389

Oblong-ovate; piceous, feebly shining; pubescent; elytra each with a median S-shaped macula and with others near base dull yellow. Pronotum distinctly transverse; base slightly wider than apex; disk rather sparsely and finely punctate. Elytra rather finely punctate; apices each broadly rounded, exposing part of the pygidium. Length 3–4 mm.

This species may be collected at carrion.

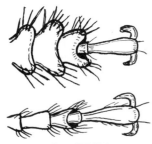

Figs. 308-309

Fig. 310

Fig. 311

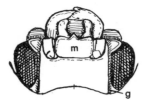

Fig. 312

Figs. 308–309. Tarsus of *Nitidula* (308) and of *Phenolia* (309).
Fig. 310. Head of *Epuraea* from below. *g*, antennal grooves.
Fig. 311. Labrum of *Epuraea*. *c*, clypeus; *l*, labrum.
Fig. 312. Head of *Prometopia* from beneath. *g*, antennal grooves; *m*, mentum.

Genus II. *OMOSITA* Erichson

Small, oblong-ovate, subconvex; front not lobed over antennae; antennae distinctly capitate; mentum not covering maxillae; mandibles entire at apex, not bifid; pronotum not narrowed apically; elytra rounded at apex, exposing the pygidium, without trace of costae; prosternum depressed behind procoxae, not prolonged; tarsi feebly or not dilated.

Omosita colon (Linné)   Plate XXXIX, No. 2, p. 395

Oblong-ovate, subconvex; piceous, rather shining; pronotum margined with yellowish; elytra each with three or four yellowish maculae on basal half and a large, yellowish fascia near apex, enclosing on each side a piceous dot. Pronotum distinctly transverse; disk coarsely punctate and somewhat rugose. Elytra smooth; apices separately rounded, exposing only the pygidium. Length 2–3 mm.

This species may be found on decaying vegetable or animal matter.

Genus III. *EPURAEA* Erichson

Small, oval, robust, subdepressed; antennae with a distinct, three-segmented club; labrum bilobed; antennal grooves strongly converging; pronotum transverse; elytra truncate or entire at apex, disk without costae or rows of punctures; tarsi distinctly dilated.

Epuraea helvola Erichson   Plate XXXIX, No. 4, p. 395

Broadly ovate, robust, subdepressed; dark reddish brown, feebly shining, sparsely pubescent; margins often paler. Pronotum strongly transverse; apex deeply emarginate; sides slightly narrowed basally, margins broadly flattened, slightly reflexed; disk finely granulate and rather densely punctate. Elytra together slightly longer than wide, strongly tapering posteriorly, margins reflexed; disk finely granulate and rather densely punctate; apices separately rounded, exposing pygidium. Length 2.5–3.5 mm.

This species occurs in spring at sap and in summer in decaying fleshy fungi.

Genus IV. *STELIDOTA* Erichson

Small, oval, subdepressed; antennae distinctly clubbed, club three-segmented; antennal grooves parallel; pronotum transverse; elytra more or less costate, covering abdomen above; prosternum depressed behind procoxae, not prolonged; tarsi very distinctly dilated.

Stelidota geminata (Say)   Plate XXXIX, No. 5, p. 395

Oval, narrowed posteriorly, subdepressed; dark brown or piceous, margins paler; elytra with a basal and a postmedian band of indistinct, pale-yellowish maculae. Pronotum strongly transverse; base wider than apex, which is deeply emarginate; lateral margins broadly flattened; posterior angles rectangular; disk coarsely, densely punctate. Elytra narrowing gradually to the rounded apices, which are subtruncate at suture, covering abdomen entirely; disk feebly costate, each costa with a single row of fine punctures bearing short hairs; intervals densely punctate. Length 2–3.5 mm.

In spring this species may be found at sap, and on decaying fruit in fall.

Genus V. *PROMETOPIA* Erichson

Small, oval, depressed; antennal club distinctly three-segmented; mentum broad, covering the base of the maxillae; mandibles bifid at apex; pronotum transverse, apex deeply emarginate; lateral margins of pronotum and elytra broad, flat, and translucent; elytra entire, covering abdomen; prosternum depressed behind procoxae, not prolonged; tarsi feebly dilated.

Prometopia sexmaculata (Say)   Plate XXXVIII, No. 8, p. 389

Broadly ovate, rather robust, depressed; piceous, margined with reddish brown; body beneath grayish brown; elytra with an irregular band on humerus and a macula near apex pale reddish brown. Pronotum strongly transverse, narrowed apically; posterior angles rectangular; disk sparsely, coarsely punctate, with fine punctures interspersed. Elytra coarsely, sparsely punctate; apices together rounded, concealing abdomen. Length 5–6 mm.

This species hibernates in numbers beneath logs and bark in the winter, and in spring feeds on sap.

Genus VI. *PHENOLIA* Erichson

Rather small, oblong-ovate; antennae distinctly capitate; mandibles with apex slightly bifid; mentum not covering the maxillae; pronotum transverse; elytra feebly costate, entirely covering abdomen; tarsi not dilated.

Phenolia grossa (Fabricius)   Plate XXXVIII, No. 7, p. 389

Oblong-ovate; piceous, slightly shining; elytra each with seven indistinct, reddish maculae—an oblique row of three at base, another similar row of

PLATE XXXIX
Family NITIDULIDAE II

1. *Nitidula rufipes* (Linné) (p. 391)
Dark brown to blackish; legs reddish brown; 3.5–4 mm.

2. *Omosita colon* (Linné) (p. 392)
Dark brown and dull yellowish; 2–3 mm.

3. *Conotelus obscurus* Erichson (p. 386)
Deep brown to black; legs light brown; 3.5–4 mm.

4. *Epuraea helvola* Erichson (p. 392)
Dark brown and dull yellowish; 2.5–3.5 mm.

5. *Stelidota geminata* (Say) (p. 393)
Deep ochraceous-yellow, with paler margins and spots; 2–3.5 mm.

Family CUCUJIDAE

6. *Cucujus clavipes* Fabricius (p. 400)
Brownish red; 10–14 mm.

7. *Laemophloeus biguttatus* Say (p. 401)
Fulvous to dark brown; elytral spots yellowish; 3–4 mm.

8. *Catogenus rufus* (Fabricius) (p. 400)
Brownish red to dark reddish brown; 5–11 mm.

9. *Laemophloeus adustus* LeConte (p. 401)
Yellowish brown; 1.5–2.5 mm.

10. *L. testaceus* (Fabricius) (p. 401)
Light reddish brown; 1.5–2.5 mm.

11. *Silvanus bidentatus* (Fabricius) (p. 399)
Reddish brown; 2.7 mm.

12. *Oryzaephilus surinamensis* (Linné) (p. 400)
Fuscous; 2.5 mm.

13. *Silvanus planatus* Germar (p. 399)
Reddish brown; 2.2–2.7 mm.

14. *Uleiota debilis* LeConte (p. 402)
Blackish; elytral margins and legs reddish brown; 4–5 mm.

15. *U. dubius* Fabricius (p. 402)
Reddish brown; elytral sides paler; 4.5–5.5 mm.

16. *Telephanus velox* Haldeman (p. 402)
Dull yellow and black; elytral band brownish; 3.5–4.5 mm.

```
MM
0    10    20    30    40    50    60    70
```

PLATE XXXIX

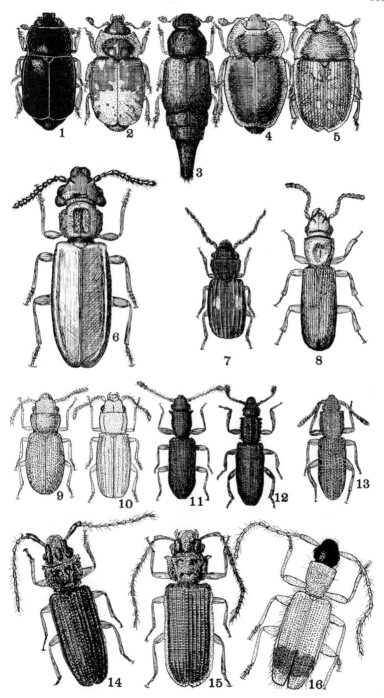

three near middle, and a single macula near scutellum. Pronotum strongly transverse, slightly wider at base than at apex, which is deeply emarginate; sides arcuate, sinuate basally; posterior angles acute; disk coarsely and rather densely punctate. Elytral apices separately, narrowly rounded, completely covering abdomen; disk feebly costate, each costa finely, seriately punctate, punctures each with a short hair; intervals each with three indistinct rows of punctures. Length 6.5–8 mm.

This species hibernates beneath bark and is also found in fungi.

Subfamily CRYPTARCHINAE

KEY TO GENERA

Pronotum margined basally, slightly overlapping the base of elytra;
   body pubescent ....I. *Cryptarcha* (p. 396)
Pronotum not margined basally; body glabrous ....II. *Glischrochilus* (p. 396)

Genus I. *CRYPTARCHA* Shuckard

Small, oval; antennae distinctly capitate; labrum indistinct, connate with epistoma (Fig. 302); antennae eleven-segmented, club three-segmented; pronotum margined basally, slightly overlapping base of elytra; prosternum prolonged and platelike at apex, partially concealing mesosternum (Fig. 313); body pubescent.

Cryptarcha ampla Erichson   Plate XXXVIII, No. 14, p. 389

Oval; piceous or fuscous; sparsely pubescent. Pronotum transverse, base feebly wider than apex, which is slightly emarginate; lateral margins not flattened, narrowly reflexed; posterior angles obtuse; disk densely punctate. Elytral lateral margins narrowly reflexed; sides converging gradually apically; apices separately, broadly rounded, covering abdomen; disk with irregular rows of punctures. Length 6–7 mm.

This species may be found at sap in spring.

Genus II. *GLISCHROCHILUS* Reitter

Small, oblong-ovate, subconvex; antennae eleven-segmented, club distinct; labrum indistinct, connate with epistoma (Fig. 302); pronotum not margined basally; body glabrous; prosternum prolonged and platelike at apex, partially concealing mesosternum (Fig. 313).

In this genus are some of the most common and best-known species of this family. They come to sap or decaying fruit.

KEY TO SPECIES

1. Elytra reddish, each with two black maculae ....c. *sanguinolentus*
   Elytra dark reddish brown to black, each with two yellowish or reddish
   maculae 2
2. Body beneath entirely black ....a. *fasciatus*
   Body beneath reddish brown ....b. *quadrisignatus*

a. *Glischrochilus fasciatus* (Olivier)   Plate XXXVIII, No. 11, p. 389
   Oblong-ovate, subconvex; black, shining; elytra each with two transverse yellowish or reddish maculae, one at humerus, one near apex, these often reduced in size. Pronotum transverse, sides feebly arcuate; disk finely punctate. Elytra finely punctate; apices of male oblique, covering abdomen, of female rounded and partially exposing the pygidium. Length 4–7 mm.

   The adults are frequently found in spring beneath bark of decaying and injured maple trees; throughout the summer they come to sap and decaying vegetable matter.

b. *Glischrochilus quadrisignatus* (Say)   Plate XXXVIII, No. 12, p. 389
   Oblong-ovate, tapering posteriorly, subdepressed; dark reddish brown, shining; elytra each with two pale-yellowish maculae, basal one frequently broken into two, one at apical third smaller. Pronotum strongly transverse, slightly narrowed apically; sides narrowly margined; disk finely, sparsely punctate. Elytra rather coarsely, densely punctate; in male each elytral apex oblique, covering abdomen, in female separately, broadly rounded, exposing pygidium. Length 4.5–6 mm.

c. *Glischrochilus sanguinolentus* (Olivier)   Plate XXXVIII, No. 13, p. 389
   Oblong-ovate, subconvex; black, shining; elytra red, each with a black macula at middle and at apex; beneath largely reddish. Pronotum transverse, sides feebly arcuate; disk finely, sparsely punctate. Elytra finely punctate; in male, apex oblique, covering abdomen, in female, rounded, partially exposing pygidium. Length 4–6 mm.

   The adults are found on sap and decaying vegetable matter. This species is not quite so common as *fasciatus*.

FIG. 313

Fig. 313. Prosternum of *Glischrochilus*. *c*, procoxae; *m*, mesosternum; *p*, prosternum.

Family CUCUJIDAE

The Flat Bark Beetles

A small family of flat, elongate beetles, having antennae of eleven segments, usually without a club, inserted at the frontal margin; procoxae rounded or subglobose, not prominent, their cavities open or closed posteriorly; elytra rounded at apex, usually covering abdomen, and frequently strongly margined; five abdominal sternites present.

These insects are adapted for existence under loose but close-fitting bark of trees, where both adult and larva feed on insects. However, several species of the genera *Oryzaephilus* and *Silvanus* are pests in stored grains and their products.

KEY TO GENERA

1. Procoxal cavities closed posteriorly (Fig. 25B) 2
   Procoxal cavities open posteriorly (Fig. 25A) 4
2. Antennal club distinct; tarsi not lobed beneath, fourth segment small 3
   Antennae not clubbed, but slender and filiform (Figs. 10, 11); third tarsal segment lobed beneath, fourth segment very small ......
   ....VII. *Telephanus* (p. 402)
3. Pronotum ovate; sides with six teeth each ....II. *Oryzaephilus* (p. 399)
   Pronotum elongate or quadrate, sides not dentate ....I. *Silvanus* (p. 398)
4. Maxillae concealed by corneous plates which extend from sides of mouth (Fig. 314) ....III. *Catogenus* (p. 400)
   Maxillae not concealed (Fig. 315) 5
5. Head widest behind eyes ....IV. *Cucujus* (p. 400)
   Head widest across eyes 6
6. Pronotal sides not serrate, sometimes with a single tooth at anterior angles ....V. *Laemophloeus* (p. 401)
   Pronotal sides distinctly serrate (Plate XXXIX–A, No. 5) ..VI. *Uleiota* (p. 401)

Genus I. *SILVANUS* Latreille

Small, oblong beetles; head subquadrate; antennae with first and second segments long, third to seventh shorter, subequal, eighth shortest, ninth to eleventh forming a loose club; pronotal sides finely crenulate (Plate XXXIX–A, No. 3); sometimes anterior angles with a tooth; elytra seriately punctate, punctures large, round.

Under bark and in grains and cereals are the usual places in which these beetles occur.

KEY TO SPECIES

Each anterior angle of pronotum with a sharp, divergent tooth; elytra opaque, strongly punctate ....a. *bidentatus*
Tooth at anterior angle feeble; elytra rather shining, not densely punctate .....
....b. *planatus*

a. *Silvanus bidentatus* (Fabricius)   Two-toothed Grain Beetle
Plate XXXIX, No. 11, p. 395

Elongate, subdepressed; dark reddish brown, opaque. Pronotum one-half longer than wide; anterior angles sharply dentate; disk scabrose, densely punctate, with traces of three raised longitudinal lines. Elytra densely, coarsely punctate, punctures in close-set rows; intervals very narrow. Length 2.7 mm.

b. *Silvanus planatus* Germar   Plate XXXIX, No. 13, p. 395

Elongate-oblong, depressed; dark reddish brown. Pronotum feebly longer than wide, anterior angles feebly dentate; disk finely scabrose, without trace of longitudinal raised lines, near base with a shallow, rounded impression. Elytra with rows of moderately coarse punctures; intervals minutely punctate, nearly as wide as rows of punctures. Length 2.2–2.7 mm.

Genus II. *ORYZAEPHILUS* Ganglbauer

Small, oblong, depressed; antennal club two- or three-segmented, first segment nearly equal in width to second; pronotal sides each with six sharp teeth; elytra seriately granulate-punctate, the series placed between four feeble costae; mesocoxal cavities open posteriorly.

 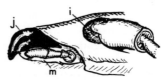

Fig. 314   Fig. 315

Figs. 314–315. Anterior part of head of *Catogenus* (314) and of *Laemophloeus* (315) viewed obliquely from the side. *c*, corneous plate; *i*, antennal insertions; *j*, mandible; *m*, maxilla.

Oryzaephilus surinamensis (Linné)   Saw-toothed Grain Beetle
                                                    Plate XXXIX, No. 12, p. 395

Elongate, depressed; dark reddish brown, clothed with pale pubescence. Pronotum elongate; disk with three feeble but distinct longitudinal costae; sides evenly arcuate, with six rather acute teeth. Elytra each with four costae; intervals granulate-punctate. Length 2.5 mm.

A pest in stored grains and dried fruits, this beetle may be taken at any time of the year.

Genus III. *CATOGENUS* Westwood

Moderate-sized, elongate-oblong, depressed; head as wide as pronotum; disk flat and smooth; front bistriate apically; antennae robust, moniliform, first segment largest, second smallest, eleventh compressed and carinate; elytra sulcate; procoxal cavities open posteriorly (Fig. 25A).

Catogenus rufus (Fabricius)   Plate XXXIX, No. 8, p. 395

Elongate-oblong, depressed; dark reddish brown. Head transversely grooved behind eyes; eyes almost invisible from above. Pronotum narrowed posteriorly; disk distinctly punctate, on basal half with an impressed median line. Elytra not punctate, deeply striate. Length 5–11 mm.

This beetle occurs beneath bark.

Genus IV. *CUCUJUS* Fabricius

Moderate to large in size, elongate-oblong, rather robust; head broader than pronotum, widest behind eyes, posterior angles produced; pronotal disk rugose, sides gradually narrowed posteriorly, constricted suddenly at apex; antennae moniliform; elytra at most with only indistinct striae, a longitudinal raised line near external edge; procoxal cavities closed posteriorly.

Cucujus clavipes Fabricius   Plate XXXIX, No. 6, p. 395

Elongate, very depressed, sides parallel; above, bright yellowish red; beneath, dull red; tibiae and tarsi darker; antennae black. Antennae extending to base of pronotum. Pronotum coarsely punctate; disk with three broad, slightly elevated ridges. Elytra finely punctate. Length 10–14 mm.

This species is one of the largest and most brilliantly colored members of the family; they are common beneath bark of ash and poplar, especially of recently felled trees.

Genus V. *LAEMOPHLOEUS* Laporte

Small, flattened or subconvex, oblong; antennae frequently elongate, especially in males; eyes rather small, near anterior edge of prothorax; labrum large, transverse, rounded anteriorly; pronotum margined and with an impressed line each side of middle; procoxal cavities closed posteriorly; protibial spurs unequal in length; meso- and metatarsi four-segmented in male.

KEY TO SPECIES

1. Pronotum distinctly transverse, about twice as wide as long 2
   Pronotum quadrate, almost parallel-sided; pale red to brown; elytra not
     spotted ....c. *testaceus*
2. Elytra each with a pale spot before middle; labrum emarginate ..a. *biguttatus*
   Elytra not spotted; labrum entire ....b. *adustus*

a. *Laemophloeus biguttatus* Say   Plate XXXIX, No. 7, p. 395
  Oblong, depressed; dark brown; legs and antennae slightly paler. Pronotum narrowed posteriorly; sides distinctly curved, very finely crenate. Elytra striate, twice as long as head and pronotum combined, strongly margined. Length 3–4 mm.

b. *Laemophloeus adustus* LeConte   Plate XXXIX, No. 9, p. 395
  Oblong, subconvex; head and pronotum reddish brown, densely and coarsely punctate; elytra darker, shining, glabrous. Head as wide as pronotum; antennae two-thirds as long as body. Pronotum twice as wide as long, narrowed basally; sides rounded, sinuate near posterior angles. Elytra finely striate, surface punctate. Length 1.5–2.5 mm.
  This species may be taken by sweeping herbage.

c. *Laemophloeus testaceus* (Fabricius)   Plate XXXIX, No. 10, p. 395
  Elongate-oblong, depressed; light reddish brown. Head sparsely punctate; antennae in male nearly as long as body, of female equal in length to elytra. Pronotum quadrate, finely punctate, sides almost parallel; anterior angles distinctly dentate; posterior angles rectangular, with distinct grooves laterally. Length 1.5–2.5 mm.

Genus VI. *ULEIOTA* Latreille

Small, broad, depressed; first antennal segment elongate; pronotum with sides finely and acutely serrate, anterior angles strongly dentate; procoxal cavities open posteriorly (Fig. 25A); mesosternum emarginate anteriorly; metatarsi of male five-segmented.

KEY TO SPECIES

Pronotum distinctly wider than long; elytral lateral margins pale ....a. *dubius*
Pronotum subquadrate; elytra unicolorous ....b. *debilis*

a. *Uleiota dubius* Fabricius   Plate XXXIX, No. 15, p. 395

Moderately elongate, very depressed; brownish black, legs and margins of elytra paler. Head and pronotum often paler than elytra, their surfaces densely and coarsely punctate. Antennae as long as body. Pronotum one-half broader than long, anterior angles very prominent. Elytra broader at base than pronotum, a distinct costa extending from humerus to apex; sides strongly emarginate; intervals each with a row of minute granules. Length 4.5–5.5 mm.

This species may be found beneath bark.

b. *Uleiota debilis* LeConte   Plate XXXIX, No. 14, p. 395

Elongate, slender, depressed; piceous or black, with short, yellowish hairs; antennae and legs brownish, the former slightly shorter than body. Pronotum almost quadrate, narrowed behind middle; anterior angles acute, posterior ones obtusely rounded. Elytra with a distinct costa extending from humerus to apex; intervals each with a row of minute granules; sides between costa and margin nearly perpendicular. Length 4–5 mm.

These beetles may be taken by sifting forest-floor debris.

Genus VII. *TELEPHANUS* Erichson

Elongate, slender, subdepressed; first antennal segment long, spindle-form; elytra broader than pronotum, apices rounded; procoxae closed posteriorly (Fig. 25A); metafemora swollen; tarsi with five segments, fourth small, fifth one bilobed.

Telephanus velox Haldeman   Plate XXXIX, No. 16, p. 395

Small, elongate, slender; pale brownish yellow; closely and coarsely punctate, rather coarsely pubescent; head deep brown; antennae on apical half dusky; elytra frequently with apical third fuscous. Antennae as long as elytra. Pronotum one-half longer than wide, narrowed behind middle. Length 3.5–4.5 mm.

This species is usually found beneath stones and bark. When exposed, they generally remain quiet with antennae folded, but, when touched, run very quickly.

Family LANGURIIDAE

The Slender Plant Beetles

Long, slender, small to large beetles, with a color combination of either deep blue and red or black and red; ligula with winglike, lateral, membranous lobes; antennae eleven-segmented, short, club three- to six-segmented (Fig. 316), inserted close together above base of mandibles (Fig. 317); head narrowed at base of mandibles; eyes hemispherical and finely granulate; procoxal cavities open posteriorly (Fig. 25A); tarsi five-segmented, fourth segment usually very small (Fig. 318), first three broad, pubescent beneath.

These beetles are found on foliage and stems of plants; the larvae live in the stems, frequently doing considerable damage to crop plants.

KEY TO GENERA

Apices of elytra simple, rounded or truncately rounded (Fig. 319)
....I. *Languria* (p. 403)
Apices of elytra acuminate (Fig. 320) ....II. *Acropteroxys* (p. 405)

Genus I. *LANGURIA* Latreille

Long, slender, small to large beetles; ocular stria present, extending from antennal socket to end of eye (Fig. 317); antennal club asymmetrical (Fig. 316), usually of three or more segments; body very narrow in form; apices of elytra simple, rounded or truncately rounded.   .

KEY TO SPECIES

1. Head red 2
   Head entirely or mostly black 3
2. Undersurface red, last abdominal sternite black; pronotum red, usually with a black discal macula; antennal club distinctly six-segmented ..a. *bicolor*
   Undersurface red, at least three abdominal sternites black; pronotum red, immaculate; antennal club five-segmented ....b. *mozardi*
3. Antennae at least in part reddish yellow 4
   Antennae entirely black; elytra bluish black, reddish yellow at sides, sometimes extended into a reddish-yellow fascia ....d. *angustata*
4. Elytra entirely bluish black ....c. *taedata*
   Elytra with a median reddish fascia ....e. *trifasciata*

a. *Languria bicolor* (Fabricius)   Color Plate D; Plate XL, No. 3, p. 409

Moderate-sized, elongate, slender; head and pronotum red, pronotum with a black macula on disk; elytra very dark blue, shining; undersurface red; legs, last abdominal segment, and antennae black. Antennal club six-segmented. Pronotum subquadrate, narrowed to apex, sides arcuate; disk with fine, sparse punctures. Elytra with regular rows of deep, elongate punctures. Length 7–13 mm.

This species may be collected from leaves of Indian plantain and by sweeping herbage.

b. *Languria mozardi* Latreille   Plate XL, No. 1, p. 409

Small to moderate-sized, elongate, slender, parallel; head and pronotum red; elytra very dark blue, shining; undersurface red; last two or three abdominal segments, legs except for basal half of femora, and antennae black. Antennal club five-segmented. Pronotum quadrate, feebly narrowing toward apex; sides slightly arcuate; disk sparsely punctate, coarse and fine punctures intermingled. Elytra with regular rows of coarse, deep, elongate punctures. Length 4–9 mm.

This is the commonest and most widespread species of the family; the larvae are the "clover-stem borers."

c. *Languria taedata* LeConte   Plate XL, No. 4, p. 409

Moderate-sized, elongate, slender; head, elytra, femora, and antennae black or piceous with a bluish cast; pronotum, undersurface, and labrum yellowish red, pronotum with a black macula on disk. Antennal club five-segmented. Pronotum quadrate; sides slightly arcuate; disk with sparse, fine punctures. Elytra with regular rows of coarse, deep, elongate punctures. Length 9–11 mm.

d. *Languria angustata* (Beauvois)   Plate XL, No. 2, p. 409

Small to moderate-sized, elongate, very slender, parallel; head, antennae, and elytra bluish black, the latter with two lateral red maculae which sometimes are joined into a red fascia at middle; pronotum reddish yellow; beneath, reddish yellow, except last two abdominal segments, tarsi, and apical tips of femora, which are black. Pronotum quadrate, sides almost parallel; disk with fine, sparse punctures. Elytra with regular rows of coarse, deep, elongate punctures. Antennal club five-segmented. Length 6–9 mm.

This species is especially common on *Ranunculus,* chard, and parsley.

e. *Languria trifasciata* Say   Plate XL, No. 5, p. 409

Small, elongate, very slender, tapering to an obtuse point; head and basal and apical third of elytra blue-black; pronotum, a broad median fascia on elytra, and antennal segments two to six, inclusive, reddish yellow; undersurface reddish yellow, last two abdominal sternites black. Antennae with a five-segmented club. Pronotum with sides arcuate; disk finely and sparsely punctate. Elytra with regular rows of coarse, deep, elongate punctures. Length 6–7.5 mm.

The adults may be found on wild lettuce and *Ranunculus;* the larvae bore in the stems of these plants.

Genus II. *ACROPTEROXYS* Gorham

Small to moderate-sized forms, long, slender; usually black and red or dark blue and red; ocular stria absent; club of antennae asymmetrical (Fig. 316), usually with three or more segments; body very narrow in form; elytral apices acuminate but neither dentate nor rounded.

Acropteroxys gracilis Newman   Plate XL, No. 6, p. 409

Elongate, very slender, parallel; head, at least in part, red; pronotum red, with a greenish-black median discal macula extending from apex almost to base; elytra and antennae black with greenish tinge; undersurface of head and prothorax red; meso- and metathorax, abdomen, and legs

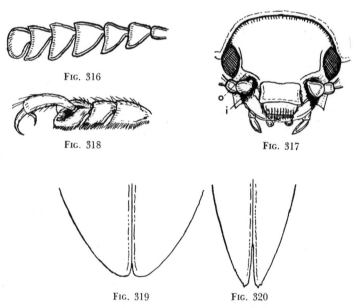

Fig. 316. Antennal club of *Languria bicolor.*
Fig. 317. Head of *Languria,* viewed from above. *i,* antennal insertion; *o,* ocular stria.
Fig. 318. Tarsus of *Languria,* the fourth segment minute.
Figs. 319–320. Elytral apices of *Languria* (319) and of *Acropteroxys* (320).

greenish black. Antennae with five-segmented club. Pronotum usually deeply, evenly, or sometimes shallowly punctate. Elytra with rows of deep punctures. Length 6–12 mm.

The larvae may be found in stems of nettle, fleabane, ragweed, and other low herbs; the adults frequent flowers of wild rose, Jersey tea, clover, and willows.

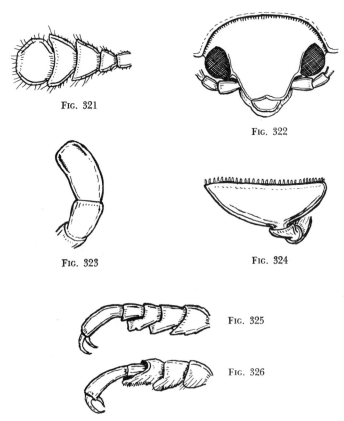

Fig. 321.

Fig. 322.

Fig. 323.

Fig. 324.

Fig. 325.

Fig. 326.

Fig. 321. Antennal club of *Tritoma*.
Fig. 322. Head of *Tritoma* from the front.
Figs. 323–324. Maxillary palpus of *Megalodacne* (323) and of *Tritoma* (324).
Figs. 325–326. Tarsus of *Megalodacne* (325) and of *Tritoma* (326).

Family EROTYLIDAE

The Pleasing Fungus Beetles

Moderate-sized, elongate-ovate beetles, usually yellow or brown with black or blue markings; sometimes prettily bicolored, the pronotum red, the elytra black, or vice versa. Other characters which distinguish them as a family are: antennae eleven-segmented, abruptly clavate (Fig. 321), club three- or four-segmented, inserted on sides of front before eyes; head retracted into prothorax to eyes; front more or less prolonged into a short beak (Fig. 322); procoxal cavities closed posteriorly; pro- and mesocoxae globose, metacoxae transverse, not contiguous; tarsi five-segmented, fourth segment sometimes very small (Fig. 326), first to third more or less broad and pubescent beneath.

The adults are common during the summer on fungus or under bark of decaying logs in deep woods; some species are attracted to sap in the spring.

KEY TO TRIBES

Mentum strongly transverse; terminal segment of maxillary palpus not
    transverse (Fig. 323); tarsi distinctly five-segmented (Fig. 325) DACNINI   (p. 412)
Mentum not transverse; terminal segment of maxillary palpus strongly
    transverse (Fig. 324); tarsi apparently four-segmented, fourth minute
    and attached closely to fifth (Fig. 326) .... TRIPLACINI   (p. 407)

Tribe TRIPLACINI

KEY TO GENERA

1. Pronotum yellow, with four black, rounded spots in a transverse row
    ....I. *Ischyrus*   (p. 410)
    Pronotum black or reddish, without any maculae 2
2. Pronotum black ....II. *Tritoma*   (p. 410)
    Pronotum reddish or yellowish ....III. *Triplax*   (p. 411)

PLATE XL

Family LANGURIIDAE

1. *Languria mozardi* Latreille (p. 404)

Orange-red; elytra, femoral apices, and tip of abdomen blue-black; 4–9 mm.

2. *L. angustata* (Beauvois) (p. 404)

Yellow to dull reddish; head and elytra partly blue-black; 6–9 mm.

3. *L. bicolor* (Fabricius) (p. 404)

Reddish; elytra, pronotal macula, and legs black; 7–13 mm.

4. *L. taedata* LeConte (p. 404)

Reddish and black; 9–11 mm.

5. *L. trifasciata* Say (p. 404)

Reddish and blue-black; 6–7.5 mm.

6. *Acropteroxys gracilis* Newman (p. 405)

Black; sides of pronotum yellowish or red; 6–12 mm.

Family EROTYLIDAE I

7. *Megalodacne heros* (Say) (p. 413)

Black and red; 18–21 mm.

8. *M. fasciata* (Fabricius) (p. 413)

Black and red; 9–15 mm.

9. *Dacne quadrimaculata* (Say) (p. 412)

Black, with red maculae; legs and antennae pale yellow; 2.5–3.2 mm.

10. *Ischyrus quadripunctatus* (Olivier) (p. 410)

Yellowish and black; 7–8 mm.

11. *Tritoma pulcher* (Say) (p. 410)

Black; elytral base orange or reddish; 3.2–4 mm.

12. *T. sanguinipennis* (Say) (p. 410)

Black; elytra dark reddish yellow; 4–5 mm.

13. *Triplax flavicollis* Lacordaire (p. 411)

Yellow; elytra and antennal club black; 3–4 mm.

14. *Tritoma biguttata* Say (p. 411)

Black, with reddish maculae; 3–4 mm.

15. *Triplax festiva* Lacordaire (p. 411)

Black and orange; 5–6 mm.

16. *Tritoma humeralis* Fabricius (p. 411)

Black and reddish; 3–4 mm.

MM | 0 | 10 | 20 | 30 | 40 | 50 | 60 | 70

PLATE XL

409

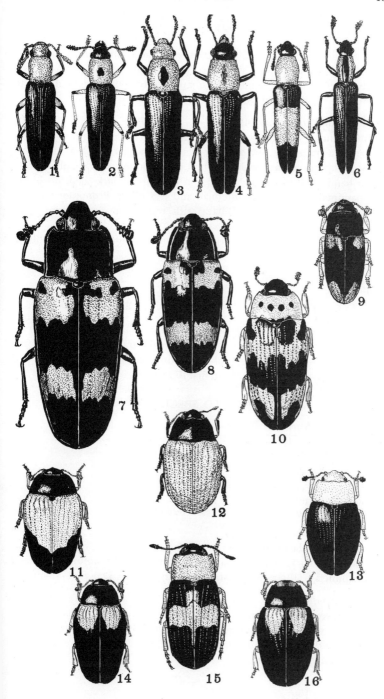

Genus I. *ISCHYRUS* Lacordaire

Rather small, elongate or oval species; mentum triangular; last segment of maxillary palpus hatchet-shaped; antennal club three-segmented; eyes coarsely faceted; tibiae slender; tarsi apparently four-segmented, fourth segment very small, united with fifth.

Ischyrus quadripunctatus (Olivier)   Plate XL, No. 10, p. 409

Ovate, slender, convex; head black; pronotum yellow, with four black maculae in a transverse row on disk; elytra yellow, each with a large common, scutellar macula and a small round one on humerus, a deeply dentate median band, and an oblong macula on each apex black; beneath black, sides margined with yellow; antennae and legs black. Pronotum more or less finely, sparsely punctate. Elytra with regular rows of coarse, deep punctures. Length 7–8 mm.

This species may be found during the winter months beneath rubbish, in the summer on fungi.

Genus II. *TRITOMA* Fabricius

Small, oval, convex beetles; black, or red and black; last segment of maxillary palpus broadly dilated and strongly transverse; mentum triangular, not transverse; antennal club three- or four-segmented; basal three tarsal segments widening from first to third.

KEY TO SPECIES

1. Color entirely black ....e. *unicolor*
   Elytra at least in part reddish 2
2. Elytra entirely reddish yellow ....a. *sanguinipennis*
   Elytra largely black 3
3. Elytral red area extending almost to apex ....b. *pulcher*
   Elytral red area confined to base 4
4. Abdominal sternites entirely red ....c. *biguttata*
   Abdominal sternites, except for apices of terminal one, black ....d. *humeralis*

a. *Tritoma sanguinipennis* (Say)   Plate XL, No. 12, p. 409

Oval, convex; head and pronotum black; elytra dark reddish yellow; body beneath black; abdomen tipped with reddish. Pronotum finely and sparsely punctate. Elytra with distinct, punctate striae. Length 4–5 mm.

b. *Tritoma pulcher* (Say)   Plate XL, No. 11, p. 409

Oval, convex; black, shining; elytra together with a large, triangular, red area basally, extending at suture almost to apex. Pronotum sparsely punctate, fine and coarse punctures intermingled. Elytral striae distinctly punctate. Length 3.2–4 mm.

c. *Tritoma biguttata* Say   Plate XL, No. 14, p. 409
Oval, rather slender, convex; black, shining; elytra with large, triangular, reddish area at base; body beneath pale red. Elytra more deeply striate, punctures more distinct, especially basally. Length 3–4 mm.

d. *Tritoma humeralis* Fabricius   Plate XL, No. 16, p. 409
Broadly oval; black, shining; elytra with a reddish-yellow, subquadrate macula near humerus; undersurface black, with apex of last abdominal sternite red. Pronotum finely, sparsely punctate. Elytra with rows of fine punctures; intervals obsoletely punctate. Length 3–4 mm.

e. *Tritoma unicolor* Say   Plate XLI, No. I, p. 417
Broadly ovate; black, shining. Pronotum sparsely and coarsely punctate. Elytra with rows of distinct punctures, which become finer apically; intervals smooth. Length 4–5 mm.

Genus III. *TRIPLAX* Herbst

Rather small, elongate or ovate beetles; mentum triangular, not transverse; terminal segment of maxillary palpi strongly transverse; eyes finely faceted; basal three tarsal segments successively wider from first to third.

KEY TO SPECIES

1. Body beneath, black ....b. *flavicollis*
   Body beneath, red 2
2. Elytra entirely black ....c. *thoracica*
   Elytra black, with a reddish-yellow fascia at middle ....a. *festiva*

a. *Triplax festiva* Lacordaire   Plate XL, No. 15, p. 409
Elongate-oblong, subconvex; black, shining; pronotum, scutellum, and a broad fascia on middle of elytra reddish yellow; body beneath reddish yellow. Pronotum with sides feebly rounded, only slightly narrowing to apex; disk finely, sparsely punctate. Elytral disk with rows of rather deep punctures, not extending onto humeral region. Length 5–6 mm.
This form is more abundant in the southern part of the area covered by this book.

b. *Triplax flavicollis* Lacordaire   Plate XL, No. 13, p. 409
Oblong-ovate; head, pronotum, antennae (except club), and legs reddish yellow; antennal club, elytra, and body beneath, shining black. Pronotum distinctly, finely, and closely punctate. Elytral striae with coarse, rather close punctures; intervals very feebly punctate. Length 3–4 mm.

c. *Triplax thoracica* Say   Plate XLI, No. 2, p. 417
Oblong-ovate; head and pronotum reddish yellow; elytra and apical half of antennae black; body beneath and legs reddish yellow. Pronotum slightly

narrowed apically; disk finely and closely punctate. Elytral striae with fine, close punctures; intervals very feebly, finely punctate. Length 3.5–5 mm.

This species is common on fleshy fungi and beneath bark.

Tribe DACNINI

KEY TO GENERA

Second to fourth tarsal segments of equal length, small; length of body not over 4 mm. . . . . .I. *Dacne* (p. 412)
Fourth tarsal segment much smaller; length of body 9–25 mm. . . . . . .
. . . . .II. *Megalodacne* (p. 412)

Genus I. *DACNE* Latreille

Small, oval, convex species; last segment of maxillary palpi bluntly pointed, not transverse; mentum strongly transverse; antennae distinctly eleven-segmented; tarsi distinctly five-segmented, narrow, second to fourth segments of equal length, small, pubescent beneath.

Dacne quadrimaculata (Say)   Plate XL, No. 9, p. 409
Oblong-ovate, subparallel, subconvex; black; elytra each with a round, reddish-yellow macula on humerus and one at apex; beneath, piceous or dark reddish brown; antennae, legs, and clypeus paler. Pronotum and head finely and sparsely punctate. Elytra with numerous irregular rows of fine punctures. Length 2.5–3.2 mm.

This species occurs on fungi and is frequent in the southern half of the corn belt.

Genus II. *MEGALODACNE* Cramer

Moderate- or large-sized, elongate-oblong, convex beetles; mentum without lateral angles dentate; last segment of maxillary palpus blunted and hatchet-shaped; eyes coarsely faceted; tarsi distinctly five-segmented, dilated, spongy-pubescent beneath, fourth segment smaller than either second or third.

KEY TO SPECIES

No punctures on median or apical black fasciae; 9–15 mm. in body length . . . .
. . . . .b. *heros*
Entire elytra with rows of punctures; 18–21 mm. in body length . . . . . .a. *fasciata*

a. *Megalodacne fasciata* (Fabricius)   Plate XL, No. 8, p. 409

Oblong-ovate; black, shining; elytra with two reddish fasciae, the basal one irregular and enclosing a small, round macula on each humerus and one common quadrangular one just behind scutellum, black, the latter entirely enclosed by the red fascia, apical fascia narrower and interrupted at suture. Pronotum short, transverse, very feebly and finely punctate; sides straight, broadly margined; base with an impression each side. Elytra with a few rows of distant, fine, feeble punctures, these also appearing on black areas. Length 9–15 mm.

This species is usually found in colonies in dry, rotten wood and beneath loose bark at almost any time of the year.

b. *Megalodacne heros* (Say)   Plate XL, No. 7, p. 409

Oblong-ovate; black, shining; elytra with two reddish fasciae, the basal one irregular and enclosing a small, round macula on each humerus and one common transverse one just behind the scutellum, black, the latter not enclosed entirely by the red fascia. Pronotum transverse, moderately margined. Elytra with indistinct rows of distant, fine punctures, which do not appear on the black areas. Length 18–21 mm.

The adults and larvae of this species feed usually on fungi that grow on tree trunks; they are also found under the bark of decaying logs.

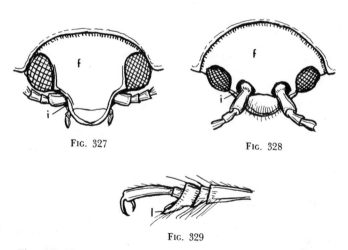

Fig. 327   Fig. 328

Fig. 329

Figs. 327–328. Head of *Tomarus* (327) and of *Anchicera* (328), viewed from above and anteriorly. *f*, front; *i*, antennal insertion.
Fig. 329. Tarsus of *Tomarus*, viewed from the side. *l*, lobe.

Family CRYPTOPHAGIDAE

The Silken Fungus Beetles

Oblong or oval, convex beetles, usually coarsely pubescent and frequently with longer hairs on elytra; antennae eleven-segmented, nine to eleven forming a loose club; pronotal side margins thickened into nodules or serrate; elytra rounded posteriorly, entirely covering abdomen; abdomen with five free ventral segments; procoxae oval, rarely globose, sometimes transverse, separated by prosternum; tarsi five-segmented, occasionally metatarsi with four segments in males.

These are small, yellow to black beetles that live on fungi, about wood-chip piles, beneath dead leaves, in decaying logs, or on flowers.

KEY TO GENERA

1. Antennae widely separated at base, inserted under sides of front
   (Fig. 327) 2
   Antennae approximate at base (Fig. 328), inserted on front . . . .
   . . . . .III. *Anchicera* (p. 415)
2. Tarsi with third segment strongly lobed beneath (Fig. 329), second
   segment less strongly so, fourth segment very small . . . .I. *Tomarus* (p. 414)
   Tarsi with second or third segment not lobed beneath . . . .
   . . . . .II. *Antherophagus* (p. 415)

Genus I. *TOMARUS* Erichson

Very small, elongate-oval, convex; basal segment of antennal club nearly as large as second; pronotum not impressed basally; elytra irregularly punctate; procoxal cavities open posteriorly (Fig. 25A); prosternal process truncate apically; tarsi five-segmented, third segment strongly, second feebly, lobed beneath, fourth segment very short.

Tomarus pulchellus LeConte   Plate XLI, No. 3, p. 417
Elongate-oval, convex; brownish yellow or piceous; legs and basal half of antennae paler; elytra each with a large humeral macula and a broad subapical fascia yellow. Pronotum finely but distinctly punctate, not as broad as elytra, as wide at apex as at base. Elytra widest just before middle, thence narrowed to the acute apices; surface finely and sparsely punctate. Length 1.3–1.7 mm.

This species is frequent in spring under dead leaves and stones and in summer on fungi.

Genus II. *ANTHEROPHAGUS* Latreille

Small, elongate-oval, subcylindrical; front not prolonged beyond antennae; clypeus deeply emarginate in male; antennae robust, compactly segmented; elytra with rows of punctures, sides not margined at base; mesosternum deeply emarginate on anterior margin, receiving prosternum (Fig. 313); tarsi filiform, simple, never lobed beneath, five-segmented, metatarsi four-segmented in male.

Antherophagus ochraceus Melsheimer   Plate XLI, No. 4, p. 417
Elongate-oblong, convex; brownish yellow to bronze-brown, feebly shining; in male, antennae and tibiae black basally. Pronotum strongly transverse, sides feebly arcuate; disk finely, densely punctate. Elytra as wide as pronotum; disk densely, finely punctate. Length 4–4.5 mm.
The adults occur on flowers, especially those of wild hydrangea.

Genus III. *ANCHICERA* Thomson

Small, oblong-oval, subconvex, sparsely pubescent; antennae approximate at base, inserted on front; antennal club feeble, first two segments about as long as wide; pronotum narrowed apically, transversely impressed basally; elytra irregularly punctate, sides not margined basally; procoxal cavities open posteriorly (Fig. 25A); tarsi five-segmented, not lobed beneath.

Anchicera ephippiata Zimmermann   Plate XLI, No. 5, p. 417
Oblong-oval, convex; head and pronotum piceous, shining; elytra reddish yellow, with a piceous fascia anterior to middle, this sometimes the full width of elytra but frequently broken into maculae. Head and pronotum rather coarsely, sparsely punctate; pronotal transverse impression deep, closely approximate to basal margin. Elytra distinctly wider than pronotum; finely, irregularly, distinctly punctate. Length 1–2 mm.

PLATE XLI

Family EROTYLIDAE II

1. *Tritoma unicolor* Say (p. 411)

   Black or piceous; 4–5 mm.

2. *Triplax thoracica* Say (p. 411)

   Orange-fulvous; elytra black; 3.5–5 mm.

Family CRYPTOPHAGIDAE

3. *Tomarus pulchellus* LeConte (p. 414)

   Orange-brown; 1.3–1.7 mm.

4. *Antherophagus ochraceus* Melsheimer (p. 415)

   Dark brown and dull yellow; 4–4.5 mm.

5. *Anchicera ephippiata* Zimmermann (p. 415)

   Dull ochraceous-yellow; 1–2 mm.

Family PYROCHROIDAE

6. *Schizotus cervicalis* Newman (p. 301)

   Black; pronotum and mouthparts dull yellowish brown; 6–8 mm.

7. *Dendroides cyanipennis* Latreille (p. 302)

   Dull yellowish; head largely and elytra entirely blackish; 9–13 mm.

8. *Neopyrochroa flabellata* (Fabricius) (p. 301)

   Dull yellowish; elytra and antennae (except at base) fuscous; 15–17 mm.

9. *Dendroides concolor* Newman (p. 302)

   Entirely dull yellowish; 11–13 mm.

MM ⌊0   10   20   30   40   50   60   70

PLATE XLI 417

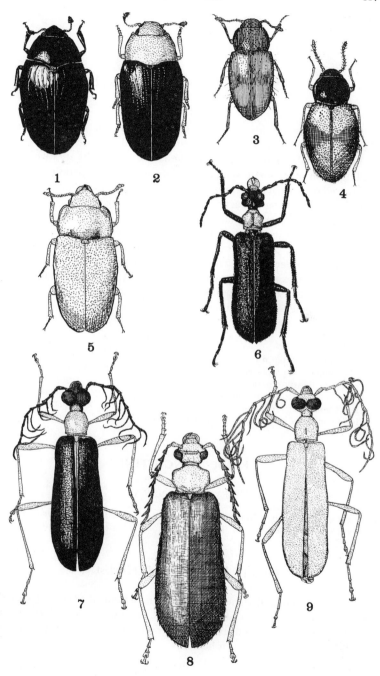

Family COLYDIIDAE

The members of this family of small, elongate or cylindrical beetles resemble the Cucujidae not only in form but in habits as well. They also live in fungi or under bark, and some of the larvae and adults are carnivorous, feeding upon other small wood-boring forms; others are parasitic, and still others feed on decaying vegetable matter. From their allies they may be separated by the following characters: antennae ten- or eleven-segmented, rarely eight-segmented, inserted under the margin of the front, sometimes gradually thickened but usually the last one or two segments are enlarged to form a club (Figs. 330, 331); elytra entire, always covering the abdomen; procoxal cavities either open or closed behind; the pro- and mesocoxae small, globular; metacoxae transverse, not prominent; legs short, tibiae not dilated, tarsi four-segmented, claws simple; abdomen with five ventral segments visible, the first three or four segments fused.

KEY TO TRIBES

1. Last segment of palpi not acicular 2
   Last segment of palpi acicular (Fig. 332) ....CERYLONINI (p. 421)
2. Procoxae slightly separated 3
   Procoxae distant; first abdominal sternite elongate ..... BOTHRIDERINI (p. 421)
3. First segment of tarsi short ....SYNCHITINI (p. 418)
   First segment of tarsi longer than second ....COLYDIINI (p. 420)

Tribe SYNCHITINI

KEY TO GENERA

Procoxal cavities open behind (Fig. 25A) ....I. *Bitoma* (p. 418)
Procoxal cavities closed behind (Fig. 25B) ....II. *Coxelus* (p. 419)

Genus I. *BITOMA* Herbst

Very small, oblong, flattened beetles, having antennae eleven-segmented, inserted under the margin of the front, the last two segments forming an abrupt club; eyes large, convex, coarsely granulate; head without antennal grooves; procoxal cavities open behind.

418

Bitoma quadriguttata Say — Plate XXXVI, No. 5, p. 361

Oblong, elongate, depressed; black, feebly shining; each elytron with three dull-reddish spots, one oblique, elongate, extending from humerus to suture, a rounded one behind middle, and a smaller subsutural one near apex; antennae and legs reddish brown. Pronotum broader than long; sides nearly straight, disk finely granulate and with four carinae, each curving inward anteriorly, the two median ones converging. Elytra slightly wider than pronotum, each with four discal costae, the broader intervals with two rows of coarse punctures. Length 2.5–3 mm.

The adults occur beneath bark and logs.

Genus II. *COXELUS* Latreille

In this genus the antennae are eleven-segmented and with a two-segmented club, as in the preceding genus, but are received in grooves beneath the eyes; procoxal cavities closed behind; tibiae without spurs.

Coxelus guttulatus LeConte — Plate XXXVI, No. 3, p. 361

Elongate-oblong, subconvex; piceous, with reddish-brown legs, antennae, and margins of pronotum and elytra. Pronotum strongly transverse, apex deeply emarginate, front angles prominent; sides broadly rounded; margins wide and flat, edges finely serrulate; disk coarsely granulate. Elytra with rows of coarse granules; near middle, spots of coarse, gray pubescence forming an interrupted sinuous band, another near apex. Length 4–5 mm.

The adults and larvae are found in fungi and under bark of decaying hardwoods.

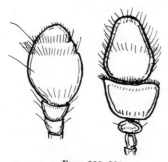

FIGS. 330–331

FIG. 332

Figs. 330–331. Antennal club of *Cerylon* (330) and of *Philothermus* (331), the former composed of a single segment, the latter of two.

Fig. 332. Last palpal segment of *Philothermus* and a portion of the preceding.

Tribe COLYDIINI

KEY TO GENERA

Protibiae finely denticulate at outer apical angle; form rather robust
....I. *Aulonium* (p. 420)
Protibiae with outer apical angle prolonged; form very slender ....
....II. *Colydium* (p. 420)

Genus I. *AULONIUM* Erichson

Antennae eleven-segmented, inserted in front of the eyes, the last three segments forming a rather loose club; eyes emarginate in front by the sides of the clypeus; metacoxae separated by an acute triangular abdominal process.

Aulonium parallelopipedum (Say)   Plate XXXVI, No. 2, p. 361

Elongate, subcylindrical; piceous, moderately shining; legs and antennae reddish. Head with two tubercles on vertex, these sometimes feeble. Pronotum quadrate; disk with a carina each side which curves and converges on anterior margin, before middle with two obtuse tubercles; surface finely punctate; sides feebly arcuate; posterior angles rectangular. Elytra slightly wider than pronotum; disk with rows of rather fine, close-set punctures. Length 4.5–6 mm.

These beetles are scavengers beneath bark.

Genus II. *COLYDIUM* Fabricius

In this genus the procoxal cavities are narrowly enclosed behind; protibiae with outer angle prolonged; palpi with last segment not acicular.

Colydium lineola Say   Plate XXXVI, No. 4, p. 361

Elongate, slender, cylindrical; piceous, moderately shining; legs and antennae paler. Pronotum much longer than wide; the disk with a strongly impressed line at middle and a shorter one either side; coarsely punctate. Elytra only very slightly wider than pronotum; each alternate interval finely carinate, intervals with two rows of punctures. Length 4–6.5 mm.

These beetles may be found beneath bark, particularly of linden and locust; the larvae follow in the tunnels of the Ambrosia beetles.

Tribe BOTHRIDERINI

Genus *BOTHRIDERES* Erichson

Head horizontal or nearly so; eyes not prominent, placed near base of head; palpi not acicular; antennae short, eleven-segmented, received in an oblique antennal groove, club two-segmented; all coxae widely separated, procoxae narrowly enclosed behind; apical angle of tibiae not prolonged; first tarsal segment longer than either second or third.

Bothrideres geminatus (Say)   Plate XXXVI, No. 6, p. 361

Oblong, subdepressed; dark reddish brown, moderately shining, thinly pubescent. Pronotum longer than wide, narrowed basally, apex feebly emarginate; sides feebly arcuate, with a small tubercle on middle of margin; disk slightly depressed, coarsely and densely punctate. Elytra slightly wider than pronotum; striate, striae finely punctate; intervals alternately wider, and with a single row of punctures, the narrower ones smooth. Length 3–4.5 mm.

This species lives beneath the bark of living hardwoods, particularly hickory and maple.

Tribe CERYLONINI

KEY TO GENERA

Antennae ten-segmented, club composed of a single segment (Fig. 330)
. . . . .I. *Cerylon*   (p. 421)
Antennae eleven-segmented, club composed of two segments (Fig. 331)
. . . . .II. *Philothermus*   (p. 422)

Genus I. *CERYLON* Latreille

Head small, deeply inserted; last segment of palpi acicular; prosternum broad; procoxal cavities closed behind; tibiae with small terminal spurs; first abdominal sternite as long as three following combined; first three segments of tarsi short, their combined length shorter than fourth.

Cerylon castaneum Say   Plate XXXVI, No. 7, p. 361

Oblong, elongate, depressed; dark reddish brown, shining. Pronotum subquadrate; posterior angles rectangular; disk with a feeble impression on each side at base, rather coarsely but not densely punctate. Elytra subequal in width to pronotum; disk striate, the striae punctate. Length 2–3 mm.

These small beetles may be found on the underside of logs and beneath the bark of hardwoods.

Genus II. *PHILOTHERMUS* Aubé

These small beetles have the antennae eleven-segmented, club two-segmented; procoxal cavities open behind; tibiae without terminal spurs; last segment of palpi acicular.

Philothermus glabriculus LeConte   Plate XXXVI, No. 8, p. 361

Elongate-oval, subdepressed; dark reddish brown, shining. Pronotum broader than long, widest at base; sides evenly arcuate from base to apex; margin distinctly reflexed; disk sparsely and finely punctate. Elytra as wide as pronotum at base; disk with rows of coarse punctures, which are less distinct toward apex. Length 2–3 mm.

The adults usually are found beneath bark, rarely beneath stones.

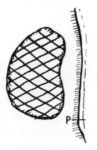

Fig. 333

Fig. 333. Eye of *Corticaria*, emarginate near pronotum (*P*).

Family LATHRIDIIDAE

The Minute Brown Scavenger Beetles

As the common name implies, the members of this family are very small, rarely exceeding 2.5 mm. in length. They inhabit decaying plant debris, especially fallen leaves, as a general rule. Exceptions occur, however, as some species are found beneath bark and stones, in drugs and other commercial products, in mammal nests, and on leaves and flowers of such plants as *Viburnum* and huckleberry.

The family characteristics are: antennae with nine or eleven segments, clavate, club two- or three-segmented, inserted on sides of front; pronotum narrower than elytra, sides often serrate or crenate, posterior angles with a small tooth; elytra covering abdomen, rarely slightly abbreviated, with six to eight rows of coarse punctures, intervals each with a row of fine ones; procoxae conical, prominent, more or less distinctly separated, their cavities usually closed posteriorly; mesocoxae rounded; metacoxae transverse, widely separated; tarsi three-segmented, third segment as long as preceding two combined; claws simple.

KEY TO GENERA

1. Pronotum with a longitudinal carina each side of middle; body
    glabrous or nearly so ....I. *Lathridius* (p. 423)
   Pronotal disk not carinate; body distinctly pubescent 2
2. Eyes vertical, posterior margin emarginate (Fig. 333) ....II. *Corticaria* (p. 424)
   Eyes oblique or circular, posterior margin rounded ....
    ....III. *Melanophthalma* (p. 425)

Genus I. *LATHRIDIUS* Herbst

Very small, oblong-ovate, subconvex; glabrous, shining; eyes on side of head; antennae eleven-segmented, club three-segmented; pronotal anterior angles more or less lobed, sides convergent to near middle, thence divergent to base, disk with costae or ridges; elytra not fused, twice as wide at base as pronotum, apices each subacuminate; prosternal process not attaining posterior border of prothorax, epimera uniting on median line; procoxae globose, narrowly but distinctly separated; protarsi in male feebly dilated.

Lathridius liratus LeConte   Plate XXVII, No. 12, p. 261

Oblong-ovate, rather robust; dark reddish brown, shining; legs and antennae slightly paler. Antennae slender, attaining posterior angles of pronotum. Pronotum slightly elongate, lateral margins reflexed; disk with two longitudinal ridges which are nearly parallel on basal two-thirds, diverging apically; basal impression distinct and divided into three by the ridges; surface coarsely, irregularly punctate. Elytra broadly, transversely impressed near base; striae coarsely, distinctly punctate; intervals convex, third slightly, seventh more strongly, elevated at base. Length 2–2.2 mm.

Genus II. *CORTICARIA* Marsham

Very small, elongate or oblong-ovate, convex; pubescence long and conspicuous, on elytra arranged in rows; eyes large, prominent; antennae not quite attaining posterior angles of pronotum, eleven-segmented, club three-segmented; pronotum usually subcordate, anterior and posterior angles obtuse, sides crenulate or denticulate, surface not carinate, and with a distinct rounded or transverse impression before base; elytra each with eight rows of punctures; abdomen of female with five ventral segments, a sixth usually visible in male; procoxae subconical, distinctly separated; male protarsi with first segment distinctly dilated.

KEY TO SPECIES

Sides of pronotum on apical half crenulate, with a prominent tooth at basal angle ....b. *elongata*
Sides of pronotum denticulate from base nearly to apex, with a feeble tooth at basal angle ....a. *serrata*

a. *Corticaria serrata* (Paykull)   Plate XXVII, No. 13, p. 261

Oblong-ovate, rather robust, moderately convex; dull reddish yellow to dark reddish brown; pubescence grayish, recumbent. Pronotum transverse, wider than head, three-fourths as wide as elytra; sides denticulate, arcuate before middle, convergent posteriorly; a short tooth at basal angle; disk coarsely, densely punctate, basal impression rounded, moderately impressed. Elytral sides broadly rounded; apices separately, broadly, and obtusely rounded; striae feebly impressed, punctures coarse basally, finer apically; intervals more finely punctate. Length 2–2.2 mm.

These beetles occur in fungi and come to light.

b. *Corticaria elongata* Gyllenhal   Plate XXVII, No. 14, p. 261

Elongate-ovate, parallel, subdepressed; light brownish or reddish yellow; elytra tinged with fuscous each side of scutellum; pubescence pale yellow, short, recumbent. Pronotum distinctly transverse; sides feebly arcuate and finely crenulate apically, slightly convergent and denticulate posteriorly, a prominent tooth at basal angles; disk finely, sparsely punctate; basal impression rounded, moderately impressed. Elytral sides broadly rounded, apices separately, obtusely rounded; striae finely punctate; intervals more finely so. Length 1.4–1.8 mm.

These beetles may be collected by sifting dead leaves and other debris in damp localities.

Genus III. *MELANOPHTHALMA* Motschulsky

Very small, oval or elongate-oval, convex; pubescence variable; eyes very large, prominent; antennae eleven-segmented, club three-segmented, last segment much longer; pronotum scarcely wider than head, about as wide as long, sides unarmed, anterior and posterior angles rounded, disk with a transverse impression basally; elytra broad, with distinct rows of punctures; procoxae subglobose, narrowly but distinctly separated.

KEY TO SPECIES

Second segment of tarsi as long as or slightly longer than first; protibiae of male
  with apices bearing longer, denser, and more bristle-like hairs . . a. *distinguenda*
Second segment of tarsi distinctly shorter than first; protibiae of male with a
  short, acute tooth on inner side beyond middle . . . . .b. *cavicollis*

a. *Melanophthalma distinguenda* Comstock   Plate XXVII, No. 15, p. 261
  Elongate-ovate, moderately convex, robust; dull fuscous or brownish yellow; elytra usually darker; legs dull yellowish; yellowish pubescence long and conspicuous. Pronotum transverse; sides angulate medially, margin obsoletely crenulate; disk strongly, coarsely punctate; basal impression moderately deep, extending nearly the width of base. Elytral striae not impressed, punctures coarse on basal half, finer apically, the hairs arising from intervals more erect than those from the striae. Length 1.5–1.8 mm.

The adults may be taken in spring by sifting, or in summer from the flowers of black haw and allied shrubs.

b. *Melanophthalma cavicollis* Mannerheim   Plate XXVII, No. 16, p. 261
  Ovate, convex, moderately robust; usually head and pronotum dull reddish brown, elytra fuscous; apex of abdomen, legs, and bases of antennae dull pale yellow; pubescence rather short and recumbent. Pronotum transverse, subcordate; anterior margin strongly rounded; posterior angles with a small tooth at apex; disk evenly, finely punctate; basal impression rather deep, transverse. Elytral base slightly wider than that of pronotum; apices separately rounded; striae feebly impressed, punctures moderate in size; intervals more finely punctate. Length 1.2–1.5 mm.

These beetles may be collected in spring by sifting debris.

Family ENDOMYCHIDAE

The Handsome Fungus Beetles

In this small family of moderately small beetles, the adults are strikingly colored, often being clear orange or reddish, marked with handsome patterns of black. Not all are bright-hued, however, for some are entirely black or brown; nor are all members of the family small, some foreign species attaining a length of an inch or more. For the most part, the adults and larvae are found feeding in fungi, beneath bark of decaying logs, or beneath fallen timber. The structure of the tarsi is a distinctive feature of the adults, each tarsus appearing to be composed of but three segments, the first two being broad and dilated, the last long and slender. Actually, as shown in Figure 334, there are four segments present, the third being minute and fused to the last. The peculiar linear impressions usually found on the pronotum are also diagnostic. From their close relatives, the ladybird beetles, they are distinguished by the long, stout antennae and the prominent head, as well as by the simple tarsal claws. Other characteristics of the family are as follows: antennae nine- to eleven-segmented, inserted on front, the last three segments forming a distinct, loose club; pronotum subquadrate, margins somewhat expanded, sometimes narrowly reflexed; elytra entire; legs moderately long, pro- and mesocoxae globose, metacoxae transverse; procoxal cavities open posteriorly.

KEY TO GENERA

1. Ligula longer than wide, rounded at apex (Fig. 335); pronotum without a transverse basal impressed line ....IV. *Endomychus* (p. 429)
   Ligula at least as wide as long, truncate or rounded at apex (Fig. 336); pronotum with a distinct transverse impressed line at base ..2
2. Prosternum prolonged posteriorly, partly covering the mesosternum (Fig. 337); procoxae separated; elytra usually maculate or vittate ..3
   Prosternum not prolonged posteriorly (Fig. 338); procoxae subcontiguous; elytra unicolorous ....I. *Lycoperdina* (p. 428)
3. Prosternum narrow between coxae (Fig. 337); elytra usually vittate ....II. *Aphorista* (p. 428)
   Prosternum broad, margined (Fig. 339); elytra not vittate ....
   ....III. *Mycetina* (p. 429)

426

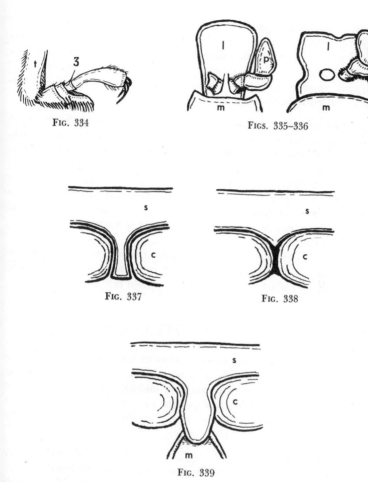

Fig. 334

Figs. 335–336

Fig. 337   Fig. 338

Fig. 339

Fig. 334. A tarsus of an endomychid (lateral view), the third segment
(*3*) much reduced in size. Portion of the tibia (*t*) is also
shown.

Figs. 335–336. Portion of labium of *Endomychus* (335) and of *Aphorista*
(336), a portion of one palpus removed on each figure.
l, ligula; *m*, mentum; *p*, palpus.

Figs. 337–339. Prosternum of *Aphorista* (337), of *Lycoperdina* (338), and
of *Mycetina* (339). *s*, prosternum; *c*, procoxa; *m*, mesosternum.

Genus I. *LYCOPERDINA* Latreille

Small, oblong-ovate; pronotum depressed, moderately transverse, apical margin rounded, anterior angles distinctly prolonged, sides arcuately widened near apex, disk with a transverse impressed line at base, joining a short longitudinal one each side; elytra strongly convex; procoxae sub-contiguous; prosternum not prolonged posteriorly; antennae with last two segments flattened, suddenly wider than preceding.

Lycoperdina ferruginea LeConte   Plate XXXI, No. 6, p. 315
Oblong-ovate, robust; varying from dark brownish red to nearly black, the elytra and pronotal disk frequently darker than remainder of body, shining. Pronotum minutely, densely alutaceous; disk sparsely, finely punctate, longitudinal impressed lines deep, feebly arcuate, scarcely oblique. Scutellum strongly transverse, sides narrowed anteriorly. Elytra scarcely impressed at base, feebly margined along suture briefly behind scutellum; disk minutely, densely alutaceous and sparsely, feebly punctate. Length 4.5–6 mm.

While this species may be found in many types of fungi, it most frequently occurs inside the little pear-shaped or rounded mushroom (*Lycoperdon pyriforme*) which grows in numbers on old fallen logs.

Genus II. *APHORISTA* Gorham

Small, ovate, subdepressed; pronotum strongly depressed, distinctly transverse, apical margin excavated, narrowly produced at middle; anterior angles greatly prolonged, sides widest near middle, disk with a transverse line at base joining a short, longitudinal one each side; elytra subdepressed; procoxae well separated; antennae with last three segments gradually widened.

Aphorista vittata (Fabricius)   Plate XXXI, No. 7, p. 315
Ovate, moderately robust, subdepressed; dull orange to brownish red; pronotum edged with blackish and often with an indistinct brownish macula each side of middle; elytra with a broad, tapering, common black vitta on suture and each with another shorter one laterally; antennae reddish to piceous, paler apically. Pronotum distinctly margined laterally; disk finely, irregularly punctate, basal line deep, arcuate, prolonged nearly to sides, longitudinal lines shallow, nearly straight, sometimes indistinct. Scutellum strongly transverse, sides subparallel. Elytra with a broad, shallow impression near humerus; suture distinctly margined on basal third; disk minutely, rather densely punctate and with fine, sparse punctures intermingled. Length 5.5–6.2 mm.

Genus III. *MYCETINA* Mulsant

Small, oblong-ovate, convex forms; pronotum depressed, strongly transverse, nearly twice as wide as long, apical margin excavated, feebly angularly produced at middle, anterior angles prolonged, sides widest just anterior to middle, disk with a deep transverse impressed line at base, joining a longitudinal short line each side; elytra strongly convex; procoxae separated; antennae with last three segments successively wider.

Mycetina perpulchra (Newman) Plate XXXI, No. 9, p. 315

Oblong-ovate, robust; piceous to black, shining; pronotum, except extreme side margins, reddish yellow, sometimes with a blackish macula at middle of disk or at base; elytra each with two reddish-yellow maculae, one at base, the other before apex, former generally larger. Pronotum distinctly margined laterally; disk minutely, indistinctly punctate, basal line broad, deep, not prolonged laterally, longitudinal lines shallow, distinctly arcuate. Scutellum about as long as wide, rounded. Elytra each with a deep impression at the middle of base; suture distinctly margined on basal third; disk finely coriaceous, and with fine, sparse punctures. Length 3.5–4 mm.

This species is more abundant on the Atlantic coastal region and in the South than in the central states.

Genus IV. *ENDOMYCHUS* Panzer

Small, ovate, subconvex; pronotum subdepressed, distinctly transverse, apical margin somewhat excavated, arcuate, anterior angles somewhat prolonged, sides widest at base, tapering to apex, disk without a transverse impressed line at base, a longitudinal impressed line each side basally; elytra subconvex; procoxae well separated; prosternum flat, margined; antennae with last three segments successively wider apically.

Endomychus biguttatus Say Plate XXXI, No. 8, p. 315

Ovate, robust, subconvex; black, shining; elytra orange to reddish, each with two rounded black maculae, one before middle and a much larger one before apex. Pronotum distinctly margined each side and along base; disk very finely, sparsely punctate, longitudinal impressed lines deep, arcuate. Scutellum as long as wide, apex rounded. Elytra each with a shallow, sublinear impression near humerus; suture indistinctly margined on basal two-fifths; disk moderately finely, rather densely punctate. Length 3.5–5 mm.

This is probably the most common member of the family within the area covered in this book.

Family PHALACRIDAE

The Shining Flower Beetles

In their glabrous, highly convex, and broadly oval or rounded body form, the adult members of this family bear a strong resemblance to their close relatives, the ladybird beetles, from whom, however, they are at once distinguishable by the presence of five segments in the tarsi instead of only three. However, the fourth tarsal segment is reduced in size (Fig. 340) and may be difficult to find. Other distinguishing features of the family are, in addition to their small size, which is not over 3 and usually less than 2 mm. in length: antennae eleven-segmented, inserted on or under sides of front, with a three-segmented, oval club; elytra entire, rounded apically; prothoracic sidepieces indistinct; prosternum prolonged and declivous posteriorly, its bent portion received in an emargination of the mesosternum; metasternum large, produced anteriorly (Figs. 343, 344); procoxae small, globose, procoxal cavities open posteriorly; mesocoxae transverse, widely separated; metacoxae transverse, contiguous.

Most of the members of this family are found on flowers, especially of composites such as goldenrod, daisy, and boneset, and on Queen Anne's lace and other umbelliferous plants. By no means are the insects confined to flowers of these sorts, for they can be found on many kinds, ranging from skunk cabbage to sedges. While the larvae are known to live in the heads of various flowering plants, adults may also occur on leaves, and some species seem to live solely beneath bark of logs.

Males may be distinguished by the more compact antennal club and by the strongly expanded metatibiae.

KEY TO GENERA

1. Metatarsi equal in length to protarsi; antennae inserted beneath sides of front, the base not visible from above (Fig. 341) ....I. *Phalacrus* (p. 432)
   Metatarsi distinctly longer than protarsi; antennae inserted on front, the base readily visible from above (Fig. 342) 2
2. Metasternum strongly produced anteriorly, largely concealing mesosternum, the latter appearing as beading on the former (Fig. 343) ....II. *Olibrus* (p. 432)
   Metasternum less strongly produced anteriorly, not concealing mesosternum, which is readily discernible behind the prosternum (Fig. 344) 3

3. Eyes large, more than half as wide as the front between them;
   pronotum with a broad lobe at middle of base ....
   ....III. *Acylomus* (p. 433)
   Eyes smaller, less than half as wide as the front between them; pro-
   notum with basal margin entirely straight, not lobed medially ....
   ....IV. *Stilbus* (p. 433)

Fig. 340

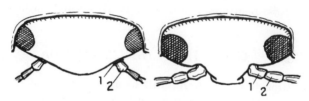

Figs. 341–342

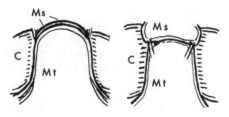

Figs. 343–344

Fig. 340. A tarsus of a phalacrid viewed from the side, the fourth
         segment (*4*) small.
Figs. 341–342. Head of *Phalacrus* (341) and of *Stilbus* (342) viewed from
         above, the first two antennal segments appropriately
         numbered.
Figs. 343–344. Portion of sternum of *Olibrus* (343) and of *Stilbus* (344).
         In the former the metasternal process (*Mt*) extends an-
         terior to the mesocoxae (*C*), the mesosternum (*Ms*)
         being scarcely discernible.

Genus I. *PHALACRUS* Paykull

Very small, convex species; antennae inserted beneath sides of front of head (Fig. 341), third segment as long as fourth and fifth together, last segment of club greatly elongate; pronotum strongly transverse, about twice as wide as long, sides narrowly but distinctly margined; scutellum large, triangular; elytra each with a distinct stria near suture, more deeply impressed posteriorly and with indistinct rows of punctures; metatarsi not elongate, equal in length to protarsi.

Phalacrus politus (Melsheimer)　　　　　　　　Plate XXXI, No. 1, p. 315

Broadly ovate, sometimes nearly circular, robust, convex; black, shining; body beneath piceous; antennae and legs fuscous. Head and entire upper surface of body densely, minutely alutaceous. Head small, less than half as wide as pronotum. Pronotum with lateral marginal line continued around the moderately prolonged anterior angles, reaching to behind eye. Elytra only slightly longer than wide at base; disk with a number of indefinite rows of coarse punctures; apices broad, nearly square. Length 1.5–2.2 mm.

Genus II. *OLIBRUS* Erichson

Oval, strongly convex, very small species; head half as broad as pronotum, eyes small, not more than one-third as wide as the front between them; antennae with third segment one-half again as long as fourth, last segment of club as long as the first two combined; pronotum strongly transverse, more than twice as wide as long, lateral marginal line indistinct, continued along the declivous anterior angles; scutellum large, triangular; elytra each with two distinct striae on apical two-thirds; prosternum strongly declivous posteriorly, the declivity not marked off by a transverse line; metasternum anteriorly very strongly produced, reaching anterior of the mesocoxae; mesosternum medially reduced to beading on the mesosternal process (Fig. 343).

Olibrus semistriatus LeConte　　　　　　　　Plate XXXI, No. 2, p. 315

Very convex, elongate-oval, robust; dark orange-brown to fuscous, polished; body underneath, legs, and antennae yellow-brown to reddish brown. Head rather coarsely, moderately densely punctate. Pronotum distinctly margined along base, lateral margin shallow; disk rather coarsely, very sparsely punctate. Elytra more than twice as long as wide; disk with two distinct, straight striae, one near suture, the second close to first, approaching the latter posteriorly, both confined to apical two-thirds of elytron, remainder of surface with rows of distinct punctures, apical margin densely, minutely alutaceous; apices separately, rather narrowly rounded. Length 1.7–2.3 mm.

Genus III. *ACYLOMUS* Sharp

Very small, broadly oval, strongly convex; head half as broad as pronotum, eyes large, more than half as wide as the front between them; antennal third segment nearly equal in length to next two combined, club elongate, nearly as long as remaining segments together; pronotum very strongly transverse, lateral marginal line prolonged around anterior angles to behind eyes; scutellum as long as wide, triangular; elytra each with a single deep stria along suture and with a short indistinct one just anterior to middle, entire disk minutely and feebly alutaceous; prosternum declivous posteriorly, the upper edge of declivity sharply defined by an elevated line which bears short setae; mesosternum short, but extending partially between mesocoxae, emarginate behind to receive the long, rounded anterior process of metasternum; metatarsi long, second segment strongly elongate.

Acylomus ergoti Casey   Plate XXXI, No. 5, p. 315

Broadly ovate, convex; dark reddish brown to black, strongly shining; legs, body underneath, and antennae often yellowish, usually light reddish brown. Head minutely, rather densely punctate. Pronotum more than twice as wide as long, sides only moderately tapering anteriorly, evenly arcuate; basally broadly lobed at middle, the lobe distinctly margined; disk minutely, rather sparsely punctate. Elytra about twice as long as pronotum, sides subparallel basally; disk with indistinct rows of punctures, entire surface indistinctly alutaceous; apices together nearly semicircularly rounded. Length 1.6–1.8 mm.

Genus IV. *STILBUS* Seidlitz

Ovate, convex, very small; head about half as wide as pronotum, eyes large, less than half as wide as the front between them; pronotum with lateral marginal line extending around anterior angles to behind eye; scutellum distinctly wider than long, triangular; elytra each with only one stria, close to suture, indistinct basally, deeply impressed apically, surface nearly entirely smooth; prosternum declivous posteriorly, the upper edge of declivity elevated, the elevation bearing a loose fringe of stiff, erect setae; mesosternum well developed, extending partly between mesocoxae, posteriorly feebly emarginate, metasternal anterior process weakly rounded (Fig. 344); metatarsi rather short, second segment only moderately elongate; antennal scape with a small tubercle near base.

KEY TO SPECIES

Elytra with a distinct yellowish macula at apex ....b. *apicalis*
Elytra uniformly orange-brown, not maculate ....a. *nitidus*

a. *Stilbus nitidus* (Melsheimer)   Plate XXXI, No. 4, p. 315

Broadly elliptical, convex, robust; entirely orange-brown, shining. Head more than half as wide as pronotum; minutely, sparsely punctate and feebly alutaceous. Pronotum scarcely twice as wide as long, briefly margined at middle of base; disk very feebly alutaceous and with sparse, minute punctures. Elytra as long as wide, broadly rounded, sides parallel near base; disk with sutural stria fine but distinct, entire surface feebly alutaceous and with sparse, minute punctures. Length 1.2–1.4 mm.

b. *Stilbus apicalis* (Melsheimer)   Plate XXXI, No. 3, p. 315

Ovate, robust; dark brown, shining; elytra each with an elongate macula of yellowish or yellowish brown at apex; body underneath, legs, and antennae light orange-brown. Head about half as wide as pronotum, minutely, irregularly punctate. Pronotum not margined at base; disk feebly, finely coriaceous and with minute, scattered punctures. Elytra distinctly longer than wide; disk with sutural stria deep, not attaining base, and with a number of rows of fine punctures, apical area minutely alutaceous. Length 1.5–1.8 mm.

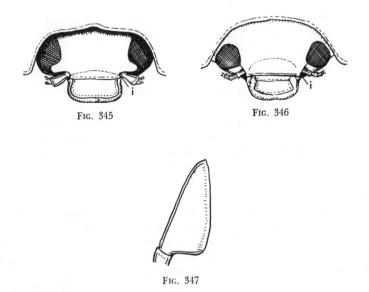

FIG. 345   FIG. 346

FIG. 347

Figs. 345–346. Head of *Coccinella* (345) and of *Hippodamia* (346), the latter not retractile into prothorax. *i*, antennal insertion.

Fig. 347. Last segment of maxillary palpus of *Coccinella*.

Family COCCINELLIDAE

The Lady Beetles

The members of this family are familiar to everyone, as they occur frequently on the leaves of garden plants. In color, they vary from red or yellow, sometimes with black spots, to black, sometimes with red or yellow spots. Their shape is usually nearly hemispherical, but some species are more elongate-oval and less convex. Both adults and larvae occur about leaves or stems of plants, where they are predaceous upon plant lice and other small insects. However, one species, *Epilachna borealis,* is not predaceous but is herbivorous, feeding on and doing considerable damage to squash and allied plants, while *Epilachna varivestis* is the notorious Mexican bean beetle. When handled, some lady beetles emit a yellowish fluid from between the segments of their legs that has a rather disagreeable odor.

Other family characters are as follows: antennae eleven-segmented, inserted at inner margin of eyes below front (Fig. 345), club three-segmented; maxillary palpi with last segment hatchet-shaped (Fig. 347); head retracted into prothorax; pronotum transverse, sides usually arcuate, anterior margin emarginate; pro- and metacoxae transverse, separated; tarsi three-segmented, second segment dilated, spongy beneath; elytra convex.

KEY TO TRIBES

1. Mesocoxae narrowly separated; body elongate-oval, glabrous; legs long, free, femora extending beyond sides of body; abdomen with sixth segment visible in both sexes; head not deeply inserted into prothorax; pronotum strongly sinuate but not covering the eyes (Fig. 346) .... COCCINELLINI (p. 442)
    Mesocoxae widely separated; legs shorter, femora usually not extending beyond sides of body; head deeply inserted into prothorax, the pronotum covering a large portion of the eyes (Fig. 345) 2
2. Body loosely articulated, usually rounded; epipleura wide (Fig. 348), concave, strongly descending externally 3
    Body compact, usually oval; epipleura narrow (Fig. 349), horizontal, flat or feebly concave; abdomen with sixth segment well developed, fifth shorter; body glabrous 6
3. Frontal plate narrowed from base, not covering the base of antennae (Fig. 345) 4
    Frontal plate broadly dilated, concealing base of antennae and subdividing eyes .... CHILOCORINI (p. 454)

4. Upper surface of body glabrous 5
   Upper surface of body pubescent ....EPILACHNINI (p. 454)
5. Antennae shorter, last segment truncate (Fig. 351) .....COCCINELLINI (p. 442)
   Antennae slender, last segment elongate .............PSYLLOBORINI (p. 442)
6. Body glabrous; epipleura usually slightly descending externally but
   narrow (Fig. 349); legs moderately retractile or free ..HYPERASPINI (p. 436)
   Body pubescent; epipleura usually flat and horizontal (Fig. 350); legs
   always free ....SCYMNINI (p. 441)

Tribe HYPERASPINI

KEY TO GENERA

Eyes with a small emargination at anterior edge of front; protibiae
   spinose externally at basal two-fifths ....II. *Brachyacantha* (p. 440)
Eyes entire; tibiae not spinose ....I. *Hyperaspis* (p. 436)

Genus I. *HYPERASPIS* Redtenbacher

Small, oval or rounded, black beetles; elytra spotted or margined with
yellowish; epipleura foveate for receiving tips of metafemora; protibiae
slender, outer margin unarmed, apical plate never more than feebly
oblique at apex (Fig. 352); tarsal claws with an internal quadrate tooth
at base, variable in size.

KEY TO SPECIES

1. Lateral margins of elytra with a reddish or yellowish vitta, this sometimes,
   but rarely, broken to form a subapical macula 2
   Lateral margins of elytra without reddish or yellowish vitta 3
2. Elytra with marginal vittae strongly undulating on inner margin, sometimes
   broken into two or three distinct maculae ....d. *undulata*
   Elytra with marginal vittae of nearly uniform width except for a constriction
   at apical third, this portion sometimes forming a separate macula ....
   ....c. *fimbriolata*
3. Elytra with a single small subapical macula; sides and apical margin of pronotum yellow in male ....a. *signata*
   Elytra with two subapical maculae; sides of pronotum yellow in both sexes
   ....b. *proba*

a. *Hyperaspis signata* (Olivier)   Plate XLII, No. 1, p. 439
   Rounded, strongly convex; black, shining; elytra with a large discal
macula and a smaller subapical one reddish yellow; male with head and
narrow apical and side margins of pronotum yellow; head and pronotum
in female entirely black. Entire upper surface densely, distinctly, finely
punctate. Length 2.5–3 mm.

b. *Hyperaspis proba* (Say)   Plate XLII, No. 2, p. 439

Rounded, moderately convex; black, shining; elytra with a large discal macula and two small subapical ones orangeish; head and pronotum of male as in *signata;* in female entirely black. Head and pronotum densely, minutely punctate, elytra densely, finely so. Length 2–3 mm.

c. *Hyperaspis fimbriolata* Melsheimer   Plate XLII, No. 3, p. 439

Rounded, moderately convex; black, shining; elytra margined narrowly with yellow, this vitta often broken near apical third, forming a free, oval, subapical macula; head and pronotum in male on front and sides yellow. Entire upper surface coarsely, rather sparsely punctate. Length 2–3 mm.

This species may be captured by sweeping.

d. *Hyperaspis undulata* (Say)   Plate XLII, Nos. 4, 5, p. 439

Elongate, oval, subdepressed; black, shining; elytra with an oval macula near center and a narrow marginal vitta, with inner side undulating, yellow; male with head yellow and pronotum apically and laterally narrowly yellow; female with only the sides of pronotum yellow. Head and pronotum densely, finely punctate; elytra more sparsely so. Length 2–2.5 mm.

This species may be taken by sweeping foliage in low, moist areas.

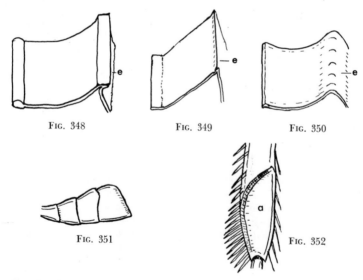

Figs. 348–350. Section through epipleuron of *Coccinella* (348), of *Hyperaspis* (349), and of *Scymnus* (350). *e*, side of elytron.

Fig. 351. Antennal club of *Coccinella*, the apical segment truncate.

Fig. 352. Apical portion of protibia of *Hyperaspis*, the outer face bearing the apical plate (*a*).

PLATE XLII
Family COCCINELLIDAE I

1. *Hyperaspis signata* (Olivier) (p. 436)

Black; elytra each with two reddish spots; 2.5–3 mm.

2. *H. proba* (Say) (p. 437)

Black; pronotum with a spot each side and elytra each with three orangeish spots; 2–3 mm.

3. *H. fimbriolata* Melsheimer (p. 437)

Black; elytra with sides largely orange; sometimes front of head and sides of pronotum orange; 2–3 mm.

4, 5. *H. undulata* (Say) (p. 437)

Black, with yellow markings which are variable in extent, as indicated in the two figures; 2–2.5 mm.

6. *Brachyacantha ursina* (Fabricius) (p. 440)

Black, with yellow markings; 2.5–3.5 mm.

7. *B. felina* (Fabricius) (p. 440)

Black, with yellow markings; 1.8–2.3 mm.

8. *Psyllobora vigintimaculata* (Say) (p. 442)

Pale straw-yellow, with black markings which vary in extent, as shown; 2–2.5 mm.

9, 10. *Anisosticta strigata* Thunberg (p. 444)

Yellowish, with black markings which vary in extent, as indicated; 3–4 mm.

11. *Naemia seriata* (Melsheimer) (p. 444)

Brown-yellow or brown-orange, with black markings; 5–6 mm.

12. *Coleomegilla fuscilabris* Mulsant (p. 445)

Ranging from light yellow to red-orange, with black markings; 5–7 mm.

13. *Hippodamia tridecimpunctata tibialis* (Say) (p. 445)

Orange or reddish, with black markings; 4.5–5.2 mm.

14. *H. parenthesis* (Say) (p. 448)

Orange or reddish, with black markings; 4–5 mm.

15. *H. glacialis* (Fabricius) (p. 448)

Yellow to deep orange, with black markings; 6–7.5 mm.

16. *H. convergens* Guérin (p. 448)

Yellow to deep orange, with black markings; 4–6 mm.

MM |0 10 20 30 40 50 60 70

PLATE XLII   439

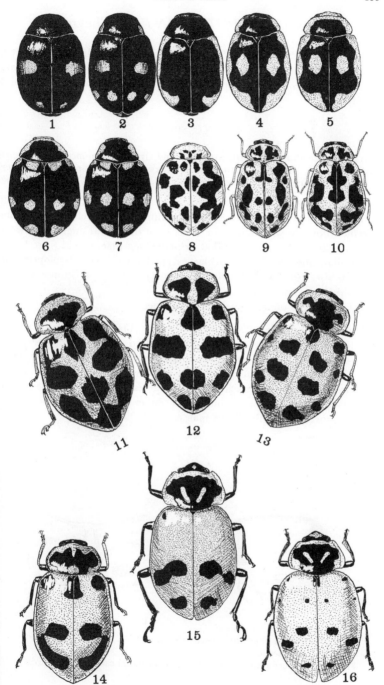

Genus II. *BRACHYACANTHA* Chevrolat

Oval, strongly convex; black, shining; elytra with distinct, rounded, yellowish maculae; eyes finely emarginate anteriorly; epipleura foveate for receiving tips of metafemora; protibiae with external spines at basal two-fifths.

KEY TO SPECIES

Elytral maculae all equal in size; pronotum and elytra finely punctate ..a. *ursina*
Medial maculae of elytra smaller than others; pronotum and elytra rather
coarsely punctate ....b. *felina*

a. *Brachyacantha ursina* (Fabricius)   Plate XLII, No. 6, p. 439

Elongate-ovate, robust, convex; black, shining; head yellow; pronotum margined apically with yellow in male, only the apical angles yellow in female; elytra each with five yellow or orange maculae, two of these basal, two medial, one apical, all maculae except humeral well developed and equal in size; legs pale yellowish, femora darker at base. Pronotum and elytra distinctly, finely punctate. Length 2.5–3.5 mm.

Milkweed is the preferred habitat of this species.

b. *Brachyacantha felina* (Fabricius)   Plate XLII, No. 7, p. 439

Oval, subrotund, convex; black, shining; head orange, in female sometimes black with vertex orange; pronotum apically orange in male, near basal angles spotted in female; elytra each with five orange or yellow maculae, two basal, two medial, and one apical, the two medial smaller and less distinct. Pronotum and elytra rather coarsely and moderately densely punctate. Length 1.8–2.3 mm.

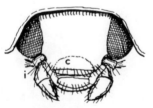
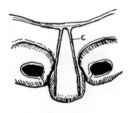

Fig. 353   Fig. 354

Fig. 353. Head of *Scymnus* viewed from the front. *c*, clypeus; *i*, antennal insertion.

Fig. 354. Prosternum of *Scymnus*, with a carina (*c*) each side of process.

Tribe SCYMNINI

Genus *SCYMNUS* Kugelann

Very small, pubescent species; antennae shorter than head, inserted in the small, shallow emargination just before eyes (Fig. 353); clypeus prolonged, sides converging (Fig. 353); pronotum deeply emarginate at apex, rounded at base; front and middle legs more or less contractile; pro- and metatibiae sulcate for reception of tarsi; prosternum flat, not at all deflexed apically, usually bicarinate (Fig. 354).

KEY TO SPECIES

Metacoxal line incomplete, gradually curving into first ventral suture, which it sometimes joins (Fig. 355); pubescence on upper surface long ....a. *americanus*
Metacoxal line forming an entire arc beginning at the inner border of coxal cavity and ending at or near the outer anterior angle of the abdominal segment (Fig. 356); pubescence on upper surface short ....b. *puncticollis*

a. *Scymnus americanus* Mulsant   Plate XLIV, No. 1, p. 453
Broadly ovate, strongly convex; piceous; pronotum frequently orangeish red, with a piceous discal macula, sometimes entirely black; elytra narrowly margined with red at apex; legs yellowish or piceous. Pronotum narrowed apically; sides feebly arcuate; disk sparsely punctate. Elytra coarsely, sparsely punctate, pubescence coarse, long, and ashy. Length 2–2.5 mm.

These beetles may be taken by sweeping or beating grass and foliage.

b. *Scymnus puncticollis* LeConte   Plate XLIV, No. 2, p. 453
Broadly oval, convex; dull black; head piceous; pronotum usually with sides yellowish, sometimes only apical angles yellowish; apex of elytra narrowly reddish; tibiae and tarsi pale yellow; femora piceous; entire upper surface with short, fine, moderately dense, whitish pubescence. Pronotal disk sparsely punctate, sides more densely so. Elytra closely and rather coarsely punctate. Length 2–2.5 mm.

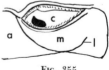 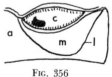

FIG. 355   FIG. 356

Figs. 355–356. Metacoxa of *Scymnus americanus* (355) and *S. puncticollis* (356). *a*, first abdominal sternite; *c*, metacoxa; *l*, metacoxal line; *m*, metacoxal plate.

Tribe Psylloborini

Genus *PSYLLOBORA* Chevrolat

Small, oval or rounded, rather convex beetles; above pale-colored, with darker maculae; antennae slender, last segment elongate; scutellum very small; mesosternum truncate anteriorly; tarsal claws near apex with a large quadrate tooth internally.

Psyllobora vigintimaculata (Say)   Plate XLII, No. 8, p. 439

Broadly ovate or rounded, convex; pale yellowish; pronotum with five blackish maculae, one before scutellum smaller than others; elytra each with nine maculae, the two discal usually merged and sometimes partly joining the others together; beneath pale brownish yellow, the pro-, meso-, and metasterna, and abdominal sternites medially, black. Pronotum finely, elytra more strongly, densely punctate. Length 2–2.5 mm.

In early spring this species occurs in numbers about the base of skunk cabbage and on leaves of various shrubs.

Tribe Coccinellini

KEY TO GENERA

1. Mesocoxae narrowly separated; head not deeply inserted; pronotum strongly sinuate but not covering eyes (Fig. 346); body elongate-ovate 2
   Mesocoxae widely separated; head deeply inserted (Fig. 345); pronotum covering a large part of eyes 5
2. Tarsal claws simple, evenly arcuate, slender, and very acutely pointed, with a slight bulbiform enlargement at base (Fig. 357) 3
   Tarsal claws with a large basal tooth, or bifid (Fig. 358) ....
   ....IV. *Hippodamia* (p. 445)
3. At least the sternal or the abdominal metacoxal plates distinct (Fig. 356) 4
   Both coxal plates obsolete ....III. *Coleomegilla* (p. 444)
4. Sternal and abdominal metacoxal plates both distinct ..I. *Anisosticta* (p. 444)
   Sternal plates distinct, the abdominal obsolete ....II. *Naemia* (p. 444)
5. Limiting line of metacoxal plate arcuate, continuous, not quite entire (Fig. 355), metacoxal plates shorter than the segment; body oval
   ....VII. *Adalia* (p. 450)
   Limiting line of metacoxal plate curving outward to the sides of the body along the first abdominal suture, the included area (metacoxal plate) frequently divided by an oblique line (Fig. 359); body usually rounded 6
6. A large, subquadrate tooth at base of claws (Fig. 26G) 7
   Claws cleft (Fig. 358) ....X. *Neomysia* (p. 451)

7. Metacoxal plates divided by a distinct oblique line, joining the
limiting arc at about its middle point, forming an angulate inner
plate (Fig. 359) ....V. *Coccinella* (p. 448)
Metacoxal plates not or only partially divided, the oblique line
obsolete or feeble (Fig. 360) 8
8. Mesosternum on apical margin deeply and broadly sinuate (Fig.
361) 9
Mesosternum truncate apically, with a minute notch medially
(Fig. 362) ....VIII. *Mulsantina* (p. 450)
9. Metacoxal plate partially divided, the oblique line obsolete near
middle of limiting arc (Fig. 360) ....VI. *Cycloneda* (p. 449)
Metacoxal plate not distinctly divided ....IX. *Anatis* (p. 451)

FIGS. 357–358

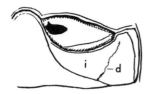
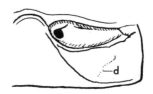

FIGS. 359–360

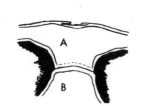
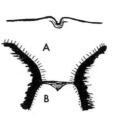

FIGS. 361–362

Figs. 357–358. Tarsal claws of *Coleomegilla* (357) and of *Hippodamia*
(358).
Figs. 359–360. Metacoxa of *Coccinella* (359) and *Cycloneda* (360) with
abdominal sternite. *d*, dividing line; *i*, inner metacoxal
plate.
Figs. 361–362. Mesosternum of *Cycloneda* (361) and of *Mulsantina* (362).
A, mesosternum; *B*, metasternum.

Genus I. *ANISOSTICTA* Chevrolat

Small, elongate-ovate, subconvex; head not deeply inserted; pronotum strongly sinuate but not covering the eyes, basal angles obtuse but distinct; elytra maculate and strongly punctate, lateral margins strongly and widely reflexed; metasternal and ventral abdominal coxal plates both distinct; mesocoxae narrowly separated; tarsal claws simple, evenly arcuate, slender and very acutely pointed, with a slight bulbiform enlargement basally.

Anisosticta strigata Thunberg   Plate XLII, Nos. 9, 10, p. 439

Elongate-ovate, slightly convex; yellow; base of head, two triangular maculae on pronotum, the outer anterior corner of each of these often isolated as a dot, black; elytra each with a common, bilobed macula at scutellar region and eight others black, some of these often united to form fewer and larger maculae; body beneath black; legs, antennae, sides of abdomen, and last ventral abdominal segment yellow. Pronotum finely and densely punctate. Elytra more coarsely and shallowly punctate. Length 3–4 mm.

This species is found in more or less swampy places on herbs and shrubs.

Genus II. *NAEMIA* Mulsant

Small, elongate-ovate, convex; head not deeply inserted; anterior pronotal margin strongly sinuate but not covering eyes, posterior angles obtuse, not rounded; metasternal coxal plates distinct, the abdominal ones obsolete; mesocoxae narrowly separated; tarsal claws simple, evenly arcuate, slender, and acutely pointed, with a slight bulbiform enlargement basally.

Naemia seriata (Melsheimer)   Plate XLII, No. 11, p. 439

Elongate-ovate, convex; body beneath and head black, shining; pronotum and elytra yellow or orange, maculate with black, the former with entire disk and basal margin black, the latter each with a lateral row of three large maculae, more or less coalescing, and with a common row of three maculae, which are usually confluent along suture. Pronotum and elytra finely punctate. Length 5–6 mm.

Genus III. *COLEOMEGILLA* Timberlake

Small, elongate-ovate, subconvex; head not deeply inserted, pronotum subquadrate, anterior margin strongly sinuate but not covering eyes, a narrow but distinct margin basally; mesocoxae narrowly separated; tarsal claws acutely pointed, with a large, quadrate, basal tooth separated from the apical portion by a deep, acute groove.

Coleomegilla fuscilabris Mulsant   Plate XLII, No. 12, p. 439
    Elongate-ovate, subconvex; head black, with a triangular, red macula on front; pronotum and elytra reddish, the former with an oval, black macula on each side of median line, these touching base but not apex; elytra with two common black maculae on suture, one at base, the second on apical third, and each with four black maculae, the second largest, arranged longitudinally near the lateral margin; beneath black, the prosternum and a row of maculae on each side of abdomen reddish. Head and pronotum densely, minutely alutaceous and with sparse, minute punctures; elytra minutely alutaceous and sparsely, finely punctate. Length 5–7 mm.
    This species is fairly common on foliage.

Genus IV. *HIPPODAMIA* Dejean

    Small, elongate-ovate; head not deeply inserted; pronotum transverse, apex sinuate, base not sinuate or margined; mesocoxae narrowly separated; femora not grooved; metatibial spurs distinct; tarsal claws slender, bifid, the two lobes of unequal length, acutely pointed.

KEY TO SPECIES

1. Pronotum black, with broad, pale-yellowish lateral margins, within each of which is a small, black macula; tibiae and tarsi pale yellowish . . . .
. . . . .a. *tridecimpunctata tibialis*
Pronotum with a narrower, white lateral margin, without a small, distinct macula but sometimes intruded upon by a more or less pronounced angulation of the central black area; legs black 2
2. Black disk of pronotum nearly divided by a white, quadrate spot at middle of base, and with an elongate, triangular macula at apex . . . . .b. *parenthesis*
Black disk of pronotum without white spot at base and apex but with two discal, divergent, white dashes 3
3. Anterior half of elytra without markings or with only a small, humeral, black macula . . . . .c. *glacialis*
Elytra each with six small maculae, three of which are on anterior half; all maculae small and widely separated . . . . .d. *convergens*

a. *Hippodamia tridecimpunctata tibialis* (Say)   Plate XLII, No. 13, p. 439
    Elongate-ovate; orangeish red; base of head black; pronotum black, with broad, pale-yellowish lateral margins, within each of which is a small black macula; elytra each with six small, round maculae and a common scutellar one black; undersurface and femora black; tibiae and tarsi pale yellowish. Pronotum finely and densely punctate. Elytra with shallow punctures, fine and coarse intermingled. Length 4.5–5.2 mm.

PLATE XLIII
Family COCCINELLIDAE II

1. *Coccinella trifasciata* Linné (p. 449)

   Yellow or orangeish, with black markings; 4.5–5.5 mm.

2. *Cycloneda sanguinea* (Linné) (p. 449)

   Yellow or orangeish, with black markings on pronotum; 4–5 mm.

3. *Adalia bipunctata* (Linné) (p. 450)

   Orange or reddish, with black markings; 4–5.5 mm.

4. *Chilocoris stigma* Say (p. 454)

   Black; elytral spot orange or red; 4–5 mm.

5, 6. *Mulsantina picta* (Randall) (p. 450)

   Pale straw-yellow, with black markings which are extremely variable; four common variations are shown; 4–5 mm.

7. *Coccinella novemnotata* Herbst (p. 449)

   Dull yellowish, with black markings; 5.5–7 mm.

8. *C. transversoguttata* Faldermann (p. 449)

   Orange, with black markings; 6–7 mm.

9. *Neomysia pullata* (Say) (p. 451)

   Dull yellow to fulvous, with very variable blackish markings, those of elytra sometimes absent; 6–7 mm.

10. *Anatis quindecimpunctata* (Olivier) (p. 451)

    Ground color very variable, ranging from pale yellow through brown-orange to maroon; the black markings are occasionally pale-ringed; 6.5–8.5 mm.

11. *Epilachna borealis* (Fabricius) (p. 454)

    Brownish yellow, with black spots; 7–8 mm.

12. *E. varivestis* Mulsant (p. 455)

    Pale yellow to dull brownish, with black spots; 6–7 mm.

MM | 0 | 10 | 20 | 30 | 40 | 50 | 60 | 70

PLATE XLIII

447

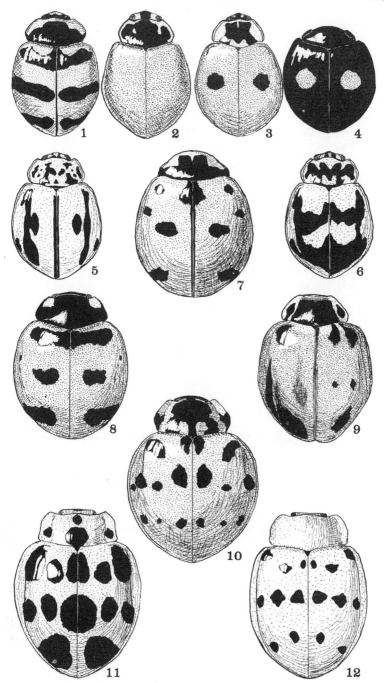

b. *Hippodamia parenthesis* (Say)   Plate XLII, No. 14, p. 439

Elongate-ovate; yellowish red; head black at base and apex; pronotum black, with a narrow, white lateral margin, a small macula at middle of base, and a short line at apex white, these sometimes lacking; elytra each with a large, common scutellar macula, a small, round one on humerus, and a strongly curved subapical lunule black, the latter sometimes broken into two maculae. Head and pronotum finely, rather sparsely punctate; elytra minutely alutaceous and with fine, indistinct punctures. Length 4–5 mm.

c. *Hippodamia glacialis* (Fabricius)   Plate XLII, No. 15, p. 439

Elongate-ovate; head black, with a triangular, yellow macula medially; pronotum black, lateral margins broadly, apical margin narrowly, white, as are two small, oblique maculae on disk; elytra red, each disk with an oblique band just behind middle and a large subapical macula black; humerus sometimes with a very small, black macula; beneath black; mes- and metepimera white; abdominal segments each with a reddish macula laterally. Head and pronotum minutely, rather sparsely punctate. Elytra minutely alutaceous and with dense, fine punctures. Length 6–7.5 mm.

d. *Hippodamia convergens* Guérin   Plate XLII, No. 16, p. 439

Elongate-ovate; head black, medially with a transverse, pale macula which attains eyes; pronotum black, lateral and apical margins and two oblique discal bars white; elytra reddish, with a small, common scutellar macula and each with six small maculae black, these sometimes only partly present or entirely missing; beneath entirely black. Pronotum finely and densely punctate. Elytra finely, feebly punctate. Length 4–6 mm.

Genus V. *COCCINELLA* Linné

Small, more or less rounded, convex; head deeply inserted, pronotum covering greater part of eyes; antennal apical segment truncate; pronotal anterior margin more or less emarginate, side margins finely reflexed; mesosternum transversely truncate anteriorly; mesocoxae widely separated; tarsal claws with a large, subquadrate tooth basally.

KEY TO SPECIES

1. Pronotal apical margin whitish or yellowish white 2
   Pronotal apical margin not whitish ....c. *transversoguttata*
2. Elytra with nine black maculae; procoxae black, in males with a white macula
   ....b. *novemnotata*
   Elytra with transverse black fasciae; coxae entirely black in both sexes ....
   ....a. *trifasciata*

a. *Coccinella trifasciata* Linné   Plate XLIII, No. 1, p. 447

Narrowly ovate, convex; head black, in male with a transverse white fascia, in female with a white spot near each eye; pronotum black, apical margin and a broad area at each apical angle white; elytra reddish orange, with three black fasciae, the subbasal not attaining the side margins, the other two interrupted at suture; legs and undersurface black, sidepieces of meso- and metasternum white. Pronotum finely and sparsely punctate. Elytra coarsely and deeply punctate. Length 4.5–5.5 mm.

This species is often found on white birches infested with aphids; it may also be taken by sweeping herbs.

b. *Coccinella novemnotata* Herbst   Plate XLIII, No. 7, p. 447

Broadly ovate, convex; head black, with a broad, yellowish-white fascia across front, clypeus with anterior margin narrowly yellowish; pronotum black, with a narrow apical margin and a large, subquadrate macula at each apical angle pale yellowish; elytra yellow or orange, with a common scutellar macula and each with four others, black, the anterior two smaller, sometimes maculae united into two oblique, curved fasciae; undersurface and legs black; procoxae in males with a small, white macula; mes- and metepimera whitish. Head and pronotum alutaceous and finely, densely punctate. Elytra alutaceous and with sparse, indistinct, fine punctures. Length 5.5–7 mm.

c. *Coccinella transversoguttata* Faldermann   Plate XLIII, No. 8, p. 447

Broadly ovate, convex; head black, with a white spot on each side near eyes; pronotum black, with white, quadrangular maculae in apical angles; elytra yellow or red, with a common subbasal fascia, a very small macula near external margin (sometimes absent), a large, transversely oval macula on disk, and a subapical transverse fascia, all black. Head, pronotum, and elytra densely, strongly punctate, punctures deeper near lateral margin of elytra. Length 6–7 mm.

Genus VI. *CYCLONEDA* Crotch

Small, broadly rounded, very convex; pronotum black, lateral markings pale yellowish; elytra immaculate; head deeply inserted, the pronotum covering most of eyes; metacoxal plates very rarely with a distinct trace of the dividing line; mesocoxae widely separated; claws with a large, subquadrate tooth basally.

Cycloneda sanguinea (Linné)   Plate XLIII, No. 2, p. 447

Broadly rounded, very convex; head black; male white on front of head, female with two white spots; pronotum black, sides, anterior and posterior angles bordered with white, apical margin with three white spurs toward base, lateral ones sometimes attaining base; elytra dull reddish yellow, immaculate, reflexed margins paler; undersurface and legs black, tibiae and tarsi paler. Entire upper surface alutaceous and sparsely, finely punctate. Length 4–5 mm.

This species is common on flowers of goldenrod.

Genus VII. *ADALIA* Mulsant

Small, ovate, convex; head deeply inserted, the pronotum covering a large part of the eyes; limiting line of metacoxal plates arcuate, continuous, not quite entire, the plates shorter than the segment (Fig. 355); mesocoxae widely separated; femora not extending beyond sides of body.

Adalia bipunctata (Linné)   Plate XLIII, No. 3, p. 447

Oval, convex; head black, with two yellowish frontal maculae; pronotum with a black, M-shaped macula on disk, side margins broadly pale whitish yellow, immaculate; elytra reddish, with a small, round, black macula on center of disk; beneath black; tarsi and sides of abdomen reddish brown. Pronotum very finely and densely punctate. Elytra very finely and densely but not so distinctly punctate. Length 4–5.5 mm.

This species is among the commonest of those occurring in the eastern half of the country.

Genus VIII. *MULSANTINA* Nunenmacher

Small, ovate, convex; head deeply inserted, the pronotum covering most of the eyes; mesosternum apically truncate, with a minute notch at middle; mesocoxae widely separated; claws with a large, quadrate tooth at base.

Mulsantina picta (Randall)   Plate XLIII, Nos. 5, 6, p. 447

Broadly ovate, convex; brownish yellow, shining; head with several, pronotum with numerous, irregular black maculae; elytra with a black vitta toward side of disk, extending from humerus to near apex and expanded at tip, a macula before middle on disk and another behind middle near lateral margin black, these maculae sometimes large, forming wide bands across base and apex; suture frequently blackish; beneath piceous. Head and pronotum alutaceous, rather densely, finely punctate. Elytra densely, rather coarsely punctate. Length 4–5 mm.

Genus IX. *ANATIS* Mulsant

Small, body rounded, convex; head deeply inserted, pronotum covering a large part of eyes; prosternal process broad, strongly convex in a transverse direction and prominent at apical margin; mesosternum with anterior margin broadly and deeply sinuate; limiting line of metacoxal plates curving outward to the sides of the body along the first suture (Fig. 360), the included area (metacoxal plate) frequently but indistinctly divided by an obsolete line; mesocoxae widely separated; a large, subquadrate tooth at base of tarsal claws.

Anatis quindecimpunctata (Olivier)   Plate XLIII, No. 10, p. 447

Small, round, convex; head black, with two small, yellow maculae on front; pronotum with disk black, lateral margins broad and pale, with a black macula near base, two small, pale maculae near posterior margin of black discal area; elytra yellow or reddish brown, each with eight small, black maculae, the one at scutellum sometimes partially joined to humeral, three forming a transverse median line, and three forming a transverse subapical line; beneath and femora black, tibiae and tarsi pale yellowish or reddish brown. Pronotum and elytra very finely, feebly, and densely punctate. Length 6.5–8.5 mm.

The adults may be found frequently on red haw.

Genus X. *NEOMYSIA* Casey

Small, round, strongly convex; head deeply inserted, pronotum covering a large portion of eyes; limiting line of metacoxal plates curving outward to the sides of the body along the first suture (Fig. 360), the included area (metacoxal plate) frequently divided by an oblique line; mesocoxae widely separated; claws cleft.

Neomysia pullata (Say)   Plate XLIII, No. 9, p. 447

Round, strongly convex; head black, with two spots on sides of front brownish yellow; pronotum of male with disk black, narrow anterior margin and wide side margins (enclosing a small, black macula), pale yellow, a small, yellow macula at base in front of scutellum which is extended sometimes into a median pale space; female with disk brown; elytra uniformly dull reddish brown; undersurface black, paler medially. Pronotum minutely punctate. Elytra finely, rather shallowly punctate. Length 6–7 mm.

PLATE XLIV
Family COCCINELLIDAE III

1. *Scymnus americanus* Mulsant (p. 441)   Black; pronotal margins and elytral apex broadly reddish; 2–2.5 mm.

2. *S. puncticollis* LeConte (p. 441)   Black; pronotal sides and elytral apex reddish, the former very variable in extent; 2–2.5 mm.

Family OSTOMATIDAE

3. *Airora cylindrica* (Serville) (p. 381)   Deep brown to blackish; 5–14 mm.

4. *Tenebroides americanus* (Kirby) (p. 382)   Deep brown to piceous; 9–11 mm.

5. *T. mauritanicus* (Linné) (p. 382)   Deep brown to piceous; 6–11 mm.

Family PTINIDAE

6. *Gibbium psylloides* (Czenpinski) (p. 493)   Dark reddish brown, shining; antennae and legs pale-yellowish-pubescent; 2–3.5 mm.

7. *Ptinus fur* (Linné) ♂ (p. 494)   Dull reddish brown; pronotum often with yellowish markings medially; elytra with indistinct patches of white scales; 2.5–4.5 mm.

8. *P. fur* (Linné) ♀ (p. 494)   Deep brown; elytra often paler at base, marked with white scales; pronotum with pale-yellowish markings; 2.5–4.5 mm.

9. *Mezium affine* Boieldieu (p. 493)   Elytra dark reddish brown, shining; remainder of body densely pale-yellowish-pubescent; 3–4 mm.

Family BOSTRICHIDAE

10. *Xylobiops basilare* (Say) (p. 501)   Black; base of elytra and antennae reddish; 4–7 mm.

11. *Endecatomus rugosus* (Randall) (p. 501)   Densely covered with ashy scales; markings black; 4–4.5 mm.

12. *Lichenophanes bicornis* (Weber) (p. 502)   Dark brown, covered with ashy or pale-brown pubescence; 7–12 mm.

13. *Amphicerus hamatus* (Fabricius) (p. 502)   Dark brown to blackish; the female lacks the apical tooth on the elytra; 6–11.5 mm.

MM 0   10   20   30   40   50   60   70

PLATE XLIV   453

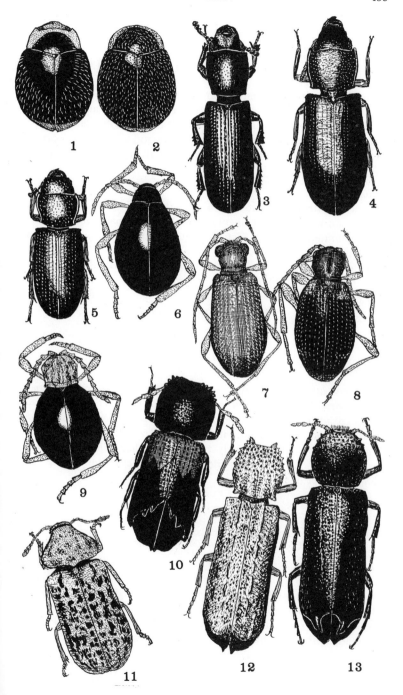

Tribe Chilocorini

Genus *CHILOCORUS* Leach

Small, oval, strongly convex; antennae long, with a loose club; eyes coarsely faceted; clypeus broadly dilated, concealing the antennae and subdividing the eyes; pronotum with a double marginal line laterally at base; posterior legs moderately retractile, abdomen and epipleura concave to receive the femora; tibiae obtusely dentate externally near base; tarsal claws dentate.

Chilocorus stigma Say   Plate XLIII, No. 4, p. 447

Broadly ovate, strongly convex; black, shining; elytra each with a round, red spot on center of disk; beneath black, abdominal segments red. Pronotum minutely punctate. Elytra minutely and densely punctate. Length 4–5 mm.

These are most frequent on flowers of red haw in spring.

Tribe Epilachnini

Genus *EPILACHNA* Chevrolat

Rather small, broadly ovate, convex; head deeply inserted, eyes coarsely faceted, partially covered by pronotum; clypeus narrowed from base, sometimes expanded slightly at apex, antennal fossa more or less exposed; mandibles bifid at apex and with several teeth on inner margin; lateral margin of elytra rather strongly reflexed; epipleura horizontal, broadly concave; legs moderately retractile; tarsal claws cleft, lower cusp nearly as long as upper one.

KEY TO SPECIES

Pronotum maculate; maculae of elytra large, irregular in size ....a. *borealis*
Pronotum immaculate; elytral maculae small, uniform in size ......b. *varivestis*

a. *Epilachna borealis* (Fabricius)   Squash Ladybird Beetle
                                       Plate XLIII, No. 11, p. 447

Broadly ovate, convex; pale orangeish yellow, slightly shining, covered with very short pubescence; pronotum with a large basal macula and a small apical one on median line, a small one each side near margin, black; elytra each with seven black maculae, the largest at apex; metasternum black; remainder of undersurface pale yellow. Pronotum finely and densely punctate. Elytra with coarse and finer punctures intermingled. Length 7–8 mm.

This species is found on foliage; the larvae feed on leaves of squash and pumpkin and allied plants.

b. *Epilachna varivestis* Mulsant   Mexican Bean Beetle

Plate XLIII, No. 12, p. 447

Broadly ovate, convex; brownish yellow, feebly shining; elytra each with eight small, uniform, black maculae, three basally, three medially, two apically. Pronotum transverse, finely and densely punctate. Elytra finely, irregularly punctate. Length 6–7 mm.

Both the larvae and adults of this species do much damage to beans of all kinds, attacking both the leaves and the fruit of the plants.

Family ALLECULIDAE

The Comb-clawed Beetles

In this family belong many brownish or black, small to moderate-sized beetles, which are clothed with minute hairs, giving a silky gloss to the upper surface. None have any markings or maculae, except a few in the genus *Mycetochara* which have reddish spots on the humeri of the elytra. In form they are usually elongate-oval, strongly convex, and resemble the Tenebrionidae, from which they may be easily distinguished by the comb-like (pectinate) tarsal claws (Fig. 26J). In addition the maxillary palpi are four-segmented, often long and much dilated; head narrowed behind eyes, which are large, transverse, and emarginate; clypeus not distinct, labrum prominent, mandibles short; antennae long, more or less serrate, eleven-segmented, the segments, except for three or four of the basal ones, with large, sparsely placed pits. Mesosternum short, the sidepieces reaching the coxal cavities; metasternum long; elytra rounded at apices; abdomen with five or six visible sternites, the third and fourth prolonged apically and with their posterior margins leatherlike; mesocoxae with distinct trochantins; metacoxae transverse, not widely separated; tarsi slender, often lobed beneath some of the segments (Fig. 363), pro- and mesotarsi five-segmented, the metatarsi four-segmented.

The adults are found on flowers and foliage or under bark, while the larvae, which resemble wireworms, are gregarious in burrows in dead or decaying stumps and logs on the ground. Some of the larvae are associated with termite nests and buzzard nests.

KEY TO GENERA

1. Tarsi lobed beneath (Fig. 363) .... I. *Hymenorus* (p. 457)
   Tarsi not lobed beneath 2
2. Antennae robust, shorter, segments obconical; protarsi shorter than tibiae; form oblong, subparallel; punctation and pubescence generally coarse and sparse .... II. *Mycetochara* (p. 460)
   Antennae slender, longer, segments parallel-sided or feebly obconical; form oval; punctation and pubescence usually minute and dense ..
   .... III. *Isomira* (p. 461)

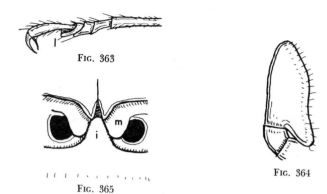

FIG. 363

FIG. 364

FIG. 365

Fig. 363. Mesotarsus of *Hymenorus*. *l*, lobes.
Fig. 364. Apical segments of maxillary palpus of *Hymenorus*.
Fig. 365. Intercoxal process of first abdominal sternite of *Hymenorus*.
      i, intercoxal piece; *m*, metacoxa.

Genus I. *HYMENORUS* Mulsant

Small, more or less oblong-oval, parallel species, having the last segment of the maxillary palpi in the shape of a right-angled triangle, the apex and outer sides subequal in length (Fig. 364); process of first abdominal sternite between metacoxae narrow, acute, and angulate (Fig. 365); pro- and mesotarsi never having more than two segments lobed and metatarsi with but one; head not covered by pronotum; prosternum before the coxae only slightly declivous; pronotum rounded at apex, the sides never convergent toward base, the basal angles right-angled or slightly obtuse.

KEY TO SPECIES

Femora dark brown, tibiae and tarsi paler; antennae one-half length of body; size 7–8 mm. ....a. *pilosus*
Femora reddish yellow, tibiae darker; antennae two-fifths length of body; size 5–6 mm. ....b. *niger*

a. *Hymenorus pilosus* (Melsheimer)   Plate XLV, No. 3, p. 459
Oblong-oval; dark reddish brown to piceous, shining; antennae, tibiae, and tarsi paler. Eyes separated above by more than their own width. Pronotum as wide at base as elytra, nearly twice as wide as long; sides rounded.

PLATE XLV

Family BYRRHIDAE

1. *Byrrhus americanus* LeConte (p. 380)
Black; elytra with grayish markings, sometimes forming a band at middle; 8.5–9.5 mm.

2. *Cytilus alternatus* (Say) (p. 379)
Bronzy black; elytra metallic green; 4.5–5.5 mm.

Family ALLECULIDAE

3. *Hymenorus pilosus* (Melsheimer) (p. 457)
Orange-brown to blackish; legs and antennae paler; 7–8 mm.

4. *H. niger* (Melsheimer) (p. 460)
Orange-brown to blackish; 5.3–6 mm.

5. *Mycetochara foveata* LeConte (p. 461)
Dark brown, shining; legs and antennae orange-brown; head and pronotum blackish; 5–6 mm.

6. *Isomira quadristriata* Couper (p. 461)
Orange-brown to blackish, slightly shining; head and pronotum blackish; 5–6.5 mm.

7. *I. sericea* (Say) (p. 461)
Brown-orange, not shining; 5–5.5 mm.

Family ANOBIIDAE

8. *Sitodrepa panicea* (Linné) (p. 496)
Brown-orange; 2.5–3.5 mm.

9. *Ptilinus ruficornis* Say (p. 499)
Dark reddish brown (female) to blackish (male); females do not possess the flabellate antennae; 3–4.5 mm.

10. *Xestobium rufovillosum* (DeGeer) (p. 496)
Deep brown, with dull-yellowish markings; 6–7.5 mm.

11. *Trypopitys sericeus* (Say) (p. 498)
Dark brown, with pale-yellowish pubescence; 5–6.2 mm.

12. *Lasioderma serricorne* (Fabricius) (p. 499)
Dark brownish red; 2.2–3 mm.

13. *Hadrobregmus carinatus* (Say) (p. 498)
Dark reddish brown to piceous; 3.5–6.5 mm.

MM 0 10 20 30 40 50 60 70

PLATE XLV

459

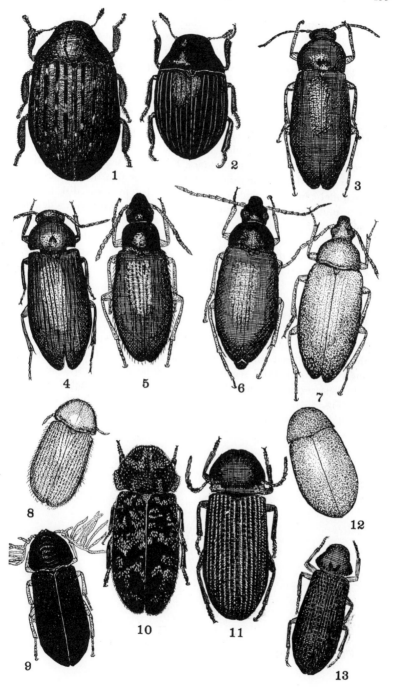

into apex; posterior angles rectangular; surface strongly sloping on sides, coarsely, deeply, and sparsely punctate, basally with a shallow impression each side and at middle. Elytra nearly four times as long as pronotum, sides parallel; disk with rows of feebly impressed punctures; intervals slightly convex, sparsely and finely punctate, rugulose near apex. Length 7–8 mm.

This species occurs on and beneath bark of black willow.

b. *Hymenorus niger* (Melsheimer)   Plate XLV, No. 4, p. 459

Elongate-oval, rather slender, and parallel; black or piceous, shining; covered with fine, ash-gray pubescence. Eyes above separated by a distance equal to their width. Pronotum three-fifths wider than long, sides straight and parallel almost to middle, thence rounded to apex; disk finely and sparsely punctate, without impressions near base. Elytra with sides nearly straight, parallel; disk with rows of small, deep punctures which are impressed only on basal half, obsolete near apex; intervals finely, deeply, and sparsely punctate. Length 5.3–6 mm.

The adults occur on dead branches of oak.

Genus II. *MYCETOCHARA* Berthold

Small, oblong, subparallel, brownish species, usually having the humeri of the elytra dull red; antennae somewhat short, generally robust, segments strongly obconical, third segment usually subequal to fourth, at least in female; last segment of maxillary palpi a robust right-angled triangle in shape (Fig. 364); punctation and pubescence usually coarse and sparse; tarsi not lobed beneath.

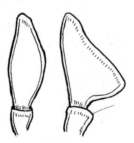

Figs. 366–367

Figs. 366–367. Apical segment of *Isomira sericea* (366) and of *I. quadristriata* (367).

Mycetochara foveata LeConte — Plate XLV, No. 5, p. 459

Elongate, subovate; dark reddish brown to piceous, shining; antennae and legs reddish brown; elytra with a small, pale-reddish spot on each humerus; pubescence fine, short, and semierect. Eyes small, separated by nearly four times their width. Pronotum one-third wider than long; sides strongly rounded at middle, then converging to apex, posterior angles rectangular; disk distinctly sloping on sides toward front angles, finely, deeply, and sparsely punctate; basal impression on sides deep, rounded, one at middle linear, shallow. Elytra with feebly impressed rows of rather coarse, close-set punctures; intervals each with a single row of very fine punctures. Protarsi not as long as tibiae. Length 5–6 mm.

These beetles are usually found under the bark of maple and walnut.

Genus III. *ISOMIRA* Mulsant

Rather small, oval, brownish species; antennae slender and filiform, segments feebly obconical or subparallel, the third segment usually subequal to or slightly shorter than fourth in female and more frequently shorter in the male; elytral striae often obliterated; punctation and pubescence usually minute and very dense; tarsi not lobed beneath.

KEY TO SPECIES

Fourth segment of maxillary palpi long and slender (Fig. 366); elytral punctation and pubescence exceedingly dense, color pale brownish yellow ......a. *sericea*
Fourth segment of maxillary palpi robust, the outer side but slightly longer than apex (Fig. 367); dark reddish brown to piceous; elytral punctation sparse ....
....b. *quadristriata*

a. *Isomira sericea* (Say) — Plate XLV, No. 7, p. 459

Elongate-oval; entirely pale brownish yellow, feebly shining, densely covered with fine, short pubescence. Antennae two-thirds as long as body, the third and fourth segments subequal. Fourth segment of maxillary palpi long and slender. Pronotum one-half wider than long, sides straight and parallel to middle, thence rounded to apex, which is truncate and one-half the width of the base; disk densely, finely punctate. Elytra with two or three feebly impressed striae near the suture, these more strongly marked near apex. Length 5–5.5 mm.

The adults occur on flowers of Jersey tea, wild hydrangea, etc.

b. *Isomira quadristriata* Couper — Plate XLV, No. 6, p. 459

Rather broadly oval, convex; dark reddish brown to piceous, feebly shining; head and pronotum nearly black, antennae and tibiae usually paler. Fourth segment of maxillary palpi robust, rather triangular. Pronotum nearly twice as wide as long, sides rounded on basal half, converging toward apex, which is two-thirds as wide as base; disk finely, densely punctate. Elytra at middle one-fourth wider than pronotum at base, surface finely and sparsely but distinctly punctate, each with two striae visible on apical half near the suture. Length 5–6.6 mm.

The adults are usually found on huckleberry and other shrubs along the borders of marshes.

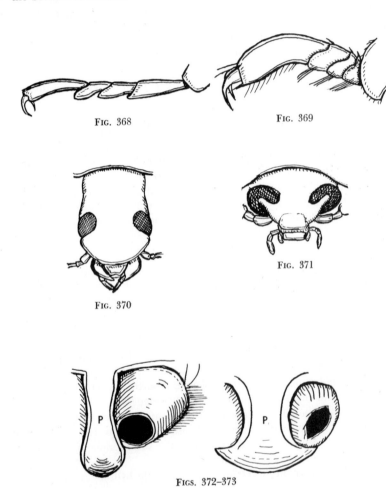

Fig. 368

Fig. 369

Fig. 370

Fig. 371

Figs. 372–373

Figs. 368–369. Metatarsus of *Paratenetus* (368) and *Boletotherus* (369).
Figs. 370–371. Head of *Alobates* (370) and of *Diaperis* (371), the eyes strongly projecting from the head in the latter.
Figs. 372–373. Procoxa of *Uloma* (372) and of *Iphthimus* (373). P, prosternal process.

Family TENEBRIONIDAE

The Darkling Beetles

This is a family of very plain, rather clumsy, and loosely constructed beetles, some of which resemble members of the Carabidae. While this family is a very large one, it is not as common in our territory as it is further west, where it largely displaces the Carabidae. The adults and larvae occur under bark, in dead wood, fungi, and in dry vegetable matter. A few species are obnoxious; for example, the "meal worm," which occurs in dried, ground grains, and the "false wireworms," which often destroy thousands of acres of wheat. Members of the genus *Tribolium* are museum pests, attacking dried insects, plants, and mounted bird and animal specimens.

Other family characters are: mostly dull black or brown, oblong or oval in form; mandibles short, robust, and usually with a basal tooth; antennae eleven-segmented, moniliform, rarely subserrate, inserted beneath front; eye emarginate on anterior margin; procoxal cavities closed behind; procoxae short, globose, separated by prosternum; metacoxae transverse; elytra concealing abdomen and often embracing the sides; tarsi 5–5–4, first segment of metatarsi always longer than second; claws simple.

KEY TO SUBFAMILIES

1. All ventral abdominal segments entirely corneous ..TENTYRIINAE (p. 464)
   Third and fourth ventral abdominal segments with a coriaceous posterior margin 2
2. Front of head with a coriaceous margin, or coriaceous between front and labrum; distal antennal segments broader 8
   Front entirely corneous 3
3. Tarsi not compressed, first segment moderate or elongate, never strongly shortened (Fig. 368); genae not sulcate 4
   Tarsi compressed (Fig. 369), first segment short; genae sulcate ....BOLETOPHAGINAE (p. 465)
4. Eyes less prominent than sides of front (Fig. 370) 5
   Eyes more prominent than sides of front (Fig. 371) ..DIAPERINAE (p. 465)
5. Next to last segment of tarsi bilobed (Fig. 368) ....HETEROTARSINAE (p. 475)
   Next to last segment of tarsi entire 6
6. Procoxae transverse (Fig. 372); mesocoxae without trochantin; antennae with third segment short ....ULOMINAE (p. 468)
   Procoxae rounded (Fig. 373); mesocoxae with trochantin; antennal third segment longer than those following 7

7. Length over 12 mm. .........................TENEBRIONINAE   (p. 472)
   Length less than 6 mm. ....PEDININAE   (p. 464)
8. Metacoxae narrowly separated (Fig. 374); sides of front of head not
    obliquely elevated ....HELOPINAE   (p. 478)
   Metacoxae widely separated (Fig. 375); sides of front of head ob-
    liquely elevated ..........................MERACANTHINAE   (p. 479)

Subfamily TENTYRIINAE

Genus *PHELLOPSIS* LeConte

Medium-sized, oblong, depressed, very roughly and densely sculptured beetles; mentum small, leaving maxillae and the much smaller ligula exposed; palpi distinct; mandibles bifid at apex; eyes minutely faceted, flat, more widely separated above; antennae small, all segments free, last three segments not fused; elytra without true epipleura; procoxae separated; mesocoxae without trochantin; tarsi variable.

Phellopsis obcordata (Kirby)   Plate XLVI, No. 2, p. 471

Elongate-oblong, slender, depressed; yellow-brown to deep brown, opaque. Pronotum as long as wide; sides evenly arcuate, base narrower than apex, apical margin deeply emarginate; anterior angles prominent; disk roughly tubercled. Elytra each with two long carinae and with several rows of punctures; several acute tubercles near apex. Length 12–15 mm.

Subfamily PEDININAE

Genus *BLAPSTINUS* Latreille

Small, oblong or oblong-ovate; eyes entirely divided; mentum not trilobed; antennae robust, segments four to eight longer than broad; base of pronotum as wide as elytra, bisinuate; scutellum triangular, separating elytra at base; epipleura entire; wings always present but sometimes rudimentary; protibiae straight, simple; protarsi of male usually dilated.

Blapstinus metallicus (Fabricius)   Plate XLVI, No. 1, p. 471

Oblong-ovate, convex; bronzed, shining. Pronotum one-third wider than long, sides almost straight, thence converging to apical angles; apex broadly emarginate; surface densely, coarsely, and deeply punctate, more sparsely and finely so medially; basal fovea deeply impressed. Elytral punctures very coarse, deep, in regular rows; intervals flat, with fine and sparse punctures. Length 4–4.8 mm.

Subfamily BOLITOPHAGINAE

Genus *BOLITOTHERUS* Candèze

Medium-sized, oblong, rather robust beetles; surface roughly sculptured; antennae not pectinate, ten-segmented, the third elongate; prothorax pedunculate and in males with two horns, slightly curved, broader at apex, projecting forward on dorsal surface, in females strongly tuberculate; clypeus of male with a feeble horn, bifid at apex; epipleura entire; third and fourth ventral abdominal segments with coriaceous posterior margin; tarsi compressed, first segment short.

Bolitotherus cornutus (Panzer)   Plate XLVI, No. 4, p. 471

Oblong, robust; dark brown to black, dull. Pronotum three times as broad as long; margins broadly flattened and serrate; disk with horns in male, tubercles in female. Elytra each with four rows of large, irregular tubercles; intervals with smaller ones. Length 10–11.5 mm.

The adults are found especially in the woody bracket fungi, which grow on dead and dying tree trunks; they feign death when disturbed.

Subfamily DIAPERINAE

KEY TO GENERA

1. First metatarsal segment longer than second 2
   First metatarsal segment not longer than second ....I. *Diaperis* (p. 466)
2. First metatarsal segment longer than second and third together ....
   ....III. *Platydema* (p. 467)
   First metatarsal segment only as long as second and third ....
   ....II. *Hoplocephala* (p. 466)

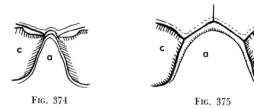

FIG. 374   FIG. 375

Figs. 374–375. Portions of metacoxae and first abdominal sternite. *Tarpela* (374) with metacoxae narrowly separated. *Meracantha* (375) with metacoxae widely separated. *a,* intercoxal piece of first sternite; *c,* inner portion of metacoxa.

Genus I. *DIAPERIS* Geoffroy

Small, broadly oval, convex; front entirely corneous; eyes emarginate; antennae gradually broadened at apex; epipleura slightly abbreviated apically; ventral abdominal segments three and four with coriaceous posterior margin; procoxae transverse; mesocoxae with distinct trochantins; first metatarsal segment not longer than second; tarsi pubescent beneath.

Diaperis maculata Olivier   Plate XLVI, No. 3, p. 471
  Broadly oval, strongly convex; black; head between eyes reddish; elytra dark orangeish red, each with a sutural vitta, wider at apex, not attaining scutellum, a rounded macula on middle of basal third, another small, elongate one laterally, and a large, irregular macula on apical half, all black. Pronotum nearly three times as wide as long, finely, sparsely punctate. Elytra with rows of fine, feebly impressed punctures; intervals flat, finely and sparsely punctate. Length 6–6.5 mm.
  The adults occur beneath bark of elm especially, and in fungi.

Genus II. *HOPLOCEPHALA* Castelnau and Brullé

Small, elongate, oval, convex; front of head entirely corneous; eyes emarginate (Fig. 371); antennae gradually broadened to apex; epipleura slightly abbreviated apically; ventral abdominal segments three and four with leathery posterior margins; first metatarsal segment longer than second but only as long as second and third together; males with two short horns on clypeus and two longer ones on vertex.

KEY TO SPECIES

Pronotum red ....a. *viridipennis*
Pronotum black. rarely brown ....b. *bicornis*

a. *Hoplocephala viridipennis* (Fabricius)   Plate XLVI, No. 5, p. 471
  Elongate-oval, convex; pronotum, legs, and undersurface red; abdomen brownish red; head and apical half of antennae piceous; elytra metallic green or blue. Pronotum more than twice as wide as long; sides slightly arcuate; posterior angles rounded; disk finely, sparsely punctate. Elytral striae with close-set, coarse, deep punctures; intervals finely and sparsely punctate. Length 3–3.5 mm.
  This species is found beneath bark of fungus-covered logs.

b. *Hoplocephala bicornis* (Fabricius)   Plate XLVI, No. 6, p. 471
  Elongate-ovate, convex; metallic bluish green, shining; pronotum sometimes brownish; undersurface, except prosternum, brownish to piceous. Pronotum finely, sparsely punctate. Elytral striae with close-set, coarse, deep

punctures; intervals very finely, sparsely, and obsoletely punctate. Length 3–4 mm.

This species is very common on fungi of various kinds.

Genus III. *PLATYDEMA* Castelnau and Brullé

Small, usually broadly oval, slightly convex; last segment of maxillary palpi broadly triangular, inner and outer sides subequal (Fig. 376); eyes emarginate; antennae gradually broadened to apex; epipleura entire; intercoxal process of prosternum acute; mesosternum short, concave; first metatarsal segment longer than second and third together.

KEY TO SPECIES

1. Head with horns or tubercles; front concave; upper surface black, shining ....
   ....a. *excavatum*
   Head without horns or tubercles 2
2. Pronotum and elytra black; surface opaque 3
   Pronotum and elytra black; surface shining 4
3. Elytra without red maculae; antennae wholly pale ....b. *ruficorne*
   Elytra each with an oblique red macula on basal half ....c. *ellipticum*
4. Prosternum horizontal, its apex prominent (Fig. 377); form oval, rather
   slender ....d. *americanum*
   Prosternum convex between coxae, its apex deflexed and obtuse (Fig. 378);
   form broadly oval ....e. *subcostatum*

a. *Platydema excavatum* (Say)   Plate XLVI, No. 10, p. 471
   Broadly ovate, slightly convex; black, shining; antennae dark reddish brown; legs either dark reddish brown or piceous. Male with two parallel, prominent, cylindrical horns between eyes; front concave between the bases of the horns; head of female with tubercles instead of horns. Pro-

Fig. 376

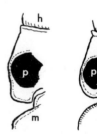

Figs. 377–378

Fig. 376. Apical segment of maxillary palpus of *Platydema*.
Figs. 377–378. Prosternum of *Platydema americanum* (377) and of *P. subcostatum* (378), in profile. *h*, head; *m*, mesosternum; *p*, procoxal cavity.

notum more than twice as wide as long, narrowed from base to apex, finely and sparsely punctate. Elytral striae deep, coarsely and deeply punctate; intervals very finely and sparsely punctate. Length 4.5–5.5 mm.

This species is common under bark.

b. *Platydema ruficorne* Sturm   Plate XLVI, No. 7, p. 471

Broadly ovate; dull black or sometimes piceous with a purplish tinge; undersurface and legs dark reddish brown; antennae pale reddish yellow. Pronotum twice as wide at base as long, narrowed to apex; disk finely, densely punctate. Elytral striae coarsely and deeply punctate; intervals flat, very minutely punctate. Length 4–5.5 mm.

The adults are common on fleshy fungi and beneath bark.

c. *Platydema ellipticum* (Fabricius)   Plate XLVI, No. 9, p. 471

Elongate-ovate; dull black; elytra each with an oblique reddish macula extending from humerus to suture; undersurface and legs dark reddish brown. Pronotum more than twice as wide as long, narrowing from base to apex; disk finely, densely punctate. Elytral striae with coarse, distant punctures; intervals obsoletely punctate. Length 5.5–7 mm.

Beneath bark on fungus-covered logs is the usual habitat of this species.

d. *Platydema americanum* Castelnau and Brullé   Plate XLVI, No. 8, p. 471

Elongate-ovate, robust, convex; black, shining. Head with a distinct, transverse groove and a frontal impression. Pronotum transverse, sides arcuate, narrowed apically; disk coarsely, regularly punctate. Elytral striae punctate; intervals finely punctate. Length 5–6 mm.

e. *Platydema subcostatum* Castelnau and Brullé   Plate XLVI, No. 12, p. 471

Broadly oval; dark reddish brown or black, shining; antennae and legs reddish brown, sometimes almost piceous. Head with a transverse impression in front of eyes. Pronotum at base more than twice as wide as long, narrowed apically; disk sparsely, very finely punctate. Elytral striae with coarse, deep punctures; intervals very minutely, sparsely punctate. Length 5.5–6.5 mm.

Subfamily ULOMINAE

Genus *ULOMA* Castelnau

Medium-sized, elongate-oblong, slightly convex; last segment of maxillary palpi triangular, rarely obliquely truncate; antennae gradually widened apically; base of pronotum not margined; epipleura abbreviated; pygidium not exposed; protibiae dilated, serrate.

KEY TO SPECIES

1. Last segment of antennae with apex rounded 2
   Last segment of antennae with apex oblique and acuminate ....b. *imberbis*
2. Elytral intervals very minutely and sparsely punctate; middle plate of mentum
   elongate-oval (Fig. 379) ....a. *impressa*
   Elytral intervals very densely, finely punctate; middle plate of mentum transversely oval (Fig. 380) ....c. *punctulata*

a. *Uloma impressa* Melsheimer   Plate XLVI, No. 11, p. 471
Elongate-oblong, subparallel; dark reddish brown, shining. Front of
head with a deep, curved impression; last segment of antennae rounded
at tip. Pronotum almost one-third wider than long; base as wide as elytra;
sides feebly arcuate; posterior angles obtuse; disk with a deep, transverse
impression at middle of apex, finely, sparsely punctate. Elytra parallel on
basal three-quarters, thence narrowed apically; striae deep, with close-set,
deep, coarse punctures; intervals slightly convex, minutely punctate. Length
11–12 mm.
The adults are usually found beneath bark of oak and beech.

b. *Uloma imberbis* LeConte   Plate XLVI, No. 14, p. 471
Elongate-oblong, subparallel; dark reddish brown to piceous, shining.
Head with a curved impression at apex; last segment of antennae oblique,
acuminate. Pronotum almost one-half wider than long, narrowed in front
of posterior angles; without a transverse impression at apex; sides arcuate;
disk finely, sparsely punctate. Elytral striae with very coarse, deep punctures; intervals very minutely, sparsely punctate. Length 8.5–9 mm.

c. *Uloma punctulata* LeConte   Plate XLVII, No. 7, p. 477
Oblong-ovate, subparallel; pale reddish brown. Last segment of antennae
rounded at apex. Pronotum with sides parallel behind middle, arcuately
narrowed apically; disk densely, rather finely punctate, both sexes not impressed apically. Elytral striae deeply punctate; intervals feebly convex,
densely, minutely punctate. Male with mesotibiae mucronate. Length
7–8.5 mm.
This species is more frequent in the southern states and is found beneath
bark of pine.

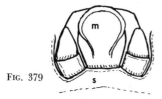

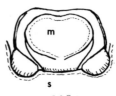

FIG. 379   FIG. 380

Figs. 379–380. Mentum of *Uloma impressa* (379) and of *U. punctulata*
(380). *m*, middle plate of mentum: *s*. submentum.

PLATE XLVI
Family TENEBRIONIDAE I

1. *Blapstinus metallicus* (Fabricius) (p. 464) Brassy black; 4–4.8 mm.
2. *Phellopsis obcordata* (Kirby) (p. 464) Yellowish brown to blackish; 12–15 mm.
3. *Diaperis maculata* Olivier (p. 466) Black; elytra dull red, with black markings; 6–6.5 mm.
4. *Bolitotherus cornutus* (Panzer) (p. 465) Dull brown to black; 10–11.5 mm.
5. *Hoplocephala viridipennis* (Fabricius) (p. 466) Head black; pronotum reddish; elytra brilliant dark green or blue; 3–3.5 mm.
6. *H. bicornis* (Fabricius) (p. 466) Deep brown to blackish, with a green reflex; antennae and legs yellowish brown; 3–4 mm.
7. *Platydema ruficorne* Sturm (p. 468) Dull black; antennae and legs dark reddish brown; 4–5.5 mm.
8. *P. americanum* Castelnau and Brullé (p. 468) Dark brown or blackish, shining; 5–6 mm.
9. *P. ellipticum* (Fabricius) (p. 468) Black; elytra with a deep-red mark; legs blackish; 5.5–7 mm.
10. *P. excavatum* (Say) (p. 467) Black, shining; legs and antennae dark brown; 4.5–5.5 mm.
11. *Uloma impressa* Melsheimer (p. 469) Deep reddish brown, shining; 11–12 mm.
12. *Platydema subcostatum* Castelnau and Brullé (p. 468) Dark brown to black; legs and antennae reddish brown; 5.5–6.5 mm.
13. *Helops aereus* Germar (p. 479) Deep brown, very shining; 7–9 mm.
14. *Uloma imberbis* LeConte (p. 469) Blackish; legs and antennae reddish brown; 8.5–9 mm.
15. *Alobates pennsylvanica* (DeGeer) (p. 473) Black, rather shining; 20–23 mm.
16. *Iphthimus opacus* LeConte (p. 473) Black, not shining; 15–20 mm.
17. *Upis ceramboides* (Linné) (p. 474) Blackish, somewhat shining; 14–18 mm.
18. *Paratenetus punctatus* Spinola (p. 478) Rather dark yellowish brown; 3–4 mm.
19. *Anaedus brunneus* (Ziegler) (p. 475) Dark brown; antennae and legs reddish yellow; 5–5.5 mm.

MM 0 10 20 30 40 50 60 70

PLATE XLVI

471

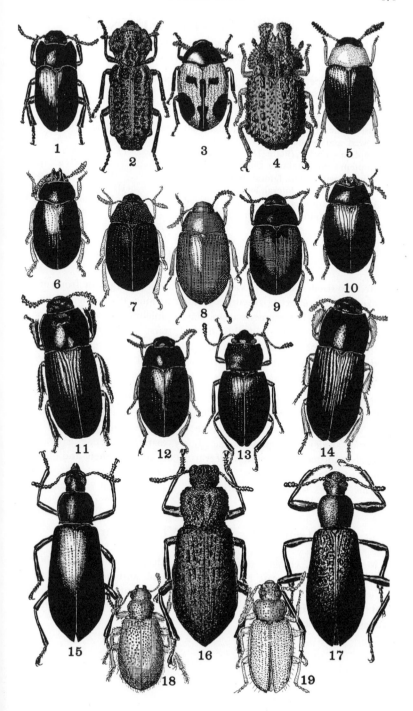

Subfamily TENEBRIONINAE

KEY TO GENERA

1. Tarsi with fine, usually silky, pubescence beneath 2
   Tarsi spinose or setose beneath ....VI. *Tenebrio*   (p. 474)
2. Last segment of antennae perfoliate (Fig. 19); antennae shorter than head and pronotum 3
   Last segment of antennae triangular; antennae slender, longer than head and pronotum 5
3. Epipleura entire (Plate II) 4
   Epipleura not attaining the apices of elytra ....V. *Upis*   (p. 474)
4. Mentum with small, lateral, inflexed lobes ....IV. *Alobates*   (p. 473)
   Mentum without lateral lobes ....III. *Iphthimus*   (p. 473)
5. Anterior margin of front of head reflexed ....I. *Scotobates*   (p. 472)
   Anterior margin of front not reflexed ....II. *Xylopinus*   (p. 472)

Genus I. *SCOTOBATES* Horn

Medium-sized, elongate-ovate, convex; anterior margin of front of head thickened and reflexed; antennae slender, as long as or longer than head and pronotum, last segment triangular; epipleura not attaining apex of elytra; protarsi of male feebly dilated; tarsi with fine, usually silky, pubescence beneath. Males with an elongate patch of yellowish hairs on underside of profemora and protibiae and with a short, blunt tooth at middle.

Scotobates calcaratus (Fabricius)   Plate XLVII, No. 2, p. 477

Elongate-ovate, convex; black, shining; elytra bluish black. Pronotum only slightly wider than long, sides feebly arcuate; anterior angles obtuse; posterior angles rectangular; surface finely, sparsely punctate. Elytral striae coarsely and deeply punctate; intervals feebly convex, finely and obsoletely punctate. Length 14–17 mm.

This species is found beneath stones, logs, bark, and rubbish.

Genus II. *XYLOPINUS* LeConte

Medium-sized, elongate-ovate, rather slender; anterior margin of front not reflexed but truncate or feebly emarginate; antennae slender, as long as or longer than head and pronotum, last segment triangular; epipleura not attaining tip of elytra; protarsi of male dilated; tarsi with silky pubescence beneath.

Xylopinus saperdioides (Olivier)   Plate XLVII, No. 1, p. 477

Elongate-oval, subparallel, convex; piceous to black, feebly shining; undersurface very dark reddish brown. Pronotum subquadrate, narrowed apically; sides feebly arcuate; anterior angles rounded; posterior angles acute; surface finely and densely punctate, with a slight impression each side near basal angles. Elytra parallel, narrowed at apex; striae with coarse, close-set punctures; intervals convex, finely and sparsely punctate. Length 12–16 mm.

The adults are found especially beneath bark of oak.

Genus III. *IPHTHIMUS* Truqui

Medium-sized, elongate-ovate, convex; mentum without lateral lobes; antennae shorter than head and pronotum, apical segments perfoliate (Fig. 19), last segment subquadrate, rounded at apex; pronotum narrowing basally, sides crenulate; epipleura entire, narrowed at apex; tarsi with fine, usually silky, pubescence beneath.

Iphthimus opacus LeConte   Plate XLVI, No. 16, p. 471

Elongate-oval, convex; black, opaque. Pronotum subquadrate; sides distinctly arcuate; posterior angles acutely dentate; surface coarsely, confluently punctate at sides. Elytral striae interrupted, coarsely and distinctly punctate. Length 15–20 mm.

Genus IV. *ALOBATES* Motschulsky

Medium-sized, elongate-oval, convex; mentum with small, lateral, inflexed lobes; pronotum not narrowed at base; antennae shorter than head and pronotum, outer segments perfoliate (Fig. 19), last segment subquadrate, rounded at apex; epipleura entire, narrower at apex; tarsi with fine, usually silky, pubescence beneath.

Alobates pennsylvanica (DeGeer)   Plate XLVI, No. 15, p. 471

Elongate-ovate, convex; black, feebly shining. Mentum coarsely punctate. Pronotum quadrate, slightly narrowed at apex; anterior angles rounded, posterior ones acute; surface finely and sparsely punctate. Elytral striae coarsely, deeply punctate; intervals minutely alutaceous and minutely, sparsely punctate. Length 20–23 mm.

This species may be found throughout the year beneath bark and logs. Both adults and larvae feed upon other insects.

Genus V. *UPIS* Fabricius

Medium-sized, elongate-ovate, rather slender; eyes feebly emarginate, broad at middle; antennae shorter than head and pronotum, outer segments perfoliate (Fig. 19); epipleura entire, not attaining apices of elytra; intercoxal process narrow, acute; tarsi with fine, silky pubescence beneath.

Upis ceramboides (Linné)   Plate XLVI, No. 17, p. 471

Elongate-ovate, rather slender, subconvex; piceous or black, feebly shining. Pronotum slightly elongate; sides arcuate; surface rather densely and irregularly punctate. Elytra entirely covered with interlacing carinae, the interspaces with small, smooth tubercles. Length 14–18 mm.

Genus VI. *TENEBRIO* Linné

Medium-sized, elongate-ovate or parallel, subconvex; black or brownish; palpi short; eyes not completely divided; antennae gradually thickened toward apex; epipleura entire; third and fourth ventral abdominal segments with coriaceous posterior margin; tarsi short, spinose or setose beneath.

KEY TO SPECIES

1. Entire surface opaque ....a. *obscurus*
   Surface distinctly shining 2
2. Sides of elytra feebly curved, only a trace wider behind middle ..b. *molitor*
   Sides of elytra curved and distinctly wider behind middle ....c. *picipes*

a. *Tenebrio obscurus* Fabricius   Plate XLVII, No. 5, p. 477

Oblong-ovate, slender; piceous or dark reddish brown, opaque. Pronotum subquadrate, narrowed slightly to apex; sides feebly arcuate, margins wide, reflexed; posterior angles acute; disk coarsely, densely punctate, a rounded, rather shallow impression each side near base. Elytra parallel, narrowed to apex; striae indistinct, punctate; intervals granulate-punctate. Length 14–17 mm.

An introduced species, it is found in granaries, storehouses, and barns as well as in flour and meal. The larva is the "dark meal-worm."

b. *Tenebrio molitor* Linné   Plate XLVII, No. 3, p. 477

Oblong-oval, slender; piceous or dark reddish brown, slightly shining. Pronotum transverse, narrowed slightly toward apex; margins broad and strongly reflexed; anterior angles prominent, posterior ones subacute; disk finely, densely punctate, a rounded, distinct impression each side near base. Elytral striae with rather fine, indistinct punctures; intervals minutely and densely punctate. Length 13–16 mm.

This species is also introduced and occurs with *obscurus;* the larva is known as the "yellow meal-worm."

c. *Tenebrio picipes* Herbst   Plate XLVII, No. 4, p. 477

Elongate-ovate, robust; black or dark reddish brown, shining. Pronotum transverse; sides feebly arcuate, margins narrow, slightly reflexed; sinuate at base, angles not prominent; disk with coarse and fine punctures intermingled, coarse ones more numerous laterally. Elytral striae with close-set punctures; intervals subconvex, minutely, densely punctate. Mesocoxae with trochantin very small. Length 12–13 mm.

The adults are common beneath bark.

Subfamily HETEROTARSINAE

KEY TO GENERA

Antennae gradually thicker distally ....I. *Anaedus* (p. 475)
Antennae with last three segments clubbed ....II. *Paratenetus* (p. 475)

Genus I. *ANAEDUS* Blanchard

Small, oblong-oval, subdepressed; body pubescent; front of head entirely corneous; eyes less prominent than the sides of front, more or less transverse, always emarginate anteriorly; antennae gradually thickened distally; third and fourth abdominal sternites with coriaceous posterior margin; epipleura entire; protibiae sometimes dilated, other tibiae not dilated; first tarsal segment moderate or elongate, never very short, not compressed, next to last segment bilobed.

Anaedus brunneus (Ziegler)   Plate XLVI, No. 19, p. 471

Oblong-ovate, subdepressed; dark reddish brown, with sparse, long, yellowish hairs; antennae and legs dark reddish yellow. Head coarsely punctate, a rounded elevation above base of antennae. Pronotum transverse; distinctly narrowed each side in front of posterior angles, which are acute; margins reflexed; disk very coarsely and sparsely punctate. Elytra irregularly, coarsely, deeply punctate. Length 5–5.5 mm.

The adults occur throughout the year beneath bark, logs, and stones in dry localities.

Genus II. *PARATENETUS* Spinola

Small, oval, convex; body pubescent; front of head entirely corneous; eyes less prominent than the side of front, more or less transverse, always

PLATE XLVII

Family TENEBRIONIDAE II

1. *Xylopinus saperdioides* (Olivier) (p. 473) — Blackish, shining; 12–16 mm.
2. *Scotobates calcaratus* (Fabricius) (p. 472) — Black, shining; elytra blue-black; 14–17 mm.
3. *Tenebrio molitor* Linné (p. 474) — Dark brown to blackish; 13–16 mm.
4. *T. picipes* Herbst (p. 475) — Dark brown to black; 12–13 mm.
5. *T. obscurus* Fabricius (p. 474) — Dark brown to blackish; 14–17 mm.
6. *Tarpela micans* (Fabricius) (p. 478) — Black, bronzed with green, red, and bluish; bronzing on elytra arranged in stripes; 10–17 mm.
7. *Uloma punctulata* LeConte (p. 469) — Light reddish brown; 7–8.5 mm.
8. *Meracantha contracta* (Beauvois) (p. 479) — Black, with a feeble bronze; 11–13 mm.

Family MELANDRYIDAE I

9. *Penthe obliquata* (Fabricius) (p. 482) — Black; last antennal segment whitish; scutellum orange; 11.5–14 mm.
10. *Synchroa punctata* Newman (p. 483) — Dark brown to blackish; legs reddish brown; 10–13 mm.
11. *Dircaea quadrimaculata* (Say) (p. 487) — Dark brown to piceous, with orange markings; 7–9 mm.
12. *Penthe pimelia* (Fabricius) (p. 483) — Black; last segment of antennae whitish; scutellum black; 10–14 mm.

MM 0 10 20 30 40 50 60 70

PLATE XLVII

477

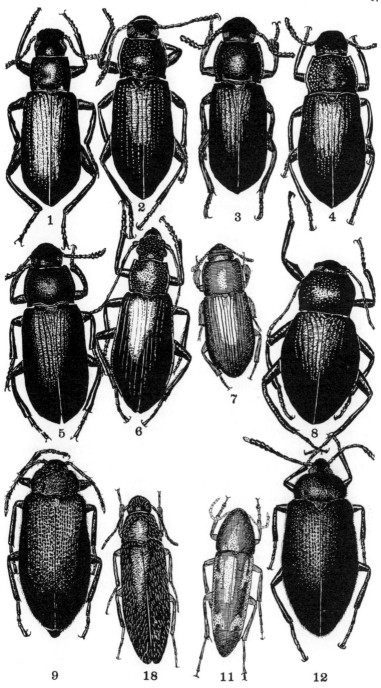

emarginate anteriorly; antennae distinctly clubbed; pronotum narrower than elytra, margin denticulate; epipleura entire; third and fourth abdominal sternites with coriaceous posterior margin; protibiae alone or none of tibiae dilated; first tarsal segment moderate or elongate, never short, not compressed, next to last segment bilobed.

Paratenetus punctatus Spinola   Plate XLVI, No. 18, p. 471

Oval, slender, convex; brown, somewhat shining; covered with silvery pubescence. Pronotum feebly transverse, apex wider than base; sides oblique, finely and irregularly serrate; disk coarsely, deeply punctate. Elytra with rows of short setae, surface coarsely punctate. Length 3–4 mm.

Subfamily HELOPINAE

KEY TO GENERA

Mesosternum short, distinctly shorter than metasternum at middle
....II. *Helops* (p. 479)
Mesosternum longer, equal in length to metasternum at middle ......
....I. *Tarpela* (p. 478)

Genus I. *TARPELA* Bates

Small or medium-sized, elongate-ovate, convex; anterior angles of pronotum very strongly produced, extending nearly to the upper edge of the eyes, subrectangular, lateral margins crenulate; epipleura slightly abbreviated at apex; mesosternum rather long, deeply excavated before process; prosternum bent down behind procoxae and prolonged posteriorly.

Tarpela micans (Fabricius)   Plate XLVII, No. 6, p. 477

Elongate-ovate, convex; black, bronzed, shining; elytra with blue or greenish and reddish metallic stripes. Antennae slender, one-half length of body, three apical segments shorter. Pronotum transverse, emarginate at apex, margins feebly sinuate; disk coarsely, irregularly, and densely punctate. Elytral striae indistinctly punctate; intervals very minutely, almost obsoletely, and sparsely punctate. Apex of last abdominal sternite with a broad, hairy depression in male, a longitudinal, narrow one in female. Length 10–17 mm.

This species occurs in colonies beneath loose bark of logs, especially those of red oak.

Genus II. *HELOPS* Fabricius

Small or medium-sized beetles; elongate-ovate, convex; apical segments of antennae broader; eyes ovate, feebly emarginate anteriorly; epipleura very slightly abbreviated apically; pronotal apical angles acute; mesosternum short, excavated, declivous anteriorly; tarsi slender.

Helops aereus Germar   Plate XLVI, No. 13, p. 471

Elongate-ovate, strongly convex; black, bronzed, shining. Antennae with last three segments almost equal, shorter than those preceding. Pronotum slightly transverse; anterior angles subacute; disk densely and finely punctate. Elytra with rows of elongate punctures; intervals flat, without punctures. Length 7–9 mm.

This species is also gregarious beneath loose bark.

Subfamily MERACANTHINAE

Genus *MERACANTHA* Kirby

Of medium size, ovate, strongly convex; wingless; head retracted into pronotum nearly to eyes; eyes large, transverse, emarginate anteriorly; sides of head covering base of antennae and obliquely elevated; antennae long, slender, apical segments only slightly wider; last segment of maxillary palpi hatchet-shaped; epipleura slightly abbreviated at apex; procoxae rounded, mesocoxae with distinct trochantins; metacoxae widely separated; profemora beneath with an obtuse tooth.

Meracantha contracta (Beauvois)   Plate XLVII, No. 8, p. 477

Broadly ovate, robust, strongly convex; blackish, bronzed; elytra, antennae, and legs piceous. Pronotal sides strongly narrowed to apex; anterior and posterior angles subrectangular; disk coarsely, irregularly, and rather densely punctate, especially laterally. Elytral striae feebly impressed, rather finely punctate; intervals nearly flat, minutely, densely punctate. Length 11–13 mm.

This species is not gregarious and may be found beneath logs and bark, especially that of oak.

Family MELANDRYIDAE

The Melandyrid Bark Beetles

Small to moderate-sized, oval, convex or flattened, often very slender beetles, usually clothed with fine, silky hair; antennae eleven-segmented, filiform or somewhat clavate apically, inserted beneath the very narrow frontal margins; head usually inserted in prothorax to eyes; pronotum margined laterally, almost as broad at base as elytra; tarsi 5–5–4-segmented, first segment of metatarsi elongated, sometimes very strongly so.

The adults and larvae occur beneath bark, in dried fungi, in dry wood, and other vegetable matter; several aberrant members are found chiefly on foliage of trees and shrubs.

KEY TO SUBFAMILIES

1. Next to last tarsal segment simple (Fig. 381); protarsi of male not dilated; procoxae well separated (Fig. 372) ..TETRATOMINAE (p. 480)
   Next to last tarsal segments excavated and emarginate, more or less lobed beneath (Fig. 382), or rarely those of the metatarsi simple; protarsi of males dilated; procoxae contiguous (Fig. 215) 2
2. Head not constricted behind eyes ..............MELANDRYINAE (p. 486)
   Head suddenly constricted behind eyes into a short neck ....
   ....SCRAPTIINAE (p. 491)

Subfamily TETRATOMINAE

KEY TO TRIBES

1. Procoxal cavities angulate externally (Fig. 383); femora slender and cylindrical ....TETRATOMINI (p. 481)
   Procoxal cavities not angulate externally; femora broad and flat, with a sharp posterior edge 2
2. Metatibiae as long as femora, longer than first tarsal segment, with short, simple spurs apically; antennae without a club ....
   ....HALLOMENINI (p. 483)
   Metatibiae shorter than femora, or than first tarsal segment, apical spurs pectinate (Fig. 384), as long as tibiae; antennae clubbed
   ....ORCHESIINI (p. 485)

Tribe Tetratomini

KEY TO GENERA

1. Last three antennal segments abruptly wider than preceding ones, forming a loose, parallel-sided club (Fig. 385) ....I. *Pisenus* (p. 482)

   Antennae with apical segments gradually widened (Fig. 386) or filiform 2

2. Antennae gradually thickened apically, third segment as long as fourth and fifth combined; body form broadly ovate, robust ....II. *Penthe* (p. 482)

   Antennae filiform, not thickened apically, third segment scarcely longer than fourth; body form elongate, slender ....III. *Synchroa* (p. 483)

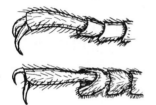

FIGS. 381–382   FIG. 383

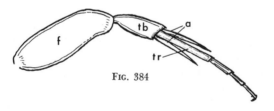

FIG. 384

FIG. 385   FIG. 386

Figs. 381–382. Apical tarsal segments of *Penthe* (381) and of *Melandrya* (382).

Fig. 383. Procoxal cavity of *Penthe*. *a*, lateral angulation.

Fig. 384. Hind leg of *Orchesia*. *a*, apical spurs; *f*, metafemur; *tb*, metatibia; *tr*, first metatarsal segment.

Figs. 385–386. Apical segments of antenna of *Pisenus* (385) and of *Penthe* (386).

Genus I. *PISENUS* Casey

Small, ovate, subconvex; head with eyes moderately large, narrow, strongly erect, narrowly emarginate on anterior margin; antennae with last three segments forming an abrupt club; pronotum not flattened along sides, basal margin broadly lobed medially, nearly as wide as elytra at base, disk near base with a small, deep fovea each side; all coxae distinctly separated; tarsi shortened, robust.

Pisenus humeralis (Kirby)   Plate XLVIII, No. 9, p. 489

Elongate-ovate, moderately slender, subconvex; dark reddish brown to piceous, shining, sparsely covered with short, silky, yellowish pubescence; elytra sometimes with a rounded, poorly defined, reddish macula on humeri. Pronotum almost twice as wide as long, sides nearly straight and tapering basally, strongly rounded anteriorly; disk finely, rather densely punctate, distinctly foveate each side of middle. Elytral apices rounded together; disk a little more coarsely and less densely punctate than pronotum. Length 3–4 mm.

Adults of this species are especially common on woody fungi.

Genus II. *PENTHE* Newman

Moderate-sized, broadly oval, subdepressed; eyes large, transverse, feebly emarginate anteriorly, lower lobe much wider than upper; antennae gradually clavate, third segment as long as fourth and fifth together; procoxae well separated, their cavities open posteriorly, angulate externally (Fig. 383); femora cylindrical; first metatarsal segment elongate, nearly as long as remaining segments combined.

KEY TO SPECIES

Scutellum densely covered with orange pubescence ....a. *obliquata*
Scutellum entirely black ....b. *pimelia*

a. *Penthe obliquata* (Fabricius)   Plate XLVII, No. 9, p. 477

Broadly oval, robust, subdepressed; black, feebly shining; scutellum covered with long, orangeish pubescence. Pronotum transverse, sides rounded to apex; disk densely and finely granulate-punctate, deeply, linearly impressed each side near base. Elytra with rows of deep punctures; intervals not as wide as the rows of punctures, densely, finely granulate. Length 11.5–14 mm.

Throughout the year this species may be found beneath bark of decaying trees and in dry fungi.

b. *Penthe pimelia* (Fabricius)   Plate XLVII, No. 12, p. 477

Broadly oval, robust, subdepressed; black, feebly shining. Pronotum transverse, sides strongly arcuate; disk densely, coarsely, more or less rugosely punctate, rather shallowly impressed each side near base. Scutellum densely, finely granulate-punctate. Elytra with closely set rows of deep punctures; intervals as wide as rows of punctures, densely granulate-punctate. Length 10–14 mm.

The adults live throughout the year beneath bark of decaying trees and in dry fungi.

Genus III. *SYNCHROA* Newman

Moderate-sized, elongate, subdepressed beetles that resemble click beetles in form; antennae slender, feebly serrate (Fig. 20), third segment slightly longer than fourth; eyes moderately large, feebly emarginate anteriorly, lower lobe broader than upper; procoxal cavities open posteriorly (Fig. 25A), angulate externally; femora cylindrical; tarsi slender, meso- and metatarsi elongate, first segment of latter as long as remaining segments combined.

Synchroa punctata Newman   Plate XLVII, No. 10, p. 477

Elongate-ovate, slender; dark brown to piceous, covered with long, ashy pubescence. Pronotum slightly transverse, sides gradually narrowing from base to apex; disk finely, rather sparsely punctate, deeply impressed each side near base. Elytra finely, sparsely punctate, sulcate along suture on apical third. Length 10–13 mm.

Beneath bark and at light are the chief places where this species may be collected.

Tribe HALLOMENINI

KEY TO GENERA

1. Prosternum narrowing to a point, not prolonged behind the coxae (Fig. 387); elytra with striae of moderate or coarse punctures ..2
   Prosternum prolonged behind coxae, separating them, apex not pointed (Fig. 388); elytra finely, irregularly punctate ....
   ....III. *Holostrophus* (p. 485)
2. Eyes less widely separated than their width, or, if nearly as wide, then the prothorax is shining beneath ....II. *Eustrophus* (p. 484)
   Eyes as widely separated as their width; prothorax densely, rugosely punctate beneath ....I. *Eustrophinus* (p. 484)

Genus I. *EUSTROPHINUS* Seidlitz

Small, oval, subconvex; head retracted into prothorax to eyes; eyes large, subapproximate above, separated by less than their width, deeply emarginate anteriorly; pronotum transverse, posterior angles rectangular; elytra with rows of punctures; prosternal process not prolonged behind coxae, gradually acute to apex; femora flattened; tibiae nearly as long as femora, meso- and metafemora finely dentate on outer margin; tarsi not elongate, metatarsi with first segment not as long as remaining ones together; antennae with last seven segments forming a loose club.

Eustrophinus bicolor (Fabricius)   Plate XLVIII, No. 1, p. 489

Oval, subconvex, rather robust; piceous to black, shining, covered with short, fuscous pubescence; body beneath in part, legs, and antennae at base and extreme apex reddish brown. Pronotum with basal margin distinctly bisinuate each side, the median lobe pronounced; disk rather densely, finely punctate, each side at base with a broad, feeble impression, in each of which is a group of four or five coarse punctures. Elytra with rows of coarse punctures; intervals broad, flat, and densely, finely punctate. Length 4.5–6 mm.

For the most part, this beetle may be found beneath the bark of decaying logs.

Genus II. *EUSTROPHUS* Illiger

Small, oval, subconvex; head retracted into prothorax to eyes; eyes rather small, much more widely separated above than their width, deeply emarginate anteriorly; pronotum transverse, posterior angles broadly rounded; elytra with rows of punctures; prosternal process not prolonged behind procoxae, its apex gradually acute; femora flattened; tibiae nearly as long as femora, meso- and metatibiae finely dentate on outer margin; tarsi not elongate, metatarsi with first segment not as long as remaining ones combined; antennae with last seven segments forming a loose club.

Eustrophus tomentosus Say   Plate XLVIII, No. 2, p. 489

Oval, subconvex, rather robust; reddish brown, somewhat shining, covered with short, yellowish pubescence; body beneath and legs slightly paler brown. Pronotum with basal margin weakly bisinuate each side, the median lobe broad, prominent; disk densely, finely punctate, each side at base with a shallow, longitudinal impression. Elytra with rows of fine punctures; intervals broad, flat, densely punctate. Length 4–5 mm.

This species occurs in dry fungi and beneath bark.

Genus III. *HOLOSTROPHUS* Horn

Small, ovate, subconvex; head retracted into prothorax to eyes; eyes rather small, widely separated above, anteriorly deeply emarginate, the lower portion much larger than upper; pronotum transverse, posterior angles subacute; elytra without rows of punctures; prosternal process distinctly prolonged behind procoxae, apically slightly expanded and abruptly acute (Fig. 388); femora somewhat flattened; tibiae nearly as long as femora, meso- and metatibiae not or feebly dentate on outer margin; antennae with last six segments gradually thickened into a tapering club.

Holostrophus bifasciatus (Say)   Plate XLVIII, No. 3, p. 489

Oval, rather slender, subconvex; reddish brown, shining, covered with short, yellowish pubescence; elytra piceous, with a broad, yellowish fascia on basal third and another on apical third, both broadly interrupted at suture. Pronotum with a prominent lobe at middle of base; disk densely, finely punctate, linearly impressed each side near base. Elytra uniformly densely, finely punctate. Length 4–5.5 mm.

Tribe ORCHESIINI

Genus *ORCHESIA* Latreille

Small, elongate-elliptical, subconvex; eyes large, subapproximate above, deeply emarginate anteriorly, upper lobe much larger than lower; antennae

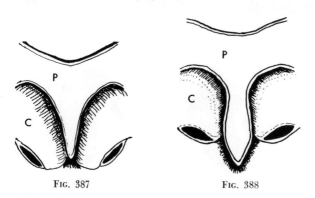

FIG. 387   FIG. 388

Figs. 387–388. Prosternum of *Eustrophinus* (387) and of *Holostrophus* (388). *C,* procoxa; *P,* prosternum.

clavate; metatibiae shorter than femora, with apical spurs pectinate, as long
as tibiae (Fig. 384); metatarsi strongly elongate, nearly as long as metafemora and metatibiae combined.

Orchesia castanea Melsheimer   Plate XLVIII, No. 4, p. 489

Elongate-elliptical, subconvex; dark brown, covered with silky, brown
pubescence; legs slightly paler. Pronotum transverse; disk basally densely
and coarsely punctate, toward apex more finely so, shallowly but distinctly
impressed each side near base. Elytra densely and coarsely punctate, a
shallow sulcus along suture. Length 4–5 mm.

Subfamily MELANDRYINAE

KEY TO TRIBES

1. Procoxal cavities at least narrowly angulate externally (Figs. 389,
   390); pronotum transverse, at least slightly so 2
   Procoxal cavities not at all angulate externally (Fig. 391); pronotum
   at least slightly longer than wide ..................SERROPALPINI   (p. 487)
2. Procoxal cavities with angulation narrow, often closed (Fig. 390);
   eyes deeply emarginate anteriorly ....HYPULINI   (p. 487)
   Procoxal cavities with angulation broad, open (Fig. 389); eyes not or
   obsoletely emarginate anteriorly ....MELANDRYINI   (p. 490)

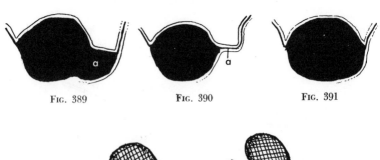

FIG. 389   FIG. 390   FIG. 391

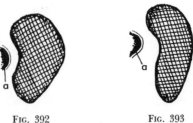

FIG. 392   FIG. 393

Figs. 389–391. Procoxal cavity of *Melandrya* (389), of *Mystaxus* (390),
and of *Dircaea* (391). *a*, lateral angulation.

Figs. 392–393. Eye of *Symphora* (392) and of *Mystaxus* (393). *a*, antennal socket.

Tribe SERROPALPINI

Genus *DIRCAEA* Fabricius

Elongate-elliptical, moderately small; head retracted into prothorax; pronotum at base as wide as elytra, margined at base and sides; meso- and metatibiae obliquely truncate at apex; procoxal cavities without an external fissure; tarsi with next to last segment emarginate, more or less lobed beneath; male with protarsi dilated.

Dircaea quadrimaculata (Say)   Plate XLVII, No. 11, p. 477
Elongate-elliptical, convex; dark brown to piceous, slightly shining; pronotum with apex, and elytra each with a more or less H-shaped macula on basal third and an irregularly shaped one on apical third, yellowish. Pronotum transverse, finely and densely punctate and with a very feeble impression each side at base. Elytra coarsely, rather sparsely punctate, more finely so toward apex. Length 7–9 mm.

Tribe HYPULINI

KEY TO GENERA

Eyes broadly ovate, except for anterior emargination (Fig. 392) ......
....I. *Symphora* (p. 487)
Eyes vertical, nearly straight (Fig. 393) ....II. *Mystaxus* (p. 490)

Genus I. *SYMPHORA* LeConte

Small, elongate, convex; antennae filiform; head not constricted posteriorly; eyes oval in outline; maxillary palpi with last segment hatchet-shaped; pronotum somewhat narrower at base than base of elytra, base margined; procoxal cavities with external fissure closed (Fig. 391); tarsi with next to last segment emarginate, more or less bilobed beneath; male with protarsi dilated.

Symphora flavicollis (Haldeman)   Plate XLVIII, No. 7, p. 489
Elongate, convex; piceous, shining; head, pronotum, and legs brownish yellow. Pronotum transverse, sides broadly arcuate, apex truncate; disk sparsely and coarsely punctate, broadly impressed near posterior angles. Elytra broader at base than pronotum, sparsely and coarsely punctate. Length 3–3.5 mm.
The adults are found beneath bark and on foliage.

PLATE XLVIII

Family MELANDRYIDAE II

1. *Eustrophinus bicolor* (Fabricius) (p. 484) — Deep brown to black; antennae and legs bright reddish brown, the former black medially; 4.5–6 mm.

2. *Eustrophus tomentosus* Say (p. 484) — Reddish brown; 4–5 mm.

3. *Holostrophus bifasciatus* (Say) (p. 485) — Bright reddish brown; elytra nearly black, with dull-orangeish markings; 4–5.5 mm.

4. *Orchesia castanea* Melsheimer (p. 486) — Reddish brown; 4–5 mm.

5. *Melandrya striata* Say (p. 490) — Black, shining; 8–15 mm.

6. *Mystaxus simulator* Newman (p. 490) — Dull yellowish, with blackish markings; 5–7 mm.

7. *Symphora flavicollis* (Haldeman) (p. 487) — Brownish yellow; elytra blackish; 3–3.5 mm.

8. *Emmesa labiata* (Say) (p. 491) — Blackish, shining; 9–11 mm.

9. *Pisenus humeralis* (Kirby) (p. 482) — Dark brown to black, shining; legs and antennae brown; 3–4 mm.

10. *Canifa pallipes* (Melsheimer) (p. 491) — Blackish; legs yellowish brown; 2–2.5 mm.

Family LYCTIDAE

11. *Lyctus opaculus* LeConte (p. 503) — Dark yellowish brown to blackish, shining; 3.5–5 mm.

12. *L. striatus* Melsheimer (p. 504) — Dark brown, somewhat shining; 3.5–5 mm.

13. *L. planicollis* LeConte (p. 504) — Black; 4–6 mm.

MM 0 10 20 30 40 50 60 70

PLATE XLVIII

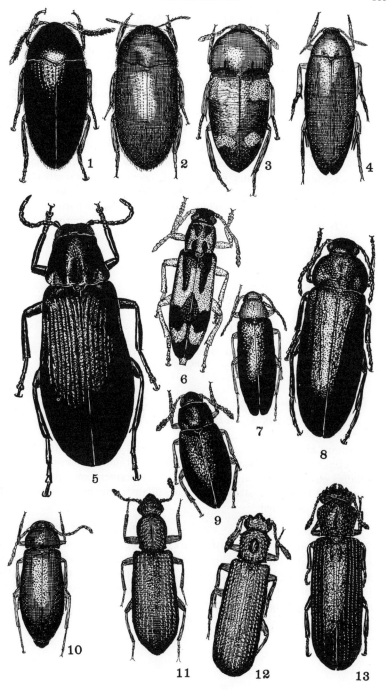

Genus II. *MYSTAXUS* Kugelann

Small, elongate-oval, convex; antennae filiform; head not constricted posteriorly; eyes elongate, vertical, nearly parallel-sided; last segment of maxillary palpi long, curved, and flat, the preceding segments rather serrate; pronotum feebly transverse, somewhat narrower at base than elytra; procoxal cavities with external fissure closed; metatarsi with third segment emarginate, shorter than second.

Mystaxus simulator Newman   Plate XLVIII, No. 6, p. 489
    Elongate-oval, slender, convex; brownish yellow, feebly shining, pubescent; head black; pronotum with a black fascia near apex; elytra each with a long, comma-shaped macula at base, a diagonal band behind middle, and apex black. Pronotum feebly transverse; sides arcuate, narrowed anteriorly; posterior angles acute; disk with a long, deep impression each side at base, densely, moderately punctate. Elytra densely, rather coarsely punctate. Length 5–7 mm.

Tribe MELANDRYINI

KEY TO GENERA

Base of pronotum emarginate at middle ....I. *Melandrya* (p. 490)
Base of pronotum with a broad lobe; elytra punctate, not striate
  ....II. *Emmesa* (p. 491)

Genus I. *MELANDRYA* Fabricius

Small or moderate-sized, elongate-ovate; head not constricted behind eyes; eyes obsoletely emarginate anteriorly; pronotal base emarginate medially; elytra striate; tarsi with next to last segment emarginate, more or less lobed beneath; males with protarsi dilated; antennae robust, apical segments not thickened.

Melandrya striata Say   Plate XLVIII, No. 5, p. 489
    Elongate-ovate, rather robust; black, shining. Pronotum finely and sparsely punctate, with three broad, rather deep sulci on basal half; apex narrower than base but only slightly wider than the head. Elytra gradually widened posteriorly, deeply striate; intervals convex, irregularly, rather finely punctate. Length 8–15 mm.

Genus II. *EMMESA* Newman

Moderately small, elongate-oblong; head not constricted behind eyes; eyes not emarginate anteriorly; pronotum with base broadly lobed medially; elytra not striate; tarsi with next to last segment emarginate, more or less lobed beneath; male with protarsi dilated; antennae robust, apical segments gradually thickened.

Emmesa labiata (Say)   Plate XLVIII, No. 8, p. 489
Elongate-oblong; black, shining. Pronotum slightly transverse; sides gradually arcuate from base to apex; disk finely and densely punctate, deeply, obliquely impressed each side near base. Elytra finely, densely punctate, each with two or three indistinct costae. Length 9–11 mm.
On foliage of trees and shrubs of various types, the adults may frequently be captured.

Subfamily SCRAPTIINAE

Genus *CANIFA* LeConte

Very small, elongate, slender, subdepressed; head constricted behind eyes into a short neck; pronotum transverse, posterior angles rectangular; elytra not striate; tarsi with next to last segment emarginate, more or less lobed beneath; metatarsi with first segment nearly twice as long as remaining segments together; male with protarsi dilated; antennae feebly serrate, apical segments not expanded.

Canifa pallipes (Melsheimer)   Plate XLVIII, No. 10, p. 489
Elongate, oblong-ovate, slender, subdepressed; dark brown to fuscous, covered with fine, yellowish pubescence; legs brownish yellow. Pronotum strongly transverse, about twice as wide as long; base and apex truncate; disk finely and densely granulate-punctate, broadly and shallowly impressed each side near base. Elytra rather finely and moderately densely punctate. Length 2–2.5 mm.
This form occurs on the foliage of shrubs and low trees.

Family PTINIDAE

The Spider Beetles; Drugstore Beetles

Very small beetles; head small, retractile into prothorax; maxillae exposed at base; palpi short, four-segmented; antennae inserted upon front, more or less approximate basally (Fig. 394), rather long and moderately robust, filiform or feebly serrate, eleven-segmented; pronotum not margined laterally, disk frequently swollen or tuberculate; elytra often strongly swollen and partially enclosing the abdomen, giving the insects the hunched appearance of certain spiders; hind wings often absent; legs long, tibiae with two small or minute spurs at apex, tarsal claws simple, strongly divergent (Fig. 26B); abdomen with five sternites.

For the most part, these insects live in dried animal substances. Occasionally, however, some of the species are harmful to articles made from silk, and others attack cereal products and dried herbs formerly sold in drugstores. Still others are, like the dermestids, pests in insect collections.

KEY TO GENERA

1. Elytra polished, impunctate, widely overlapping abdomen at sides, so that the exposed surface of body beneath is only about one-half to one-third as wide as elytra 2
   Elytra punctate and pubescent, less strongly overlapping abdomen at sides, so that the body beneath is nearly as wide as elytra ....III. *Ptinus* (p. 494)
2. Head and pronotum smooth, shining, glabrous ....I. *Gibbium* (p. 492)
   Head and pronotum rugose, opaque, densely covered with small scales and short pubescence ....II. *Mezium* (p. 493)

Genus I. *GIBBIUM* Scopoli

Small, ovate, strongly convex beetles; elytra greatly swollen; entire body glabrous above; eyes small, placed toward front; elytra concealing much of the abdomen, impunctate, polished; hind wings absent; abdomen with only four visible sternites; legs rather long, slender, metatrochanter elongate, two-thirds as long as metafemur (Fig. 395); antennae as long as body, segments cylindrical.

Gibbium psylloides (Czenpinski)   The Humpback Beetle
                                                     Plate XLIV, No. 6, p. 453
   Strongly convex, ovate; dark reddish brown, shining; upper surface entirely glabrous, body beneath, legs, and antennae with dense, short, pale-yellowish hairs. Head above sparsely, finely punctate. Pronotum strongly transverse; sides straight, tapering apically; disk with a few fine punctures. Elytra strongly swollen, ovate, impunctate, fused along suture. Length 2–3.5 mm.
   This cosmopolitan species occurs the year round in houses, hotels, mills, latrines, and granaries, where it feeds on grain and vegetable products in general, including bread, cake, yeast, cotton and other seeds, paprika, cayenne pepper and other spices, hay, woolen material, leather, and even rubber mats. The adult is flightless and walks with a slow, characteristic gait.

Genus II. *MEZIUM* Curtis

   Small, ovate, strongly convex forms; elytra strongly swollen, nearly hemispherical; head and pronotum densely pubescent and scaled; eyes small, placed toward sides of head; elytra concealing much of abdomen, impunctate, glabrous; hind wings absent; abdomen with five visible sternites; legs rather long, moderately slender, metatrochanter not elongate, not more than one-third as long as metafemur; antennae robust, not quite as long as body, segments flattened, serrate.

Mezium affine Boieldieu   Plate XLIV, No. 9, p. 453
   Strongly convex, ovate, robust; dark reddish brown, shining; entire body (including legs and antennae) except elytra densely covered with

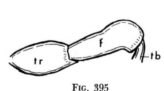

Fig. 394

Fig. 395

Fig. 394. Head of *Mezium*, viewed from in front.
Fig. 395. Upper segments of hind leg in *Gibbium*. *f*, femur; *tb*, tibia; *tr*, the greatly elongated trochanter.

shining, pale-yellowish, matted pubescence and scales. Pronotum transverse; sides straight, slightly divergent to apex; disk each side of middle with a broad, linear elevation, these parallel to each other, a shorter, lower, similar elevation laterally. Elytra feebly elongate, strongly swollen, nearly hemispherical, fused along suture. Length 3–4 mm.

Although wingless, this originally European species is now found throughout the world, having been dispersed by commercial activities. It is known to occur in seeds, grains, and cereals and in various types of decaying animal and vegetable refuse. Occasionally it also becomes a pest in insect and plant collections and attacks silk products.

Genus III. *PTINUS* Linné

Very small; male elongate-oblong, convex, elytra parallel-sided, female broadly ovate, robust, with swollen elytra; head partly concealed by pronotum; eyes large, rounded in male, smaller and ovate in female; pronotum strongly constricted posteriorly; scutellum distinct; elytra pubescent; abdomen with five sternites, distinctly separated by sutures; metatrochanters not elongate, not more than one-fourth as long as metafemora; antennae filiform, first segment robust, second smallest, third to eleventh elongate, subequal.

Ptinus fur (Linné)   The White-marked Spider Beetle
                                                Plate XLIV, Nos. 7, 8, p. 453

Elongate-oblong in male, broadly ovate in female; dull reddish yellow or pale brown, female darker brown; pronotum with a tuft of yellowish hairs each side of middle; elytra with irregular patches of whitish scales behind humeri and forming a fascia near apex, more conspicuous in female. Pronotum a little narrower than head, nearly as wide as long, sides parallel anteriorly, strongly constricted toward base; disk feebly tuberculate and with a distinct median impressed line. Elytra elongate, parallel, with prominent humeri in male, ovate and without humeri in female; striae slightly impressed, coarsely punctate. Length 2.5–4.5 mm.

Like the preceding two forms, this is found throughout the world, attacking a wide variety of animal and vegetable products. It has been reported as feeding on flour, cacao, seeds, meal, and other grain products as well as on herbarium specimens, stuffed birds, and insect collections.

Family ANOBIIDAE

The Drugstore and Deathwatch Beetles

Small, subcylindrical, broadly oval to nearly globular; head deflexed, nearly or completely invisible from above; antennae distant at base, inserted just in front of the prominent eyes; antennae nine- to eleven-segmented, filiform, serrate or pectinate; pronotum usually margined laterally; five abdominal segments; pro- and mesocoxae cylindrical or subglobose, metacoxae transverse, usually sulcate to receive the femora.

These small beetles live in vegetable matter in the first stages of decay, in dried materials such as tobacco, cayenne pepper, etc., and in woodwork, furniture, and dead trees. Their common name, "deathwatch beetles," stems from the ticking noise they make as they bore through wood, because superstitious people believe the sound foretells a death.

KEY TO GENERA

1. Protibiae not dentate on outer apical angle; form and sculpture similar in both sexes; antennae of male never flabellate (at most pectinate) (see Fig. 21) 2
   Protibiae with outer margin prolonged at apex into a horizontal tooth (Fig. 396); form and sculpture varying in sexes; antennae of male flabellate (Fig. 22) ....VI. *Ptilinus* (p. 499)
2. Head at rest received upon the undersurface of prothorax (Fig. 397) 3
   Head at rest very strongly deflexed and retracted, mandibles nearly or quite attaining the metasternum (Fig. 398) .....V. *Lasioderma* (p. 498)
3. Prothorax not excavated beneath, head free (Fig. 397)..I. *Xestobium* (p. 496)
   Prothorax excavated beneath for reception of head 4
4. Procoxae contiguous or narrowly separated; prosternal process usually ending in a sharp point (Fig. 399) ....II. *Sitodrepa* (p. 496)
   Procoxae distinctly or even widely separated; prosternal process with parallel sides (Fig. 400) 5
5. Antennae not serrate; segments nine to eleven each longer than the preceding ....III. *Hadrobregmus* (p. 498)
   Antennae serrate (Fig. 20); segments nine to eleven not distinctly longer than those preceding ....IV. *Trypopitys* (p. 498)

Genus I. *XESTOBIUM* Motschulsky

Small, oblong, moderately robust; antennae eleven-segmented, segments nine to eleven each longer than those preceding; head free, moderately deflexed; prothorax not excavated beneath for reception of head; elytra parallel-sided, not striate; procoxae moderately prominent, narrowly but distinctly separated; legs not received in cavities; tarsi broad, densely pubescent beneath.

Xestobium rufovillosum (DeGeer)   Plate XLV, No. 10, p. 459

Elongate-oblong, robust, parallel, convex; dark brown, with scattered areas of dull-black and yellow hairs. Antennae longer than head and pronotum; second segment much narrower and half as long as first, third twice as long as wide, third to eighth subequal in length and gradually wider. Pronotum distinctly transverse, sides broadly flattened and feebly reflexed; anterior and posterior angles rounded; surface of pronotum as well as elytra densely granulate-punctate. Length 6–7.5 mm.

This species occurs particularly on pine.

Genus II. *SITODREPA* Thomson

Small, oblong, moderately robust; head received in excavation on underside of prothorax; last segment of maxillary palpi parallel and obliquely truncate, last segment of labial palpi broadly triangular; mandibles not attaining mesosternum; antennae less than half body length, eleven-segmented, first segment elongate, robust, third to eighth small, ninth equal to the five preceding combined, tenth and eleventh each equal to ninth; procoxae separated by a triangular intercoxal process (Fig. 399); mesocoxae distinctly separated; prosternal process acuminate apically; elytra striate.

Sitodrepa panicea (Linné)   Plate XLV, No. 8, p. 459

Oblong, moderately robust, convex; reddish brown, clothed with long, rather stiff, yellowish pubescence. Pronotum as wide as elytra, narrowed apically; side margins anteriorly finely serrate; anterior angles distinctly rounded, posterior ones very broadly rounded; disk sparsely granulate. Elytral striae fine, punctate; intervals with a single row of punctures, each of which bears a semierect hair. Length 2.5–3.5 mm.

A very cosmopolitan species, it is found in all kinds of dried vegetable materials, in drug and grocery stores, and in homes. It has also been known to be injurious to paper items, such as books and manuscripts.

Fig. 396

Fig. 397

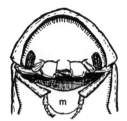

Fig. 398

Fig. 399

Fig. 400

Fig. 396. Apical portion of protibia of *Ptilinus*. *t*, tooth.
Figs. 397–398. Head of *Xestobium* (397) and of *Lasioderma* (398), viewed from beneath. In the former and in allied genera, the undersurface of the head and the prothorax are plainly visible, whereas in *Lasioderma* the upper surface of the head is visible, the latter structure attaining the metasternum (*m*) and concealing the remainder of the thorax.
Figs. 399–400. Prosternum and procoxae of *Sitodrepa* (399) and of *Hadrobregmus* (400).

Genus III. *HADROBREGMUS* Thomson

Small, elongate, subcylindrical; head received in excavation on underside of prothorax; antennae ten-segmented, last three segments elongate, together longer than all those preceding; pro- and mesocoxae widely separated to receive antennae in repose; prosternal process with sides parallel; tibiae not produced on outer angle at apex; metasternum not deeply excavated anteriorly, at most slightly concave; elytra striate.

Hadrobregmus carinatus (Say)   Plate XLV, No. 13, p. 459

Elongate, slender, subcylindrical, strongly convex; reddish brown to piceous. Pronotum nearly equal to elytra in width; sides arcuate, convergent and feebly sinuate apically; posterior angles broadly rounded; disk slightly gibbous, compressed posteriorly, finely granulate-punctate, frequently with a median carina on basal third. Elytral striae strongly and closely punctate. Length 3.5–6.5 mm.

These beetles are usually found in beech and soft-maple logs in moist woods; they also come to light.

Genus IV. *TRYPOPITYS* Redtenbacher

Small, oblong, cylindrical; head deeply retracted into prothorax in repose; eyes nearly covered; antennae eleven-segmented, more or less serrate, last three segments not conspicuously longer than those preceding; pro- and mesocoxae widely separated to receive antennae; metasternum strongly excavated anteriorly; elytra punctate-striate.

Trypopitys sericeus (Say)   Plate XLV, No. 11, p. 459

Oblong, cylindrical, convex; fuscous, sparsely clothed with short, recumbent, brownish-yellow hairs. Pronotum not as wide as elytra at base, about as long as wide; sides parallel, broadly sinuate medially; posterior angles nearly rectangular; disk with a median impressed line and a transverse impression each side on basal third. Elytra with regular rows of close-set, deep, quadrate punctures; intervals feebly convex, about as wide as punctures, finely, densely punctate. Length 5–6.2 mm.

The adults of this species occur beneath bark and on dead branches of wild cherry and oak.

Genus V. *LASIODERMA* Stephens

Very small, elongate-ovate, moderately convex; prothorax excavated beneath for reception of head in repose; head deeply excavated beneath for reception of antennae; antennae also resting against procoxae, eleven-segmented, moderately serrate, apical segments not noticeably elongate; elytra not striate; metasternum short, suddenly sloping anteriorly from side to side (Fig. 398), the declivity limited posteriorly by a transverse raised line across body.

Lasioderma serricorne (Fabricius)   Plate XLV, No. 12, p. 459
Elongate-ovate, moderately convex; dull reddish yellow or brownish red. Head broad, eyes small. Antennae slender, second and third segments shorter than first, third distinctly triangular, fourth to tenth nearly as wide as long, eleventh oval. Pronotum strongly convex; anterior angles acute, posterior ones lacking. Entire upper surface finely, uniformly punctate. Length 2.2–3 mm.

These beetles are mostly found in dried vegetable products, such as tobacco, cayenne pepper, yeast, figs, etc.

Genus VI. *PTILINUS* Geoffroy

Small, cylindrical; prothorax not distinctly excavated beneath to receive head in repose; antennae in male with third segment elongate, cylindrical, with a basal process equal in length, and segments four to ten strongly flabellate (Fig. 22), in female third segment scarcely longer than second, subparallel, fourth to tenth strongly serrate, about twice as wide as long, eleventh oval; tarsi as long as tibiae, first segment as long as next two or three combined; pro- and mesosternum not excavated for reception of antennae; elytra not striate.

Ptilinus ruficornis Say   Plate XLV, No. 9, p. 459
Elongate, cylindrical, convex; black or piceous, subopaque; female dark reddish brown; antennae and legs reddish yellow, femora frequently darker. Branch of fourth segment of male antennae six or seven times the length of segment. Pronotum slightly wider than elytra, widest anterior to base; sides broadly arcuate; posterior angles rounded, anterior ones rectangular; anterior margin rounded, narrowly reflexed medially; surface finely granulate basally, more coarsely so on apical half; median line feebly impressed, terminating at base in a smooth tubercle. Elytra finely scabrous, rather closely and distinctly punctate. Length 3–4.5 mm.

The adults occur on dead branches of oak and maple, the larvae live in the branches.

Family BOSTRICHIDAE

The Branch and Twig Borers

Rather small, robust, cylindrical species, mostly black or dark brown in color; head bent downward, largely concealed from above by front part of pronotum; eyes small; antennae ten-segmented, inserted before eyes on margin of front, last three or four segments forming a distinct club; abdomen with five visible sternites; procoxae prominent, subconical; meso- and metatibiae with distinct spurs, protibiae usually serrate, with a single long spur at apex; tarsi with first segment very short, sometimes nearly lacking (Fig. 403), fifth segment long, with simple claws.

Most of the species of this family attack wood, either living trees or well-seasoned lumber. In the latter case, they in rare instances cause extensive damage to older dwellings and furniture, reducing the wood to a fine powder. Other species are found in woody fungi; one Californian species occasionally damages cables by drilling through the lead sheathing.

KEY TO GENERA

1. Pronotal side margins flattened, reflexed; head covered in part by pronotum ....I. *Endecatomus* (p. 500)
   Pronotum rounded on sides, without distinct margins; head entirely covered by pronotum 2
2. Middle segments of antennae together shorter than first and second, the club much longer than the entire funicle (Fig. 401) ....
   ....II. *Xylobiops* (p. 501)
   Middle segments of antennae together longer than first and second, the club not as long as funicle (Fig. 402) 3
3. Front of head with an elevated margin, at least at sides ....
   ....IV. *Lichenophanes* (p. 502)
   Front not margined ....III. *Amphicerus* (p. 502)

Genus I. *ENDECATOMUS* Mellié

Small, cylindrical, robust; head only partially inclined, largely visible from above (Fig. 484); pronotum distinctly transverse, sides compressed, reflexed; elytra not elongate, each scarcely more than twice as long as wide; protibiae with terminal spur large and hooked (Fig. 403); tarsi with last segment strongly elongate; antennae eleven-segmented, with a loose, three-segmented club.

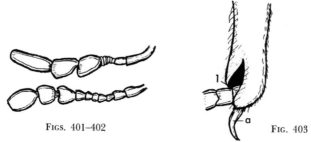

FIG. 403

Figs. 401–402. Antenna of *Xylobiops* (401) and of *Lichenophanes* (402).
Fig. 403. Apex of protibia of *Endecatomus*. *a*, apical spur; *1*, first tarsal
segment.

Endecatomus rugosus (Randall)   Plate XLIV, No. 11, p. 453
Elongate-oblong, robust; dark brown to piceous, irregularly covered with
tufts of ashy, woolly pubescence. Pronotum widest near base; sides arcuate,
tapering gradually to apex; disk densely, rather coarsely granulate. Scutellum small, subquadrate. Elytra at base with two broad, low gibbosities; apical declivity nearly vertical, at its base with a prominent, elongate elevation
which continues forward on disk nearly to middle; disk with small granules
arranged reticularly, covered with hairs. Length 4–4.5 mm.
Usually this form can be collected on woody fungi and beneath bark of
trees; in spring it sometimes comes to sap.

Genus II. *XYLOBIOPS* Casey

Small, cylindrical species; head concealed under pronotum, which is
covered anteriorly with small tubercles; elytra strongly declivous apically,
the declivity bordered by small tubercles as in the Scolytidae; abdomen
with first sternite linearly elevated between metacoxae; antennae ten-
segmented, with five segments between second segment and first segment of
club, each of these intermediate segments smaller than either the first or
second segments of antennae.

Xylobiops basilare (Say)   Plate XLIV, No. 10, p. 453
Elongate-oblong, rather slender, convex; blackish to dark reddish brown;
elytra dull reddish yellow on humeri or entire basal third; antennae, palpi,
and tarsi brownish yellow. Pronotum convex, strongly declivous on anterior
half; sides gradually narrowing apically; all angles rounded; disk densely
punctate, with numerous small tubercles anteriorly. Apical fourth of elytra
strongly sloping, declivity coarsely punctate, margined with three tubercles;
elytral disk rather coarsely, densly punctate, each with three smooth, prominent costae. Length 4–7 mm.

Genus III. *AMPHICERUS* LeConte

Moderately small, oblong, cylindrical beetles; head entirely covered above by pronotum; front not margined, clypeus with anterior angles usually acute; pronotum not margined laterally, usually serrulate along apical margin, anteriorly moderately declivous, the declivity with small tubercles; elytral apical declivity nearly vertical, with a single gibbosity or spine; abdomen with intercoxal piece tabular; antennae with intermediate segments longer than first and second, club segments traversed on each face by two fine, longitudinal sulci; tarsi as long as tibiae, slender, second segment elongate.

Amphicerus hamatus (Fabricius)   The Apple Twig Borer
Plate XLIV, No. 13, p. 453

Elongate, cylindrical, uniformly reddish brown to brownish black; antennae and legs slightly paler. Pronotum subglobose; sides strongly arcuate, each apical angle produced into a short, clawlike horn; disk densely, coarsely punctate on basal half, coarsely tuberculate apically. Elytra at extreme apex abruptly declivous, above each declivity with a single spine or tubercle which curves inward toward suture; disk coarsely, rugosely punctate, without costae. Length 6–11.5 mm.

The larvae of this species occur in diseased or dying wood of all kinds; the adults bore in living twigs of ash, hickory, pecan, apple, pear, grape, cherry, peach, and plum.

Genus IV. *LICHENOPHANES* Lesne

Moderately small, elongate, cylindrical species; head with front bearing an elevated margin, at least laterally; pronotum globose, with hind angles prominent, depressed; apical margin often armed with two curved processes; elytra abruptly declivous at apex, the declivity margined along suture and gibbous or spined at base; antennae eleven-segmented, middle segments short, subglobose, together distinctly longer than first two combined.

Lichenophanes bicornis (Weber)   Plate XLIV, No. 12, p. 453

Elongate-oblong, convex, slender; fuscous to piceous, subopaque, covered with short, pale-yellow pubescence arranged in irregular patches. Pronotum armed at apex with two hooklike processes, apical margin truncate between processes; disk with median line impressed, basally rather finely granulate, apically coarsely so. Elytra with apical declivity coarsely, densely punctate, at base in female with a low, rounded gibbosity, which in the male is prolonged into a long, curved spine; disk rather coarsely, rugosely punctate, each with two feeble costae. Length 7–12 mm.

In old fungi and beneath bark are the usual places to find this species.

Family LYCTIDAE

The Powder-Post Beetles

Small, elongate, slender species; head porrect, not covered by prothorax; antennae eleven-segmented, club two-segmented, inserted on sides of front; pronotum trapezoidal, narrowly margined laterally; procoxae prominent, narrowly separated (Fig. 404), cavity closed posteriorly (Fig. 404); metacoxae widely separated; tarsi with first segment very short, fifth segment elongate; abdomen with five sternites, first much longer than any of the remainder.

Many species are serious pests, the larvae living in the sapwood of hickory, ash, oak, and other timber trees. They attack seasoned timber, preferring a moisture content of 10–28 per cent, and do great damage to older buildings. Other substances attacked include the pith of vines and the dried roots of herbaceous plants.

Genus *LYCTUS* Fabricius

Antennal club with both segments subequal, neither one very elongate; pronotum varying in shape from subquadrate to cordate; elytra punctate, punctures either in rows or confused, pubescence confusedly or seriately arranged; protibiae slender, acutely produced externally; tarsi slender.

KEY TO SPECIES

1. Elytra with a single row of coarse but very shallow punctures between the elevated longitudinal lines ....c. *striatus*
   Elytra with two or more rows of fine, deep punctures between the elevated longitudinal lines 2
2. Pronotum distinctly elongate, one-half again as long as wide, without a median discal impression ....a. *opaculus*
   Pronotum not or scarcely elongate, with a distinct, elongate impression at middle of disk ....b. *planicollis*

a. *Lyctus opaculus* LeConte   The Opaque Powder-Post Beetle
                                Plate XLVIII, No. 11, p. 489
   Elongate-oblong, slender, subconvex; reddish brown to piceous, very sparsely covered with pale-yellowish hairs; head, pronotum, and antennae usually darker than rest of body. Pronotum elongate, one-half again as

503

long as wide, sides nearly straight basally, gradually widened apically and rounded into apical margin; posterior angles distinct; disk very densely, moderately finely punctate, without a median impression. Elytra each with about six feebly elevated, broad, longitudinal lines, between each set of which are two irregular rows of moderately coarse, close-set punctures; entire surface finely alutaceous. Length 3.5–5 mm.

As a rule this species may be taken on the dead limbs of oak or other hardwood trees.

b. *Lyctus planicollis* LeConte   The Flat-necked Powder-Post Beetle
                                       Plate XLVIII, No. 13, p. 489

Elongate-oblong, slender, subconvex; piceous to black, sparsely covered with short, yellowish-white hairs. Pronotum about as long as wide, sides straight, feebly divergent apically, rounded into apical margin; posterior angles prominent; disk coarsely, rather densely punctate, with an elongate impression medially that is not sharply defined. Elytra each with eleven fine, feebly elevated, longitudinal lines bearing hairs; between each set of lines are two regular rows of rather fine, well-spaced punctures. Length 4–6 mm.

This species may be found throughout the year in dwellings but is especially common during the warmer months. It also occurs in dried timber and lumber and in wood products.

c. *Lyctus striatus* Melsheimer   Plate XLVIII, No. 12, p. 489

Elongate-oblong, slender, subconvex; dull reddish brown, sparsely covered with pale-yellowish pubescence. Pronotum feebly longer than wide, sides straight, nearly parallel, apical and basal angles prominent; disk finely, densely, rugosely punctate, medially with an elongate, deep, sharply defined impression. Elytra each with eleven feebly elevated, longitudinal lines bearing hairs; between each pair of lines is a single row of coarse, shallow punctures; entire surface finely, densely alutaceous. Length 3.5–5 mm.

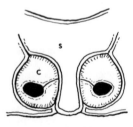

FIG. 404

Fig. 404. Prosternum and procoxae of *Lyctus*. *c*, procoxa; *s*, prosternum.

Family SCARABAEIDAE

The members of this large family are quite varied in color, form, and feeding habits. In color many species are dull brown or black, but there are many which are brilliant metallic blue or green or attractively variegated in contrasting colors. The form of the species ranges from convex to compressed, from broadly oval to elongate-oblong. Frequently males, and occasionally females, of some species are adorned with prominent horns on the head or pronotum. Two distinct subdivisions are apparent because of the feeding habits of the individuals. In one group both adults and larvae feed on dung, carrion, excreta, skin, feathers, and the like. In these beetles the metasternum is very elongate, placing the hind legs far back on the body. The second group feeds on leaves, flowers, and pollen as adults and on roots, juices of plants, and decaying wood as larvae. This latter group includes those of great economic importance. Here the metasternum is short, placing the middle and hind pairs of legs close together.

The family as a whole is characterized by the antennae being seven- to eleven-segmented, usually ten-segmented, with a lamellate, oval club of from three to seven leaves, the leaves capable of being expanded or folded together (Fig. 405), inserted under sides of front before eyes; protibiae broad, toothed or crenate; protarsi variable in number of segments, meso- and metatarsi five-segmented, generally long; usually six ventral abdominal sternites visible (rarely five); pro- and mesocoxae large, transverse, the procoxal cavities large and closed behind; metacoxae flat, transverse; tarsal claws usually equal.

FIG. 405

Fig. 405. Antenna of a scarab with the club composed of three tightly folded, platelike segments, as is typical of the family.

KEY TO SUBFAMILIES

1. At least last two segments of the three-segmented club gray-tomentose, not shining; spiracles in lateral membrane of abdomen; dung beetles 2
   Antennal club glabrous, polished, or sparsely hairy, never tomentose, often with more than three segments; on flowers, roots, leaves, and wood 4
2. Metatibiae with one apical spur; metacoxae usually separated; pygidium exposed ..........................SCARABAEINAE (p. 506)
   Metatibiae with two apical spurs; all coxae approximate; pygidium rarely exposed 3
3. Antennae nine- or ten-segmented ....APHODIINAE (p. 516)
   Antennae eleven-segmented ....GEOTRUPINAE (p. 523)
4. Mandibles bent, expanded and leaflike, often notched, plainly visible from above (Fig. 406) ....DYNASTINAE (p. 548)
   Mandibles not bent or leaflike, only exceptionally visible from above, in which case the claws are usually dissimilar 5
5. Claws, especially on hind legs, almost always of unequal length; metatibiae with two apical spurs ....RUTELINAE (p. 542)
   Claws of equal length, or metatibiae without apical spurs 6
6. Clypeus emarginate laterally before eyes, so that the antennal insertion is visible from above (Fig. 407) 7
   Clypeus not emarginate laterally ............MELOLONTHINAE (p. 525)
7. Epimera of mesothorax visible from above (Fig. 408) .CETONIINAE (p. 551)
   Epimera of mesothorax not visible from above 8
8. Metacoxae contiguous (Fig. 409) ....TRICHIINAE (p. 553)
   Metacoxae widely separately (Fig. 410) ....VALGINAE (p. 558)

Subfamily SCARABAEINAE

KEY TO TRIBES

1. Meso- and metatibiae slender, curved, scarcely enlarged ....
   ....Scarabaeini (p. 506)
   Meso- and metatibiae dilated apically 2
2. Third segment of labial palpi distinct ....Coprini (p. 509)
   Third segment of labial palpi obsolete (Fig. 411) ....Onthophagini (p. 513)

Tribe Scarabaeini

Genus *CANTHON* Hoffmansegg

Small or moderate-sized species; black or bronzed; clypeus with prominent teeth medially; meso- and metatibiae curved and slender, scarcely enlarged apically, the metatibiae usually with a single spur; metacoxae separated; pygidium exposed. The sexes are usually alike.

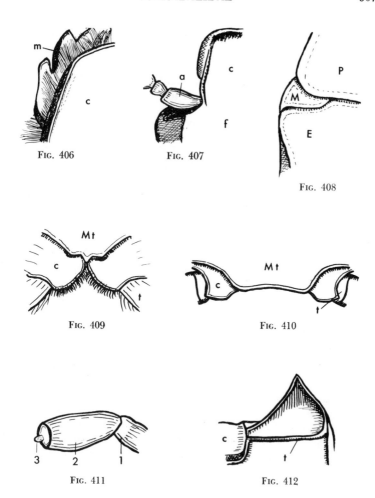

Fig. 406
Fig. 407
Fig. 408
Fig. 409
Fig. 410
Fig. 411
Fig. 412

Fig. 406. Anterior portion of left side of head of *Dynastes*, the mandibles (*m*) produced into lobes visible from above and extending beyond the clypeus (*c*).

Fig. 407. Left side of head of *Euphoria*, the clypeus (*c*) incised laterally, exposing the base of antenna (*a*). *f*, front.

Fig. 408. Portion of left side of upper surface of *Euphoria*. P, pronotum; E, elytron; M, mesepimeron.

Figs. 409–410. Metacoxae of *Osmoderma* (409) and of *Valgus* (410). Mt, metasternum; *c*, metacoxa; *t*, metatrochanter.

Fig. 411. Apical segments of a labial palpus of *Onthophagus*, the segments appropriately numbered.

Fig. 412. Left anterior angle of prothorax of *Canthon viridis* viewed from below. *c*, procoxa; *t*, transverse carina.

These insects may frequently be seen along country roads and paths, working in pairs, rolling balls of dung. The dung balls are at least twice as large as the beetle itself and are shaped by the curved tibiae of the hind legs. Having tumbled their burden to a suitable situation, often at some considerable distance, the beetles bury it in the ground, where the female then oviposits in one side of it.

KEY TO SPECIES

1. Prothorax beneath on sides without an entire, transverse carina 2
   Prothorax beneath on sides with an entire, transverse carina (Fig. 412); size small, 4–6 mm.; clypeus with two teeth; bright bronze or greenish .c. *viridis*
2. Pronotum distinctly granulate; pygidium and last abdominal sternite granulate ....a. *laevis*
   Pronotum finely rugose, without distinct granules; pygidium and last abdominal sternite smooth ....b. *chalcites*

a. *Canthon laevis* (Drury)   Common Tumble Beetle
                                               Plate XLIX, No. 5, p. 511

Robustly ovate, subdepressed; black, not shining, but tinged with cupreous, occasionally dark blue or greenish. Clypeal teeth obtuse, not very prominent. Pronotum rather densely granulate; convex, transverse, broadest at middle, narrowed to base and apex; basal margin broadly rounded. Elytra rather densely granulate, with eight feebly impressed striae. Length 11–19 mm.
This species is found rather commonly in cow dung.

b. *Canthon chalcites* Haldeman   Plate XLIX, No. 7, p. 511
Broadly oval; black, above uniformly, rather feebly bronzed, moderately shining. Clypeus obtusely bidentate. Pronotum transverse, convex; sides broadly rounded, widest at middle, base arcuate; disk not granulate, but finely rugose. Elytra granulate, but less densely so than in *laevis;* striae almost totally obsolete. Protibiae in male more elongate, slender, and curved than in female. Length 13–20 mm.

FIG. 413

Fig. 413. Antennal club of *Phanaeus* viewed from its upper surface, the first segment (*1*) of the club partially enveloping the other two.

c. *Canthon viridis* (Beauvois)   Plate XLIX, No. 1, p. 511
Broadly oval, subrotund; bronzy green, very shining. Clypeus distinctly
bidentate. Pronotum transverse, convex; sides curved; base rounded; disk
very finely punctate. Elytra smooth or nearly so, with obsolete striae. Prothorax beneath at sides with a fine, transverse carina (Fig. 412). Metatibiae
slightly curved. Length 4–5 mm.

Tribe COPRINI

KEY TO GENERA

1. Procoxae strongly transverse, not prominent ....I. *Ateuchus* (p. 509)
   Procoxae short, prominent 2
2. First segment of antennal club not receiving the others (Fig. 405);
   tarsal claws distinct; protarsi present 3
   First segment of antennal club hollowed to receive the others (Fig.
   413); tarsal claws wanting; protarsi absent ....IV. *Phanaeus* (p. 513)
3. Elytra with seven striae each ....II. *Pinotus* (p. 509)
   Elytra with eight or nine striae each ....III. *Copris* (p. 512)

Genus I. *ATEUCHUS* Weber

Small, rotund, convex beetles which resemble a *Hister* in appearance.
Prothorax beneath on sides transversely carinate; procoxae very transverse,
not prominent; meso- and metatibiae strongly dilated apically; third segment of labial palpi distinct.

Ateuchus histeroides Weber   Plate XLIX, No. 2, p. 511
Rounded, convex; above black, bronzed; beneath dark chestnut-brown,
very shining. Clypeus emarginate, occasionally bidentate. Pronotum feebly
sulcate at middle basally, with a small fovea on each side; disk sparsely,
shallowly punctate. Elytra with finely punctate striae. Protibiae of male
with a small, circular disk at apex. Length 6–7 mm.
This species is abundant in warm weather in half-dried cow dung and on
dead fish.

Genus II. *PINOTUS* Erichson

Large, oblong-ovate, robust species; clypeus anteriorly produced, at apex
rounded or subtruncate; labial palpi broad, compressed, three-segmented;
first segment of antennal club not receiving others; elytra with seven striae;
prothorax beneath with sides not carinate; procoxae conical, prominent;

PLATE XLIX

Family SCARABAEIDAE I

1. *Canthon viridis* (Beauvois) (p. 509) — Coppery or greenish black; 4–5 mm.

2. *Ateuchus histeroides* Weber (p. 509) — Black; 6–7 mm.

3. *Onthophagus hecate* Panzer (p. 514) — Dull brassy black; 6.5–9 mm.

4. *O. janus* Panzer (p. 515) — Black, feebly reflexed with bronze, green, or bluish; elytra often with brown maculae near apex; 4–8 mm.

5. *Canthon laevis* (Drury) (p. 508) — Bronzy or greenish black, not shining; 11–19 mm.

6. *Onthophagus orpheus* Panzer (p. 514) — Black, brightly reflexed with blue or bronze; 5–7 mm.

7. *Canthon chalcites* Haldeman (p. 508) — Purplish black, not shining; elytra with striae; 13–20 mm.

8. *Pinotus carolinus* (Linné) (p. 512) — Black; elytra with apical markings dull clay-colored; 20–28 mm.

9. *Copris minutus* (Drury) (p. 512) — Black; 8–11 mm.

10. *C. tullius* Olivier (p. 512) — Black; 13–18 mm.

11. *Onthophagus nuchicornis* (Linné) (p. 515) — Black; elytra ochre-yellow, with blackish maculae; 6.5–8 mm.

12. *O. pennsylvanicus* Harris (p. 515) — Dull brassy black; 3.5–5 mm.

13. *O. tuberculifrons* Harold (p. 515) — Brassy black; elytra brown, markings dull yellow to reddish; 4–5 mm.

14. *Ataenius strigatus* (Say) (p. 522) — Dark brown to blackish, shining; 4.5–5 mm.

MM
0   10   20   30   40   50   60   70

PLATE XLIX

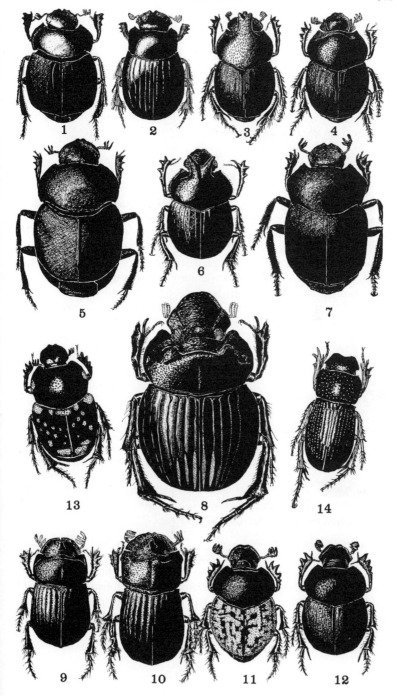

protarsi present, all tarsi with distinct claws; head and pronotum horned or tuberculate in male.

Pinotus carolinus (Linné)   Plate XLIX, No. 8, p. 511

Broadly oval, convex, strongly robust; black, rather shining. Clypeus at most subtruncate apically, finely rugose, not punctate; vertex of male with a short, blunt horn. Pronotum convex, disk broadly elevated in male; entire surface finely, rather sparsely punctate. Elytral striae shallow, feebly punctate, eight in number. Length 20–28 mm.

Genus III. *COPRIS* Geoffroy

Of small or moderate size, oval, robust; labial palpi broad, compressed, three-segmented; first segment of antennal club not receiving the others; clypeus anteriorly semicircular; prothorax beneath with sides transversely carinate; elytra each with eight or nine striae; procoxae short, conical, prominent; protarsi present, all tarsi with distinct claws, without bristle-tipped process between them (onychium); metasternum rectangular; head or pronotum (sometimes both) horned or tuberculate in male.

These beetles, instead of transporting balls of dung for some distance, as in *Canthon,* bury it in burrows nearby.

KEY TO SPECIES

Clypeus densely punctate at sides, nearly smooth at middle; size small, 8–11 mm.
....a. *minutus*
Clypeus evenly and densely punctate over entire surface; larger, 13–18 mm.
....b. *tullius*

a. *Copris minutus* (Drury)   Plate XLIX, No. 9, p. 511

Broadly oval, convex; black, feebly shining. Clypeus on anterior margin acutely and deeply emarginate, surface nearly smooth medially, laterally densely and coarsely punctate; vertex of male with a short, slender horn. Pronotum densely and coarsely punctate, with a broad, rounded impression on each side; sometimes transversely tuberculate near apex in male. Elytra with eight punctate striae. Length 8–11 mm.

b. *Copris tullius* Olivier   Plate XLIX, No. 10, p. 511

Broadly oval, convex, robust; black, feebly shining. Vertex of head in male with a blunt horn, which varies greatly in length, in female tuberculate; clypeus sharply notched medially. Pronotum densely and coarsely punctate; disk trituberculate, medial tubercle deeply emarginate, in female less prominent. Elytra with rather broad striae transversely punctate. Length 13–18 mm.

This species is common in burrows under manure; it also comes to light.

Genus IV. *PHANAEUS* MacLeay

Broadly oval, robust, bright metallic-colored species; antennal club with first segment hollowed, receiving the others; clypeus in male usually with a long horn; metasternum rhomboidal; protarsi lacking in male, slender and feeble in female; tarsal claws absent on all legs.

These beetles dig tubular burrows near or under dung, often to a considerable depth.

KEY TO SPECIES

Male with posterior angles of pronotum directed outward; female with elytral
    intervals bearing elevated lines as well as punctures ....b. *vindex*
Male with posterior angles of pronotum directed inward; female with elytral
    intervals coarsely punctate, without elevated lines ....a. *difformis*

a. *Phanaeus difformis* LeConte   Plate L, No. 3, p. 519
Broadly oval, robust, subconvex; bright metallic green; pronotal disk often wholly or in part cupreous; elytra sometimes deep blue or purplish. Clypeus entire, in male with a long, curved horn, in female tuberculate. Pronotum in male with disk flattened into a horseshoe-shaped area, the posterior angles directed inward and more prominent than in female; female with a transverse tubercle at apical third; surface transversely rugose medially in both sexes, becoming rugosely punctate laterally. Elytral striae distinctly impressed; intervals feebly convex, coarsely, densely punctate, and without elevated lines in both sexes. Length 20–22 mm.

This species is more southerly in its distribution than the following.

b. *Phanaeus vindex* MacLeay   Color Plate D; Plate L, Nos. 1, 2, p. 519
Broadly oval, robust, subconvex; head bronzed, pronotum bright coppery red, elytra metallic green, frequently tinged with bluish. Clypeus entire, in male with a long, curved horn, in female tuberculate. Pronotum in male with disk flattened and posterior angles directed outward and much more prominent than in female; surface in both sexes strongly rugose. Elytra striate; intervals broad, finely and intricately rugose, deeply punctate, and feebly costate. Length 14–22 mm.

Tribe ONTHOPHAGINI

Genus *ONTHOPHAGUS* Latreille

Small, broadly oval, rather robust forms, usually dull brown or black, some with metallic reflexes; third segment of labial palpi obsolete; procoxae large, conical, prominent; tarsal claws distinct, between each pair a long process with setae or onychium; pronotum in some species tuberculate or horned anteriorly, most prominent in the male, where it varies in development even in the same species; clypeus and vertex usually transversely carinate, most distinctly so in female; protibiae in male longer, more slender, and more curved than in female.

The members of this genus burrow into the ground beneath the dung or carrion they feed upon, as do the species of *Copris*.

KEY TO SPECIES

1. Pronotum of male protuberant anteriorly, frequently with a long process which is more or less deeply emarginate at apex; protuberance in female very short but evident 2
   Pronotum of both sexes simply convex or at most with a feeble tubercle either side of middle anteriorly 4
2. Pronotum punctate, sometimes granulate-punctate anteriorly, especially on protuberance 3
   Pronotum with entire surface distinctly granulate ....a. *hecate*
3. Elytral intervals finely punctate, surface smooth, shining ....b. *orpheus*
   Elytral intervals with irregular rows of fine granules; surface minutely alutaceous and subopaque ....c. *janus*
4. Elytra yellow or dull orange, with numerous small, brown maculae ....
   ....e. *nuchicornis*
   Elytra blackish, with or without maculae 5
5. Anterior margin of clypeus strongly notched medially; blackish, elytra with dull-reddish maculae at apex and base ....f. *tuberculifrons*
   Anterior margin of clypeus feebly emarginate or entire; elytra black ....
   ....d. *pennsylvanicus*

a. *Onthophagus hecate* Panzer   Plate XLIX, No. 3, p. 511

Broadly ovate, robust; black with purplish tinge, opaque, with sparse, short, grayish hairs. Head in male moderately reflexed, with a triangular, elevated process anteriorly; clypeus and vertex feebly carinate, carina sometimes wholly absent, in female strongly transversely carinate. Pronotum rather densely granulate; in male with a process on disk which is variable in length, often as long as pronotum itself, emarginate apically and bidentate finely at middle of emargination; in female, protuberance transverse. Elytra finely striate, intervals with two or three rows of fine granules. Length 6.5–9 mm.

This species is abundant in fresh cow dung and is also found in carrion.

b. *Onthophagus orpheus* Panzer   Plate XLIX, No. 6, p. 511

Broadly oval, robust; brilliant bronze or metallic green, highly polished, elytra occasionally bluish. Clypeus in male with margin moderately reflexed and elevated, feebly emarginate medially, carina indistinct; in female distinctly carinate; vertex feebly carinate in male, strongly so in female. Pronotum in male with a long process, deeply emarginate or forked apically, sides divergent; in female, disk with a transverse, low, distinct protuberance; surface rather sparsely punctate. Elytra finely striate, intervals with two series of fine punctures; surface smooth, shining. Length 5–7 mm.

This species is found in fungi and carrion.

c. *Onthophagus janus* Panzer Plate XLIX, No. 4, p. 511
Broadly ovate, robust; varying in color from blackish to bronze or greenish, feebly shining, slightly pubescent. Head in male usually with a feeble transverse carina that terminates on each side in a slender horn. Pronotum with sparse, coarse punctures that become more or less granulate anteriorly; protuberance in male low, transverse, and not as long and prominent as in *hecate*. Elytra finely striate, intervals with two or three series of fine granules; surface minutely alutaceous, subopaque. Length 4–8 mm.

The adults are found especially in decaying fungi.

d. *Onthophagus pennsylvanicus* Harris Plate XLIX, No. 12, p. 511
Broadly oval, robust; black, slightly shining, sparsely pubescent. Clypeus medially entire or feebly truncate, surface densely and coarsely punctate; vertex with a feeble transverse carina. Pronotum finely and rather sparsely punctate, with at most only a feeble discal tubercle in both male and female. Elytra finely striate, intervals each with two rows of punctures. Length 3.5–5 mm.

These beetles are found in carrion, dung, and fungi.

e. *Onthophagus nuchicornis* (Linné) Plate XLIX, No. 11, p. 511
Oblong-oval, robust; deep brown, slightly metallic, not very shining; elytra orange, with numerous uniform brown spots. Clypeus feebly emarginate, margin slightly reflexed; near occiput, in male, with a short tubercle. Pronotum in both sexes anteriorly with a small tubercle either side of middle. Elytra feebly striate; intervals with two rows of fine granules. Length 6.5–8 mm.

f. *Onthophagus tuberculifrons* Harold Plate XLIX, No. 13, p. 511
Oblong-oval; dull black, feebly bronzed; elytra at base and apex with small, dull-red spots, sometimes remainder of surface with minute spots of same color; legs piceous to black; antennae red, club black. Head rounded anteriorly, rather sparsely, strongly punctate, posteriorly with a short, arcuate carinule. Pronotum rather densely punctate, punctures subasperate. Elytra striate, intervals flat, opaque, obsoletely granulate. Length 4–5 mm.

Subfamily APHODIINAE

KEY TO GENERA

Head usually deflexed, often with tubercles; meso- and metatibiae with transverse carinae; outer apical angle of metatibiae not prolonged or spiniform (Fig. 414) ....I. *Aphodius*   (p. 516)

Head not deflexed, never tuberculate; tibiae without transverse carinae, although the mesotibiae sometimes have traces of them; outer apical angle of metatibiae spiniform (Fig. 415) ....II. *Ataenius*   (p. 521)

Genus I. *APHODIUS* Illiger

Small or moderate-sized, oblong-ovate, convex forms; head usually deflexed, often tuberculate; genae small, lying somewhat horizontally; elytra striate with rows of deep punctures, lateral rows abbreviated; protibiae expanded apically, outer margin dentate; meso- and metatibiae with transverse carinae.

KEY TO SPECIES

1. Scutellum long, one-fourth or one-fifth as long as elytral suture; first metatarsal segment simple ....a. *fossor*
   Scutellum small, not more than one-eighth or one-tenth as long as elytral suture; all metatarsal segments simple 2
2. Apex of metatibiae with short, equal spinules; head more or less tuberculate; pronotum with a distinct basal marginal line 3
   Apex of metatibiae with unequal spines; head rarely with tubercles 5
3. Mesosternum not carinate between coxae 4
   Mesosternum distinctly carinate between coxae ....d. *granarius*
4. Pronotum dissimilar between sexes, compressed anteriorly in male; elytra clear red ....b. *fimetarius*
   Pronotum similar in both sexes; elytra black ....c. *ruricola*
5. Elytra not pubescent 7
   Elytra more or less pubescent 6
6. Elytra with an oily appearance, pubescence well marked; color almost entirely fuscous ....i. *femoralis*
   Elytra shining, pubescence feeble and deciduous; color more yellow than fuscous ....j. *prodromus*
7. Mesosternum distinctly carinate between coxae; protibiae punctate on anterior face; first tarsal segment longer than second; first metatarsal segment longer than the next three combined ....e. *stercorosus*
   Mesosternum not carinate; protibiae smooth in front; species in great part piceous, head and pronotum always piceous, sometimes with sides pale; elytra variable in color, either black, dull red, or yellow-maculate 8
8. Clypeus denticulate or angulate each side of middle 9
   Clypeus broadly emarginate at middle, obtusely rounded each side; basal marginal line of pronotum distinct; first segment of metatarsus longer than next two; head black; elytral spots forming stripes ....h. *distinctus*

9. Elytra piceous, alternate intervals with small, red spots; body beneath and
   legs pale yellow .... f. *bicolor*
   Elytra yellow, with black maculae; sides of pronotum somewhat paler. g. *serval*

a. *Aphodius fossor* (Linné)   Plate L, No. 10, p. 519
   Elongate-oblong; piceous, shining. Head margined, emarginate anteriorly;
above with three small tubercles, middle one occasionally acute. Pronotum
rounded anteriorly; disk with somewhat scattered punctures. Scutellum
large, about one-fourth as long as elytral suture. Elytra rounded apically,
with distinct striae; sutural stria subfoveate near scutellum. Length 12–
13 mm.

b. *Aphodius fimetarius* (Linné)   Plate L, No. 4, p. 519
   Oblong-oval, very convex; black, shining; elytra red, occasionally piceous-
clouded; front angles of pronotum reddish yellow. Head sparsely and finely
punctate, male with three tubercles; clypeus broadly and feebly emarginate,
with an indistinct transverse carina. Pronotum coarsely, irregularly punctate, intermingled with finer punctures. Elytral striae crenately punctate,
intervals slightly convex and finely, sparsely punctate. Length 6–8 mm.
   The adults occur throughout the year, especially in or beneath cow dung,
as well as beneath logs on sandy places. They may frequently be taken in
flight in early spring.

c. *Aphodius ruricola* Melsheimer   Plate L, No. 5, p. 519
   Elongate, oblong-oval, frequently slightly widened behind; piceous,
shining; elytral sides and apices usually paler. Head distinctly but finely
trituberculate, sparsely punctate; clypeus broadly emarginate medially, the
angles formed obtuse. Pronotum narrowed from base to apex; posterior
angles distinct, obtuse; sides rounded; disk finely and rather sparsely

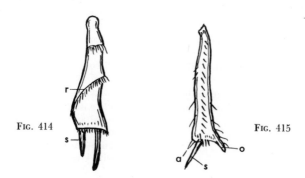

FIG. 414   FIG. 415

Figs. 414–415. Left metatibia of *Aphodius* (414) and of *Ataenius* (415)
            viewed obliquely from beneath. *r*, ridge or carina; *s*,
            spur; *o*, outer spine; *a*, accessory spinule.

PLATE L

Family SCARABAEIDAE II

1. *Phanaeus vindex* MacLeay ♀ (p. 513) ⎫   Head bronzed; pronotum coppery red; elytra green or bluish; 14–22 mm.
2. *P. vindex* MacLeay ♂ (p. 513) ⎭

3. *P. difformis* LeConte (p. 513) — Bright metallic green or bluish; pronotal disk often cupreous; 20–22 mm.

4. *Aphodius fimetarius* (Linné) (p. 517) — Black; elytra reddish, sometimes tinged with blackish; 6–8 mm.

5. *A. ruricola* Melsheimer (p. 517) — Blackish; elytra paler on sides; 4.5–6 mm.

6. *A. granarius* (Linné) (p. 520) — Blackish; legs reddish brown; 4–6 mm.

7. *A. stercorosus* Melsheimer (p. 520) — Brown-yellow; elytra sometimes clouded with black; 3.5–5 mm.

8. *A. bicolor* Say (p. 520) — Black; legs pale yellow; 4.5–6 mm.

9. *A. serval* Say (p. 520) — Black, with pale margins; elytra yellowish, with black spots; 4–5 mm.

10. *A. fossor* (Linné) (p. 517) — Blackish, shining; 12–18 mm.
11. *A. femoralis* Say (p. 521) — Black, pronotal sides and elytra yellowish; 4.5–7 mm.

12. *A. prodromus* (Brahm) (p. 521) — Black; pronotal sides and elytra yellow, spots brown; 5.5–7.5 mm.

13. *A. distinctus* (Müller) (p. 521) — Black; elytra yellowish, with black spots; 4.5–6 mm.

14. *Ataenius abditus* (Haldeman) (p. 522) — Piceous; legs and antennae pale reddish brown; 3.5–4.5 mm.

15. *A. gracilis* (Melsheimer) (p. 522) — Piceous; legs, antennae, and pronotal margins fuscous; 3–4 mm.

16. *Geotrupes balyi* Jekel (p. 523) — Blackish, shining; 14–18 mm.
17. *Ataenius spretulus* (Haldeman) (p. 523) — Piceous; legs and extreme pronotal apex reddish brown; 4.5–5 mm.

18. *Geotrupes blackburnii* (Fabricius) (p. 524) — Purple or blackish, often bronzed with green or purple; 14–20 mm.

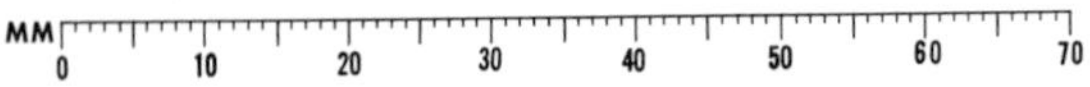

MM | 0   10   20   30   40   50   60   70

PLATE L 519

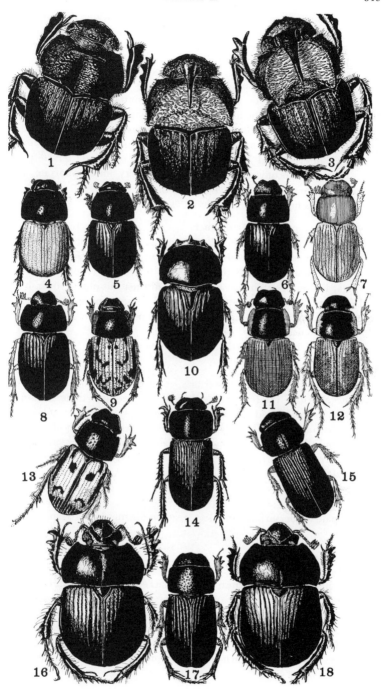

punctate, more coarsely so laterally. Elytra slightly wider than pronotum, deeply striate, striae coarsely and crenately punctate; intervals convex, finely and sparsely punctate. Mesosternum not carinate between coxae. Length 4.5–6 mm.

4. *Aphodius granarius* (Linné) Plate L, No. 6, p. 519

Elongate, oblong-ovate, convex; piceous, shining; legs reddish brown; antennae paler. Head distinctly trituberculate, sparsely punctate medially, more densely and roughly so laterally; clypeus feebly emarginate, sides broadly rounded. Pronotum almost smooth in male, with coarse and fine punctures intermingled in female. Elytral striae finely and serrately punctate; intervals subconvex, only sparsely and very finely punctate. Mesosternum distinctly carinate. Length 4–6 mm.

This species may be taken on fungi as well as in dung.

e. *Aphodius stercorosus* Melsheimer Plate L, No. 7, p. 519

Oblong, convex; brownish yellow, shining; head and pronotum darker, elytra sometimes clouded with black. Head nearly smooth in male, sparsely punctate in female; clypeus truncate, sides rounded. Pronotum with basal marginal line entirely absent; hind angles distinct but obtuse; disk sparsely and finely punctate, sides more coarsely and densely punctate. Elytra finely striate, the striae finely punctate in male, more coarsely so in female; intervals flattened, smooth. Length 3.5–5 mm.

This species is found mostly on cattle dung.

f. *Aphodius bicolor* Say Plate L, No. 8, p. 519

Oblong, slightly broader posteriorly, subdepressed; piceous; elytra piceous, the alternate intervals finely dotted with reddish; undersurface and legs pale yellow. Head densely and coarsely punctate, not tuberculate; clypeus broadly and distinctly emarginate, angles each side of notch distinct. Pronotum transverse, almost twice as wide as long, densely punctate, with intermixed coarse and fine punctures; hind angles rounded; basal marginal line distinct. Elytra rather deeply striate, striae finely, crenately punctate; intervals convex, sparsely, irregularly punctate. Length 4.5–6 mm.

The pale undersurface and legs readily distinguish this species from others.

g. *Aphodius serval* Say Plate L, No. 9, p. 519

Oblong, moderately elongate, convex; head and pronotum piceous, margins paler; elytra brownish yellow, marked with quadrate, black spots in an oblique row from base of fifth interval to suture, a sinuate band at apical three-fourths, and laterally with a broad, black stripe on seventh and ninth intervals; these marks sometimes so enlarged as to entirely cover the elytra. Head coarsely and roughly punctate; clypeus deeply emarginate, the angles each side of notch distinct. Pronotum transverse, nearly twice as wide as long, almost parallel-sided; covered with coarse and fine punctures intermixed. Elytra finely striate, striae fine, impunctate; intervals flat, sparsely, obsoletely punctate. Length 4–5 mm.

This species may be found throughout the year beneath leaves and rubbish.

h. *Aphodius distinctus* (Müller)   Plate L, No. 13, p. 519
Elongate-oblong, convex; black, shining; elytra grayish yellow, marked with blackish, very much as in *serval,* but spots are somewhat larger and often connected as well as more elongated, as follows: one at base of fifth interval, one or two obliquely arranged at middle near suture, an irregular, usually arcuate blotch near apex, and an elongated stripe toward the lateral margin, all markings being variable in exact form. Head sparsely punctate, more roughly so laterally; vertex bluntly trituberculate; clypeus feebly emarginate, the angles obtusely rounded each side of notch. Pronotum very sparsely punctate in male, more densely so in female. Elytra finely striate, the striae crenately punctate; intervals subconvex in male, in female convex, very finely punctate near striae. Length 4.5–6 mm.

i. *Aphodius femoralis* Say   Plate L, No. 11, p. 519
Elongate-oblong, moderately convex; black, shining; pronotal sides dull yellow; elytra pubescent, light yellowish brown, opaque, more yellowish basally and sometimes laterally; antennae and legs reddish brown. Head with vertex feebly trituberculate; in male finely and sparsely punctate, in female more coarsely and densely so; clypeus truncate or feebly and broadly emarginate, angles broadly rounded. Pronotum transverse, basal marginal line distinct; in male finely, sparsely punctate, in female more densely and coarsely so. Elytral striae deep, finely punctate; intervals convex, with a row of distinct punctures on each side near striae. Length 4.5–7 mm.

j. *Aphodius prodromus* (Brahm)   Plate L, No. 12, p. 519
Oblong, convex; black, shining; pronotum with sides pale yellow; elytra pale yellow, with an elongate, brown spot extending from humerus to apex, broad posteriorly and narrow anteriorly. Clypeus broadly and feebly emarginate; head with a slight elevation at middle in male; surface sparsely punctate. Pronotum rounded anteriorly; disk nearly impunctate, sides with a few coarse punctures toward posterior angles. Elytral striae moderately deep, punctate; intervals convex, sparsely, finely punctate in female, densely punctate on each side in male. Length 5.5–7.5 mm.

Genus II. *ATAENIUS* Harold

The species of this genus resemble those of *Aphodius* in general form but are usually smaller and more slender. Head convex, not tuberculate;

522 SCARABAEIDAE

eyes usually concealed; elytra finely striate, striae usually finely, sparsely
punctate, intervals with sides crenulate, the crenulation being independent
of the punctation of the striae; metatibiae simple, straight, the outer apical
angle more prolonged than in *Aphodius* and frequently spined, on underside near spurs a prolongation of the apical margin referred to as the
"accessory spinule" (Fig. 415).

KEY TO SPECIES

1. Clypeus feebly emarginate anteriorly at middle, broadly rounded on each side,
   never dentate or subangulate 2
   Clypeus angulate, or sometimes denticulate, each side of median emargination;
   piceous ....a. *abditus*
2. Metatibiae without accessory spinule ....b. *gracilis*
   Metatibiae with accessory spinule (Fig. 415) 3
3. Clypeus finely punctate, without trace of wrinkles; pronotum sparsely, coarsely
   punctate, denser laterally ....c. *strigatus*
   Clypeus more or less transversely wrinkled; pronotum with coarse and fine
   punctures intermingled ....d. *spretulus*

a. *Ataenius abditus* (Haldeman)   Plate L, No. 14, p. 519

Elongate, parallel, subdepressed; piceous, feebly shining; legs pale
reddish brown; antennae and palpi paler. Clypeus roughly punctate or
nearly granulate, broadly, feebly emarginate, angles of emargination pronounced or subdentate; vertex densely punctate. Pronotum almost twice
as wide as long, narrowed slightly behind, posterior angles rounded; disk
densely, rather coarsely punctate. Elytra finely punctate; striae deep,
punctate; intervals subdepressed, with sides crenate, each with one or two
more or less distinct rows of fine punctures. Mesosternal process longitudinally carinate. Length 3.5–4.5 mm.

b. *Ataenius gracilis* (Melsheimer)   Plate L, No. 15, p. 519

Elongate, slender, parallel, subdepressed; piceous, shining; legs brownish;
tarsi, palpi, antennae, and narrow margin of pronotum paler. Clypeus
emarginate anteriorly, broadly rounded each side, surface smooth; vertex
coarsely punctate. Pronotum transverse, base curved, basal marginal line
distinct; posterior angles broadly rounded; disk coarsely and densely
punctate, distinctly impressed near anterior angles and feebly so laterally
at middle. Elytra as wide as pronotum, deeply and broadly striate, striae
indistinctly punctate; intervals convex, each with a row of slightly elongate
elevations on the sides. Mesosternal process strongly longitudinally carinate
between the coxae. Length 3–4 mm.

c. *Ataenius strigatus* (Say)   Plate XLIX, No. 14, p. 511

Elongate, slender, parallel, subdepressed; black; legs and antennae paler.
Clypeus anteriorly emarginate, broadly rounded each side, surface finely
punctate, coarser basally, without a trace of wrinkles; occiput coarsely
punctate. Pronotum transverse; posterior angles obtusely rounded; disk

coarsely, sparsely punctate, punctures denser laterally. Elytra deeply striate, striae punctate; intervals feebly convex, impunctate. Mesosternal process strongly longitudinally carinate between coxae. Length 4.5–5 mm.

d. *Ataenius spretulus* (Haldeman) Plate L, No. 17, p. 519

Elongate-oblong, parallel, subconvex; piceous, shining; legs, clypeus at sides, and pronotum with narrow apical margin reddish brown. Clypeus slightly impressed anteriorly, sides broadly rounded, surface with numerous fine wrinkles; vertex coarsely and sparsely punctate basally, more finely so anteriorly. Pronotum transverse, sides feebly curved; base arcuate, marginal line deep; posterior angles rounded; disk with coarse and fine punctures intermingled. Elytra as broad as pronotum, with punctate striae; intervals crenulate on inner side, very finely punctate; humeri dentate. Mesosternal process longitudinally carinate. Length 4.5–5 mm.

The adults of this species are active on the first warm days of spring. They may be found in and beneath dry cow dung, in fungi, and are attracted to lights.

Subfamily GEOTRUPINAE

Genus *GEOTRUPES* Latreille

This genus varies in color from black to dark metallic green or purple. Of moderate size, broadly ovate, robust, convex; antennae eleven-segmented, club of three segments, plates all of equal width; clypeus rounded anteriorly, sometimes feebly tubercled in male and female; elytra at base equal in width to pronotum, striate, frequently punctate.

The adults occur on excrement, especially in open, somewhat moist places. They frequently burrow into the ground beneath to a considerable depth.

KEY TO SPECIES

1. Striae of elytra impunctate; head without tubercles; basal marginal line of pronotum absent ....d. *semiopacus*
   Striae of elytra punctate; head with tubercle medially; basal marginal line of pronotum present 2
2. Median impressed line of pronotum distinct from base to apex ......a. *balyi*
   Median impressed line present only on basal half, indistinct 3
3. First metatarsal segment equal to next three combined ....b. *blackburnii*
   First metatarsal segment shorter than the next three combined ..c. *splendidus*

a. *Geotrupes balyi* Jekel Plate L, No. 16, p. 519

Broadly oval, robust; piceous or black, shining. Clypeus rounded anteriorly, very roughly punctate, distinctly tuberculate behind middle; front coarsely punctate. Pronotum transverse; disk sparsely punctate; median impressed line distinct, punctate, extending from base almost to apex; sides densely and coarsely punctate. Elytral striae distinct, punctate. Length 14–18 mm.

b. *Geotrupes blackburnii* (Fabricius)   Plate L, No. 18, p. 519

Broadly oval, robust; purple, piceous, or black, frequently bronzed with green or purple, in whole or in part. Clypeus rounded anteriorly, roughly punctate, distinctly tuberculate behind middle. Pronotum transverse, sides coarsely, rather sparsely punctate; disk nearly free of punctures; median impressed line confined to basal half, feeble. Elytra distinctly striate, impunctate or nearly so. Length 14–20 mm.

c. *Geotrupes splendidus* (Fabricius)   Plate LI, No. 2, p. 527

Broadly oval, robust; color variable, brilliant metallic green, purple, or bronze. Clypeus rounded anteriorly; surface roughly and coarsely punctate; median tubercle distinct. Pronotum transverse; disk finely and sparsely punctate, more coarsely and densely so on sides. Elytral striae deep, with well-defined punctures; intervals smooth, flat, or subconvex. Mesotarsi of male short and robust. Length 12–18 mm.

This species may be found throughout the year beneath dung and carrion.

d. *Geotrupes semiopacus* Jekel   Plate LI, No. 1, p. 527

Broadly oval, robust; purple, piceous, or black, frequently bronzed with green or purple, in whole or in part. Clypeus rounded anteriorly, roughly punctate, distinctly tuberculate behind middle. Pronotum transverse, sides coarsely, rather sparsely punctate; disk nearly free of punctures; median impressed line on basal half very feeble. Elytral striae distinct, impunctate or nearly so, except at sides. Length 14–20 mm.

Fig. 416

Fig. 417

Figs. 416–417. Mesotarsal claws of *Hoplia* (416) and of *Phyllophaga* (417). *o*, onychium.

Subfamily MELOLONTHINAE

KEY TO TRIBES

1. Tibiae with one spur or none; pro- and mesotarsal claws chelate, unequal (Fig. 416), onychium not present .... Hopliini (p. 541)
   Meso- and metatibiae with two spurs; tarsal claws equal, sometimes chelate; onychium present (Fig. 417) 2
2. Anterior coxae conical, prominent 3
   Anterior coxae transverse, not prominent, or prominent internally .... Melolonthini (p. 529)
3. Labrum connate; claws not chelate .... Sericini (p. 525)
   Labrum not connate; claws chelate .... Macrodactylini (p. 539)

Tribe Sericini

Genus *SERICA* MacLeay

Rather small, oblong, robust; brown, often covered with a silky, iridescent pubescence; body widened posteriorly; labrum indistinct, connate with the undersurface of clypeus; elytra shallowly striate; metacoxae flat, dilated, as wide as any two sternites together; metafemora, and especially the metatibiae, slender.

In habit and in general appearance, the members of this genus resemble small May beetles (*Phyllophaga*), from which they can most readily be distinguished by the possession of regularly spaced elytral striae. By day they may be found beneath logs and stones in shady places, where they conceal themselves until evening. They are leaf-feeders and come readily to light.

KEY TO SPECIES

1. Clypeus with an acute notch each side; body smooth, shining, not iridescent .. 2
   Clypeus without notch on sides; body usually with silky pubescence and more or less iridescent 3
2. Notch of clypeus deep, distinct, the margin in front of notch strongly reflexed; surface of clypeus and front coarsely, confluently punctate, wrinkled between punctures .... a. *vespertina*
   Notch of clypeus small and indistinct, margin less strongly reflexed; surface finely punctate, without wrinkles or rugosities .... b. *intermixta*
3. Head and pronotum with numerous short, erect, yellowish hairs ....c. *iricolor*
   Head and pronotum not distinctly hairy 4
4. Size larger, 8 mm. long or longer; upper surface purplish brown or piceous, distinctly iridescent; clypeus more sparsely and finely punctate .....d. *sericea*
   Size smaller, not more than 6 mm. long; head and pronotum black or piceous, elytra usually reddish brown .... e. *trociformis*

PLATE LI
Family SCARABAEIDAE III

1. *Geotrupes semiopacus* Jekel (p. 524)

    Black; elytra with a green, bronze, or purple sheen; 14–20 mm.

2. *G. splendidus* (Fabricius) (p. 524)

    Black, shining; elytra with a green, bronze, or purple sheen; 12–18 mm.

3. *Serica iricolor* (Say) (p. 528)

    Dark brown to black, not shining; elytra reflexed with many colors, as in a film of oil; 6–7.5 mm.

4. *S. vespertina* (Gyllenhal) (p. 528)

    Dull yellowish to yellowish brown; 8–11 mm.

5. *S. sericea* (Illiger) (p. 528)

    Dull blackish; elytra with an oily appearance; 8–10 mm.

6. *S. trociformis* Burmeister (p. 528)

    Blackish; elytra dull orange-brown; legs reddish brown; 5–6.5 mm.

7. *Diplotaxis sordida* (Say) (p. 529)

    Dark brown to blackish, covered with dull-yellowish pubescence; pronotum often encrusted with dirt; 10–12 mm.

8. *D. atlantis* Fall (p. 529)

    Dark brown to blackish, shining; 11–12.5 mm.

9. *D. liberta* (Germar) (p. 530)

    Reddish brown to blackish, shining; 12–13 mm.

10. *Serica intermixta* Blatchley (p. 528)

    Dull brownish yellow to black; 7.5–9.5 mm.

11. *Dichelonyx elongata* (Fabricius) (p. 539)

    Dark brown; elytra with a green reflex; 8–10 mm.

12. *D. subvittata* LeConte (p. 539)

    Orange-brown; pronotum and elytra marked with black; 10–11.5 mm.

13. *D. albicollis* Burmeister (p. 540)

    Reddish brown; elytra with a green reflex; 11–13 mm.

14. *Diplotaxis frondicola* (Say) (p. 530)

    Chestnut-brown; 7–8 mm.

MM 0 10 20 30 40 50 60 70

PLATE LI 527

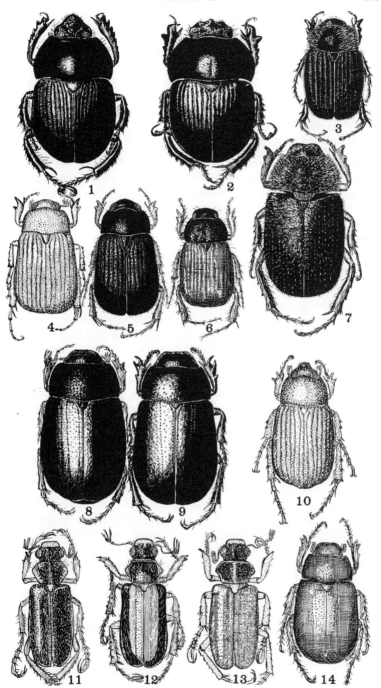

a. *Serica vespertina* (Gyllenhal)   Plate LI, No. 4, p. 527
    Oblong-ovate, robust; subconvex; color ranging from light to dark brown,
glabrous, shining. Clypeus short, truncate; surface coarsely, densely, rugosely
punctate; margin distinctly reflexed, deeply notched just behind anterior
angles. Pronotum strongly transverse; sides feebly arcuate, rather densely
and roughly punctate, disk more finely and sparsely so; posterior angles
rectangular. Elytra with broad, fairly distinct striae, each stria with two
rows of coarse, confluent punctures; intervals subdepressed, sparsely punctate. Length 8–11 mm.

b. *Serica intermixta* Blatchley   Plate LI, No. 10, p. 527
    Oblong, convex; smooth, shining; dull brownish yellow, sometimes brown
or black. Clypeus long, notch small, indistinct; surface finely, sparsely
punctate; front more sparsely, coarsely punctate. Pronotum convex, sides
feebly arcuate; disk finely, sparsely, evenly punctate. Elytral striae deep,
each with two or three irregular rows of rounded, more or less confluent
punctures; intervals feebly convex, sparsely punctate, punctures as large as
those of striae. Length 7.5–9.5 mm.
    These beetles may be found beneath bark of decayed logs.

c. *Serica iricolor* (Say)   Plate LI, No. 3, p. 527
    Oblong-ovate, robust, convex; piceous or black, feebly shining, iridescent;
pronotum densely pubescent. Clypeus short, broadly and distinctly emarginate anteriorly, margin only feebly reflexed, not notched behind anterior
angles; front rather densely pubescent. Pronotum transverse, sides straight
to middle, then curved to apex; entire surface roughly punctate and densely
covered with long, erect pubescence. Elytral striae broad, shallow, coarsely,
biseriately punctate; intervals subconvex, narrow; surface thinly covered
with rather long, erect hairs. Length 6–7.5 mm.

d. *Serica sericea* (Illiger)   Plate LI, No. 5, p. 527
    Oblong, convex, robust, female widened behind middle; purplish brown,
feebly shining, strongly iridescent. Clypeus short, rugosely punctate, feebly
emarginate anteriorly, margin distinctly reflexed, not notched; surface
densely and roughly punctate; vertex finely, sparsely punctate. Pronotum
transverse, sides feebly curved at base, more distinctly so at apex; disk
finely and shallowly punctate. Elytra deeply striate in male, more shallowly
so in female, in both sexes striae finely, irregularly punctate; intervals
convex in male, subconvex in female, sparsely punctate in both sexes.
Length 8–10 mm.
    The adults are often taken at lights and beneath various kinds of debris.

e. *Serica trociformis* Burmeister   Plate LI, No. 6, p. 527
    Broadly oblong-ovate, convex, smooth; dark brown to black, feebly shin-
ing; elytra reddish brown, lateral margins piceous, or sometimes entire
elytra piceous. Clypeus feebly emarginate anteriorly, margin reflexed, not

notched; densely and coarsely punctate. Pronotum transverse, convex; sides feebly rounded, apex much narrower than base; disk coarsely punctate, more densely so at base, a median impressed line on basal half. Elytra feebly striate, striae and intervals sparsely punctate, the latter subconvex. Length 5–6.5 mm.

Tribe MELOLONTHINI

KEY TO GENERA

Procoxae prominent, conical; claws cleft or toothed ......I. *Diplotaxis*   (p. 529)
Procoxae not prominent, transverse; claws with a single tooth beneath
....II. *Phyllophaga*   (p. 530)

Genus I. *DIPLOTAXIS* Kirby

Rather small or moderate-sized species, elongate-oblong, robust, convex; antennae ten-segmented, laminae of club rather short; five abdominal sternites visible; procoxae prominent, conical; claws cleft or dentate; elytra not striate, either with scattered punctures, seriately punctate, or feebly costate, wider intervals irregularly punctate; body not wider behind middle.

The species of this genus occur beneath stones, logs, and bark, especially on dry hillsides.

KEY TO SPECIES

1. Body pubescent; elytra without distinct rows of punctures ....a. *sordida*
   Body not pubescent above; elytra with some or all of punctures arranged in rows 2
2. Pronotum with impression at basal angles distinct. ....c. *liberta*
   Pronotum with impression at basal angles very shallow 3
3. Elytral intervals coarsely, sparsely punctate; elytra not costate ....b. *atlantis*
   Elytral intervals coarsely, densely punctate; elytra feebly costate .d. *frondicola*

a. *Diplotaxis sordida* (Say)   Plate LI, No. 7, p. 527
   Elongate-oblong, robust, convex; reddish brown, piceous, or black, feebly shining; pronotum with dense, yellowish, suberect pubescence; elytra with moderately dense, yellowish pubescence. Clypeus short, broadly and shallowly emarginate; surface densely and subrugosely punctate. Pronotum distinctly impressed near anterior and posterior angles, basal impressions less distinct; margins crenate; surface finely, densely punctate. Elytra finely, transversely rugose between punctures. Length 10–12 mm.

b. *Diplotaxis atlantis* Fall   Plate LI, No. 8, p. 527
   Elongate-oblong, robust, convex; chestnut-brown or piceous, shining, not pubescent. Clypeus coarsely and densely punctate, vertex coarsely but

less densely so. Pronotum transverse, sides feebly arcuate; surface rather densely and coarsely punctate, with a smooth space at middle basally, shallowly impressed near posterior angles. Elytra not costate but with several rows of coarse punctures arranged in pairs and within each pair a row of fine punctures; intervals between these double rows rather coarsely, irregularly, and rather sparsely punctate. Length 11–12.5 mm.

c. *Diplotaxis liberta* (Germar)   Plate LI, No. 9, p. 527
   Elongate-oblong, robust, convex; dark chestnut-brown to piceous, shining, not pubescent. Clypeus and vertex coarsely and densely punctate. Pronotum transverse, sides feebly arcuate; surface coarsely punctate, densely so on apical and basal angles, moderately so basally and rather sparsely so on disk, with many irregular, smooth spaces; apical and basal angles distinctly impressed. Elytra as in *atlantis,* but the wide intervals coarsely and fairly densely punctate. Length 12–13 mm.

d. *Diplotaxis frondicola* (Say)   Plate LI, No. 14, p. 527
   Oblong-oval, convex; pale to dark chestnut-brown, feebly shining. Clypeus subtruncate anteriorly, anterior margin strongly reflexed; surface finely punctate. Pronotum transverse; sides broadly rounded; disk finely, densely punctate. Elytra each with three feeble costae, each costa with a single row of punctures and a row each side; intervals with coarse, more or less regularly placed punctures. Length 7–8 mm.
   This species may be found beneath stones and logs.

Genus II. *PHYLLOPHAGA* Harris

The "June bugs" or "May beetles" make up this genus of the scarabs. As "white grubs" they spend their larval stage underground, feeding on the roots of grass, corn, and allied crops. When they emerge as adults, they are nocturnal, coming out after dusk to feed on leaves of trees and shrubs. They are usually very difficult to identify, as the species resemble each other very closely. They may be separated from related genera by the following characters: antennae nine- or ten-segmented, club of three laminiform segments, resting at right angles to remainder of segments; meso- and metasternum covered with dense, long hair; six visible abdominal sternites; procoxae transverse, not very prominent; tarsal claws dentate, beneath never serrate (Fig. 417).

The males are most precisely identified by their genitalia and may be distinguished also by being less robust, less widened posteriorly, and less convex. In most species the abdomen of the male is more or less flattened and the last two abdominal sternites are more or less modified, the next to last often bearing a transverse ventral ridge and the last segment a depression or concavity.

KEY TO SPECIES

1. Body pubescent above, hairs either long or short, sometimes both, on elytra usually indefinitely arranged but on some species in definite rows; infrequently more or less pruinose 2
   Body above without pubescence, either dull or shining, sometimes pruinose or iridescent or both 6
2. Hairs long, with definite rows on elytra ....m. *hirticula*
   Hairs of different lengths and not in rows on elytra 3
3. Antennae nine-segmented ....j. *hirsuta*
   Antennae ten-segmented 4
4. Body more or less pruinose ....n. *ilicis*
   Body not pruinose but sometimes iridescent 5
5. Clypeus emarginate ....o. *crenulata*
   Clypeus entire ....p. *tristis*
6. Body pruinose ....c. *micans*
   Body not pruinose or iridescent 7
7. Antennae nine-segmented 8
   Antennae ten-segmented 9
8. Clypeal emargination deep, acute (Fig. 418) ....k. *implicita*
   Clypeal emargination arcuate, shallow (Fig. 419) ....l. *balia*
9. Apex of clypeus feebly emarginate (Fig. 420) 10
   Apex of clypeus moderately to deeply emarginate (Fig. 421) 13
10. Body dark brown to piceous; larger, 17–24 mm. long 12
    Body orange-brown to dark testaceous; smaller, 12–18 mm. long 11
11. Entire clypeal margin strongly reflexed (Fig. 420) ....a. *ephilida*
    Clypeal margin narrowly and feebly reflexed anteriorly ....b. *futilis*
12. Clypeal margin slightly reflexed anteriorly ....e. *fervida*
    Clypeal margin distinctly reflexed anteriorly ....d. *fusca*
13. Pronotum with median line distinctly raised, surface densely covered with large, deep punctures ....i. *rugosa*
    Pronotum with median line not raised; surface at most with moderate-sized punctures 14
14. Pronotum with lateral margin crenulate its entire length ....h. *forsteri*
    Pronotum with lateral margin smooth or feebly crenulate at middle 15
15. Blackish or very dark brown; body length 18–21 mm. ....f. *anxia*
    Reddish brown; body length 15–18 mm. ....g. *fraterna*

FIG. 418

FIG. 419

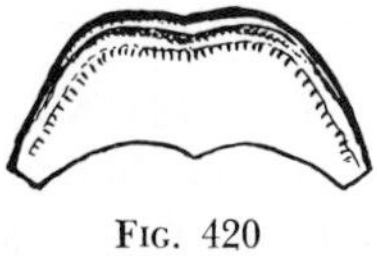

FIG. 420

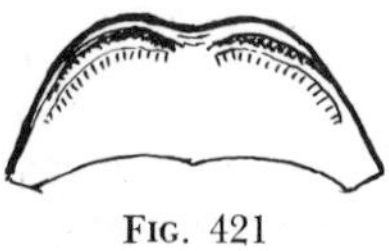

FIG. 421

Figs. 418–421. Clypeus from above. *Phyllophaga implicita* (418). *P. balia* (419). *P. ephilida* (420). *P. rugosa* (421).

a. *Phyllophaga ephilida* (Say)   Plate LV, No. 1, p. 563

Elongate, subcylindrical; brownish yellow, shining; head and pronotum darker. Clypeus broadly rounded anteriorly or very feebly emarginate, more coarsely and less densely punctate than front; entire margin strongly reflexed. Pronotum narrowed apically, coarsely but not densely punctate. Elytra more coarsely and deeply punctate than pronotum, submarginal costae obsolete. Metasternum densely punctate, hairs sparse and long. Tarsal claws with strong median tooth. Male with antennal club slightly shorter than funicle; next to last ventral segment feebly and broadly emarginate, last one more deeply emarginate and abruptly concave, both segments rugose or granulate anterior to emarginations. Length 14–18 mm.

This species is more common in the South.

b. *Phyllophaga futilis* LeConte   Plate LII, No. 1, p. 537

Oblong, convex, slightly broader behind middle; color varying from light reddish brown to brownish yellow; head darker; moderately shining. Clypeus very feebly emarginate, margin scarcely reflexed at middle. Pronotum rather short, sides curved, narrowing anteriorly, covered with long hairs; disk coarsely and rather sparsely punctate, usually with a smooth median space. Elytra as coarsely punctate as pronotum but more densely so; costae variable. Pygidium convex. Metasternum with extremely long hairs. Last abdominal sternite of male deeply, circularly concave; next to last broadly emarginate at apex. Length 12–17 mm.

c. *Phyllophaga micans* (Knoch)   Plate LII, No. 2, p. 537

Oblong, subconvex, slightly wider posteriorly; brownish black; surface, especially that of elytra, opaque, due to the hoary, pruinose covering. Clypeus concave, feebly emarginate anteriorly, entire margin slightly reflexed; both clypeus and front rather coarsely, not very densely punctate. Pronotum with sides parallel at base, arcuately narrowed anteriorly, moderately punctate, punctures sparse and irregularly placed, median line smoother. Elytra as coarsely punctate as pronotum, not densely so; sutural costa distinct, as are one or two discal ones. Pygidium opaque, at least laterally, and coarsely, indistinctly punctate. Metasternum densely punctate, hairs long and dense. Male with antennal club shorter than funicle; fifth abdominal sternite with a feebly curved ridge medially; last segment irregularly concave; inner spur of metatibiae more than half the length of outer, slender, and feebly curved outwardly. Length 15–17 mm.

This species is most easily recognized by the pruinose body covering.

d. *Phyllophaga fusca* (Froelich)   Plate LII, No. 5, p. 537

Broadly oblong, convex; dark reddish brown or piceous, shining. Clypeus scarcely emarginate anteriorly; surface rather finely and densely punctate; frontal margin strongly reflexed; front more coarsely, less densely punctate. Pronotum always widest at base, sides curved and narrowed to apex, punctation variable but never very coarse or very dense; not sulcate along base, median line usually smooth. Elytra more densely punctate than pronotum, costae variable, distinct or wanting, submarginal always distinct. Pygidium usually punctate, finely or coarsely but always sparsely. Metasternum densely punctate, hairs long and dense. Male with antennal club as long as or slightly longer than funicle; abdomen beneath flattened medially, last segment feebly transversely concave. Last abdominal sternite of female not emarginate at apex. Claws arcuate, dentate at middle, always more strongly so in female. Length 17–24 mm.

This species is very frequent at light.

e. *Phyllophaga fervida* (Fabricius)   Plate LV, No. 3, p. 563

Oblong, feebly widened posteriorly; deep reddish brown to piceous, shining. Clypeus distinctly emarginate anteriorly, margin feebly reflexed medially; surface densely, finely punctate; front more coarsely and sparsely punctate. Pronotum much wider at middle than base, which is distinctly wider than apex; disk covered with moderate-sized, well-spaced punctures; median line not entirely smooth; not transversely sulcate basally. Elytra feebly punctate, basally becoming rugose posteriorly; sutural costa distinct, discal ones obsolete, submarginal one present only on posterior two-thirds. Metasternum densely clothed with long hairs. Male with last abdominal segment broadly emarginate, next to last with a transverse, arcuate ridge, hollowed on posterior side. Length 19.5 mm.

f. *Phyllophaga anxia* LeConte   Plate LV, No. 2, p. 563

Broadly oblong, wider posteriorly; dark brown to piceous, shining. Clypeus distinctly emarginate anteriorly, slightly reflexed on anterior margin, densely, finely punctate; front more coarsely and sparsely punctate. Pronotum slightly wider at middle than at base, strongly narrowed apically; disk rather coarsely, sparsely punctate; median line more or less smooth; basal transverse sulcus interrupted at middle. Elytra finely, densely, somewhat rugosely punctate, punctures shallow; sutural costa distinct, discal ones feeble, submarginal one feeble, nearly entire. Pygidium shining, very finely punctate, in female punctures more deeply impressed. Metasternum with long, dense hairs. Male with last abdominal sternite shallowly impressed, next to last emarginate at apex, with transverse, crescent-shaped ridge at middle; antennal club longer than funicle. Length 17–21 mm.

g. *Phyllophaga fraterna* Harris   Plate LII, No. 3, p. 537

Oblong-ovate, feebly widened posteriorly; reddish brown, shining; head frequently blackish. Clypeus deeply emarginate at apex, margin slightly reflexed anteriorly; surface very densely, finely punctate; front slightly less densely punctate. Pronotum widest medially; base slightly wider than apex; disk sparsely covered with moderate-sized punctures; median line not smooth; basal sulcus absent. Elytra rather densely, coarsely punctate, toward suture somewhat rugose; sutural costa broad, slightly elevated, submarginal and discal ones obsolete or wanting. Metasternum moderately covered with long hairs. Male with last abdominal sternite feebly emarginate apically, at middle with a broad, shallow impression, next to last indistinctly, arcuately ridged, outlining a shallow depression. Length 15–18 mm.

h. *Phyllophaga forsteri* Burmeister   Plate LV, No. 4, p. 563

Oblong-ovate, scarcely widened posteriorly; reddish brown, shining; head and pronotum frequently darker. Clypeus deeply emarginate anteriorly, the margin strongly reflexed except at extreme sides; entire surface and front with dense, moderate-sized punctures. Pronotum widest slightly behind middle, base distinctly wider than apex; entire lateral margin coarsely crenulate; disk moderately densely, coarsely punctate; median line partly smooth; basal sulcus absent. Elytra more finely and densely punctate than pronotum; sutural costa distinct, discal ones obsolete, submarginal one distinct on posterior half. Metasternum densely covered with long hairs. Male with last abdominal sternite subtruncate at apex and with a deep, transverse impression medially; next to last deeply, broadly emarginate at apex, on each side of middle with a low, oblique ridge. Length 16–17 mm.

i. *Phyllophaga rugosa* (Melsheimer)   Plate LII, No. 6, p. 537

Oblong, rather robust, broader posteriorly; reddish brown to piceous, shining. Clypeus acutely, rather deeply emarginate anteriorly; margin scarcely reflexed anteriorly; surface densely and rather coarsely punctate, the front more coarsely so. Pronotum widest at middle; sides obtusely angulate, distinctly narrowed at base, more obliquely narrowed in front; basal margin broadly, shallowly depressed at middle of each side; disk coarsely and deeply punctate, punctures irregularly and moderately closely placed, median line raised. Elytra more finely and densely punctate than pronotum, somewhat finely rugose near suture, sides and apex smoother; costae of disk moderately distinct. Metasternum with rather dense, long hairs. Male with last abdominal sternite triangularly emarginate at apex and with a broad, transverse, oval impression medially; next to last truncate medially at apex, with an arcuate ridge each side followed by a flattened area. Length 18–23 mm.

j. *Phyllophaga hirsuta* (Knoch)   Plate LII, No. 8, p. 537

Oblong, rather slender, subparallel; dark brown to piceous, moderately shining, covered with sparse, long, yellowish, erect hairs not arranged in rows, longer on pronotum. Clypeus broadly, distinctly emarginate, anterior margin rather strongly reflexed; surface finely and densely punctate, front more coarsely so. Pronotum widest at middle, slightly narrowed at base, more so at apex; basal margin sulcate laterally; coarsely and fairly densely punctate. Elytra more finely and densely punctate than pronotum, rather finely rugose; costae of disk not distinct. Metasternum with long, dense hairs. Male with last abdominal sternite broadly, strongly emarginate apically, with a broad, shallow impression medially; next to last sternite broadly emarginate at apex, with an arcuate, transverse ridge; club of antennae much longer than funicle. Length 15–18 mm.

k. *Phyllophaga implicita* Horn   Plate LII, No. 9, p. 537

Oblong-oval, convex; orange-brown to brown; head and pronotum always darker, shining. Clypeus deeply, acutely emarginate, margin slightly reflexed anteriorly; surface densely and rather coarsely punctate; front more densely punctate. Pronotum narrowed from base to apex, more obliquely near apex; surface coarsely, regularly, but not closely punctate; median line smoother; basal margin sulcate laterally. Elytra as coarsely but more densely punctate than pronotum, somewhat rugose; discal costae feeble. Metasternum with moderately dense, long hairs. Male with last abdominal sternite narrowly emarginate at apex; next to last broadly, feebly emarginate, densely and finely punctate each side. Length 14–18 mm.

l. *Phyllophaga balia* (Say)   Plate LII, No. 10, p. 537

Oblong, distinctly broader posteriorly; brown to dark brown, shining; head and pronotum slightly darker than elytra. Head coarsely, rather densely punctate; front convex; clypeus broadly, shallowly emarginate anteriorly, entire margin narrowly reflexed. Pronotum widest at middle, narrowed anteriorly, less so posteriorly; punctures coarse, not close, irregularly placed; median space usually smooth; basal margin sulcate laterally. Elytra a little more finely and much more densely punctate than pronotum, with a somewhat scabrous appearance; costae indistinct. Metasternum with rather dense, long hairs. Male with last abdominal sternite narrowly emarginate at apex, transversely concave medially; next to last sternite broadly emarginate, with a long, arcuate, transverse ridge; club of antennae much longer than funicle. Length 15–16 mm.

m. *Phyllophaga hirticula* (Knoch)   Plate LII, No. 11, p. 537

Oblong, slightly wider posteriorly; orange-brown to dark brown, moderately shining; head and pronotum with erect hairs, elytra with lines of erect hairs along the costae. Clypeus moderately deeply emarginate anteriorly; margin narrowly reflexed; surface very densely punctate; front more coarsely punctate and with erect hairs. Pronotum widest at middle, apex narrower than base; punctation extremely coarse, sometimes dense, sometimes rather sparse; basal margin sulcate laterally. Elytra finely, rather closely punctate, somewhat scabrose, especially near suture; five rows of long, erect hairs along costae. Metasternum with rather dense, long hairs. Male with last abdominal sternite feebly emarginate apically and with a shallow, irregular impression medially; next to last sternite broadly, deeply emarginate; club of antennae slightly longer than funicle. Length 16.5–19 mm.

PLATE LII
Family SCARABAEIDAE IV

1. *Phyllophaga futilis* LeConte (p. 532) — Light to medium orange-brown; 12–17 mm.

2. *P. micans* (Knoch) (p. 532) — Dark brown; elytra pruinose; 15–17 mm.

3. *P. fraterna* Harris (p. 533) — Reddish brown; head often blackish; 15–18 mm.

4. *P. tristis* Fabricius (p. 538) — Brown-orange or dull yellowish; elytra paler; 11.5–15 mm.

5. *P. fusca* (Froelich) (p. 532) — Dark brown to fuscous, shining; 17–24 mm.

6. *P. rugosa* (Melsheimer) (p. 534) — Dark brown to fuscous, shining; 18–23 mm.

7. *P. ilicis* (Knoch) (p. 538) — Dark orange-brown; 19–23 mm.

8. *P. hirsuta* (Knoch) (p. 534) — Orange-brown to fuscous; 15–18 mm.

9. *P. implicita* Horn (p. 535) — Dark brown to fuscous; 14–18 mm.

10. *P. balia* (Say) (p. 535) — Orange-brown to chestnut; 15–16 mm.

11. *P. hirticula* (Knoch) (p. 535) — Dark brown; elytra paler; 16.5–19 mm.

12. *P. crenulata* Froelich (p. 538) — Orange-brown; 17–20 mm.

13. *Hoplia trifasciata* Say ♂ (p. 541) — Black; covered with fine, white pubescence; 6.5–9 mm.

14. *H. trifasciata* Say ♀ (p. 541) — Brown; head black; covered with yellowish or orangeish scales; markings brown; 6.5–9 mm.

15. *H. limbata* LeConte (p. 542) — Reddish brown; head and pronotum deep brown; elytra dull yellow; sparsely covered with silvery scales; 6–9 mm.

MM | 0 | 10 | 20 | 30 | 40 | 50 | 60 | 70

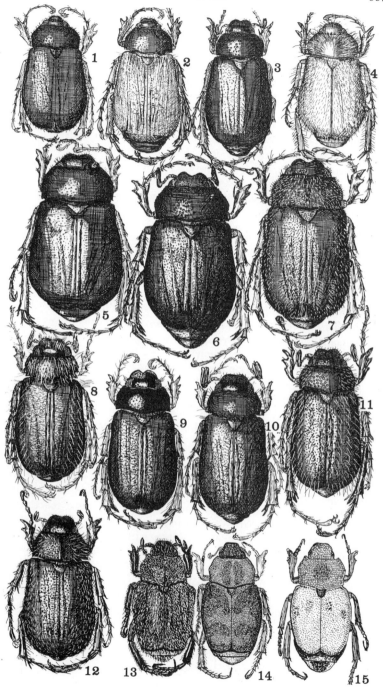

PLATE LII

n. *Phyllophaga ilicis* (Knoch)   Plate LII, No. 7, p. 537

Oblong, slightly wider posteriorly, robust; brown, more or less pruinose; sparsely clothed with short, equal, recumbent hair. Clypeus rather deeply emarginate anteriorly, only sides slightly reflexed; surface very densely and coarsely punctate, as is the front. Pronotum widest at middle, apex narrower than base, sides crenate and ciliate, very densely granulate-punctate; median line usually feebly elevated and smooth. Elytra densely punctate and finely rugose, punctures shallow and indistinct; costae indistinct, submarginal costae distinct beyond middle. Metasternum with moderately sparse, long hairs. Male with last abdominal sternite narrowly, deeply emarginate and with a broad, transverse impression; next to last broadly, rather strongly emarginate and with a long, transverse impression outlined anteriorly by a similarly shaped ridge; antennal club distinctly longer than funicle. Length 19–23 mm.

o. *Phyllophaga crenulata* Froelich   Plate LII, No. 12, p. 537

Oblong, indistinctly widened behind; brown, feebly shining, covered with short, yellowish, recumbent hairs, often with erect hairs intermixed. Clypeus broadly, moderately emarginate anteriorly, margin very narrowly reflexed; surface coarsely and densely punctate and with short, erect hairs; front more densely punctate and with longer hairs Pronotum with lateral margin coarsely serrate, widest at middle, apex narrower than base; median line smooth, interrupted; surface very coarsely and closely punctate, less densely so at sides. Elytra uniformly punctate, punctures finer than those on pronotum, rather closely placed; sutural costa feeble, discal costae usually indistinct, submarginal one well marked, entire, extending from apex to basal quarter. Metasternum with very sparse, rather short hairs. Male with last abdominal sternite straight on apical margin; next to last sternite feebly emarginate, scarcely impressed medially; antennal club shorter than funicle. Length 17–20 mm.

p. *Phyllophaga tristis* (Fabricius)   Plate LII, No. 4, p. 537

Elongate-oblong, feebly wider posteriorly; light or dark yellowish brown, shining, sparsely clothed with short hair on elytra, longer on base and pronotum. Clypeus entire, broadly rounded anteriorly, entire margin distinctly reflexed, surface coarsely and sparsely punctate; front more densely punctate. Pronotum widest at middle, apex narrower than base; margin entire; disk coarsely and densely punctate. Elytra evenly punctate, punctures closer than on pronotum, costae indistinct. Metasternum with dense, long hairs. Male with first abdominal sternite feebly emarginate apically; next to last bilobedly emarginate, with a rather deep impression outlined anteriorly with a curved ridge; antennal club much longer than funicle. Length 11.5–15 mm.

Tribe MACRODACTYLINI

KEY TO GENERA

Last spiracle in fifth sternite; claws chelate; eyes large and prominent
....I. *Dichelonyx* (p. 539)
Last spiracle on suture between fifth sternite and propygidium; claws
not chelate; eyes of moderate size ....II. *Macrodactylus* (p. 540)

Genus I. *DICHELONYX* Harris

Very elongate, oblong, subdepressed species; usually metallic green, or brown with a green reflex, covered with fine, silky pubescence; eyes large to moderately large, prominent; first abdominal sternite in great part visible, not hidden by metacoxae; claws cleft at apex.

These species occur in late spring on young shoots or leaves of trees and shrubs.

KEY TO SPECIES

1. Pronotum without a well-defined median groove 2
   Pronotum with a rather broad and deeply impressed median groove; elytra
   with a distinct greenish cast ....c. *albicollis*
2. Color dull brownish yellow; elytra bronzed, a narrow, dark stripe on sides,
   more distinct at base and apex; subapical marginal grooves of pronotum distinct; tibiae and tarsi entirely pale ....b. *subvittata*
   Color dark; elytra with greenish or purplish cast; metatibiae and metatarsi
   with apex piceous ....a. *elongata*

a. *Dichelonyx elongata* (Fabricius)   Plate LI, No. 11, p. 527
   Elongate-oblong, slender, parallel-sided; upper surface shining; head and pronotum brown or piceous; elytra brownish yellow, usually with a greenish or purplish cast; antennae and legs pale brownish yellow, apex of metatarsi and metatibiae piceous. Head above densely and rather coarsely punctate. Pronotum laterally produced at middle, sides sinuate behind promi-nence; posterior angles prominent; disk densely punctate, sparsely pubes-cent in male but densely so in female. Elytra rather coarsely, not closely punctate, sparsely and finely pubescent. Pygidium and abdominal sternites laterally covered with dense, white, prostrate hairs. Length 8–10 mm.

The adults may be collected on blooms of wild rose, wild plum, and other flowers, as well as on leaves of oak and willow, but they are chiefly nocturnal in habit.

b. *Dichelonyx subvittata* LeConte   Plate LI, No. 12, p. 527
   Elongate-oblong, more robust than *elongata,* parallel-sided; brownish

yellow to orange-brown, shining; above with green or bronze reflex; elytra with a fuscous or dark-green stripe laterally which is often obsolete except at humerus and apex. Head coarsely and rugosely punctate. Pronotum with a feeble median line; laterally produced at middle, sides sinuate behind middle; disk more coarsely, less densely punctate than in *elongata,* sparsely pubescent in both sexes. Elytra rugose, rather coarsely punctate, very sparsely pubescent. Pygidium and abdominal sternites rather densely covered laterally with white pubescence. Length 10–11.5 mm.

The adults are usually found on leaves of witch hazel and oak.

c. *Dichelonyx albicollis* Burmeister   Plate LI, No. 13, p. 527

Elongate-oblong, rather robust, parallel-sided; dull brownish yellow, with sparse, short pubescence; elytra with a green reflex, suture and margins paler. Head coarsely and densely punctate. Pronotum coarsely and sparsely punctate; widest at middle, sides behind middle straight, posterior angles obtuse. Elytra coarsely punctate, sparsely pubescent. Length 11–13 mm.

The adult feeds on pine foliage and is both nocturnal and diurnal.

Genus II. *MACRODACTYLUS* Latreille

Elongate, rather slender species; eyes of moderate size; last spiracle on suture between fifth sternite and propygidium, which are closely connate; tarsi elongate, slender; claws divergent, apices cleft, more deeply so in female. In the male the pro- and metatibiae are without spurs, the prosternum is spined behind procoxae, and the pygidium is elongate-ovate, not almost equilaterally triangular, as is the case in the female.

Macrodactylus subspinosus (Fabricius)   Rose Chafer
                                                Plate LV, No. 6, p. 563

Elongate, slender, female more robust, rather ovate; reddish brown, densely covered with dull-yellow scales or hairs; head, pronotum, and body beneath often darker; tarsi black. Pronotum convex, slightly elongate, widest at middle, distinctly narrowed at base and apex. Elytra indistinctly striate. Tarsi about as long as femora and tibiae combined. Length 8–10 mm.

This is the "rose chafer," whose damage to the rose garden is well known. It occurs also in large numbers on wild grape and other wild flowers.

Tribe Hopliini

Genus *HOPLIA* Illiger

Small, oblong, rather robust, subdepressed beetles; antennal club three-segmented; tibiae with but one spur or none; tarsi without onychium; claws of pro- and mesotarsi unequal in size, the external one larger, bifid at apex; metatarsi, and sometimes mesotarsi, with only one claw.

The adults of this genus may be found on flowers during the day.

KEY TO SPECIES

1. Metatarsal claw not cleft 2
   Metatarsal claw cleft near tip; sides of pronotum strongly angulate; body black, sides of pronotum, suture and margins of elytra, and two oblique branches with silvery scales ....c. *limbata*
2. Sexes dissimilar in color, male black and hairy, with grayish pubescence; female brown, with pale-brown and yellowish scales; pronotum wide, narrowed at apex, sides subangulate and rounded ....a. *trifasciata*
   Both sexes dull black, thinly clothed with elongate, grayish scales; pronotal sides oblique, slightly rounded ....b. *trivialis*

a. *Hoplia trifasciata* Say   Plate LII, Nos. 13, 14, p. 537

Oblong, robust, subdepressed; male dull black, pronotum and elytra rather densely covered with flattened, yellowish-gray hairs, pygidium and abdominal sternites densely covered with silvery scales; female with head black, pronotum and elytra orange- or red-brown, covered rather densely with pale-yellowish scales, which are denser on parts of the elytra, forming three irregular, transverse patches near suture; body beneath with silvery scales. Clypeus truncate anteriorly, apical margin reflexed. Pronotum wide, narrowed apically, sides angulate and rounded. Metatarsal claws not cleft. Length 6.5–9 mm.

The adults may be collected from flowers of haw and oak leaves.

b. *Hoplia trivialis* Harold   Plate LIII, No. 1, p. 547

Elongate-oblong, robust, subconvex; dark reddish brown to deep gray, dorsally covered with elongate scales, these usually arranged on elytra to form an indistinct band at middle and a narrower band at apex; pygidium and abdominal sternites with sparsely placed, flat, silvery scales. Clypeus truncate anteriorly, apical margin strongly reflexed. Pronotum with sides oblique, slightly rounded. Metatarsal claw not cleft. Length 6–8 mm.

The adults are found beneath boards, stones, and rubbish on sandy areas near water during the day.

c. *Hoplia limbata* LeConte   Plate LII, No. 15, p. 537

Elongate-oblong, robust, subdepressed; reddish brown; head and pronotum usually dark brown; elytra dull yellow; sides of pronotum and suture and margins of elytra with silvery scales or hairs, those on elytra sometimes arranged in more or less distinct, oblique lines near apex; body beneath more or less densely covered with silvery scales. Clypeus rather narrow, truncate apically, anterior margin feebly reflexed. Pronotum depressed, sides oblique, variable, feebly rounded or angulate. Metatarsal claws cleft near apex. Length 6–9 mm.

The adults may be taken on flowers of bittersweet and other plants.

Subfamily RUTELINAE

KEY TO TRIBES

Tribe ANOMALINI

KEY TO GENERA

1. Mesepimera not ascending before elytral shoulders 2
   Mesepimera narrowly and inconspicuously ascending before shoulders (Fig. 408) 3
2. Mesosternum flat or but feebly convex between coxae; meso-metasternal suture always evident ....I. *Anomala* (p. 542)
   Mesosternum tumid and smooth between coxae; more or less prominent anteriorly and sometimes greatly produced, gradually acuminate and anteriorly porrect; meso-metasternal suture obliterated ....II. *Pachystethus* (p. 544)
3. Pronotum grooved and impressed ....III. *Strigoderma* (p. 544)
   Pronotum smooth, not grooved or impressed ....IV. *Popillia* (p. 545)

Genus I. *ANOMALA* Samouelle

Small or moderate-sized, ovate, convex species; antennae nine-segmented; pronotum not pubescent; elytra convex, shallowly striate and punctate, laterally with a membranous border; mesosternum flat or nearly so between the coxae, the meso-metasternal suture always visible; mesepimera not at all visible from above.

KEY TO SPECIES

1. Claw-bearing segment of protarsi distinctly toothed on underside 2
   Claw-bearing segment of protarsi not toothed on underside; pronotum with
   disk dark, side margins paler ....c. *undulata*
2. Pronotum entirely reddish yellow; clypeus distinctly concave, margin broadly
   reflexed ....b. *flavipennis*
   Pronotum either bicolored or entirely piceous; clypeus flat, margin narrowly
   reflexed 3
3. Larger, 10–11 mm.; sides of clypeus nearly parallel ....a. *binotata*
   Smaller, not over 8 mm.; sides of clypeus divergent behind middle . .d. *innuba*

a. *Anomala binotata* Gyllenhal   Plate LIII, No. 6, p. 547

Oblong-ovate, robust; piceous, greenish-bronzed, shining; elytra dull
yellow, reddish, or dark brown, and, except in the latter case, with the
suture, side margins, a spot at middle, and a short stripe on humerus dark
brown. Head densely and finely punctate. Pronotum strongly transverse,
narrowed anteriorly, sides curved; disk finely and sparsely punctate, more
densely so laterally. Elytra with rows of coarse punctures; each with three
feeble costae. Pygidium rather finely, densely rugose, sparsely pubescent.
Length 9–12 mm.

The adults are found on foliage and flowers of shrubs and occasionally
may be found at light.

b. *Anomala flavipennis* Burmeister   Plate LV, No. 8, p. 563

Oblong-ovate, moderately robust; head, pronotum, and undersurface
reddish yellow; elytra pale dull yellow, with or without darker areas; pronotum frequently with a greenish-bronze tinge. Pronotum strongly transverse, sides arcuate; disk sparsely, finely punctate and with two or three
small impressions laterally. Elytra each with three or four indistinct costae,
the intervals broad and with several irregular rows of punctures. Pygidium
coarsely punctate. Length 10–12 mm.

c. *Anomala undulata* Melsheimer   Plate LIII, Nos. 3, 4, p. 547

Elongate-oval, convex, robust; brownish yellow, shining; head darker;
pronotal disk piceous, with greenish bronze; elytra usually with a curved,
transverse row of dark-brown, oval dots near middle and another series at
apical third, but these dots sometimes entirely wanting or reduced in number or confused and enlarged so as to almost cover the elytra. Head depressed at middle of front; clypeus and depressed portion of front densely
and rugosely punctate, the former with margin narrowly reflexed, angles
broadly rounded. Pronotum strongly transverse; sides arcuate; disk finely
and rather sparsely punctate. Elytra with rows of rather coarse punctures,
inner rows somewhat irregular; intervals subequal and nearly flat. Length
8–9.5 mm.

The adults may be taken on foliage and flowers of shrubs and at light.

d. *Anomala innuba* (Fabricius) Plate LIII, No. 5, p. 547

Elongate-ovate, convex, rather robust; color variable, often dull yellow, with pronotal disk and one to three transverse rows of dots on elytra dark brown, sometimes entirely piceous or dark brown. Head densely and finely punctate; clypeus nearly semicircular, sides divergent, not parallel behind middle, margin narrowly reflexed. Pronotum transverse, sides arcuate; disk coarsely, rather deeply, not densely punctate. Elytra with rows of coarse, deep, closely placed punctures, rows near suture very irregular. Pygidium finely rugose, smoother apically. Length 6–7.5 mm.

The adults occur on wild flowers, especially wild rose and Jersey tea; they also come to light.

Genus II. *PACHYSTETHUS* Blanchard

Ovate, convex, robust; antennae nine-segmented; elytra convex, with a membranous lateral border; mesosternum smooth, with a broad, obtuse prominence between coxae; meso-metasternal suture obliterated; mesepimera not at all visible from above.

Pachystethus lucicola (Fabricius) Plate LIII, No. 2, p. 547

Oval, robust; color varying from entirely brownish yellow to wholly black; pronotum often with a piceous discal area, which is sometimes divided at middle. Clypeus nearly twice as long as broad, densely punctate. Pronotum convex, sides arcuate; surface rather coarsely, not densely punctate. Elytra with double rows of rather coarse, close punctures, which are confused near suture; intervals feebly convex, finely punctate. Length 8.5–10 mm.

The adults may be found on foliage of vines and shrubs.

Genus III. *STRIGODERMA* Burmeister

Oblong-ovate, robust, subconvex; antennae nine-segmented; pronotum broadly impressed laterally; elytra with a distinct humeral callus, lateral margin membranous, disk with numerous deep, subequal striae; mesepimera visible from above, between the humerus of elytra and basal angle of pronotum; larger claw of pro- and mesotarsi always cleft.

Strigoderma arboricola (Fabricius) Plate LIII, Nos. 7, 8, p. 547

Elongate, oblong-ovate, subconvex; blackish green, shining; pronotum in part or entirely paler; elytra light yellowish brown, sometimes dark brown in whole or in part; undersurface piceous, with sparse, long, grayish hairs. Head coarsely, roughly punctate. Pronotum rather hairy, slightly transverse, sides arcuate, posterior angles broadly rounded, anterior angles acute; disk rather sparsely punctate, impressed median line visible apically, laterally with two irregular depressions. Elytra distinctly, deeply striate. Length 10–12 mm.

The adults may be taken on flowers of wild rose, blackberry, and water willow.

Genus IV. *POPILLIA* Serville

Broadly oval, robust, subdepressed; antennae nine-segmented; pronotum with a feeble fovea laterally; elytra with humeral callus indistinct, disk with numerous shallow striae; mesepimera narrowly visible between pronotum and elytra; larger claw of pro- and mesotarsi always cleft.

Popillia japonica Newman   Japanese Beetle
                                                       Plate LIII, No. 9, p. 547

Ovate, robust, subdepressed; deep green, shining; elytra brownish orange, margined with deep green; undersurface piceous, abdominal sternites each with transverse spots of white pubescence laterally; pygidium with two white-pubescent basal spots. Clypeus rugosely punctate; front densely punctate. Pronotum convex, transverse; sides distinctly arcuate; disk densely, rather coarsely punctate, medially less densely so. Elytra with broad, feebly impressed, punctate striae; intervals feebly convex, feebly punctate. Length 8–12 mm.

The "Japanese beetle," introduced on iris roots from Japan, in the past few years has done much damage to almost every kind of plant in the eastern part of the United States.

Tribe RUTELINI

Genus *PELIDNOTA* MacLeay

Large, elongate-ovate, convex, robust species; mandibles obtusely bidentate externally; suture between front and clypeus absent; pronotum beaded along basal margin; antennae ten-segmented; elytra without membranous margin.

Pelidnota punctata Linné   Grapevine Beetle
                                                       Plate LIII, No. 11, p. 547

Broadly elongate-ovate, robust, convex; brownish yellow to light brown, shining; head sometimes with occiput black; pronotum with a round, black spot on each side laterally; elytra each with three more or less distinct, rounded, black spots along sides; undersurface, legs, and scutellum

PLATE LIII
Family SCARABAEIDAE V

1. *Hoplia trivialis* Harold (p. 541)

Dark brown to blackish, sparsely covered with long scales; 6–8 mm.

2. *Pachystethus lucicola* (Fabricius) (p. 544)

Ranging from brownish yellow, with blackish markings, to entirely black; 8.5–10 mm.

3, 4. *Anomala undulata* Melsheimer (p. 543)

Very variable, ranging from brownish yellow to dark brown, with many intermediates between the two extremes illustrated; 8–9.5 mm.

5. *A. innuba* (Fabricius) (p. 544)

Variable, from yellow, with dark-brown markings, to entirely dark brown; 6–7.5 mm.

6. *A. binotata* Gyllenhal (p. 543)

Blackish, greenish-bronzed; elytra variable, dull yellow to dark brown, markings dark brown; 9–12 mm.

7, 8. *Strigoderma arboricola* (Fabricius) (p. 544)

Blackish green; elytra varying from light brown to dark brown, in whole or in part; 10–12 mm.

9. *Popillia japonica* Newman (p. 545)

Deep green, shining; elytra brown-orange, with green margins; 8–12 mm.

10. *Ligyrus relictus* (Say) (p. 549)

Blackish, shining; 18–23 mm.

11. *Pelidnota punctata* Linné (p. 545)

Brownish yellow to brown, shining; markings black; 17–25 mm.

12. *Ligyrus gibbosus* (DeGeer) (p. 549)

Dark brown to black, shining; 11–16 mm.

13. *Xyloryctes jamaicensis* (Drury) ♂ (p. 550)

Dark brown to nearly black; 25–28 mm.

14. *X. jamaicensis* (Drury) ♀ (p. 550)

Dark brown to nearly black; 25–28 mm.

15. *Valgus seticollis* (Beauvois) (p. 558)

Blackish, with pale-yellow scales; 6.5–7.5 mm.

16. *V. canaliculatus* (Fabricius) (p. 558)

Dark brown, with pale-yellow and blackish scales; 5–6 mm.

MM 0 10 20 30 40 50 60 70

PLATE LIII 547

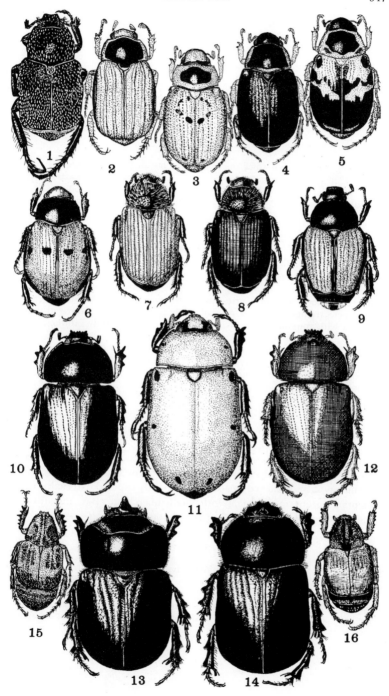

deep green or piceous. Entire upper surface finely, sparsely, and irregularly punctate. Length 17–25 mm.

The adults occur particularly on grape, both wild and cultivated; the larvae live on decaying roots and stumps of various trees.

Subfamily DYNASTINAE

KEY TO TRIBES

Tarsi long, filiform, but thick, basal segment not or scarcely triangular (Fig. 422); protarsi of male elongate .... DYNASTINI (p. 550)
Tarsi shorter, more tapering, with triangular and externally produced basal segment (Fig. 423); protarsi of male not elongate ..... ORYCTINI (p. 548)

Tribe ORYCTINI

KEY TO GENERA

1. Elytra without rows of coarse punctures, smooth, strongly shining; clypeus triangular, with a median tooth at apex ..... II. *Strategus* (p. 549)
   Elytra with rows of coarse, distinct punctures, rather feebly shining; clypeus bidentate at apex 2
2. Head in both sexes with at least a short horn; length over 25 mm.
   .... III. *Xyloryctes* (p. 550)
   Head without horn in either sex but with a transverse ridge; length less than 22 mm. .... I. *Ligyrus* (p. 548)

Genus I. *LIGYRUS* Burmeister

Of moderate size, oblong-ovate, robust, convex; head armed with small, transverse, toothed ridges in both sexes; clypeus triangular, bidentate at extreme apex, and reflexed; mandibles distinctly exposed externally, usually tridentate; pronotum of male with small tubercle at apex; metatibiae expanded (sometimes but slightly), truncate and ciliate at apex.

KEY TO SPECIES

Clypeus with teeth separated distinctly basally; front with transverse carina more or less evenly elevated; pronotum with a low but distinct tubercle at middle of apex .... b. *gibbosus*
Clypeus with teeth contiguous basally; front with transverse carina obsolete medially and forming a tooth each side of middle; pronotum not tuberculate .... a. *relictus*

a. *Ligyrus relictus* (Say) Plate LIII, No. 10, p. 547

Oblong-ovate, robust, convex; piceous, shining. Transverse carinae of head interrupted at middle; clypeus with two teeth. Pronotum very convex; posterior angles broadly rounded; surface finely and sparsely punctate. Elytral punctures fine, those of disk arranged in three double rows, those on sides and near suture confused. Inner claw of male protarsi thickened, dilated, and abruptly curved. Length 18–23 mm.

The adults may be taken at light and under rubbish.

b. *Ligyrus gibbosus* (DeGeer) Carrot Beetle
Plate LIII, No. 12, p. 547

Oblong, slightly dilated posteriorly; black, shining; underside reddish brown, densely pilose. Head with an acute raised line between antennae; clypeus with two teeth anteriorly. Pronotal sides obtusely angulate near apex, apex slightly emarginate, tubercled at middle, with a round impression behind tubercle; disk feebly punctate, more coarsely so laterally. Elytra slightly broader than pronotum, punctate-striate, the lateral striae confused externally. Length 11–16 mm.

The adult is often attracted to lights and also attacks the roots of beets, carrots, ornamental flowers, and celery.

Genus II. *STRATEGUS* Hope

Large, robust, oblong-ovate beetles; head unarmed in both sexes; clypeus triangular, with a single reflexed tooth at apex; mandibles exposed externally, tridentate; pronotum with three long, erect horns in male, in female with a single horn at middle of apex; elytra without striae; metatibiae sinuate externally at apex.

FIG. 422 FIG. 423

Figs. 422–423. First three segments of left mesotarsus of *Dynastes* (422) and of *Xyloryctes* (423), viewed from below.

Strategus antaeus (Drury)   Plate LV, Nos. 5, 7, p. 563

Oblong-ovate, feebly tapering posteriorly; dark reddish brown, shining; slightly paler beneath, with rather sparse, long hairs. Head unarmed, with feeble, transverse carina, especially in female; surface irregularly, coarsely rugose. Pronotum widest just behind middle, base somewhat wider than apex; in male with three erect horns, surface finely punctate; in female with a feeble horn, surface more densely punctate on basal half, anteriorly becoming coarsely, irregularly rugose. Elytra minutely, sparsely punctate in both sexes. Pygidium and propygidium exposed, transversely rugose, pygidium punctate at apex. Length 28–31 mm.

Genus III. *XYLORYCTES* Hope

Large, robust beetles with mandibles small, nearly concealed, feebly bilobed at tip; male with a long, curved horn arising from middle of head; prothorax unarmed in male; clypeus obtuse, reflexed and bilobed anteriorly; mentum deeply excavated at base; metatibiae not sinuate externally at apex, the dilated apex evenly truncate but distinctly crenulate.

Xyloryctes jamaicensis (Drury)   The Rhinoceros Beetle
                                                      Plate LIII, Nos. 13, 14, p. 547

Oblong, robust, dark reddish brown to piceous brown, slightly shining; undersurface rather thickly clothed with light-reddish-brown hairs. Male with anterior half of pronotum almost perpendicular, slope with coarse, transverse punctures; basal half convex, finely and sparsely punctate; sides rounded and fringed with long, brown hairs. Female with pronotum strongly convex, but slightly declivous before middle. Elytra striate, with rows of rather fine, feebly impressed punctures, the striae deeper and punctures larger in female. Length 25–28 mm.

Tribe DYNASTINI

Genus *DYNASTES* Kirby

To this genus belong some of the largest of the known beetles; some of the tropical members are three inches long and an inch or more in thickness. Central horn of male pronotum usually long, the lateral spines protruding from the surface near the base of the horn or from the sides of the horn itself; the cephalic horn long, curving upward toward the pronotal horn; mandibles sharply bidentate; anterior legs differing but little between sexes, tibiae tridentate externally, more finely and acutely so in male; postcoxal process of prosternum large, triangular.

Dynastes tityus Linné   Plate LIV, Nos. 1, 2, p. 557
  Broadly oval, convex; yellowish gray; elytra irregularly marked with brown to piceous spots, rarely uniformly dark reddish brown. Male with three pronotal horns, side ones short and curved, median one with orangeish hair beneath, bifid at tip, and curving forward to meet the long, curved horn arising from the head; female with a very slight tubercle on middle of head. Entire upper surface of male almost entirely smooth; female with pronotum sparsely and finely punctate, more densely and coarsely so on sides and anterior angles; elytra with coarse and very fine punctures intermingled on basal half, apical half smooth. Length of male, 40–50 mm. (exclusive of horns); female, 40–45 mm.

Subfamily CETONIINAE

KEY TO GENERA

Scutellum covered by basal lobe of pronotum (Fig. 424) ......I. *Cotinis*   (p. 551)
Scutellum free, pronotal lobe usually feebly sinuate at scutellum ......
....II. *Euphoria*   (p. 552)

Genus I. *COTINIS* Burmeister

  Elongate-oval, subdepressed, medium-sized beetles; clypeus with a hornlike process at apical margin in both sexes; mesosternal process flattened and usually somewhat horizontal; pygidium usually shining and with fine, transverse, wavy, incised lines.

Cotinis nitida (Linné)   The Green June Beetle; Fig-eater
                                      Color Plate B; Plate LIV, No. 3, p. 557
  Elongate-oblong, somewhat narrowed apically, subdepressed; dull, velvety green above, with sides of pronotum and elytra brownish yellow; head, middle of metasternum, and tibiae shining metallic green; femora and

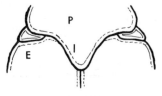

FIG. 424

Fig. 424. Portion of pronotum (*P*) and of elytra (*E*) of *Cotinis,* a lobe
(*l*) of the former entirely concealing the scutellum.

usually abdomen orange-yellow. Head deeply excavated, front with a horizontal spine extending forward nearly to upturned clypeal spine. Pronotum triangular; apex truncate, less than half as wide as base, latter with a triangular lobe covering the scutellum. Upper surface smooth, with the exception of two very feeble costae on each elytron. Length 20–23 mm.

The adults visit flowers, especially hollyhocks, and ripening fruit, especially peaches; they are also nocturnal and fly in great numbers, usually in sandy areas, with a loud, buzzing noise.

Genus II. *EUPHORIA* Burmeister

Elongate-ovate, robust, and rather broad, more or less hairy species; clypeus varying in form from obtusely acuminate to broadly obtuse, sometimes bilobed; mandibles feeble, in great part membranous; pronotum triangular, nearly as wide at base as elytra, sinuate to truncate medially at base; scutellum distinct; mesosternal process forming a smooth and generally glabrous knob between coxae; metatarsi variable in length but generally short, sometimes strongly compressed; last spiracles placed midway between the anterior and posterior margins of the segment.

KEY TO SPECIES

1. Elevation between mesocoxae oval or semicircular 2
   Elevation between mesocoxae transverse; elytra brownish yellow, with numerous small, black spots ....c. *inda*
2. Pronotum either shining, or punctured and pubescent 3
   Pronotum opaque, scarcely punctate, not pubescent; dull green to opaque brown ....b. *herbacea*
3. Pronotum densely punctate, surface pubescent; dark brown, feebly bronzed, with narrow, white markings ....d. *sepulchralis*
   Pronotum sparsely punctate, shining, not pubescent; green, tinged with brown ....a. *fulgida*

a. *Euphoria fulgida* (Fabricius)   Plate LIV, No. 4, p. 557

Oblong-ovate, depressed; head and pronotum bright green, latter margined at sides with brownish orange, sometimes with minute, whitish spots; abdomen green, with white spots laterally, four similar spots on base of pygidium; legs orange-brown, tinged with green. Entire upper surface sparsely and finely punctate; elytra with traces of costae, rugose laterally. Length 13–18 mm.

The adults are found on flowers. This species is easily separated from *Cotinis nitida*, which it resembles, in that the elytra are shining, not dull and velvety.

b. *Euphoria herbacea* (Olivier) Plate LIV, No. 5, p. 557

Broadly oval, subdepressed; above olive-green to brown, opaque; elytra sometimes reddish, with more or less distinct, small dots of white pubescence, especially on apical half, margin of apex densely pubescent; sternites reddish brown or green, smooth, shining. Head coarsely, moderately densely punctate. Pronotum densely, coarsely punctate laterally, rather sparsely so toward middle. Elytra seriately punctate on disk; on sides and at apex with numerous fine, transverse, irregular, raised lines. Length 12–15 mm.

c. *Euphoria inda* (Linné) Bumblebee Flower Beetle; Brown Fruit Chafer
Plate LIV, No. 6, p. 557

Broadly oval, robust; brownish yellow; head and pronotum piceous, feebly bronzed, sometimes with brownish-yellow spots, clothed with dense, yellow pubescence; elytra mottled with black spots which often tend to form crossbands; beneath piceous; legs and apical margins of abdominal segments often paler; vertex of head, pronotum, pro- and mesosterna, femora, and sides of abdomen generally densely clothed with light-yellow pubescence. Elytra each with two feeble costae which converge apically. Length 13–16 mm.

On the first warm days of spring these beetles appear and fly close to the ground with a loud, buzzing noise similar to that of the bumblebee. The adults often eat corn, peaches, grapes, and apples; the larvae live in decaying wood.

d. *Euphoria sepulchralis* (Fabricius) Plate LIV, No. 7, p. 557

Oblong-oval; dark brown, bronzed, slightly shining; pronotum sometimes with an indistinct, fine, white line on side and clothed with short, pale-yellowish, persistent pubescence; elytra with numerous short, transverse, whitish lines; underneath purplish-bronzed. Pronotum triangular; base emarginate at middle; disk coarsely punctate, more densely so toward sides. Elytra each with two costae; intervals with numerous coarse punctures, on sides changing to short, deep, transverse wrinkles; apex subtruncate, distinctly sinuous. Pro- and mesosterna, femora, and sides of abdomen hairy. Length 9–13 mm.

The adults may be found on flowers and feign death when touched.

Subfamily TRICHIINAE

KEY TO GENERA

Scutellum elongate, triangular, apically attenuate; size larger, 18–30 mm.
. . . . .I. *Osmoderma* (p. 554)
Scutellum small, oval or rounded; size smaller, 9–12 mm. . . . .
. . . . .II. *Trichiotinus* (p. 554)

Genus I. *OSMODERMA* LePeletier and Serville

Large, broadly ovate, dark brown, sometimes slightly bronzed beetles with pronotum distinctly narrower than elytra, rounded on sides; scutellum elongate, triangular, apically attenuate; last spiracle nearer to anterior than to posterior margin of segment.

Because of the strong odor of Russian leather they give off when captured, they are known as "odor-of-leather beetles."

KEY TO SPECIES

Larger, 25–29 mm.; dark chestnut- or mahogany-brown, shining . . . .b. *eremicola*
Smaller, 18–25 mm.; purplish black, bronzed . . . . .a. *scabra*

a. *Osmoderma scabra* (Beauvois)   Plate LIV, No. 11, p. 557

Broadly oval, depressed; purplish black, slightly bronzed. Head of male deeply excavated between eyes, the clypeus more strongly reflexed in front; head of female nearly flat, with clypeus narrowly reflexed. Pronotum with a rather deep median groove; disk deeply and rather coarsely punctate near base, more finely so near apex. Elytra very rugosely and irregularly punctate. Length 18–25 mm.

The adults are nocturnal and occur in orchards and open woods.

b. *Osmoderma eremicola* Knoch   Hermit Flower Beetle
                                             Plate LIV, No. 12, p. 557

Broadly oval, depressed; dark reddish brown, shining. Head deeply excavated between eyes in both sexes; margin with a small tubercle above base of antennae. Pronotum with a deeply impressed median groove on basal half, in front of which is a broad, rather deep excavation which is bordered anteriorly by a sharp, elevated line; disk finely and sparsely punctate. Elytra finely and sparsely punctate. Length 25–29 mm.

This species is also taken at lights and about the edges of open woods.

Genus II. *TRICHIOTINUS* Casey

Medium-sized beetles having the upper surface in great part pubescent; pronotum rounded, narrower than elytra; elytra short, almost truncate; pygidium prominent in male and female, with apex slightly inflexed; metatarsi very long in male, not so long and generally more slender in female.

The species of this genus occur on flowers during the day and readily take flight when disturbed.

KEY TO SPECIES

1. Elytra with white, transverse bands and velvety spots on sides 2
   Elytra reddish brown, tinged with green, without transverse, whitish bands
   or velvety spots on sides ....c. *bibens*
2. Elytra with third and fifth intervals distinctly more convex than second and
   fourth, the latter two rather densely punctate; protibiae of male without
   spur ....a. *piger*
   Elytra with third and fifth intervals but slightly convex, second and fourth very
   sparsely punctate; protibiae with spur in both sexes, that of male more
   slender and straight than that of female ....b. *affinis*

a. *Trichiotinus piger* (Fabricius)   Color Plate B; Plate LIV, No. 8, p. 557

Oblong-oval, robust; head and pronotum piceous, slightly bronzed with
green, clothed with dense, yellow, erect pubescence; elytra orangeish brown
to piceous, sparsely pubescent, each with two short, white crossbars, one
slightly in front of, the other slightly behind the middle, and reaching
from the margin to the fifth, or rarely the third, interval; sides with a black,
or slightly reddish, velvety spot reaching from the margin to the fifth interval behind the front crossbar and divided by the posterior one; pygidium
piceous, with white stripe either side and clothed with pale-yellow hair;
body underneath and femora piceous and slightly bronzed, clothed with
long, silky, pale-yellow hairs; abdomen, tibiae, and tarsi reddish brown.
Head and pronotum densely punctate. Length 9–11 mm.

The adults are common on Queen Anne's lace, Jersey tea, wild hydrangea,
and other flowers.

b. *Trichiotinus affinis* (Gory and Percheron)   Plate LIV, No. 9, p. 557

Oblong-oval, slightly smaller than *piger;* head, pronotum, and underside black, tinged with green, slightly shining; head and pronotum with
short, fine, pale-yellow hair; body beneath with long, pale, silken hairs;
elytra greenish black, with second and fourth intervals often reddish brown,
the sides with whitish, transverse bars and velvety space as in *piger;* also
frequently a short, whitish bar next to suture, just behind scutellum;
pygidium dark reddish brown to piceous, with white spaces or lines on
sides, densely clothed with pale-yellow pubescence. Length 9–10 mm.

This species is usually found with *piger,* which it closely resembles, but
is smaller and more shining and has the pronotum more sparsely punctate
and the punctation of the second and fourth elytral intervals coarser.

c. *Trichiotinus bibens* (Fabricius)   Plate LIV, No. 10, p. 557

Oblong-oval; head, pronotum, body beneath, and femora bright metallic
green, slightly shining; clothed with dense, erect, pale-yellow pubescence;
elytra orange-brown, green-bronzed, and with very fine, sparse pubescence; undersurface and femora with long, white, silky hairs. Head densely

PLATE LIV
Family SCARABAEIDAE VI

1. *Dynastes tityus* Linné ♂ (p. 551)
2. *D. tityus* Linné ♀ (p. 551)

Usually yellowish gray, with brown markings, as shown in the male; sometimes entirely dark brown, as shown in the female; 40–50 mm.

3. *Cotinis nitida* (Linné) (p. 551)

Dull velvety green, with brownish-yellow markings; 20–23 mm.

4. *Euphoria fulgida* (Fabricius) (p. 552)

Bright green, shining; elytra and pronotal sides brownish orange; 13–18 mm.

5. *E. herbacea* (Olivier) (p. 553)

Olive-green to brown; elytra sometimes reddish, markings white; 12–15 mm.

6. *E. inda* (Linné) (p. 553)

Brownish yellow; head and pronotum largely blackish; markings black; 13–16 mm.

7. *E. sepulchralis* (Fabricius) (p. 553)

Dark brown, with fine, whitish lines; 9–13 mm.

8. *Trichiotinus piger* (Fabricius) (p. 555)

Blackish, with a faint green sheen; elytra orange-brown to blackish, with white markings; 9–11 mm.

9. *T. affinis* (Gory and Percheron) (p. 555)

Black, tinged with green; elytra reddish brown and black, with white markings; 9–10 mm.

10. *T. bibens* (Fabricius) (p. 555)

Bright green; elytra orange-brown, with a green reflex; black markings may be absent; 11–12 mm.

11. *Osmoderma scabra* (Beauvois) (p. 554)

Purplish black, with a green or bronzy sheen; 18–25 mm.

12. *O. eremicola* Knoch (p. 554)

Dark brown, shining; 25–29 mm.

MM |0 10 20 30 40 50 60 70

PLATE LIV 557

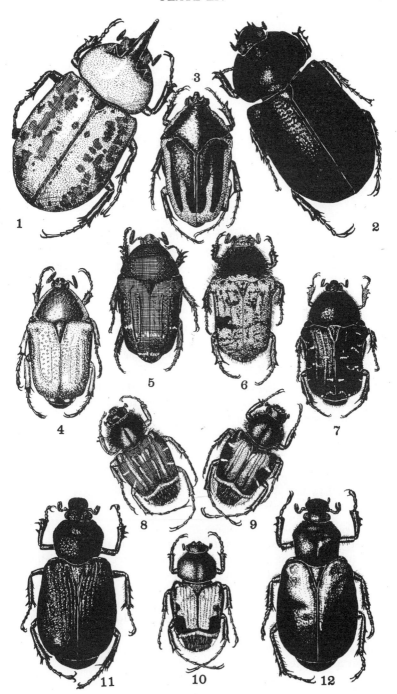

punctate; pronotum more coarsely but sparsely punctate. Elytra with intervals nearly equal, second and fourth intervals more densely punctate than others. Pygidium sometimes with an oblong, white space each side. Protibiae of male with a slender, straight spur. Length 11–12 mm.

This beetle may be taken on many species of flowers, particularly dogwood.

Subfamily VALGINAE

Genus *VALGUS* Scriba

Small, brownish, strongly flattened species; elytra short, exposing the pygidium; body more or less covered with whitish scales; apex of pygidium of female prolonged obliquely into a long, straight, gradually acuminate process, the upper side of which is feebly sulcate; metacoxae widely separated.

KEY TO SPECIES

Protibiae with three or more slender, widely separated teeth on outer side;
  size smaller, not over 6 mm.; color dark reddish brown ......b. *canaliculatus*
Protibiae with five or six closely placed, stout, rounded teeth; size larger, 6.5–
  7.5 mm.; usually piceous ....a. *seticollis*

a. *Valgus seticollis* (Beauvois)   Plate LIII, No. 15, p. 547
Small, oval, very depressed; piceous; undersurface sparsely clothed with pale-yellow scales. Pronotum coarsely punctate, margin coarsely denticulate; median groove feeble on basal half, often with a short, oblique ridge on each side. Surface of elytra and pygidium densely granulate. Length 6.5–7.5 mm.

This species occurs in spring and summer on various flowers, particularly red haw and dogwood, and usually hibernates in colonies beneath logs and mullein leaves in winter.

b. *Valgus canaliculatus* (Fabricius)   Plate LIII, No. 16, p. 547
Oval, very depressed, smaller than preceding; dark reddish brown, slightly shining; sides of pronotum, base, middle, and apex of elytra, and pygidium sparsely clothed with pale-yellow scales; undersurface and femora densely clothed with pale-yellow scales. Pronotum longer than wide, narrowed apically, sides feebly curved; margin denticulate nearly to base, surface with a deep median groove, which is wider at base, and with an impression on the middle of each side. Elytral disk slightly concave; intervals each with two rows of shallow punctures. Length 5–6 mm.

This species occurs with the preceding.

Family TROGIDAE

This group was formerly included as a tribe in the Scarabaeidae, but on the basis of larval and adult structure and habit it has recently been given family rank. It includes a small number of oblong, convex beetles which are dull grayish brown in color; the surface is rough and tuberculate, usually covered with a hard incrustation which is difficult to remove. When disturbed, they usually draw the legs against the body and lie motionless, appearing much as a small lump of dirt or excrement. Other characters which distinguish them are: antennae composed of ten segments, club of three segments, lamellate (segments flattened and capable of being closely folded together; Fig. 405); eyes not divided; scutellum very small; elytra covering abdomen entirely dorsally; legs slender, weak, scarcely fossorial; coxae contiguous; profemora enlarged; tarsal claws simple; five abdominal sternites visible.

The family name comes from the Greek word meaning "to gnaw," which describes the habit of these beetles. They live in and about carrion, feathers, dried carcasses of all sorts, and also in the nests of birds or small animals which contain animal debris.

Genus *TROX* Fabricius

Since there is only the one genus in the family, the characters listed above will distinguish these beetles.

KEY TO SPECIES

1. Scutellum spear-shaped, narrowed strongly near base, sides angulate at middle (Fig. 425) 2
   Scutellum oval, never spear-shaped 3
2. Elytra with rows of distinct, rounded, widely separated tubercles on alternate intervals; pronotal margins without long, fine hairs ....i. *monachus*
   Elytra feebly tuberculate; pronotal margins with long, fine hairs ..h. *suberosus*
3. Pronotum mostly glabrous, smooth, not tomentose or noticeably setose, nor ridged, nor tuberculate 4
   Pronotum tomentose, setose, ridged, or tuberculate, or a combination of these characters 5
4. Elytral patches of setae uniform on all intervals (in size, spacing, and number), less elongate, setae sparse and short ....b. *aequalis*
   Elytral patches of setae contrasting, those on odd intervals more elongate, closer together, setae longer and more numerous, those on even intervals smaller, wider apart, placed in tufts of from five to six setae, the setae shorter ....a. *scaber*

559

5. Pronotum with four rounded foveae enclosed by setose ridges 6
   Pronotum without four rounded foveae enclosed by setose ridges 7
6. Metatibiae of male greatly enlarged at middle, with a large tooth within, near
   apex; of female, keeled narrowly on outer margin from base to external
   tooth (Fig. 426) ....c. *hamatus*
   Metatibiae not enlarged or toothed within in either sex, outer margin not
   keeled (Fig. 427) ....d. *foveicollis*
7. Posterior angles of pronotum not extended posteriorly, basal margin near
   angles straight at sides (Fig. 428) 8
   Posterior angles of pronotum extended posteriorly, basal margin near angles
   sinuate (Fig. 429) ....e. *tuberculatus*
8. Elytra with large, square, strial punctures in regular rows; long lines of fine,
   yellow setae in double rows on odd intervals; pronotum with sides nearly
   parallel ....g. *unistriatus*
   Elytral strial punctures not visible; conspicuous tufts of dense, erect, long
   setae on odd intervals; pronotal sides rounded ....f. *variolatus*

a. *Trox scaber* (Linné)   Plate LV, No. 9, p. 563

Oblong-oval; black; antennal club fulvous. Head densely punctate. Pronotum nearly twice as wide as long, not tomentose, densely punctate;
median longitudinal groove distinct, ending in a rounded fovea at base, two
foveae laterally, these three foveae well defined; marginal setae short. Elytra
not tomentose, the third interval and sometimes fifth feebly elevated,
clothed with tufts of yellowish setae, on odd intervals the setae usually
denser and in more-elongate patches; sides without setae, reflexed. Metatarsi with first segment shorter than last segment; metatibiae with serrations
interrupted before apex. Length 5–7 mm.

This species may be found beneath carrion and rubbish, on fur and
feathers, and in nests of birds and mammals.

b. *Trox aequalis* Say   Plate LV, No. 16, p. 563

Oblong-oval; dull blackish brown; antennal club fulvous. Head densely
punctate. Pronotum almost twice as wide as long, not tomentose; median
longitudinal groove and basal median fovea often obsolete, lateral foveae
present but not deep; sides feebly arcuate; marginal setae short. Elytra
not tomentose; all intervals flat, not elevated; clothed with small, round,
equidistant tufts of yellow setae (these tufts sometimes elongated or confluent); reflexed sides without setae. First metatarsal segment shorter than
last segment; metatibiae with serrations interrupted before apex. Length
5–6.5 mm.

This species may be found in mammal and bird nests and also beneath
bark and under dead leaves.

c. *Trox hamatus* Robinson   Plate LV, No. 11, p. 563

Oblong-ovate; blackish brown; antennal scape with fulvous hairs, club
fulvous. Head quadrituberculate. Pronotum nearly twice as wide as long,
densely tomentose; disk with four, large, deep, rounded foveae, ridges
separating them sharply elevated and narrow; sides feebly or not at all

sinuate before posterior angles; marginal setae dense, contiguous. Elytra with surface of tubercles usually covered by dense, long setae, much longer than marginal setae; marginal setae not contiguous. Metatibiae of male flattened, half as wide as long, externally with a keel expanding into a blunt tooth at apical third, internally with a large, curved tooth near apex, this covered by hairs; in female nearly one-third as wide as long, keel on outer margin scarcely expanded into a tooth at apical one-third, no tooth on inner side. Length 5–6 mm.

These beetles have been taken from carrion, chicken feathers, mammal nests, and at light.

d. *Trox foveicollis* Harold   Plate LV, No. 14, p. 563

Oblong-ovate; blackish brown; antennal scape with fulvous hairs, club fulvous. Head quadrituberculate. Pronotum nearly twice as wide as long, densely tomentose; disk with four large, rounded foveae, sometimes the two anterior foveae indistinct, ridges sharply elevated, narrow; sides sinuate before posterior angles; marginal setae moderately separated. Elytra with surface of tubercles bearing short, erect, brownish setae which are as long

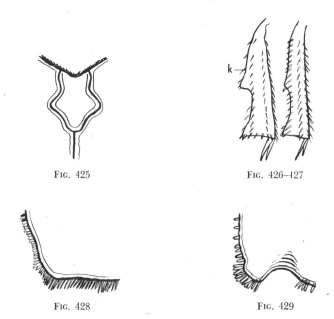

FIG. 425   FIG. 426–427

FIG. 428   FIG. 429

Fig. 425. Scutellum of *Trox monachus*.
Figs. 426–427. Left metatibia of female *T. hamatus* (426) and of *T. foveicollis* (427), viewed from above. *k*, keel.
Figs. 428–429. Left basal angle of pronotum of *T. unistriatus* (428) and of *T. tuberculatus* (429).

PLATE LV
Family SCARABAEIDAE VII

1. *Phyllophaga ephilida* (Say) (p. 532) — Brownish yellow; head and pronotum darker; 14–18 mm.

2. *P. anxia* LeConte (p. 533) — Dark brown to blackish; 17–21 mm.

3. *P. fervida* (Fabricius) (p. 533) — Dark brown to blackish; 19.5 mm.

4. *P. forsteri* Burmeister (p. 534) — Reddish brown; head and pronotum often darker; 16–17 mm.

5. *Strategus antaeus* (Drury) ♂ (p. 550) — Dark brown, shining; 28–31 mm.

6. *Macrodactylus subspinosus* (Fabricius) (p. 540) — Reddish brown; head and pronotum often darker; 8–10 mm.

7. *Strategus antaeus* (Drury) ♀ (p. 550) — Dark brown, shining; 28–31 mm.

8. *Anomala flavipennis* Burmeister (p. 543) — Reddish yellow; elytra pale yellow, with or without darker areas; 10–12 mm.

Family TROGIDAE

9. *Trox scaber* (Linné) (p. 560) — Black; 5–7 mm.

10. *T. monachus* Herbst (p. 565) — Deep brown; 12–16 mm.

11. *T. hamatus* Robinson (p. 560) — Blackish; 5–6 mm.

12. *T. tuberculatus* (DeGeer) (p. 564) — Blackish; 7.5–11 mm.

13. *T. unistriatus* Beauvois (p. 564) — Dull blackish; 9–12 mm.

14. *T. foveicollis* Harold (p. 561) — Blackish; 5–6.5 mm.

15. *T. suberosus* Fabricius (p. 564) — Dull grayish brown; 9–17 mm.

16. *T. aequalis* Say (p. 560) — Dull blackish brown, with light-brown scales and hairs; 5–6.5 mm.

17. *T. variolatus* Melsheimer (p. 564) — Dull black; 6–8.5 mm.

MM | 0 | 10 | 20 | 30 | 40 | 50 | 60 | 70

PLATE LV   563

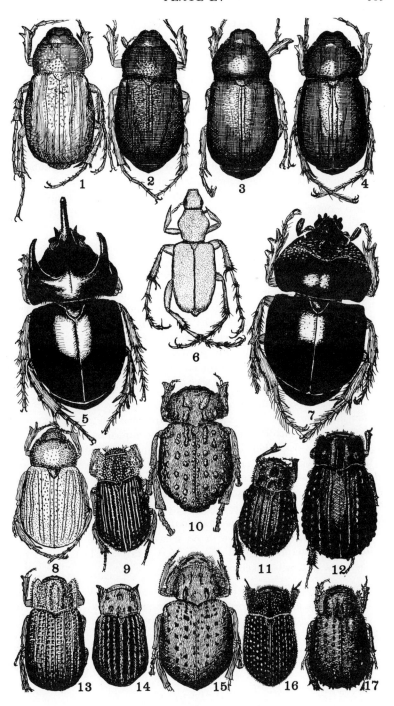

as or longer than marginal setae; marginal setae not contiguous. Metatibiae feebly toothed. Length 5–6.5 mm.

This species may be collected from carrion, feathers, dung, and in some bird nests.

e. *Trox tuberculatus* (DeGeer)   Plate LV, No. 12, p. 563
Oblong, slightly broader behind middle; black or piceous; antennal scape with fulvous hairs, club fulvous. Head not tuberculate, with four tufts of setae or scattered, conspicuous setae. Pronotum densely tomentose, lateral tubercles feebly covered with dark, erect setae. Elytra tomentose; the odd intervals, except third at base, not elevated between setae-bearing tubercles which are round or elongate, setae dark or bronzed, occasionally yellow, long; marginal setae usually separated by about their own length. Metatibiae on outer side feebly serrate, strongly spined on inner side. Length 7.5–11 mm.

f. *Trox variolatus* Melsheimer   Plate LV, No. 17, p. 563
Oblong-oval; dull black, sometimes somewhat shining; antennal scape with fulvous hairs, antennal club fulvous. Head bituberculate, setae conspicuous. Pronotum about twice as wide as long, tomentose; median ridges behind middle, anterior margin, and lateral tubercles with dark, erect setae. Elytra tomentose, all intervals flat, not raised; conspicuous tufts of erect, long setae on odd intervals; reflexed margins with a row of setose tubercles; marginal setae usually separated by nearly their own length. Prosternum behind procoxae bituberculate. Length 6–8.5 mm.

This species has been taken in owl pellets, carrion, fur, and dung.

g. *Trox unistriatus* Beauvois   Plate LV, No. 13, p. 563
Elongate-ovate; dull brownish black; antennal club fulvous. Head bituberculate or quadrituberculate, setae inconspicuous. Pronotum less than twice as wide as long, tomentose; median ridges, tubercles, and anterior margin with sparse, erect, yellow setae. Elytra rather shining; suture and odd intervals slightly raised, each with a double row of fine, yellow setae which are more or less continuous on third but are separated into elongate, widely spaced patches on others; even intervals with same arrangement of setae but in shorter patches; strial punctures large, in rows as wide as intervals; reflexed margins with no setae or tubercles; marginal setae contiguous. Prosternum behind procoxae feebly carinate. Length 9–12 mm.

These beetles may be taken on carrion.

h. *Trox suberosus* Fabricius   Plate LV, No. 15, p. 563
Oblong; dull grayish brown; antennal scape with fulvous hairs; club fulvous. Head bituberculate. Pronotum transverse, tomentose; surface not ridged, tubercles and lateral depressions confluent, obsolete; lateral margins notched in front of posterior angles; all margins with long, fine hairs. Elytral humeri prominent; odd intervals either not raised, not tuberculate,

and almost entirely tomentose or odd intervals feebly raised and with small, black, shining, flattened tubercles alternating with tomentose patches; even intervals flat or slightly rugose; reflexed margins without tubercles or setae. Denuded specimens have large strial punctures, and elytra appear nearly smooth. Length 9–17 mm.

These beetles may be collected from carrion, cow dung, feathers, and at light.

i. *Trox monachus* Herbst   Plate LV, No. 10, p. 563

Oblong; dark brown or fuscous; antennal scape with fulvous hairs, club fulvous. Head bituberculate. Pronotum transverse, tomentose; surface ridged and tuberculate, the depressions distinct; sides notched in front of posterior angles. Elytral humeri prominent; odd intervals strongly raised, tuberculate to apical declivity, tubercles large, round, widely separated and tomentose, no black spaces present; third interval at base with tubercles somewhat confluent; even intervals flat, tomentose, with scattered patches of setae; reflexed elytral margins with irregularly placed tomentose tubercles. Length 12–16 mm.

This species may be taken on carrion and feathers.

Family LUCANIDAE

Stag Beetles or Pinching Beetles

This family is closely related to the Scarabaeidae but differs in having the three or four outer antennal segments enlarged and platelike to form a club, the plates not fitting together compactly (Fig. 430). Mostly moderate-sized beetles, living by day in or beneath dead or decaying logs and stumps. Some take to flight at dusk and are attracted in large numbers to light; others are said to feed on exudations of leaves and bark of trees. The grublike larvae resemble those of the May beetles and live in damp, decaying wood.

The antennae ten-segmented, inserted under the margin of the front; elytra rounded at apex, covering the abdomen; abdomen ventrally with five visible segments, which are not fused (six in *Platycerus*); legs adapted for digging; procoxae large, transverse, without trochantin, cavities closed behind; protibiae more or less toothed on outer side; meso- and metatibiae with two teeth on outer side; tarsi slender, five-segmented; claws simple, with a short, bristle-bearing pad (onychium) between them (Fig. 431).

KEY TO GENERA

1. Antennae geniculate (Fig. 430), scape nearly or quite as long as others combined 2
   Antennae straight 5
2. Elytra smooth or nearly so; protibiae with large teeth on outer edge; large, 20–35 mm. long 3
   Elytra striate and punctate; protibiae serrulate or multidentate; medium-sized beetles, 10–20 mm. long 4
3. Mandibles of male at least as long as elytra; labrum elongate, triangular, apex narrowly rounded in female (Fig. 432), in male acute (Fig. 433) ....II. *Lucanus*   (p. 568)
   Mandibles of male no longer than pronotum; labrum transverse, triangular, apex broadly rounded or truncate in female (Fig. 434), notched at apex in male (Fig. 435) ....I. *Pseudolucanus*   (p. 568)
4. Eyes strongly emarginate (Fig. 436) ....III. *Dorcus*   (p. 569)
   Eyes almost entire (Fig. 437) ....IV. *Platycerus*   (p. 569)
5. Form oblong, elongate, sides parallel or nearly so; elytra striate, glabrous; front excavated ....V. *Ceruchus*   (p. 572)
   Form short, oval, convex, sides not parallel; elytra not striate, coarsely punctate; front not excavated ....VI. *Nicagus*   (p. 572)

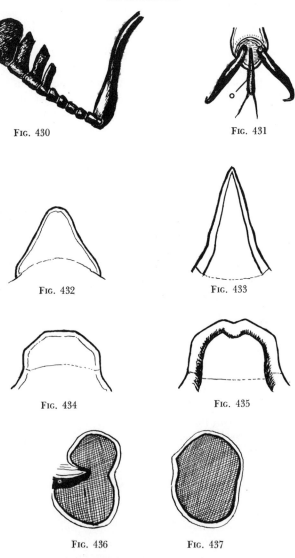

Fig. 430.

Fig. 431.

Fig. 432.

Fig. 433.

Fig. 434.

Fig. 435.

Fig. 436.

Fig. 437.

Fig. 430. Antenna of *Pseudolucanus* of the sort typical of the family, with a loosely lamellated club; not always are the antennae geniculate as here.

Fig. 431. Tarsal claws of *Pseudolucanus*. *o,* onychium.

Figs. 432–435. Labrum of lucanids. *Lucanus* female (432). *Lucanus* male (433). *Pseudolucanus* female (434). *Pseudolucanus* male (435).

Figs. 436–437. Left eye of *Dorcus* (436) and of *Platycerus* (437).

Genus I. *PSEUDOLUCANUS* Hope

Very large, smooth, brown to piceous species; in male, mandibles prominent, as long as pronotum, head subequal in width to pronotum, mentum broad, concealing maxillae; in female, mandibles shorter than head; head narrower than pronotum; labrum transversely triangular, apex truncate or broadly rounded in female, in male notched; antennae geniculate; abdomen with five visible ventral segments.

KEY TO SPECIES

Femora light brown; mandible of male with but one tooth internally ....
....a. *capreolus*
Femora dark brown or black; mandible of male with several internal teeth ....
....b. *placidus*

a. *Pseudolucanus capreolus* (Linné)   Plate LVI, Nos. 2, 3, p. 571
Elongate-oblong; dark reddish brown, smooth, shining; femora light brown. Mandibles with one tooth on inner edge in male, and twice as long as those of female. Head of male broader than pronotum. Elytra smooth or very finely punctate. Length 22–35 mm.
This species varies greatly in color and size. It is usually taken by sugaring, at light, and around decaying logs and stumps.

b. *Pseudolucanus placidus* (Say)   Plate LVI, No. 4, p. 571
Elongate-oblong; very dark reddish brown or piceous, smooth, shining; femora dark brown or nearly black. Mandibles of male as long as pronotum, straight, with several teeth on inner side, female with two indistinct teeth. Head of male not broader than pronotum. Entire upper surface distinctly punctate. Length 19–32 mm.
This species is often collected at lights.

Genus II. *LUCANUS* Scopoli

Very large, smooth, brown beetles; mandibles prominent, in male as long as elytra, in female shorter than head; head wider than pronotum in male, narrower in female; mentum very broad, entirely concealing the maxillae; labrum narrowly elongate, triangular, apex narrowly rounded in female, acute in male; antennae geniculate; abdomen with five visible sternites.
This genus occurs most frequently in the southern portion of the region included in this book.

Lucanus elaphus Fabricius — Giant Stag Beetle
Plate LVI, Nos. 5, 6, p. 571

Dark chestnut-brown, shining; legs and antennae black or nearly so. Head of male much wider than pronotum, a distinct crest present above the eyes; mandibles very long, widely forked at apex, inner edge with numerous small teeth. Exclusive of the mandibles the length is 31–40 mm. in male and 28 mm. in female.

This species occurs about oak stumps and at light. The females are very rare.

Genus III. *DORCUS* MacLeay

Moderate-sized, more or less parallel-sided species; body distinctly pedunculate; elytra striate and punctate; protibiae serrulate or with many teeth; eyes strongly emarginate; antennae geniculate; abdomen with five visible ventral segments.

Dorcus parallelus Say — Antelope Beetle
Plate LVI, No. 8, p. 571

Oblong, parallel; dark brown, nearly black. Head and pronotum shining, finely and sparsely punctate; mentum with a distinct transverse stria in male, rugose in female; head of male nearly as broad as pronotum; mandibles with a large, medial tooth. Elytra deeply striate, both striae and intervals finely, densely punctate. Length 15–26 mm.

This beetle is common about lights during warmer parts of the summer and may also be found about roots and stumps of decayed oak, linden, and maple trees, in which their larvae live.

Genus IV. *PLATYCERUS* Geoffroy

Small, oblong; eyes nearly entire; antennae geniculate; six ventral abdominal sternites visible; protibiae armed externally with many fine, serrulate teeth; mandibles of male incline upward and are larger than in female.

Platycerus virescens Fabricius — Plate LVI, No. 1, p. 571

Oblong, subdepressed; piceous or dark reddish brown, occasionally with brassy or greenish tinge, shining. Mandibles of male as long as head and with about six teeth near apex, in female much shorter. Pronotum one-half wider than long, sides rounded, hind angles obtuse; disk sparsely punctate

PLATE LVI
Family LUCANIDAE

1. *Platycerus virescens* Fabricius (p. 569)

Dark brown to blackish; elytra sometimes reflected with dull greenish and blue; 10–12 mm.

2. *Pseudolucanus capreolus* (Linné) ♂ (p. 568)
3. *P. capreolus* (Linné) ♀ (p. 568)

Dark brown, shining; 22–35 mm.

4. *P. placidus* (Say) (p. 568)

Dark brown to blackish; 19–32 mm.

5. *Lucanus elaphus* Fabricius ♂ (p. 569)
6. *L. elaphus* Fabricius ♀ (p. 569)

Dark brown; elytra a little paler; 28–40 mm.

7. *Nicagus obscurus* (LeConte) (p. 572)

Dull brown to blackish; elytra sometimes slightly paler; 7–9.5 mm.

8. *Dorcus parallelus* Say (p. 569)

Dark brown or blackish; 15–26 mm.

9. *Ceruchus piceus* (Weber) (p. 572)

Black or nearly so, shining; 10–15 mm.

Family PASSALIDAE

10. *Popilius disjunctus* (Illiger) (p. 573)

Black, very shining; 32–36 mm.

MM | 0 | 10 | 20 | 30 | 40 | 50 | 60 | 70

PLATE LVI

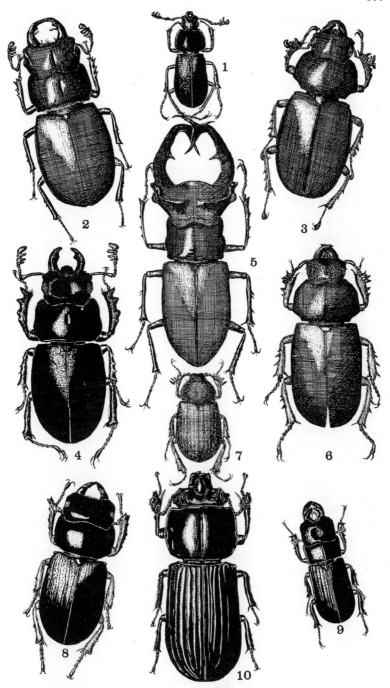

in male, more densely and coarsely so in female. Elytra with three or four more or less distinct striae near suture; surface deeply, sparsely punctate. Length 10–12 mm.

This species is found especially beneath bark and in logs of decaying oak and frequently on flowers such as blackberry.

Genus V. *CERUCHUS* MacLeay

Oblong or elongate, sides nearly parallel or parallel, slightly convex; antennae straight, not geniculate; front excavated; elytra glabrous; procoxae contiguous; head of male broader and longer than that of female, and with a deep frontal excavation in both sexes.

Ceruchus piceus (Weber)   Plate LVI, No. 9, p. 571

Subcylindrical, parallel-sided, slightly convex; piceous or dark reddish brown, very shining. Head deeply striate laterally; male with mandibles as long as head and with a very large tooth at middle of inner edge, in female one-half as long as head, with three or four rounded teeth on inner edge. Pronotum coarsely and densely punctate. Elytra coarsely and densely punctate, feebly striate in both sexes, more obsoletely so on sides. Length 10–15 mm.

These beetles breed in decaying logs of beech, oak, and other trees.

Genus VI. *NICAGUS* LeConte

Short, oval, convex species in which the sides are not parallel; mentum triangular; antennae ten-segmented, with a club of three segments; elytra not striate but coarsely punctate. In general appearance these beetles resemble scarabs.

Nicagus obscurus (LeConte)   Plate LVI, No. 7, p. 571

Oval, convex; piceous or dark brown, with sparse, short, indistinct, pale, suberect hairs; entire upper surface coarsely and rather densely punctate. Pronotum one-half wider than long, broadest at middle, apex distinctly narrower than base; margins finely crenate; anterior angles prominent, posterior ones obtuse. Elytra not striate; pubescence denser than that on pronotum. Length 7–9.5 mm.

This species usually occurs about piles of damp debris in sandy localities.

Family PASSALIDAE

Horn or Bess Beetles

The single United States species is a large, somewhat flattened, parallel-sided, black beetle, with deeply striate elytra; mentum deeply emarginate, the notch being filled with the large, hornlike ligula (Fig. 438); body distinctly pedunculate; antennae stout, not geniculate but, in repose, curved so as to appear so (Fig. 439).

These beetles live in half-decayed logs and stumps, in company with their larvae, and are of particular biological interest because of their social habits. Larvae and adults live together in colonies and communicate with each other by stridulating, the adults tending the larvae in the brood galleries.

Genus *POPILIUS* Kaup

This genus is characterized sufficiently by the above description.

Popilius disjunctus (Illiger)   Bess Beetle

Plate LVI, No. 10, p. 571

Elongate, more or less flattened, robust; black, shining. Head with a short, curved hook. Pronotum quadrate, disk smooth, with a deep median impressed line; posterior angles rounded. Elytra deeply striate, striae finely punctate. Length 32–36 mm.

The name "*Passalus cornutus* Fabricius" has been in use for this insect for many years, but recently it has been found to have been so employed in error.

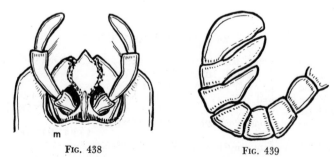

Fig. 438   Fig. 439

Fig. 438. Ligula of *Popilius*. *m*, mentum.
Fig. 439. Antenna of *Popilius*.

573

Family CERAMBYCIDAE

Longhorn Beetles

This family is a popular one among collectors, as many forms are hand-somely or strikingly colored, the species numerous, and many of them very common. They are very active fliers or runners and often feign death when disturbed. Many forms, when picked up, make a squeaking or rasp-ing sound by rubbing the thorax over the scutellum. The very elongate antennae, in extreme cases extending more than four times the length of the body, and the form of the tarsi serve to distinguish the members of this group. They are moderate- or large-sized, less than one-fourth of an inch to over three inches in length, cylindrical or sometimes flattened, elongate beetles. Antennae usually serrate or with segments cylindrical, sometimes moniliform, very elongate, generally as long as or longer than the body. Tarsi five-segmented, but the fourth segment always small, ap-pearing as a node at the base of the fifth, the third deeply bilobed (Fig. 440). The adults occur on tree trunks and limbs, on foliage, flowers, and beneath bark; some forms come freely to light and others to sugar. The larvae are known as the "round-headed wood-borers" and may take up to two or three or more years to mature.

Of the 1,500 species found in North America, about 450 are within the range included in this book.

Some species are very destructive in the immature stages, as their larvae bore in the trunks of living orchard and forest trees, but primarily they are feeders on decaying wood. A few live in the stems or about the roots of herbs.

KEY TO SUBFAMILIES

1. Pronotum margined; labrum connate ....PRIONINAE (p. 575)
   Pronotum not margined; labrum free 2
2. Protibiae not grooved; palpi not acute at tip 3
   Protibiae grooved (Fig. 441); last palpal segment cylindrical and pointed ....LAMIINAE (p. 624)
3. Head strongly constricted behind eyes; procoxae conical ....
   ....LEPTURINAE (p. 606)
   Head not strongly constricted behind eyes; procoxae depressed ....
   ....CERAMBYCINAE (p. 580)

574

Subfamily PRIONINAE

KEY TO TRIBES

1. Antennae short, of similar simple segments, not extending beyond
   the base of pronotum (Fig. 442) ....PARANDRINI (p. 575)
   Antennae elongate, extending beyond base of pronotum, the segments
   dissimilar or complicated 2
2. Pronotal sides with many fine teeth; eyes not or very feebly emarginate ....MACROTOMINI (p. 576)
   Pronotal sides with two or more large teeth; eyes rather strongly
   emarginate ....PRIONINI (p. 576)

Tribe PARANDRINI

Genus *PARANDRA* Latreille

Brown, moderate-sized, oblong beetles, having eyes transverse, feebly
emarginate; antennae attaining base of pronotum, second segment half as
long as third, segments three to ten equal, almost as wide as long, flattened; prosternum distinct between procoxae, which are large and transverse, cavities closed behind.

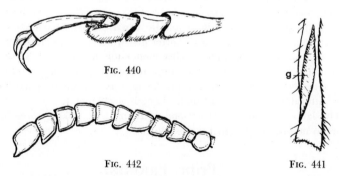

Fig. 440

Fig. 442

g

Fig. 441

Fig. 440. Tarsus of *Prionus,* showing the reduced fourth segment
    characteristic of the family and its relatives.

Fig. 441. Protibia of *Monochamus;* posterior face of apex, showing the
    groove (*g*).

Fig. 442. Antenna of *Parandra,* the segments more or less similar and
    somewhat moniliform.

Parandra brunnea (Fabricius)   Pole Borer
                                                                       Plate LVII, No. 2, p. 579

Elongate-oblong, subdepressed; yellowish brown to deep reddish brown, shining. Pronotum subquadrate, widest anteriorly; the sides nearly straight, margined, gradually converging to base. Elytra with sides parallel, margined, rounded at apex, not striate. Length 9–18 mm.

This species is one of the most destructive borers, attacking poles, cross-ties, shade trees, and any structural wood in contact with moist ground. Sometimes the adults do not emerge, but mate and lay eggs in the same cavity in which they are working.

Tribe MACROTOMINI

Genus *STENODONTES* Serville

Large, elongate, nearly parallel-sided beetles. The antennae are eleven-segmented, extending to just beyond middle of elytra, rather slender, not serrate, segments feebly widened apically. Eyes with upper lobes separated two to three times the width of a lobe; finely granulate. Mandibles robust, in male sometimes much elongated. Pronotum strongly transverse; lateral margins nearly straight, multidenticulate.

Stenodontes dasystomus (Say)   Hardwood-Stump Borer
                                                                       Plate LVII, No. 8, p. 579

Elongate, parallel-sided, feebly convex; medium reddish brown to nearly piceous, moderately shining. Head coarsely, rugosely punctate. Pronotum with a broad area either side of middle, a narrow band basally at middle and a long, broad carina and a shorter one which is more lateral, smooth, without punctures, remainder of disk moderately finely, rugosely punctate; the median line sometimes smooth to near the apex; hind angles not spined but obtusely dentate. Elytra smooth, finely, very sparsely, obsoletely punctate; sutural angle with small tooth. Length 30–46 mm.

The larvae live in the heartwood of living trees, taking three or four years to mature. Lights attract the adults.

Tribe PRIONINI

KEY TO GENERA

Elongate, parallel in form; apex of each antennal segment simple, the
    apical segments elongate, none imbricate ....I. *Orthosoma* (p. 577)
Robust in form; antennal segments often all overlapping and at least
    the apices of the more apical ones produced into lobes, the apical seg-
    ments not elongate ....II. *Prionus* (p. 577)

Genus I. *ORTHOSOMA* Serville

Large, elongate, parallel; eyes strongly granulate; antennae eleven-segmented, rather slender, apex of each segment simple, apical segments elongate, none imbricate; pronotum with two or three distinct teeth laterally.

Orthosoma brunneum (Forster)   Plate LVII, No. 5, p. 579
Elongate, cylindrical, parallel; light reddish brown, strongly shining. Head with a deep impression between antennae. Pronotum transverse, margined, and with three teeth laterally. Elytra each with three fine, raised lines; surface finely and densely punctate. Fifth sternite rounded in female, broadly truncate in male. Length 22–45 mm.

This species breeds in crossties, poles, and all structural timbers in contact with the ground or in moist, exposed situations. Adults are also attracted to lights.

Genus II. *PRIONUS* Fabricius

Very large, robust, reddish-brown to black forms that have the antennal segments conical, stout, and overlapping in male, more slender and sub-serrate in female, fourth and following antennal segments finely reticulate with elevated lines which bear special sense organs. Pronotum laterally curved, with two or three spines; elytra broadly rounded at apex, disk indistinctly costate.

KEY TO SPECIES

1. Antennae 16- to 20-segmented ....c. *imbricornis*
   Antennae 12-segmented 2
2. Pronotum almost or quite as broad as base of elytra; antennae robust; distance between upper lobes of eyes at least as great as width of lobe; color piceous-black ....a. *laticollis*
   Pronotum narrower than base of elytra; antennae more slender; distance between upper lobes of eyes less than the width of a lobe; color light reddish brown ....b. *pocularis*

a. *Prionus laticollis* (Drury)   Broad-necked Root Borer
                                                  Plate LVII, No. 1, p. 579
Broad, robust; piceous-black, shining; male with antennae attaining apical third of elytra; female with antennae one-half or less than body length. Pronotum as wide as base of elytra, laterally armed with three teeth, these often slightly reflexed, the basal one sometimes feeble; disk shining, sparsely punctate. Elytra widest at base; disk roughly and irregularly punctate, with three longitudinal, indistinct costae. Female much larger than the male. Length 22–47 mm.

PLATE LVII
Family CERAMBYCIDAE I

1. *Prionus laticollis* (Drury) (p. 577) — Fuscous to black, somewhat shining; 22–47 mm.

2. *Parandra brunnea* (Fabricius) (p. 576) — Yellowish brown to deep reddish, shining; 9–18 mm.

3. *Prionus pocularis* Dalman (p. 580) — Orange-brown, somewhat shining; 25–45 mm.

4. *Smodicum cucujiforme* (Say) (p. 582) — Uniformly tan, rather shining; 7–10 mm.

5. *Orthosoma brunneum* (Forster) (p. 577) — Orange-brown, strongly shining; 22–45 mm.

6. *Oeme rigida* (Say) (p. 584) — Pale orange-brown, scarcely shining; 7–9 mm.

7. *Prionus imbricornis* Linné (p. 580) — Dark reddish brown to blackish, shining; 22–47 mm.

8. *Stenodontes dasystomus* (Say) (p. 576) — Dark reddish brown to piceous, shining; 30–46 mm.

9. *Asemum atrum* Eschscholtz (p. 582) — Dull reddish brown to blackish, feebly shining; 8.5–12 mm.

10. *Psyrassa unicolor* Randall (p. 589) — Light reddish brown, shining; 8–12 mm.

11. *Tylonotus bimaculatus* Haldeman (p. 584) — Deep brown or blackish; elytra each with two orange or yellow spots; 12–16 mm.

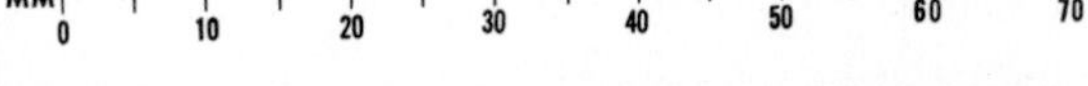

MM 0 10 20 30 40 50 60 70

PLATE LVII

579

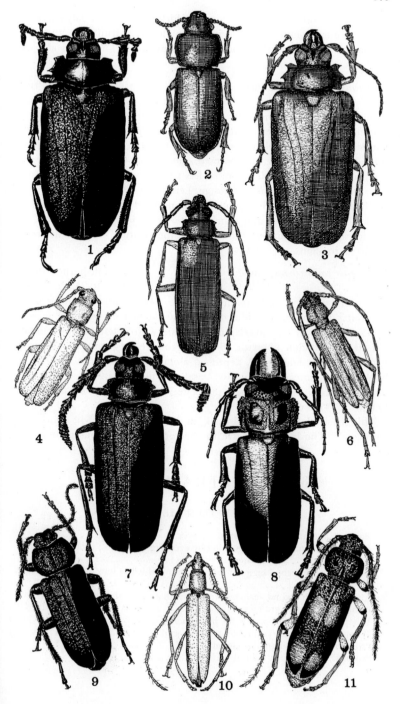

580 CERAMBYCIDAE

Unlike the other species of *Prionus* which breed in the large trees, this species is more commonly found in the smaller trees, fruit trees, and shrubs, the larvae feeding on the roots of the living trees. The adults also come to lights.

b. *Prionus pocularis* Dalman   Pine-Stump Prionus
                                          Plate LVII, No. 3, p. 579

Broad but more slender than *laticollis;* light reddish brown, shining. Antennae more slender than in preceding species. Pronotum slightly narrower than base of elytra, laterally with three teeth, these never reflexed, the two anterior ones sharply pointed, one at basal angle obtuse; disk finely punctate. Elytra with sides more or less parallel; disk rather densely punctate, with three very indistinct costae. Length 25–45 mm.

The only species of this genus not found solely in living trees but also in dead coniferous logs and stumps. The larvae feed under the root bark in the early stages but enter the wood as they mature. The adults are also attracted to lights.

c. *Prionus imbricornis* Linné   Tile-horned Prionus
                                          Plate LVII, No. 7, p. 579

Robust, shining, dark reddish brown. Male with antennae robust, extending beyond the middle of elytra, composed of 18 to 20 segments which are conical and overlapping; female with antennae more slender, not attaining middle of elytra, 16- to 18-segmented, segments simply serrate. Pronotum short and broad, depressed along lateral margins; anterior two lateral teeth more or less obtuse, basal one not as distinct; disk densely, finely punctate. Elytra rugosely punctate; three indistinct costae on each. Length 22–47 mm.

This species breeds mostly in oak and chestnut, but it will attack other hardwoods. The larvae also live in the roots of herbaceous plants.

Subfamily CERAMBYCINAE

KEY TO TRIBES

1. Bases of antennae not enveloped by eyes 2
   Bases of antennae partly enveloped by eyes (Figs. 444, 445); procoxae
     not conical 4
2. Antennae with second segment more than one-third as long as third;
     eyes variable 3
   Antennae with second segment not more than one-third as long as
     third; eyes finely granulate ....CALLIDIINI   (p. 593)
3. Mesepimera acutely pointed on inner side (Fig. 443) ....SMODICINI   (p. 581)
   Mesepimera normal, truncated at inner end ....ASEMINI   (p. 582)
4. Procoxal cavities angulate, closed behind 5
   Procoxal cavities open behind 6

Tribe Smodicini

Genus *SMODICUM* Haldeman

Moderate-sized, elongate, flattened forms. The front broad, short, and perpendicular; eyes coarsely granulate, very deeply emarginate, not enveloping base of antennae; antennae about as long as body in male, shorter in female, the segments shining, sparsely punctate; mesepimera acutely pointed in inner side. They resemble the cucujids in habit and form.

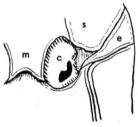

Fig. 443

Fig. 443. Mesosternum and its sidepieces of *Smodicum*. *c*, mesocoxa; *e*, mesepimeron; *m*, mesosternum; *s*, mesepisternum.

Smodicum cucujiforme (Say)   Flat Oak Borer
                                                  Plate LVII, No. 4, p. 579

Elongate, slender, subdepressed; pale, dull yellow, shining. Pronotum slightly elongate, feebly constricted before middle; disk sparsely and irregularly punctate. Elytra with sides parallel, surface finely and sparsely punctate. Femora dilated toward apex. Length 7–10 mm.

The eggs are laid in crevices of exposed wood. The heartwood of oak and hickory is often riddled by this beetle; it also infests stored wood.

Tribe ASEMINI

Genus *ASEMUM* Eschscholtz

Of moderate size, elongate-oblong, subcylindrical; antennae extending to about basal quarter of elytra, finely pubescent; eyes hairy, finely granulate, transverse, emarginate; pronotum slightly transverse, broadest at middle, sides rounded but never margined, subglobular; disk with a broad, longitudinal, shallow impression; elytra parallel-sided, apex rounded.

Asemum atrum Eschscholtz   Pine-Stump Borer
                                                  Plate LVII, No. 9, p. 579

Elongate-oblong, subconvex; dull red-brown to piceous; base of head black; pronotum before and behind margined with black; elytra sometimes covered with dull-yellowish pubescence. Head with longitudinal impression between antennae that extends to occiput. Pronotum densely, rugosely punctate. Elytra with several longitudinal, shallow striae; punctate apically. Length 8.5–12 mm.

The eggs are deposited under bark scales of recently cut or dying trees and stumps; the larvae mine the heartwood or sapwood.

Tribe OEMINI

Genus VI. *OEME* Newman

Small to moderate-sized, elongate, subcylindrical, very slender forms; antennae as long as or one-fourth longer than body, the segments elongate, cylindrical; second segment minute, from fifth segment to apex suddenly more slender than basal five segments, which are hairy and rough; pronotum subglobose, sides gradually rounded from behind middle to apex, base

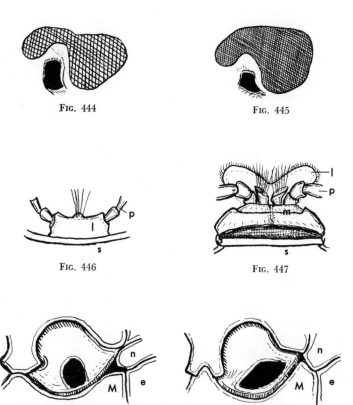

FIG. 444

FIG. 445

FIG. 446

FIG. 447

FIG. 448

FIG. 449

Figs. 444–445. Eye of *Romaleum* (444) and of *Cyllene* (445). In the latter the eye appears smooth, with the individual facets scarcely perceptible, whereas in the former the eye has a rough appearance, with each facet readily distinguishable.

Figs. 446–447. Ligula of *Oeme* (446) and of *Romaleum* (447); the mentum is vertical in the former and, hence, does not appear in the figure. *l*, ligula; *m*, mentum; *p*, labial palpus; *s*, submentum.

Figs. 448–449. Mesocoxa of *Cerasphorus* (448) and of *Romaleum* (449). In the latter the metasternum (*M*) has grown forward along the side of the mesocoxal cavity so that the latter contacts the mesepimeron (*n*) briefly but not the metepisternum (*e*), whereas in the former the cavity contacts all three of these structures.

constricted, with a longitudinal sulcus at middle; elytra slender, tapering gradually to the rounded apex; procoxae strongly angulate externally.

Oeme rigida (Say)   Cypress and Cedar Borer
                                           Plate LVII, No. 6, p. 579

Elongate, slender; pale reddish yellow. Head impressed between eyes. Pronotum sparsely punctate, with a fine median impressed line. Elytra with two discal, longitudinal carinae; sides tapering gradually to apex. Length 7–9 mm.

The larvae bore beneath bark of dead or dying cedar or juniper.

Tribe HESPEROPHANINI

KEY TO GENERA

Pronotum laterally unarmed ....I. *Tylonotus* (p. 584)
Pronotum laterally spinose, sometimes also tuberculate ....
....II. *Cerasphorus* (p. 584)

Genus I. *TYLONOTUS* Haldeman

Medium-sized, elongate, subdepressed forms, with the antennae as long as body; segments compressed and each with two sulci externally, these grooves more distinct on third and fourth segments; pronotum laterally unarmed; femora strongly clubbed.

Tylonotus bimaculatus Haldeman   Ash and Privet Borer
                                           Plate LVII, No. 11, p. 579

Elongate, rather robust, subdepressed; dark brown or piceous; each elytron with two rather large, rounded, yellow spots, one near middle, the other apical. Pronotum short, subcylindrical; disk densely punctate, with median line and two small elevations smooth, shining. Elytra sparsely and coarsely punctate. Length 12–16 mm.

The eggs are laid beneath scales of living or dying ash, hickory, and birch trees or at the base of privet plants. In ash the young larvae feed on bast tissue but go deeper as they mature.

Genus II. *CERASPHORUS* Serville

Large, elongate, slender forms, with antennae sulcate, as long as body in female, much longer in male; pronotum spined at sides; scutellum acute, triangular; femora with two short spines at apex; procoxae rounded.

Cerasphorus cinctus (Drury)   Banded Hickory Borer
Plate LVIII, No. 7, p. 591

Elongate, slender, cylindrical; yellowish brown, covered with gray pubescence; elytra usually marked obliquely with yellow before middle. Pronotum cylindrical, on each side armed with a short, acute spine at middle. Elytra densely and finely punctate, each apex with two short spines. Length 16–35 mm.

The adults deposit eggs in bark crevices or directly in the wood. During the first season the larvae feed beneath the bark, later going into the deeper wood as they mature. Lights attract the adults.

Tribe Eburiini

Genus *EBURIA* Serville

Large, elongate, slender species distinguished by the polished, ivory-colored spots of the elytra. Antennae feebly sulcate from third segment; slightly shorter than body in female, one and one-fourth times the length of the body in male; pronotum spined laterally; scutellum rounded behind; procoxae rounded; femora with two spines apically.

Eburia quadrigeminata (Say)   Ivory-marked Beetle
Plate LIX, No. 2, p. 601

Elongate, slender, subcylindrical; pale brownish yellow; elytra each with two pairs of ivory-white, elongate-oblong spots, one pair basally, the other just behind middle, these spots usually margined with blackish and occasionally with blackish lines connecting the pairs. Pronotum cylindrical, on sides with a short, sharp spine; disk with two small, blackish tubercles near middle. Elytra rather densely and finely punctate; apices each bispinose, the outer spine longer. Meso- and metafemora bispinose apically. Length 14–24 mm.

The larva of this species is a true heartwood-borer and prefers dry, solid wood; it also occurs in lumber in the process of seasoning. Trees attacked are oak, hickory, ash, chestnut, maple, and cypress.

Tribe Elaphidionini

KEY TO GENERA

Large, robust species; metathoracic episterna narrowed behind (Fig. 450) ....I. *Romaleum* (p. 586)
Smaller, more slender species; metathoracic episterna with sides parallel (Fig. 451) ....II. *Elaphidion* (p. 586)

Genus I. *ROMALEUM* White

Large, robust; antennae as long as body in female, longer in male, apical segments more or less flattened, each segment basally with a distinct, dense punctation which contains sense organs; antennae spinose, spines not elongate; pronotum densely and finely punctate, the sculpture and form varying greatly in sexes; metepisternum broad, distinctly narrowed from apex to base; femora not spined.

KEY TO SPECIES

Dark brown, speckled with yellowish-gray pubescence ....a. *atomarium*
Reddish brown, nearly entirely covered with tawny pubescence ..... b. *rufulum*

a. *Romaleum atomarium* (Drury)   Plate LVIII, No. 6, p. 591

Elongate, robust, subcylindrical; very dark brown, variegated above with short, yellowish-gray pubescence. Pronotum rounded at sides, not spined; disk coarsely punctate, medially at base with a short, longitudinal, smooth tubercle and a smaller one each side before middle. Elytra rather coarsely and densely punctate; humeri prominent; apices each with two spines, the outer one longer. Length 19–28 mm.

The larvae feed beneath bark on the bases of dead trees and stumps, going into sapwood, as they mature, to pupate.

b. *Romaleum rufulum* (Haldeman)   Red Oak Borer
       Plate LVIII, No. 8, p. 591

Elongate, robust, subcylindrical; reddish brown, almost uniformly covered above with short, dense, tawny pubescence. Pronotum usually with a small tubercle each side of the median line before middle, behind with a smooth, slightly raised space medially, not always distinct; surface finely and densely punctate in male, coarsely and roughly in female. Elytra with humeri prominent; disk densely and finely punctate; apices bidentate. Length 22–28 mm.

The adults may be taken at lights. The eggs are laid beneath the scales of bark on living oak trees. During the first year the young larva lives beneath bark and the second season migrates to the heartwood.

Genus II. *ELAPHIDION* Serville

Moderate-sized, subcylindrical, slender beetles, having the antennae longer than the body in male, shorter in female, lacking the dense punctations containing the sense organs found in *Romaleum*, basal segments spined, third segment often with a very long and conspicuous spine; metepisternum more or less parallel-sided.

KEY TO SPECIES

1. Antennae and elytra with long spines; femora spinose at tips ....
   ....a. *mucronatum*
   Antennal and elytral spines small; femora not spinose 2
2. Pronotum rounded on sides, with five large dorsal callosities; punctures coarse
   ....b. *incertum*
   Pronotum feebly rounded on sides, dorsal callosities small, punctures small ..3
3. Pronotum stout, wider than long; third segment of antenna considerably
   longer than fourth ....c. *villosum*
   Pronotum slender, longer than wide; third segment of antenna about equal
   to fourth ....d. *parallelum*

a. *Elaphidion mucronatum* (Say)   Spined Bark Borer
Plate LVIII, No. 12, p. 591

Elongate, slender, subcylindrical; dull reddish brown, irregularly covered with grayish-yellow pubescence. Antennae with segments three to five distinctly spinose. Pronotum cylindrical; laterally finely punctate; disk with median line and two small, rounded tubercles each side smooth. Elytra coarsely punctate; apices bispinose, outer one longer. Length 15–20 mm.

The eggs are laid beneath bark scales of dead hardwoods, the larvae feeding beneath bark for the first year and entering the sapwood the second year.

b. *Elaphidion incertum* Newman   Plate LVIII, No. 9, p. 591

Elongate, subcylindrical, moderately robust; dark reddish brown, variegated with light-yellowish-gray pubescence. Antennal segments three to five with small spines apically. Pronotum subglobose, slightly longer than wide; sides broadly rounded; median line smooth, shining, widest behind middle; disk convex, irregular median and lateral callosities separated by

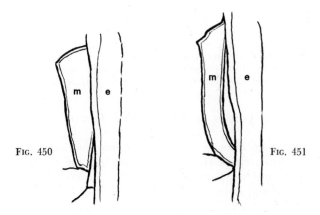

Figs. 450–451. Metepisternum of *Romaleum* (450) and of *Elaphidion* (451). *e*, sides of elytron; *m*, metepisternum.

coarse punctures. Elytra deeply, coarsely punctate at base, punctures becoming finer toward apices; apices bispinose. Length 11–20 mm.

The larvae are found in hickory and mulberry.

c. *Elaphidion villosum* Fabricius   Twig Pruner

Plate LVIII, No. 10, p. 591

Elongate, slender, subcylindrical; dark brown, with pale-grayish-yellow pubescence in scattered, small patches. Antennal segments three to five with short spines. Pronotum feebly transverse, nearly cylindrical, unarmed; disk coarsely and rather roughly punctate. Elytra parallel-sided, deeply and coarsely punctate; apices bispinose, the outer spine somewhat longer. Length 10–17 mm.

The eggs are laid in the axils of leaves near the tip of twigs of hardwoods. The larva mines down the stem and in late summer severs the branch by several cuts from the center outward, except for the bark. This weakens the stem, and it is usually broken off the tree by wind, but the larva remains in the twigs and pupates.

d. *Elaphidion parallelum* Newman   Plate LVIII, No. 11, p. 591

Elongate, subcylindrical; brown, with rather uniform, light-yellowish-gray pubescence; pronotum on each side and elytra usually with one or two elongate, narrow, straight stripes without pubescence. Pronotum slender, cylindrical, elongate, distinctly longer than wide. Elytra parallel, finely and densely punctate, apices bispinose, inner spine minute, dentiform. Length 10–13 mm.

The larvae live in hardwoods.

Tribe SPHAERIONINI

KEY TO GENERA

Eyes coarsely granulate (Fig. 444); prothorax cylindrical; third antennal
   segment with spine often very long .... I. *Psyrassa*   (p. 588)
Eyes finely granulate (Fig. 445); prothorax wedge-shaped; antennal third
   segment with spine always moderate in length ...... II. *Stenosphenus*   (p. 589)

Genus I. *PSYRASSA* Pascoe

Of moderate size, elongate, rather slender, subcylindrical; pronotum narrower than elytra, rather elongate; antennae with the spines very small, not visible beyond the fourth segment; mesocoxal cavities open behind; tibiae longitudinally carinate.

Psyrassa unicolor Randall   Plate LVII, No. 10, p. 579

Elongate, slender, subcylindrical; uniformly light reddish brown, sparsely pubescent. Pronotum cylindrical, nearly one-eighth longer than wide, convex, transversely sulcate near base; sides broadly curved; disk sparsely, irregularly, and coarsely punctate. Elytra densely and coarsely punctate; apices with short spines on outer angle. Length 8–12 mm.

The adults have been taken at lights and have been found pruning small branches from redbud, oak, hickory, beech, and walnut.

Genus II. *STENOSPHENUS* Haldeman

Elongate, subparallel forms of medium size, having eyes finely granulate and deeply emarginate; antennae as long as body, somewhat longer in male, second segment small, third longer than fourth, segments three to seven with short, apical spines on inner side; tibiae carinate; tarsi with first segment as long as the next two together.

Stenosphenus notatus (Olivier)   Plate LVIII, No. 15, p. 591

Short, moderately robust, subparallel; black, shining; pronotum reddish, with an oval, denuded, black spot on disk; undersurface of head and thorax reddish. Pronotum transverse, not narrowed apically, sparsely and coarsely punctate, each puncture bearing a gray hair. Each elytron with apex emarginate, bispinose; disk sparsely, finely punctate. Length 9–12 mm.

The adults and larvae are usually found in dead hickory.

Tribe IBIDIONINI

Genus *HETERACHTHES* Newman

Very elongate species, having the antennae elongate, in male segments three to six robust and seven to eleven slender, entirely slender in female, not spined in either sex; eyes large and coarsely granulate; metacoxal cavities rounded; femora clavate.

KEY TO SPECIES

Uniformly dark brown, elytra immaculate; femora moderately clavate ...a. *ebenus*
Yellowish brown to dark reddish brown, each elytron with two cream-colored spots; femora strongly clavate ....b. *quadrimaculatus*

PLATE LVIII
Family CERAMBYCIDAE II

1. *Phymatodes dimidiatus* (Kirby) (p. 595) — Dark brown to blackish, shining, basal half of elytra dull tan; 9–13 mm.

2. *Obrium rufulum* Gahan (p. 592) — Uniformly pale reddish yellow; 5.5–6.5 mm.

3. *Phymatodes amoenus* (Say) (p. 595) — Reddish orange or tan; elytra shining blue; 5–8 mm.

4. *Molorchus bimaculatus* Say (p. 593) — Brownish black; elytra yellowish, apices and margin black; 5–7 mm.

5. *Phymatodes varius* (Fabricius) (p. 595) — Blackish; elytral markings light reddish brown; 6–9 mm.

6. *Romaleum atomarium* (Drury) (p. 586) — Deep brown, with yellowish markings; 19–28 mm.

7. *Cerasphorus cinctus* (Drury) (p. 585) — Yellowish brown, covered with gray pubescence; elytral markings pale yellow; 16–35 mm.

8. *Romaleum rufulum* (Haldeman) (p. 586) — Light reddish brown, with tawny-pubescent markings; 22–28 mm.

9. *Elaphidion incertum* Newman (p. 587) — Dark reddish brown, with yellowish-gray markings; pronotal sides rounded; 11–20 mm.

10. *E. villosum* Fabricius (p. 588) — Dark brown, with grayish-yellow markings; pronotal sides nearly straight; 10–17 mm.

11. *E. parallelum* Newman (p. 588) — Dark brown, with light-yellowish-gray markings; elytra narrow, parallel-sided; 10–13 mm.

12. *E. mucronatum* (Say) (p. 587) — Dull reddish brown, with grayish-yellow markings; 15–20 mm.

13. *Heterachthes quadrimaculatus* (Fabricius) (p. 592) — Yellowish brown to dark brown, shining; elytral spots pale yellow; 8–11 mm.

14. *Phymatodes testaceus* (Linné) (p. 595) — Head blackish; pronotum reddish; elytra ranging from deep blue to orange-tan; 8–13 mm.

15. *Stenosphenus notatus* (Olivier) (p. 589) — Largely blackish, shining; pronotum reddish, discal spot black; 9–12 mm.

16. *Heterachthes ebenus* Newman (p. 592) — Deep brown, feebly shining; 7–11 mm.

MM 0 10 20 30 40 50 60 70

PLATE LVIII   591

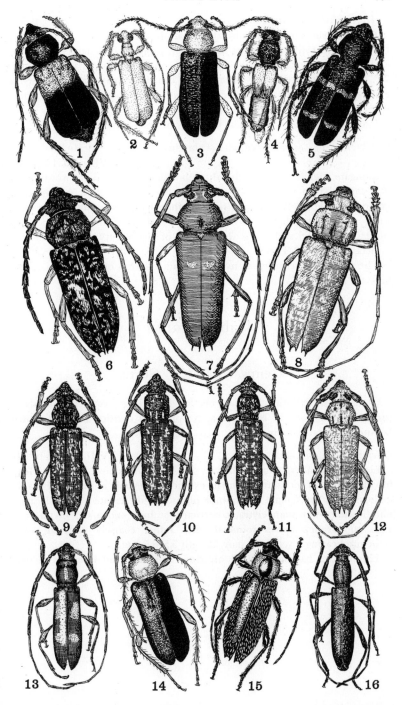

a. *Heterachthes ebenus* Newman   Plate LVIII, No. 16, p. 591

Elongate, slender, subcylindrical; uniformly dark brown, opaque. Pronotum elongate, cylindrical; sides subparallel; pronotal disk densely, coarsely, and roughly punctate, with median line smooth, slightly expanded at middle, and tuberculate; at base deeply and broadly foveate each side. Elytra elongate, sides subparallel; apices rounded; disk smooth, with large punctures widely spaced. Length 7–11 mm.

Usually this species breeds in branches of dead pines.

b. *Heterachthes quadrimaculatus* (Fabricius)   Hickory Borer
Plate LVIII, No. 13, p. 591

Elongate, slender, subcylindrical; yellowish brown to dark brown, shining; each elytron with two circular, paler spots, one before and one just behind middle, and apex usually paler than base. Pronotum longer than wide, sides subparallel; disk with a wide, shallow, median groove, interrupted at middle; surface, as well as that of elytra, very sparsely, coarsely punctate. Length 8–11 mm.

The larvae are recorded as living in dead branches of tulip, poplar, and hickory.

Tribe OBRIINI

Genus *OBRIUM* Curtis

Elongate, subcylindrical, small beetles. Eyes large, coarsely granulate; pronotum narrowed at base and apex; procoxal cavities angulate, closed behind; femora strongly clavate.

Obrium rufulum Gahan   Plate LVIII, No. 2, p. 591

Elongate, slender, subcylindrical; pale reddish yellow, shining. Head broader than pronotum; antennae extending beyond apices of elytra in male, shorter in female. Pronotum obtusely tuberculate each side near middle; narrower than elytra, constricted at base and apex. Elytra with sides subparallel, apices rounded; disk rather coarsely punctate, each puncture bearing a yellowish hair. Length 5.5–6.5 mm.

This species has been found breeding in small dead branches of oak.

Tribe MOLORCHINI

Genus *MOLORCHUS* Fabricius

Small, slender, parallel forms, with elytra only one-half the length of abdomen; antennae longer than body in male, in female about three-fourths length of body; eyes finely granulate; base of antennae partly enveloped by eyes; procoxal cavities angulate, closed behind; femora strongly clavate.

Molorchus bimaculatus Say   Plate LVIII, No. 4, p. 591

Elongate, slender, subdepressed; brownish black, feebly shining; sparsely pubescent with long, grayish hairs; elytra yellowish, apices and margin black; antennae and legs reddish brown. Pronotum subcylindrical, longer than wide, rounded at sides, much constricted basally; surface coarsely and rather densely punctate between callosities. Elytra short, apices broadly rounded; surface coarsely punctate. Length 5–7 mm.

Sumac and wild-cherry flowers especially attract the adults, while the larvae live in many of the hardwoods and also in grapevines.

Tribe CALLIDIINI

KEY TO GENERA

1. Mesonotum with a large, undivided, very finely striate, stridulating surface, the sides neither punctate nor pubescent 2
   Mesonotum without stridulating surface, or if with a median one, then sides of mesonotum are punctate and pubescent ....
   ....II. *Callidium* (p. 594)
2. Metacoxae very prominent; femora strongly clavate; metasternum with scent pores; elytra with ivory-colored lines ...I. *Physocnemum* (p. 593)
   Metacoxae not prominent; elytra without ivory lines ....
   ....III. *Phymatodes* (p. 594)

Genus I. *PHYSOCNEMUM* Haldeman

Elongate-oblong, depressed forms, with eleven-segmented antennae, longer than body and gradually tapering in male, as long as body and almost filiform in female; elytra with ivory lines, humeri prominent, rectangular; metacoxae very prominent; metasternum with scent pores; femora strongly clavate.

Physocnemum brevilineum (Say)   Elm-Bark Borer
Plate LIX, No. 14, p. 601

Elongate-oblong; black; elytra bluish black, with a bronze reflex, each with three short, ivory lines at middle, inner one slightly oblique, middle one largest, curved, interrupted at middle, lateral one rather broad, short. Pronotum wider than long, constricted basally, subglobose, with rounded tubercle laterally at middle; apical portion of disk and sides covered with a dense, velvety pubescence. Elytra with sides subparallel, surface granulate-punctate, punctures much finer toward apices. Length 12–16 mm.

The larvae feed on the corky bark of living elm trees. On bright days the adults can be collected on the trunks of these trees.

Genus II. *CALLIDIUM* Fabricius

Elongate, oblong, subdepressed forms; antennae stout, especially so in male; mesosternum obtusely triangular; femora strongly clavate.

Callidium antennatum Newman   Black-horned Pine Borer
Plate LIX, No. 1, p. 601

Elongate-oblong, robust, subdepressed; very deep blue or purple, shining above, purplish brown beneath; antennae longer than body, thickened basally, each segment clubbed apically in male. Pronotum strongly transverse, constricted basally, disk flattened, without callosities, a smooth, rounded, feeble impression each side of middle, confluently punctate laterally; sides broadly rounded. Elytra with sides subparallel; apices broadly rounded; disk finely, confluently punctate between indistinct costae. Length 13–14 mm.

The eggs are laid in wood that has seasoned over winter. The larvae feed in the sapwood of conifers.

Genus III. *PHYMATODES* Mulsant

Rather small, oblong, slender forms; prosternum very narrow, pointed; metasternum with scent pores; metacoxae not prominent and not enclosed; femora clavate.

KEY TO SPECIES

1. Elytra each with two distinct, yellowish-white crossbars ....d. *varius*
   Elytra without crossbars 2
2. Pronotum uniformly brown or piceous ....c. *dimidiatus*
   Pronotum brown-orange or reddish, sometimes with black markings on disk ..3
3. Length 5–8 mm. ....a. *amoenus*
   Length 12–13 mm. ....b. *testaceus*

a. *Phymatodes amoenus* (Say)   Plate LVIII, No. 3, p. 591

Oblong, slender, subdepressed; reddish yellow, shining; elytra blue; antennae, tibiae, and tarsi dark brown to piceous. Antennae of male extending beyond middle of elytra, those of female not attaining middle. Pronotum subcylindrical, transverse, sides broadly rounded; disk with irregular median and lateral collosities, remainder of surface finely punctate. Elytra with sides parallel; apices rounded; disk rather densely, finely punctate, each puncture bearing a short hair. Length 5–8 mm.

The adults are found on flowers, and the larvae live in dead grapevines.

b. *Phymatodes testaceus* (Linné)   Tanbark Borer
Plate LVIII, No. 14, p. 591

Elongate-oblong, depressed; head blackish; pronotum reddish, disk sometimes darker; elytra yellow, or blue with yellow laterally, very variable in color. Antennae in male extending beyond apices of elytra, in female attaining the apical fourth. Pronotum transverse, sides rounded; disk flattened, sparsely and rather coarsely punctate. Elytra with sides parallel; apices rounded; surface densely, finely punctate. Length 8–13 mm.

The eggs are laid beneath the scales of dead oak or stored hemlock; the larvae mine entirely in the bark.

c. *Phymatodes dimidiatus* (Kirby)   Plate LVIII, No. 1, p. 591

Elongate-oblong, slender, subdepressed; dark brown, shining. Elytra with a paler space basally; body beneath orange-brown. Pronotum convex, transverse; sides rounded, basally constricted; median and lateral callosities present; remaining surface densely, minutely punctate. Elytra rather densely covered with recumbent pubescence; sides subparallel; apices broadly rounded. Length 9–13 mm.

This species is known to breed in spruce, hemlock, and larch.

d. *Phymatodes varius* (Fabricius)   Plate LVIII, No. 5, p. 591

Elongate, rather slender, subdepressed; dark brown to black, covered with prostrate pubescence; pronotum in part or entirely reddish brown. Elytra each with two narrow crossbars, one arcuate, before middle, the other nearly transverse at apical third, and base frequently, reddish brown. Pronotum transverse; sides rounded, constricted basally; indistinct callosities present, surface rather coarsely punctate. Elytra with sides subparallel, apices rounded; surface granulate-punctate basally, simply punctate on remainder of surface. Length 6–9 mm.

These beetles are usually found beneath bark of dead hickory and oak trees.

Tribe CLYTINI

KEY TO GENERA

1. Metepimera not produced, metepisterna linear; front large; process of first abdominal sternite between metacoxae acute . . . .
. . . . IX. *Cyrtophorus*   (p. 604)
Metepimera produced over the angles of first ventral segment (Fig. 452) so as to enclose the metacoxae externally; metepisterna usually wide 2
2. Antennae with some segments spined distally 3
Antennal segments without distal spines 4
3. Prosternum between coxae declivous (Fig. 453) . . . . .II. *Glycobius*   (p. 598)
Prosternum between coxae perpendicular . . . . .I. *Megacyllene*   (p. 596)
4. Front not carinate 5
Front with a Y-shaped or bicarinate ridge (Fig. 454) . .V. *Xylotrechus*   (p. 599)
5. Pronotum with transverse carinae .VI. *Neoclytus*   (p. 602)
Pronotum not transversely carinate 6
6. Pronotal base as broad or broader than apex 7
Pronotal apex wider than base .VIII. *Clytoleptus*   (p. 604)
7. Metepisternum not more than three times as long as broad 8
Metepisternum four times as long as broad . . . . .IV. *Sarosesthes*   (p. 599)
8. Front elevated above the anterior margin of the eyes (Fig. 455) . . . .
. . . . III. *Calloides*   (p. 598)
Front not elevated above the anterior margin of eyes . . . . .VII. *Clytus*   (p. 603)

Genus I. *MEGACYLLENE* Casey

Moderate-sized, oblong, rather robust forms; antennae eleven-segmented; intercoxal process of first abdominal segment bluntly rounded or truncate at apex; prosternum flat, broad between coxae, posterior edge prominent, the posterior wall vertical or even concave.

KEY TO SPECIES

Each metepisternum with two spots of pubescence, the anterior one about one-third as large as posterior spot; adult occurs mainly in spring . . . . .b. *caryae*
Each metepisternum completely covered with pubescence, or with two large, sub-equal spots; most abundant in fall . . . . .a. *robiniae*

a. *Megacyllene robiniae* (Forster)   The Locust Borer
                                        Color Plate C; Plate LIX, No. 12, p. 601
Elongate, rather robust; black, pubescent; head, pronotum, and elytra with narrow, yellow crossbars, the third one on elytra shaped like a W, the three behind this sinuous; legs reddish brown. Antennae of male slender, reaching apical fourth of elytra; female antennae not attaining middle of elytra. Pronotum transverse, constricted at base; sides rounded. Elytra parallel-sided, tapering behind middle; apices obliquely truncate. Prosternum as wide as procoxal cavity. Length 12–18 mm.

The adults feed on goldenrod pollen and lay their eggs beneath the bark scales of black locust. The larvae feed in the bark and later enter the wood.

b. *Megacyllene caryae* (Gahan)   The Painted Hickory Borer
Plate LIX, No. 13, p. 601

Elongate, rather robust; velvety black; head, pronotum, and elytra with narrow, yellow crossbands, the third one on base of elytra W-shaped, the following three sinuous; legs reddish brown. Male with antennae extending beyond apices of elytra; female antennae attaining middle of elytra. Pronotum transverse, sides rounded. Elytra tapering behind middle, more so than in *robiniae;* apices obliquely truncate. Length 12–20 mm.

The adults lay eggs beneath the scales of cut hickory, ash, hackberry, and Osage orange. The larvae feed under the bark and later enter the sapwood.

FIG. 452

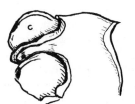

FIG. 453

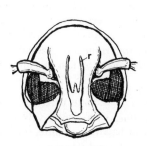

FIG. 454

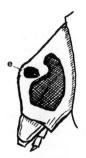

FIG. 455

Fig. 452. Metepimeron of *Glycobius,* the elytron removed to expose the parts. *W,* metepisternum; *X,* metepimeron; *Y,* metacoxa; *Z,* first abdominal sternite.

Fig. 453. Prosternum of *Glycobius* in oblique profile, its process declivous between the procoxae (*c*).

Fig. 454. Head of *Xylotrechus* from the front. *r,* ridge.

Fig. 455. Head of *Calloides* viewed from the side. *e,* elevation of front.

Genus II. *GLYCOBIUS* LeConte

Large, elongate, robust forms, having the antennae rather short and very stout, rapidly tapering distally, the segments basally very broad, strongly flattened, obtriangular, with their apices deeply emarginate and acutely bidentate, three to seven subequal, thence narrower and shorter, the eleventh somewhat appendiculate at tip; prosternum narrowed between coxae, gradually sloping posteriorly; mesosternum also gradually sloping anteriorly; metepimera produced over the angles of the first sternite so as to enclose the metacoxae externally.

Glycobius speciosus (Say)   Sugar-Maple Borer
                                        Plate LIX, No. 4, p. 601

Elongate, robust, subconvex; black; head with dense, yellow pubescence; pronotum with two short, oblique bands of yellow pubescence on each side; elytra with five pubescent bands of yellow, first arcuate and extending obliquely forward to scutellum, second W-shaped, third medial, fourth arcuate, similar to first, almost joining fifth, which is widened on apex. Pronotum transverse; sides rounded, constricted basally; disk convex, surface with fine punctures in male, larger in female. Elytra with sides subparallel, apices truncately emarginate. Length 23–27 mm.

The eggs are laid in the bark crevices of hard maples; the larvae mine between the bark and wood.

Genus III. *CALLOIDES* LeConte

Elongate, robust, rather large species. Antennae moderately slender, of equal thickness beyond the scape, cylindrical; segments not emarginate, three and five subequal, longer than fourth; prosternum narrow between the coxae, posteriorly gradually sloping; mesosternum also gradually sloping anteriorly; metepimera produced over the angle of first sternite; metepisterna usually wide.

Calloides nobilis (Harris)   Plate LIX, No. 6, p. 601

Elongate, robust; brownish black, opaque, with dense, velvety pubescence; elytra each with a round, yellow spot basally, a minute, submarginal one near humerus, a larger one before middle, and two narrow, transverse bands apically, these markings often almost obsolete. Pronotum globose, sides rounded; disk finely, confluently punctate. Elytra with apices rounded, not spined; surface minutely punctate. Length 20–24 mm.

The larvae are usually found in the bases of dead ash and oak.

Genus IV. *SAROSESTHES* Thomson

Large, elongate, subcylindrical beetles, having the antennae as long as the body in male, about three-fifths the length of body in female; antennal segments not spinose at apex, sometimes very acutely angulate; prosternum horizontal or nearly so, very narrow between coxae; mesosternum broadly and evenly sloping; metepimera produced over the angles of the first sternite, so as to enclose the metacoxae externally; metepisterna usually wide.

Sarosesthes fulminans (Fabricius)   Plate LIX, No. 11, p. 601

Elongate, rather robust, subcylindrical; black; head and pronotum with grayish pubescence, the latter with a large, black spot in center of disk and a small, round one each side; elytra with indistinct, angulate, grayish bands. Pronotum transverse, cylindrical; disk convex, with a transverse basal impression, median line glabrous on basal half, remainder of surface finely punctate. Elytra slightly depressed on disk; sides feebly curved; apices emarginately truncate. Length 12–20 mm.

The larvae are found beneath bark of dead butternut, chestnut, and oak trees.

Genus V. *XYLOTRECHUS* Chevrolat

Moderate-sized, elongate, slender, subcylindrical beetles; front of head with a carina, which varies in form; sometimes it is a smooth line, beginning below the eyes and extending slightly beyond them, dividing at about the middle into two V-shaped lines; in some species the V-shaped lines are absent. Antennal cavities margined above by a long, acute carina; first segment of metatarsi longer than any of the following.

KEY TO SPECIES

Elytra brown, with two broad, yellowish-gray or pale-gray crossbars ...b. *colonus*
Elytra brown, with very narrow, irregular, bright-yellow transverse lines ......
....a. *undulatus*

a. *Xylotrechus undulatus* (Say)   Plate LIX, No. 7, p. 601

Elongate, slender, subcylindrical; black or brown; elytra with a narrow stripe extending from scutellum along suture to middle and curving to outer margin, a short crossbar below humerus, a band near apex, and an apical curved line of yellow pubescence, these markings often broken into dots. Head with V-shaped carina on front. Pronotum wider than long, constricted basally; sides rounded; surface rugose. Elytra with sides subparallel;

PLATE LIX
Family CERAMBYCIDAE III

1. *Callidium antennatum* Newman (p. 594)

   Deep blue-black or purplish, slightly shining; 13–14 mm.

2. *Eburia quadrigeminata* (Say) (p. 585)

   Brown-yellow; markings of elytra ivory-white, margined with blackish; 14–24 mm.

3. *Clytus marginicollis* Castelnau (p. 603)

   Dark brown to black, marked with pale-yellow bands; elytral base sometimes pale reddish; 8–10 mm.

4. *Glycobius speciosus* (Say) (p. 598)

   Black, with bright-yellow markings; 23–27 mm.

5. *Clytus ruricola* (Olivier) (p. 603)

   Dark brown to blackish, elytra paler on apical half; markings bright yellow; 8–14 mm.

6. *Calloides nobilis* (Harris) (p. 598)

   Deep brown, with yellow markings; 20–24 mm.

7. *Xylotrechus undulatus* (Say) (p. 599)

   Brown or blackish, with yellowish-white marks; 11–21 mm.

8. *Clytoleptus albofasciatus* (Laporte) (p. 604)

   Black or light to deep brown; markings white, often indistinct; 8–10 mm.

9. *Euderces picipes* (Fabricius) (p. 605)

   Black; elytra often reddish on basal half; markings ivory-white; 5–8 mm.

10. *Xylotrechus colonus* (Fabricius) (p. 602)

    Deep brown or black; elytral markings indistinct, whitish or yellowish; 8–17 mm.

11. *Sarosesthes fulminans* (Fabricius) (p. 599)

    Black, with grayish markings; 12–20 mm.

12. *Megacyllene robiniae* (Forster) ♂ (p. 596)

    Black, with yellow bands; 12–18 mm.

13. *M. caryae* (Gahan) ♂ (p. 597)

    Black, with yellow bands; 12–20 mm.

14. *Physocnemum brevilineum* (Say) (p. 594)

    Black; elytra at middle pale, each with three whitish lines; 12–16 mm.

MM |᠎᠎᠎᠎|᠎᠎᠎᠎|᠎᠎᠎᠎|᠎᠎᠎᠎|᠎᠎᠎᠎|᠎᠎᠎᠎|᠎᠎᠎᠎|

0   10   20   30   40   50   60   70

PLATE LIX

601

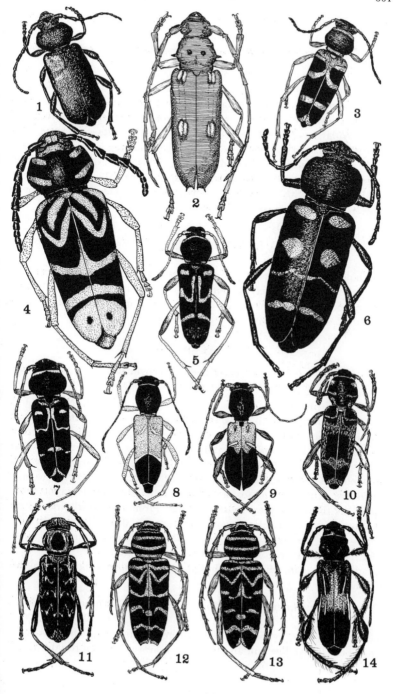

apices obliquely truncate; surface finely, rugosely punctate. Length 11–21 mm.

The larvae feed under bark of almost any dead hardwood or conifer.

b. *Xylotrechus colonus* (Fabricius) Rustic Borer
Plate LIX, No. 10, p. 601

Elongate, slender, subcylindrical; black or dark brown; pronotum usually with four to six small, rather vague, white or yellowish spots; elytra with a semicircular, subhumeral, yellowish line, which encloses a brown spot, and with two broad crossbars and a smaller spot at apex white or yellowish. Head with a median V-shaped carina. Pronotum cylindrical, slightly elongate; sides rounded; surface roughly asperate medially, finely granulate laterally. Elytra with sides subparallel; apices obliquely truncate; finely, rugosely punctate. Length 8–17 mm.

Genus VI. *NEOCLYTUS* Thomson

Of moderate size, elongate, slender, subcylindrical; front not carinate; antennal fossae not acutely margined above; pronotum with short, transverse carinae disposed in one or more longitudinal lines or series; first segment of metatarsi longer than the following.

KEY TO SPECIES

Elytral apices acutely spined on outer angle of emargination ....a. *scutellaris*
Elytral apices at most dentate on outer angle of emargination .....b. *acuminatus*

a. *Neoclytus scutellaris* (Olivier) Plate LX, No. 1, p. 613

Elongate, subcylindrical; black or dark brown, covered with fine, dark-brownish pubescence; head with two vertical stripes of yellow on front; pronotum with apex and base yellow and with a transverse band that does not attain sides; elytra basally reddish brown, with three narrow, yellow bands, the first curving back from scutellum, then recurved to side margin, the second curving forward from middle of suture, then posteriorly to side, the third, on apical fourth, oblique. Pronotum slightly transverse; sides rounded; moderately rugosely punctate on disk. Elytra with sides tapering from base to apex; apices obliquely truncate, spined at outer angle; surface finely, rugosely punctate. Length 8–15 mm.

Dead hickory, elm, white oak, and grape are recorded as breeding places for this beetle.

b. *Neoclytus acuminatus* (Fabricius) Red-headed Ash Borer
Plate LX, No. 2, p. 613

Elongate, slender, cylindrical; reddish brown; elytra with four straight, narrow bands of yellow and an area of dark brown between the third and fourth crossbands, the first band basal, feebly curved at suture, the second oblique, distinctly ascending to suture at basal quarter, the third behind middle, feebly ascending and broader internally, the fourth at apical quarter. Pronotum with sides straight, slightly tapering apically; base constricted; tuberculate at middle near apex, tubercle transversely carinate. Elytra parallel-sided; apices feebly truncate, dentate on outer angle and widely dehiscent. Length 6–18 mm.

This is one of the most common of the wood-borers. The larvae live in unseasoned material with the bark left on. Nearly all the hardwoods are attacked, but chiefly ash, oak, and hickory.

Genus VII. *CLYTUS* Laicharteg

Moderate-sized, elongate, rather robust, subcylindrical beetles; antennae three-fifths the length of body; femora elongate, the metafemora longest, not spined apically; pronotum transverse, at base as broad as or broader than apex; surface not elevated near base; front not bicarinate; antennal fossae not acutely margined above.

KEY TO SPECIES

Elytra with basal margin deep brown, apex brown ....a. *ruricola*
Elytra with basal margin pale yellow-brown, apex marked with yellow ....
....b. *marginicollis*

a. *Clytus ruricola* (Olivier)   Plate LIX, No. 5, p. 601
Elongate, rather robust, subcylindrical; dark brown to black; pronotum apically and basally margined with yellow; scutellum bright yellow; elytra with several bright-yellow crossbands, consisting of an oval, oblique spot on basal third, a strongly angulated band extending from suture caudally to middle, then forward and laterally to side margin, and an oblique bar behind middle; sternites laterally marked with yellow; antennae and legs reddish brown, the femoral clubs blackish. Pronotum subglobose; surface finely granulate. Elytra with sides subparallel, the apices obliquely truncate, not spinose. Length 8–14 mm.

The adults may be taken on flowers, and the larvae live in many of the hardwoods.

b. *Clytus marginicollis* Castelnau   Plate LIX, No. 3, p. 601
Elongate, rather robust, subcylindrical; dark brown to black; pronotum finely margined at base and apex with pale yellow; elytra paler at base, with four crossbands of pale reddish yellow, the first crossband near base, straight, the second just before middle, slightly arcuate and ascending obliquely to suture, the third at apical quarter and feebly oblique, the

fourth at apex; legs light brown; sternites each margined apically with pale yellow. Pronotum subglobose; surface finely and rugosely punctate. Elytra rounded at apex; surface finely, rugosely punctate. Length 8–10 mm.

The larvae are recorded as living in dead branches of hard pines.

Genus VIII. *CLYTOLEPTUS* Casey

Moderate-sized, elongate, slender, subcylindrical forms. Pronotum elongate; apex wider than base; disk with feeble elevations near base. Head with front not carinate; antennal fossae not acutely margined above.

Clytoleptus albofasciatus (Laporte)   Plate LIX, No. 8, p. 601

Elongate, slender, subcylindrical; light to deep brown or black; elytra often with basal half light brown, each elytron with two transverse, fine lines of white, apices white; antennae and legs dark reddish brown. Pronotum elongate, sides evenly rounded, base constricted; disk finely alutaceous, with a raised area each side. Elytra with sides subparallel, apices broadly truncate; surface finely and sparsely punctate. Length 8–10 mm.

Dead and dying grapevines are breeding places for these beetles.

Genus IX. *CYRTOPHORUS* LeConte

Of moderate size, elongate, slender, subcylindrical; antennae with second segment short, not equal to fourth, third longer than fourth and distinctly spined at apex; front large; metepimera not produced; metepisterna linear.

Cyrtophorus verrucosus (Olivier)   Plate LX, No. 3, p. 613

Elongate, slender, subcylindrical; black; elytra from base to beyond middle reddish brown and with three narrow, oblique, white lines and a fourth similar line at end of brown portion; femora reddish brown. Pronotum elongate, constricted basally; sides broadly rounded; disk with a prominent crest at middle; surface finely, rugosely punctate. Elytra with sides subparallel, apices truncate; basal gibbosities with long pubescence. Length 6–10 mm.

The adults come to flowers of trees and shrubs and breed beneath bark of walnut and other hardwoods.

Tribe TILLOMORPHINI

Genus *EUDERCES* LeConte

Small, elongate, oblong-ovate, cylindrical; antennae slender, not quite as long as body; eyes oval, feebly emarginate above; elytra with raised, ivory-colored bands near middle; mesocoxal cavities closed; tibiae not carinate.

Euderces picipes (Fabricius)   Plate LIX, No. 9, p. 601
Elongate, slightly cylindrical; black, sometimes dark reddish brown, shining; covered with sparse, grayish pubescence; elytra each with an oblique, elevated, ivory band at middle and usually a broad, pale-reddish-brown area basally. Pronotum elongate, cylindrical, constricted at base; surface densely strigose. Elytra with sides subparallel; apices rounded; surface coarsely, sparsely punctate on basal two-thirds. Length 5–8 mm.

The adults are common on flowers, especially on sumac; they usually breed in the dead branches of many different hardwoods.

Tribe STENASPINI

KEY TO GENERA

1. Pronotum with a spine at middle on each side; opaque 2
   Pronotum without lateral spine; shining ....III. *Batyleoma* (p. 606)
2. Pronotum pubescent ....I. *Tragidion* (p. 605)
   Pronotum not pubescent ....II. *Purpuricenus* (p. 606)

Genus I. *TRAGIDION* Serville

Rather large, elongate, robust beetles; scutellum small; head with front large, quadrate, perpendicular, sharply defined laterally; antennae filiform, segments five to eleven carinate externally; pronotum spined laterally; entire body densely pubescent.

Tragidion coquus (Linné)   Plate LX, No. 7, p. 613
Elongate, robust, subcylindrical; black, densely pubescent; elytra each with a large, round, yellowish-brown spot basally. Pronotum subquadrate; constricted at base; sides rounded, with an acute spine near middle; disk with a median and two lateral callosities on each side. Elytra with sides subparallel; apices rounded; each elytron with three costae; surface minutely punctate. Length 16–25 mm.

Genus II. *PURPURICENUS* Germar

Moderate-sized, elongate, robust beetles; head with front large, quadrate, and perpendicular; pronotum laterally spined; the scutellum broadly triangular, acute at tip; pronotum glabrous, not pubescent.

Purpuricenus humeralis (Fabricius)   Plate LX, No. 8, p. 613

Elongate, robust, subcylindrical; black, not shining; each elytron with a large, triangular, reddish spot on humerus. Pronotum transverse, constricted at base; each side with a spine near middle; disk with one median and two lateral tubercles on each side; surface coarsely, confluently punctate. Elytra with sides subparallel; apices emarginately truncate; surface deeply and rather coarsely punctate basally, more finely and densely so apically. Length 14–18 mm.

This species is found especially in dead branches of oak, hickory, black locust, and birch.

Genus III. *BATYLEOMA* Casey

Small, rather robust, cylindrical, shining beetles; head with front short, not sharply defined laterally; pronotum with sides rounded, not tuberculate, margined apically; elytra feebly tapering, apices separately, broadly rounded.

Batyleoma suturale (Say)   Plate LX, No. 6, p. 613

Elongate, robust; dark red, shining; antennae, apices of femora, tibiae, tarsi, and sterna dark brown to black. Pronotum transverse, constricted at apex; sides rounded; surface smooth, minutely, sparsely punctate, each puncture bearing a long, black hair. Elytra with sides subparallel; apices rounded; surface coarsely, sparsely punctate. Length 6–8.5 mm.

Adults are common on Jersey tea, dogwood, and wild carrot. The larvae live in dead branches of hickory, chestnut, and oak.

Subfamily LEPTURINAE

KEY TO TRIBES

Mandibles slender, acute, inner margin fringed with pubescence ....
....LEPTURINI (p. 607)
Mandibles short, broad, not fringed ....DORCASOMINI (p. 623)

Tribe LEPTURINI

KEY TO GENERA

Genus I. *PIDONIA* Mulsant

Elongate, slender, subcylindrical beetles. Head abruptly and strongly constricted far behind the eyes. Pronotum constricted at apex and base, only slightly narrower in front than at base, sides inflated and subangulate at middle, hind angles rounded; scarcely more than one-half the width of elytra at base. Metatarsi with a distinct pubescent patch on sole of first three segments; procoxal cavities widely open behind.

KEY TO SPECIES

Body color reddish; elytra reddish, with two brown vittae, one sutural, the other lateral ....a. *aurata*
Body color black or gray; elytra either entirely piceous, or reddish and black ....
....b. *ruficollis*

a. *Pidonia aurata* Horn   Plate LX, No. 4, p. 613

Elongate, slender, subcylindrical; reddish yellow to red-brown; elytra with sides and suture narrowly margined with black. Pronotum elongate, constricted apically; sides sinuate; disk convex, with an apical and basal transverse depression; surface densely, minutely punctate. Elytra with sides nearly straight; apices rounded; surface coarsely, densely punctate. Length 8–10 mm.

The adults may be collected on flowers.

b. *Pidonia ruficollis* (Say)   Plate LX, No. 5, p. 613

Elongate, slender, parallel. Extremely variable in color; black, pronotum frequently reddish; elytra typically black, sometimes brown, and frequently with a yellowish, longitudinal vitta which varies in distinctness. Pronotum elongate, convex, deeply constricted at apex and base; surface minutely, densely punctate. Elytra rather coarsely and sparsely punctate; apices rounded. Length 6–10 mm.

The adults may be taken on flowers.

Genus II. *GRAMMOPTERA* Serville

Small, elongate, slender, subconvex; pronotum campanulate; hind angles acute and moderately produced; elytral apices evenly rounded; metepisternum very slender; procoxal cavities widely open behind; first metatarsal segment with a distinct pubescent sole; prosternum convex.

Grammoptera exigua (Newman)   Plate LX, No. 9, p. 613

Elongate-ovate, slender, subconvex; black, shining; pronotum sometimes margined with red, covered with golden pubescence; legs reddish, bicolored, or black. Pronotum transverse, constricted at apex; sides sinuate, hind angles produced; disk with a feeble median impressed line; surface finely, densely punctate. Elytra with sides nearly parallel; apices rounded; surface densely, coarsely punctate. Length 4–7 mm.

The adults are found on flowers, and they breed in dead poplar and linden.

Fig. 456

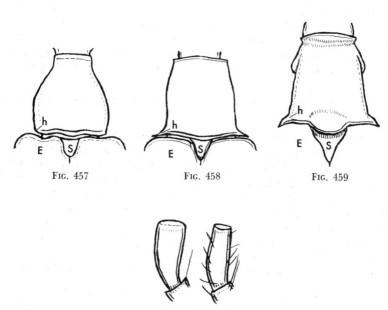

Figs. 460–461

Fig. 456. Eye of *Evodinus* viewed obliquely from the front, its anterior margin narrowly emarginate above the antennal insertion.

Figs. 457–459. Pronotum of *Anoplodera* (457), *Grammoptera* (458), and *Leptura* (459). E, elytron; h, hind angle of pronotum; S, scutellum.

Figs. 460–461. Last segment of labial palpus of *Typocerus* (460) and of *Strangalina* (461).

Genus III. *LEPTURA* Linné

Elongate, rather slender, small to large species; pronotum subcampanulate or trapezoidal, the hind angles prolonged and acute; head constricted shortly behind eyes; elytra wedge-shaped, apices usually emarginate and dentiform; procoxal cavities usually narrowly open behind.

KEY TO SPECIES

1. Size large, 25 mm. or more ....a. *emarginata*
   Size small or moderate, not over 15 mm. 2
2. Elytra with a fine, linear discal stripe and the sutural and lateral margins black ....c. *lineola*
   Elytra with median crossband and the sutural and lateral margins black; in male, the markings are considerably broadened, with the apices black as well ....b. *subhamata*

a. *Leptura emarginata* Fabricius   Plate LXI, No. 3, p. 621

Elongate, robust; black, with silky pubescence; elytra reddish brown, except apices, which are black. Pronotum transverse; broadest at base, narrowed strongly to apex, basal margin broadly and deeply bisinuate; hind angles produced; disk finely, sparsely punctate. Elytra with sides tapering gradually; apices deeply emarginate; surface finely, densely punctate. Length 27–31 mm.

This species breeds in the decaying logs of many hardwoods. The adults come readily to fermenting baits.

b. *Leptura subhamata* Randall   Plate LX, Nos. 10, 12, p. 613

Elongate, rather slender; male black, except bases of legs and a curved elytral vitta of variable shape and extent, which are yellow; female reddish, except the vertex, an irregular median spot on pronotum, the scutellum, and sutural and lateral margins and a transverse band of elytra black. Pronotum transverse, constricted apically; sides sinuate, hind angles produced; disk only moderately convex; surface finely and densely punctate. Elytra densely and finely punctate; apices obliquely truncate-emarginate. Length 10–14 mm.

The adults are found on flowers, particularly those of wild hydrangea.

c. *Leptura lineola* Say   Plate LX, No. 11, p. 613

Elongate, slender; black; legs and elytra testaceous, the latter narrowly margined at suture, broadly vittate laterally, and finely vittate on disk with black, the lateral vitta frequently broken into spots. Pronotum transverse; constricted apically; disk very strongly convex, without median impressed line; hind angles produced; surface densely and finely punctate. Elytra coarsely but not densely punctate; apices almost transversely truncate and feebly emarginate. Length 8–11 mm.

The above species is recorded as breeding in birch, but the abundance of the insect would suggest that it also breeds in other hardwood species. The adult occurs on flowers of various sorts, especially wild rose and Jersey tea.

Genus IV. *TYPOCERUS* LeConte

Elongate-oval, rather robust; pronotum trapezoidal, hind angles produced over humeri; distal segments of antennae with distinct poriferous area; prosternum convex; elytra wedge-shaped; first mesotarsal segment barely longer than second and third together; procoxal cavities narrowly open behind.

KEY TO SPECIES

1. Antennae brown, rarely distal segments black; segments 7–11 with poriferous
   areas ....d. *sinuatus*
   Antennae black; segments 6–11 with poriferous areas 2
2. Elytra uniformly black ....b. *lugubris*
   Elytra black or reddish, with yellow crossbars 3
3. Elytral apices emarginate; elytra reddish brown, with yellow bands ....
   ....c. *velutinus*
   Elytral apices obliquely truncate-acuminate; elytra black, with yellow bands
   ....a. *zebratus*

a. *Typocerus zebratus* Olivier   Plate LX, No. 16, p. 613
Elongate, robust, tapering behind middle; black, densely clothed with pale pubescence; pronotum with yellow pubescence basally and apically; elytra with four transverse yellow bands, these sometimes reduced to spots and may be completely absent. Pronotum transverse; widest at base, constricted apically; disk closely punctate. Elytral apices obliquely truncate, acuminate at tip; surface finely, densely punctate. Length 8–14 mm.
Adults are found on flowers, especially sumac; the larvae usually live in decayed pine stumps.

b. *Typocerus lugubris* (Say)   Plate LX, No. 15, p. 613
Elongate, slender, tapering behind middle; black, with prostrate black hairs; humeri sometimes with a reddish spot; undersurface black, with yellow hairs. Pronotum transverse, constricted apically; surface finely and closely punctate. Elytra with apices submarginate, outer angle acute; surface finely and densely punctate. Length 9–11 mm.
The adults occur on flowers and are recorded as breeding in pine stumps.

c. *Typocerus velutinus* (Olivier)   Plate LX, No. 14, p. 613
Elongate, robust, strongly tapering behind middle; head, pronotum, antennae, and undersurface black; pronotum with yellow pubescence; elytra reddish brown, with narrow, transverse, yellow bands. Pronotum widest basally; disk with small, granulate punctures. Elytra with small,

PLATE LX
Family CERAMBYCIDAE IV

1. *Neoclytus scutellaris* (Olivier) (p. 602) — Black, with pale-yellow markings; elytral base reddish; 8–15 mm.

2. *N. acuminatus* (Fabricius) (p. 602) — Brown or yellow-brown, with pale-yellow markings; 6–18 mm.

3. *Cyrtophorus verrucosus* (Olivier) (p. 604) — Black, with snow-white marks; 6–10 mm.

4. *Pidonia aurata* Horn (p. 608) — Reddish yellow to red-brown; elytral lines black; 8–10 mm.

5. *P. ruficollis* (Say) (p. 608) — Variable; black; pronotum, frequently, and scutellum reddish; elytra sometimes brown, each with a yellowish vitta; 6–10 mm.

6. *Batyleoma suturale* (Say) (p. 606) — Reddish, shining; 6–9 mm.

7. *Tragidion coquus* (Linné) (p. 605) — Black; elytral spot yellowish brown; 16–25 mm.

8. *Purpuricenus humeralis* (Fabricius) (p. 606) — Black; elytral humeral spot orange or red; 14–18 mm.

9. *Grammoptera exigua* (Newman) (p. 608) — Black; pronotum margined with reddish and with yellow pubescence; 4–7 mm.

10. *Leptura subhamata* Randall ♂ (p. 610) — Black; markings yellowish; 10–14 mm.

11. *L. lineola* Say (p. 610) — Black; elytra light tan, with blackish markings; 8–11 mm.

12. *L. subhamata* Randall ♀ (p. 610) — Reddish, with blackish markings; 10–14 mm.

13. *Anoplodera pubera* (Say) (p. 617) — Black, shining; 8–12 mm.

14. *Typocerus velutinus* (Olivier) (p. 611) — Black; elytra light reddish brown, with dull-reddish bands; 8–14 mm.

15. *T. lugubris* (Say) (p. 611) — Black; humeri sometimes with a reddish spot; 9–11 mm.

16. *T. zebratus* Olivier (p. 611) — Black, with yellow or tan markings; 8–14 mm.

17. *Anoplodera nitens* (Forster) (p. 615) — Black; elytra with yellowish bands 10–15 mm.

18. *A. biforis* (Newman) (p. 615) — Dull reddish brown; pronotum paler; elytra marked with blackish; 11–16 mm.

19. *A. proxima* (Say) (p. 616) — Black; elytra tan, tipped with black; 14–17 mm.

MM 0 10 20 30 40 50 60 70

PLATE LX   613

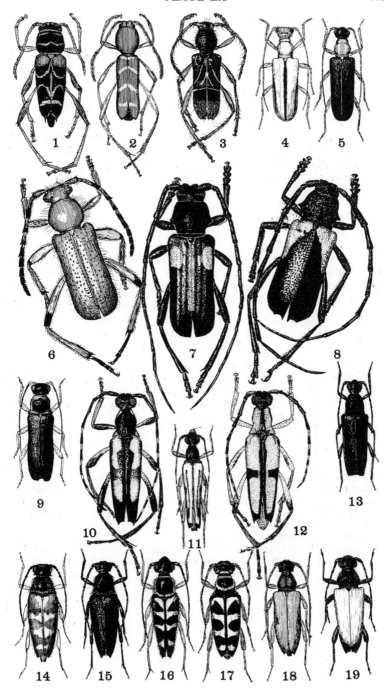

close-set punctures, then finer and denser toward apex; apices emarginate. Length 8–14 mm.

This is one of the most common cerambycids; the adults are found on flowers and usually breed in decaying hardwoods and conifers.

d. *Typocerus sinuatus* (Newman)   Plate LXI, No. 9, p. 621
Elongate, robust; black to dark brown; elytra light reddish brown or reddish yellow, with a longitudinal row of four lateral, black spots, the last two pairs sometimes fused across the suture, forming short fasciae. Pronotum transverse, widest at base, constricted at apex; surface finely, densely punctate. Elytra with apices obliquely, emarginately truncate; surface densely, finely punctate. Length 10–12.7 mm.

Genus V. *ANOPLODERA* Mulsant

Of moderate size; elongate-ovate, tapering behind; pronotum campanulate or quadrate, not tuberculate laterally, rarely strongly angulate, basal angles acute, laminate or obtuse, not prolonged over humeri; prosternum convex, sulcate only near anterior margin; procoxal cavities narrowly open or closed behind.

KEY TO SPECIES

1. Entirely black, piceous, or deep brown 2
   At least elytra entirely or in part with some color other than blackish 3
2. Black, shining; pronotum distinctly elongate, bell-shaped ....j. *pubera*
   Black, piceous, or deep brown, shining; pronotum slightly longer than wide, sides nearly straight ....d. *mutabilis*
3. Elytra black, with red markings 4
   Elytra not black 7
4. Elytra with base or humerus red 5
   Elytra with discal spots or vitta 6
5. Length 10–20 mm.; elytral bases red ....g. *canadensis*
   Length 7–9 mm.; elytral humeri red ....i. *vagans*
6. Elytra black, with a red stripe from base to beyond middle ....k. *vittata*
   Elytra black, each with four red spots ....c. *octonotata*
7. Elytra distinctly red 8
   Elytra brown-orange or yellowish 9
8. Length 10–13 mm.; elytra uniformly red ....h. *rubrica*
   Length 7–9 mm.; elytra red, or red with apices or sutural margin black .....
   ....i. *vagans*
9. Elytra with one or more black discal spots, the apex may or may not be black in addition 10
   Elytra without discal black spots, its apex black or not 11
10. Elytra bright yellow, each with at least four large, black, transverse spots ....
    ....b. *nitens*
    Elytra brownish yellow, each with one or two spots and apex black ......
    ....a. *cordifera*

11. Pronotum and body beneath reddish brown or yellowish brown ....e. *biforis*
    Pronotum black; body beneath largely black 12
12. Length 8–13 mm.; elytra orange-brown, sometimes clouded in part with
    black ....d. *mutabilis*
    Length 14–17 mm.; elytral apices distinctly marked with black....f. *proxima*

a. *Anoplodera cordifera* (Olivier)   Plate LXI, No. 6, p. 621
Elongate-ovate, moderate to robust, convex; black, covered with golden
pubescence; elytra yellow, each with two black maculae, variable in size
and shape, one laterally just before middle, the other behind middle; apices
also black. Pronotum campanulate, transverse; constricted at apex; hind
angles acute; surface densely, finely punctate. Elytra wedge-shaped, apices
dehiscent. First segment of metatarsus densely hairy. Length 9–12 mm.
This species is common on flowers.

b. *Anoplodera nitens* (Forster)   Plate LX, No. 17, p. 613
Elongate, robust; dark brown to black; antennae, legs, and abdomen
partially light brown; body beneath, margin of pronotum, and four elytral
bands with golden-yellow pubescence. Pronotum transverse; convex;
widened just before middle and at base, constricted apically; disk transversely sulcate at apex and base, densely, finely punctate. Elytra subparallel;
apices obliquely truncate, subemarginate; surface finely punctate. Length
10–15 mm.
The adults may be collected on flowers. They breed in living chestnut
and oak trees, the larvae mining beneath the bark at the bases of the trees.

c. *Anoplodera octonotata* (Say)   Plate LXI, No. 10, p. 621
Elongate, rather slender; black, shining; each elytron with four more
or less yellowish spots, these sometimes reduced in number or very large and
confluent; metafemora basally and metatarsi pale. Pronotum subquadrate,
widened basally; disk with an apical and basal transverse depression present, surface finely and sparsely punctate. Elytra with sides subparallel;
apices obliquely truncate; surface rather finely punctate. Length 10–12 mm.
The adults frequent flowers and are recorded as breeding in oak.

d. *Anoplodera mutabilis* (Newman)   Plate LXI, Nos. 7, 8, p. 621
Elongate-ovate, slender; black; elytra shining, sometimes brownish orange,
or brownish orange with apices shaded with black. Pronotum subquadrate;
sides feebly narrowed to apex; surface minutely, confluently punctate.
Elytra with sides subparallel; apices rounded or truncate; surface coarsely,
densely punctate. Length 8–14 mm.
These beetles breed in numerous decaying hardwoods, and the adults
may be taken on flowers.

e. *Anoplodera biforis* (Newman)   Plate LX, No. 18, p. 613
Elongate-ovate, rather robust; dark brown; antennae, pronotum, legs,
and undersurface rufous; each elytron with two small, black spots laterally

near base. Pronotum subquadrate; strongly narrowed apically; disk with a median impressed line; hind angles obtuse, slightly prominent; surface finely, densely punctate. Elytra with sides subparallel; apices obliquely truncate, the angles formed by the truncations acute. Length 11–16 mm.

This species is recorded as breeding in dead wood of chestnut and hemlock. The adults may be collected on flowers.

f. *Anoplodera proxima* (Say)   Plate LX, No. 19, p. 613
Elongate-ovate, robust; black; elytra light orangeish brown, apices broadly and obliquely marked with black; entire surface covered with sparse, short, yellowish hairs. Pronotum strongly narrowed apically; sides strongly angulate at middle; disk inflated, with a median impressed line, deeply, transversely sulcate at base; hind angles rounded, not prominent. Elytra at base feebly lobed; apices strongly dehiscent, broadly, obliquely emarginate, the angles formed acute. Length 14–17 mm.

The adults frequent flowers, and they are recorded as breeding in the wood of decayed gum.

g. *Anoplodera canadensis* (Olivier)   Plate LXI, No. 1, p. 621
Elongate, rather slender; black; elytra usually with basal portion reddish, sometimes, however, entirely black or entirely reddish. Pronotum subquadrate, strongly narrowed apically; disk inflated, the basal and apical impressions wide and deep, the former abrupt, median line broadly impressed; surface very coarsely, confluently punctate, more sparsely so laterally, with irregular, smooth spaces, covered with dark-grayish pubescence. Elytra with sides feebly arcuate; apices deeply emarginate, angles acute; disk coarsely, deeply, and sparsely punctate, with short, black, indistinct pubescence. Length 10–20 mm.

This beetle breeds in dead pine, spruce, and hemlock.

h. *Anoplodera rubrica* (Say)   Plate LXI, No. 2, p. 621
Elongate, robust; black; elytra reddish brown, opaque; sternites black in female, reddish in male. Pronotum subquadrate, strongly narrowed apically; disk inflated, transversely impressed at base and without median impressed line; a strong carina extends toward the procoxae from the apex of the lateral margin, which gives the pronotum a subquadrate appearance as viewed from above. Elytra distinctly more than twice as long as wide; sides strongly sinuate; apices obliquely truncate or emarginate, angles acute; surface coarsely and rather densely punctate. Length 10–16 mm.

This species usually breeds in many of the decayed hardwoods and conifers. The adults may be collected on flowers.

i. *Anoplodera vagans* (Olivier)   Plate LXI, Nos. 4, 5, p. 621
Elongate-ovate, rather robust; black; elytra variable, either entirely reddish or black, or reddish with broad, black sutural margins, or black with

red humeral angles. Pronotum transverse; strongly narrowed apically, not carinate as in *rubrica;* disk inflated, transversely impressed at base and apex, and without median impressed line; surface densely, coarsely punctate. Elytra elongate, sides strongly sinuate; apices dehiscent and usually rounded; surface densely, coarsely punctate, except at apex. Length 7–9 mm.

The adults of these beetles are common on flowers in pine areas. Breeding takes place in decayed pine, butternut, hickory, and birch.

j. *Anoplodera pubera* (Say)   Plate LX, No. 13, p. 613

Elongate-oblong, rather slender; entirely black, shining. Pronotum transverse, strongly narrowed apically, not carinate laterally; disk inflated, impressed at base, without impressed median line; surface densely, coarsely punctate. Elytra elongate, sides almost parallel, feebly sinuate, apices only feebly dehiscent, emarginately truncate; rather coarsely and sparsely punctate on surface. Length 8–12 mm.

The adults occur on wild-rose and other flowers.

k. *Anoplodera vittata* (Swederus)   Plate LXI, No. 19, p. 621

Elongate, slender; varying from entirely black to light brown, with darker head and pronotum; elytra with a reddish median vitta extending to beyond middle, this sometimes reduced to a feeble basal spot or entirely lacking. Pronotum strongly narrowed at apex; disk inflated, without median impressed line; surface finely, sparsely punctate. Elytra narrow and elongate; transversely impressed near scutellum; apices truncate; surface finely, sparsely punctate. Length 10–13 mm.

The adults are very abundant on flowers and breed in conifers and some hardwoods.

Genus VI. *ENCYCLOPS* Newman

Elongate, oblong, slightly widened behind, subdepressed; front vertical, meeting vertex at nearly a right angle; tarsi slender; second metatarsal segment longer than third, the first pubescent beneath; prosternum narrow, only slightly prominent between coxae.

Encyclops coerulea (Say)   Plate LXI, No. 16, p. 621

Elongate-oblong, subdepressed; metallic bluish black or greenish black, feebly shining; head and pronotum reddish brown, the latter with a narrow, elongate, black median stripe; elytral humeri reddish brown. Pronotum elongate, sides sharply rounded from base to apex, which is very narrow; surface very densely, coarsely punctate. Elytral sides subparallel, broader near apex; apices rounded, shortly bidentate; disk densely, coarsely punctate, medially with rather long hairs. Length 7–9.5 mm.

This species may usually be collected on flowers.

Genus VII. *TOXOTUS* Dejean

Elongate, subcyclindrical forms of moderate or large size; front of head oblique; pronotum constricted at apex and base, spined laterally; elytra strongly tapering to apices; tibial spurs inserted at base of a deep excavation, not terminal.

Toxotus vittiger (Randall)   Plate LXI, No. 18, p. 621

Elongate, subcylindrical; black, rather shining; elytra reddish, each with two longitudinal vittae, one from humerus near side margin, extending almost to apex, the other sutural. Pronotum transverse; deeply constricted near apex and base; median impressed line extending between basal and apical transverse impressions; surface finely, confluently punctate. Elytra with humeri prominent, sides narrowed to middle, then parallel almost to apices, which are obliquely truncate; surface finely, densely punctate. Length 11–21 mm.

The adults frequent flowers of *Viburnum* and wild hydrangea.

Genus VIII. *STENOCORUS* Geoffroy

Elongate, rather robust forms; antennae short, scarcely reaching base of elytra, segments five to eleven thickened apically; eyes rather small, oblong, slightly emarginate; front of head oblique, meeting vertex at an angle of much more than 90 degrees; prosternum prominent between procoxae; tibial spurs terminal.

Stenocorus inquisitor (Linné)   Plate LXI, No. 17, p. 621

Elongate, rather robust; black, variegated with brown and grayish pubescence; elytra with reddish-brown spots. Pronotum transverse, much narrower than elytra, laterally with an acute tubercle at middle. Elytra feebly narrowed to apex; apices rounded; each elytron with four smooth, distinct costae; intervals coarsely punctate. Length 11–18 mm.

This widely distributed species breeds in many of the conifers.

Genus IX. *EVODINUS* LeConte

Elongate, rather robust forms of moderate size; head with front oblique, eyes distinctly emarginate; pronotal sides obtusely rounded or feebly tuberculate before middle; metepisternum broad at base, converging behind; tibial spurs terminal.

Evodinus monticola (Randall)   Plate LXI, No. 11, p. 621

Elongate, rather robust; dark brown to black, subopaque; antennae brown; elytra yellow, with three rather large spots or blotches along side margins (these sometimes connected) and apices black, usually with a small round dot of black on disk at basal quarter. Pronotum elongate; sides with an obtuse tubercle at middle; disk with median impressed line. Elytra with humeri rather prominent; sides subparallel; apices dehiscent, obliquely truncate; surface minutely punctate. Length 8–12 mm.

The larvae are recorded as breeding under bark of dead hemlock. The adults may be found on flowers.

Genus X. *GAUROTES* LeConte

Elongate-oblong, robust; head with front oblique; eyes entire; pronotum and elytra polished, feebly punctate, almost entirely devoid of pubescence, the former with sides obtusely rounded, or feebly tuberculate before middle; tibial spurs terminal.

Gaurotes cyanipennis (Say)   Plate LXI, No. 12, p. 621

Elongate-oblong, rather robust; black, shining; elytra blue, green, or dark cupreous, very shining; antennae and legs brownish yellow. Pronotum transverse; constricted before apex; sides sinuate; surface of disk smooth, minutely, sparsely punctate. Elytra much wider at base than pronotum, sparsely and finely punctate; humeri prominent; apices truncate. Length 9–12.5 mm.

The adults are found on flowers, especially those of sumac. They are recorded as breeding in various dead hardwoods.

Genus XI. *ACMAEOPS* LeConte

Small or moderate-sized, elongate, rather depressed beetles; head with front oblique, eyes small, entire; antennae as long as body; pronotum variable in form but always punctate and distinctly pubescent, sides obtusely rounded, sometimes subtuberculate; tibial spurs terminal.

KEY TO SPECIES

Slender; pronotum with sides rounded, not at all tuberculate near middle......
....a. *directus*
Robust; pronotum subtuberculate laterally at middle ....b. *bivittatus*

a. *Acmaeops directus* (Newman)   Plate LXI, No. 13, p. 621

Elongate, slender; light brown; elytra dull yellow, with suture, discal stripe, and side margin black, all three of these vittae sometimes lacking; antennal segments yellow at base, with apices darker. Pronotum subquadrate, convex, narrowed at apex; sides rounded, not tuberculate laterally; disk with a very narrow apical and a broader basal transverse depression;

PLATE LXI

Family CERAMBYCIDAE V

1. *Anoplodera canadensis* (Olivier) (p. 616)
Black; elytral bases usually reddish; 10–20 mm.

2. *A. rubrica* (Say) (p. 616)
Black; elytra reddish orange; 10–16 mm.

3. *Leptura emarginata* Fabricius (p. 610)
Black; elytra brown-red, apices black; 27–31 mm.

4, 5. *Anoplodera vagans* (Olivier) (p. 616)
Black; elytra very variable, usually black, with red humeral patches, sometimes entirely black, sometimes entirely reddish; 7–9 mm.

6. *A. cordifera* (Olivier) (p. 615)
Black; elytra dull yellow, with black marks; 9–12 mm.

7, 8. *A. mutabilis* (Newman) (p. 615)
Black; elytra varying from entirely dull yellow to entirely black; 8–14 mm.

9. *Typocerus sinuatus* (Newman) (p. 614)
Dark brown to black; elytra yellow-tan, with brownish or black markings; 10–13 mm.

10. *Anoplodera octonotata* (Say) (p. 615)
Black, shining; elytral spots yellowish; 10–12 mm.

11. *Evodinus monticola* (Randall) (p. 618)
Dark brown to black; elytra pale yellow, with black marks; 8–12 mm.

12. *Gaurotes cyanipennis* (Say) (p. 619)
Black; elytra deep metallic green or blue; 9–12.5 mm.

13. *Acmaeops directus* (Newman) (p. 619)
Light brown; elytra dull yellow, sometimes with black vittae; 6–8 mm.

14, 15. *A. bivittatus* (Say) (p. 622)
Very variable in color; tan; head and markings of pronotum black; elytral vittae black, sometimes expanded and conjoined to cover most of disk; 6–10 mm.

16. *Encyclops coerulea* (Say) (p. 617)
Head and pronotum reddish brown; elytra metallic green or blue, humeri reddish brown; 7–10 mm.

17. *Stenocorus inquisitor* (Linné) (p. 618)
Black; pronotum reddish at base and apex; elytra reddish, with black marks and costae; 11–18 mm.

18. *Toxotus vittiger* (Randall) (p. 618)
Black; elytra reddish, with black stripes; 11–21 mm.

19. *Anoplodera vittata* (Swederus) (p. 617)
Black; elytral stripes reddish; 10–13 mm.

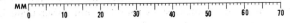

MM 0 10 20 30 40 50 60 70

PLATE LXI   621

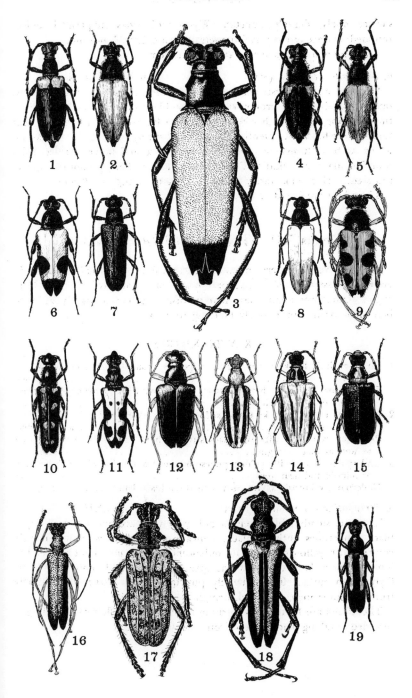

surface finely, densely punctate. Elytra with sides subparallel; apices rounded; surface coarsely and densely punctate. Length 6–8 mm.

This common species may be taken on flowers.

b. *Acmaeops bivittatus* (Say)   Plate LXI, Nos. 14, 15, p. 621

Elongate-ovate, robust; very variable in color, usually brownish yellow, rarely entirely black; pronotum with two black discal spots, these sometimes lacking; elytra each with a broad vitta laterally and a finer one near suture blue-black, frequently the elytra entirely blue-black. Pronotum widest at base, transversely impressed near base and before middle; sides subtuberculate at middle. Elytra much wider than pronotum; apices rounded; surface moderately coarsely punctate. Length 6–10 mm.

The adults are found on flowers.

Genus XII. *STRANGALINA* Aurivillius

Elongate, very slender; antennal segments 6–11 with small, oval, poriferous depressions near apices; prothorax much narrowed at apex, hind angles acute, prominent, basal margin bisinuate; elytra slightly wider at base than prothorax, strongly tapering to apex.

KEY TO SPECIES

1. Elytra entirely black or blue-black; stripes on pronotum pale, indistinct ....
   ....c. *bicolor*
   Elytra brown-yellow or brown-orange, marked with black; pronotum entirely
   black or distinctly striped 2
2. Pronotum entirely black; elytra striped along suture and sides with black,
   without spots ....a. *acuminata*
   Pronotum yellowish, with two black stripes; elytra with black spots or bands
   as well as black margins 3
3. Underparts black, with golden pubescence; elytra usually with a black spot
   at middle and near apex ....b. *famelica*
   Underparts yellowish; elytra each with three black bands ......d. *luteicornis*

a. *Strangalina acuminata* (Olivier)   Plate LXII, No. 3, p. 631

Elongate, slender; black; elytra dull yellow, suture and lateral margins black, sometimes entirely black; beneath densely, above more sparsely covered with yellowish, prostrate pubescence. Pronotum about as broad as long, widest at base, constricted at apex; disk finely and densely punctate. Elytra with surface finely, densely punctate; apices distinctly obliquely truncate, outer angle produced. Length 7–11.5 mm.

The adults are found on viburnum and other wild flowers. Breeding is recorded as taking place in dead ironwood and alder.

b. *Strangalina famelica* (Newman)   Plate LXII, No. 4, p. 631
   Elongate, very slender; dull brownish yellow, with brighter-yellow
pubescence; pronotum with two broad, black vittae; elytra with some
lateral spots and a band near apex black; antennae and undersurface
piceous, though the sternites are sometimes partly yellowish. Pronotum
transverse, widest at base, constricted at apex, surface finely and sparsely
punctate. Elytra slender, strongly narrowed to apices; apices acuminate;
surface finely, sparsely punctate. Length 12–14 mm.
   The adults are usually abundant on flowers and have been recorded as
breeding in decayed yellow birch and oak.

c. *Strangalina bicolor* (Swederus)   Plate LXII, No. 1, p. 631
   Elongate, very slender; pale reddish yellow; elytra black. Pronotum wider
than long; hind angles acute, strongly divergent; constricted at apex; disk
finely and densely punctate. Elytra with sides strongly tapering to apex;
apices obliquely emarginate, outer angles acute, strongly dehiscent; surface
densely, finely punctate. Length 10–14 mm.
   This species is recorded as breeding in dead maple and oak; the adults
are found on flowers.

d. *Strangalina luteicornis* (Fabricius)   Plate LXII, No. 2, p. 631
   Elongate, slender; yellowish brown; pronotum black-bivittate; elytra
with three bands of black; metafemora black apically. Pronotum widest at
base, constricted at apex; surface densely and finely punctate. Elytra attenuate; surface finely and rather sparsely punctate; apices obliquely
emarginate, outer angle acute. Length 9–14 mm.
   The adults frequent sumac flowers especially. This species is recorded as
breeding in decaying grape, beech, and elm.

Tribe DORCASOMINI

Genus *DESMOCERUS* Serville

Large, elongate, robust, subcylindrical; very brightly colored; bases of
antennae not enveloped by eyes; antennal segments three to five widened
apically; mandibles simple, not fringed on inner margin; procoxae conical;
elytra entire, not abbreviated.

Desmocerus palliatus (Forster)   Color Plate B; Plate LXII,
                                            No. 6, p. 631
   Elongate, robust, subdepressed; dark blue, rather shining; elytra with
basal one-third reddish yellow or yellow. Pronotum transverse, constricted

at apex, gradually widening to base; hind angles acute; disk transversely rugose. Elytra nearly parallel-sided; apices obliquely rounded; disk densely and rather coarsely punctate, more finely so apically; each elytron with three fine carinae. Length 17–24 mm.

This species breeds in elderberry, and the adults are found on the flowers of the same plant.

Subfamily LAMIINAE

KEY TO TRIBES

Tribe Monochamini

KEY TO GENERA

FIG. 462

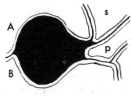

FIG. 463

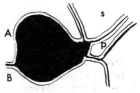

FIG. 464

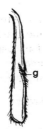

FIG. 465

Fig. 462. First and second antennal segments of *Monochamus*, the former with a cicatrix (*c*) at its apex.

Figs. 463–464. Mesocoxal cavity of *Dorcaschema* (463) and of *Lepturges* (464). *A*, mesosternum; *B*, metasternum; *p*, mesepimeron; *s*, mesepisternum.

Fig. 465. Mesotibia of *Dorcaschema*. *g*, sulcus or groove.

Genus I. *MONOCHAMUS* Guérin

Large, elongate, robust; antennae very long, roughly punctate, and without pubescence in male, shorter, smoother, and finely pubescent on base of each segment beyond third in the female, scape with a distinct cicatrix; pronotum strongly spined laterally; legs elongate, the front pair even longer in male.

As the larvae feed, they make a buzzing sound, hence the common name, "sawyers." Most species of this genus attack felled or dead pines. The larvae feed under the bark for a short period and then enter the sapwood and heartwood.

KEY TO SPECIES

1. Elytral apices rounded, sutural angle dentate or spinose 2
   Elytral apices rounded, sutural angle not toothed or spined 3
2. Elytral apices elongate, forming an acute angle with the suture (not taking into account the tooth, which is usually short) ....b. *carolinensis*
   Elytral apices rounded, forming a right angle with suture (not taking into account the tooth, which is usually long) ....a. *titillator*
3. Black, bronzed; elytra entirely bare of pubescence or almost so ...d. *scutellatus*
   Brown, entirely mottled with grayish and brownish pubescence ....c. *notatus*

a. *Monochamus titillator* (Fabricius)   Southern Pine Sawyer
Plate LXIII, No. 6, p. 643

Elongate, robust, subcylindrical; brownish; elytra irregularly mottled with patches of brown, piceous, and grayish pubescence. Pronotum cylindrical, slightly elongate; sides spined at middle; punctation variable, from very sparse to dense. Elytra with humeri prominent; sparsely, rather coarsely punctate; apical tooth long, often spinelike. Length 20–30 mm.

b. *Monochamus carolinensis* (Olivier)   Pine Sawyer
Plate LXIII, No. 5, p. 643

Elongate, robust, subcylindrical; grayish or reddish brown, variegated with dark brown, very much as in *titillator,* but elytra paler. Pronotum coarsely, roughly punctate on center of disk, finely, transversely wrinkled near base and apex. Elytra coarsely and rather closely punctate on basal half, more finely and sparsely so toward apices, which are elongate in both sexes; tooth of sutural angle short. Length 13–18 mm.

c. *Monochamus notatus* (Drury)   Northeastern Sawyer
                                               Plate LXIII, No. 1, p. 643

Elongate, robust, subcylindrical; dark yellow-brown, mottled with light gray and white; pronotum with four small, whitish, irregular patches; elytra with numerous scattered patches of gray and brown, the latter being slightly elevated. Pronotum with a broad tubercle at sides; constricted rather feebly at base and apex. Elytra elongate, sides feebly curved, slightly tapering toward apices; apices rounded. Length 18–32 mm.

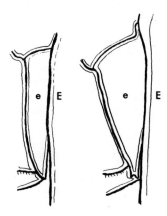

Figs. 466–467

Fig. 468

Figs. 466–467. Metepisternum of *Eupogonius* (466) and of *Saperda* (467). *E*, sides of elytron; *e*, metepisternum.
Fig. 468. Procoxal cavity of *Cyrtinus*. *l*, lateral angulation.

d. *Monochamus scutellatus* (Say)   White-spotted Sawyer
Plate LXIII, No. 3, p. 643

Elongate, subcylindrical; black, distinctly bronzed; elytra with small patches of gray and brown pubescence; scutellum covered with white pubescence. Pronotum transversely rugose, especially near apical and basal margins. Elytra coarsely and roughly punctate, especially in male. Length 15–28 mm.

Genus II. *GOES* LeConte

Large, elongate, rather robust, subcylindrical; antennae as long as body in female, slightly longer in male, scape with distinct cicatrix; head as wide as pronotum; front concave between antennae, deflexed portion short; procoxal cavities completely closed; protibiae with two small, terminal spurs. In some of the members of this genus the larvae enter the sapwood very shortly after hatching, while others feed beneath the bark for some time before going into the heartwood.

KEY TO SPECIES

1. Elytra with conspicuous bare spaces, forming distinct transverse bands 2
   Elvtra almost uniformly covered with pubescence .... d. *pulverulentus*
2. Length 18 mm. or more 3
   Length not over 15 mm. .... a. *debilis*
3. Pubescence white or gray .... b. *tigrinus*
   Pubescence tawny or clay-colored .... c. *pulcher*

a. *Goes debilis* LeConte   Oak-Branch Borer
Plate LXII, No. 11, p. 631

Elongate, rather robust, subcylindrical; reddish brown to piceous; head, pronotum, and elytra apically with reddish-yellow pubescence, basal half of elytra mottled with grayish pubescence. Pronotum transverse; surface coarsely and sparsely punctate; sides distinctly tubercled, tubercles terminating in a blunt spine. Elytra sparsely and feebly tuberculate basally, thence rugosely, coarsely punctate, more finely so apically; apices rounded. Length 11–16 mm.

This species breeds usually in the small branches of living hickory and oak.

b. *Goes tigrinus* (DeGeer)   White-Oak Borer
Plate LXII, No. 10, p. 631

Elongate, robust, cylindrical; dark brown, covered with rather dense, recumbent, white pubescence; elytra with a dark-brown transverse band before and behind middle. Pronotum transverse, armed laterally with a robust tubercle; disk with three smaller, obtuse tubercles. Elytra with sides nearly parallel; disk at base with small, black tubercles, remainder of surface finely and sparsely punctate; apices rounded. Length 25–30 mm.

This species breeds in oak, especially white oak.

c. *Goes pulcher* (Haldeman)   Living-Hickory Borer
                                                Plate LXII, No. 9, p. 631

Elongate, robust, subcylindrical; brownish yellow; elytra with base broadly brown, thence to beyond middle pale grayish yellow, apex brownish yellow, with a broad, brown band on apical quarter, interrupted at suture. Pronotum transverse, finely and acutely tuberculate laterally, sulcate at basal and apical margins. Elytra with sides subparallel; base feebly tuberculate, then coarsely punctate, punctures finer apically; apices feebly truncate. Length 18–25 mm.

This species is found breeding in oak and hickory.

d. *Goes pulverulentus* (Haldeman)   Living-Beech Borer
                                                Plate LXII, No. 5, p. 631

Elongate, robust, subcylindrical; brown, covered with short, prostrate, gray and whitish pubescence; elytra with an indistinct band at base, and another behind middle, of darker-brown pubescence; scutellum sometimes nearly ochraceous. Pronotum transverse; sides with a small tubercle; disk coarsely punctate. Elytra with sides subparallel; disk at base with small tubercles, then coarsely punctate, more finely so apically; apices feebly truncate. Length 12.5–25.5 mm.

This species is recorded as breeding in the small branches and trunks of white oak, beech, blue beech, elm, and sycamore.

Genus III. *PLECTRODERA* LeConte

Large, elongate-ovate, robust beetles; antennae as long as or slightly longer than body, the cicatrix of scape not rimmed, indistinct; pronotum with strong lateral spines; procoxal cavities closed behind.

Plectrodera scalator (Fabricius)   Plate LXIII, No. 2, p. 643

Elongate, robust, subcylindrical; black, shining; pronotum with four broad, dense, white vittae, one either side of middle and one below each lateral tubercle; elytra with dense, white pubescence in irregular, transverse bands, usually connected with the others in several places, beneath partly clothed with dense, white pubescence; legs and antennae thinly grayish-white-pubescent. Pronotum transverse; disk with three callosities and a basal and apical transverse impression. Elytra with sides nearly parallel;

PLATE LXII
Family CERAMBYCIDAE VI

1. *Strangalina bicolor* (Swederus) (p. 623) — Tan; elytra black; 10–14 mm.

2. *S. luteicornis* (Fabricius) (p. 623) — Light tan, with black markings; 9–14 mm.

3. *S. acuminata* (Olivier) (p. 622) — Black; elytra dull yellow, margined with black; 7–11.5 mm.

4. *S. famelica* (Newman) (p. 623) — Light brown; pronotum and elytra with variable black markings; 12–14 mm.

5. *Goes pulverulentus* (Haldeman) (p. 629) — Reddish brown, concealed by brown and whitish pubescence; 12–25 mm.

6. *Desmocerus palliatus* (Forster) (p. 623) — Deep, shining blue; elytra at base yellowish; 17–24 mm.

7. *Dorcaschema wildii* Uhler (p. 632) — Reddish brown, concealed by ashy, brownish, and yellowish pubescence; 15–22 mm.

8. *D. alternatum* (Say) (p. 632) — Light brown, with ashy- and yellowish-pubescent markings; 8–13 mm.

9. *Goes pulcher* (Haldeman) (p. 629) — Entirely covered with yellowish-brown and dark-brown pubescence; 18–25 mm.

10. *G. tigrinus* (DeGeer) (p. 628) — Covered with ashy pubescence and marked with dark brown; 25–30 mm.

11. *G. debilis* LeConte (p. 628) — Reddish brown to piceous, ashy- and tawny-pubescent; 11–16 mm.

12. *Psenocerus supernotatus* (Say) (p. 634) — Dark brown or black, with white markings; 3–6 mm.

13. *Dorcaschema nigrum* (Say) (p. 633) — Grayish black, not shining; 8–10 mm.

14. *Eupogonius vestitus* (Say) (p. 634) — Light to dark brown; yellowish-brown-pubescent markings; 6–9 mm.

15. *E. tomentosus* (Haldeman) (p. 634) — Brown; markings grayish white; 5.5–8 mm.

MM 0 10 20 30 40 50 60 70

PLATE LXII 631

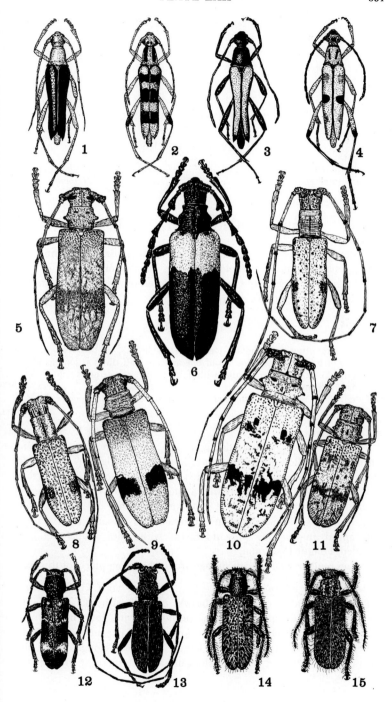

disk with nonpubescent areas sparsely, finely punctate; apices rounded. Length 22–40 mm.

Usually the adults are abundant about cottonwood and poplar trees, in which they breed.

Tribe DORCASCHEMATINI

KEY TO GENERA

Elytra rounded at apices . . . . I. *Dorcaschema* (p. 632)
Elytra pointed at apices . . . . II. *Hetoemis* (p. 633)

Genus I. *DORCASCHEMA* LeConte

Moderate-sized or large, elongate-oblong, subcylindrical; antennae twice as long as body in male, one and one-fourth times as long as body in female, third segment longest, rest gradually shorter; elytra rounded at apex; mesotibiae carinate; claws divaricate.

KEY TO SPECIES

1. Black; pronotum only slightly longer than wide . . . . c. *nigrum*
   Brown or grayish; pronotum about one and one-half times as long as wide . . 2
2. Length 15–22 mm.; pronotum with fine, transverse wrinkles and a few indistinct punctures . . . . a. *wildii*
   Length 8–12 mm.; pronotum not wrinkled but distinctly punctate . . . .
   . . . . b. *alternatum*

a. *Dorcaschema wildii* Uhler   Plate LXII, No. 7, p. 631
Elongate, slender, subcylindrical; brown; pronotum and elytra densely covered with yellow-gray pubescence, laterally with light-gray pubescence; elytra with numerous small, rounded, bare spots and a large, irregular spot behind middle, frequently with a lateral stripe of yellowish pubescence extending from middle to apex. Pronotum elongate; disk with numerous fine, transverse carinae, median impressed line smooth, transverse basal and apical impressions present. Elytra with sides subparallel; apices rounded. Length 15–22 mm.

Living mulberry and Osage orange are the breeding places of this species.

b. *Dorcaschema alternatum* (Say)   Plate LXII, No. 8, p. 631
Elongate, slender, cylindrical; brown, covered with sparse, recumbent, gray and light-brown pubescence; pronotum with four fine stripes of yellow pubescence; elytra each with three rows of irregular spots of yellow pubescence, those of middle row larger. Pronotum elongate; disk finely, rugosely punctate and with an elongate, smooth space at middle. Elytra

with sides subparallel; disk sparsely and coarsely punctate, with an irregular space behind middle devoid of pubescence and densely punctate; apices rounded. Length 8–13 mm.

This species is recorded as breeding in dead and dying mulberry and Osage orange.

c. *Dorcaschema nigrum* (Say) Plate LXII, No. 13, p. 631
Elongate, slender, cylindrical; uniformly black, not shining. Head subequal in length to pronotum, finely carinate. Pronotum feebly elongate or feebly transverse, slightly narrowed behind middle; disk coarsely and roughly punctate. Elytra with sides subparallel; disk minutely granulate, sparsely, rather finely, and deeply punctate. Length 8–10 mm.

This species is recorded as breeding in dead hickory branches.

Genus II. *HETOEMIS* Haldeman

Elongate, slender; antennae slender, tapering, twice length of body in male, about as long as body in female, third segment longest, twice as long as fourth, the fifth slightly longer than fourth; elytra narrowed and pointed apically; mesotibiae carinate; claws divaricate.

Hetoemis cinerea (Olivier) Plate LXIII, No. 4, p. 643
Elongate, slender, cylindrical; black, covered with dense, short, recumbent, gray pubescence; antennae glabrous, black. Pronotum transverse, not as wide as elytra; disk with a smooth median line, surface with fine, transverse striae. Elytral disk densely and finely punctate, punctures concealed by dense pubescence. Length 8–12 mm.

This species breeds in dead limbs of walnut, mulberry, hickory, hackberry, linden, and Osage orange.

Tribe APODASYINI

KEY TO GENERA

Elytra with a spine or protuberance near scutellum; claws divergent ..
....I. *Psenocerus* (p. 633)
Elytra neither spinose nor protuberant at base; claws divaricate ......
....II. *Eupogonius* (p. 634)

Genus I. *PSENOCERUS* LeConte

Small, elongate, slender, cylindrical; antennae about two-thirds as long as body, third and fourth segments equal and longer than the other segments, scape stout, without a cicatrix; pronotum much constricted behind middle; elytra each with a distinct protuberance at base; mesotibiae not sulcate; claws divergent.

Psenocerus supernotatus (Say)   Currant-Tip Borer
Plate LXII, No. 12, p. 631

Elongate, cylindrical; dark reddish brown or blackish, densely and coarsely punctate; scutellum with white pubescence; elytra with a narrow, oblique band near middle and a curved band on apical third (not attaining suture) of white pubescence. Pronotum transverse, constricted at base; sides rounded. Elytra parallel-sided; disk near scutellum with an oval, obtuse elevation; apices rounded. Length 3–6 mm.

The adults frequent flowers of shrubs and breed in various shrubs and vines.

Genus II. *EUPOGONIUS* LeConte

Rather small, elongate, cylindrical species; antennae not longer than body, covered with long, flying hairs, first segment feebly clavate, shorter than third, segments five to ten equal; eyes coarsely granulate; mesotibiae not sulcate on outer side; claws divaricate.

KEY TO SPECIES

Light brown, with fine, transverse streaks of pubescence on elytra ....
....a. *tomentosus*
Dark brown; elytra with patches of pubescence ....b. *vestitus*

a. *Eupogonius tomentosus* (Haldeman)   Plate LXII, No. 15, p. 631

Elongate, slender, subdepressed; reddish brown to orange-brown, sparsely covered with long, erect hairs, more densely so on head and pronotum, the latter with a medial bare space; elytra with irregular, transverse, fine, whitish streaks and dots. Pronotum transverse, acutely tuberculate laterally, sides feebly curved; disk uniformly, coarsely, and densely punctate. Elytra subparallel to beyond middle, disk coarsely punctate, punctures finer apically; apices rounded. Length 5.5–8 mm.

This species breeds in dead pine, spruce, and cedar. The adults may be collected on fresh pine slash.

b. *Eupogonius vestitus* (Say)   Plate LXII, No. 14, p. 631

Elongate, slender; light to piceous brown, covered with sparse, erect hairs; elytra mottled with small patches of dense, yellowish-brown pubescence. Pronotum transverse; sides acutely tuberculate at middle; disk densely, deeply, and rather coarsely punctate. Elytra with sides subparallel; disk coarsely, densely punctate, punctures becoming finer apically; apices rounded. Length 6–9 mm.

This species is recorded as breeding in dead branches of various hardwoods. The adults may be taken on fresh slash.

TRIBE POGONOCHERINI

Genus *ECYRUS* LeConte

Small, rather robust beetles; antennae very hairy; protibiae abruptly dilated apically; pronotum unarmed; pubescence short.

Ecyrus dasycerus (Say)   Plate LXIV, No. 4, p. 649

Short, moderately robust, parallel; dark brown, with brown, gray, white, and black pubescence; elytra with an oblique, black stripe basally and a transverse band of same color near apex, the costae with small, light-colored pubescent tubercles. Pronotum subquadrate, cylindrical, constricted at base; anterior margin arcuate, with two small tubercles at middle; surface densely, finely punctate. Elytra with apices subtruncate; disk coarsely and densely punctate. Length 6–9 mm.

The adults may be beaten from foliage of elm, wild grape, and branches of dead oak. They are recorded as breeding in various hardwoods.

Tribe ONCIDERINI

Genus *ONCIDERES* Serville

Elongate, cylindrical, of moderate size; antennae fringed beneath, scape elongate, clubbed apically, third segment longest; head retractile; pronotum transverse, tuberculate laterally, disk usually with transverse striae; mesotibiae sulcate.

Oncideres cingulata Say   The Hickory Girdler
                                                            Plate LXIII, No. 8, p. 643

Elongate, robust; blackish or reddish brown to ochraceous, with fine, ashy pubescence that usually forms a broad, median band on elytra; pronotal disk with three small, black spots. Pronotum transverse, constricted at base; sides sinuate, usually tuberculate, tubercle sometimes absent; surface rugose, with large scattered punctures. Elytra with sides subparallel; disk with base granulate-punctate, then rugosely punctate to near apex, apical quarter coarsely punctate; apices rounded. Length 9–17 mm.

The female deposits eggs in the tips of the twigs of various hardwoods and proceeds to girdle the twig below the egg toward the trunk. The twig dies, is broken off by wind, and falls to the ground, where the larvae mature.

Tribe HIPPOPSINI

Genus *HIPPOPSIS* Serville

Of moderate size, very elongate, sublinear, convex above; antennae very long, about three times length of body in male, setaceous, fringed beneath, approximate at base, first segment elongate, cylindrical, third segment longest; head with front long and strongly inclined posteriorly so that the mouth is near the prosternum; palpi not slender, the last segment almost conical and pointed; pronotum unarmed laterally; procoxae angulate; mesotibiae sulcate; tarsi as long as tibiae, first segment of metatarsi slightly elongate, last segment longer, claws divergent.

Hippopsis lemniscata (Fabricius)   Plate LXIII, No. 7, p. 643
    Elongate, very slender, cylindrical; pale to dark reddish brown; pronotum with two whitish lines on each side, elytra each with three whitish lines; antennae pale brown, darker apically. Antennae twice as long as body in female, longer in male, fringed beneath. Pronotum elongate; sides unarmed; disk coarsely and densely punctate. Elytra very elongate, sides gradually convergent toward acute, dehiscent apices; disk coarsely and deeply punctate, punctures in rows. Length 10–13 mm.
    The adults may be taken by sweeping *Coreopsis,* ragweed, tickweed, and daisy fleabane.

Tribe ACANTHODERINI

Genus *AEGOSCHEMA* Aurivillius

Of moderate size, elongate-oblong, robust, subdepressed; antennae as long as body in female, slightly longer in male, first segment large, clavate, second short, third longest; pronotum almost as long as wide, tuberculate laterally, disk irregular or tuberculate; procoxae globose; femora clavate; tibiae slender; mesotibiae sulcate; protarsi of male broader than those of female and fringed on sides with long hairs.

Aegoschema modesta Gyllenhal   Plate LXIII, No. 9, p. 643
    Elongate, oblong, rather robust, subdepressed; dark brown, covered with dense, short, prostrate, yellowish and gray pubescence, the gray pubescence forming three obscure, oblique bands on the elytra. Pronotum finely but

deeply punctate; base at middle with an oblong, obtuse tubercle. Elytra each with an oblong, obtuse raised space at middle; apices rounded. Length 10–13 mm.

This species is recorded as breeding in many of the dead hardwoods.

Tribe ACANTHOCININI

KEY TO GENERA

Genus I. *AMNISCUS* Haldeman

Rather small, oblong, subconvex species; front narrowed to mouth and between eyes; pronotum feebly tuberculate or angulate at sides, slightly behind middle; female without an elongated ovipositor.

KEY TO SPECIES

Elytra without scattered tufts of hairs ....a. *maculus*
Elytra with scattered, small tufts of fuscous hairs ....b. *sexguttatus*

a. *Amniscus maculus* (Say)   Plate LXIV, No. 2, p. 649

Elongate, oblong, robust; dark reddish brown, sparsely pubescent; pronotum broadly white-pubescent at sides and with a broad, brown streak either side of middle bounded on each side by a line of two or three bare tubercles; elytra with a broad, whitish band behind middle and with six longitudinal series of irregularly spaced, fuscous maculae. Pronotum transverse; constricted apically; lateral tubercles broad; disk with five obtuse tubercles, surface coarsely punctate, more sparsely so laterally. Elytra with basal gibbosities broad; disk rather sparsely, coarsely punctate; apices obliquely truncate to suture. Length 4–9 mm.

This species is recorded as breeding in walnut, oak, apple, butternut, beech, buckeye, hickory, and dogwood.

b. *Amniscus sexguttatus* (Say)   Plate LXIV, No. 3, p. 649

Elongate, oblong, robust; reddish brown or dull yellow, mottled with grayish pubescence; each elytron near base with an elongate, dark spot, another at middle, and a third near apex. Pronotum transverse; lateral tubercles short, acute; disk with five small, blunt tubercles, remainder of surface finely and densely punctate. Elytra coarsely, densely punctate; basal gibbosities distinct; each elytron with four costae; apices strongly, obliquely truncate, the sutural angle with a small tooth. Length 6–10 mm.

This species is recorded as breeding in dead pine, larch, and spruce branches.

Genus II. *ASTYLEIOPUS* Dillon

Elongate-ovate, robust; antennae feebly fringed ventrally on basal segments; pronotum transverse, lateral tubercles not distinct and with a short, upturned spine; disk with three feeble tubercles, surface irregularly punctate.

Astyleiopus variegatus (Haldeman)   Plate LXIII, No. 10, p. 643

Rather robust; reddish brown or yellowish brown, mottled with black; pronotum on disk with a dark M-shaped marking, this sometimes broken

or reduced; elytra with three common blackish bands, frequently interrupted or reduced, and with a black, chevron-shaped macula at apex, suture
and four elevated lines on disk whitish. Pronotum transverse; lateral tubercles small, ending in a short tooth; disk sparsely, finely punctate. Elytra
with basal gibbosities variable in size; disk of each elytron with four costae,
these not bearing tufts or small tubercles; surface with deep, moderate-
sized punctures which are denser medially; apices separately, broadly
rounded. Length 6–12 mm.

This species is recorded as breeding in honey locust, elm, walnut, Virginia
creeper, and poison ivy.

Genus III. *GRAPHISURUS* Kirby

Of moderate size, rather robust, elongate; antennae with third and fourth
segments densely fringed beneath with short hairs; pronotum each side
laterally with a blunt tubercle a little behind middle, disk nearly impunctate; elytra emarginate at tip; females with an elongated ovipositor.

Graphisurus fasciatus (DeGeer)　　　　　Plate LXIV, No. 1, p. 649
Elongate, rather slender; dark reddish brown, with dense, ashy or fulvous
pubescence; pronotum with two black dots; elytra sprinkled with small
dark dots and blotches, the latter forming an irregular fascia in front of
middle and another, more conspicuous, behind middle. Pronotum transverse; lateral tubercles very obtuse, with a short, blunt spine at apex; disk
with scattered, fine punctures, a few coarser ones at base. Elytra with basal
gibbosities distinct; surface coarsely, sparsely punctate, punctures finer behind middle; apices distinctly emarginate, the angles formed acute. Length
8–14 mm. (excluding ovipositor in female).

This species is recorded as breeding in many dead hardwoods.

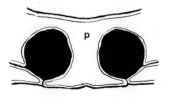

FIG. 469

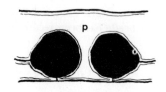

FIG. 470

Figs. 469–470. Prosternum and procoxal cavities of *Amniscus* (469)
and of *Graphisurus* (470). *p,* prosternal process.

Genus IV. *STERNIDIUS* LeConte

Feebly elongate, convex, rather small species; antennae not ciliate beneath, long in male; pronotum distinctly tuberculate laterally behind middle, disk rather irregular; femora clavate; first metatarsal segment equal to second and third together; females without elongated ovipositors.

KEY TO SPECIES

Antennae with fourth segment distinctly longer than first; pronotal punctation distinct ....b. *alpha*
Antennae with fourth segment subequal to or shorter than first; pronotal punctation usually concealed by pubescence ....a. *mimeticus*

a. *Sternidius mimeticus* (Casey)   Plate LXIII, No. 12, p. 643
Elongate-oblong, slender; dark reddish brown, entirely clothed with dense, hoary, gray pubescence; head usually piceous; pronotal disk and base of elytra with light-fulvous-brown pubescence; pronotum with three fuscous maculae, these sometimes indistinct or absent; elytra with a narrow band around scutellum, a large spot near humeri, and an irregular band behind middle all fuscous, the disk on basal three-fifths with small, fuscous spots arranged in rows. Pronotum transverse; lateral tubercles distinct, not spined or toothed at apex; disk with three small tubercles medially. Elytra with basal gibbosities not distinct; disk with four costae each side, these interrupted at basal third and with small, sometimes tufted, tubercles along their length; apices broadly, obliquely truncate. Length 4.8–7 mm.

b. *Sternidius alpha* (Say)   Plate LXIII, No. 11, p. 643
Elongate, slender; dark reddish brown, with sparse, grayish pubescence; pronotum with three small, fuscous maculae; elytra with four rows of small, black dots and with an acute, angular, fuscous band behind middle which usually has three or four fuscous tufts. Pronotum transverse; lateral tubercles small and at apex with an obtuse tooth; disk trituberculate; surface finely, densely punctate. Elytra with basal gibbosities prominent; surface finely punctate, almost smooth at apex, base sometimes coarsely punctate, in which case the apex is distinctly punctate; each elytron with four indistinct costae which bear small, tufted tubercles; apices narrowly, obliquely truncate at suture. Length 4–7 mm.
This beetle has been recorded as breeding in dead sycamore twigs.

Genus V. *URGLEPTES* Dillon

Small to very small beetles, subdepressed; antennae fringed beneath with widely scattered hairs; third segment slightly longer than first; prosternal process narrow, mesosternal process slightly broader than prosternal; first metatarsal segment nearly equal to remaining segments combined.

KEY TO SPECIES

1. Elytra with a broad, dark band across apices ....c. *facetus*
   Elytra without a dark band at apices 2
2. Elytra each with a dark vitta laterally which extends without interruption to apical third, postscutellar macula with its posterior margin arcuately merging with sutural vitta ....b. *querci*
   Elytra each without a continuous dark vitta laterally, postscutellar margin separated from sutural vitta by a pale line ....a. *signatus*

a. *Urgleptes signatus* (LeConte)   Plate LXIV, No. 8, p. 649

Elongate, rather slender; head and pronotum dark ferrugineous; elytra, body underneath laterally, and antennae paler, legs much paler; pronotum with four indistinct, brownish vittae; each elytron with seven irregular, fuscous markings. Pronotum transverse, narrowed apically; lateral tubercles small, armed at apex with a long, acute spine; disk without punctures except for a row of coarse punctures in basal sulcus. Elytra with basal gibbosities rounded, prominent; disk finely, sparsely punctate; apices narrowly, separately rounded. Length 4.5–6.5 mm.

This species is recorded as breeding in sumac.

b. *Urgleptes querci* (Fitch)   Plate LXIV, No. 9, p. 649

Elongate, slender; ferrugineous to piceous on upper side, beneath pale yellowish to black; sparsely covered with cinereous pubescence; pronotum either side of middle with two indistinct, irregular, fuscous vittae; elytra with six to seven dark-brown or fuscous markings. Pronotum transverse; sides gradually narrowing toward apex, constricted at base; lateral tubercles feeble, each armed with a short, robust tooth; disk impunctate except for a row of coarse punctures in the basal sulcus. Elytra with basal gibbosities broad, not prominent; disk coarsely, sparsely, confusedly punctate; apices broadly, separately rounded. Length 4–5 mm.

c. *Urgleptes facetus* (Say)   Plate LXIV, No. 5, p. 649

Elongate, slender; dark reddish brown, sparsely covered with fuscous pubescence; pronotum at middle usually with a large W-shaped macula of cinereous pubescence, this sometimes variously interrupted; elytra each with two large, cinereous markings. Pronotum transverse; lateral tubercles small but prominent, each armed with an acute, slender spine; sides strongly constricted behind lateral tubercles; disk impunctate except for a row of coarse, close-set punctures in the basal sulcus. Elytra with basal gibbosities nearly obsolete; disk coarsely, sparsely, irregularly punctate; apices separately, strongly rounded. Length 3.1–4.2 mm.

This species is recorded as breeding in hawthorns and black oak.

PLATE LXIII

Family CERAMBYCIDAE VII

1. *Monochamus notatus* (Drury) (p. 627)

White- and silvery-gray-pubescent, spotted with blackish; 18–32 mm.

2. *Plectrodera scalator* (Fabricius) (p. 629)

Black, with dense, white markings; 22–40 mm.

3. *Monochamus scutellatus* (Say) (p. 628)

Blackish or deep brown, with white markings; 15–28 mm.

4. *Hetoemis cinerea* (Olivier) (p. 633)

Black; uniformly densely ashy-pubescent 8–12 mm.

5. *Monochamus carolinensis* (Olivier) (p. 626)

Whitish-pubescent, tinged with yellow and marked with deep brown; elytral apices dentate; 13–18 mm.

6. *M. titillator* (Fabricius) (p. 626)

As above, but elytral apices spined and antennae longer; 20–30 mm.

7. *Hippopsis lemniscata* (Fabricius) (p. 636)

Pale to dark reddish brown, with pale-yellowish stripes; 10–13 mm.

8. *Oncideres cingulata* Say (p. 635)

Ashy-pubescent, spotted with yellowish; elytral band sometimes absent; 9–17 mm.

9. *Aegoschema modesta* Gyllenhal (p. 636)

Dull-yellowish- and ashy-pubescent, spotted or banded with white and deep brown; 10–13 mm.

10. *Astyleiopus variegatus* (Haldeman) (p. 638)

Ashy-pubescent, varied with white and blackish; 6–12 mm.

11. *Sternidius alpha* (Say) (p. 640)

Ashy- to brownish-pubescent; fuscous markings very variable; 4–7 mm.

12. *S. mimeticus* (Casey) (p. 640)

Ashy- and brownish-pubescent, marked with black and white; 4.8–7 mm.

MM |||||||||||||||||||||||||||||||||||||||||||||||||||
0   10   20   30   40   50   60   70

PLATE LXIII   643

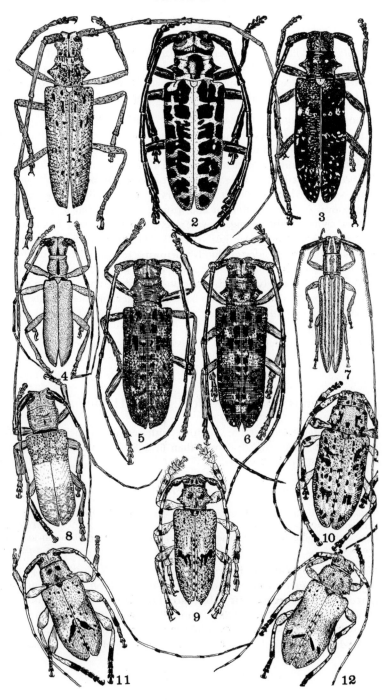

Genus VI. *LEPTURGES* Bates

Small, rather flattened species; antennae very sparsely fringed beneath with very short hairs, scape always longer than third segment; pro- and mesosternum very narrow, linear, scarcely separating the coxae; first metatarsal segment longer than rest of segments combined.

Lepturges confluens (Haldeman)   Plate LXIV, No. 6, p. 649

Elongate-ovate; red-testaceous to dark ferrugineous, covered with dull, ashy pubescence; pronotum with four ovate maculae of dull-fulvous pubescence, these sometimes confluent, forming a vitta either side of middle, and with usually a dark vitta laterally which is frequently broken into small, lunate spots; elytra each with the following dull-fulvous markings: an elongate-oval one near scutellum and a smaller one behind it, laterally a series of eight or nine elongate-ovate spots, extending from humerus to apex, and two discal maculae just at middle, these all sometimes confluent. Pronotum transverse; sides gradually narrowing to apex; lateral tubercles placed almost at base, robust, with a short, robust tooth at apex; disk tumid apically, at base coarsely, densely punctate, punctures not placed in a distinct row in basal sulcus. Elytra with basal gibbosities elongate, arcuate; disk coarsely, densely punctate; apices separately, broadly rounded. Length 6–9 mm.

This species has been recorded as breeding in decaying beech and black walnut.

Genus VII. *HYPERPLATYS* Haldeman

Small, subdepressed beetles; antennae with very few fringing hairs beneath, third segment slightly longer than first; first metatarsal segment as long as following three together.

KEY TO SPECIES

Elytra each with a distinct, blackish vitta laterally; abdomen beneath usually ferrugineous ....a. *maculatus*
Elytra each without a distinct, blackish vitta laterally; abdomen beneath usually blackish ....b. *aspersus*

a. *Hyperplatys maculatus* Haldeman   Plate LXIV, No. 13, p. 649

Elongate, slender, subdepressed; light to dark reddish brown, entirely covered with sparse, cinereous pubescence; head often blackish; pronotum with a transverse series of four dark, rounded spots, the two outer ones sometimes reduced or wanting; elytra sprinkled with fine, blackish spots and with a large, dark one behind middle, on sides with a vitta of same color extending from humeri to apices. Pronotum transverse, sides rounded, constricted at base; lateral tubercles obsolete, replaced by a small, acute tooth just before basal constriction; disk uniformly, finely punctate. Elytra with basal gibbosities broad, prominent; disk uniformly, coarsely punctate, with a distinct carina laterally; apices emarginate, the angles acutely toothed, the outer one larger. Length 4–6.5 mm.

This species is recorded as breeding in dead willow branches.

b. *Hyperplatys aspersus* Say   Plate LXIV, No. 12, p. 649

Short, slender; reddish brown, covered with dense, grayish pubescence; pronotum with four small, round, blackish spots arranged in a transverse row, the two inner ones larger; each elytron sprinkled with rounded, blackish maculae and usually with a large, black blotch behind middle; sides never vittate with black. Antennae twice as long as body. Pronotum transverse, constricted basally; disk finely and sparsely punctate; acutely spined laterally near base. Elytra with basal gibbosities broad, prominent; disk coarsely, densely punctate, lateral carina distinct; apices emarginate, angles dentate, outer one larger. Length 4–6.5 mm.

This species is recorded as breeding in poplar and Juneberry.

Genus VIII. *DECTES* LeConte

Elongate, slender, cylindrical; antennae not fringed with hairs beneath; third antennal segment either shorter or longer than first; pronotal disk without transverse impression and tubercles; elytra without costae or basal gibbosities; prosternum very narrow, linear; mesosternal process narrow, tapering; first metatarsal segment as long as next two together.

KEY TO SPECIES

Antennae with second segment one-fourth as long as first; front not transverse, quadrate or elongate; tarsi and femora without fuscous annuli at apex ..a. *sayi*
Antennae with second segment never more than one-eighth as long as first; front distinctly transverse; tarsi and femora with fuscous annuli at apex ..b. *texanus*

a. *Dectes sayi* Dillon and Dillon   Plate LXIV, No. 10, p. 649

Elongate, cylindrical; dark reddish brown to black, uniformly covered with dense, gray pubescence; elytra on anterior margin below each humerus frequently with a poorly defined brown or fuscous macula. Pronotum quadrate or feebly elongate; lateral tubercles feeble, each armed with an acute spine; disk convex, densely, finely punctate. Elytra with basal gibbosities feeble; disk with dense, fine punctures, which become finer at apex; apices obliquely truncate, the outer angle frequently subdentate. Length 6–10.5 mm.

This species is recorded as breeding in living stems of ragweed, *Eupatorium*, and *Xanthium*. The adult may usually be found head downward in the whorl of leaves at the top of ragweed.

b. *Dectes texanus* LeConte   Plate LXIV, No. 11, p. 649

Elongate, cylindrical; piceous or black, with dense, uniformly pale-gray pubescence; elytra on anterior margin of each humerus with a transverse, fuscous bar. Pronotum transverse; lateral tubercles feeble, each armed with a slender, subacute spine; disk convex, densely, finely punctate. Elytra with basal gibbosities feeble; disk finely, densely punctate, punctures finer and more dense apically; apices broadly, obliquely truncate, the lateral angles more or less distinctly dentate. Length 6–10 mm.

Tribe CYRTININI

Genus *CYRTINUS* LeConte

Very small, elongate, subcylindrical; head broad; eyes small, divided, coarsely granulate; antennae slightly longer than body, scape slender, each segment with one or two hairs apically; legs robust, femora strongly clavate.

Cyrtinus pygmaeus (Haldeman)   Plate LXIV, No. 7, p. 649

Elongate, subcylindrical; dark brown; elytra with a transverse blotch of white pubescence basally and an oblique band of white before middle; antennae annulate with yellow. Pronotum elongate, widest at apex, constricted basally; disk very convex, smooth, with sparse, minute punctures. Elytra convex, each with a large, acute spine near scutellum; surface finely, densely punctate on flattened area. Length 2–3.7 mm.

This species breeds in dead branches of various hardwoods. The adults may be collected by beating dead branches.

Tribe SAPERDINI

Genus *SAPERDA* Fabricius

Large or medium-sized beetles; elongate, cylindrical; head with front flat, quadrate, vertical; eyes finely granulate, deeply emarginate; antennae as long as or slightly shorter than body, scape subcylindrical; pronotum cylindrical, unarmed laterally; elytra wider at base than pronotum, apices either rounded, spinose, or acuminate; femora cylindrical; first metatarsal segment much elongated; tarsal claws divaricate.

KEY TO SPECIES

1. Antennae distinctly annulate 9
   Antennae unicolorous 2
2. Elytra and pronotum with conspicuous white markings 3
   Elytra and pronotum without white markings 4
3. Each elytron with a single, continuous white stripe ....b. *candida*
   Each elytron with two unconnected white spots ....e. *cretata*
4. Pronotum bright yellow, with four black dots ....i. *puncticollis*
   Pronotum otherwise colored 5
5. Elytra with a reddish stripe laterally 6
   Elytra without stripes 7
6. Pronotum and elytra black; elytra without darker spots and usually without
   reddish crossbands ....h. *lateralis*
   Pronotum and elytra gray; elytra with several small, black spots and with three
   reddish crossbands ....d. *tridentata*
7. Uniformly grayish yellow, with several small, rounded spots of brown on
   elytra ....g. *vestita*
   Not uniformly colored—gray, brown, or black 8
8. Gray, with yellowish patches and tiny black dots; length over 25 mm. ......
   ....c. *calcarata*
   Brown to black; male unicolorous, length 10 mm.; female with olive-yellow
   markings on elytra, length 15 mm. ....f. *discoidea*
9. Color uniformly gray ....j. *concolor*
   Color light brown, with oblique, dark bands ....a. *obliqua*

a. *Saperda obliqua* Say   Plate LXV, No. 6, p. 655

Elongate, robust; light reddish brown; pronotum with four dark-brown stripes; elytra with four oblique, parallel bands of dark brown; antennae annulate, scape and second segment dark. Pronotum transverse, narrowed anteriorly; disk coarsely, confluently punctate. Elytra with apices divaricate and armed with a spine at tip; surface densely, coarsely punctate. Length 16–20 mm.

This species breeds in the bases of living alder and birch.

b. *Saperda candida* Fabricius   Round-headed Apple Borer
                                              Plate LXV, No. 4, p. 655

Elongate, cylindrical; light brown above, with two white vittae extending from front of head to apex of elytra; underneath white. Pronotum transverse; disk convex; surface coarsely punctate medially. Elytral disk coarsely, densely punctate; apices rounded. Length 15–20 mm.

In the larval stage this species is very destructive to apple trees, quince, and *Crataegus* species.

c. *Saperda calcarata* Say   Poplar Borer
                                              Plate LXV, No. 1, p. 655

Elongate, cylindrical, rather robust; densely covered with gray pubescence, variegated with patches of yellow hairs on elytra and on head; pronotum with three yellow stripes; front of head and scutellum yellow; underneath gray, with yellow patches. Pronotum transverse; disk with a

PLATE LXIV
Family CERAMBYCIDAE VIII

1. *Graphisurus fasciatus* (DeGeer) (p. 639) — Ashy-pubescent, marked with blackish; 8–14 mm.

2. *Amniscus maculus* (Say) (p. 638) — Dark reddish brown, with fuscous and white markings; 4–9 mm.

3. *A. sexguttatus* (Say) (p. 638) — Light to dark reddish brown, with pale ashy and black markings; 6–10 mm.

4. *Ecyrus dasycerus* (Say) (p. 635) — Brownish, ashy, and white, marked with dark brown or black; 6–9 mm.

5. *Urgleptes facetus* (Say) (p. 641) — Blackish, with ashy-pubescent marks; 3.1–4.2 mm.

6. *Lepturges confluens* (Haldeman) (p. 644) — Dull ashy, marked with dark brown or fulvous; 6–9 mm.

7. *Cyrtinus pygmaeus* (Haldeman) (p. 646) — Shining brown; elytra with white lines; 2–3.7 mm.

8. *Urgleptes signatus* (LeConte) (p. 641) — Deep brown; elytra paler; ashy-pubescent; fuscous markings: 4.5–6.5 mm.

9. *U. querci* (Fitch) (p. 641) — Deep brown; elytra pale, with brown markings; 4–5 mm.

10. *Dectes sayi* Dillon and Dillon (p. 645) — Ashy- or gray-pubescent; fuscous markings; 6–10.5 mm.

11. *D. texanus* LeConte (p. 646) — Ashy- or gray-pubescent, with fuscous markings; 6–10 mm.

12. *Hyperplatys aspersus* Say (p. 645) — Ashy-pubescent, with black spots; 4–6.5 mm.

13. *H. maculatus* Haldeman (p. 644) — Ashy, with black spots; elytra usually with white lines; 4–6.5 mm.

14. *Saperda puncticollis* Say (p. 651) — Black; head and pronotum yellow-pubescent; elytra with a yellow marginal and sutural stripe; 9–11.5 mm.

15. *S. discoidea* Fabricius ♂ (p. 650) — Deep brown, with ashy pubescence; 14–16 mm.

16. *S. discoidea* Fabricius ♀ (p. 650) — Reddish brown, with yellowish-white-pubescent markings; 14–16 mm.

17. *S. lateralis* Fabricius (p. 651) — Black; elytra with orange vittae; 9–15 mm.

MM | 0 | 10 | 20 | 30 | 40 | 50 | 60 | 70

PLATE LXIV

649

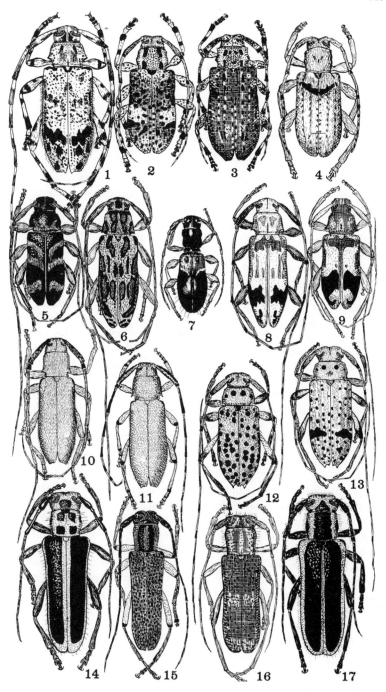

transverse basal impression; surface densely, coarsely punctate. Elytral disk coarsely, densely punctate basally, punctures becoming smaller apically; apices rounded in female, acute in male, in both sexes with sutural angle produced into a spine. Length 25–31 mm.

The larvae of this species bore in poplar and willow trees.

d. *Saperda tridentata* Olivier   Color Plate D; Plate LXV, No. 2, p. 655

Elongate, cylindrical; dark brown, densely clothed with gray pubescence above, more densely so on underside; pronotum either side of middle with two black spots as well as an orange-red vitta, these bands joined basally and attaining the head, disk sometimes with two black spots each side; elytra with several rounded, black spots near base and apex and with a more or less distinct, lateral, orange stripe, from which arise three crossbars of the same color, the one near base nearly transverse, the other two oblique, the middle one attaining suture. Pronotum transverse; sides sinuate; surface coarsely, densely punctate. Elytra with a submarginal ridge extending from humeral angle to near apex; surface coarsely, densely punctate; apices rounded. Length 9–16.5 mm.

This species breeds in dead twigs of elm and maple.

e. *Saperda cretata* Newman   Spotted Apple-Tree Borer
Plate LXV, No. 7, p. 655

Elongate, robust, cylindrical; cinnamon-brown, with a white stripe on the side of pronotum; a large, oblong, white spot (twice as long as wide) at middle of each elytron and another small spot before apex; occasionally with small, white spots at base of pronotum and humeral angles; beneath brown, sides white. Pronotum transverse; disk convex, with transverse basal impression; surface coarsely, densely punctate. Elytral surface coarsely punctate basally, more finely so apically; apices rounded. Length 12–20 mm.

This beetle is recorded as breeding in living apple and *Crataegus* species.

f. *Saperda discoidea* Fabricius   Hickory Saperda
Plate LXIV, Nos. 15, 16, p. 649

Elongate, moderately robust, cylindrical; reddish brown to black; male usually blackish, with gray pubescence which forms an indistinct vitta on disk and sides of pronotum, femora reddish brown, tibiae and tarsi often darker; female reddish brown, the pubescence olive or grayish yellow, each elytron with a small basal spot, another on apical one-third, and a broad, crescent-shaped spot at middle densely yellow-pubescent. Pronotum transverse; surface densely, coarsely punctate. Elytral apices rounded; surface densely, coarsely punctate. Length of male, 10–11 mm.; female, 14–16 mm.

The sexes are very different in color and markings in this species.

The adults are to be found breeding in dead or dying hickory and butter-nut trees.

g. *Saperda vestita* Say   Linden Borer
                                                Plate LXV, No. 8, p. 655

Elongate, robust, cylindrical; black, densely covered with light-olive-yellow or gray pubescence; elytra usually with three small, round, denuded spots, two of which are placed obliquely before middle and one behind middle, these spots occasionally absent. Pronotum transverse; sides sinuate; surface densely, coarsely punctate. Elytral disk coarsely punctate at base, concealed on apical half by pubescence; apices rounded. Length 12–21 mm.

The larvae live in dead linden trees.

h. *Saperda lateralis* Fabricius   Plate LXIV, No. 17, p. 649

Elongate, rather robust, cylindrical; black or piceous; coarsely punctate and covered with brownish-black pubescence above and gray beneath; pronotum with two black spots at base and a lateral, orange-red stripe that extends anteriorly on the head to the eyes and posteriorly is continuous with a submarginal elytral stripe which joins a sutural stripe of same color at apex, the latter sometimes absent. Pronotum transverse; sides sinuate; surface densely, coarsely punctate. Elytral disk coarsely, densely punctate; apices broadly rounded. Length 9–15 mm.

The adults of this species may be beaten from foliage of hickory, elm, and hazel. They breed in dead trees of the same species.

i. *Saperda puncticollis* Say   Plate LXIV, No. 14, p. 649

Elongate, rather slender, cylindrical; black or piceous, with sparse, black pubescence above and dense, gray pubescence beneath; head and pronotum densely yellow-pubescent; pronotum with a round, black spot laterally and four others on disk; each elytron with a broad, yellow marginal and sutural stripe. Pronotum transverse; surface densely, coarsely punctate. Elytral disk coarsely punctate; apices rounded. Length 9–11.5 mm.

This beetle is recorded as breeding in poison ivy and Virginia creeper.

j. *Saperda concolor* LeConte   Plate LXV, No. 3, p. 655

Elongate, rather slender, cylindrical; black, finely punctate, entirely covered by a dense, gray or yellowish-gray pubescence except on pronotal disk, where it is less dense; pronotum laterally with a deeper-gray stripe; antennae black, annulated with gray. Pronotum transverse; constricted basally; sculpturing concealed by pubescence. Elytral punctation concealed; apices acutely rounded. Length 11–13.8 mm.

The larvae bore in the stems of willow and poplar.

Tribe Phytoeciini

KEY TO GENERA

Body above nearly uniformly gray; tarsal claws cleft (Fig. 26E) ....
....I. *Mecas* (p. 652)
Body above never uniformly gray, usually bicolored; tarsal claws appendiculate (Fig. 26F) ....II. *Oberea* (p. 652)

Genus I. *MECAS* LeConte

The species of this genus resemble the *Saperda* in appearance. Elongate, slender, cylindrical; head with front short and subconvex; eyes deeply emarginate, but not divided; prothorax cylindrical; epipleura indistinct.

Mecas inornata (Say)   Plate LXV, No. 17, p. 655
Slender, elongate; black, densely gray-pubescent; pronotum with a small denuded area each side of middle. Pronotum transverse, sides rounded; punctures concealed by pubescence. Elytral apices rounded; surface finely but sparsely punctate. Length 8–15 mm.

This species resembles *Saperda concolor* in size, shape, and color, but it breeds in stems of shrubs, herbs, and weeds rather than in wood, as the *Saperda* do.

Genus II. *OBEREA* Mulsant

Of moderate size, elongate, cylindrical; eyes not divided; pronotum laterally neither spined nor tuberculate, disk with four, two, or no tubercles; epipleura distinct; mesotibiae sinuate on external edge; tarsal claws broadly appendiculate.

KEY TO SPECIES

1. Pronotum without callosities ....f. *ruficollis*
   Pronotum with elevated, black callosities 2
2. Pronotum with four callosities ....a. *schaumii*
   Pronotum with two callosities (often a third spot black) 3
3. Pronotum with basal border black ....c. *basalis*
   Pronotum without a black basal border 4
4. Abdomen entirely reddish ....e. *ocellata*
   Abdomen entirely or in large part black 5
5. Abdomen entirely black ....d. *bimaculata*
   Abdomen black, with several reddish segments ....b. *tripunctata*

a. *Oberea schaumii* LeConte   Plate LXV, No. 9, p. 655

Elongate, slender; color variable, usually pale brownish yellow; elytra, antennae, and tarsi frequently nearly black; pronotum with four round, black, smooth callosities arranged in a curved line; disk coarsely punctate between callosities. Elytra elongate; surface indistinctly costate, coarsely punctate, apices subtruncate. Length 10–14 mm.

This species is recorded as breeding in branches of living poplar and cottonwood.

b. *Oberea tripunctata* (Swederus)   Plate LXV, No. 13, p. 655

Elongate, slender, cylindrical; color variable, head dark brown, rarely yellow; pronotum yellow, disk with three black spots, one before scutellum, the other two on apical half; elytra black, each with a wide, yellowish discal stripe; body beneath usually in great part yellow, sometimes entirely black. Pronotum with two discal callosities; surface sparsely, not deeply punctate. Elytra with rows of coarse, deep punctures; apices truncate. Length 8–16 mm.

This species is recorded as breeding in living cottonwood, elm, dogwood, and *Viburnum*.

c. *Oberea basalis* LeConte   Plate LXV, No. 5, p. 655

Elongate, slender, cylindrical; black, shining; pronotum reddish yellow, with one small, round dot on each side and basal margin black. Pronotum quadrate, widest behind middle, constricted at base, narrowed feebly to apex, which is narrower than head; disk with two callosities. Elytra elongate, sides broadly sinuate from base to near apex; apices obliquely truncate and finely bidentate; surface rather coarsely punctate, the punctures seriate, and finer apically. Length 7–10 mm.

This species is recorded as breeding in stems of living raspberry and blackberry plants.

d. *Oberea bimaculata* (Olivier)   Raspberry-Cane Borer
                                                Plate LXV, No. 12, p. 655

Elongate, slender, cylindrical; black, shining; pronotum yellow, disk with two round, black spots and frequently a third spot before scutellum; lower portion of sides black. Pronotum deeply and coarsely punctate; disk with two callosities. Elytral disk with rows of coarse punctures; apices truncate. Length 8–13 mm.

This species is recorded as breeding in the same plants as *O. basalis*.

e. *Oberea ocellata* Haldeman   Plate LXV, No. 10, p. 655

Elongate, slender, subcylindrical; head, pronotum, femora, and ventral surface reddish; tibiae and tarsi and antennae dark brown or black; elytra

PLATE LXV
Family CERAMBYCIDAE IX

1. *Saperda calcarata* Say (p. 647)

Silvery-gray-pubescent, with yellow markings; 25–31 mm.

2. *S. tridentata* Olivier (p. 650)

Dark-gray-pubescent, with red and black markings; 9–16.5 mm.

3. *S. concolor* LeConte (p. 651)

Black, with dense gray or yellowish-gray pubescence; 11–13.8 mm.

4. *S. candida* Fabricius (p. 647)

Light brown, with snow-white vittae; 15–20 mm.

5. *Oberea basalis* LeConte (p. 653)

Dark brown or black; pronotum partially yellow; 7–10 mm.

6. *Saperda obliqua* Say (p. 647)

Dull reddish, with brown markings; 16–20 mm.

7. *S. cretata* Newman (p. 650)

Dark brown-orange, with snow-white markings; 12–20 mm.

8. *S. vestita* Say (p. 651)

Densely grayish-tan-pubescent; elytral spots black; 12–21 mm.

9. *Oberea schaumii* LeConte (p. 653)

Tan, with variable black markings; elytra black, except at base and below humeri; 10–14 mm.

10. *O. ocellata* Haldeman (p. 653)

Reddish; elytra and markings black; 13–14 mm.

11. *O. ruficollis* (Fabricius) (p. 656)

Tan; elytra black, gray-pubescent; 15–18 mm.

12. *O. bimaculata* (Olivier) (p. 653)

Black; pronotum yellow, usually with black spots; 8–13 mm.

13. *O. tripunctata* (Swederus) (p. 653)

Dark brown; pronotum yellow, with black spots; elytra each with a wide, discal yellowish stripe; 8–16 mm.

14. *Tetraopes tetraophthalmus* (Forster) (p. 657)

Red; legs and maculae black; 9–14 mm.

15. *T. femoratus* LeConte (p. 657)

Red; maculae black; legs black, except the reddish femora; 12–17 mm.

16. *T. melanurus* Schönherr (p. 656)

Red; markings deep gray and black; 8–12 mm.

17. *Mecas inornata* (Say) (p. 652)

Black; grayish-pubescent; 8–15 mm.

MM 0 10 20 30 40 50 60 70

PLATE LXV   655

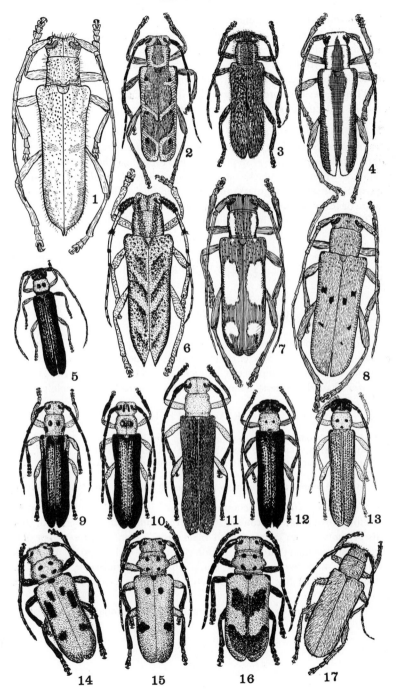

black, with gray pubescence; pronotum with two small, black, rounded dots on disk. Pronotum transverse; sides sinuate; disk with a small, flattened callosity either side of middle; surface sparsely, deeply, coarsely punctate. Elytral disk with rows of coarse punctures; apices rounded, sometimes feebly truncate. Length 13–14 mm.

This species is recorded as breeding in sumac and blackberry. The adults may be collected by sweeping these plants.

f. *Oberea ruficollis* (Fabricius)   Plate LXV, No. 11, p. 655
Elongate, subcylindrical, slender; orange; antennae, elytra, tibiae, and tarsi black; elytra with gray pubescence. Pronotum subquadrate; disk without callosities and black spots; surface coarsely, confluently punctate. Elytral disk with irregular rows of rather fine, oblong punctures; apices more or less truncate. Length 15–18 mm.

These beetles breed in living sassafras and spicebush.

Tribe TETRAOPINI

Genus *TETRAOPES* Serville

Elongate, robust, cylindrical; antennae shorter than body, hairy beneath, rather short; eyes entirely divided; pronotum subquadrate, tuberculate laterally; metepisterna moderately wide; sternites two to four shorter than the others; femora cylindrical; tarsi with claws cleft.

KEY TO SPECIES

1. Elytra with dark patches that meet along the suture . . . . a. *melanurus*
   Elytra with several black spots, but these not reaching suture 2
2. Antennae black, not annulate; larger median spot of elytra oblong. . . . .
   . . . . b. *tetraophthalmus*
   Antennae more or less distinctly annulate; elytral spots rounded . . c. *femoratus*

a. *Tetraopes melanurus* Schönherr   Plate LXV, No. 16, p. 655
Elongate-oblong, subconvex; red; pronotum with four round, black discal spots; elytra marked with black from before middle to apex, this spot nearly divided near its middle; humerus with a small, black spot; scutellum and body beneath black. Pronotum transverse; disk almost smooth. Elytral disk rather coarsely, densely punctate; apices rounded. Length 8–12 mm.

This beetle breeds in milkweed and is more common in the South.

b. *Tetraopes tetraophthalmus* (Forster) Milkweed Beetle
Plate LXV, No. 14, p. 655

Elongate-oblong, robust; red; pronotum with four black spots on disk, sometimes with black apical angles and basal margin; elytra with a humeral and three discal spots black, the first discal spot round (near suture), a second oblong (near middle), the third rounded (on apical third); scutellum and body beneath black. Pronotum transverse, with a smooth median tubercle, the sides of which merge gradually with the disk; surface sparsely and finely punctate; apices rounded. Length 9–14 mm.

This beetle also breeds in milkweed.

c. *Tetraopes femoratus* LeConte Color Plate D; Plate LXV,
No. 15, p. 655

Elongate-oblong, robust; pronotum, elytra, and femora red; ventral surface, tibiae, tarsi, four rounded dots on pronotum, scutellum, humeri, and three rounded spots on each elytron black; antennae black, annulate with gray. Pronotum transverse; median tubercle prominent, sides abrupt; surface finely, irregularly punctate. Elytral disk basally finely punctate, the punctures becoming obsolete apically; apices rounded. Length 12–17 mm.

This species breeds in milkweed.

Family CHRYSOMELIDAE

Leaf-eating Beetles

To the agriculturist this family is very destructive, to the collector very interesting, to the systematist very difficult. Many of our commonest beetles belong to it. In color they are prettily variegated, many being spotted or striped in brightly contrasting colors, some with metallic hues, while others are dull brown or black. As their common name implies, nearly all adults and larvae feed on leaves of plants or on flowers during the day.

In size they are small or moderate; usually oval in shape, but varying greatly. Head either prominent and more or less constricted posteriorly, inserted to the eyes, or concealed under a shieldlike pronotum; eyes entire or feebly emarginate (Fig. 471) on inner side, finely granulate (Fig. 471); antennae eleven-segmented, variable in position and form, may be serrate, lamellate, or clavate; labial palpi three-segmented; mentum transverse; maxillary palpi four-segmented, cylindrical, rarely dilated or elongate. Pronotum often margined laterally; elytra usually covering abdomen, sometimes last dorsal segment of abdomen exposed, in females sometimes smaller and not covering the enlarged abdomen. Legs short; metatibiae often dilated for jumping; tibiae never serrate, usually without spines; tarsi 5–5–5-segmented, segments one to three broad, fourth small and nearly concealed by third, fifth with two variable, equal claws.

The larvae are for the most part soft-bodied and more or less brightly colored. Some are flattened and armed with spines, others are partially covered with their excrement. Most of them are free-living, but some are leaf-miners, case-bearers, or root-feeders. When ready for pupation many of the free-living forms fasten themselves by the tip of the abdomen to a leaf and enter their resting period much as the butterflies do; others pupate in the ground, and the case-bearers pupate in their larval cases.

KEY TO SUBFAMILIES

1. Front normal; mouth anterior (Fig. 471) 2
   Front inflexed; mouth turned backward (Fig. 472) 10
2. Intermediate abdominal sternites not narrowed; pygidium not exposed 3
   Intermediate sternites narrowed medially (Fig. 473); pygidium exposed, declivous 8

3. Pronotum narrower than elytra, without a lateral margin 4
   Pronotum as wide as elytra or approximately so, with a lateral margin 6
4. Antennae separated by the entire width of the front; first visible abdominal sternite no longer than second and third together ..5
   Antennae somewhat approximate; first sternite as long as all others together ....DONACIINAE (p. 660)
5. Ligula well developed, membranous, or, if sclerotized, it is cleft (Fig. 474); prosternal process distinctly widened ......................................ORSODACNINAE (p. 663)
   Ligula small, sclerotized, entire; prosternal process very narrow ....CRIOCERINAE (p. 666)
6. Antennae at base separated by the entire width of the front 7
   Antennae approximate at base ....GALERUCINAE (p. 692)
7. Third tarsal segment deeply bilobed, nearly dividing the segment (Fig. 475); procoxal cavities circular ....EUMOLPINAE (p. 675)
   Third tarsal segment entire or moderately emarginate (Fig. 476); procoxal cavities transversely oval ..........CHRYSOMELINAE (p. 683)
8. Prothorax with antennal grooves on underside (Fig. 477) ....FULCIDACINAE (p. 669)
   Prothorax without antennal grooves on underside 9
9. Antennae filiform or clavate ..............CRYPTOCEPHALINAE (p. 671)
   Antennae dentate or pectinate beyond third or fourth segment ....CLYTRINAE (p. 668)
10. Head free; pronotum and elytra without broadly expanded margins ....HISPINAE (p. 720)
    Head concealed; pronotum and elytra with strongly expanded margins ....CASSIDINAE (p. 724)

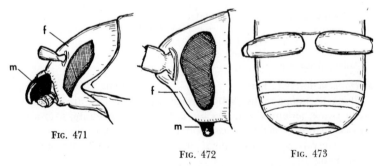

Fig. 471

Fig. 472

Fig. 473

Fig. 471. Head of *Labidomera* from the side, with normal front (*f*) and anteriorly placed mouth. *m*, mandible.

Fig. 472. Head of *Baliosus* from the side, with front (*f*) inflexed and mouth placed posteriorly. *m*, mandible.

Fig. 473. Ventral view of abdomen of *Pachybrachys*, with second, third, and fourth sternites narrower at middle than at sides.

Subfamily DONACIINAE

Genus *DONACIA* Fabricius

Small or moderate-sized beetles; elongate, rather slender, subdepressed; elytral apices simply rounded; pygidium of female more or less elongate, always rounded; tarsi dilated, spongy beneath, third segment bilobed, never much shorter, usually as long as or longer than second, the last segment rarely as long as the two segments preceding taken together, claws slightly appendiculate at base (Fig. 478).

KEY TO SPECIES

1. Elytra truncate at apex 2
   Elytra rounded at tip 5
2. Mesocoxae separated by about their own width (Fig. 479) 3
   Mesocoxae separated by less than their own width (Fig. 480); pronotal sides
     nearly straight, punctures coarse and distinct, uniform in size; third antennal
     segment one-half longer than second ....d. *subtilis*
3. Third antennal segment at most half again as long as second 4
   Third segment of antennae about twice length of second; sides of pronotum
     strongly tuberculate ....c. *piscatrix*
4. Color brownish or fuscous-yellow; form more slender; metatibiae of male
     curved, serrate; elytral punctures in rows, finer, separated by at least their
     own length in the row ....b. *cincticornis*
   Color purplish black; form broader, more robust; metatibiae of male straight;
     elytral punctures in rows, coarser, separated by less than their own length
     in the row ....a. *proxima*
5. Femora at least in part blackish 6
   Femora entirely brownish orange ....g. *flavipes*
6. Pronotum with median line deeply impressed, broad, sides of the groove
     sharply defined at least at middle ....e. *emarginata*
   Pronotum with median line very narrow, not deeply impressed, sides of groove
     obscured by fine rugosities 7
7. Antennal scape for the most part black ....f. *metallica*
   Antennal scape pale ....h. *rufa*

a. *Donacia proxima* Kirby   Plate LXVI, No. 1, p. 665
   Elongate, rather robust, subdepressed; purplish black, frequently with a
green reflex; antennae and legs black. Pronotum quadrate, with a median
impressed line; punctate at base and apex. Elytra with coarse punctures in
rows, intervals not rugose. Metafemora swollen, armed with one to three
teeth. Length 8–11 mm.

b. *Donacia cincticornis* Newman   Plate LXVI, No. 2, p. 665
   Elongate, rather slender, subdepressed; dark brownish yellow, strongly
shining, often tinged with green; head and pronotum darker; clothed beneath with dense, dark-gray pubescence; antennae and legs reddish brown

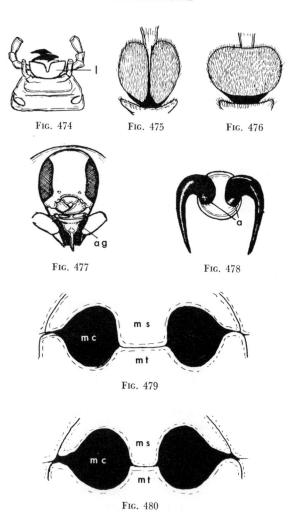

FIG. 474   FIG. 475   FIG. 476

FIG. 477   FIG. 478

FIG. 479

FIG. 480

Fig. 474. Mouthparts and surrounding portion of head of *Orsodacne* viewed from beneath, with ligula (*l*) well developed.

Fig. 475. Third tarsal segment (ventral aspect) of *Chrysochus*, with deep cleft.

Fig. 476. Third tarsal segment of *Labidomera* from beneath.

Fig. 477. Head and part of prothorax of *Chlamisus* from beneath. *ag*, antennal groove of prothorax.

Fig. 478. Tarsal claws of *Donacia*, with small appendix (*a*) at base.

Fig. 479. Mesocoxal cavities (*mc*) of *Donacia proxima* equal to the mesosternal process (*ms*) in width. *mt*, metasternum.

Fig. 480. Mesocoxal cavities (*mc*) of *D. subtilis* wider than mesosternal process (*ms*). *mt*, metasternum.

to piceous, the tips of antennal segments often darker. Pronotum wider than long, slightly narrowed near base; disk nearly smooth, median line distinct; sides finely and somewhat rugosely punctate, with an irregular depression in front of middle. Elytral disk with two feebly transverse impressions; punctures moderate in size, in rows; intervals flat, nearly smooth. Metafemora swollen and armed with one to three teeth. Length 7-11 mm.

The adult of this species is found on yellow water lily and pondweed.

c. *Donacia piscatrix* Lacordaire　　　　　　Plate LXVI, No. 3, p. 665

Oblong-oval, slender, subconvex; color variable, bronze, green, or brownish yellow, strongly shining; underneath with gray pubescence; antennae and legs reddish yellow, femora in part darker. Antennae with second segment about one-half length of third. Pronotum quadrate, sides each with two rounded tubercles, the anterior one most prominent; disk finely alutaceous, sparsely, finely, and shallowly punctate; median line slightly elevated. Elytra with rather coarse punctures in rows; intervals nearly flat, finely, transversely rugose. Length 6.5–9 mm.

The adults are found on the yellow water lily.

d. *Donacia subtilis* Kunze　　　　　　　Plate LXVI, No. 5, p. 665

Elongate, slender, subconvex; dark bronze to green or purplish black, rarely bluish, shining; antennae and legs reddish brown to piceous. Pronotum longer than wide; sides almost straight; disk transversely rugose, with punctures between the wrinkles; median line shallow but distinct. Each elytron with two shallow impressions near middle; punctures in irregular rows; intervals almost flat, transversely rugose; apices somewhat narrowed, squarely truncate. Length 7–10 mm.

The adults occur on leaves and stems of sedges and arrow arum along banks of ponds and lakes.

e. *Donacia emarginata* Kirby　　　　　　Plate LXVI, No. 6, p. 665

Elongate, slender, convex; bright metallic blue, rarely purple, green, or bronzed; antennae black, segments sometimes reddish at base. Second and third antennal segments subequal. Pronotum longer than wide; median line distinct; sides with rounded tubercle near apex; surface minutely rugose, finely, densely punctate. Elytra with a slight impression in front of middle; apices rounded; sutural margin strongly sinuate on apical quarter; intervals slightly convex, transversely rugose. Length 6–8 mm.

This species may be taken by beating sedges.

f. *Donacia metallica* Ahrens　　　　　　Plate LXVI, No. 7, p. 665

Elongate, convex, rather slender; color variable, usually greenish or bronzed, sometimes blackish, strongly shining; legs dark. Second and third antennal segments subequal. Pronotum longer than wide, slightly narrowed near base; tubercles on sides feeble; median line fine but distinct; disk rugulose, finely and densely punctate. Elytra convex, punctures coarse, intervals flattened, nearly smooth; apices rounded. Length 5.5–7 mm.

The adults may be found on skunk-cabbage leaves.

g. *Donacia flavipes* Kirby   Plate LXVI, No. 4, p. 665

Elongate, rather slender, convex; bronze, rarely dark blue or green, rather shining; antennae and legs brownish orange. Antennae with third segment one-third longer than second. Pronotum one-half longer than wide; median impression wide and deep; tubercles on sides prominent and rounded; surface finely, transversely rugose and finely, densely punctate. Elytra with two shallow, transverse impressions near middle; punctures coarse and in rows; intervals transversely rugose and irregular near apices, which are rounded. Mesosternum narrower than coxae; first abdominal sternite shorter than metasternum. Length 6–8.5 mm.

The adults of this species may be found on reeds, rushes, and arrow arum.

h. *Donacia rufa* Say   Plate LXVI, No. 8, p. 665

Elongate-oval, convex, subcylindrical; dark reddish brown, bronzed, shining; antennae and legs pale brown, femora largely blackish. Third antennal segment one-half longer than second. Pronotum longer than wide, broadest near apex; tubercles on sides not prominent; median line distinct; surface shining, with fine, scattered punctures. Elytra with two very shallow impressions near middle; intervals somewhat flattened, smooth; apices rounded. Length 5.5–7.5 mm.

The adults are found on and about roots of skunk cabbage.

This species may be distinguished from *flavipes* by the more convex and shining pronotum, which is wider at the apex.

Subfamily ORSODACNINAE

KEY TO GENERA

Elytral punctation entirely confused; procoxal cavities separated and closed behind; pronotum campanulate (Fig. 24D), sides evenly rounded, without lateral teeth or tubercles ....I. *Orsodacne* (p. 663)
Elytral punctation, at least in part, serially arranged; procoxal cavities contiguous and open behind; sides of pronotum dentate ..II. *Syneta* (p. 666)

Genus I. *ORSODACNE* Latreille

Elongate-ovate, subconvex; antennae less than half as long as body; elytra wider at base than pronotum, punctation confused, not arranged in rows; entire upper surface either more or less destitute of pubescence or with a single erect seta in each puncture.

PLATE LXVI
Family CHRYSOMELIDAE I

1. *Donacia proxima* Kirby (p. 660) — Black, with a moderate green or bluish reflex; 8–11 mm.

2. *D. cincticornis* Newman (p. 660) — Blackish, scarcely reflexed with green; elytra entirely and legs and antennae in part dark orange-brown; 7–11 mm.

3. *D. piscatrix* Lacordaire (p. 662) — Bronze, green, or brownish yellow; antennae and legs yellowish; 6–9 mm.

4. *D. flavipes* Kirby (p. 663) — Bronze, rarely blue or green; legs and antennae brown-orange; 6–9 mm.

5. *D. subtilis* Kunze (p. 662) — Bronze, green, or purplish black; legs and antennae blackish; 7–10 mm.

6. *D. emarginata* Kirby (p. 662) — Metallic blue, purple, green, or bronze; 6–8 mm.

7. *D. metallica* Ahrens (p. 662) — Green or bronzed, sometimes blackish; 5–7 mm.

8. *D. rufa* Say (p. 663) — Bronzed reddish brown; antennae and legs light brown, femora blackish; 5–8 mm.

9. *Syneta ferruginea* (Germar) (p. 666) — Brownish yellow; 6–8 mm.

10. *Crioceris asparagi* (Linné) (p. 667) — Largely metallic blue; pronotum red; elytra with yellow spots; 6–7 mm.

11. *Lema collaris* Say (p. 667) — Head black or red; pronotum red; elytra dark green or blue; 4–5 mm.

12. *Crioceris duodecimpunctata* (Linné) (p. 667) — Orange-red; spots black; 6–7 mm.

13. *Lema trilineata* (Olivier) (p. 668) — Reddish yellow; markings black; 6–8 mm.

14, 15, 16. *Orsodacne atra* (Ahrens) (p. 666) — Very variable, ranging from brownish yellow to black, colors variously arranged; 4–8 mm.

17. *Acalymma vittata* (Fabricius) (p. 694) — Yellowish and black; 5–7 mm.

MM | 0 | 10 | 20 | 30 | 40 | 50 | 60 | 70

PLATE LXVI

665

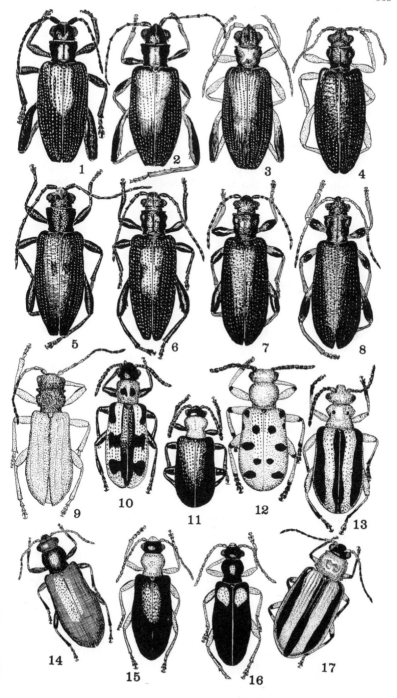

Orsodacne atra (Ahrens) Plate LXVI, Nos. 14–16, p. 665

Elongate-ovate, slender, subconvex; color very variable, ranging from entirely piceous to almost pale brownish yellow or a combination of the two colors; pronotum sometimes with a single large, dark spot; elytra sometimes striped; legs either wholly piceous or piceous with tibiae and tarsi yellowish. Antennae less than half as long as body, segments subequal in length. Pronotum campanulate (Fig. 24D), strongly narrowed at base, without lateral teeth or tubercles; disk roughly and rather sparsely, coarsely punctate. Elytra wider than pronotum, irregularly and coarsely punctate; apices rounded. Length 4–8 mm.

This is the only species in the genus, and it displays such a variation in the color pattern that it has been described under several names. There are all intergrades known, from those which are entirely piceous to those which are pale brownish yellow. They are found most frequently in spring on the catkins of willow, and several different color-varieties may be found together on the same tree.

Genus II. *SYNETA* Lacordaire

Elongate-oblong, subcylindrical; antennae less than half as long as body; body sparsely, finely pubescent; elytra wider basally than pronotum; pronotal sides dentate.

Syneta ferruginea (Germar) Plate LXVI, No. 9, p. 665

Elongate, subcylindrical, convex; head, pronotum, and antennae brownish yellow; elytra, legs, and undersurface paler. Antennae slender, almost half as long as body; segments four to ten nearly equal in length, eleventh longer than tenth. Pronotum longer than wide, rather broadly angulate and obtusely tridentate at sides; surface densely and coarsely punctate. Each elytron with four feeble costae; each interval with from three to five irregular rows of coarse, close punctures. Metatibiae of male slightly broader at tip and with terminal spurs, the inner edge sinuate below the middle. Length 6–8 mm.

The adults may be taken on foliage of oak and hazel.

Subfamily CRIOCERINAE

KEY TO GENERA

Genus I. *CRIOCERIS* Geoffroy

Elongate, oblong, subdepressed; head constricted behind eyes into a neck; pronotum cylindrical; tarsal claws separated, contiguous only at base, always for less than basal third.

The two North American species of this genus were introduced from Europe.

KEY TO SPECIES

Elytra dark metallic blue, each with yellow dots on sides which merge into a reddish-yellow margin ....a. *asparagi*
Elytra orange-red, each with six black dots ....b. *duodecimpunctata*

a. *Crioceris asparagi* (Linné)   The Asparagus Beetle
                                                   Plate LXVI, No. 10, p. 665

Elongate-oblong, subdepressed; smooth, shining; head dark metallic blue; pronotum red, with two bluish spots; elytra dark blue, with three or four large, yellow spots on sides which merge into a reddish-yellow margin. Pronotum distinctly elongate; disk finely, sparsely punctate; sides evenly arcuate. Elytra with sides parallel; disk with numerous rows of coarse punctures, scarcely finer apically; apex rounded. Length 6–7 mm.

Both larvae and adults feed on the green parts of asparagus.

b. *Crioceris duodecimpunctata* (Linné)   Plate LXVI, No. 12, p. 665

Elongate-oblong, rather robust, subdepressed; dull orange-red, smooth, shining; head and pronotum reddish brown; each elytron with six small, black spots; pro-, meso-, and metasterna black. Pronotum quadrate; disk minutely punctate and alutaceous; sides smoothly rounded, strongly narrowed basally. Elytra parallel-sided; disk with numerous rows of coarse punctures, becoming finer apically; apex rounded. Length 6–7 mm.

The adults and larvae are both found on asparagus.

Genus II. *LEMA* Fabricius

Small or moderate-sized, oblong-ovate, subdepressed species; elytra much wider than pronotum, which is abruptly sinuate behind middle and constricted at middle; tarsal claws contiguous for at least the basal third.

KEY TO SPECIES

Elytra wholly dark blue ....a. *collaris*
Elytra reddish yellow, with three black stripes ....b. *trilineata*

a. *Lema collaris* Say   Plate LXVI, No. 11, p. 665

Elongate-oblong, rather subdepressed; head black, occasionally red; pronotum red; elytra shining dark green or blue. Head with a median groove;

antennae a little longer than one-third of the body length. Pronotum short, very finely and sparsely punctate. Elytra with irregular rows of coarse, oblong punctures. Length 4–5 mm.

The adults are found on foliage of low-growing plants, particularly on spiderwort and other herbs in moist, sandy localities.

b. *Lema trilineata* (Olivier) Three-lined Potato Beetle
Plate LXVI, No. 13, p. 665

Elongate-oblong, rather robust; reddish yellow; pronotum usually with two small, black spots on disk; elytra slightly paler, with sutural margin and rather wide lateral stripe black; antennae (except basal segments), apical half of tibiae, and tarsi black. Pronotum strongly constricted at middle; disk smooth, except for a few coarse punctures on sides near apex. Elytra with rows of punctures, the punctures coarser and more distinct on basal half. Length 6–7.5 mm.

This is known as the "old-fashioned potato beetle" or the "three-lined potato beetle" and is found on foliage of potato or other solanaceous plants.

Subfamily CLYTRINAE

KEY TO GENERA

Tarsal claws simple ....I. *Anomoea* (p. 668)
Tarsal claws appendiculate (Fig. 26F) ....II. *Babia* (p. 669)

Genus I. *ANOMOEA* Lacordaire

Elongate, subcylindrical, rather small; male with antennae more deeply serrate and protibiae longer than in female; tarsal claws simple; procoxae contiguous.

Anomoea laticlavia (Forster) Plate LXVII, Nos. 2, 3, p. 679

Elongate, subcylindrical, robust; head, pronotum, and femora reddish yellow; elytra paler yellow, the suture and lateral edges narrowly margined with black; antennae, tibiae, and tarsi black; undersurface except prosternum black, clothed with dense, gray pubescence. Pronotum transverse, sides rounded; posterior margin sinuate; surface smooth and somewhat shining. Elytra finely and indistinctly punctate. Length 6–8 mm.

The adults are usually found on foliage of low-growing plants such as bush clover, ragweed, and Jersey tea, as well as on honey locust and willow.

Genus II. *BABIA* Lacordaire

Oblong-oval, convex; head vertical; pronotum without antennal grooves; prosternal process invisible; mesosternal process very narrow or short and perpendicular; eyes oblong; epipleural lobe but little expanded (Fig. 481); tarsal claws appendiculate.

Babia quadriguttata (Olivier)   Plate LXVII, No. 6, p. 679
    Broadly oblong-oval, convex; black, shining; each elytron with a large humeral and a smaller apical reddish-orange spot. Pronotum slightly narrower than elytra and tapering slightly to apex; disk finely and rather densely punctate. Elytra not striate, but with irregular rows of larger punctures; intervals with scattered punctures. Length 3–5.3 mm.
    The short, stout, subserrate antennae will distinguish this from other red-and-black species of this group.
    The adults are found on milkweed and other roadside plants.

Subfamily FULCIDACINAE

KEY TO GENERA

Antennae serrate beyond the fourth or fifth segment ......I. *Chlamisus* (p. 669)
Antennae serrate beyond sixth segment ....II. *Exema* (p. 670)

Genus I. *CHLAMISUS* Rafinesque

Small, oblong, very convex beetles; pygidium exposed, declivous; pronotum on underside with antennal grooves; antennae serrate beyond the fourth or fifth segment.

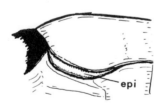

Fig. 481

Fig. 481. *Babia,* with portions of elytron and prothorax from the side. *epi,* epipleural fold.

Chlamisus gibbosa Fabricius   Plate LXVII, No. 5, p. 679

Robust, oblong; brown, with slight bronze; elytra and legs sometimes black. Pronotum finely and densely rugulose; disk at middle with a large tubercle, which is sparsely and coarsely punctate and bifid at tip. Each elytron with twelve to fifteen tubercles, of which the four largest are arranged in an oblique row extending from humerus to suture; intervals between tubercles sparsely and coarsely punctate, either flat or covered with smaller tubercles. Length 2.6–4.5 mm.

The adults are found on foliage of plants along roadsides; when disturbed, they retract their legs and roll off the leaves.

Genus II. *EXEMA* Lacordaire

Very small, oblong, convex species; pygidium exposed, declivous; pronotum with antennal grooves on underside; antennae serrate beyond sixth segment.

KEY TO SPECIES

Pronotum with yellow markings, punctures circular, dense, and moderately coarse, sculpture not at all strigose; elytra usually with yellow maculae; tarsal claws appendiculate (Fig. 26F) ....a. *pennsylvanica*
Pronotum entirely black, punctures fine, elongate, their form and arrangement producing a substrigose sculpture; elytra always entirely black; tarsal claws simple (Fig. 26D) ....b. *canadensis*

a. *Exema pennsylvanica* Pierce   Plate LXVII, No. 1, p. 679

Oblong, robust; black; head of male largely yellow, frequently with a median black macula, female with markings reduced; anterior declivity of pronotum with a yellow area, irregular in size and shape, disk with a few small, yellow maculae; elytra usually with a few yellow maculae, sometimes more numerous; antennae and legs yellow, femora and tibiae sometimes in part blackish. Pronotum transverse, sides strongly narrowed apically; disk prominent, not at all strigose, punctures dense, circular, and rather coarse. Elytra coarsely, densely punctate, with about eleven coarse tubercles scattered over disk. Length 3–3.6 mm.

b. *Exema canadensis* Pierce   Plate LXVII, No. 4, p. 679

Oblong, robust; black, moderately shining; head of male with a large, triangular macula and a longitudinal vitta near upper lobe of each eye yellow, these vittae sometimes joining the triangular macula, in female markings greatly reduced or lacking; antennae yellow, blackish on apical half; femora sometimes marked with yellow; tibiae annulate basally and apically with yellow; tarsi brown, rarely yellowish. Pronotal gibbosity feebly and broadly sulcate; three small, transverse tubercles near base at each side; disk with fine, elongate punctures, substrigose. Elytra with about eleven coarse tubercles scattered over disk, punctures coarse and dense, but less so than in the preceding species. Length 2.3–2.7 mm.

Subfamily CRYPTOCEPHALINAE

KEY TO GENERA

1. Claws simple, or if appendiculate, then prosternal process is longer than wide 2
   Claws appendiculate . . . . .III. *Diachus* (p. 674)
2. Pronotum margined at base; sides not crenulate . . . .I. *Pachybrachys* (p. 671)
   Pronotum not margined at base; sides crenulate. . .II. *Cryptocephalus* (p. 673)

Genus I. *PACHYBRACHYS* Redtenbacher

Small, compact, subcylindrical beetles; pronotum without antennal grooves on underside, as wide as elytra, margined at base, sides not crenulate; prosternum feebly sulcate (Fig. 482); profemora distinctly stouter than metafemora; claws simple.

A number of the species vary greatly in color and merge from one color to another, making identification rather difficult.

KEY TO SPECIES

1. Upper surface uniformly black, densely punctate; pubescent; punctures of elytra everywhere much confused; size larger, 4–4.5 mm. . . . . .a. *pubescens*
   Upper surface not uniformly black 2
2. Colors of upper surface arranged in definite pattern 3
   Colors of upper surface irregularly mottled; elytra black, with a broad, irregular band that extends from the side almost to suture red . . . .b. *subfasciatus*
3. Elytra with stripes; colors yellow and black or brown; pronotum black, with margins and a narrow median line on anterior half yellow . . . .d. *othonus*
   Pronotum or elytra with spots 4
4. Colors black and red; rows of elytral punctures very irregular at sides and behind middle; pronotum black, usually with margins and two basal spots red . . . . .f. *trinotatus*
   Colors black and yellow 5
5. Pronotum black, with margins and three basal spots yellow; larger, 3.5–4 mm. . . . . .e. *m-nigrum*
   Pronotum yellow, with either a Y-shaped or an entire, oblong, median spot and a smaller, rounded one on each side black; smaller, not over 3 mm. . . . . .c. *tridens*

a. *Pachybrachys pubescens* (Olivier) Plate LXX, No. 1, p. 705

Small, subcylindrical, robust; black, feebly shining; covered with short, sparse pubescence; antennae and legs reddish brown. Pronotum with dense, coarse punctures. Elytra with confused, coarse punctures; humeral umbone prominent, nearly smooth. Length 3.4–4.8 mm.

b. *Pachybrachys subfasciatus* LeConte   Plate LXX, No. 2, p. 705

Short, subcylindrical; black, feebly shining; pronotum with sides and often a small, dorsal spot reddish; elytra with a median angulate, reddish band extending from sides almost to suture, frequently a small spot near apex. Pronotum densely and irregularly punctate; posterior angles slightly rounded. Elytra with irregular rows of punctures and with convex intervals at sides and behind middle, punctation confused on basal half. Length 2.5–3.5 mm.

c. *Pachybrachys tridens* (Melsheimer)   Plate LXX, No. 5, p. 705

Oblong, subcylindrical, convex; head light yellow, vertex and often a spot on the front black; pronotum light yellow, with either a Y-shaped spot or an entire, oblong, median spot and a smaller, round one each side black; elytra light yellow, with a common cruciform, black spot on disk, this wider at base, narrowed at middle, and much widened on apical third, each elytron also with a narrow marginal line and small humeral spot black; undersurface black; antennae and legs yellow; metafemora often with a black spot. Pronotum sparsely and coarsely punctate. Elytra with rather irregular rows of coarse punctures. Length 2–3 mm.

The adults are found on foliage of both roadside plants and hickory, elm, and willow.

d. *Pachybrachys othonus* (Say)   Plate LXX, No. 4, p. 705

Subcylindrical, robust; black; labrum and three spots on front of head yellow; margins and median line of pronotum and two discal stripes of elytra yellow; legs and ventral margins yellow; antennae blackish. Pronotum nearly three times wider than long, densely and rugosely punctate. Elytra with a few sinuous rows of coarse, closely set punctures. Length 3.5–4 mm.

This species is found on foliage of roadside plants.

e. *Pachybrachys m-nigrum* (Melsheimer)   Plate LXX, No. 6, p. 705

Subcylindrical, robust; yellow; pronotum usually with markings resembling the letter M and margins black; elytra with suture and margins narrowly black, a black, irregular discal stripe more or less broadly connected with suture before and behind middle and to three spots near lateral margin of same color; undersurface and legs black, the latter spotted with yellow. Pronotum with coarse, deep punctures. Elytra with prominent humeral umbones; surface with irregular rows of punctures which are confused on basal half. Length 3.2–4 mm.

This species may be taken by sweeping roadside herbs.

f. *Pachybrachys trinotatus* (Melsheimer)   Plate LXX, No. 3, p. 705
Subcylindrical, robust; black, opaque; head with two red spots between eyes; pronotum with narrow apical and lateral margins, two basal spots, and a small median line reddish; elytra rarely with pale spots. Pronotum strongly convex, evenly, deeply, and coarsely punctate. Elytra coarsely and irregularly punctate; umbone prominent. Length 4–5 mm.

These beetles may be found on Jersey tea, *Baptisia,* and *Ceanothus.*

Genus II. *CRYPTOCEPHALUS* Geoffroy

A large genus of small, compact, subcylindrical forms that have the head entirely retracted within the thorax in repose; pronotum without antennal grooves on underside, base as wide as elytra and not margined; claws simple; front edge of prothoracic flanks straight.

KEY TO SPECIES

1. Elytra black, each with a humeral and apical red spot 2
   Elytra not black, or if black, without red spots 3
2. Humeral spot of elytra extending almost entirely across base ....a. *notatus*
   Humeral spot of elytra oblong, slightly wider behind ....b. *quadruplex*
3. Elytra brown or black, each with seven yellowish spots ....c. *guttulatus*
   Elytra yellow, with brown stripes or spots 4
4. Elytra yellow, each with one or two diagonal brown or black stripes.
   ....d. *venustus*
   Elytra yellow, with a large, common, brown spot and each with several scattered spots, large spot broken into several lines at times ....e. *mutabilis*

a. *Cryptocephalus notatus* Fabricius   Plate LXX, No. 7, p. 705
Robust, cylindrical; black, shining; elytra with a reddish, oblong humeral spot, extending across the base and along sides to middle, and another rounded one apically; base of antennae pale. Pronotum very finely and sparsely punctate. Elytra with ten regular rows of coarse punctures. Length 4–5.5 mm.

This species may be found on foliage of low-growing plants.

b. *Cryptocephalus quadruplex* Newman   Plate LXX, No. 8, p. 705
Elongate, cylindrical, rather robust; black; red humeral spot oblong, wider near middle of elytra, apical spot rounded; antennae dusky, base yellowish. Elytra with rows of very coarse punctures. Length 2.5–4 mm.

This species may be taken by beating and sweeping foliage of low-growing plants.

c. *Cryptocephalus guttulatus* Olivier   Plate LXX, No. 11, p. 705
Oblong, cylindrical, robust; reddish brown; elytra sometimes almost

black, with seven rounded, yellow spots arranged in three transverse rows of two and a single one at apex, sometimes a very small, yellow spot on humerus; apical portion of antennae black. Pronotum smooth, shining. Elytra with rows of coarse, distant punctures, the sixth and seventh rows confused near middle. Male much smaller than female and with surface color of elytra black. Length 3.5–5.5 mm.

d. *Cryptocephalus venustus* Fabricius   Plate LXX, No. 9, p. 705

Robust, subcylindrical; head and pronotum reddish brown; pronotal sides and two oblique basal spots yellow; elytra yellow, each with two broad, oblique, black or brown stripes, one of these sometimes absent; undersurface and legs reddish brown. Pronotum finely punctate. Elytra with rows of fine punctures. Length 4.5–6 mm.

This species varies in color, the pronotum often being entirely reddish or the elytra often black, with sides, a narrow line at suture, and a basal spot yellow.

The adults are found on flowers, particularly in meadows.

e. *Cryptocephalus mutabilis* Melsheimer   Plate LXX, No. 10, p. 705

Robust, cylindrical; reddish brown, shining; pronotum with apical and side margins narrowly yellow, with or without two narrow, oblique, basal spots; elytra pale yellow, with a large, common, brown spot that extends backward along suture, each also with six or seven small, brown spots: three in row basally, one or two at middle, two near apex (these may be more or less confluent or absent). Pronotum finely and sparsely punctate. Elytra with rows of distant punctures, the sixth and seventh rows slightly confused. Prosternum emarginate and acutely dentate behind. Length 4–6.5 mm.

The male has the spots of pronotum and elytra black.

This species may be found on flowers and foliage of herbs and shrubs.

Genus III. *DIACHUS* LeConte

Very small, oblong, cylindrical beetles; eyes feebly emarginate; antennae not more than half as long as body, segments six to eleven broader; pronotum without antennal grooves on underside, as wide as elytra at base, not margined, sides crenulate; prosternum usually quadrate and flat (Fig. 483).

Diachus auratus (Fabricius)   Plate LXX, No. 12, p. 705

Oblong, cylindrical; head and pronotum dark reddish brown, slightly bronzed; elytra either metallic green or brown; antennae, legs, and undersurface brownish yellow; abdomen black. Pronotum very finely alutaceous. Elytra with rows of very fine punctures. Length 1.4–2 mm.

This species may be taken by beating and sweeping roadside plants.

Subfamily EUMOLPINAE

KEY TO GENERA

1. Apical margin of prosternum lobed laterally, forming postocular
    lobes (Fig. 484) 2
    Apical margin straight beneath 5
2. Body pubescent above 3
    Body glabrous above 4
3. Pronotal sides not distinctly margined ....VIII. *Adoxus*   (p. 681)
    Pronotal sides distinctly margined ....IX. *Glyptoscelis*   (p. 681)
4. Meso- and metatibiae emarginate apically on outer edge; length 3–4
    mm. ....X. *Paria*   (p. 682)
    Tibiae not emarginate apically; length 8–11 mm. . .XI. *Chrysochus*   (p. 682)
5. Pronotum without a distinct lateral margin 6
    Pronotum distinctly margined laterally 8
6. Head without grooves above eyes; body without metallic color 7
    Head with grooves above eyes; body above with metallic colors
    ....V. *Graphops*   (p. 677)
7. Pronotum transverse; profemora with a small tooth; third antennal
    segment not longer than second ....VI. *Xanthonia*   (p. 680)
    Pronotum cylindrical; femora unarmed; third antennal segment
    longer than second ....VII. *Fidia*   (p. 681)
8. Pronotal lateral margin irregular or undulating 9
    Pronotal lateral margin regular and entire 10
9. Prosternum narrow, constricted between the coxae ....III. *Colaspis*   (p. 676)
    Prosternum wide, nearly parallel-sided ....IV. *Rhabdopterus*   (p. 677)
10. Pronotum with a basal marginal line ....II. *Nodonota*   (p. 676)
    Pronotum without a basal marginal line ....I. *Chrysodina*   (p. 676)

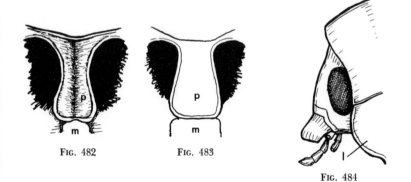

Figs. 482–483. Prosternum (*p*) of *Pachybrachys* (482) and of *Diachus*
        (483), along with portions of mesosternum (*m*) and pro-
        coxal cavities.
Fig. 484. Head and portion of prothorax of *Chrysochus* viewed from
        side. *l*, postocular lobe on apical margin of prosternum.

Genus I. *CHRYSODINA* Baly

Small, broadly ovate, convex beetles; supraorbital grooves not distinct; third antennal segment distinctly longer than second, last five segments not abruptly widened; anterior margin of prothorax straight beneath; pronotum margined but without a basal ·marginal line, lateral margin regular and entire; claws appendiculate, usually broadly so.

Chrysodina globosa (Olivier)   Plate LXVII, No. 8, p. 679
Ovate, convex, subglobose; dark blue or black, with bronze or greenish reflex, shining; legs brownish yellow. Pronotum strongly transverse; sides arcuate; apex only half as wide as base; surface minutely punctate, more densely so laterally and at basal margin. Elytral surface finely, evenly, and densely punctate. Length 2.5–3.5 mm.

Genus II. *NODONOTA* Lefèvre

Small, oval, convex; greenish, bronzed, or bluish beetles; supraorbital grooves indistinct; antennal insertions separated by the entire width of the front; third antennal segment distinctly longer than the second, the succeeding not abruptly wider; pronotum margined, not grooved basally, the lateral margin regular and entire; third tarsal segment bilobed; tarsal claws appendiculate, usually broadly so; anterior margin of prothorax straight beneath.

Nodonota puncticollis (Say)   Plate LXVII, No. 7, p. 679
Oblong, nearly parallel, convex; bluish, greenish, or bronzed, rather shining; basal segments of antennae and legs reddish yellow. Head and pronotum very minutely alutaceous, the latter twice as wide as long, sides feebly arcuate, anterior angles acute, surface with dense, elongate punctures. Elytra coarsely and irregularly punctate, punctures arranged in rows near apex; umbone distinctly impressed, followed by a short costa. Length 3.5–4.5 mm.
The adults are found on flowers and on foliage.

Genus III. *COLASPIS* Fabricius

Small, oblong or oval beetles; supraorbital grooves not distinct; antennae separated by the entire width of the front; pronotum not grooved basally, lateral margin irregular or undulating; third tarsal segment bilobed; procoxal cavities circular; tarsal claws appendiculate, usually broadly so; all tibiae entire; anterior margin of prothorax straight beneath.

Colaspis brunnea (Fabricius)   Plate LXVII, No. 13, p. 679

Oblong-oval, convex; dull brownish yellow, undersurface darker; legs pale yellowish; outer segments of antennae often black. Head coarsely and sparsely punctate. Pronotum transverse; sides broadly arcuate, angles prominent; sparsely, evenly punctate on disk. Elytral intervals costate, two or three rows of coarse, deep punctures between the costae. Male with first tarsal segment dilated. Length 4–6 mm.

Both larvae and adults feed on many wild and cultivated plants.

Genus IV. *RHABDOPTERUS* Lefèvre

Oblong-ovate, subconvex forms; antennal insertions separated by the entire width of the front; supraorbital grooves not distinct; pronotum without grooves, lateral margins irregular or undulating; anterior margin of prothorax straight underneath; prosternum wide, nearly parallel-sided; all tibiae entire; third tarsal segment bilobed; procoxal cavities circular; claws appendiculate, usually broadly so.

Rhabdopterus picipes (Olivier)   Plate LXVII, No. 9, p. 679

Oblong-ovate, convex; dark brown to black, shining; elytral margins sometimes greenish-bronzed; antennae, tibiae, and tarsi reddish yellow, femora and apices of antennae often dark brown; undersurface of body greenish; abdomen black, its apex paler. Head coarsely and sparsely punctate, clypeus more closely so. Pronotum twice as wide as long; slightly narrowed in front; sides strongly rounded; finely and sparsely punctate; posterior angles prominent. Elytra coarsely and somewhat closely and irregularly punctate, a line representing the third interval smooth. Length 4–6 mm.

Genus V. *GRAPHOPS* LeConte

Small, subcylindrical, pubescent, metallic species; head with supraorbital grooves present; antennal insertions separated by entire width of front; pronotum as wide as elytra, without grooves and without a distinct lateral margin; anterior margin of prothorax straight beneath; procoxal cavities circular; third tarsal segment bilobed.

KEY TO SPECIES

Clypeus truncate at apex, not emarginate; pronotum punctate on disk, rugose on sides ....a. *pubescens*
Clypeus deeply emarginate; pronotum irregularly punctate and with indistinct smooth areas ....b. *nebulosus*

PLATE LXVII
Family CHRYSOMELIDAE II

1. *Exema pennsylvanica* Pierce (p. 670) — Black; pronotum and usually elytra with yellow markings; 2.5–3 mm.

2, 3. *Anomoea laticlavia* (Forster) (p. 668) — Reddish yellow; elytra paler, variously marked with black; 2.5–3 mm.

4. *Exema canadensis* Pierce (p. 670) — Black; 2.5–3 mm.

5. *Chlamisus gibbosa* Fabricius (p. 670) — Dark brown; 2.5–4.5 mm.

6. *Babia quadriguttata* (Olivier) (p. 669) — Black, elytral marks reddish orange; 3–5 mm.

7. *Nodonota puncticollis* (Say) (p. 676) — Black, with bronze, green, or blue reflex; 3.5–4.5 mm.

8. *Chrysodina globosa* (Olivier) (p. 676) — Dark blue or black, with bronze or greenish reflex; 2.5–3.5 mm.

9. *Rhabdopterus picipes* (Olivier) (p. 677) — Dark brown or black, partly greenish-reflexed; 4–6 mm.

10. *Graphops pubescens* (Melsheimer) (p. 680) — Black, with coppery reflex; 3.5–4 mm.

11. *Xanthonia villosula* (Melsheimer) (p. 680) — Reddish yellow; elytra and legs paler; 3–4 mm.

12. *X. decemnotata* (Say) (p. 680) — Dull yellowish to brown; spots black; 2.5–4 mm.

13. *Colaspis brunnea* (Fabricius) (p. 677) — Brownish yellow; 4–6 mm.

14. *Hydrothassa vittata* (Olivier) (p. 684) — Greenish black, with reddish-yellow markings; 3.5–4.5 mm.

MM ¦ 0 ¦ 10 ¦ 20 ¦ 30 ¦ 40 ¦ 50 ¦ 60 ¦ 70

PLATE LXVII 679

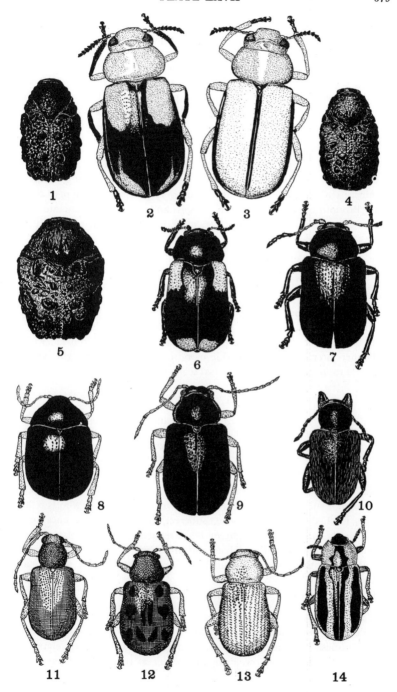

a. *Graphops pubescens* (Melsheimer)   Plate LXVII, No. 10, p. 679
Oblong-ovate, subcylindrical; black, coppery-bronzed, sparsely clothed with ash-gray pubescence. Clypeus truncate at apex. Pronotum feebly transverse, not margined laterally; disk finely and sparsely punctate, densely and finely alutaceous on sides and basal half. Elytra one-third wider than pronotum; disk with rows of fine punctures which become obsolete apically; sutural stria confined to apical third. Length 3.5–4 mm.
The adults are found on roadside plants, particularly evening primrose.

b. *Graphops nebulosus* (LeConte)   Plate LXVIII, No. 1, p. 687
Oblong-ovate, subcylindrical; black, feebly bronzed, shining, sometimes greenish; covered uniformly with a thin, gray pubescence. Clypeus emarginate. Pronotum transverse, finely, densely, and irregularly punctate. Elytra rather coarsely, irregularly punctate, more finely so apically. Length 3.3–4 mm.

Genus VI. *XANTHONIA* Baly

Very small, oblong, brownish species; head without supraorbital grooves; antennal insertions separated by entire width of front, third antennal segment not longer than second; pronotum transverse, not grooved, without a distinct lateral margin; anterior margin of prothorax straight beneath; procoxal cavities circular; third tarsal segment bilobed.

KEY TO SPECIES

Punctures of elytra very confused; color usually dull reddish brown or clay-yellow, with piceous spots; sometimes wholly reddish yellow ..a. *decemnotata*
Punctures of elytra much finer, arranged in regular rows, but slightly confused near suture; color usually pale reddish yellow, often dark, never spotted ....
....b. *villosula*

a. *Xanthonia decemnotata* (Say)   Plate LXVII, No. 12, p. 679
Oblong or subquadrate; dull reddish brown, clay-yellow, or wholly reddish yellow, clothed with very sparse, suberect, brownish pubescence; elytra each usually marked with eight or ten irregular, piceous spots; antennae and legs pale reddish yellow. Head and pronotum finely and densely punctate. Elytra with large, close punctures. Profemora of male with a small tooth. Length 2.5–4 mm.
The adults may be found on oak, beech, and elm.

b. *Xanthonia villosula* (Melsheimer)   Plate LXVII, No. 11, p. 679
Oblong or subquadrate; pale reddish yellow or darker, with reddish-yellow pubescence; head and pronotum usually darker than elytra; antennae and legs dull yellow. Pronotum wider at base than at apex; sides

strongly arcuate; rather finely and densely punctate on disk. Elytra with distinct, close-set rows of rather fine punctures, a single row of erect hairs on each elytral interval. Length 3–4 mm.

The adults may be taken on oak foliage.

Genus VII. *FIDIA* Baly

Small, oblong, robust, brownish species; head without suborbital grooves; antennal insertions separated by entire width of front; third antennal segment longer than second; pronotum cylindrical, not grooved, without a distinct lateral margin; anterior margin of prothorax straight beneath; procoxal cavities circular; third tarsal segment bilobed.

Fidia viticida Walsh   Plate LXVIII, No. 13, p. 687

Elongate, oval, subcylindrical, robust; dark reddish brown, densely clothed with short, grayish-yellow pubescence; antennae and legs paler. Pronotum wider than long in female, often longer than wide in male, widest at or just behind middle; finely and densely punctate. Elytra with coarse punctures in rather irregular rows; humeri prominent. Length 5.5–7 mm.

The larva is the grape rootworm, and the adult may be found on the leaves of grapes.

Genus VIII. *ADOXUS* Kirby

Small, subquadrate forms; antennal insertions separated by entire width of front; pronotum as wide as elytra, without grooves, not distinctly margined; anterior margin of prothorax arcuate beneath, forming postocular lobes; procoxal cavities circular; third tarsal segment bilobed.

Adoxus obscurus (Linné)   Plate LXVIII, No. 6, p. 687

Small, broadly oval; head, pronotum, undersurface, and femora dark brown or blackish; elytra, tibiae, and basal half of antennae brown, clothed with prostrate, yellow pubescence. Pronotum subglobose, much narrower than elytra. densely and rather finely punctate. Elytra with irregular rows of fine punctures. Length 4–6 mm.

The larvae feed on grape roots.

Genus IX. *GLYPTOSCELIS* LeConte

Moderately small beetles with body pubescent above; antennal insertions separated by the entire width of the front; pronotum with a distinct lateral margin and without grooves; anterior margin of prothorax arcuate beneath, forming postocular lobes; prosternum much longer than wide, narrowed between coxae; procoxal cavities circular; third tarsal segment bilobed.

Glyptoscelis pubescens (Fabricius)   Plate LXVIII, No. 7, p. 687

Moderately small, oblong, robust, convex; dark brown, with a metallic lustre, shining; surface irregularly clothed with thin, short, white pubescence, which is sometimes arranged in rows on elytra. Pronotum transverse, widest at middle, narrowed to base, suddenly so to apex, densely and finely punctate. Elytra parallel-sided; apices each broadly rounded; densely and finely punctate. Length 7–10 mm.

This species has been collected on pine, hickory, and wild grape.

Genus X. *PARIA* LeConte

Very small beetles; antennal insertions separated by entire width of front; pronotum margined, without grooves; anterior margin of prothorax arcuate beneath, forming postocular lobes; procoxal cavities circular; meso- and metatibiae emarginate on the outer edge near apex; third tarsal segment bilobed.

Paria canella (Fabricius)   Plate LXVIII, Nos. 2, 3, p. 687

Oblong-oval, convex; reddish yellow, shining; pronotum black or yellow; elytra wholly black, entirely yellowish, or yellowish with black spots; when spotted, usually with two black spots which are sometimes united to form a stripe, or three black spots, on each elytron. Pronotum variably punctate, sometimes nearly smooth, often in the black varieties alutaceous and subopaque. Elytra with rows of fine punctures, these often indistinct on sides and apical third. Length 3–4 mm.

This species is very variable in color and markings. The adults may be taken by sweeping roadside and other plants.

Genus XI. *CHRYSOCHUS* Redtenbacher

Medium-sized beetles; antennal insertions separated by entire width of front; pronotum with lateral margin and without grooves; anterior margin of prothorax arcuate beneath, forming postocular lobes; procoxal cavities circular; tibiae entire; third tarsal segment bilobed; claws simply divergent.

Chrysochus auratus (Fabricius)   The Goldsmith Beetle
                              Color Plate C; Plate LXVIII, No. 5, p. 687

Oblong, convex; green, strongly shining; elytra often with a coppery, brassy, and sometimes bluish tinge; antennae, legs, and undersurface bluish

green. Head and pronotum with sparse, coarse, deep punctures intermingled with fine ones. Elytra finely, irregularly, and sparsely punctate.
Length 8–11 mm.

The adults are found on representatives of the milkweed family and
especially on Indian hemp.

Subfamily CHRYSOMELINAE

KEY TO TRIBES

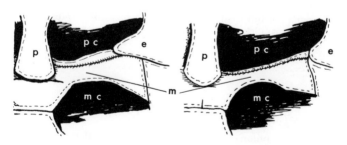

FIGS. 485–486

Figs. 485–486. Portion of mesosternum (*m*) and prosternum (*p*) of *Hydrothassa* (485) and *Lina* (486). The mesosternum is
broad between the procoxal cavities (*pc*) and the mesocoxal cavities (*mc*), though in the former it is much narrower than in the latter. *e*, proepimeron.

Tribe PRASOCURINI

Genus *HYDROTHASSA* Thomson

Rather small, elongate or oval, feebly convex species; last segment of maxillary palpi oval, attenuate toward apex, at least as long as the one preceding it; antennal insertions separated by entire width of front; pronotum with a lateral margin, basal margin without a fine, elevated line, disk without grooves; third tarsal segment usually bilobed or emarginate, sometimes simple; claws simple.

Hydrothassa vittata (Olivier)   Plate LXVII, No. 14, p. 679

Elongate, narrow, subconvex; greenish black, shining; pronotum margined on sides with reddish yellow; elytra each with a reddish-yellow marginal stripe and a narrow, paler one on disk, the two united at base and apex; undersurface, legs, and antennae black; tibiae sometimes pale. Pronotum slightly transverse; apex deeply emarginate; disk finely, sparsely punctate. Elytra with sides parallel; umbone carinate; punctures in rows, somewhat fine and deep, those of first row rather confused. Length 3.5–4.5 mm.

Tribe ZYGOGRAMMINI

KEY TO GENERA

1. Last palpal segment shorter than preceding one, truncate at apex . . 2
   Last palpal segment at least as long as the preceding one, dilated . . 3
2. Mesosternum forming a blunt tubercle between mesocoxae; profemora
   of male strongly toothed . . . . I. *Labidomera* (p. 684)
   Mesosternum not tubercled; profemora simple . . . . . . II. *Leptinotarsa* (p. 685)
3. Tarsal claws parallel, united at base; last tarsal segment dentate
   beneath . . . . III. *Zygogramma* (p. 685)
   Tarsal claws divergent; last tarsal segment unarmed . . . .
   . . . . IV. *Calligrapha* (p. 688)

Genus I. *LABIDOMERA* Chevrolat

Medium-sized, oblong-ovate, convex, robust beetles; last segment of maxillary palpi subquadrangular or dilated; broadly truncate at apex, shorter than preceding segment; antennal insertions separated by entire width of front; pronotum with lateral margins and without grooves; mesosternum forming a blunt tubercle between the mesocoxae; procoxal cavities open, or closed by an extension of the mesosternum; profemora of male strongly toothed; third tarsal segment entire or scarcely emarginate; claws simple.

Labidomera clivicollis (Kirby)   Color Plate B; Plate LXIX, No. 7, p. 697

Oblong-ovate, convex, robust; dark bluish or greenish black; elytra orange-yellow, with a large, black, cruciform common spot in front of middle, each with a triangular spot behind humerus and a V-shaped one near apex, these spots sometimes in part or all confluent to form one or two broad, transverse bands. Pronotum transverse, sparsely and finely punctate. Elytra with rather sparse, fine punctures, arranged in irregular, double rows. Profemora of male with a large tooth at middle and one near apex on inner side. Length 9–11 mm.

These beetles are usually found on swamp milkweed, but sometimes they attack cultivated members of the genus *Asclepias*. They are known to hibernate in the woolly leaves of mullein.

Genus II. *LEPTINOTARSA* Stål

Medium-sized, broadly oval, convex beetles; last palpal segment shorter than the preceding, broadly truncate at apex, subquadrangular or dilated; antennal insertions separated by entire width of front; pronotum with a lateral margin; mesosternum not tuberculate; procoxal cavities transversely oval, open, or closed by an extension of the mesosternum; profemora simple; third tarsal segment entire; claws simple.

Leptinotarsa decimlineata (Say)   Colorado Potato Beetle
                                                      Plate LXIX, No. 8, p. 697

Broadly oblong-oval, strongly convex; robust; dull yellow; pronotum with a narrow V-shaped spot on disk and six small spots on each side black; elytra each with suture and five narrow discal lines black, the second and third united near apex; undersurface reddish yellow, legs darker, apices of femora and tarsi blackish. Elytra with an undulating row of punctures on the two sides of the black stripes. Length 5.5–11 mm.

Besides potatoes, this beetle often attacks the foliage of ornamental plants belonging to the nightshade family.

Genus III. *ZYGOGRAMMA* Chevrolat

Medium-sized or small, oval, convex beetles; elytra marked with spots or stripes; last palpal segment not shorter than the preceding, subquadrangular or dilated, broadly truncate at apex; antennal insertions separated by

PLATE LXVIII
Family CHRYSOMELIDAE III

1. *Graphops nebulosus* (LeConte) (p. 680)

   Black, slightly bronzed; 3.5–4 mm.

2, 3. *Paria canella* (Fabricius) (p. 682)

   Very variable; black to yellowish, or yellowish with black spots; 3–4 mm.

4. *Phaedon viridis* (Melsheimer) (p. 690)

   Black, with brassy or green reflex; 2–3 mm.

5. *Chrysochus auratus* (Fabricius) (p. 682)

   Brilliant green, often brassy- or bluish-tinged; 8–11 mm.

6. *Adoxus obscurus* (Linné) (p. 681)

   Dark brown or blackish; elytra paler; 4–6 mm.

7. *Glyptoscelis pubescens* (Fabricius) (p. 682)

   Dark brown; 7–10 mm.

8. *Zygogramma suturalis* (Fabricius) (p. 688)

   Brown and dull yellow; 5–7 mm.

9. *Calligrapha lunata* (Fabricius) (p. 688)

   Brown and yellow; 7–8 mm.

10. *C. bidenticola* Brown (p. 689)

   Dark brown and yellow; 5–7 mm.

11. *Gastrophysa cyanea* Melsheimer (p. 691)

   Black, with metallic blue or green sheen; 4–5.5 mm.

12. *Calligrapha californica coreopsivora* Brown (p. 689)

   Black and yellowish; 5–6 mm.

13. *Fidia viticida* Walsh (p. 681)

   Dark reddish brown; antennae and legs paler; 5–7 mm.

14. *Gastrophysa polygoni* (Linné) (p. 691)

   Metallic blue or green; pronotum and legs reddish; 4–5 mm.

PLATE LXVIII 687

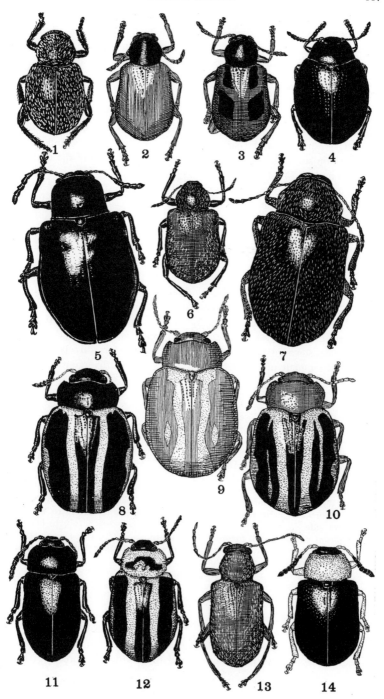

the entire width of the front; pronotum with a lateral margin; procoxal cavities transversely oval, open, or closed by an extension of the mesosternum; third tarsal segment entire, scarcely emarginate, last tarsal segment dentate beneath; claws simple, parallel, united at base.

Zygogramma suturalis (Fabricius)   Plate LXVIII, No. 8, p. 687
Broadly oval, convex; brown, with a feeble bronze or greenish lustre; elytra dirty yellow, with suture, first and second intervals, and a broad discal stripe dark brown; epipleura pale, with dark margins. Pronotum transverse, sparsely and coarsely punctate. Elytra coarsely and shallowly punctate on sides, coarsely and deeply so along the sides of the dark-brown lines. Length 5–7 mm.

The adults occur in spring on ragweed in low, moist places and on flowers of goldenrod in autumn.

Genus IV. *CALLIGRAPHA* Erichson

Small, oval or rounded, convex species; last palpal segment shorter than the preceding, subquadrangular or dilated, broadly truncate at apex; antennal insertions separated by entire width of front; pronotum with a lateral margin, sides thickened; elytral dark markings outlined by punctures; procoxal cavities transversely oval, open, or closed by an extension of the mesosternum; third tarsal segment entire or scarcely emarginate; last tarsal segment unarmed beneath; claws simple, divergent.

KEY TO SPECIES

1. Elytra with brown and yellow stripes 2
   Elytra with irregular spots, suture usually dark 4
2. Pronotum entirely brown; epipleura dark 3
   Pronotum in part yellow; epipleura pale yellowish; elongate-oval, slightly convex; discal spot of pronotum irregular, not attaining base ....
   ....c. *californica coreopsivora*
3. Last segment of palpi strongly dilated; discal brown stripe of elytra more or less divided by yellow ....a. *lunata*
   Last segment of palpi normal; discal brown stripe of elytra entire, notched on outer side ....b. *bidenticola*
4. Pronotum entirely dark green or olive-green 5
   Pronotum pale yellow, with reddish-brown discal spots; elytra with numerous small, greenish or black spots ....f. *multipunctata*
5. Elytra with a dark, rather broad, common sutural stripe, irregular on outer edge ....d. *rhoda*
   Elytra without a sutural stripe but with a narrow subsutural vitta ....
   ....e. *philadelphica*

a. *Calligrapha lunata* (Fabricius)   Plate LXVIII, No. 9, p. 687
Oblong-oval, very convex; light red-brown to brown, smooth, shining; elytra yellow, each with the suture and three vittae red-brown or brown,

the two inner ones broadly curved, outer one straight, except near base, and connected with middle one, these three vittae often wholly united into a broad stripe. Pronotum transverse, sides curved near apex; sparsely and finely punctate. Elytra coarsely and irregularly punctate, the vittae outlined in coarse punctures. Length 7–8 mm.

b. *Calligrapha bidenticola* Brown   Plate LXVIII, No. 10, p. 687

Oval, convex, robust; dark brown, feebly bronzed; elytra pale yellow, with a broad sutural stripe and a discal stripe dark brown, the latter notched near middle on outer side. Pronotum transverse, coarsely and sparsely punctate. Elytra laterally confusedly punctate, the stripes outlined with coarse, rather deep punctures. Length 5.5–7 mm.

c. *Calligrapha californica coreopsivora* Brown   Plate LXVIII, No. 12, p. 687

Elongate-oval, convex; black, slightly bronzed; pronotum pale reddish yellow, with black, W-shaped spot near, but not attaining, base; elytra pale yellow, with a common sutural stripe and a discal stripe on each bronzed black. Pronotum coarsely and rather sparsely punctured. Elytral sides with irregular rows of punctures; stripes outlined with coarse, rather deep punctures. Length 5–6 mm.

The adults occur on various plants, especially those of the Composite family, such as bur marigold, boneset, tickseed, and solidago. In gardens, they sometimes damage the foliage of *Coreopsis* and *Calliopsis*.

d. *Calligrapha rhoda* Knab   Plate LXIX, No. 1, p. 697

Subovate, convex; dark olive-green, slightly metallic; legs, antennae, and palpi reddish brown; elytra yellowish white, often with apical two-thirds dull reddish yellow, a common sutural stripe with three short spurs on each side, a large, curved, humeral lunule double to near middle and enclosing two small spots, which are often confluent, disk behind lunule with about eleven small spots, all of dull-green color. Head and pronotum finely alutaceous, coarsely, sparsely, and irregularly punctate, the pronotum with an irregular impression each side. Pale area of elytra more coarsely and closely punctate. Length 7–8 mm.

The adults feed on hazel.

e. *Calligrapha philadelphica* (Linné)   Plate LXIX, No. 3, p. 697

Subovate, very convex; dark olive-green, metallic; legs, antennae, and palpi dark reddish brown; elytra yellowish white, suture pale, with a narrow, subsutural, black line on basal half and two or three dark spots, humeral lunule not sharply curved, rather narrow, and enclosing a smaller lunule and spot, discal spots small and numerous. Pronotum coarsely, sparsely, and irregularly punctate. Elytra with sparse, shallow punctures. Length 8–9 mm.

The adults occur on foliage of linden and elm.

f. *Calligrapha multipunctata* (Say) Plate LXIX, No. 2, p. 697

Subovate, convex; dark reddish brown or dark olive-green, slightly bronzed; pronotum pale yellowish, with a large, dark-reddish-brown discal spot; elytra pale yellow, with narrow sutural and subsutural dark stripes, on pale area between them are numerous black or greenish spots. Pronotum rather finely and sparsely punctate. Elytra with finer, sparse punctures. Length 6.5–8.5 mm.

These beetles are usually found on red haw.

Tribe CHRYSOMELINI

KEY TO GENERA

1. Prosternum produced posteriorly as a distinct process 2
   Prosternum not produced posteriorly as a process . . . . II. *Gastrophysa* (p. 690)
2. Third tarsal segment distinctly emarginate . . . . I. *Phaedon* (p. 690)
   Third tarsal segment scarcely or not at all emarginate . . . . III. *Lina* (p. 691)

Genus I. *PHAEDON* Latreille

Small, subglobose, convex beetles; last segment of maxillary palpi oval, attenuate toward apex, at least as long as the preceding; antennae separated by entire width of front; pronotum without grooves and with a lateral margin; mesosternum not long, without distinct lateral prolongations; procoxal cavities open; third tarsal segment distinctly emarginate and bilobed; claws simple.

Phaedon viridis (Melsheimer) Plate LXVIII, No. 4, p. 687

Subglobose, robust, convex; black, brassy- or greenish-bronzed, shining. Pronotum transverse, disk strongly alutaceous. Elytra with rows of punctures; intervals rather rugulose; humerus not calloused. Length 2–3 mm.

Genus II. *GASTROPHYSA* Chevrolat

Small, oblong, subconvex, metallic forms; last segment of maxillary palpi oval, attenuate toward apex, at least as long as the preceding; pronotum without grooves and with a lateral margin; prosternum not produced posteriorly as a process; mesosternum not long, without distinct, broad, lateral prolongations; procoxal cavities open; claws simple.

KEY TO SPECIES

Head, elytra, and undersurface brilliant green or blue; pronotum, legs, base of antennae, and tip of abdomen reddish ....a. *polygoni*
Uniformly brilliant green or blue; antennae, legs, and undersurface purplish black ....b. *cyanea*

a. *Gastrophysa polygoni* (Linné)   Plate LXVIII, No. 14, p. 687
Oblong-oval, subconvex; head, elytra, and undersurface metallic green or blue; pronotum, legs, base of antennae, and tip of abdomen reddish; tarsi and apical two-thirds of antennae black. Pronotum transverse, sides arcuate; surface rather coarsely, sparsely, irregularly punctate. Length 4–5 mm.
The adults of this species are usually found on knotgrass.

b. *Gastrophysa cyanea* Melsheimer   Plate LXVIII, No. 11, p. 687
Oblong-oval, subconvex; metallic green or blue, shining; antennae, legs, and undersurface black. Head and pronotum finely and sparsely punctate. Elytra rather densely and roughly punctate. Length 4–5.5 mm.
The adults frequent dock and rhubarb.

Genus III. *LINA* Megerle

Rather small, oblong, subconvex species; last segment of maxillary palpi oval, attenuate toward apex, at least as long as the preceding; pronotum not acutely narrowed from base to apex, with a longitudinal, lateral impression; sides of pronotum and elytra thickened; mesosternum not long, without distinct, broad, lateral prolongations; mesosternum not arcuate anteriorly but produced between the mesocoxae; tibiae grooved externally; third tarsal segment scarcely or not at all emarginate.

KEY TO SPECIES

Elytra red or yellow, with small, round, black spots ....a. *interrupta*
Elytra dull reddish or greenish yellow, with elongate, black spots ......b *scripta*

a. *Lina interrupta* (Fabricius)   Plate LXIX, No. 4, p. 697
Oblong-oval, subconvex; black or dark metallic green; pronotum with a broad, yellow margin laterally; elytra red or dull yellow, each with seven small, black spots, which are more or less confluent and appear as transverse bands; bases of antennae and tibiae reddish. Dark area of pronotum finely punctate, the thickened, yellow sides coarsely punctate. Elytra coarsely and irregularly punctate. Length 6.5–9 mm.

The adults are common on willow, aspen, cottonwood, lombardy poplar, and alder.

b. *Lina scripta* (Fabricius) Plate LXIX, No. 5, p. 697

Oblong, rather parallel-sided, subconvex; dull reddish or greenish yellow; pronotum black, sides yellow; elytra yellow with suture black, two small, basal spots, three short, median lines, one small spot near suture, and a curved, lateral line near apex black, these markings sometimes confluent. Pronotum with dark area very finely and very sparsely punctate, the yellow sides coarsely and sparsely punctate. Elytra rather coarsely and densely punctate. Length 6.5–9 mm.

The larvae and adults are found on willow and poplar.

Tribe PHRATORINI

Genus *PHRATORA* Chevrolat

Small, oblong, convex species; procoxal cavities open; tibiae neither dilated nor toothed near apex; third tarsal segment much wider and longer than first and second, deeply bilobed; tarsal claws toothed.

Phratora americana (Schaeffer) Plate LXIX, No. 6, p. 697

Oblong, convex; purple, metallic blue-green, or bronze, shining; legs and antennae black, sometimes bronzed, tibiae and tarsi sometimes paler. Pronotum transverse; anterior angles prominent, posterior ones rectangular; surface sparsely and irregularly punctate, disk with rather fine punctures, those on side coarser. Elytra with rows of moderate punctures, sides with coarser and more or less irregularly placed punctures. Length 4–5 mm.

These beetles frequent willows and poplars.

Subfamily GALERUCINAE

KEY TO TRIBES

1. Metafemora slender, not adapted for jumping 2
   Metafemora thickened, adapted for jumping (Fig. 487) ....ALTICINI (p. 700)
2. Claws bifid (Fig. 26E) ....OIDINI (p. 693)
   Claws with a broad basal tooth or lobe (Fig. 26G) 3
3. Procoxal cavities closed (Fig. 25B) ....MONOLEPTINI (p. 700)
   Procoxal cavities open (Fig. 25A) ....LUPERINI (p. 699)

Tribe OIDINI

KEY TO GENERA

1. Tibiae without terminal spurs 3
   At least some of tibiae with terminal spurs 2
2. Punctation of elytra confused ....I. *Diabrotica* (p. 693)
   Punctation of elytra in regular rows ....II. *Acalymma* (p. 694)
3. Third antennal segment shorter than fourth ....IV. *Trirhabda* (p. 698)
   Third antennal segment longer than fourth ....III. *Galerucella* (p. 694)

Genus I. *DIABROTICA* Chevrolat

Of small to moderate size, oblong-ovate; head not inserted in the pronotum to eyes; antennae slender, more than half as long as body, second segment nearly equal to third; pronotum transverse, subquadrate, disk bifoveate, the foveae separated; procoxae contiguous, cavities open behind; meso- and metatibiae usually carinate on outer edge and with terminal spurs; metatarsi with first segment distinctly longer than next two combined; claws bifid.

Diabrotica undecimpunctata howardi Barber Spotted Cucumber Beetle
Plate LXXI, No. 3, p. 711

Oblong-oval, widened behind, subconvex; greenish yellow, shining; head and metasternum black; elytra each with three pairs of black spots arranged transversely, one pair basally, another before middle, the third pair at apical third; antennae dark brown, the three basal segments yellowish. Pronotum transverse, not punctate; disk deeply foveate each side of middle. Elytra very finely and irregularly punctate. Length 6–7 mm.

The adults are found on cucumber, melon, and goldenrod, feeding on the pollen, flowers, and foliage. The larvae do considerable damage to crops by attacking the roots.

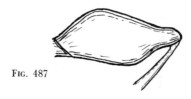

FIG. 487

Fig. 487. Metafemur of *Altica,* much thickened and adapted for jumping; upper portion of tibia is also shown.

Genus II. *ACALYMMA* Barber

Small, oblong-oval beetles; head not inserted into pronotum to eyes; antennae slender, more than half body length, the second segment much shorter than third; pronotum transverse, subquadrate, bifoveate, the foveae contiguous at middle; elytra usually sulcate, punctate, striate, and vittate; procoxae contiguous; meso- and metatibiae carinate on outer edge, with terminal spurs at apex; first metatarsal segment as long as second and third combined; claws bifid.

Acalymma vittata (Fabricius)   Striped Cucumber Beetle
                                                                 Plate LXVI, No. 17, p. 665

Oblong-ovate, very slightly wider posteriorly, subconvex; pale yellow or orange-yellow; head and scutellum black; elytra with a common sutural stripe and each with a single lateral stripe black; beneath piceous; antennae piceous, three basal segments yellowish. Pronotum transverse, impunctate; disk either side of middle with a fovea, the foveae contiguous. Elytra striate; striae each with two rows of punctures, intervals convex. Length 5–6.5 mm.

This beetle is very injurious to cucumber and melon vines. In addition to destroying many plants by devouring the leaves and stems, this beetle and the preceding do further damage by carrying the cucumber wilt disease from an infected plant to a healthy one. Moreover, the bacteria that produce the wilt live during the winter months within the digestive tract of these beetles. In spring the bacteria are excreted with the feces and enter cucumber plants through a break in the epidermis.

Genus III. *GALERUCELLA* Crotch

Small, oblong-ovate; head usually with a distinct median impressed line; antennae one-half or more the length of body, third segment longer than fourth; pronotum impressed medially and bifoveate; procoxal cavities open behind; tibiae without terminal spurs, carinate externally; first metatarsal segment not longer than next two together; claws bifid.

The species of this genus as a whole occur on herbs in moist places.

KEY TO SPECIES

1. Elytra vittate 2
   Elytra not vittate or maculate (margins sometimes pale) 3
2. Elytra each with a broad, black, submarginal vitta and a short one at middle
   of base ....e. *xanthomelaena*
   Elytra each with three vittae, nearly uniform in width, narrow ....a. *americana*

3. Color dull brick-red; head entirely dull red ....b. *cavicollis*
   Color dull yellow, brownish, or piceous; head above at least with a median
   spot black or piceous 4
4. Head above entirely black or blackish; mesocoxae separated by mesosternal
   process ....c. *nymphaeae*
   Head above with only a small black median spot; mesocoxae contiguous ....
   ....d. *decora*

a. *Galerucella americana* (Fabricius)   Plate LXXI, No. 2, p. 711
   Broadly oval, strongly convex; brown-yellow to gray-brown, feebly shining; head and pronotum with median black spot; antennal segments darker
apically; elytra each with three narrow, black stripes which are often reduced. Pronotum transverse, base wider than apex; sides arcuate; surface
coarsely and densely punctate, in female more sparsely so; disk with a
feeble median impression. Elytral humeri rounded, not prominent; disk
coarsely and rather densely punctate. Length 4–6 mm.

b. *Galerucella cavicollis* (LeConte)   Plate LXX, No. 14, p. 705
   Elongate-oval, widened posteriorly, convex; orange- or red-brown, rather
shining; antennae black, tibiae and tarsi sometimes black; sparsely, finely
pubescent. Pronotum convex, base wider than apex; sides arcuate; disk
with a broad median impression, foveate each side, coarsely, rather densely
punctate. Elytra coarsely, not densely punctate. Length 4.3–6 mm.
   The adults may be taken on wild cherry.

c. *Galerucella nymphaeae* (Linné)   Plate LXX, No. 15, p. 705
   Oblong-ovate, widened posteriorly, subconvex; dull brownish yellow,
finely pubescent; head above nearly entirely black; antennae annulate,
apices of segments blackish; pronotum with three black spots; elytra
piceous, lateral margins and apex yellowish; body beneath largely piceous.
Pronotum transverse, sides angulate, anterior angles rather prominent,
subdentate; disk narrowly impressed medially, with a fovea on each side
which is coarsely punctate, remainder of surface impunctate or nearly so.
Elytra coarsely and densely punctate. Length 4.5–6 mm.
   The adults are found on leaves and flowers of water lilies, spatterdock,
and *Polygonum* species.

d. *Galerucella decora* (Say)   Plate LXX, No. 13, p. 705
   Oblong, scarcely wider posteriorly, convex; brownish red or yellow,
covered with fine, silky pubescence; elytra usually darker; antennae either
entirely piceous or with basal segments dull yellow. Pronotum transverse,
narrowed anteriorly; sides arcuate, basal angles slightly prominent, base
oblique toward sides. Elytra coarsely, deeply, densely punctate. Length
4.5–5.5 mm.

PLATE LXIX
Family CHRYSOMELIDAE IV

1. *Calligrapha rhoda* Knab (p. 689) — Dark olive-green and yellowish; 7–8 mm.

2. *C. multipunctata* (Say) (p. 690) — Dark brown or olive-green and yellowish; 6–9 mm.

3. *C. philadelphica* (Linné) (p. 689) — Dark olive-green and yellowish; 8–9 mm.

4. *Lina interrupta* (Fabricius) (p. 691) — Black or deep green and yellowish; 6–9 mm.

5. *L. scripta* (Fabricius) (p. 692) — Dull yellowish, with black marks; 6–9 mm.

6. *Phratora americana* (Schaeffer) (p. 692) — Dull yellowish, with black markings; elytra sometimes maroon, without black spots; 4–5 mm.

7. *Labidomera clivicollis* (Kirby) (p. 685) — Bluish or greenish black; elytral markings orange-yellow; 9–11 mm.

8. *Leptinotarsa decimlineata* (Say) (p. 685) — Dull yellow, with black marks; 6–11 mm.

MM 0 10 20 30 40 50 60 70

PLATE LXIX   697

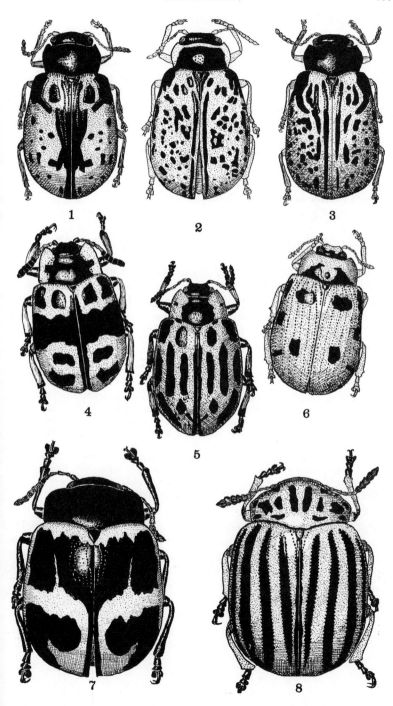

1

2

3

4

5

6

7

8

e. *Galerucella xanthomelaena* (Schrank)   Elm-Leaf Beetle
                                                      Plate LXXI, No. 1, p. 711

Oblong, subconvex; olive-brown or yellowish brown, pubescent; head spotted with black on vertex and behind eyes; pronotum with three black spots; elytra with a broad, lateral stripe and a short line on disk black; underside piceous. Pronotum transverse, slightly narrowed anteriorly, sides feebly angulate; disk obliquely impressed on each side and shallowly so at middle near apex; surface sparsely punctate. Elytral sides subparallel; disk finely, evenly punctate. Length 5–7 mm.

This beetle is an "immigrant" and, like other insects that have come into this country, has become a serious pest on elm trees; it is suspected of helping to spread the dreaded Dutch elm disease. Both larvae and adults do much damage to the foliage of elms.

Genus IV. *TRIRHABDA* LeConte

Moderate-sized, elongate-oblong, convex; head not impressed, a spot of color usually present on the occiput; antennae one-half as long as body or longer, fourth segment always longer than third; pronotum transverse, disk transversely impressed; elytra with sides subparallel; procoxal cavities open behind; tibiae without terminal spurs, carinate externally; first tarsal segment longer than following; claws cleft.

KEY TO SPECIES

1. Elytra with lateral and sutural vittae united behind (sometimes before) middle, or with traces of a median vitta coalescing with sutural vitta ......
....a. *bacharidis*
   Elytra with lateral and sutural vittae not united or narrowly united at extreme apex 2
2. Occipital spot of head small, oblong, not forming a transverse basal band or extending broadly down the front; elytra densely pubescent, finely punctate ....b. *canadensis*
   Occipital spot of head widely oblong and extending down front; elytra not densely pubescent, coarsely punctate ....c. *virgata*

a. *Trirhabda bacharidis* (Weber)   Plate LXXI, No. 6, p. 711

Robust, elongate-oblong, slightly widened posteriorly; pale yellow, feebly shining; head with a triangular, black spot on occiput extending narrowly down vertex; elytra each with a lateral vitta, which gradually widens and connects behind middle with a sutural stripe, black; scutellum black. Pronotum transverse, sides nearly straight, feebly angulate at middle; sparsely, coarsely punctate. Elytra densely, shallowly, confluently punctate, covered with short, dense, pale-yellowish pubescence. Length 7.5–12 mm.

The food plant of this species is groundsel bush.

b. *Trirhabda canadensis* (Kirby) Plate LXXI, No. 7, p. 711

Elongate-oblong, rather robust; pale yellow, feebly shining; head with a small, oblong, black spot on occiput, not covering base of head or extending on front; antennae, tarsi, and sides of abdomen blackish; elytra with a lateral and sutural stripe, narrow and black, joined at apex; scutellum entirely black. Pronotum transverse, sides feebly arcuate, narrowly angulate at middle; surface sparsely, coarsely punctate. Elytra densely, finely punctate, covered with dense, pale pubescence. Length 7–10 mm.

Both larvae and adults may be found on goldenrod.

c. *Trirhabda virgata* LeConte Plate LXXI, No. 5, p. 711

Elongate-oblong, rather robust; yellowish; head with a moderate-sized, black spot on occiput that extends broadly down the front and covers the base of head; antennae dark; pronotum with three black spots; elytra with wide lateral and sutural vittae black, the former usually wider than the enclosed yellow portion, not usually united at apex. Pronotum transverse, sides obtusely angulate; disk sparsely and coarsely punctate. Elytra coarsely, densely, confluently punctate; inconspicuously and sparsely pubescent. Length 6–9 mm.

The adults may be collected on goldenrod.

Tribe LUPERINI

Genus *LUPERODES* Motschulsky

Small, oblong-ovate, convex beetles; head transversely sulcate between eyes, carinate between antennae; antennae slender, more than half as long as body, second and third segments together not longer than fourth segment; pronotum never distinctly impressed; elytral epipleura extending nearly to apex; procoxal cavities open behind; tibiae with a terminal spur; first metatarsal segment longer than second and third together, slender; claws appendiculate, divaricate.

Luperodes meraca (Say) Plate LXXI, No. 13, p. 711

Elongate-oblong, convex; deep metallic blue, shining; antennae, tibiae, and tarsi brown-yellow, femora darker. Pronotum subquadrate, wider anteriorly; disk sparsely and rather finely punctate. Surface of elytra finely, transversely rugose, a few fine punctures intermingled. Length 4–5 mm.

Tribe MONOLEPTINI

Genus *CEROTOMA* Chevrolat

Small, oval, convex forms; first antennal segment longer than fourth, the third elongate, almost as long as first; metafemora not adapted for jumping; procoxal cavities closed behind; first metatarsal segment as long as the rest combined; tarsal claws with a broad basal tooth or lobe.

Cerotoma trifurcata (Forster)   The Bean-Leaf Beetle
                                                    Plate LXXI, No. 4, p. 711

Oval, convex; yellow or red, shining; underside black; head black or deep blue; elytra with a lateral stripe, almost attaining apex, and three rounded spots in a line close to suture, all black or dark blue; scutellum black or dark blue, sometimes spots and lines more or less connected or lacking in part or entirely. Pronotum transverse, sides slightly narrowing from base to apex; disk finely and densely punctate. Elytra with irregular rows of fine, sparse punctures. Length 4–8.5 mm.

This beetle is found on legumes and is sometimes very destructive.

Tribe ALTICINI

KEY TO GENERA

1. Last segment of metatarsi globose ....II. *Oedionychis* (p. 702)
   Last segment of metatarsi normal, not globose 2
2. Procoxal cavities open behind 3
   Procoxal cavities closed behind 6
3. Pronotum without transverse basal impression 4
   Pronotum with transverse basal impression ....IV. *Altica* (p. 707)
4. First segment of metatarsi slender and long; species not over 3.5 mm.
  5
   First segment of metatarsi short as compared to tibia; size 4 mm. or
   larger ....III. *Disonycha* (p. 706)
5. Metatibiae not grooved on outer edge ....XII. *Phyllotreta* (p. 715)
   Metatibiae grooved on outer edge (Fig. 488); first metatarsal segment
   nearly half as long as tibia ....XI. *Longitarsus* (p. 715)
6. Antennae eleven-segmented 7
   Antennae ten-segmented ....XIV. *Psylliodes* (p. 719)
7. Bases of antennae distant; tarsal claws bifid (Fig. 26E) ....
   ....I. *Blepharida* (p. 701)
   Bases of antennae approximate; claws simple (Fig. 26D) or appendiculate (Fig. 26F) 8
8. Metatibiae sinuate near apex (Fig. 489) ....IX. *Chaetocnema* (p. 712)
   Metatibiae without sinuation or tooth 9

9. Pronotum with a distinct transverse basal impression (Fig. 490) . . . 10
Pronotum without a basal impression 13
10. Elytra pubescent . . . . V. *Epitrix* (p. 709)
Elytra glabrous 11
11. Pronotal transverse basal impression interrupted laterally by a sharp longitudinal impression each side (Fig. 490) 12
Pronotal transverse basal impression not interrupted laterally by a sharp longitudinal impression . . . . VI. *Orthaltica* (p. 709)
12. Space between pronotal transverse basal impression and base flat . . . . VIII. *Chalcoides* (p. 712)
Space between pronotal transverse basal impression and base convex . . . . VII. *Derocrepis* (p. 709)
13. Spur of metatibiae small, slender . . . . X. *Systena* (p. 714)
Spur of metatibiae broad, emarginate or bifid at apex (Fig. 491) . . . . XIII. *Dibolia* (p. 719)

Genus I. *BLEPHARIDA* Rogers

Small, elongate-oval, convex, rather robust forms; antennae not approximate at base, eleven-segmented, first four segments smooth, the second half as long as first, third and fourth slender and each longer than second, fifth

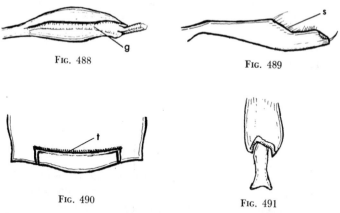

FIG. 488

FIG. 489

FIG. 490

FIG. 491

Fig. 488. Left metafemur and part of tibia of *Longitarsus* viewed from beneath, with groove (*g*).
Fig. 489. Left metatibia of *Chaetocnema* from below, sinuate (*s*) near apex.
Fig. 490. Basal portion of pronotum of *Chalcoides,* the transverse impression (*t*) interrupted by longitudinal sulci each side.
Fig. 491. Tip of metatibia of *Dibolia,* with a broad spur which is emarginate at apex.

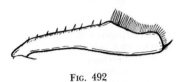

Fig. 492

Fig. 492. Metatibia of *Blepharida;* the sinuation at apex possesses a comblike row of bristles.

to tenth broader than fourth and gradually very slightly shorter and pubescent, eleventh longer and with a very small, conical terminal appendage; pronotum without distinct impressions; elytra with punctures in regular rows or striae; meso- and metatibiae with a preapical tooth, followed by an emargination in which there is a comblike brush of bristles (Fig. 492); tarsi robust, first segment broadly triangular, last slender; claws cleft, the inner point shorter.

Blepharida rhois (Forster)   Plate LXXIII, No. 5, p. 723

Oval, strongly convex, robust; reddish brown; elytra irregularly marked with pale yellow; antennae piceous, the four basal segments pale; undersurface and legs reddish brown. Pronotum more than twice as wide as long, narrowed apically, sides sharply arcuate, anterior angles prominent, posterior ones obtuse; disk finely and sparsely punctured and with a row of coarse punctures at margin. Each elytron with nine rows of coarse, deep punctures. Length 5–6.5 mm.

The markings of the elytra vary greatly in size. These beetles occur especially on sumac.

Genus II. *OEDIONYCHIS* Latreille

Small or medium-sized species; varying from pale yellowish to metallic green, blue, purple, or opaque black, either spotted, uniformly colored, striped, or banded; pronotum always much wider than long and more or less margined; elytra margined, either widely or narrowly so, disk usually glabrous or smooth, punctation when present always confused, never in rows; body beneath generally slightly pubescent; epipleura varying with the width of the margins; procoxal cavities open; legs rather short; metatarsus with first segment shorter than second and third combined; metatibiae with a preapical emargination, bordered by a sharp angle or small tooth; claw segment swollen and globular; claws appendiculate.

KEY TO SPECIES

1. Antennae stouter, scarcely half as long as body; species larger, 4.5 mm. long
   or more; convex; front of head oblique; elytral margins not flattened 2
   Antennae slender, half or a little more than half as long as body; smaller,
   less than 4.5 mm. long; depressed; front vertical; elytral margins flattened ..4
2. Elytra concolorous, punctures distinct, often coarse and dense; pronotal margin
   pale ....b. *vians*
   Elytra bicolored, either with a pale margin or with discal stripes, rarely dull
   reddish yellow with suture black 3
3. Elytra bluish, margin pale; pronotum and elytra coarsely and closely punctate ....a. *thoracica*
   Elytra dull yellow, each with a sutural and median stripe black; disk minutely
   alutaceous ....c. *miniata*
4. Elytra dirty yellow, with indistinct black lines; sides strongly arcuate; disk
   coarsely punctate ....d. *circumdata*
   Elytra in great part piceous; sides feebly arcuate or nearly parallel; disk
   finely, closely punctate ....e. *quercata*

a. *Oedionychis thoracica* (Fabricius) Plate LXXIII, No. 7, p. 723

Broadly ovate, subconvex; head, pronotum, and undersurface brownish
yellow; pronotum with seven black dots which are often more or less confluent; elytra dark metallic blue, a narrow margin on basal half and
epipleura reddish yellow; antennae and tarsi piceous. Antennae half as
long as body, segments three and four equal. Pronotum strongly transverse,
sides feebly arcuate, angles acute; disk coarsely and closely punctate. Elytral
surface coarsely and densely punctate. Length 5.5–8 mm.

b. *Oedionychis vians* (Illiger) Plate LXXIII, No. 8, p. 723

Oblong-oval, subconvex; dull black, sometimes with a slight greenish or
purplish tinge; pronotum brownish yellow, with an inverted W-shaped
black spot or with a large, transverse discal spot, so that only the margins
are pale; tip of abdomen brownish yellow. Antennae almost half as long
as body, third segment longer than fourth. Pronotum twice as wide at base
as long, narrowed apically, sides feebly arcuate, angles prominent; surface
very finely alutaceous, coarsely and sparsely punctate. Elytral surface very
finely alutaceous, finely and sparsely punctate. Length 4–7 mm.

These beetles have been collected from oak and *Polygonum pennsylvani-
cum*.

c. *Oedionychis miniata* (Fabricius) Plate LXXIII, No. 12, p. 723

Oblong-oval, subconvex; brownish yellow, slightly shining; pronotum
with a transverse brown spot; elytra each with a sutural and a median
discal black stripe; antennae except basal three or four segments, pro- and
mesotibiae, and all tarsi piceous; body beneath reddish brown. Pronotum
about three times as wide as long, sides arcuate, narrowed apically; disk
very minutely alutaceous. Elytra finely, sparsely punctate. Length 4–7 mm.

These beetles may be taken by sweeping herbs and low-growing shrubs.

PLATE LXX
Family CHRYSOMELIDAE V

1. *Pachybrachys pubescens* (Olivier) (p. 671) — Black; 3.5–5 mm.

2. *P. subfasciatus* LeConte (p. 672) — Black; pronotal and elytral markings dull reddish or orangeish, variable in shape and size; 2.5–3.5 mm.

3. *P. trinotatus* (Melsheimer) (p. 673) — Black, with reddish marks; 4–5 mm.

4. *P. othonus* (Say) (p. 672) — Black, with yellow marks; 3.5–4 mm.

5. *P. tridens* (Melsheimer) (p. 672) — Light yellow and black; 3.5–4 mm.

6. *P. m-nigrum* (Melsheimer) (p. 672) — Yellow, with black marks; 3–4 mm.

7. *Cryptocephalus notatus* Fabricius (p. 673) — Black; elytral marks reddish; 4–5.5 mm.

8. *C. quadruplex* Newman (p. 673) — Black; elytral marks reddish; 2.5–4 mm.

9. *C. venustus* Fabricius (p. 674) — Yellow and brownish, with black marks on elytra; 4.5–6 mm.

10. *C. mutabilis* Melsheimer (p. 674) — Yellow or orange, with black or brown markings which are variable in extent; 4–6.5 mm.

11. *C. guttulatus* Olivier (p. 673) — Brown, with yellow spots, those on elytra variable in size; 3.5–5.5 mm.

12. *Diachus auratus* (Fabricius) (p. 674) — Dark brown, often bronzed or greenish-reflexed; 1.5–2 mm.

13. *Galerucella decora* (Say) (p. 695) — Brownish red or brownish yellow; 4.5–5.5 mm.

14. *G. cavicollis* (LeConte) (p. 695) — Dark reddish; tibiae and tarsi sometimes black; 4–6 mm.

15. *G. nymphaeae* (Linné) (p. 695) — Dull yellow and blackish; median spot of pronotum often obsolete; 4–6 mm.

MM 0 10 20 30 40 50 60 70

PLATE LXX

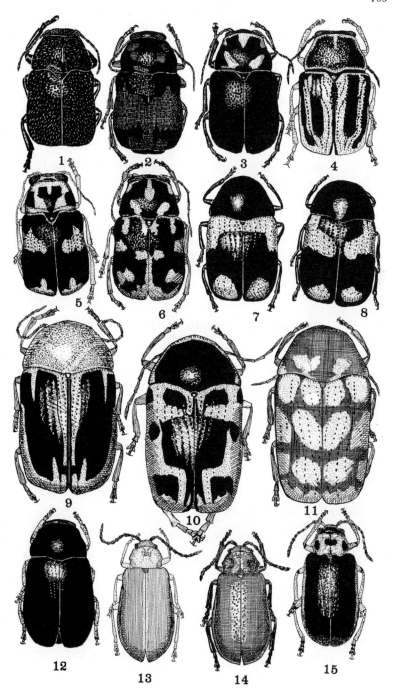

d. *Oedionychis circumdata* (Randall)   Plate LXXIII, No. 15, p. 723

Rather broadly ovate, subconvex; brownish yellow; elytra each with four narrow, fuscous or piceous stripes (one or all of these may be absent or all may be confluent); antennae fuscous, basal segments pale yellowish. Pronotum nearly three times as wide as long; lateral margins broadly flattened; anterior angles not dentiform; surface very minutely alutaceous. Elytra broadly oval; umbone rather prominent; surface closely and coarsely punctate. Length 3.5–5.5 mm.

These beetles may be collected by beating and sweeping foliage.

e. *Oedionychis quercata* (Fabricius)   Plate LXXIII, No. 11, p. 723

Broadly ovate, subconvex; piceous, slightly shining; front of head, pronotum, legs, epipleura, and narrow margins of elytra pale yellow. Antennae more than half as long as body, outer segments piceous. Pronotum twice as wide as long; lateral margins widely flattened, anterior angles dentiform; disk very finely alutaceous, finely and very sparsely punctate. Elytral umbone distinct; disk finely, closely punctate. Length 3.5–4.5 mm.

These beetles are found on various kinds of foliage.

Genus III. *DISONYCHA* Chevrolat

Of moderate size, oblong-oval, convex; head inserted into pronotum as far as eyes; front distinctly carinate and bituberculate; pronotum as wide as elytra at base, narrowed apically, basal margin near hind angles obliquely truncate for a short distance; procoxal cavities open behind; metatibiae not deeply grooved; first tarsal segment twice length of second; claw segment slender, appendiculate, that of metatarsi not inflated; last abdominal sternite truncate in male, the pygidium vertical and convex, last abdominal sternite oval in female, pygidium horizontal.

KEY TO SPECIES

1. Elytra unicolorous, not vittate 2
   Elytra vittate 3
2. Head coarsely and densely punctate; ventral surface and legs entirely dark ....a. *triangularis*
   Head smooth, or with a few punctures across occiput and front; abdomen usually with a pale-yellowish margin on last ventral segment, sometimes entire abdomen pale yellowish ....b. *xanthomelas*
3. Head entirely pale yellowish ....d. *caroliniana*
   Head entirely dark except for base of antennae and sometimes a pale-yellowish streak along lower edge of front ....c. *pennsylvanica*

a. *Disonycha triangularis* (Say)   Plate LXXII, No. 6, p. 717

Oval, rather depressed; black or blue-black, shining; entire prothorax yellow, pronotal disk with three black dots arranged in a triangle, the lateral ones rounded, the middle one basal, linear, sometimes reduced. Pronotum transverse, sides feebly arcuate, margins very narrow; finely, not densely punctate. Elytra finely and rather densely punctate. Length 4.5–7 mm.

This has been recorded as being taken from chickweed, beets, spinach, etc., and may be collected by sweeping low-growing herbs in moist or damp areas.

b. *Disonycha xanthomelas* (Dalman) Spinach Flea Beetle
Plate LXXII, No. 5, p. 717

Oblong-oval, rather depressed; black or blue-black, shining; pronotum not spotted; prothorax entirely yellow; meso- and metasterna black; abdominal sternites yellow. Pronotum transverse, nearly impunctate. Elytra obsoletely punctate. Length 4.5–6 mm.

The adults may be taken on spinach and chickweed.

c. *Disonycha pennsylvanica* (Illiger) Plate LXXII, No. 3, p. 717

Oblong, nearly parallel, convex; black, shining; head blackish, bases of antennae yellow; pronotum yellow, usually with three black spots, these sometimes fused to form a wide, transverse band; elytra yellow, with suture, a narrow stripe close to side margin, and a median stripe (not attaining apex), wider than the yellow spaces on each side of it, black; last abdominal segment pale. Pronotum transverse; side margins wide; surface nearly smooth. Elytra sparsely, finely, but distinctly punctate, sometimes feebly sulcate between discal stripes in female. Length 5.5–7.5 mm.

d. *Disonycha caroliniana* (Fabricius) Plate LXXII, No. 1, p. 717

Oval, slightly narrower anteriorly, convex; yellow, shining; antennae, tibiae, and tarsi black; pronotum (on apical half) with two piceous spots of variable size; elytra with a narrow stripe along suture, another near lateral margin, and a discal one, narrower than the yellow spaces on each side of it, black; beneath reddish yellow. Pronotum transverse, sides feebly arcuate, margins narrow; disk smooth or very feebly punctate. Elytral disk finely and sparsely punctate. Length 5.5–6.5 mm.

Genus IV. *ALTICA* Geoffroy

Small, oblong or oval species; head short, deeply inserted into the prothorax; antennae half as long as body, segments two to four gradually longer; pronotum transversely sulcate in front of base; prosternum rather narrow between the coxae; procoxal cavities open behind; meso- and metatibiae not toothed above near apex; metatibiae not or feebly sulcate, apex with a short spur; tarsal claws dilated at base.

KEY TO SPECIES

1. Prebasal sulcus extending entirely across pronotum 2
   Prebasal sulcus never extending entirely across pronotum, sometimes obsolete . 3
2. Pronotum conspicuously wider at base than at apex ....a. *chalybea*
   Pronotum only slightly wider at base than at apex ....b. *ignita*
3. Legs concolorous with body 4
   Legs in part reddish yellow, contrasting with body ....e. *fuscoaenea*
4. Prebasal sulcus deep, evanescent laterally ....c. *carinata*
   Prebasal sulcus shallow or obsolete ....d. *marevagans*

a. *Altica chalybea* Illiger   The Great Flea Beetle
                                                  Plate LXXII, No. 8, p. 717

Oblong-oval, robust; dark metallic blue, shining, occasionally metallic green or cupreous; underside and legs blue-black. Pronotum transverse, prebasal sulcus rather deep, extending entirely across pronotum; disk nearly smooth, with minute, scattered punctures. Elytra finely and sparsely punctate, smoother toward apex. Length 4–5.2 mm.

The adults are found on wild grape and poison ivy, as well as on Virginia creeper.

b. *Altica ignita* Illiger   Plate LXXII, No. 9, p. 717

Oblong-oval, rather slender; bronze, green, or brassy green, shining, infrequently dark blue; underside and legs blue-black. Pronotum transverse, prebasal sulcus deep, extending entirely across pronotum; disk minutely and sparsely punctate. Elytra distinctly but sparsely punctate near base, gradually smoother near apex. Length 3–4 mm.

The adult are very common on *Ludwigia* (the water purslane) and on foliage of many other plants.

c. *Altica carinata* Germar   Plate LXXII, No. 10, p. 717

Oblong-ovate, rather slender; cupreous-black, shining, with a purple or blue reflex. Pronotum transverse, distinctly wider at base than at apex; prebasal sulcus rather deep at middle, evanescent laterally, not attaining side margins; disk finely and fairly densely punctate. Elytra more or less coarsely and densely punctate. Length 3.5–5 mm.

d. *Altica marevagans* Horn   Plate LXXII, No. 11, p. 717

Oblong-oval, slightly robust; metallic bluish green, shining. Pronotum transverse, base slightly wider than apex; prebasal sulcus shallow, sometimes nearly obsolete, not extending across disk; minutely and densely punctate on surface. Elytra rather coarsely and densely punctate. Length 4–5 mm.

e. *Altica fuscoaenea* Melsheimer   Plate LXXII, No. 12, p. 717

Oblong-oval, convex, slender; olive-green or bronze, shining; underside and metafemora piceous or bronze; tibiae and tarsi reddish yellow. Pronotum feebly transverse, apex as wide as base; prebasal sulcus deep, extending from margin to margin; surface minutely and sparsely punctate, smoother near apex. Elytra finely punctate. Length 2.5–3.5 mm.

The adults are commonly found on primrose.

Genus V. *EPITRIX* Foudras

Very small, convex species; body above with patches or series of hairs; head inserted into prothorax to eyes; front with a V-shaped carina, ending on vertex above an impressed line; antennae half as long as body; pronotum transverse, punctate, prebasal impression curved toward base; procoxal cavities closed.

The most obvious distinction between this and the two preceding genera is the presence of pubescence on the pronotum and elytra, as well as the smaller size.

Epitrix cucumeris (Harris)   Potato Flea Beetle
Plate LXXII, No. 15, p. 717

Oblong-oval; piceous, shining; antennae and legs brownish orange, metafemora piceous. Pronotum transverse, finely and rather densely punctate; prebasal impression deep, ends slightly curved toward base. Elytral punctures coarse, rather close, arranged in series. Length 1.5–2.5 mm.

Genus VI. *ORTHALTICA* Crotch

Small, elongate-oblong; antennae more than half as long as body, nearly as long as body in male, the segments dissimilar in the two sexes; pronotum transverse, prebasal sulcus deep, not ending at sides in a longitudinal impression, ends curved toward base; metatibiae with a short spur.

Orthaltica copalina (Fabricius)   Plate LXXIII, No. 1, p. 723

Elongate-oblong, subconvex; brown or piceous, shining; when piceous, the head and pronotum are paler; legs reddish yellow. Pronotum transverse, base and apex subequal, coarsely and rather sparsely punctate. Elytra wider than pronotum, with nine rows of coarse, dense punctures, inner rows confused at base. Length 2–3 mm.

This species is common on sumac and poison ivy.

Genus VII. *DEROCREPIS* Weise

Small, oblong-oval species; head inserted into prothorax to eyes; front sulcate, sulci not extending behind eyes; antennae half as long as body,

PLATE LXXI
Family CHRYSOMELIDAE VI

1. *Galerucella xanthomelaena* (Schrank) (p. 698) — Olive-brown or yellowish brown, with black spots; 5–7 mm.

2. *G. americana* (Fabricius) (p. 695) — Brownish yellow, with black markings; 4–6 mm.

3. *Diabrotica undecimpunctata howardi* Barber (p. 693) — Greenish yellow, with black spots; 6–7 mm.

4. *Cerotoma trifurcata* (Forster) (p. 700) — Orangeish, with black maculae; elytral markings variable; 4–9 mm.

5. *Trirhabda virgata* LeConte (p. 699) — Yellowish and black; 6–9 mm.

6. *T. bacharidis* (Weber) (p. 698) — Yellowish, with black marks; 7–12 mm.

7. *T. canadensis* (Kirby) (p. 699) — Pale yellow and black; 7–10 mm.

8. *Phyllotreta zimmermanni* (Crotch) (p. 718) — Blackish; elytral vitta yellow; 1.8–3.4 mm.

9. *P. striolata* (Fabricius) (p. 718) — Blackish; elytral vitta yellow; 1.5–2.5 mm.

10. *P. bipustulata* (Fabricius) (p. 718) — Blackish; elytral spots orangeish; 1.6–2.5 mm.

11. *P. armoraciae* (Koch) (p. 718) — Black and yellow; 2.6–4 mm.

12. *Longitarsus testaceus* (Melsheimer) (p. 715) — Dull yellowish, head darker; 2–3 mm.

13. *Luperodes meraca* (Say) (p. 699) — Deep metallic blue; legs yellowish; 4–5 mm.

14. *Systena frontalis* (Fabricius) (p. 714) — Blackish; head and legs in part brownish; 3.5–4.8 mm.

15. *Longitarsus melanurus* (Melsheimer) (p. 715) — Dark brown to blackish; legs and antennae brown; 2–2.5 mm.

MM 0 10 20 30 40 50 60 70

PLATE LXXI 711

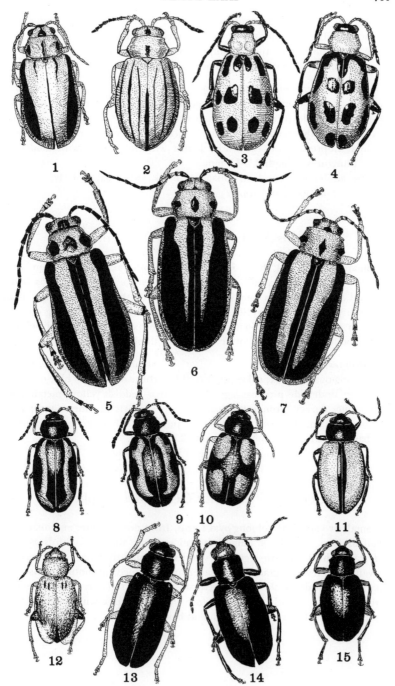

second segment half as long as first, third to tenth subequal and longer than second; pronotum transverse, impunctate; prebasal sulcus ending each side in a short, longitudinal impression; procoxal cavity closed behind; first abdominal sternite as long as next three together.

Derocrepis erythropus (Melsheimer)   Plate LXXII, No. 13, p. 717
    Oblong-oval, convex; brown-orange, shining; elytra dark, metallic blue-green; underside piceous. Pronotum transverse, sides feebly arcuate; disk entirely smooth except for prebasal sulcus, which ends in a short, longitudinal impression on each side. Elytra with regular rows of moderate-sized punctures. Length 2.5–3.5 mm.
    The adults are found on foliage of black locust particularly; they are also a pest on peach and apple.

Genus VIII. *CHALCOIDES* Foudras

    Small, oblong-oval; head inserted into prothorax to eyes; front with curved sulci which extend behind eyes; antennae half as long as body, second segment half as long as first, third to tenth subequal, longer than second; pronotum transverse, punctate, the prebasal sulcus ending on each side in a short, longitudinal impression; procoxal cavities closed behind; first abdominal sternite shorter than next three together.

Chalcoides nana (Say)   Plate LXXII, No. 14, p. 717
    Oblong-oval, convex; color very variable; bronze or metallic blue or green, shining; underside piceous; legs and antennae reddish yellow, metafemora sometimes darker. Pronotum transverse; apex nearly as wide as base; sides feebly arcuate; disk coarsely, sparsely punctate. Elytra coarsely punctate at base, more finely so apically. Length 2.3–3.5 mm.
    This species is common on foliage of willow and poplar.

Genus IX. *CHAETOCNEMA* Stephens

    Small or very small, oblong-oval forms; front not carinate; antennae one-half as long as body or longer, second segment about two-thirds as long as scape, third to sixth segments slender and slightly longer than second, seventh to eleventh gradually broader and flattened; pronotum transverse, narrower apically, without a prebasal sulcus; elytra seriately punctate; meta-tibiae sinuate apically, dentate before the sinus, apex with a rather long spur; tarsal claws divaricate, dentate at base.

KEY TO SPECIES

1. Sides of pronotum regularly curved from base to apex, the anterior angles not obliquely truncate 2
   Sides of pronotum obliquely truncate at anterior angles and with an angulation in front of middle; without basal marginal line ....d. *confinis*
2. Head punctate, sometimes indistinctly so 3
   Head without punctures; pronotum subopaque, distinctly alutaceous ......
   ....c. *pulicaria*
3. Punctures of head distinct, those of front and clypeus dense and rugulose; surface subopaque ....a. *denticulata*
   Punctures of head small, indistinct; punctures of elytral striae well impressed to apex; pronotum with a distinct basal row of punctures ......b. *minuta*

a. *Chaetocnema denticulata* (Illiger)   Plate LXXIII, No. 2, p. 723
Elongate-oval, robust; piceous, with a brassy-bronze lustre; antennae with fifth or sixth segment orangeish, remaining segments piceous; pro- and mesofemora brown, metafemora bronzed, remainder of legs orangeish. Pronotum transverse, rather coarsely and regularly punctate; sides evenly arcuate; basal marginal line feeble at sides. Elytra coarsely, deeply, but not closely punctate; intervals subdepressed discally, on sides subconvex, very finely, seriately punctate. Length 2.3–2.5 mm.
These beetles may be collected by sweeping grasses in moist meadows.

b. *Chaetocnema minuta* Melsheimer   Plate LXXIII, No. 3, p. 723
Oval, robust, convex; piceous, bronzed, shining; basal four antennal segments brownish yellow; legs sometimes with tibiae and tarsi paler. Pronotum transverse, widest at middle, finely and sparsely punctate; sides evenly arcuate; a row of distinct, coarse punctures at base. Elytra with rows of coarse, closely set punctures; intervals subconvex, impunctate. Length 1.5–2.5 mm.
This beetle is usually found in damp or marshy places.

c. *Chaetocnema pulicaria* Melsheimer   Corn Flea Beetle
                                               Plate LXXIII, No. 4, p. 723
Oblong-oval, convex; black, faintly bronzed with blue or green, shining; antennae with basal three or four segments orangeish, remaining segments piceous; femora piceous, tibiae and tarsi brownish yellow. Pronotum transverse, narrowed apically; sides evenly arcuate; basal marginal line punctate to near middle; disk alutaceous. Elytra with rows of coarse, close-set punctures; intervals feebly convex, minutely and seriately punctate. Length 1.5–2.5 mm.
This beetle is very destructive to corn.

d. *Chaetocnema confinis* Crotch   Sweet-Potato Flea Beetle
                                                     Plate LXXIII, No. 6, p. 723

Oval, robust, convex; piceous, bronzed, slightly shining; legs reddish yellow; metafemora piceous. Pronotum transverse, narrowed apically; disk coarsely, not densely punctate; sides angulate before middle; apical angles obliquely truncate; basal marginal line absent. Elytra with rows of coarse, closely placed, deep punctures; intervals slightly convex, very finely punctate. Length 1.5–1.8 mm.

This beetle does extensive damage to young sweet-potato plants.

Genus X. *SYSTENA* Clark

Small, elongate-oblong, subdepressed species; antennae slender, half as long as body, fourth segment longer than third or fifth, second shorter than third; pronotum not oblique behind basal angles; procoxae feebly separated, the cavities closed behind; metatibiae sulcate and carinate on outer edge; tarsal claws appendiculate.

KEY TO SPECIES

1. Elytra entirely piceous or dark brown, slightly bronzed 2
   Elytra dull yellow or vittate 3
2. Head entirely black ....a. *hudsonias*
   Head dull reddish yellow ....b. *frontalis*
3. Surface shining, the punctation never very coarse; elytra each with a paler
     median stripe ....c. *blanda*
   Surface subopaque, the punctation coarse, close, and deep; elytra without a
     paler median stripe ....d. *marginalis*

a. *Systena hudsonias* (Forster)   Plate LXXII, No. 4, p. 717

Elongate-oval, subdepressed; piceous, shining; antennal segments three to seven brown. Pronotum transverse; disk finely alutaceous and indistinctly punctate. Elytra coarsely, densely punctate, subrugose. Length 3.5–4.7 mm.

The adults are common on the greater ragweed, elder, and other weeds.

b. *Systena frontalis* (Fabricius)   Plate LXXI, No. 14, p. 711

Elongate-oblong, subdepressed; piceous, feebly shining; head reddish or yellowish; legs in part pale. Pronotum transverse, distinctly punctate. Elytra not coarsely but densely punctate, subrugose. Length 3.5–4.8 mm.

This species has been recorded on smartweed, ragweed, and pigweed.

c. *Systena blanda* Melsheimer   Plate LXXII, No. 2, p. 717

Elongate-oblong, subdepressed; reddish brown or yellowish brown, shining; pronotum narrowly margined laterally with piceous; elytra sometimes darker, always with a pale median stripe; body beneath piceous. Pronotum transverse, finely and sparsely punctate. Elytra finely and densely punctate. Length 2.7–4.5 mm.

This beetle occurs on ragweed and horseweed and may be a garden pest.

d. *Systena marginalis* (Illiger)   Plate LXXII, No. 7, p. 717
  Elongate-oblong, subdepressed; pale brownish yellow, feebly shining; pronotum and elytra at sides narrowly piceous. Pronotum transverse; disk coarsely, rather densely punctate. Elytra coarsely and densely punctate. Length 3–4.5 mm.

This species is recorded as having been taken from oak.

Genus XI. *LONGITARSUS* Latreille

Minute, oval or oblong, convex species; elytra with punctures not arranged in rows; tarsi slender; metatarsi with first segment half as long as tibiae and as long as the rest of the segments together; metatibiae grooved and with a long spine at apex.

KEY TO SPECIES

Pale reddish yellow; elytra not shining, punctures very indistinct ....a. *testaceus*
Dark reddish yellow to piceous; elytra shining, punctures coarse and well marked
....b. *melanurus*

a. *Longitarsus testaceus* (Melsheimer)   Plate LXXI, No. 12, p. 711
  Oblong-oval, convex; light reddish yellow, shining, head darker; elytra subopaque; undersurface darker. Pronotum transverse; sides arcuate; apex as wide as base; sparsely and finely punctate on disk. Elytral humeri obtuse; disk very finely and sparsely punctate. Length 2–3 mm.

The adults may be taken by sweeping and sifting.

b. *Longitarsus melanurus* (Melsheimer)   Plate LXXI, No. 15, p. 711
  Oblong-oval, convex; dark reddish yellow to piceous, shining. Pronotum transverse, not narrowed apically; sides feebly arcuate; disk sparsely and rather coarsely punctate. Elytra with distinct humeri; disk coarsely and rather densely punctate. Length 2–2.5 mm.

The adults may be taken by sweeping and beating.

Genus XII. *PHYLLOTRETA* Dejean

Small, elongate-oval, convex forms; frontal tubercles of head reduced to flat areas, not sharply delimited; metatibiae not grooved on outer edge, slightly excavated near apex, spur at middle beneath; first metatarsal segment less than half as long as tibia; procoxal cavities open behind.

PLATE LXXII
Family CHRYSOMELIDAE VII

1. *Disonycha caroliniana* (Fabricius) (p. 707) — Yellow, with black markings; 5–6 mm.

2. *Systena blanda* Melsheimer (p. 714) — Brownish, marked with blackish; 2.7–4.5 mm.

3. *Disonycha pennsylvanica* (Illiger) (p. 707) — Black and yellow; 6–8 mm.

4. *Systena hudsonias* (Forster) (p. 714) — Blackish; 3.5–4.7 mm.

5. *Disonycha xanthomelas* (Dalman) (p. 707) — Black or blue-black; pronotum yellow; 4–6 mm.

6. *D. triangularis* (Say) (p. 706) — Black; pronotum yellow, median black spot sometimes wanting; 4–7 mm.

7. *Systena marginalis* (Illiger) (p. 715) — Brownish yellow; pronotal and elytral sides blackish; 3–5 mm.

8. *Altica chalybea* Illiger (p. 708) — Black, with a blue, green, or purplish reflex; 4–5 mm.

9. *A. ignita* Illiger (p. 708) — Black, reflexed with bronze, green, brassy, or blue; 3–4 mm.

10. *A. carinata* Germar (p. 708) — Coppery black, reflexed with blue or purple; 3.5–5 mm.

11. *A. marevagans* Horn (p. 708) — Metallic bluish green; 4–5 mm.

12. *A. fuscoaenea* Melsheimer (p. 708) — Black, with a brassy or golden bronze; legs and antennae dark brown; 2.5–3.5 mm.

13. *Derocrepis erythropus* (Melsheimer) (p. 712) — Clay-yellow; elytra blue-black; 2.5–3.5 mm.

14. *Chalcoides nana* (Say) (p. 712) — Black, with a brilliant green or purplish bronze; legs and antennae yellowish; 2.3–3.5 mm.

15. *Epitrix cucumeris* (Harris) (p. 709) — Black; legs and antennae dull yellowish; 1.5–2.5 mm.

MM 0 10 20 30 40 50 60 70

PLATE LXXII 717

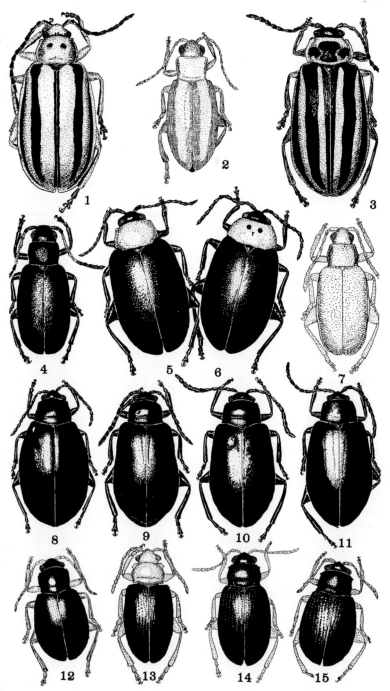

KEY TO SPECIES

1. Fifth segment of antennae longer than either fourth or sixth; male always with
   fifth segment and sometimes the fourth thickened and elongate 2
   Fifth antennal segment never longer than fourth; antennae not different between the sexes, the segments gradually but slightly stouter from the second
   to apex 3
2. Stripes of elytra parallel with suture on basal half ....b. *zimmermanni*
   Stripes of elytra curved inward at base, approaching the scutellum ..c. *striolata*
3. Elytra each with two oval, yellow spots, one humeral, the other subapical
   ....d. *bipustulata*
   Elytra dull yellow, with a common sutural stripe and a narrow marginal line
   black ....a. *armoraciae*

a. *Phyllotreta armoraciae* (Koch)   Plate LXXI, No. 11, p. 711

Elongate-oval, convex; black, shining; elytra dull yellow, with a common
sutural stripe and each with side and apical margins black. Pronotum
transverse, finely and sparsely punctate. Elytra more coarsely and densely
punctate than pronotum. Length 2.6–4 mm.

This is an imported species and does much damage to horse-radish.

b. *Phyllotreta zimmermanni* (Crotch)   Plate LXXI, No. 8, p. 711

Elongate-oval, convex; piceous or black, shining; elytra with a narrow
yellow or orangeish vitta extending from base to apex, sinute on apical
third and not incurved at base but parallel with suture. Fifth segment
of male antennae distinctly longer than third, not as long as third and
fourth combined. Elytra coarsely and rather densely punctate. Length
1.8–3.4 mm.

The adults may be taken by sweeping grasses and by sifting.

c. *Phyllotreta striolata* (Fabricius)   Turnip Flea Beetle
                                             Plate LXXI, No. 9, p. 711

Elongate-oval, convex; piceous, shining; elytra each with a narrow,
yellow stripe extending from base to apex, curved at base and apex, a
broad branch extending laterally behind humerus. Fifth segment of male
antennae as long as the third and fourth together and much more robust
than fourth. Pronotum transverse, coarsely and rather sparsely punctate.
Elytra more coarsely and densely punctate than pronotum. Length 1.5–2.5
mm.

These beetles are found particularly on plants of the cabbage family;
they often damage the flowers of alpine rock cress.

d. *Phyllotreta bipustulata* (Fabricius)   Plate LXXI, No. 10, p. 711

Elongate-oval, convex; piceous, shining; elytra each with two yellowish
or orange spots, one at base, extending behind humerus, and an oval one
near apex. Pronotum transverse, finely and sparsely punctate. Elytra
coarsely and rather densely punctate. Length 1.6–2.5 mm.

These beetles may be taken by sweeping and sifting.

Genus XIII. *DIBOLIA* Latreille

Very small, elongate-oval beetles; head retracted to eyes into prothorax; front carinate and with distinct tubercles; pronotum without distinct impressions, occasionally with indistinct, transverse furrows or shallow pits before base; elytra with punctures in regular rows or striae; metafemora strongly dilated; metatibial spurs very large and broad, deeply emarginate; last metatarsal segment not swollen; first metatarsal segment one-third length of tibia.

Dibolia borealis Chevrolat   Plate LXXIII, No. 9, p. 723
Oval, slightly oblong, convex; piceous, cupreous-bronzed, or bluish, sometimes green; antennae and legs reddish yellow, metafemora and undersurface blackish. Pronotum twice as wide at base as long, but little wider than long at apex, sides curved; disk closely punctate, fine and coarse punctures intermingled. Sides of elytra continuous with those of pronotum, umbones prominent; disk with rows of fine, close-set punctures, the third and fourth rows confused; intervals broad and flattened, the second, fourth, and sixth with coarser punctures than others. Length 2.5–3.5 mm.

In winter the adults hibernate under loose bark of sycamores. The larvae are leaf-miners in plantain leaves.

Genus XIV. *PSYLLIODES* Latreille

Small, elongate-oval, convex beetles; head inserted to eyes in prothorax; front without carinae or distinct tubercles; antennae with only ten segments; pronotum transverse, narrowed anteriorly, base arcuate, with a distinct marginal line; elytra with rows of punctures; metatarsi slender, first segment more than half length of tibiae; claws simple.

Psylliodes punctulata Melsheimer   Hop Flea Beetle
                                                    Plate LXXIII, No. 10, p. 723
Elongate-oval, convex; piceous, bronzed, sometimes brassy or greenish, shining. Pronotum slightly transverse, alutaceous, coarsely but not densely punctate; anterior angles obliquely truncate; basal marginal line distinct. Elytra with rows of punctures somewhat irregular basally, punctures coarse, in deep striae; intervals slightly convex, finely and seriately punctate. Length 2–2.7 mm.

This beetle frequents rhubarb, hops, and garden weeds.

Subfamily HISPINAE

KEY TO GENERA

Genus I. *ANOPLITIS* Chapuis

Elongate-oblong, depressed forms, widened behind; antennae eleven-segmented; eyes prominent; elytra each with three costae and with eight rows of punctures; mesotibiae straight or nearly so.

Anoplitis inaequalis Weber   Plate LXXIII, No. 13, p. 723

Elongate-oblong, wider behind, depressed; varying in color from brownish red to piceous; when brownish red, the elytra have a few irregular, black marks which are margined posteriorly with whitish; when piceous, the elytra have a few scattered, red streaks; legs pale yellowish, antennae black. Vertex with a median sulcus. Pronotum slightly transverse, coarsely and deeply punctate; sides feebly arcuate; anterior angles sometimes slightly dentate. Elytra slightly widened behind, margins and apex serrulate, each with three entire, acute costae and with eight rows of punctures. Length 3.5–4.5 mm.

The adults are found on foliage of legumes, and the larvae are leaf-miners on the same plants.

Genus II. *CHALEPUS* Thunberg

Small, wedge-shaped, depressed beetles; clypeus black, rarely with a yellow margin, surface densely and finely punctate or coarsely granulate-punctate; antennae as long as head and pronotum, eleven-segmented, all segments distinct; elytra each with four costae, the first sutural; tibiae straight.

KEY TO SPECIES

Elytra black, with red or yellowish humeri; undersurface black; pronotum red, with a dark discal marking ....a. *scapularis*
Elytra mostly yellow or orange-red, with a black sutural stripe which gradually broadens from base to apex ....*b. dorsalis*

a. *Chalepus scapularis* (Olivier)   Plate LXXIV, No. 1, p. 729
    Wedge-shaped, depressed; black; a broad stripe on each side of pronotum, humeral angles of elytra, and sometimes base of femora dull red or yellowish. Antennae short and projecting forward. Pronotum widest at base, sides slightly angulate at middle; disk depressed at base, surface deeply, coarsely punctate. Elytral humeri prominent; each elytron with four costae, the third and fourth separated by four rows of coarse, deep punctures; margins and apex serrulate. Length 5–7.5 mm.
    The adults are found on honey locust particularly.

b. *Chalepus dorsalis* Thunberg   Plate LXXIV, No. 4, p. 729
    Wedge-shaped, rather broad, depressed; orange-red; head, underparts, and sutural stripe black. Antennae short, projecting forward. Pronotum wider at base, sides slightly arcuate; disk coarsely and deeply punctate, slightly depressed at base. Elytral humeri only slightly prominent; four costae on each elytron, the first and second separated by four rows of coarse, deep punctures; margins and apex serrulate. Length 6–6.5 mm.
    The adults are common on black and honey locust and on oak.

Genus III. *BALIOSUS* Weise

Small, wedge-shaped, depressed; clypeus yellow, rarely black, surface smooth or punctate; antennae as long as head and pronotum, eleven-segmented, sometimes apparently eight- or nine-segmented; elytra with four costae and ten or ten and one-half rows of punctures; tibiae straight.

Baliosus ruber (Weber)   Plate LXXIII, No. 14, p. 723
    Wedge-shaped, broad, depressed; reddish yellow; elytra with indistinct deep-red markings along lateral edges and apical half; undersurface varying from deep red to piceous; legs reddish yellow. Antennae short, projected forward. Pronotum widened basally, sides almost straight; disk coarsely and deeply punctate, with a slight depression at base. Elytra with humeri prominent; apex much broader; margins flattened and serrate; disk with four costae, third united with an oblique, shorter one from humerus at basal third, the fourth united with a very short, oblique one almost at apex; four rows of coarse, deep punctures between third and fourth costae. Length 4.5–7 mm.
    The adults are found on locust, oak, soft maple, and basswood.

PLATE LXXIII
Family CHRYSOMELIDAE VIII

1. *Orthaltica copalina* (Fabricius) (p. 709)

Reddish brown to blackish; legs and antennae orange-brown; 2–3 mm.

2. *Chaetocnema denticulata* (Illiger) (p. 713)

Blackish, with a brassy sheen; 2.3–2.5 mm.

3. *C. minuta* Melsheimer (p. 713)

Blackish, bronzed; 1.5–2.5 mm.

4. *C. pulicaria* Melsheimer (p. 713)

Black; reflexed with blue or green; 1.5–2.5 mm.

5. *Blepharida rhois* (Forster) (p. 702)

Dull yellowish or orange; elytral brown markings variable; 5–7 mm.

6. *Chaetocnema confinis* Crotch (p. 714)

Blackish; legs yellowish; 1.5–1.8 mm.

7. *Oedionychis thoracica* (Fabricius) (p. 703)

Brownish yellow and black; elytra deep blue; 5–8 mm.

8. *O. vians* (Illiger) (p. 703)

Blackish, sometimes tinged with green or purple; pronotal margins dull yellow; 4–7 mm.

9. *Dibolia borealis* Chevrolat (p. 719)

Blackish, with blue or coppery sheen; legs mostly yellowish; 2.5–3.5 mm.

10. *Psylliodes punctulata* Melsheimer (p. 719)

Blackish, with a brassy, greenish, or bronze reflex; 2–2.7 mm.

11. *Oedionychis quercata* (Fabricius) (p. 706)

Dull tan; elytra largely dark brown or blackish; 3.5–4.5 mm.

12. *O. miniata* (Fabricius) (p. 703)

Dark tan; elytra deep maroon, black vittae often absent; 4–7 mm.

13. *Anoplitis inaequalis* Weber (p. 720)

Dull reddish, black markings variable; 3.5–4.5 mm.

14. *Baliosis ruber* (Weber) (p. 721)

Yellowish to reddish; black elytral markings sometimes reduced; 4.5–7 mm.

15. *Oedionychis circumdata* (Randall) (p. 706)

Dull orange-brown; markings black, variable; 3.5–5.5 mm.

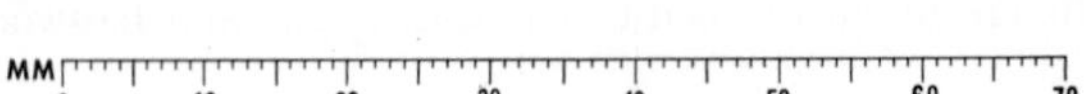

MM | 0 | 10 | 20 | 30 | 40 | 50 | 60 | 70

PLATE LXXIII   723

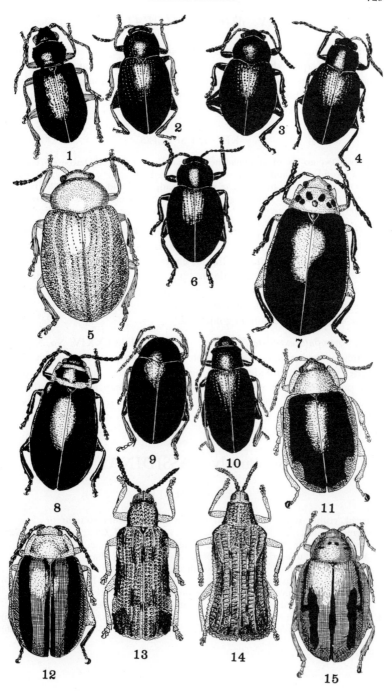

Genus IV. *MICRORHOPALA* Dejean

Small, elongate-oval, rather subdepressed species; antennae filiform or thickened at apex, the last segments so closely united that the number of segments appears to be from three to eight; elytra elongate-oval, slightly convex, costae absent or not present for entire length, and with eight rows of punctures; tibiae straight.

KEY TO SPECIES

Segments two to six of antennae nearly smooth and without hairs; elytra black, with second costa and a narrow line at side red ....a. *vittata*
Segments three to six of antennae roughly sculptured and somewhat hairy; body above entirely dark blue or greenish; punctures of outer rows of elytra much larger and of more irregular size than those of inner rows ....b. *excavata*

a. *Microrhopala vittata* (Fabricius)   Plate LXXIV, No. 6, p. 729
Oblong-oval, subdepressed; black or bluish black; head, pronotum, second costa, a narrow marginal line of elytra, and often base of femora red. Pronotum almost twice as wide as long, coarsely and sparsely punctate. Elytra with eight rows of oblong punctures arranged in pairs, intervals between slightly elevated. Length 5–7 mm.
The adults are common on goldenrod.

b. *Microrhopala excavata* (Olivier)   Plate LXXIV, No. 3, p. 729
Elongate-oval, subdepressed; bluish black, violaceous, or greenish. Front sulcate. Pronotum broader than long, widest at base, coarsely and irregularly punctate. Elytra with eight rows of coarse, deep punctures, those of the two inner rows smaller and less deep; intervals sometimes slightly elevated; margins with minute, distant teeth. Length 4–5.5 mm.

Subfamily CASSIDINAE

KEY TO GENERA

1. Head visible from above; front margin on pronotum straight or
   emarginate ....I. *Chelymorpha* (p. 725)
   Head covered by the arcuate front margin of pronotum 2
2. A groove on underside of prothorax, margined by a sharp carina, receiving antennal segments two, three, and four; third antennal segment twice as long as second ....II. *Deloyala* (p. 725)
   No antennal groove on underside of prothorax; segments free when at rest; third antennal segment but little longer than second 3
3. Elytra gibbous (anterior to middle) ....III. *Plagiometriona* (p. 726)
   Elytra smooth, evenly convex ....IV. *Metriona* (p. 726)

Genus I. *CHELYMORPHA* Chevrolat

Of medium size, convex; margins of pronotum and elytra narrow, the pronotal margin bisinuate at base and emarginate at apex, leaving the head partly visible; elytra and pronotum spotted; prosternum grooved and prolonged behind procoxae, the apex fitting into a notch in mesosternum (Fig. 493).

Chelymorpha cassidea Fabricius   The Milkweed Tortoise Beetle
                                          Plate LXXIV, No. 5, p. 729

Oblong-oval, convex; brick-red or yellow; pronotum with four black dots in a transverse row and usually two others behind them; elytra with six dots and a common sutural one near the scutellum black. Pronotum minutely alutaceous; disk with coarse and fine punctures intermingled, sparsely scattered over surface. Elytra minutely alutaceous, coarsely and rather densely, irregularly punctate. Length 8–11.5 mm.

The adults and larvae are common on milkweed and wild potato.

Genus II. *DELOYALA* Chevrolat

Rather small, broadly oval, convex species; head covered by the arcuate front margin of the pronotum; prothorax on underside with a groove, margined by a sharp carina, receiving antennal segments two, three, and four; third antennal segment but little longer than second; elytra not vittate; claws angularly dilated at base (Fig. 494).

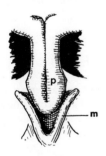

Fig. 493

Fig. 494

Fig. 493. Prosternal process (*p*) of *Chelymorpha. m,* mesosternum.
Fig. 494. A single tarsal claw of *Deloyala.*

Deloyala guttata (Olivier) The Mottled Tortoise Beetle
Plate LXXIV, No. 7, p. 729

Broadly oval; light yellow; base of pronotum sometimes with a black spot enclosing two small, pale ones; disk of elytra black, with irregular yellow spots, margins yellow, except at humeri, suture, and apex; undersurface black, with margins yellow; antennae yellow, the last two segments dusky. Explanate margins of pronotum and elytra broad, thin, and almost transparent. Elytra minutely alutaceous and with very irregular rows of deep, coarse, distant punctures. Length 5–6 mm.

This species is found on foliage, especially that of the morning-glory family.

Genus III. *PLAGIOMETRIONA* Spaeth

Small, broadly convex; prothorax without antennal groove on underside; third antennal segment but little longer than second; head covered by the arcuate front margin of pronotum; elytra gibbous, rugose, and irregularly reticulate; claws angularly dilated at base.

Plagiometriona clavata (Fabricius) Plate LXXIV, No. 8, p. 729

Broadly oval, convex; brilliant brassy or greenish gold in life, dull reddish yellow after death; undersurface and last four segments of antennae black. Margin of pronotum and elytra broadly explanate, very thin, translucent except at humeri and apical fourth of suture. Elytra with many conical tubercles, the largest on suture before middle, reticulately costate and with coarse, shallow punctures in depressions between costae. Length 6.5–7.5 mm.

The adults are found on sycamore, linden, oak, and morning-glory foliage.

Genus IV. *METRIONA* Weise

Small, broadly convex species; prothorax without antennal groove beneath; third antennal segment but little longer than second; head covered by the arcuate front margin of pronotum; elytra smooth, evenly convex; claws angularly dilated at base.

KEY TO SPECIES

Elytra yellow, with suture and two stripes on each black or dark brown ....
....a. *bivittata*
Elytra without markings ....b. *bicolor*

a. *Metriona bivittata* (Say)   Plate LXXIV, No. 9, p. 729

Oval, convex; pronotum pale yellow, with a large, triangular, brownish-red spot at base; elytra pale yellow, each with suture and two discal stripes that are connected at apex black or dark brown; undersurface and legs piceous. Pronotum more widely margined than elytra; disk coarsely, shallowly, sparsely punctate. Elytra with rows of coarse, deep punctures, the submarginal row of punctures black. Length 4.5–6 mm.

The adults are common on members of the morning-glory family.

b. *Metriona bicolor* (Fabricius)   Goldbug; Golden Tortoise Beetle
                                                   Plate LXXIV, No. 2, p. 729

Broadly oval, convex; above brilliant brassy or greenish gold in life, dull reddish yellow after death; undersurface and last four segments of antennae black. Margins of pronotum and elytra rather broadly explanate. Pronotum very finely, sparsely punctate. Elytra each with a small, rounded, depressed space at basal third and a large, oblong one (sometimes interrupted at middle) near margin; disk with small, shallow punctures arranged in regular rows. Length 5–6 mm.

The adults and larvae are found on morning-glories and roses.

PLATE LXXIV
Family CHRYSOMELIDAE IX

1. *Chalepus scapularis* (Olivier) (p. 721)

Black; pronotal disk in part and elytral humeri red or yellow; 5–7.5 mm.

2. *Metriona bicolor* (Fabricius) (p. 727)

Golden while alive, dull reddish yellow after death; 5–6 mm.

3. *Microrhopala excavata* (Olivier) (p. 724)

Black, often tinged with blue, green, or violet; 4–5.5 mm.

4. *Chalepus dorsalis* Thunberg (p. 721)

Black; pronotum and much of elytra orangeish; 6–6.5 mm.

5. *Chelymorpha cassidea* Fabricius (p. 725)

Reddish, with black spots which are variable; 8–12 mm.

6. *Microrhopala vittata* (Fabricius) (p. 724)

Blackish and reddish; 5–7 mm.

7. *Deloyala guttata* (Olivier) (p. 726)

Yellowish, with black or brown markings; side margins pale; 5–6 mm.

8. *Plagiometriona clavata* (Fabricius) (p. 726)

Greenish gold while alive, becoming yellowish after death; 6.5–7.5 mm.

9. *Metriona bivittata* (Say) (p. 727)

Yellowish and black; pronotum largely brown; 4.5–6 mm.

MM | 0 | 10 | 20 | 30 | 40 | 50 | 60 | 70

PLATE LXXIV 729

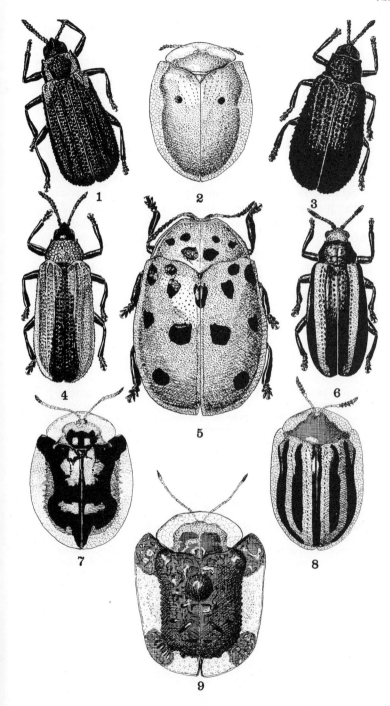

Family MYLABRIDAE

Pea and Bean Weevils

Small, chunky, robust beetles; head free, usually deflexed, mentum transverse, distinctly pedunculate, more or less emarginate anteriorly; antennae rather short, eleven-segmented, strongly serrate or pectinate, inserted before eyes on sides of front; eyes large, more or less emarginate anteriorly; pronotum margined basally, sometimes apically and laterally; elytra entire or truncate, always leaving the pygidium exposed; abdomen with five sternites; legs moderately long, procoxae oval, moderately prominent, metacoxae transverse, narrowly separated, metafemora usually dilated, often dentate; tarsi with first segment elongated, third deeply bilobed, fourth segment concealed in third and rigidly attached to fifth; claws broadly dentate basally.

The larvae of these beetles live in seeds of legumes, especially those of peas and beans, and are frequently pests, occurring in large numbers in stored leguminous seeds.

KEY TO GENERA

1. Metacoxae twice as broad as femora; metatibiae with two movable spurs (Fig. 495) ....V. *Amblycerus*   (p. 734)
   Metacoxae not twice as broad as femora; metatibiae with fixed spines or teeth at apex or unarmed 2
2. Pronotum without a median tooth on lateral margin; front of head carinate or with a glabrous line or area 3
   Pronotum emarginate on lateral margin, with a single tooth near middle anterior to emargination (Fig. 496); front of head without carina or glabrous line ....I. *Mylabris*   (p. 732)
3. Metafemora with a strong tooth or spine near apex, beneath, within, and beyond this one or more denticles (Fig. 497) 4
   Metafemora with a strong, obliquely truncate spine, often tridenticulate on truncation ....II. *Althaeus*   (p. 732)
4. Metafemora strongly thickened, broader than the coxae, outer edge crenulate or serrulate ....III. *Gibbobruchus*   (p. 733)
   Metafemora with outer margin not crenulate or serrulate, not broader than coxae ....IV. *Acanthoscelides*   (p. 733)

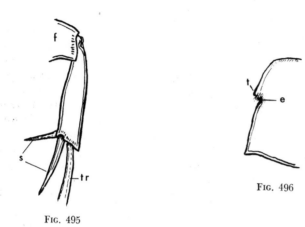

Fig. 495

Fig. 496

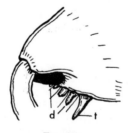

Fig. 497

Fig. 495. Metatibia of *Amblycerus*. *f*, metafemur; *s*, movable spurs; *tr*, portion of first tarsal segment.

Fig. 496. Left side of pronotum of *Mylabris*. *e*, emargination; *t*, tooth.

Fig. 497. Apex of metafemur of *Gibbobruchus*, viewed obliquely from beneath. *d*, denticles; *t*, tooth.

Genus I. *MYLABRIS* Geoffroy

Moderately small, ovate, subdepressed; pronotum with disk not surrounded by an impressed marginal line, laterally emarginate, and with a single tooth near middle before the emargination; metafemora bicarinate beneath, outer carina prominently armed near apex with a strong, acute tooth; male with specialized spines or processes at apex of mesotibiae.

Mylabris pisorum (Linné)　　　　　　　The Pea Weevil
　　　　　　　　　　　　　　　　　　Plate LXXV, No. 6, p. 737

Broadly ovate, robust, subdepressed; black, feebly shining, densely clothed above with reddish-brown and whitish pubescence; pronotum with a more or less triangular, whitish area medially at base; elytra varied with yellowish, grayish, and whitish pubescence, and with a broken band of the last color behind middle; pygidium with gray pubescence, and two oval, black maculae apically; antennae and legs black, the first three antennal segments and protibiae and tarsi reddish; body underneath black, sparsely clothed with gray pubescence. Pronotum transverse, narrowed apically, the sides emarginate and dentate; disk coarsely and densely punctate. Elytra slightly longer than broad, striate, the striae finely punctate. Length 4–5 mm.

This species may be found throughout the year, but especially in the spring, when the eggs are deposited on the very young pods of peas. After hatching, the larvae bore through the pods and enter the growing peas, where they spend the rest of the immature stages.

Genus II. *ALTHAEUS* Bridwell

Small, ovate, subconvex; pronotum not carinate laterally and without an impressed marginal line surrounding disk; sides unarmed, arcuate, not emarginate; metafemur slightly sulcate beneath, not at all carinate on either margin, the inner margin with a robust, obliquely truncate spine, the truncation often with three denticles; male without spines, teeth, or lamellae at apex of mesotibia.

Althaeus hibisci (Olivier)　　　　　　Plate LXXV, No. 2, p. 737

Broadly ovate, robust, subconvex; black, slightly shining; rather sparsely covered with grayish-yellow pubescence; elytra with many irregular, transverse, glabrous areas; antennae reddish brown, paler on basal and apical segments; legs rusty red, metafemora black, reddish at apex. Pronotum twice as broad at base as long, strongly tapering apically, sides unarmed, rounded; disk sparsely punctate. Elytra each twice as long as broad; disk with punctate striae; intervals flattened, sprinkled with irregular-sized punctures. Length 2–3 mm.

The adults may be found in seeds, especially those of the rose mallow (*Hibiscus*), throughout the year, but they are most abundant on flowers of redbud, dogwood, and other flowering plants during late spring and early summer.

Genus III. *GIBBOBRUCHUS* Pic

Small, ovate; head not elongate, antennal sockets nearly contiguous to the mandibles; pronotum strongly narrowed anteriorly, not carinate laterally, sides rounded, unarmed, strongly expanding from apex to the acute posterior angles, disk not outlined with a marginal impressed line, medially with a distinct longitudinal ridge which bears a feeble, longitudinal sulcus; metafemora robust, one-half as wide as long, the lower surface sulcate, finely bicarinate, the posterior carina with a strong tooth near apical third, followed by four acute denticles, anterior carina serrulate on apical two-thirds.

Gibbobruchus mimus (Say)   Plate LXXV, No. 1, p. 737

Broadly oblong-ovate, robust; dull reddish brown, variegated with gray, black, and white pubescence; pronotum with median ridge fuscous each side, this dark area divided by a small, white macula; elytra with a common, heart-shaped, fuscous area behind the scutellum and with numerous small, blackish, oblong maculae sprinkled over disk, each macula tipped with white basally; antennae and legs pale brownish, metafemora and metatibiae fuscous-annulate; pygidium in male entirely whitish-pubescent, in female with a large, oval, shining, denuded area. Pronotum somewhat campanuliform, much narrower at apex than at base; disk with a sulcate, median, longitudinal ridge, each side near base with a tubercle. Elytra each nearly as broad as long; disk with punctate striae; intervals flat, minutely punctate. Length 2.5–3.5 mm.

The adults are especially abundant on wild flowers in late spring and early summer.

Genus IV. *ACANTHOSCELIDES* Schilsky

Small, oblong-ovate; pronotum conical, not carinate laterally, sides unarmed, either straight or arcuate, disk not enclosed by an impressed marginal line, surface plane; metafemora feebly sulcate beneath, longitudinally bicarinate, posterior carina with a strong tooth, distad of which are usually one or two, but sometimes as many as four, denticles; abdomen with several middle sternites abbreviated; pygidium oblique or subvertical.

KEY TO SPECIES

All legs black ....b. *calvus*
Legs reddish brown, metafemora blackish beneath ....a. *obtectus*

a. *Acanthoscelides obtectus* (Say)   The Bean Weevil
                                                   Plate LXXV, No. 4, p. 737

Oblong-ovate, rather robust; black or nearly so, with dark-gray–tawny pubescence; elytra with short, transverse bands of brownish pubescence; abdomen dull reddish brown; antennae black, except for the rusty-red apical and basal segments; legs reddish brown, metafemora piceous beneath. Pronotum one-third wider at base than long, sides arcuate, strongly narrowed apically; base lobed medially; disk coarsely, sparsely punctate. Elytra each about twice as long as wide; disk with punctate striae; intervals flat, minutely, densely punctate. Length 2.5–4 mm.

This species may be found throughout the year in dried beans. It is a native of North America and has now become a pest throughout the world.

b. *Acanthoscelides calvus* (Horn)   Plate LXXV, No. 3, p. 737

Oblong-ovate, moderately robust; entirely black, very sparsely covered with grayish pubescence. Antennae as long as head and pronotum together, more or less serrate. Pronotum somewhat broader at base than long, much narrower at apex, sides moderately arcuate, unarmed; disk finely, rugosely punctate. Elytra each more than twice as long as wide, shining; disk with fine, indistinctly punctate striae, intervals flat, minutely punctate. Length 2–2.5 mm.

The adults are abundant on flowers, especially near moist places.

Genus V. *AMBLYCERUS* Thunberg

Medium-sized, oblong-oval; eyes very feebly emarginate anteriorly; pronotal disk without surrounding marginal impressed line; prosternal process separating procoxae to apex; metatibiae compressed, cylindrical, and armed with two unequal, jointed spurs, inner one short and placed at a right angle to tibia (Fig. 495).

Amblycerus robiniae (Fabricius)   Plate LXXV, No. 5, p. 737

Oblong-oval, feebly convex; dull reddish brown, clothed with grayish pubescence; pronotum sometimes partly piceous; elytra with small, black maculae arranged in five irregular, transverse rows. Pronotum nearly semicircular; apical margin truncate, basal lobe truncate, sides bisinuate; surface sparsely, rather coarsely punctate, with dense and fine punctures intermixed. Elytra widest at middle; apices each broadly rounded; surface with punctate striae, intervals feebly convex, densely, minutely punctate. Length 7–7.5 mm.

The adults may be found beneath the bark or on the foliage of black or honey locust; the larvae live in the seeds of the same trees.

PLATE LXXV

Family MYLABRIDAE

1. *Gibbobruchus mimus* (Say) (p. 733)

Reddish brown, with white and blackish markings; 2.5–3.5 mm.

2. *Althaeus hibisci* (Olivier) (p. 732)

Black, with yellowish-white pubescence; 2–3 mm.

3. *Acanthoscelides calvus* (Horn) (p. 734)

Black, with whitish pubescence; 2–2.5 mm.

4. *A. obtectus* (Say) (p. 734)

Pale-brownish-pubescent, marked with dark brown; 2.5–4 mm.

5. *Amblycerus robiniae* (Fabricius) (p. 734)

Dark reddish brown, with brownish pubescence, marked indistinctly with black and white; 7–7.5 mm.

6. *Mylabris pisorum* (Linné) (p. 732)

Black, covered with brown and white pubescence; 4–5 mm.

Family BRENTIDAE

7. *Arrhenodes minutus* (Drury) (p. 738)

Mahogany-brown and black, with orange markings; the female has a slender beak and is less robust; 7–17 mm.

Family ANTHRIBIDAE

8. *Euparius marmoreus* (Olivier) (p. 742)

Ashy- and brown-pubescent, mottled with black and white; 3.5–8.5 mm.

9. *Brachytarsus sticticus* Boheman (p. 742)

Blackish-, ashy-, and white-pubescent; 2.5–3 mm.

10. *Eurymycter fasciatus* (Olivier) (p. 741)

Deep slate-gray, with white and brown markings; 6.5–9.5 mm.

Family BELIDAE

11. *Ithycerus noveboracensis* (Forster) (p. 743)

Ashy-pubescent, marked with white and black; 12–18 mm.

Family CURCULIONIDAE I

12, 13. *Eugnamptus collaris* (Fabricius) (p. 746)

Very variable, ranging from tan, with black elytra, to nearly entirely black; 3.5–5 mm.

MM 0 10 20 30 40 50 60 70

PLATE LXXV 737

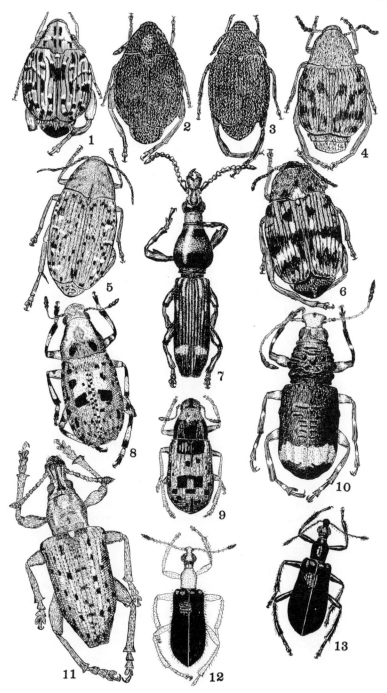

Family BRENTIDAE

The Primitive Weevils

Elongate, slender, small to moderate-sized beetles; mouthparts usually differing greatly between sexes; antennae ten- or eleven-segmented, not geniculate, and without a distinct club, the basal segment more robust and slightly longer than the second; beak straight; eyes small, rounded, not granulate; labrum not present; pronotum strongly elongate, without post-ocular lobes, truncate at apex, pedunculate at base; elytra elongate, covering pygidium, with a fold close to the margin on inner surface; prosternum long before coxae; mesosternum long and metasternum very long; five ventral abdominal segments, first and second long, third and fourth short, fifth longer, flat and rounded posteriorly; legs robust, femora clavate; tarsi with spongy pubescence ventrally, third segment bilobed.

The beak of the female (Fig. 499) in the North American species is long and slender, with pincer-shaped mandibles which enable her to bore deep holes in dead or decaying trees in which to lay the eggs. The males stand guard and assist the females in extracting the beaks that occasionally become stuck in the wood.

Genus *ARRHENODES* Schönherr

Small to moderate-sized beetles; head broad, posterior angles obsolete; mouthparts concealed by mentum; in male mandibles arcuate, flattened, acuminate, dentate on inner edge, in female small, pincer-shaped; meso-coxae rounded, distinctly separated; femora slender; protibiae sinuate and with an oblique groove on inner side, at apex with a hook on outer side and a spine on inner side; tarsal claws large, simple, and divergent.

Arrhenodes minutus (Drury) Plate LXXV, No. 7, p. 737

Elongate, slender, subcylindrical; dark reddish brown to piceous, elytra with narrow, elongate, yellowish spots, these often united to form two or three nearly complete, transverse fasciae. Beak narrow, much longer than head in female, broad and only as long as head in male. Pronotum elongate, widest behind middle, constricted at base; sides arcuate from base to middle, thence strongly converging to apex; disk shining, minutely, sparsely punctate. Elytral striae deep, lateral ones coarsely punctate; intervals smooth, convex. First two ventral abdominal segments of male deeply grooved medially, in female feebly impressed. Length 7.2–17 mm.

These beetles occur beneath bark of recently felled or dying oak, poplar, or beech.

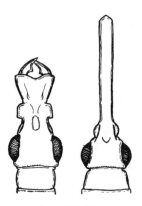

Figs. 498–499

Figs. 498–499. Head and beak of male (498) and female (499) of *Arrhenodes minutus*.

Family ANTHRIBIDAE

The Fungus Weevils

This small family of beetles is characterized by having the beak broad and flat, sometimes very short, not separated from the front by a transverse impression; antennae either long and filiform or short and with a three-segmented club; palpi visible, the labial ones three-segmented, the maxillary four-segmented; elytra together rounded at apex, nearly covering pygidium, and each with ten longitudinal striae; procoxae globose, narrowly separated, metacoxae transverse; abdomen with five visible sternites, which are nearly equal; legs slender; tibiae truncate apically, without spurs or hooks; tarsi four-segmented, second segment triangular and partially covering third, which is bilobed (Fig. 500), fourth segment slender; claws divergent, either simple or dentate.

Because some of the members of this family have long antennae, they resemble some of the Cerambycidae; but the form of the tarsi and the presence of an elevated transverse ridge near or at the base of the pronotum serve to distinguish this group. The genera are usually separable by the modifications of the basal elevated ridge of the pronotum.

Fungi, dead wood, and smut are usually the breeding places of these beetles, and the adults may be found beneath old bark or on dead twigs.

KEY TO TRIBES

Transverse ridge of pronotum anterior to base (Fig. 501) ... TROPIDERINI   (p. 740)
Transverse ridge of pronotum at base, the surface behind it perpendicular .... ANTHRIBINI   (p. 741)

Tribe TROPIDERINI

Genus *EURYMYCTER* LeConte

Small, oblong, robust beetles; surface coarsely sculptured; beak narrower than head, strongly dilated at apex, dorsally with three ridges and four broad grooves; eyes rounded; antennal foveae deep, visible only from above; antennae half as long as body, first and second segments more

740

robust, nearly equal in length, third to eighth slender, longer, and shining, ninth to eleventh forming a loose club; first and fifth ventral abdominal segments longer than remainder.

Eurymycter fasciatus (Olivier)   Plate LXXV, No. 10, p. 737

Oblong; dark brown to fuscous; a large spot of white pubescence on beak and a broad, transverse, white fascia behind middle on elytra. Pronotum with a transverse, arcuate impression before middle, surface roughly sculptured; antebasal ridge about one-fifth from base, laterally bent at an obtuse angle, forming a lateral protuberance. Elytra wider than pronotum; disk with numerous short rugosities and with rows of large, distant punctures. Length 6.5–9.5 mm.

This species may be found on dead twigs and on fungus growing on dead beech.

Tribe ANTHRIBINI

KEY TO GENERA

Genus I. *EUPARIUS* Schönherr

Small, oblong species; beak flat, as long as head; eyes oval, prominent; antennae short, attaining base of elytra in both sexes, first and second

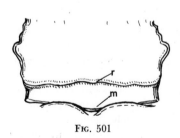

Fig. 500.   Fig. 501.   Fig. 502.

Fig. 500. Portion of tarsus of *Eurymycter,* with second segment (2) partially enclosing the third.
Fig. 501. Basal portion of pronotum of *Eurymycter,* the basal ridge (*r*) placed some distance from the basal margin (*m*).
Fig. 502. Head of *Ithycerus* from above.

segments robust, subequal, third slender, twice as long as second, fourth to eighth gradually shorter, ninth to eleventh larger, forming a loose, compressed club; pronotum with a lateral carina confined to basal half, base feebly bisinuate, with its lower margin distinct, making the transverse ridge appear to be not strictly basal.

Euparius marmoreus (Olivier)   Plate LXXV, No. 8, p. 737

Elongate-oblong, robust; fuscous, densely clothed with pale-brown and grayish-yellow pubescence, the latter covering beak, apical third of pronotum, and forming a large, common, sutural spot near middle of elytra, which is bordered posteriorly with black; remainder of surface with the two colors of pubescence intermixed; legs annulate with gray and black or dark brown. Pronotum strongly narrowed apically, sides concave anteriorly; disk with a broad, shallow, median groove on basal half in which is a low, broad carina; remainder of surface coarsely, densely punctate. Elytra not wider than pronotum; disk with rows of coarse, deep, close-set punctures; alternate intervals slightly more elevated. Length 3.5–8.5 mm.

Genus II. *BRACHYTARSUS* Schönherr

Short, oblong-oval species; antennae as long as head and pronotum, first and second segments robust, second slightly longer, third to eighth shorter, ninth to eleventh forming an oval, compressed club; eyes emarginate anteriorly; pronotum with anterior margin rounded, partially concealing the head; basal ridge of pronotum bent abruptly forward at hind angles and continued along sides for a short distance; elytral intervals equal and even; first tarsal segment scarcely longer than second, second triangular and emarginate, third deeply bilobed, as wide as second, claws dentate near apex.

Brachytarsus sticticus Boheman   Plate LXXV, No. 9, p. 737

Oblong-oval, rather slender; brown, densely clothed with short, dark-brown and grayish-yellow pubescence; pronotum varied with fuscous-brown that does not extend on anterior margin; elytra with numerous small, rounded maculae and two larger, dark-brown ones; antennae pale reddish brown, the three apical segments fuscous; legs pale reddish, femora fuscous medially. Pronotum convex, finely, densely punctate; basal ridge extending along sides nearly to middle. Elytral striae fine, obsoletely punctate. Length 2.5–3 mm.

This species has been found breeding in smut of corn and wheat; the adults may be taken by sweeping low herbs and are also found on flowers of the buttonbush.

Family BELIDAE

The New York Weevil

This family is represented by a single large species, which may be distinguished from related families by the following characters: mandibles emarginate at apex, with an inferior cusp; mentum large, quadrate; beak half as long as head (Fig. 502); eyes small, rounded; antennae straight, first and second segments subequal, third distinctly longer than second, fourth to eighth gradually shorter and more robust, club small, oval, acuminate; ventral abdominal segments nearly equal in length, sutures straight; procoxae contiguous, metacoxae narrowly separated; tibiae truncate apically; tarsi broad, pubescent beneath, third segment deeply bilobed; claws near middle with a small, acute tooth.

Genus *ITHYCERUS* Schönherr

This genus is sufficiently characterized by the preceding family description.

Ithycerus noveboracensis (Forster)   Plate LXXV, No. 11, p. 737

Elongate-oblong, robust; black, shining; sparsely ashy-gray and pale-brown-pubescent, the hairs prostrate, the ashy-gray pubescence condensed to form a narrow median and two wider lateral vittae on pronotum and a narrow stripe on each alternate interval of elytra, these each bearing three or four small, rounded tufts of black hairs; scutellum grayish white. Head and beak slightly longer than pronotum; beak carinate medially, surface densely, rugosely punctate. Pronotum about as wide as long; apex and base truncate; sides feebly arcuate; disk densely, rugosely punctate. Elytral base nearly twice the width of pronotum; sides parallel to apical quarter, then strongly converging to apices, which are separately, obtusely rounded; disk indistinctly striate, the striae coarsely punctate; intervals feebly convex, rugose. Pygidium deeply grooved in both sexes, projecting slightly beyond apices of elytra. Length 12–18 mm.

This species has been taken from oak, hickory, and beech; it breeds in twigs of bur oak and pignut hickory. It also damages fruit trees by gnawing at the bark of twigs in spring, before the buds have come out, and later by eating the tender shoots.

Family CURCULIONIDAE

The Snout Beetles; Weevils

Small or moderate-sized beetles, which have a well-defined beak, compose this large family. The beak is usually long and curved downward and frequently has a longitudinal groove or scrobe (Fig. 503) into which the antennal first segment is attached; the palpi are short and rigid, nearly always concealed; head globose; antennae sometimes straight but most usually geniculate (Figs. 503, 504), with a three-segmented club; funicle three- to seven-segmented; elytra strongly folded on underside, limiting a deep groove into which fits the upper edge of the abdomen, without epipleura; five abdominal sternites present, the first and second closely united; procoxal cavities closed behind; pro- and mesocoxae rounded, metacoxae oval and more or less widely separated; tarsal claws variable.

Weevils may be found in flowers, attacking leaves or fruit, and, in fact, on any and all parts of plants. The adults frequently bask in the sunshine and, when disturbed, may fold up their legs and antennae and drop to the ground. Some of our most destructive pests belong to this family, among which are the cotton-boll weevil, the apple curculio, the white-fringed weevil, the plum curculio, the alfalfa weevil, and the clover weevil.

KEY TO SUBFAMILIES

1. Antennae straight, without a distinct club, but last segment elongated (Fig. 504), in male longer than other segments combined; body slender, antlike ....CYLADINAE (p. 750)
   Antennae straight or geniculate, always with a distinct club; body not antlike 2
2. Antennae not geniculate; beak without scrobes 3
   Antennae more or less geniculate (Fig. 503); beak with scrobes present 5
3. Antennal club with segments well separated (Fig. 505) 4
   Antennal club with segments compact (Fig. 506) ....APIONINAE (p. 751)
4. Beak as long as head and pronotum together ....CIMBERINAE (p. 746)
   Beak no longer than head ....ATTELABINAE (p. 747)
5. Club of antennae usually annulate, not shining; tarsi usually dilated apically, third segment bilobed, brushlike beneath 6
   Club of antennae usually with basal segment enlarged or shining or both, feebly or not at all annulate; tarsi frequently narrow, not brushlike beneath ....COSSONINAE (p. 794)

6. Beak never long and slender ...............OTIORHYNCHINAE (p. 752)
   Beak usually elongate, slender, or if short and stout, then received
   on prosternum in repose ....................CURCULIONINAE (p. 757)

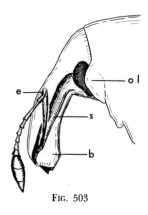

Fig. 503

Fig. 504

Fig. 505

Fig. 506

Fig. 503. Head of curculionid from side, showing beak (*b*), scrobe (*s*)
  for receipt of antenna, and ocular lobe (*ol*) on prothorax.
  The antenna here is of the geniculate sort (*e* marking the
  elbow).
Fig. 504. Antenna of female of *Cylas formicarius*, with last segment
  long and slightly thickened; that of male is still longer and
  thicker.
Fig. 505. Antennal club of *Rhynchites*, with segments well separated.
Fig. 506. Antennal club of *Apion*, with segments compactly arranged.

Subfamily CIMBERINAE

The Toothed-Nose Snout Beetles

KEY TO GENERA

Pygidium covered by elytra, the latter entire .... I. *Eugnamptus* (p. 746)
Pygidium exposed, elytra abbreviated .... II. *Rhynchites* (p. 746)

Genus I. *EUGNAMPTUS* Schönherr

Small, rather slender beetles; sparsely clothed with erect hairs; funicle of antennae with segments two to four longer than wide; head neither emarginate nor truncate at base; legs long, slender.

The males have the beak shorter, the eyes usually larger and more approximate, and the mandibles with only one tooth on outer side; the female's mandibles are externally bidentate.

Eugnamptus collaris (Fabricius)   Plate LXXV, Nos. 12, 13, p. 737

Elongate, rather slender; black; elytra bluish black. Beak carinate at base in male, sparsely and coarsely punctate. Pronotum subquadrate, widest at middle; disk coarsely, sparsely, irregularly punctate, with a shallow median impression on basal half. Elytral intervals each with a fine carina near the row of punctures and with a row of finer, setae-bearing punctures external to the larger ones. Length 3.5–4.7 mm.

This species is very variable in color; the pronotum may be reddish yellow, as may also be the head, legs, and antennae. These differences in color may occur between the sexes.

These beetles may be beaten from oak, walnut, hickory, and butternut, as well as from roadside weeds.

Genus II. *RHYNCHITES* Herbst

Small, very convex, and robust beetles; head neither emarginate nor truncate at base; antennal segments three to five longer than wide; pygidium exposed.

Rhynchites bicolor Fabricius   Rose Curculio; Black-snouted Rose Beetle
Plate LXXVI, No. 12, p. 749

Robust, convex; elytra, pronotum, and head behind eyes bright red; undersurface, femora, and beak black; tibiae, tarsi, and antennae piceous.

Beak as long as head and pronotum, with elongate punctures; antennae inserted at middle; antennal grooves distinct. Pronotum cylindrical, as long as wide, densely and finely punctate. Elytra with indistinctly punctate striae; intervals with dense, coarse punctures. Beak of female shorter and stouter than that of male. Length 5–6.5 mm.

The adults frequent blooms and leaves of wild and cultivated rose, also blackberries and raspberries.

Subfamily ATTELABINAE

The Leaf-rolling Weevils

Genus *ATTELABUS* Linné

Small, short-bodied, robust beetles; glabrous; head prominent, not deflexed; beak short, stout, wider apically; antennae straight, inserted in short, broad grooves on upper surface of beak, eleven-segmented, the first and second segments more robust, nine to eleven larger and forming a loose, elongate club; pronotum truncate apically and basally, convex; each elytron rounded at apex, not covering pygidium; pygidium with upper surface margined with a deep groove; abdomen with five short ventral segments divided by straight sutures; procoxae conical, prominent, contiguous; mesocoxae slightly transverse; metacoxae transverse, subcontiguous tibiae serrate on inner side and armed at apices with two stout hooks; tarsi dilated, third segment deeply bilobed.

The larvae live in small rolls made from leaves by the female.

KEY TO SPECIES

1. Elytra bright red 2
   Elytra black, with two reddish maculae ....c. *bipustulatus*
2. Meso- and metasterna black, remainder of undersurface red ....a. *analis*
   Entire undersurface red; profemora robust, dentate in male ......b. *nigripes*

a. *Attelabus analis* Illiger   Plate LXXVI, No. 2, p. 749
   Pear-shaped, robust, convex; elytra, pronotum, base of head, prosternum, and abdomen bright red; remainder of body and appendages bluish black. Beak stout, shorter than head, narrowed at insertion of antennae; sparsely punctate. Head with two grooves between eyes; coarsely, rather closely punctate. Pronotum campanulate, very narrow at apex, sparsely, finely punctate. Elytra with rows of shallow punctures. Ventral abdominal segments of male with two rows of minute tubercles. Length 5–6 mm.

The adults occur mostly on leaves or beneath bark of hickory and also

PLATE LXXVI

Family CURCULIONIDAE II

1. *Attelabus nigripes* LeConte (p. 750)

Bright orange-brown; legs and antennae black; 3.5–4.5 mm.

2. *A. analis* Illiger (p. 747)

Varying from bright orange to deep red; legs often black, as is head in part; 5–6 mm.

3. *A. bipustulatus* Fabricius (p. 750)

Black; humeral spots reddish; 3.5–4.5 mm.

4. *Apion patruele* Smith (p. 751)

Black; 1.6–2 mm.

5. *Cylas formicarius* (Fabricius) (p. 750)

Reddish, with head black and elytra blue-black; 5–6 mm.

6. *Tychius picirostris* (Fabricius) (p. 768)

Black, with white pubescence; tibiae and tarsi reddish brown; 2.3–2.5 mm.

7. *Phyxelis rigidus* (Say) (p. 753)

Dull brown, densely covered with gray scales; 3.5–4.5 mm.

8. *Apion griseum* Smith (p. 751)

Black, covered with sparse, white pubescence; 1.7–2 mm.

9. *Notaris puncticollis* (LeConte) (p. 767)

Blackish; sparsely covered with white and brownish pubescence; 4.5–6.5 mm.

10. *Curculio baculi* (Chittenden) (p. 770)

Blackish, with white and brownish pubescence; tibiae and antennae reddish; 6–8 mm.

11. *Tachypterellus quadrigibbosus* (Say) (p. 771)

Dark reddish brown, with white pubescence; elytra on apical portion brown-pubescent; 3–4.5 mm.

12. *Rhynchites bicolor* Fabricius (p. 746)

Dark red; legs and proboscis black; 5–6.5 mm.

13. *Tychius griseus* Schaeffer (p. 768)

Black, covered with short, white pubescence; legs reddish; tip of beak red; 2.3–2.5 mm.

14. *Magdalis barbita* Say (p. 769)

Black; 4–6 mm.

15. *M. olyra* Herbst (p. 769)

Black; legs sometimes reddish; 4–6 mm.

16. *Pandeleteius hilaris* (Herbst) (p. 754)

Black; usually densely covered with gray and blackish scales; 4–5 mm.

MM
0 10 20 30 40 50 60 70

PLATE LXXVI

749

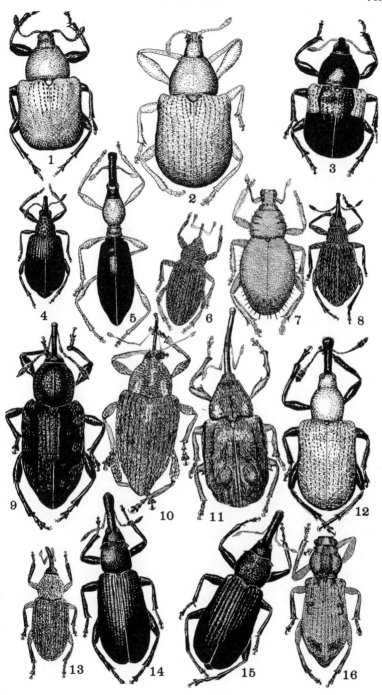

on oak and walnut. This species resembles the next one very closely in coloration but differs in the length of the beak and in other structural characters as well as in habits.

b. *Attelabus nigripes* LeConte   Plate LXXVI, No. 1, p. 749

Pear-shaped, robust, convex; base of head, pronotum, and elytra bright red; undersurface usually dull red; remainder of body black, without the bluish tinge of *analis*. Pronotum moderately narrowed to apex, disk very finely punctate. Elytra short and broad, with rows of coarse, rather deep punctures. Profemora short, thicker, and bidentate in male. Length 3.5–4.5 mm.

These beetles may be beaten from hickory and sumac.

c. *Attelabus bipustulatus* Fabricius   Plate LXXVI, No. 3, p. 749

Pear-shaped, robust; black, with a faint bluish tinge; elytra each with an oblong, reddish macula on humerus. Beak shorter than head, densely, reticulately punctate anterior to antennal insertion; head sulcate between eyes, sparsely and finely punctate. Pronotum campanulate, finely and sparsely punctate. Elytra with rows of small, feebly impressed punctures. Profemora short, robust in male and with a small, acute tooth in both sexes. Length 3–4 mm.

These beetles may be beaten from oak, hickory, and walnut.

Subfamily CYLADINAE

The Antlike Snout Beetles

Genus *CYLAS* Latreille

Elongate, slender, antlike in shape; maxillae exposed, the mentum transversely oblong; mandibles pincerlike; head widened basally; procoxae conical, prominent, contiguous; tibiae slender, straight, not mucronate at apex; tarsal claws connate basally (Fig. 524).

Cylas formicarius (Fabricius)   Plate LXXVI, No. 5, p. 749

Elongate, smooth, shining; pale reddish brown; elytra bluish black; head and beak dusky. Beak twice as long as head, robust, cylindrical, finely punctate basally. Last antennal segment cylindrical, longer than others combined in male, shorter in female. Pronotum about twice as long as wide, deeply constricted on basal third; disk smooth. Elytra elongate-oval, strongly convex, slightly wider than pronotum; humeri oblique; surface with fine, feebly punctate striae; intervals flat, smooth. Length 5–6 mm.

The larva of this beetle is known as the sweet-potato borer. This is an introduced species and attacks some Compositae and members of the morning-glory family as well as sweet potatoes.

Subfamily APIONINAE

Genus *APION* Herbst

Very small to small, broadly ovate, convex beetles; antennae straight, club three-segmented (Fig. 506), the last segment of club longer than either of the two preceding; elytra very deeply striate, entirely covering abdomen; profemora of same thickness as meso- and metafemora.

These beetles are usually found in seeds of legumes; some occur on dogwood, witch hazel, and *Viburnum*. The larvae are also found in seeds of leguminous plants but are stem-borers as well as gall-makers on leaves and stems. The members of this genus are remarkable for their uniformity of size, color, shape, and structure.

KEY TO SPECIES

Very sparsely, finely, indistinctly pubescent . . . . .a. *patruele*
Rather densely clothed with fine, whitish or yellowish hairs . . . . .b. *griseum*

a. *Apion patruele* Smith   Plate LXXVI, No. 4, p. 749
Short, robust, strongly convex; black, shining; sparsely and finely whitish-pubescent; antennae and tibiae sometimes piceous. Beak robust, finely punctate, as long as head and pronotum together in male, longer in female. Front of head strongly sulcate. Pronotum short, broader than long, narrowed apically; disk coarsely, rather densely punctate, with a distinct, rounded fovea medially at base. Elytra less than one-half longer than wide; humeri prominent; sides parallel to beyond middle; strial punctures large and deep, intervals not quite twice as wide as striae. Undersurface sparsely and finely punctate, the last ventral sternite more coarsely punctate. Length 1.6–2 mm.

These beetles have been taken by beating and sweeping hazel, and they occur also on flowers of celandine poppy and on legumes.

b. *Apion griseum* Smith   Plate LXXVI, No. 8, p. 749
Rather elongate, robust; black, faintly bronzed; rather densely clothed with prostrate whitish or yellowish pubescence. Beak as long as or slightly longer than head and pronotum together, distinctly narrowed apically; coarsely punctate and pubescent on basal two-thirds. Front of head not sulcate. Pronotum wider at base than long, sides converging from base to apex; disk densely, rather coarsely punctate; median basal fovea small,

more or less elongate. Elytra one-third longer than wide, sides subparallel at basal quarter; striae coarsely punctate; intervals more than twice width of striae. Undersurface coarsely punctate, last three abdominal sternites very finely punctate. Length 1.7–2 mm.

This species has been taken from various legumes and from beneath the bark of oak.

Subfamily OTIORHYNCHINAE

The Short-snouted Weevils; the Scarred Snout Beetles

KEY TO GENERA

1. Ocular lobes present (Fig. 507), eyes generally elongate, transverse, acuminate beneath, usually covered at least in part; scutellum not visible 2
   Ocular lobes wanting, eyes rounded or short, oval, free; scutellum generally small 3
2. Scrobes not directed below eye ....I. *Phyxelis*   (p. 752)
   Scrobes directed below eye (Fig. 507) ....II. *Anametis*   (p. 753)
3. Scrobes linear and directed below eye (Fig. 503) 4
   Scrobes sinuate and directed above eyes (Fig. 508) ....
   ....VII. *Brachyrhinus*   (p. 756)
4. Procoxae narrowly separated ....III. *Pandeleteius*   (p. 754)
   Procoxae contiguous 5
5. Elytra wider than pronotum at base; humeri angulate, often prominent ....IV. *Polydrusus*   (p. 754)
   Elytra not wider than pronotum at base, basally emarginate or truncate; humeri absent or rounded 6
6. Antennae scaled or coarsely pubescent; body beneath bearing dense scales ....V. *Graphognathus*   (p. 755)
   Antennae shining, sparsely pubescent; body beneath nearly glabrous ....VI. *Barypeithes*   (p. 756)

Genus I. *PHYXELIS* Schönherr

Small, oval, robust, convex; beak robust, longer than head, apex deeply emarginate, scrobe short, arcuate, not reaching eyes; scape of antennae gradually clavate, attaining posterior margin of eye, segments one and two of funicle longer than others, which are rounded or obconical; pronotum short, transverse, apex and base truncate; scutellum not visible; elytra convex and with rows of setae.

Phyxelis rigidus (Say)   Plate LXXVI, No. 7, p. 749

Short, oval, robust, very convex; dull brown; densely clothed with small, gray scales and sometimes with a brown or yellowish waxy crust; funicle, club, and tarsi reddish brown. Beak often with a narrow median sulcus. Pronotum transverse, sides feebly arcuate; disk with a faint median impressed line and with numerous short hairs arising from minute tubercles. Elytra with base truncate; disk feebly striate, striae coarsely punctate; intervals slightly convex, each with a row of single, coarse, long setae. Length 3.5–4.5 mm.

These insects may be captured by sweeping herbage and flowers.

Genus II. *ANAMETIS* Horn

Rather small, oval to oblong-oval, convex beetles; beak longer and narrower than head; front of head convex, separated from beak by a transverse groove; antennal scape gradually clavate; segments one and two of funicle elongate, three to seven obconical; postocular lobes short, with a slight fringe of hairs; scutellum very small, triangular; elytra truncate basally, humeri obsolete; second abdominal sternite as long as third and fourth combined, anterior margin straight.

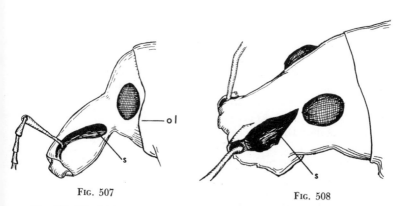

Fig. 507.   Fig. 508.

Fig. 507. Head of *Anametis* viewed from the side, with weakly developed ocular lobe (*ol*) and with scrobe (*s*) directed below eye.
Fig. 508. Head of *Brachyrhinus* (obliquely from the side and above), without ocular lobes and with scrobe (*s*) directed above eye.

Anametis granulata (Say)   Plate LXXIX, No. 10, p. 785

Oval, robust; dark brown; densely and uniformly covered with grayish scales, many with a pearly or greenish reflex; antennae and tarsi reddish brown. Head and beak equal in length to pronotum; beak convex, with a finely impressed submarginal line each side. Pronotum feebly transverse, widest medially, truncate apically and basally; sides feebly arcuate; disk convex, sculpturing concealed by scales. Elytral sides parallel on basal half; discal striae fine, with small, deep punctures; intervals nearly flat, each with two irregular rows of setae. Length 5–7 mm.

This beetle has been recorded as damaging young peach, pear, and apple trees, and it has been beaten from foliage of buckeye and other trees and shrubs and from the great ragweed. It is sometimes nocturnal in its feeding habits.

Genus III. *PANDELETEIUS* Schönherr

Small, elongate, slender, convex; beak slightly shorter than head, feebly compressed; scrobes rather deep, slightly curved, and passing beneath the eyes; scape gradually clavate, reaching posterior margin of eyes; funicle six- or seven-segmented, segments one and two elongate, five to seven short, moniliform; scutellum small, triangular; front legs longer, the profemora more robust.

Pandeleteius hilaris (Herbst)   Plate LXXVI, No. 16, p. 749

Elongate, rather slender, convex; brownish, this coloring often entirely concealed by the scales, which are silvery gray, fuscous, and pale grayish brown (on the elytra the fuscous scales often form a dark, diagonal stripe near apex); antennae and tarsi reddish brown. Beak short, upper surface punctate and with a distinct median impressed line. Antennal funicle seven-segmented; first segment as long as following two together. Pronotum subcylindrical, subquadrate, broadly constricted before and narrowly behind middle, sides arcuate; disk coarsely, deeply, rather densely punctate. Elytra truncate at base and wider than pronotum; each with ten striae, which are coarsely and deeply punctate; intervals convex, sculpturing concealed by scales. Undersurface covered with translucent scales. Length 4–5 mm.

The adults may be beaten from white, black, and scarlet oak.

Genus IV. *POLYDRUSUS* Germar

Small, elongate-oblong, convex; beak shorter and narrower than head, apex feebly notched, scrobe deep anteriorly, suddenly bent and passing beneath the eyes; eyes round; antennae long, slender, segments one and two of funicle longer, three to seven obconical, gradually decreasing in length; club elongate-oval.

Polydrusus americanus Gyllenhal   Plate LXXVIII, No. 15, p. 777
Elongate-oblong; brown, shining; densely clothed with pale-gray and orangeish-brown scales, the latter forming a dark stripe on vertex, three narrow stripes on pronotum, and a large discal spot on elytra; undersurface piceous, shining; antennae and legs reddish brown. Head and beak as long as pronotum, sparsely punctate. Pronotum quadrate, subcylindrical; apex obliquely, base squarely, truncate; sides slightly arcuate; disk sparsely punctate. Elytra almost twice as wide as long; humeri prominent; disk with finely punctured striae; intervals flat, each with a single row of short hairs. Length 4.5–5.5 mm.

This species has been recorded as taken by sweeping and on beech.

Genus V. *GRAPHOGNATHUS* Buchanan

Moderate-sized beetles; oblong-ovate to broadly oval, robust, scaly and hairy; head not constricted behind eyes; beak short, robust, distinctly notched at apex; mandibles with a shallow sulcus, either side with a blunt carina; antennal scape attaining or slightly surpassing posterior margin of eye, subequal in length to funicle; second segment of funicle much longer than first; fifth, sixth, and seventh segments combined as long as club; procoxae large; profemora more robust and longer than meso- and metafemora.

Graphognathus leucoloma (Boheman)   The White-fringed Beetle
Plate LXXIX, No. 2, p. 785
Oblong-ovate, robust; piceous to black; rather densely covered with dull ashy and gray-brown scales; scutellum whitish-scaled; elytra with long, erect, whitish hairs especially at apex, along upper border of sides with a broad, whitish vitta. Beak half the length of pronotum, a low carina each side, and at base medially with an elongate fovea. Pronotum transverse, sides broadly arcuate, base and apex subequal; disk finely, sparsely punctate. Elytra with sides broadly rounded, widest behind middle, strongly tapering to apices; disk with indistinct rows of quadrate, rather coarse punctures; intervals feebly convex, with scattered, fine granules. Length 9–12 mm.

So far as is known, no males have been found of this species; only females hatch from the unfertilized eggs, a condition known as parthenogenesis.

This is an introduced species which has spread very rapidly over the southeastern part of the United States and does extensive damage to all kinds of truck crops.

Genus VI. *BARYPEITHES* Duval

Small, elongate-oval, robust species; body hairy, not scaled; beak shorter than head, deeply notched at apex; antennae inserted near base of beak, scape attaining pronotum, first segment of funicle more robust and longer than second, segments three to seven moniliform; claws connate; second abdominal sternite as long as next two, anterior margin straight.

Barypeithes pellucidus (Boheman)   Plate LXXVIII, No. 13, p. 777

Elongate-oval; dark reddish brown to piceous, shining; sparsely covered with yellow hairs; antennae and legs pale reddish brown. Beak and head shorter than pronotum; sparsely, coarsely punctate. Pronotum more or less spherical, as long as wide, widest at middle, sides broadly arcuate; disk coarsely and sparsely punctate. Elytra widest at middle; striae deep, with coarse, close punctures; intervals slightly convex, each with a row of long, yellowish hairs. Length 2.5–3.5 mm.

This species was introduced from Europe.

Genus VII. *BRACHYRHINUS* Latreille

Rather small to moderate-sized, oblong or oblong-ovate beetles; beak as long as head, dilated and notched at apex; scrobe deep; antennae long, scape passing slightly beyond anterior margin of pronotum, club oval, acute at apex; scutellum very small; tarsi dilated, pubescent beneath, third segment deeply bilobed; second abdominal sternite shorter than third and fourth together, anterior margin arcuate.

Brachyrhinus ovatus (Linné)   Strawberry-Crown Girdler
                                       Plate LXXIX, No. 5, p. 785

Oblong-oval; piceous, shining; covered with sparse, yellowish, semiprostrate pubescence; antennae and legs reddish brown. Beak flattened, coarsely, densely, rugosely punctate; front with a deep, oblong fovea. Pronotum subglobose; basal and apical margins truncate; disk with numerous longitudinal ridges. Elytral striae more distinct laterally, all striae with coarse, deep punctures; intervals flat, sparsely and coarsely rugose. Length 5–6 mm.

This beetle is injurious to strawberries and muskmelon.

Subfamily CURCULIONINAE

KEY TO TRIBES

Tribe SITONINI

Genus *SITONA* Germar

Small, elongate-oblong, convex; beak short, free, not received by prosternum; mentum large, quadrate; elytra covering the lateral angles of first abdominal sternite; humeri not truncated by protruding mesopleura; abdominal sternites nearly equal; tibiae not fossorial; claws simple.

KEY TO SPECIES

Setae of elytral intervals very distinct, long, erect; scales dark gray and coppery ....b. *hispidulus*
Setae wholly wanting; color nearly uniformly brown; hairlike covering ....
....a. *flavescens*

a. *Sitona flavescens* Marsham   Yellow-Clover Curculio
                                            Plate LXXVIII, No. 14, p. 777

Elongate-oblong, convex; black; densely clothed above with rusty-brown and fuscous, narrow, hairlike scales, the darker ones forming two indistinct stripes on head and pronotum; beneath with fine, prostrate, grayish hairs; antennae (except club), tibiae, and tarsi reddish brown; club and femora darker. Beak and head about as long as pronotum, finely and densely punctate. Pronotum quadrate, subcylindrical, widest at middle; surface finely, densely punctate. Elytra one-third wider at base than pronotum; sides parallel to apical quarter, then strongly converging to apices; striae fine and minutely punctate. Second abdominal sternite about as long as third and fourth together. Length 4.5–5.5 mm.

This beetle may be taken by sweeping low weeds along lakes and marshes. Both adults and larvae are injurious to clover.

b. *Sitona hispidulus* (Fabricius)   Clover-Root Curculio
                                            Plate LXXIX, No. 4, p. 785

Elongate-oblong, convex; black, shining; densely clothed above with small, coppery or grayish scales, these scales forming a narrow median and two broader lateral stripes on pronotum; antennae (except club), tibiae, and tarsi reddish brown; club and femora piceous. Head and beak as long as pronotum, coarsely, deeply punctate. Pronotum subquadrate, subcylindrical, widest at middle, coarsely, sparsely, and deeply punctate. Elytra nearly one-half wider at base than pronotum, feebly striate, striae punctate; intervals slightly convex, each with one row of stout, grayish setae. Length 3–5 mm.

Both larvae and adults are injurious to clover and other legumes; the adults feed on the leaves and the larvae on the roots.

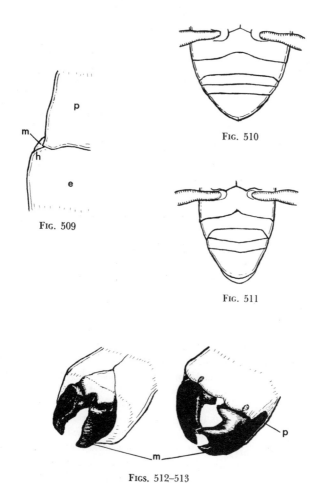

FIG. 510

FIG. 509

FIG. 511

FIGS. 512–513

Fig. 509. Portion of pronotum (*p*) and elytron (*e*) of *Trichobaris* from above, with mesopleuron (*m*) truncating the humerus (*h*).

Fig. 510. Ventral abdominal surface of *Hypera*, the sutures of sternites not angulate.

Fig. 511. Ventral surface of abdomen in *Tychius*, with apices of sternites angulate.

Fig. 512. Tip of beak of *Hypera* viewed obliquely from beneath; mandibles (*m*) with two teeth.

Fig. 513. Tip of beak of *Hylobius* viewed obliquely from beneath; mandibles (*m*) with three teeth, point of attachment (*p*) located laterally.

Tribe HYPERINI

KEY TO GENERA

1. Third and fourth abdominal sternites together not longer than second or fifth sternites 2
   Abdominal sternites nearly equal 3
2. Second funicular segment of antennae much longer than first; tibiae strongly spined ....III. *Listronotus* (p. 762)
   Second funicular segment of antennae but little if any longer than first; tibiae feebly spined ....IV. *Hyperodes* (p. 763)
3. Beak shorter than pronotum; mandibles not emarginate; pronotum much narrower than elytra (Fig. 512) ....I. *Hypera* (p. 760)
   Beak longer than pronotum; mandibles emarginate (Fig. 519); pronotum more than two-thirds as wide as elytra ....II. *Phytonomus* (p. 760)

Genus I. *HYPERA* Germar

Moderately small, elongate-oval, robust; beak shorter than pronotum; mandibles not emarginate; eyes separated by not more than their diameter; pronotum much narrower than the elongate elytra; abdominal sternites nearly equal.

Hypera punctata (Fabricius)

Clover-Leaf Weevil
Plate LXXIX, No. 3, p. 785

Elongate-oval, robust; black; densely clothed with brown, yellow-brown, or dark-brown scales and with numerous short, suberect bristles; sides of elytra paler than disk. Beak two-thirds length of pronotum, its under-surface, sides, and apex polished. Pronotum slightly transverse, sides arcuate at middle, converging to base; disk finely and densely punctate. Elytra longer than broad, sides parallel, broadly rounded at apices; striae finely punctate; sutural and each alternate interval wider and slightly elevated; all intervals finely and densely punctate. First abdominal sternite of male impressed and emarginate posteriorly. Length 5–8.5 mm.

This is a species introduced from Europe. It may be found on almost any clover. The larvae feed at night on the leaves rather than in the roots, as most of the beetles in this family do.

Genus II. *PHYTONOMUS* Schönherr

Small, elongate-oval, more or less robust; beak longer than pronotum; mandibles emarginate; eyes separated by not more than their own diameter; pronotum not much narrower than elytra; abdominal sternites almost equal.

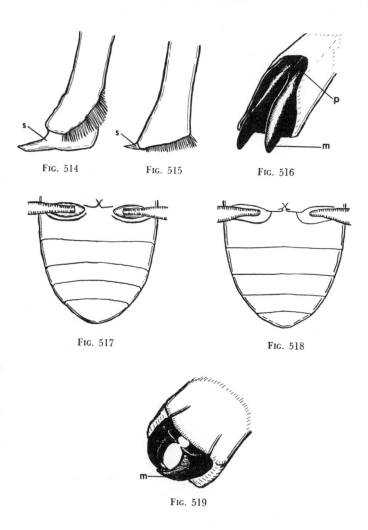

Fig. 514. Apex of metatibia of *Hylobius*, with long, curved spine (*s*).

Fig. 515. Apex of metatibia of *Notaris*, with short spine (*s*).

Fig. 516. Tip of beak of *Curculio* obliquely from below, mandibular point of attachment (*p*) located dorsally. *m*, mandible.

Fig. 517. Abdomen of *Gymnetron* in ventral view, apices of sternites angulate at extreme sides.

Fig. 518. Ventral aspect of abdomen of *Anthonomus*, the apical margins of sternites not angulated.

Fig. 519. Tip of beak of *Phytonomus* from below, with mandibles deeply emarginate or strongly bidentate (*m*).

KEY TO SPECIES

Pronotum distinctly wider than long, sides strongly arcuate; elytral scales reddish
    or greenish gray, somewhat spotted with deep brown ....a. *meles*
Pronotum not wider than long; elytra with fine, long, greenish hairs, without
    intermixed scales ....b. *nigrirostris*

a. *Phytonomus meles* (Fabricius)   Plate LXXX, No. 2, p. 793

Elongate-oval; black or piceous; pronotum sparsely covered with metallic-
gray or reddish-brown scales, a median line and sides often paler; elytra
clothed with either reddish-gray or greenish-gray scales, sometimes tessellated
with white and brown scales; antennae and legs reddish brown or piceous.
Beak slender, cylindrical, carinate dorsally, striate on sides. Antennal scape
reaching eye, first funicular segment twice as long as second, fourth to
seventh transverse. Pronotum widest at middle; disk nearly flat, densely
punctate. Elytra wider than pronotum; striae fine, punctate; intervals
feebly convex, with numerous short, scattered hairs. Third abdominal
sternite in male with a median, shallow impression. Length 3.5–5 mm.

This beetle may be collected from clover.

b. *Phytonomus nigrirostris* (Fabricius)   Lesser Clover-Leaf Weevil
                                               Plate LXXIX, No. 6, p. 785

Elongate-oval; reddish brown or black; thickly clothed with light-green,
sometimes yellowish, scalelike hairs; head black, with a median line of
whitish hairs; pronotum often with a narrow median line of whitish hairs
and a wider line of black hairs on each side of median line; antennae and
legs reddish brown. Beak as long as pronotum, longer in male than in
female, cylindrical, curved, polished, above with a median carina for the
entire length. Antennal scape extending almost to middle of eyes; first
funicular segment not twice as long as second, third to seventh shorter and
broader. Pronotum slightly longer than wide, sides feebly arcuate before
middle; disk coarsely and densely punctate. Elytral humeri rounded; sides
nearly parallel, striae distinctly punctate; intervals each with a row of
short, stiff, whitish hairs. Length 3.5–4.5 mm.

This species feeds on all varieties of clover and alfalfa.

Genus III. *LISTRONOTUS* Jekel

Medium-sized, dull-brownish species; ocular lobes of prothorax prominent, partly concealing eyes in repose (Fig. 503); first, second, and fifth
ventral abdominal segments long, third and fourth very short; legs slender;
tibiae bent inward at apex and strongly spined.

The species all breed in semiaquatic plants and readily come to light.

Listronotus caudatus (Say) Plate LXXIX, No. 1, p. 785
Elongate-oblong, robust; black; densely clothed with brownish-yellow scales; head, beak, sides of pronotum, and some scattered spots on sides of elytra paler; antennae reddish brown. Beak longer than pronotum, finely carinate dorsally, sulci on sides nearly obsolete. Pronotum transverse; sides subparallel, feebly arcuate near apex; disk finely, densely punctate. Elytra strongly emarginate basally; sides parallel, strongly narrowed on apical fourth; disk subdepressed; striae fine, minutely punctate; intervals flat, each with a row of minute setae. Length 10–12 mm.

This species has been recorded as breeding on smartweed and arrowhead.

Genus IV. *HYPERODES* Jekel

Small, oblong or elongate-oval species; eyes lateral, not encroaching on front; beak deflexed, narrower than head, slightly wider at apex, with one or more carinae dorsally; antennae inserted near apex of beak; scrobe deep anteriorly, visible from above, more or less widened and shallow posteriorly; scape clavate, reaching eye, first segment of funicle more robust than second, subequal in length, third to sixth of equal width, seventh wider; pronotum not longer than wide, ocular lobes distinct; femora clavate; tibiae feebly mucronate.

Hyperodes solutus (Boheman) Plate LXXIX, No. 7, p. 785
Elongate-oblong; reddish brown to piceous; densely clothed above with rounded, clay-yellow scales; elytra with an irregular triangular spot of black scales just behind middle; antennae and legs reddish brown; femora and antennal club darker; undersurface piceous, glabrous, last two segments paler. Beak as long as pronotum, sides parallel, median carina fine, distinct. Pronotum subquadrate, sides feebly rounded; ocular lobes only partly covering eyes in repose; surface densely, rather finely punctate. Elytra wider than pronotum, sides parallel for basal two-thirds, then narrowed to apex; striae fine, with distant punctures; intervals each with a row of short, whitish setae. Last abdominal sternite of female with a shallow, triangular fovea. Length 3–5 mm.

This species may be found on arrow arum, arrowhead, and similar aquatic plants.

PLATE LXXVII
Family CURCULIONIDAE III

1. *Madarellus undulatus* (Say) (p. 779) — Black, strongly shining; pronotum often largely reddish; 2.7–4.7 mm.

2. *Anthonomus grandis* Boheman (p. 772) — Dark reddish brown, covered with dull-gray and brownish pubescence; 4–7.5 mm.

3. *Odontocorynus scutellum-album* (Say) (p. 781) — Black; elytra sometimes partly reddish, with white scales; 3–4.8 mm.

4. *Elleschus ephippiatus* Say (p. 773) — Dark reddish brown, covered with whitish pubescence; elytra with a denuded band behind middle; 1.5–3.4 mm.

5. *Rhynchaenus ephippiatus* (Say) (p. 774) — Reddish brown and black; elytra with two white-pubescent bands; 2.5–3.5 mm.

6. *R. niger* Horn (p. 774) — Black; elytral band whitish; scutellum white; 2–3 mm.

7. *R. pallicornis* Say (p. 774) — Black; antennae yellowish; 2.5–3 mm.

8. *Acalyptus carpini* (Herbst) (p. 775) — Black, covered with gray pubescence; legs yellowish; 2.2–2.8 mm.

9. *Gymnetron tetrum* (Fabricius) (p. 775) — Black with shaggy, yellowish-brown hairs; 2.3–3.8 mm.

10. *Lixus concavus* Say (p. 778) — Black, covered with short, yellowish or gray pubescence; 10–13 mm.

11. *Trichobaris trinotata* (Say) (p. 780) — Black, covered with white scales or pubescence; 3–4 mm.

12. *Anthonomus suturalis* LeConte (p. 772) — Blackish, with indistinct white pubescence in patches on pronotum; elytral maculae dark red; 2.5–3.5 mm.

13. *A. signatus* Say (p. 773) — Piceous or black, with sparse, white hairs; elytra largely reddish, the black spots sometimes absent; 2–3 mm.

14. *Pseudobaris nigrina* (Say) (p. 780) — Black, shining; 2.5–3.7 mm.

15. *Centrinaspis picumnus* (Herbst) (p. 781) — Blackish, covered with white scales and pubescence; 2.1–2.7 mm.

MM 0 10 20 30 40 50 60 70

PLATE LXXVII

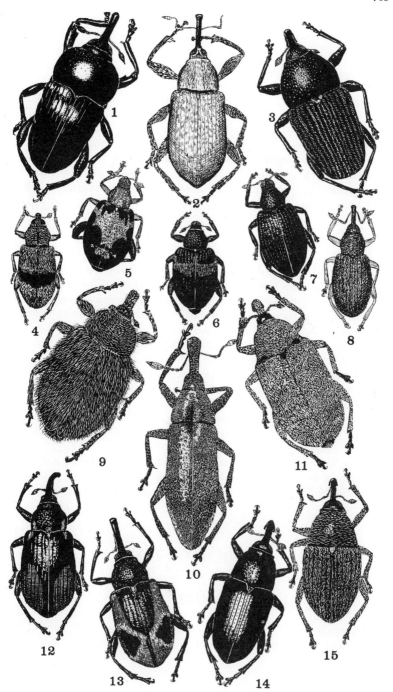

Tribe Pissodini

Genus *PISSODES* Germar

Small, oblong-oval, rather slender species; beak slender, cylindrical, as long as or longer than pronotum; head behind eyes globular; eyes not contiguous beneath; antennae inserted on sides of beak at or near middle; scape shorter than funicle, first funicular segment subequal to next two together, third to seventh subequal in length, slightly wider; first segment of club large, longer on one side, sparsely clothed with short hairs and long bristles; procoxae slightly separated; tibiae with longitudinal ridges and a long, curved, apical claw which is oblique, dilated, and ciliated; claws simple.

Pissodes strobi (Peck)   White-Pine Weevil
Plate LXXIX, No. 8, p. 785

Oblong-oval; light to dark brown; pronotum usually with three irregular basal spots and one very small, round dot on either side of median line, near middle, covered with white scales; scutellum densely covered with whitish scales; elytra near suture marked with sparse, white scales, two spots of dense, white scales on apical third, and lateral to these a transverse brownish-yellow spot; basal one-third with an irregular spot of pale or brownish-yellow scales; undersurface with sparse, irregularly placed, whitish scales; femora annulate with whitish scales near apical third. Pronotum much wider at base than at apex, sides nearly parallel on basal half, narrowed anteriorly; disk densely, finely, rugosely punctate. Elytra slightly wider than pronotum, sides parallel to beyond basal two-thirds, then strongly converging to apex; striae finely punctate; third and fifth intervals elevated. Length 4.5–6 mm.

In the white-pine stands of eastern United States this beetle is the most serious pest. It attacks the leading shoot of white pine, jack pine, pitch pine, and Scotch pine and may be found on some of the spruces and on Douglas fir.

Tribe Hylobiini

Genus *HYLOBIUS* Germar

Moderately small, elongate-oval, robust species; body with spots of fine pubescence; beak robust, cylindrical, feebly curved; antennal groove directed toward lower part of eyes; antennae robust, scape nearly attaining eye, segments one and two longer than others, first longer than second, third to sixth moniliform, seventh broader, forming a part of the club; eyes large, coarsely granulate, transverse, widely separated; pronotum transverse; procoxae contiguous; external apical angles of tibiae not dilated, tibiae not narrowed apically; femora clavate, strongly dentate; second and fifth abdominal sternites each as long as third and fourth together, the suture anterior to second broadly angulate at middle.

Hylobius pales Boheman The Pales Weevil
Plate LXXIX, No. 9, p. 785

Elongate-oval, robust; dark reddish brown; elytra with scattered, small tufts of fine, gray or yellowish hairs, those behind middle forming two oblique crossbars. Head densely punctate. Pronotum flattened; sides arcuate; disk rather coarsely punctate and alutaceous. Elytral disk flattened; striae with large, oblong punctures; intervals narrow, flat, and coarsely, rugosely punctate. Abdomen beneath sparsely and finely punctate. Length 7–10 mm.

On cutover pine lands this beetle is a serious pest, attacking the young seedlings by feeding on the bark at the base, usually at night, or beneath the cover of litter in the daytime. The eggs are laid in the inner bark of freshly cut pine logs or in freshly cut pine stumps.

Tribe ERIRHININI

Genus *NOTARIS* Germar

Small, elongate-oval, robust species; beak not separated from the head by a groove; antennae inserted at apical third of beak, third and fourth segments of equal length; eyes contiguous with thoracic margin, often partly covered by it; prosternum emarginate; metasternum as long as first abdominal sternite; femora not dentate; metatibiae feebly spined; claws divergent; apical sutures of second to fourth ventral segments very prominent.

Notaris puncticollis (LeConte) Plate LXXVI, No. 9, p. 749

Elongate-oval; black or dark reddish brown; very sparsely clothed with short, prostate, yellowish-white hairs, these hairs forming a transverse spot just behind middle of elytra. Beak slender, cylindrical, curved, longer than pronotum, coarsely punctate. Antennal club as long as preceding four segments. Pronotum subglobose, as long as wide; sides feebly arcuate; disk coarsely, densely punctate. Elytra one-half wider than pronotum at base, humeri rounded; sides parallel to behind middle, thence strongly converging to apex; striae with coarse, quadrate punctures; intervals flat, finely, densely, rugosely punctate. Length 4.5–6.5 mm.

This species is usually found on semiaquatic plants such as arrow arum but has also been recorded as attacking cabbage.

Tribe TYCHIINI

Genus *TYCHIUS* Germar

Small, oval or elongate-oblong, robust species; beak swollen at base, slightly narrowed apically; antennal funicle of six or seven segments, the two basal segments longer, the remainder short and subequal; elytral apices together rounded, concealing pygidium, disk without tubercles or erect setae; abdominal sternites unequal, first and second longer and subequal, third and fourth together longer than second, the sutural angles of second extending over the sides of third to fourth (Fig. 511).

KEY TO SPECIES

Apical third of beak distinctly reddish ....b. *griseus*
Beak entirely black ....a. *picirostris*

a. *Tychius picirostris* (Fabricius)   Plate LXXVI, No. 6, p. 749

Elongate-oval; piceous; upper surface with rather dense, narrow, grayish scales; undersurface with grayish-white scales; basal segments of antennae and tibiae and tarsi pale reddish brown. Beak as long as pronotum; sparsely scaly from base to insertion of antennae, thence to apex shining and finely, sparsely punctate. Pronotum feebly transverse; sides feebly arcuate, more strongly so at apex; disk densely, finely punctate. Elytra slightly wider than pronotum; sides converging feebly from base to apex; apex broadly rounded; striae fine, punctate; intervals flat. Length 2.3–2.5 mm.

b. *Tychius griseus* Schaeffer   Plate LXXVI, No. 13, p. 749

Elongate-oval; piceous to reddish brown; upper surface with dense, narrow, yellowish-gray scales; undersurface with grayish-white scales; beak on apical third, antennae, and legs reddish brown. Beak as long as pronotum, densely scaly from base to insertion of antennae, thence to apex shining or finely, sparsely punctate. Pronotum distinctly longer than wide; sides feebly arcuate, more strongly so near apex; disk densely, finely punctate. Elytra slightly wider than pronotum; sides feebly converging from base to apex; apex broadly rounded; striae fine, punctate; intervals flat. Length 2.3–2.5 mm.

Tribe MAGDALINI

Genus *MAGDALIS* Germar

Small, elongate-oblong, convex forms; beak distinctly longer than pronotum, slightly curved, cylindrical; antennal scape curved, slender, enlarged distally, nearly as long as remainder of antennae, second segment elongate, enlarged at apex, as long as third and fourth together, club compact, four-segmented; pronotum with several teeth near anterior angles; elytra separated at base by scutellum, separately rounded at apex in both sexes, exposing pygidium in female; abdominal sternites unequal, first and second long, connate, third to fifth short, equal; procoxae contiguous, prominent; meso- and metacoxae not widely separated, the latter small and oval; femora not club-shaped, sometimes dentate; tibiae with a strong, curved spine at apex; tarsi spongy beneath, third segment broadest and deeply bilobed.

All the members of this genus are bark-borers.

KEY TO SPECIES

Mesosternal process strongly tuberculate; scutellum sparsely grayish-pubescent
only at apex ....b. *barbita*
Mesosternal process not tuberculate; scutellum entirely densely white-pubescent
....a. *olyra*

a. *Magdalis olyra* Herbst   Plate LXXVI, No. 15, p. 749
Elongate-oblong, convex; black, feebly shining; antennae and tarsi piceous; scutellum entirely whitish-pubescent. Beak shorter than head and pronotum together, densely punctate, especially apically. Pronotum subquadrate, with several teeth near anterior angles; surface densely, rather finely punctate; posterior angles somewhat flattened, divergent. Elytral striae shallow, rather coarsely punctate; intervals convex, alutaceous. Length 4–6 mm.

These beetles are usually found under the bark of hickory and oak.

b. *Magdalis barbita* Say   Plate LXXVI, No. 14, p. 749
Elongate-oblong, convex; black, feebly shining; antennae sometimes piceous. Beak rather slender, finely punctate, nearly as long as head and pronotum combined in female, shorter in male. Pronotum subquadrate, with a short spine and several small teeth near anterior angles; disk densely and coarsely punctate. Elytra striate, striae coarsely punctate; intervals convex, finely alutaceous. Femora dentate. Length 4–6 mm.

These beetles live and breed under the bark of recently dead hickory, walnut, elm, and oak.

Tribe Curculionini

Genus *CURCULIO* Linné

The Nut and Acorn Weevils

The most noticeable characteristics of this genus are the very robust body and very long, slender beak, which in the female of some species is longer than the body, though in others it is as short as or shorter than the body, and is always shorter in the male. The beak of the female is used for drilling holes in nuts or acorns, through which the eggs are deposited.

Other characters which distinguish them are as follows: small to moderate size; antennae geniculate, very long and slender, funicle seven-segmented, club elongate-oval, acuminate, annulate, and pubescent; procoxae contiguous; pronotum without postocular lobes; femora strongly dentate; tarsi dilated; claws divergent, toothed.

Curculio baculi (Chittenden) Plate LXXVI, No. 10, p. 749

Elongate-ovate; brownish piceous; very thinly whitish- and brown-pubescent or scaled; elytra with many small patches of dull-brown scales; undersurface sparsely clothed with short, grayish-white scales. Beak of female three-fifths as long as body, more robust at base, in male usually less than half as long as body. First segment of antennal funicle longer than second. Pronotum wider than long, sides nearly parallel to basal third, thence strongly converging and sinuous to apex; disk densely and rather finely punctate. Elytra gradually tapering from behind humeri to apex; apices narrowly rounded; striae feebly punctate; intervals slightly convex and finely granulate. Length 6–8 mm.

Tribe Anthonomini

KEY TO GENERA

1. Claws simple ....V. *Acalyptus* (p. 775)
   Claws not simple 2
2. Claws toothed (Fig. 520) 3
   Claws appendiculate (Fig. 521) 4
3. Metatibiae with a curved hook at apex (Fig. 522) ..I. *Tachypterellus* (p. 771)
   Metatibiae terminating in a sharp spine (Fig. 514) ...II. *Anthonomus* (p. 772)
4. Metafemora thickened; eyes approximate above ...IV. *Rhynchaenus* (p. 773)
   Metafemora slender; eyes widely separated above ......III. *Elleschus* (p. 773)

Genus I. *TACHYPTERELLUS* Fall and Cockerell

Small, oval, robust; beak long and slender, slightly curved, as long as body in female, two-thirds as long in male; antennal grooves deep, linear, directed toward but not reaching eyes; antennae slender, inserted one-third from apex of beak in male, just anterior to middle in female; scape not attaining eyes, funicle seven-segmented, first segment as long as next four combined, second to seventh short; club elongate, acuminate; eyes not approximate beneath; pygidium covered; first and second abdominal sternites long, subequal, the third and fourth shorter, the fifth longer; mesocoxae separated; profemora bidentate, meso- and metafemora unidentate; all tibiae with a small hook at tip; claws each with a long tooth, teeth convergent.

Tachypterellus quadrigibbosus (Say)   Apple Curculio
Plate LXXVI, No. 11, p. 749

Oval, very convex, robust; dark red; beak, antennae, and legs paler; pronotum and basal half of elytra thinly covered with grayish pubescence; pronotum with three lines of white pubescence; elytral tubercles reddish; sides of pro-, meso-, and metasternum with a stripe of dense, yellowish hair. Pronotal base about twice as wide as apex; disk densely, coarsely punctate. Elytra transversely impressed behind scutellum; each with a large tubercle on third interval at declivity and another on the fourth interval nearer apex. Length 3–4.5 mm.

The larvae attack fruit of apple and hawthorn, and the adults frequent the flowers of red haw, shadbush, and fruit trees.

FIG. 521

FIG. 520

FIG. 522

Fig. 520. End view of tip of tarsus of *Anthonomus*, with dentate claws.
Fig. 521. End view of tip of tarsus of *Rhychaenus*, with appendiculate claws.
Fig. 522. Apical portion of metatibia of *Tachypterellus*, with short, curved hook (*h*).

Genus II. *ANTHONOMUS* Germar

Very small, oval, robust beetles; variable in shape but usually long and slender; antennal grooves long, directed against the eye (Fig. 503); antennal scape reaching eye or nearly so; funicle of six or seven segments; club elongate-ovate; elytra distinctly striate and punctate, apices rounded, leaving pygidium more or less exposed in male; prosternum short in front of coxae; mesocoxae separated; pro- and mesotibiae with a hook, metatibiae spined; claws toothed.

KEY TO SPECIES

1. Profemora bidentate, front tooth often very small ....a. *grandis*
   Profemora unidentate 2
2. Elytral pubescence uniform, rarely condensed in spots or bands, without denuded patches or bands ....b. *suturalis*
   Elytral pubescence condensed in spots or lines, enclosing a denuded patch or band ....c. *signatus*

a. *Anthonomus grandis* Boheman   Cotton-Boll Weevil
                                                  Plate LXXVII, No. 2, p. 765

Oblong-ovate, robust; reddish brown to piceous; clothed with coarse, pale-yellowish, scalelike hairs, denser along median line, on sides of pronotum, and on numerous small spots on elytra. Beak in female half body length, slender, shining, sparsely pubescent basally; striate and coarsely punctate laterally on basal half, finely and sparsely punctate near apex; in male about one-fourth shorter, entirely coarsely punctate. Head conical; coarsely, sparsely punctate, deeply foveate on front. Pronotum transverse; sides nearly straight on basal half, thence strongly rounded to apex; disk constricted and transversely impressed near apex, densely and coarsely punctate. Elytra oblong; sides subparallel on basal third, thence gradually narrowing to apices, which are separately rounded; striae deep, with close-set punctures; intervals feebly convex, rugose. Length 4–7.5 mm.

This beetle has been one of the greatest economic problems of the cotton-growing sections of the country. Cotton is the only food plant of both larvae and adults; the larvae live in the bolls, and the adults feed on bolls and leaves. Since the larvae and adults hibernate, eradication is difficult.

b. *Anthonomus suturalis* LeConte   Plate LXXVII, No. 12, p. 765

Oval, robust; piceous, shining, slightly pubescent; apical half of elytra reddish brown; scutellum with dense, whitish pubescence; tarsi and basal segments of antennae paler. Pronotum much wider at base than at apex, sides arcuate; disk densely, finely punctate. Beak as long as head and pronotum together, moderately slender, arcuate, feebly dilated apically; densely, finely punctate. Elytral striae not deeply impressed, with small, rather distant punctures; intervals flat, alutaceous. Length 2.5–3.5 mm.

The adults may be found on leaves of hickory, plum, and cranberry.

c. *Anthonomus signatus* Say   Strawberry Weevil
                                                   Plate LXXVII, No. 13, p. 765
Oval, robust; piceous, feebly shining; pronotum with three indistinct stripes of whitish pubescence; scutellum covered with whitish pubescence; elytra reddish brown, with a broad denuded band behind middle, interrupted at suture, and with a small denuded area around scutellum; antennae and legs reddish brown. Beak longer than head and pronotum combined, slender, slightly curved, carinate dorsally, striate and punctate laterally. Pronotum widest at base; sides arcuate; disk densely and coarsely punctate. Elytra distinctly wider than pronotum; striae deep, with large punctures; intervals convex, finely punctate. Length 2–3 mm.

The adults may be taken from flowers of redbud, raspberries, blackberries, strawberries, and dewberries. They are most destructive on the berry plants in injuring the bud so that it falls off before the flower opens.

Genus III. *ELLESCHUS* Stephens

Very small, elongate, convex species; beak short, cylindrical, robust, very slightly arcuate; antennal grooves wide and deep, directed against the lower border of eyes (Fig. 507); antennal funicle seven-segmented, club oval, pubescent; ventral abdominal segments unequal, third and fourth short, together equal to second, fifth long, rounded, carinate near apex in male; metafemora not greatly enlarged; tibiae strongly curved at apex; tarsal claws appendiculate.

Elleschus ephippiatus Say   Plate LXXVII, No. 4, p. 765
Elongate, subcylindrical; reddish brown; clothed with pale-yellowish and light-brownish pubescence; elytra with a large, dark scutellar spot and another, somewhat rhomboidal, behind middle, these usually connected along suture; scutellum pale. Beak shorter than head and pronotum combined; finely, sparsely punctate. Pronotum widest at middle, sides arcuate; disk finely but not densely punctate. Elytra feebly wider at apex; striae fine, with large, close-set punctures; intervals flat. Length 1.5–3.4 mm.

The adults occur on willow, especially on the catkins in spring.

Genus IV. *RHYNCHAENUS* Clairville and Schönherr

Very small, elongate-oval, subconvex species; beak in repose lying between front legs; antennae with first three segments of funicle elongate, others shorter, rounded; eyes large, almost meeting on front; pronotum small; elytra oval or elongate-oval, wider than pronotum at base, transversely impressed on basal third, humeri rounded; metafemora much thickened, fitted for leaping; claws appendiculate.

The species of this genus are mostly leaf-miners on willow.

KEY TO SPECIES

1. Antennal funicle seven-segmented; form short, broad 2
   Funicle six-segmented; form narrower, more elongate ....c. *pallicornis*
2. Elytra with conspicuous anterior and posterior pale bands ....a. *ephippiatus*
   Elytra with only a faint pale band on basal third ....b. *niger*

a. *Rhynchaenus ephippiatus* (Say)   Plate LXXVII, No. 5, p. 765

Broadly elongate-oval, subconvex; dark reddish brown to piceous; head and pronotum sparsely clothed with grayish or dull-yellow hairs; scutellum densely white-pubescent; elytra thinly brownish-pubescent, with two common bands of whitish or yellowish-gray pubescence, anterior one broad at basal quarter, narrowed laterally, posterior one at apical third, narrow, undulating, these two bands sometimes connected on second interval; antennae, beak, tarsi, and mesofemora reddish brown; metafemora either in part or wholly piceous. Beak robust, shorter than head and pronotum, cylindrical, feebly arcuate. Pronotum feebly transverse, sides only slightly arcuate; disk finely, densely, rugosely punctate. Elytra at middle nearly twice as wide as pronotum; striae coarsely punctate; intervals flat, rugosely punctate. Length 2.5–3.5 mm.

The adults frequent willow.

b. *Rhynchaenus niger* Horn   Plate LXXVII, No. 6, p. 765

Elongate-oval, subconvex; black; sparsely clothed above with black, prostrate hairs; antennae piceous; scutellum covered with dense, whitish pubescence; elytra with a feeble transverse band of whitish hairs at about basal third; undersurface with thin, white pubescence. Beak cylindrical, as long as head and pronotum together, slightly curved, rather sparsely and coarsely punctate. Pronotum transverse, sides arcuate; disk coarsely, deeply, and densely punctate. Elytra wider at base than pronotum; sides broadly curved from base to apex; striae broad, deeply and coarsely punctate; intervals flat, very finely punctate. Length 2–3 mm.

This species occurs mostly on low willows.

c. *Rhynchaenus pallicornis* Say   Plate LXXVII, No. 7, p. 765

Elongate-oval, subconvex; black, shining; sparsely clothed with a short, dull-yellow pubescence; antennae and tarsi pale reddish brown, club dusky. Beak robust, almost as long as head and pronotum, coarsely, sparsely punctate. Pronotum as wide at middle as long, sides feebly arcuate; disk densely covered with coarse, shallow punctures. Elytra wider than pronotum; striae feebly impressed with coarse, deep punctures; intervals flat, rugose, sparsely, finely punctate. Length 2.5–3 mm.

The adults occur on willow, alder, and apple; the larvae mine in the leaves of elm, alder, apple, and cherry.

Genus V. *ACALYPTUS* Schönherr

Small, oval, robust forms; beak slender, curved, as long as head and pronotum; antennal grooves from near middle of beak directed against middle of eyes; antennae with funicle of seven segments, scarcely longer than club, which is pubescent, first segment long, robust, second to seventh gradually wider; pro- and mesotibiae not armed; metatibiae with a short spine at apex.

Acalyptus carpini (Herbst)   Plate LXXVII, No. 8, p. 765
Oval, subdepressed; piceous; above densely clothed with short, grayish-white pubescence, less densely so beneath; antennae and legs reddish brown. Pronotum wider than long, sides feebly arcuate; disk finely, densely punctate. Elytra distinctly wider basally than pronotum, sides nearly parallel, apices separately, broadly rounded; disk indistinctly striate; intervals flat, finely punctate. Length 2.2–2.8 mm.
This is an introduced species; the adults occur abundantly on the catkins of willow.

Tribe MECININI

Genus *GYMNETRON* Schönherr

Very small, broadly oval, rather robust beetles; beak nearly straight, as long as pronotum, robust, tapering from base to apex; first segment of funicle two-thirds longer than second, the second slightly longer than third, third to fifth equal; antennal club short, oval; head short, inserted into pronotum nearly to eyes; procoxae contiguous.

Gymnetron tetrum (Fabricius)   Plate LXXVII, No. 9, p. 765
Broadly oval, strongly robust; black; densely clothed with suberect, dull-yellowish pubescence. Pronotum transverse, sides broadly arcuate; disk finely and densely punctate. Elytra slightly wider at base than pronotum; sides broadly arcuate from base to apex; striae fine, deep, and coarsely punctate; intervals flat, rugosely punctate. Femora stout, dentate beneath. Length 2.3–3.8 mm.
This species may be collected on mullein the year round; it feeds on the plant in summer and hibernates in the basal leaves during the winter.

PLATE LXXVIII
Family CURCULIONIDAE IV

1. *Ceutorhynchus punctiger* Gyllenhal (p. 786)

   Black, with white markings; 3–3.2 mm.

2. *C. rapae* Gyllenhal (p. 783)

   Black, covered with short, white hairs; 2.7–3.2 mm.

3. *Cylindrocopturus quercus* (Say) (p. 782)

   Black, usually covered with dense, tan and white scales; 2.5–3 mm.

4. *Ceutorhynchus sulcipennis* LeConte (p. 786)

   Black, sparsely whitish-pubescent; 2.5–2.7 mm.

5. *Conotrachelus anaglypticus* (Say) (p. 790)

   Black, marked with white, tan, and dark brown; 3.5–4.7 mm.

6. *Mononychus vulpeculus* (Fabricius) (p. 783)

   Black; pronotal sides and elytral suture with whitish pubescence; 4.5–5 mm.

7. *Conotrachelus nenuphar* (Herbst) (p. 788)

   Blackish, covered with tan, brown, and white pubescence; 4.5–6.5 mm.

8. *C. juglandis* LeConte (p. 788)

   Red-brown to blackish, covered with ashy and brown pubescence; 5–7 mm.

9. *C. elegans* (Say) (p. 788)

   Red-brown to black, covered with ashy, yellowish, and brown pubescence; 3.5–4.5 mm.

10. *C. crataegi* Walsh (p. 789)

    Dark reddish brown to black, with dull ashy and brown pubescence; 4–6 mm.

11. *C. geminatus* Dejean (p. 789)

    Black, covered with fuscous and whitish pubescence; 4–5 mm.

12. *Rhinoncus pyrrhopus* Boheman (p. 787)

    Black, marked with white or yellowish; 2.3–2.7 mm.

13. *Barypeithes pellucidus* (Boheman) (p. 756)

    Blackish; legs often reddish brown; 2.5–3.5 mm.

14. *Sitona flavescens* Marsham (p. 758)

    Black; densely covered with fuscous and dull-yellowish scales; 4.5–5.5 mm.

15. *Polydrusus americanus* Gyllenhal (p. 755)

    Dark brown, with light-brown, fuscous, and whitish scales; 4.5–5.5 mm.

MM |·····|·····|·····|·····|·····|·····|·····|
0   10   20   30   40   50   60   70

PLATE LXXVIII

777

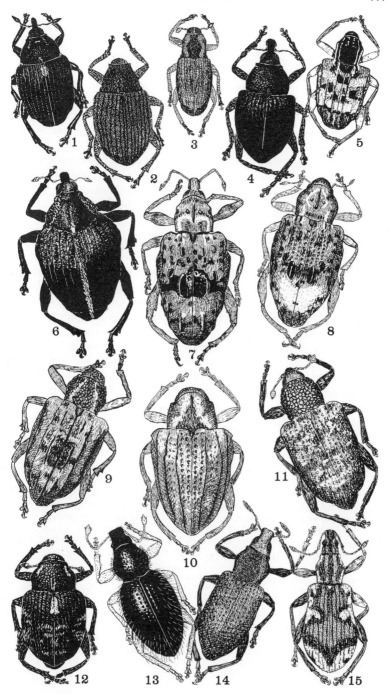

Tribe CLEONINI

Genus *LIXUS* Fabricius

Of moderate to large size, elongate, subcylindrical; beak slender, cylindrical, and arcuate, feebly dilated at apex, very rarely carinate; antennae slender, first segment of funicle more robust, second as long as or longer than the next two combined; pronotum oblong, conical, base bisinuate; scutellum minute, triangular; elytra as wide at base as pronotum, the sides continuous with those of pronotum; humeri obtusely subangulate; prosternum without a spiniform process; tarsi broad, with patches of yellowish-brown pubescence beneath, third segment deeply bilobed.

Lixus concavus Say   Rhubarb Beetle
                                                  Plate LXXVII, No. 10, p. 765

Elongate, cylindrical, robust; black; sparsely clothed with short, fine, grayish pubescence and, when specimen is fresh, covered with an orangeish pollen; antennae and tarsi reddish brown. Beak finely and densely punctate. Pronotum wider at base than long; sides feebly arcuate, constricted near apex; disk sparsely and coarsely punctate, with fine punctures intermingled; a large, deep, median impression from near apex to base and continuous with that of elytra. Elytral sides parallel to apical quarter; disk with rows of small, distinct punctures; intervals finely, densely punctate. Length 10–13.5 mm.

This beetle breeds in the stems of curly dock, sunflower, thistle, and rhubarb.

Tribe BARINI

KEY TO GENERA

1. Pygidium more or less entirely exposed, usually almost vertical 2
   Pygidium oblique or horizontal, entirely covered in female (except
   Odontocorynus), sometimes with only apex exposed in male 4
2. Tarsal claws free (Fig. 523), more or less divergent . . . . I. *Madarellus* (p. 779)
   Claws connate at base, parallel, or feebly divergent at apex (Fig. 524)
   3
3. Procoxae widely separated; body above nearly glabrous . . . .
   . . . . II. *Pseudobaris* (p. 779)
   Procoxae narrowly separated; body densely clothed with pale, scale-
   like hairs . . . . III. *Trichobaris* (p. 780)
4. Scutellum with white pubescence; apex of pygidium exposed in both
   sexes . . . . V. *Odontocorynus* (p. 781)
   Scutellum not white-pubescent; apex of pygidium entirely hidden . .
   . . . . IV. *Centrinaspis* (p. 780)

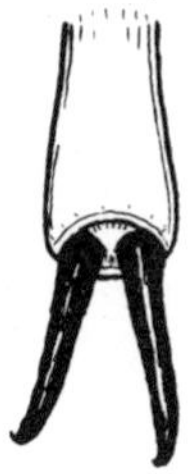

FIG. 523

FIG. 524

Fig. 523. Tip of tarsus of *Madarellus* in dorsal view, the claws free.
Fig. 524. Tip of tarsus of *Trichobaris* from above, the claws connate at base.

Genus I. *MADARELLUS* Casey

Small, oval, somewhat flattened dorsally; more or less glabrous; antennae with first segment of funicle as long as next four together, club elongate-oval, entirely pubescent; pronotum short, broadly, abruptly, and strongly constricted at apex; prosternum extending far over mesosternum, transversely truncate or broadly sinuate and always more or less angulate at sides of process, surface frequently transversely raised just behind coxae; procoxae widely separated; femora minutely dentate, profemora distinctly so; third tarsal segment broadly bilobed; tarsal claws free, slightly divergent; pygidium exposed, usually nearly vertical.

Madarellus undulatus (Say) Plate LXXVII, No. 1, p. 765

Oval, rather wedge-shaped; flattened dorsally; black, very shining; pronotum often red. Beak slender, long, and slightly curved; sides finely, densely punctate. Pronotum transverse, convex, minutely and sparsely punctate. Elytra narrower at base than pronotum, narrowing from base to apex; striae deep and narrow, very finely punctate; intervals very finely and feebly punctate, lateral ones distinctly and finely rugose. Length 2.7–4.7 mm.

These beetles may be taken from wild grape, poison ivy, and Virginia creeper.

Genus II. *PSEUDOBARIS* LeConte

Small, rather slender, subcylindrical, convex species; body above nearly glabrous; antennal club entirely pubescent; procoxae widely separated; prosternum deeply and abruptly sulcate longitudinally along middle; pygidium large, convex, not at all covered by the elytra; tarsal claws approximate, connate basally.

Pseudobaris nigrina (Say)   Plate LXXVII, No. 14, p. 765

Elongate-oval, convex; black, shining; antennae and tarsi piceous. Beak strongly arcuate, in female as long as head and pronotum, more robust and shorter in male; finely, sparsely punctate dorsally, more coarsely so laterally. Pronotum transverse, sides parallel at basal third, broadly curved and converging apically; disk deeply and very densely punctate, median line nearly entirely smooth. Elytra subequal in width to base of pronotum; striae deep, finely, sparsely punctate; intervals flat, each with a single row of large, closely placed punctures. Undersurface coarsely, densely punctate. Length 2.5–3.7 mm.

Genus III. *TRICHOBARIS* LeConte

Small, elongate-oval, robust species; body clothed with short, prostrate, whitish scales, these lacking on head and in other small areas on upper surface; beak robust, shorter, separated from head by a deep, angular impression; antennal club small, oval, entirely pubescent, funicle robust, first segment longer, others subequal and gradually wider; prosternum broadly, feebly, longitudinally impressed medially; procoxae narrowly separated; tibiae nearly smooth, clawed at apex; tarsi with third segment dilated, bilobed, last segment long; claws connate at base, approximate.

Trichobaris trinotata (Say)   Potato-Stalk Borer
                                                 Plate LXXVII, No. 11, p. 765

Narrowly elongate-oval, robust; black; densely clothed with short, white, prostrate hairs, those on disk of pronotum pointing toward median line, those on elytra in almost even rows; scutellum, head, and a round spot on each side at base of pronotum without scales. Beak coarsely and densely punctate near apex; robust, not as long as pronotum in male, more slender and longer in female. Pronotum scarcely wider than long; disk coarsely, densely punctate. Elytra finely striate; striae minutely punctate; intervals each with about three rows of scalelike hairs. Length 3–4 mm.

This species is recorded as attacking many members of the potato family, such as Jimson weed, horse nettle, ground cherry, and cocklebur, as well as potato plants.

Genus IV. *CENTRINASPIS* Casey

Small, broadly oval, robust species; surface densely scaled; mandibles elongate, prominent, not crossed in repose, inner edge never toothed; beak cylindrical, long and slender, strongly arcuate; pronotum narrowed and more or less constricted at apex; elytra scarcely wider than pronotum, narrowed toward apices; femora unarmed; tarsal claws free, divergent; apex of pygidium hidden.

Centrinaspis picumnus (Herbst) Plate LXXVII, No. 15, p. 765

Broadly oval, convex; dark reddish brown to black; legs paler; upper surface densely clothed with long, narrow, dull-yellow to white scales; undersurface with paler, denser, and broader scales; head without scales; elytral scales in more or less even rows. Beak slender, one-half as long as body, tapering to apex, arcuate, that of male finely striate-punctate, in female finely and densely punctate on basal third, apical third polished, minutely, sparsely punctate. Antennae inserted behind middle; second segment of funicle one-half longer than third. Pronotum conical, transverse, narrowed toward apex, slightly constricted apically; disk very finely, densely punctate. Elytra slightly wider at base than pronotum, narrowed to apex; striae deep, punctate; intervals flat, densely punctate, each with two or three rows of scales. Prosternum of male narrowly and deeply excavated along middle, with a short, erect, acute spine anterior to procoxae. Length 2.1–2.7 mm.

This species has been recorded as taken from flowers of dogwood, white snakeroot, and various other flowers.

Genus V. *ODONTOCORYNUS* Schönherr

Small, oval, robust species; male with outer segments of antennal funicle obliquely truncate and basal segment of club with a large, glabrous area on inner side, at middle of which there is a dentiform process; basal impression of beak almost obsolete; scutellum densely clothed with white pubescence; procoxae narrowly separated; prosternum usually with a deep, transversely oval pit behind anterior margin.

Odontocorynus scutellum-album (Say) Plate LXXVII, No. 3, p. 765

Broadly oval, convex, robust; male black, antennae and tarsi dark reddish brown; female with more or less reddish tinge; upper surface very sparsely clothed with very narrow, small, white scales; those of scutellum and undersurface very broad and dense. Beak longer than pronotum, feebly arcuate, sides flattened and coarsely striate-punctate. Antennae inserted near apical third; second segment of funicle nearly as long as next three together; basal segment of club of male on inner side with a large polished area which bears an erect, acute process; club simple in female. Pronotum transverse; sides broadly arcuate, slightly constricted near apex; disk finely, deeply, and densely punctate. Elytra distinctly wider at base than pronotum; striae deep, with coarse, deep punctures; intervals very coarsely, rugosely punctate, each puncture with a small scale. Prosternum with a large, transverse excavation just behind apex. Length 3–4.8 mm.

This beetle is found especially on the giant mullein but may be taken on other flowers.

Tribe ZYGOPINI

Genus *CYLINDROCOPTURUS* Heller

Small, robust, subcylindrical forms; antennal club short, robust, basal segment shorter than the other two combined, second segment of funicle longer than third; beak long, slender, antennal insertion near middle; femora not dentate; third, fourth, and fifth abdominal sternites subequal in length, strongly ascending.

Cylindrocopturus quercus (Say) Plate LXXVIII, No. 3, p. 777

Short, oval, robust; black, shining; undersurface, sides of pronotum, and base of beak covered with dense, rounded, grayish-white scales, this vesti-ture also forming a medial spot at base of pronotum and a sutural line and two interrupted fasciae on elytra; antennae dark reddish brown. Beak slender, strongly arcuate, feebly carinate, and shallowly punctate. Pro-notum feebly transverse, slightly constricted near apex; disk coarsely, densely punctate. Elytra distinctly wider than pronotum; sides parallel to behind middle, thence converging to apex; striae rather fine, deep, and coarsely punctate; intervals flat, each with two irregular rows of punctures concealed by scales. Length 2.5–3 mm.

Tribe CEUTORHYNCHINI

KEY TO GENERA

1. Tarsi with a single claw; upper surface of pygidium in female deeply excavated; length 4.5–5 mm. ....I. *Mononychus* (p. 783)
   Tarsi with two claws; pygidium not excavated; less than 4 mm. long 2
2. Beak longer and slender, usually one-half length of body; eyes wholly or partially concealed by postocular lobes (Fig. 503) ....
   ....II. *Ceutorhynchus* (p. 783)
   Beak robust, usually short; postocular lobes wanting (Fig. 508) ...
   ....III. *Rhinoncus* (p. 786)

Genus I. *MONONYCHUS* Germar

Small, broadly oval, robust species; beak long, cylindrical, resting in a deep groove which extends through pro- and mesosternum into the metasternum; eyes partially hidden by postocular lobes; antennal funicle seven-segmented; upper surface of female pygidium deeply excavated; second abdominal sternite as long at middle as third and fourth together; legs slender; tibiae obliquely fringed at apex; tarsi with a single claw.

Mononychus vulpeculus (Fabricius)   Plate LXXVIII, No. 6, p. 777

Broadly oval; black, feebly shining; undersurface, except middle of third and fourth abdominal sternites, sides of pronotum, and basal third of elytral suture densely clothed with yellowish-white scales; antennae dull yellow. Pronotum coarsely, densely, and shallowly punctate. Elytral striae coarsely, distantly punctate; intervals broad, flat, each with one or two rows of coarse punctures. Male pygidium protuberant, fifth abdominal sternite strongly foveate; meso- and metatibiae clawed at tip. Female pygidium strongly excavated, fifth abdominal sternite very convex; tibiae unarmed. Length 4.5–5 mm.

The adults of this species may be found on flowers of iris.

Genus II. *CEUTORHYNCHUS* Germar

Very small, ovate, robust species; beak long and slender, usually one-half as long as body; eyes wholly or partially concealed by postocular lobes; pygidium not excavated but carinate anteriorly and with transverse line for reception of elytral apices; prosternal median groove not extending beyond procoxae, limited by the acute antecoxal ridges; mesosternum oblique, not sulcate; mesocoxal cavities closed within; abdominal sternites three to five unequal; third tarsal segment bilobed; tarsi with two claws.

KEY TO SPECIES

1. Elytra uniformly pubescent or scaly and without scutellar white spot 2
   Elytra with a scutellar white spot, scales white in single rows in striae ......
   ....c. *punctiger*
2. Scales white ....a. *rapae*
   Scales brown ....b. *sulcipennis*

a. *Ceutorhynchus rapae* Gyllenhal   Cabbage Curculio
                                                  Plate LXXVIII, No. 2, p. 777

Broadly oval, robust; black; clothed above with very small, hairlike scales, yellowish in new specimens, gray in old specimens; undersurface densely clothed with large, oval, grayish scales. Beak slender, cylindrical, longer than head and pronotum combined; finely punctate, striate on

PLATE LXXIX
Family CURCULIONIDAE V

1. *Listronotus caudatus* (Say) (p. 763)

   Blackish, covered with dark-brown scales, often with a bronze reflex; pronotum with yellowish vittae; 10–12 mm.

2. *Graphognathus leucoloma* (Boheman) (p. 755)

   Ashy- and dull-brown-scaled; sides often with a broad, white vitta; 9–12 mm.

3. *Hypera punctata* (Fabricius) (p. 760)

   Black, covered with ashy or brown and blackish scales; 5–8 mm.

4. *Sitona hispidulus* (Fabricius) (p. 758)

   Black, with greenish or dull-yellowish scales which are often bronzed; 3–5 mm.

5. *Brachyrhinus ovatus* (Linné) (p. 756)

   Black, shining; legs and antennae deep brown; 5–6 mm.

6. *Phytonomus nigrirostris* (Fabricius) (p. 762)

   Blackish; densely covered with bright metallic-green, fuscous, and golden-brown pubescence; 3.5–4.5 mm.

7. *Hyperodes solutus* (Boheman) (p. 763)

   Black, covered with yellowish and blackish scales; 3–5 mm.

8. *Pissodes strobi* (Peck) (p. 766)

   Red-brown to black; pronotal spots white; elytral bands dull yellow and white; 4.5–6 mm.

9. *Hylobius pales* Boheman (p. 767)

   Blackish, with whitish markings; 7–10 mm.

10. *Anametis granulata* (Say) (p. 754)

    Dark brown to piceous, covered with white or greenish scales; 5–7 mm.

MM 0 10 20 30 40 50 60 70

PLATE LXXIX

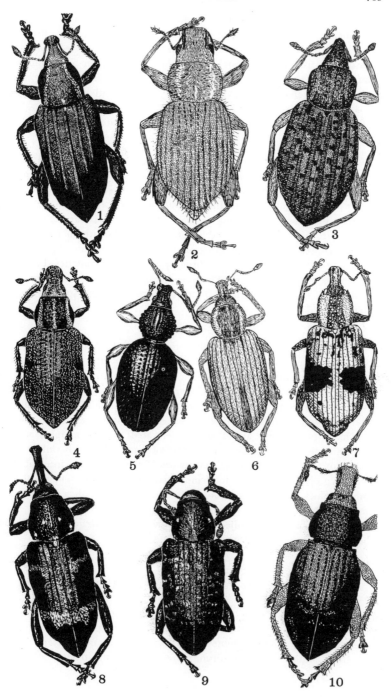

basal half. Antennae inserted near middle of beak; segments one and two of funicle each about as long as third and fourth together. Pronotum wider at base than long, narrowed to, and strongly constricted near, apex; disk densely, coarsely punctate. Elytra wider at base than pronotum, sides parallel to beyond middle, thence convergent to apices; striae fine, punctate; intervals flat, rugose, the declivity with small granules. Length 2.7–3.2 mm.

This is an introduced species and feeds on cultivated and wild forms of the mustard family.

b. *Ceutorhynchus sulcipennis* LeConte   Plate LXXVIII, No. 4, p. 777

Broadly oval, robust; black, shining, with very thin, fine, whitish pubescence; elytra with an elongate sutural spot of white scales; undersurface of body with each puncture bearing an oval, whitish scale; antennae, tibiae, and tarsi piceous. Beak as long as head and pronotum together, cylindrical, arcuate; finely punctate and striate in male, smooth in female. Eyes partially concealed by ocular lobes of pronotum. Pronotum slightly wider than long; sides strongly arcuate, broadly, not deeply constricted at apex; disk finely, densely punctate. Elytra wider basally than pronotum; striae broad, deep, coarsely punctate; intervals narrow, convex, strongly rugose. Length 2.5–2.7 mm.

This species may be collected by sweeping weeds.

c. *Ceutorhynchus punctiger* Gyllenhal   Plate LXXVIII, No. 1, p. 777

Ovate, convex; black; densely clothed with brownish hairs and white scales, the latter arranged in a single row in each stria and forming an oblong sutural spot behind scutellum; a few spots of white scales near anterior margin on either side of pronotum; tarsi reddish brown; undersurface densely clothed with white scales. Pronotum transverse, deeply constricted near apex; apical margin elevated; lateral margins with a small tubercle; a deep fovea at middle of base; disk with only coarse, dense punctures. Elytral striae narrow and finely punctate; intervals flat, finely, rugosely punctate. Metafemora strongly, the profemora feebly, toothed; claws with a long, almost bifid tooth. Male with a large, transverse impression on last abdominal sternite. Length 3–3.2 mm.

The adults have been collected from flowers of dandelion, lettuce, and other composites.

Genus III. *RHINONCUS* Schönherr

Very small, oval or oblong-oval species; beak short, robust, dilated toward apex; eyes large, convex, entirely visible in repose; antennal funicle seven-segmented, basal segment long, obconical, second segment longer than third, others short, subrotund; prosternum long in front of coxae, antecoxal ridges distinct; coxae widely separated; femora unarmed; third segment of tarsi bilobed; claws cleft or armed with a long tooth.

Rhinoncus pyrrhopus Boheman   Plate LXXVIII, No. 12, p. 777

Broadly ovate; fuscous; densely clothed above with brownish hairs and whitish scales, the latter forming a conspicuous scutellar spot, behind which is a brown, velvety line; pronotum and remainder of elytra with numerous spots of white scales; undersurface densely clothed with white scales; antennae and legs pale reddish brown. Beak scaly at base, shining on apical half; finely, sparsely pubescent; front concave between eyes. Pronotum transverse; broadly and shallowly constricted at apex; disk coarsely and densely punctate; dorsal sulcus distinct only on basal half; lateral tubercles small, acute. Elytra wider at base than pronotum; sides broadly arcuate; striae punctate; intervals convex, rugose, each with a row of very small, inclined tubercles. Last abdominal sternite of male with a small, glabrous space at apex; meso- and metatibiae with a curved hook at apex. Length 2.3–2.7 mm.

The adults frequent dock, smartweed, and some species of *Euphorbia*.

Tribe CRYPTORHYNCHINI

KEY TO GENERA

1. Ventral groove for reception of beak confined to prosternum, open
   posteriorly (Fig. 525) ....I. *Conotrachelus* (p. 787)
   Ventral groove for reception of beak extending behind procoxae into
   mesosternum, sharply limited posteriorly (Fig. 526) 2
2. Funicle of antennae six-segmented ....II. *Tyloderma* (p. 790)
   Funicle of antennae seven-segmented ....III. *Cryptorhynchus* (p. 791)

Genus I. *CONOTRACHELUS* Dejean

Small, elongate-oval, robust forms; upper surface with scales; scrobes not confluent posteriorly; head not sulcate, without tubercles; base of elytra much wider than pronotum, humeri prominent; ventral groove for reception of beak confined to prosternum, open behind; procoxae contiguous; tibiae with a strong hook; claws toothed or cleft.

KEY TO SPECIES

1. Pronotum not sulcate, usually carinate 2
   Pronotum broadly and shallowly sulcate, with two low crests anteriorly ......
   ....f. *anaglypticus*
2. Femora bidentate; elytral costae usually interrupted 3
   Femora unidentate; elytral costae either absent or entire 5

3. Costae of elytra abruptly and strongly interrupted 4
   Costae of elytra feebly or not at all interrupted ....c. *elegans*
4. Elytral band uniformly pale yellow ....b. *juglandis*
   Elytral band yellow and white ....a. *nenuphar*
5. Beak slender, much longer than head and pronotum ....d. *crataegi*
   Beak stout, curved, scarcely longer than head and pronotum .....e. *geminatus*

a. *Conotrachelus nenuphar* (Herbst)   Plum Curculio
                                              Plate LXXVIII, No. 7, p. 777

Elongate-oval, robust; dark brown; pubescence brownish yellow, forming a bifurcate line each side of pronotum and a postmedian elytral band of yellow and white hairs; a conspicuous short, white vitta at base of third interval. Beak robust, arcuate, slightly longer than head and pronotum. Pronotum as wide at base as long, strongly constricted toward apex, carinate in front of middle; disk coarsely and roughly punctate. Elytral crests abrupt, the median ones prominent. Abdominal sternites coarsely and densely punctate, the fifth with two seta-bearing tubercles. Length 4.5–6.5 mm.

The adults may be beaten from wild hawthorn and from plum, cherry, and other domestic fruit trees.

b. *Conotrachelus juglandis* LeConte   Walnut Curculio
                                              Plate LXXVIII, No. 8, p. 777

Elongate-oval; dark brown; pubescence brownish yellow, forming a bifurcate line on each side of pronotum, a broad band just behind middle of elytra, and two rings on each femur. Beak cylindrical, pubescent, longer than head and pronotum combined, with a broad, lateral groove and two short, finer ones on basal half. Pronotum transverse, broadly constricted near apex, sides rounded on basal two-thirds; disk coarsely, rugosely punctate, with a short carina before middle and four small tubercles. Elytra with rows of large, quadrate punctures; alternate intervals costate, the one on third and fifth intervals interrupted and strongly elevated just before middle. Abdominal sternites sparsely punctate. Length 5–7 mm.

This beetle attacks walnut, butternut, and hickory; the larvae live in the undeveloped nuts.

c. *Conotrachelus elegans* (Say)   Plate LXXVIII, No. 9, p. 777

Oval; dark brown; antennae, tibiae, and tarsi paler; pronotum with an oblique vitta of yellowish pubescence each side, convergent but not joining at apex; elytra yellowish-pubescent, with sparse, gray pubescence intermixed, each with a large, black, discal spot. Beak distinctly longer than head and pronotum, feebly arcuate, deeply striate and punctate. Pronotum longer than wide; disk densely, coarsely, rugosely punctate. First elytral costa twice interrupted, second interrupted just behind middle; striae with coarse, quadrate punctures. Abdominal sternites coarsely, densely punctate, the last segment more finely so. Length 3.5–4.5 mm.

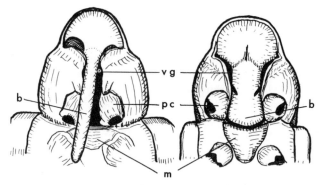

FIGS. 525–526

Figs. 525–526. Underside of anterior portion of body of *Conotrachelus* (525) and of *Tyloderma* (526). The beak (*b*) fits partly or fully into a ventral groove (*vg*) in the prothorax, more or less limited behind by the mesosternum (*m*) and bordered by the procoxae (*pc*).

The adults may be beaten from hickory and apple. The female oviposits in the rolled-up leaves and cuts the leaves off; the larvae also feed on underground stems of the rough pigweed.

d. *Conotrachelus crataegi* Walsh   Quince Curculio
                                          Plate LXXVIII, No. 10, p. 777

Broadly ovate, robust; piceous; densely clothed with yellowish and ashy scales, the latter forming a double line of paler scales on each side of pronotum, these lines meeting before middle and passing to humeri across the basal third of elytra; body beneath thinly clothed with grayish-yellow scales. Beak longer than head and pronotum, deeply striate and punctate, carinate dorsally. Pronotum as broad as long, constricted near apex; broadly, transversely impressed near apex, elevated and carinate at middle; disk coarsely punctate. Elytra with intervals three, five, seven, and nine costate, furrows between carinae with two rows of coarse punctures; humeri obliquely truncate, outer angles dentiform. Body beneath sparsely, coarsely punctate; third and fourth abdominal sternites sparsely, fifth more densely punctate. Femora with a large tooth. Length 4–6 mm.

These beetles frequent quince and hawthorn.

e. *Conotrachelus geminatus* Dejean   Plate LXXVIII, No. 11, p. 777

Ovate, robust; dark reddish brown; thinly clothed with yellowish pubescence; pronotum usually with a denser spot of pubescence on either side of median line; elytra with indistinct grayish bands and a white spot at base of third interval and rows of very short bristles; antennae, tibiae, and tarsi pale reddish brown. Beak robust; shorter than pronotum, striate, densely punctate in male; one-fourth longer than pronotum and shining at apex in female. Pronotum as wide as long; sides subparallel; disk coarsely and densely punctate. Elytra with rows of large, quadrate punctures; intervals broad, flat, the third and fifth slightly elevated near declivity. Undersurface coarsely punctate. Femora with a large, obtuse tooth. Length 4–5 mm.

This beetle may be taken by sweeping the great ragweed.

f. *Conotrachelus anaglypticus* (Say)   Plate LXXVIII, No. 5, p. 777

Broadly oval, robust; piceous or dark reddish brown; sparsely clothed with short, fine, yellowish, scalelike hairs, these concentrated to form two narrow lines on sides of pronotum, a broad, oblique, humeral spot or stripe on elytra, and a broad band on apical half of femora; elytra with an indistinct white band just behind middle. Beak almost as long as head and pronotum combined, robust, striate, carinate dorsally. Pronotum little longer than wide, sides subparallel; disk densely, finely, reticulately punctate, and with two indistinct crests on apical half. Base of elytra much wider than pronotum; humeri almost rectangular; striae punctate, with large, quadrate punctures; alternate intervals costate, second costa widely interrupted at basal third. Abdominal sternites coarsely, sparsely punctate. Length 3.5–4.7 mm.

This species is recorded as having been taken at light, on asters, under moist bark, and from hickory and quince.

Genus II. *TYLODERMA* Say

Oblong or oblong-oval, nearly glabrous species; beak short, robust, in repose barely extending to mesosternum, the pectoral groove only a shallow emargination in anterior margin of mesosternum; antennae and eyes nearly covered by the prominent postocular lobes and sides of deep pectoral groove; pronotum with apical margin rounded; second abdominal sternite longer than third; femora slender, unarmed; third tarsal segment dilated, bilobed; tarsal claws small, free, and simple.

KEY TO SPECIES

Body dull, very coarsely, deeply sculptured; pronotum with large, uneven foveae ....a. *foveolata*
Body smoother, shining; pronotum punctate, not foveate ....b. *aerea*

a. *Tyloderma foveolata* Say   Plate LXXX, No. 3, p. 793

Oblong; black, opaque; antennae and tarsi dark reddish brown; small patches of grayish-white hairlike scales on middle of vertex, between the eyes, and at apex of pronotum, a curved row each side of pronotum from before middle to near sides of base; elytra also with numerous irregular spots on disk and a broad, uneven band at apical fourth. Beak not longer than head, broad, coarsely punctate; head with a deep frontal sulcus, the surface more finely and sparsely punctate than beak. Pronotum slightly wider than long; sides strongly arcuate; disk coarsely, deeply, densely, and unevenly punctate; surface between punctures finely alutaceous. Elytral sides parallel to apical third, thence rounded to apices; disk with irregular rows of very large, irregular-sized punctures, becoming obsolete apically; intervals with scattered, small punctures. Length 3–5.8 mm.

This species breeds in stems of the evening primrose and willow herb.

b. *Tyloderma aerea* Say   Plate LXXX, No. 1, p. 793
Narrowly ovate, convex; black, bronzed, strongly shining; head, beak, and legs dull. Beak as long as head; both finely, rather densely punctate; frontal fovea obsolete. Pronotum slightly wider than long, widest at middle, thence feebly narrowed to base, more strongly so toward apex; disk minutely alutaceous, very finely, sparsely punctate; sides more coarsely, densely punctate, each puncture with a small seta. Elytra with sides nearly parallel from base to middle, thence gradually converging to apex; disk with rows of fine, widely spaced punctures, these absent on apical third; intervals flat, feebly rugose. Length 2.2–2.8 mm.

This species is taken by sweeping plants growing in bogs or near water.

Genus III. *CRYPTORHYNCHUS* Illiger

Oblong or oval, rather robust beetles; usually densely scaled; eyes widely separated; antennae inserted at middle of beak; funicle seven-segmented; ocular lobes covering eyes partially in repose; elytra with ten entire striae; mesosternal process with a deep, rounded cavity; metasternum with distinct sidepieces; abdominal sternites two to four equal or nearly so, the second sometimes one-fourth longer than third or fourth; femora robust, sulcate beneath, usually bidentate; tibiae slender, usually more or less sinuate.

The larvae of this genus are bark-borers, and the adults are usually found on bark or dead twigs.

Cryptorhynchus lapathi (Linné)   Poplar and Willow Borer
                                            Plate LXXX, No. 6, p. 793
Elongate-oval, robust; black or piceous; densely clothed with dull-black and whitish scales, with scattered tufts of erect, black bristles; apical third of elytra and an oblique band on basal third of pronotum with densely placed, whitish scales; antennae and tarsi reddish brown. Beak as long as head and pronotum combined; coarsely, densely punctate; feebly carinate.

PLATE LXXX
Family CURCULIONIDAE VI

1. *Tyloderma aerea* Say (p. 791)
   Black, with a slightly brassy reflex; 2.2–2.8 mm.

2. *Phytonomus meles* (Fabricius) (p. 762)
   Blackish, covered with sparse, ashy pubescence; antennae and legs piceous; 3.5–5 mm.

3. *Tyloderma foveolata* Say (p. 790)
   Black, feebly shining; elytra with a dull clay-yellow band near apex; 3–5.8 mm.

4. *Dryophthorus americanus* Bedel (p. 795)
   Black; often more or less encrusted with gum; 2–3 mm.

5. *Stenoscelis brevis* (Boheman) (p. 795)
   Black; elytra and legs often dark brown; 2.8–3.2 mm.

6. *Cryptorhynchus lapathi* (Linné) (p. 791)
   Black, covered by tan, white, and blackish scales; pronotum and elytra with tufts of black hairs; 7.5–10 mm.

7. *Cossonus platalea* Say (p. 795)
   Piceous to black, shining; antennae dark brown; 5.5–6.5 mm.

Family RHYNCHOPHORIDAE I

8. *Sitophilus oryzae* (Linné) (p. 803)
   Brown; markings reddish; 2.1–2.8 mm.

9. *Rhodobaenus tredecimpunctatus* (Illiger) (p. 796)
   Red, with black markings which are variable; head, body beneath, and legs black; 7–10 mm.

10. *Calendra australis* (Chittenden) (p. 798)
    Black and dark gray; 11–15 mm.

11. *C. cariosa* (Olivier) (p. 799)
    Black and dull gray; 7.5–11 mm.

12. *Sitophilus granaria* (Linné) (p. 802)
    Brown to blackish; 3–4 mm.

MM 0 10 20 30 40 50 60 70

PLATE LXXX

793

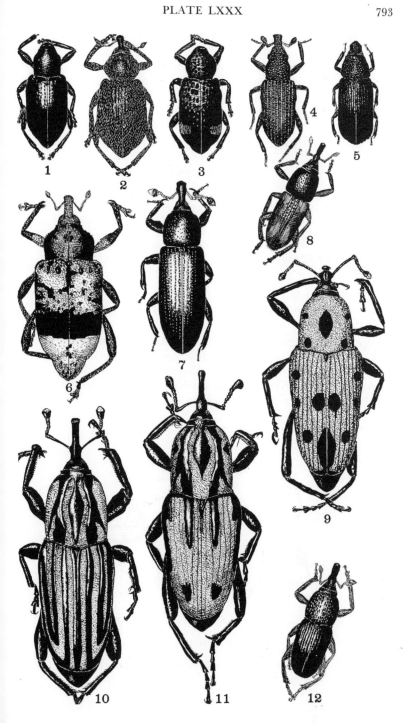

1

2

3

4

5

6

7

8

9

10

11

12

Pronotum transverse, constricted at apex; coarsely, densely punctate, with a low, nearly entire, median carina. Elytral striae punctate, the punctures large, quadrate; alternate intervals with tufts of hair. Length 7.5–10 mm.

This species was introduced from Europe and attacks willow, poplar, and other ornamental trees.

Subfamily COSSONINAE

KEY TO GENERA

1. Body uneven, covered with a crust ....I. *Dryophthorus* (p. 794)
   Body not covered with a crust, usually glabrous and shining 2
2. Beak as long as or longer than head, usually dilated at apex, grooves
   rapidly descending; no gular grooves (Fig. 527) ....II. *Cossonus* (p. 795)
   Beak usually shorter than head, continuous with front and equally
   robust, not dilated at apex; gular grooves receiving the antennae
   (Fig. 528) ....III. *Stenoscelis* (p. 795)

Genus I. *DRYOPHTHORUS* Schönherr

Very small, elongate-oval, subcylindrical forms; antennae inserted near eyes, club elongate-oval; funicle of four segments, segments one and two short and obconical, three and four slightly longer and transverse; metasternum long, sidepieces narrow; first, second, and fifth abdominal sternites very large, the third and fourth short; tarsi five-segmented.

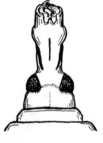

FIG. 527   FIG. 528

Fig. 527. Head of *Cossonus* in ventral view, without gular grooves and with long beak.

Fig. 528. Head of *Stenocelis* from below, with gular grooves (*gg*) and with short beak.

Dryophthorus americanus Bedel   Plate LXXX, No. 4, p. 793

Narrowly elongate-oval, subcylindrical; brownish or piceous, opaque; covered with grayish-yellow scales; antennae and legs paler. Beak slightly more than half length of pronotum, coarsely punctate dorsally. Eyes oval, transverse, coarsely granulate. Pronotum longer than wide, strongly constricted near apex; disk very coarsely, densely punctate. Elytra slightly wider than pronotum at base; striae broad, deep, coarsely punctate; intervals narrow, linear, convex. Length 2–3 mm.

These beetles may be collected from old logs and beneath bark of pine.

Genus II. *COSSONUS* Clairville

Small or moderate-sized, elongate, parallel, depressed species; body glabrous; beak more or less dilated at apex; antennae inserted near tip of beak, scrobes rapidly descending; funicle seven-segmented.

Cossonus platalea Say   Plate LXXX, No. 7, p. 793

Elongate, parallel; black, very shining; antennae and tarsi reddish brown. Beak not as long as pronotum; basal portion longer than the apical, the latter suddenly and angularly dilated. Head finely, sparsely punctate. Pronotum as wide as long, narrowed abruptly at apex; sides strongly arcuate; disk sparsely punctate, with coarse and fine punctures intermingled. Elytra slightly wider than pronotum, flattened; striate, striae with coarse, quadrate punctures; intervals flat, very finely, uniseriately punctate. Length 5.5–6.5 mm.

This beetle occurs frequently beneath bark of butternut, elm, walnut, poplar, and pine.

Genus III. *STENOSCELIS* Wollaston

Very small, subcylindrical, robust species; beak shorter than head, scrobes reduced to deep, postmedian pits; antennal scape short, slender, feebly clavate, scarcely half the length of funicle; club rounded, slightly flattened, somewhat annulate; funicle seven-segmented.

Stenoscelis brevis (Boheman)   Plate LXXX, No. 5, p. 793

Subcylindrical, robust; black, slightly shining; elytra and legs brownish or piceous; antennae and tarsi reddish brown. Head and beak coarsely, densely punctate. Pronotum short, transverse, broadly constricted near apex; sides slightly arcuate, posterior angles rounded; disk convex, coarsely, densely punctate. Elytra finely granulate at base; sides parallel, obtusely rounded at apex; striae with coarse, quadrate punctures; intervals narrow, each with a row of minute punctures. Length 2.8–3.2 mm.

These beetles may be taken from beneath bark and in decayed wood.

Family RHYNCHOPHORIDAE

The Billbugs; Grain Weevils

Small or moderate-sized, inconspicuous beetles; beak long and slender, arcuate; antennae elbowed, inserted near base of beak, scrobes short, not receiving the scape; funicle six-segmented; club not annulate, shining; elytra short, exposing pygidium; coxae separated; tibiae short, with an apical hook; tarsi rarely brushlike beneath, if pubescent with at least a broad, longitudinal, smooth area (except *Rhodobaenus,* in which the second and third segments are entirely densely hairy beneath), third segment rarely bilobed; claws divergent, simple.

The larvae and adults of this family are very injurious to both trees and crops as well as to stored grains, crackers, and other types of dried foods.

KEY TO GENERA

1. Antennal club broadly oval; mesepimera broadly truncate on outer side (Fig. 529); length of body 5 mm. or more 2
   Antennal club elongate-oval; mesepimera acute on outer side (Fig. 530); body length less than 4.2 mm. ....III. *Sitophilus* (p. 802)
2. Third segment of tarsi broad, spongy beneath, the brush not or narrowly divided (Fig. 531) ....I. *Rhodobaenus* (p. 796)
   Third segment of tarsi glabrous at middle, spongy or pilose at the sides or wholly glabrous (Fig. 532) ....II. *Calendra* (p. 798)

Genus I. *RHODOBAENUS* LeConte

Moderate-sized, convex species; usually red, with black spots; scape long, nearly attaining middle of pronotum; beak distinctly dilated behind insertion of antennae; pronotum without elevated areas; mesosternum narrow; second and third segments of tarsi densely pubescent beneath.

Rhodobaenus tredecimpunctatus (Illiger)   Plate LXXX, No. 9, p. 793
   Elongate-oval; red, with black spots, five on pronotum and four on each elytron, those on elytra often more or less confluent; undersurface and beak black. Beak two-thirds as long as pronotum, sparsely, finely punctate, more coarsely so basally. Antennal club broadly oval, apical half convex, hairy. Pronotum longer than wide, feebly constricted near apex; sides

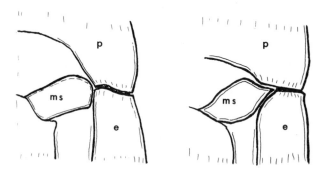

FIGS. 529–530

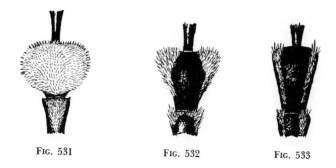

FIG. 531   FIG. 532   FIG. 533

Figs. 529–530. Body of *Calendra* (529) and of *Sitophilus* (530) from the side. Mesepimeron (*ms*) truncated laterally near prothorax (*p*) and elytron (*e*) in the former and acute in the latter.

Fig. 531. Third tarsal segment of *Rhodobaenus* from below, its entire undersurface covered by the brush.

Fig. 532. Third tarsal segment of *Calendra australis* from below, with brush largely confined to apical angles, the segment about as wide as long.

Fig. 533. Third tarsal segment of *Calendra melanocephalus* from below, pilose at sides, much longer than wide.

nearly parallel basally, distinctly curved apically; disk finely, sparsely punctate. Elytral striae fine, sparsely, finely punctate; intervals flat, smooth. Length 7–10 mm.

This beetle breeds in ironweed, joe-pye weed, cocklebur, greater ragweed, and many of the other Compositae.

Genus II. *CALENDRA* Clairville

Rather large, robust, elongate-ovate species; body glabrous, usually covered with a crust which hides the sculpture; antennae inserted near base of beak, scape long and slender, funicle six-segmented, club broadly oval; beak shorter than pronotum, slender, feebly arcuate, swollen at base; antennal scrobes very short, fovea-like, near eyes; pronotum longer than wide, disk usually with elevated smooth lines or spaces; elytra wider than pronotum, the apices separately, broadly rounded, exposing the pygidium.

KEY TO SPECIES

1. Third segment of pro- and mesotarsi strongly dilated, scarcely, if at all, longer than wide, below with spongy-pubescent pads at sides, leaving a glabrous space at middle (Fig. 532) 2
   Third segment of pro- and mesotarsi not feebly dilated, much longer than wide, entirely glabrous beneath or merely pilose at sides, leaving all of the middle glabrous (Fig. 533) 3
2. First, third, fifth, and seventh elytral intervals elevated for their entire length, elevations interrupted; remaining intervals flat; striae finely punctate; beak subcylindrical, feebly narrowed at base .... a. *australis*
   Third elytral interval strongly elevated on basal half; striae coarsely punctate .... b. *cariosa*
3. Pronotum equally punctate over the entire surface, sometimes with a smooth median line or space, neither of which is elevated, never with a trace of a lateral raised space .... c. *parvula*
   Pronotum with more or less distinct raised, smooth spaces 4
4. Median raised line of pronotum broadly dilated at middle; lateral raised spaces often more or less interrupted or obscure in front of origin of branch; elytral intervals flat, subequal .... d. *zeae*
   Median raised space of pronotum a slender apical carina, feebly dilated at middle of pronotum; lateral raised space without outer branch .... e. *melanocephala*

a. *Calendra australis* (Chittenden)   Plate LXXX, No. 10, p. 793

Elongate-ovate; reddish brown to piceous, shining; intervals of elytra covered with a clay-yellow crust. Beak subcylindrical, slightly narrowed at base, three-fourths as long as pronotum, finely and sparsely punctate, a small median basal fovea and a fine longitudinal groove also at base. Pronotum distinctly longer than wide, constricted at apex; raised lines entire, the median one widest at middle, narrowed basally and apically, the lateral ones with sinuous margins and branched; interspaces and sides of disk coarsely punctate. Elytra broadest at humeri, sides feebly converging to apical quarter, thence strongly rounded to apex; striae finely punctate; alternate intervals elevated, somewhat interrupted, minutely and sparsely punctate; remaining intervals flat, minutely, sparsely punctate. Length 11–15 mm.

This species often attacks growing corn but has also been found breeding in calamus and cattails.

b. *Calendra cariosa* (Olivier) Plate LXXX, No. 11, p. 793
Elongate-oval, convex; black, with a grayish crust; elevated portions above and undersurface shining. Beak three-fourths as long as pronotum, strongly compressed along median portion, sparsely and finely punctate, more coarsely so at base; a small median fovea or groove at base. Pronotum longer than wide, sides subparallel in male, feebly converging in female from base to near the constricted apex; disk with three raised lines, the median one beginning at apical constriction, dilated at middle to form a rhomboid, either ending there abruptly or prolonged in a fine line to base; outer raised lines broad, entire, edges sinuous, lateral branch short, broad, lines sparsely and minutely punctate, the intervals and sides of disk coarsely punctate, sometimes sides with a small, smooth space behind apical angle. Elytra slightly wider at humeri than pronotum; sides feebly arcuate to apex; striae fine, with coarse, deep, distant punctures; intervals flat, each with a single row of minute punctures; third interval strongly elevated on basal half, its elevated portion, and the humeral callosity and a small one near declivity, smooth, shining. Length 7.5–11 mm.

This species attacks growing corn but is usually found feeding on rushes and sedges.

c. *Calendra parvula* (Gyllenhal) Plate LXXXI, No. 1, p. 801
Elongate-oval, convex; black, with a gray crust; antennae, except club, reddish brown. Beak three-fourths as long as pronotum, coarsely and sparsely punctate, the base thickened and dorsally with a deep median groove. Pronotum distinctly longer than wide, slightly wider at middle than elytra, sides strongly arcuate before middle, constricted at apex; disk finely punctate, median raised line absent. Elytra finely striate, striae with distant, coarse punctures; alternate intervals slightly wider and feebly elevated, first and third with two rows, others with a single row, of coarse punctures. Length 5–8 mm.

This species breeds primarily in Kentucky bluegrass but also attacks growing corn, timothy, and wheat.

d. *Calendra zeae* (Walsh) Plate LXXXI, No. 2, p. 801
Elongate-oval, convex; black or very dark reddish brown, shining. Beak three-fourths as long as pronotum, laterally compressed at middle, finely and sparsely punctate, more coarsely so before the tumid base. Pronotum with three raised spaces, the median one entire, very slender at each end.

PLATE LXXXI

Family RHYNCHOPHORIDAE II

1. *Calendra parvula* (Gyllenhal) (p. 799) — Black, in part shining; 5–8 mm.
2. *C. zeae* (Walsh) (p. 799) — Black, shining; 6.5–9 mm.
3. *C. melanocephala* (Fabricius) (p. 802) — Black, shining; often coated with gum; 7–11 mm.

Family SCOLYTIDAE

4. *Ips grandicollis* (Eichhoff) (p. 812) — Orange-brown to fuscous; 3.2–4.5 mm.

5. *Scolytus quadrispinosus* Say (p. 805) — Dark brown to fuscous, shining; head with dense, pale, silky hairs; 4–5 mm.

6. *Hylurgops pinifex* (Fitch) (p. 809) — Orange-brown to black, feebly shining; 4.5–5 mm.

7. *Ips calligraphus* (Germar) (p. 812) — Orange-brown to piceous; 4.5–6.4 mm.

8. *I. pini* (Say) (p. 813) — Dark brown, shining; 3.5–4.5 mm.
9. *Orthotomicus caelatus* (Eichhoff) (p. 814) — Rather dark orange-brown, shining; 2.5–3 mm.

10. *Scolytus rugulosus* Ratzeburg (p. 805) — Dark brown to blackish, shining; 2–2.5 mm.

11. *Chramesus hicoriae* LeConte (p. 807) — Blackish; 1–2 mm.
12. *Phthorophloeus liminaris* (Harris) (p. 807) — Dark brown to blackish, shining; 1.5–2.2 mm.

13. *Polygraphus rufipennis* (Kirby) (p. 806) — Orange-brown to blackish; head darker; 2–2.5 mm.

14. *Hylurgopinus rufipes* (Eichhoff) (p. 808) — Deep brown to black; legs red-brown; 2–2.5 mm.

15. *Xyloterinus politus* (Say) (p. 810) — Deep brown; elytra and legs paler; 3–3.5 mm.

16. *Gnathotrichus materiarius* (Fitch) (p. 811) — Dark brown, shining; legs paler; 2.8–3.2 mm.

17. *Dendroctonus frontalis* Zimmermann (p. 808) — Reddish brown to piceous; 2.5–4 mm.

18. *Monarthrum mali* (Fitch) (p. 810) — Orange-brown, shining; 1.8–2 mm.

19. *Xyleborus pubescens* Zimmermann (p. 814) — Orange-brown, shining; 2–2.5 mm.

MM 0   10   20   30   40   50   60   70

PLATE LXXXI   801

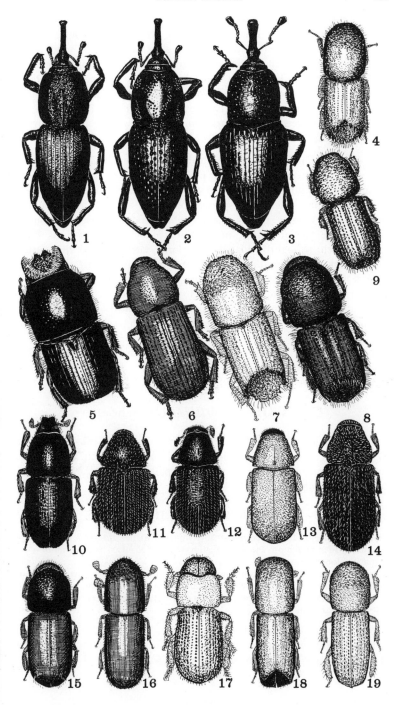

broadly dilated in front of middle; lateral raised spaces with sinuous edges, broadly interrupted in front of branches, which are strongly widened; sides of pronotum and spaces between elevations coarsely and densely punctate. Elytra with flat, subequal intervals, each having one row of fine, distinct punctures, the alternate ones basally more or less interrupted by coarse strial punctures. Pygidium coarsely and deeply punctate, with an oblique line of short, yellowish hairs each side. Length 6.5–9 mm.

This species breeds in Kentucky bluegrass as well as in timothy and corn.

e. *Calendra melanocephala* (Fabricius)   Plate LXXXI, No. 3, p. 801

Elongate-oval, convex; black or piceous; clothed with a dull-brownish crust. Beak two-thirds as long as pronotum, strongly compressed laterally before antennae, finely and sparsely punctate; abruptly tumid at base, coarsely and densely punctate and feebly grooved dorsally. Pronotum elongate, the median raised line represented by a short, apical, shining carina which is slightly dilated posteriorly; lateral raised lines usually absent; disk coarsely, rather sparsely, and irregularly punctate; each side with a small, round, shining callosity near apical angles. Elytra wider than pronotum at humeri, narrowed to apex; striae fine, with coarse, distant punctures; intervals flat, finely punctate, the third one wider; humeral umbone, subapical callosity, and scutellum shining and coarsely, sparsely punctate. Length 7–11 mm.

This species' only known host plant is cut-grass, but adults have been found on both timothy and corn.

Genus III. *SITOPHILUS* Schönherr

Small, elongate, rather slender beetles; beak usually shorter than pronotum, straight, cylindrical; antennal club not compressed, elongate-oval; third tarsal segment either narrow or expanded and rather glabrous or pilose at the sides.

KEY TO SPECIES

Elytra with deeply impressed and feebly punctate striae, intervals smooth, alternately wider and more elevated, distinctly more so near base; pronotum with sparse, elongate punctures ....a. *granaria*
Elytra with more or less contiguous double rows of coarse, deep punctures, the rows separated by narrow, punctate intervals; pronotum, especially near sides, with rather coarse, deep, very dense, rounded punctures; surface more or less depressed on disk ....b. *oryzae*

a. *Sitophilus granaria* (Linné)   Plate LXXX, No. 12, p. 793

Elongate-oblong, convex; reddish brown to piceous, shining. Beak two-thirds as long as pronotum, slender, cylindrical, finely and sparsely punctate. Pronotum with coarse, sparse, elongate punctures. Elytra deeply striate, the striae punctate but punctures not touching sides of striae; intervals smooth, alternately wider and slightly elevated, distinctly more so near base, the sutural one with a row of elongate punctures. Pygidium with small, close-set punctures. Length 3–4 mm.

This is strictly an indoor species, is wingless, and infests stored grain. A single pair is capable of producing 6,000 descendants a year, and under favorable conditions there may be from four to six broods a year.

b. *Sitophilus oryzae* (Linné)   Plate LXXX, No. 8, p. 793

Elongate-oval, robust, convex; dull brown; elytra marked with four reddish spots, two at base near humeri and two at apex. Beak slender, cylindrical, three-fourths as long as pronotum, feebly dilated basally, above with four rows of coarse punctures and a feeble fovea between the eyes. Pronotum feebly longer than wide, narrowed apically; disk densely, deeply, coarsely punctate. Elytra deeply striate, striae coarsely and closely punctate; intervals narrow, feebly convex, the sutural one with a row of coarse punctures; each puncture of pronotum and elytra bearing a short, yellowish seta. Undersurface coarsely, densely punctate. Length 2.1–2.8 mm.

This species does a great amount of damage to stored grain; it is also found beneath bark and on leaves. Both this and the preceding species are introduced forms.

Family SCOLYTIDAE

The Engraver or Bark Beetles

These small beetles are so cylindrical and compact in form and have such short legs that they resemble miniature bullets with both ends rounded. Head often concealed by pronotum; beak absent; the antennae geniculate, scape short, funicle one- to seven-segmented, club compact and, rarely, somewhat lamellate; tarsi five-segmented, first segment usually short, fourth segment sometimes very small.

As both adults and larvae, they live in timber and beneath bark of trees. Here they carve numerous undulating galleries, which often appear like engraving on the wood, when the bark is removed, and each species has its characteristic type of gallery. Usually only dead or dying trees are attacked, but some species do live in apparently healthy trees. The females eat out passageways in the cambium and later use them as egg-laying galleries. When the larvae hatch, they also feed on the cambium, helping to form more of the "engraved" designs started by the female.

KEY TO SUBFAMILIES

1. Protibiae produced into a prominent process at outer apical angle
   (Fig. 534) ....SCOLYTINAE (p. 804)
   Protibiae not produced at outer apical angle (Fig. 535) 2
2. Head visible from above ....HYLESININAE (p. 806)
   Head subglobose, concealed from above by pronotum ......IPINAE (p. 809)

Subfamily SCOLYTINAE

Genus *SCOLYTUS* Geoffroy

Small, elongate-oblong, subcylindrical; head rather flattened; lateral pronotal margins well defined; abdominal sternites flattened, obliquely ascending from posterior end of first to fifth; femora robust; protibiae not serrate externally, outer apical angle produced into a prominent process; meso- and metatibiae serrate externally, apices truncate and with two spines externally.

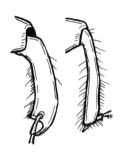

FIGS. 534-535   FIG. 536

Figs. 534-535. Right protibia of *Scolytus* (534), armed with a spine at
apex on anterior angle, and of *Ips* (535), without a spine
at anterior angle.
Fig. 536. Unsegmented antennal club of *Chramesus* attached to funicle
on one side.

KEY TO SPECIES

Elytra with distinct striae of close-set punctures ....a. *quadrispinosus*
Elytra with numerous rows of punctures ....b. *rugulosus*

a. *Scolytus quadrispinosus* Say   Hickory-Bark Borer
                                             Plate LXXXI, No. 5, p. 801

Elongate-oblong, convex; dark brown or black, shining. Head flattened
above, in male fringed with long hairs. Pronotum elongate, convex; sides
rounded, fringed with long hairs; disk finely punctate. Elytra each with
ten to twelve striae, both the striae and flattened intervals punctate, the
former coarsely, the latter finely so. Length 4–5 mm.

In the male the anterior face of the ventral declivity is deeply concave
and with four spines on the lateral margin; in the female it is simply flattened.

This beetle does extensive damage to hickory by boring into the trunk
and larger branches. The larvae bore their cylindrical chambers through
the inner bark, at first transversely, later longitudinally.

b. *Scolytus rugulosus* Ratzeburg   Shot-Hole Borer
                                             Plate LXXXI, No. 10, p. 801

Elongate-oblong, convex; gray-black, very feebly shining; tibiae, tarsi,
and elytra at apex reddish brown. Head in male flattened and with long
hairs, in female convex, without hairs. Pronotum elongate; densely punctate, with more or less elongate punctures on disk. Elytra with very numerous finely, densely punctate striae and densely punctate intervals, which
give the surface a rough appearance. Length 2–2.5 mm.

This species attacks fruit trees of various sorts. The adults may also be
found on flowers of Jersey tea.

Subfamily HYLESININAE

KEY TO GENERA

1. Third protarsal segment cylindrical; procoxae almost contiguous ...
....I. *Polygraphus* (p. 806)
   Third protarsal segment widened and emarginate or bilobed 2
2. Antennal club not segmented, funicle attached to side of club
   (Fig. 536) ....II. *Chramesus* (p. 807)
   Antennal club segmented, funicle attached to base of club 3
3. Antennal club loosely segmented, segments produced on one side,
   sublamellate ....III. *Phthorophloeus* (p. 807)
   Antennal club connate, segments not produced on one side 4
4. Antennal funicle five-segmented ....IV. *Dendroctonus* (p. 808)
   Antennal funicle seven-segmented 5
5. Procoxae rather widely separated ....V. *Hylurgopinus* (p. 808)
   Procoxae narrowly separated ....VI. *Hylurgops* (p. 809)

Genus I. *POLYGRAPHUS* Erichson

Very small, cylindrical species; head visible from above, in male with
one or two sharp frontal tubercles; elytra at base feebly crenulate, nearly
straight; procoxae almost contiguous; protibiae not strongly produced at
outer apical angle; third protarsal segment cylindrical.

Polygraphus rufipennis (Kirby)   Spruce-Bark Beetle
                               Plate LXXXI, No. 13, p. 801

Cylindrical; reddish brown to piceous; elytra, legs, mouthparts, and antennae brownish red; sparsely clothed with short, whitish pubescence; beneath glabrous. Antennal scape long, strongly clavate; funicle five-segmented, first segment robust, as long as others combined, two to five gradually increasing in thickness, short, closely united; club strongly compressed, pubescent, without sutures, elongate-oval, acute. Eyes divided, the
two parts connected by a smooth line. Pronotum transverse; sides subparallel on basal two-thirds, thence narrowed to apex; disk very densely,
minutely punctate. Elytra parallel-sided and broadly rounded at apex;
disk rugosely, minutely punctate and with rows of larger punctures; striae
obsolete. Ventral abdominal segments nearly equal, first and fifth slightly
longer. Length 2–2.5 mm.

This species bores beneath the green bark of living spruce, tamarack,
and pines; it also occurs in stumps and injured and dying individuals
of these trees.

Genus II. *CHRAMESUS* LeConte

Very small, oval, convex; body humpbacked; head visible from above; antennae with the club unsegmented, the five-segmented funicle attached to the side of the club; club compressed, pubescent, and without sutures; pronotum distinctly transverse, scabrous laterally; elytra covered with short scales and stout bristles; the protibiae not strongly produced at outer apical angle; third protarsal segment widened and emarginate.

Chramesus hicoriae LeConte   Plate LXXXI, No. 11, p. 801

Oval, convex; black, opaque; antennae yellow; dorsally clothed with short, stiff, grayish hairs. Head large, concave in male, slightly convex in female, feebly punctate. Pronotum transverse, narrowed anteriorly; sides arcuate; base feebly bisinuate; coarsely and rather sparsely punctate. Elytra with basal margin more or less serrate; disk obsoletely striate, finely, rather densely punctate; intervals with rows of long, erect bristles. Length 1–2 mm.

This species attacks injured or dying hickory, mining under partly green bark.

Genus III. *PHTHOROPHLOEUS* Reynolds

Very small, oblong, robust, cylindrical; head visible from above; antennal club loosely three-segmented, segments somewhat produced on one side; protibiae not produced at outer apical angle; tarsal segments one to three short, gradually widened, third segment not emarginate, fourth very small; basal margin of elytra serrate, acutely elevated.

Phthorophloeus liminaris (Harris)   Plate LXXXI, No. 12, p. 801

Oblong, cylindrical; light brown to nearly black, feebly shining; sparsely clothed with long, whitish pubescence. Antennal scape long, gradually clavate; first segment of funicle slightly shorter than others. Pronotum subquadrate, sides curved to apex, which is about one-half the width of base; surface finely, densely punctate; medially with a short carina. Elytra parallel-sided to apical fourth, thence strongly rounded to apex; disk with rows of deep, transverse punctures; intervals flat and feebly rugose. Length 1.5–2.2 mm.

This species is found in old stumps and in living mulberry, hackberry, peach, plum, and cherry trees.

Genus IV. *DENDROCTONUS* Erichson

Small, slender to robust species; head large, prominent; beak short, thick; antennae geniculate, the club short, obtuse, sometimes nearly globose, always composed of closely united, knob-shaped segments; basal margin of elytra acutely elevated and serrate; apical margin of fourth, fifth, and sixth abdominal sternites strongly recurved laterally; procoxae nearly contiguous; third segment of tarsi bilobed, not received in second.

Dendroctonus frontalis Zimmermann   Southern Pine Beetle
                                                                Plate LXXXI, No. 17, p. 801

Elongate-oblong; light reddish brown to piceous. Front of head with a prominent tubercle each side of a distinct median groove. Pronotum slightly wider than long; anterior margin feebly emarginate medially; female with a transverse ridge anteriorly, this lacking in male; disk coarsely, rather sparsely punctate. Elytral sides nearly parallel on basal two-thirds, thence broadly arcuate to apices, which are together rounded; striae distinctly punctate, intervals moderately rugose; the declivity in female shining, with finely granulate interspaces, in male the striae here more strongly impressed and interspatial granules coarser and more sparse. Length 2.5–4 mm.

This species attacks both pine and spruce and at times becomes so numerous as to destroy acres of the host trees.

Genus V. *HYLURGOPINUS* Swaine

Very small, oval, robust, subcylindrical species; head visible from above; antennae with compact, segmented club; funicle seven-segmented; elytra with base rounded; procoxae widely separated; protibiae not strongly produced at outer apical angle; third protarsal segment strongly dilated and bilobed.

Hylurgopinus rufipes (Eichhoff)   Plate LXXXI, No. 14, p. 801

Oval, cylindrical; fuscous, opaque; thinly covered with short, stiff, yellowish hairs. Antennal funicle seven-segmented; club subovate, transverse, shining basally. Head densely, coarsely punctate; beak short. Pronotum subequal in length and width, narrowed apically; disk densely, rather finely punctate, medially with a narrow, indistinct carina. Elytra with rows of deep, subquadrate punctures; intervals narrow, transversely rugose. Length 2–2.5 mm.

These beetles are found on elm, ash, and wild cherry.

Genus VI. *HYLURGOPS* LeConte

Small, oval, robust, subcylindrical; head visible from above; antennae with a compact, segmented club; funicle seven-segmented; elytra with base moderately rounded; procoxae nearly contiguous; protibiae not strongly produced at outer apical angle; protarsi with third segment much dilated and bilobed.

Hylurgops pinifex (Fitch) Plate LXXXI, No. 6, p. 801

Oval, robust, subcylindrical; deep reddish brown to black, tinged with brownish; elytra with short, fine pubescence; undersurface black. Beak carinate; dorsally transversely impressed; antennal funicle seven-segmented; the club four-segmented, the first segment as long as the rest combined. Pronotum broader than long, narrowed apically; disk finely, densely punctate, median carina fine. Basal margin of elytra subacute and subserrate; apex slightly wider than base; discal striae with coarse, quadrate punctures; intervals with rows of small granules. Length 4.5–5 mm.

This species mines in green bark or dying trees.

Subfamily IPINAE

KEY TO GENERA

1. Eyes divided (Fig. 537); antennal club without distinct sutures ......
   ....II. *Xyloterinus* (p. 810)
   Eyes not divided; club with sutures at least at apex 2
2. Funicle with more than three segments 3
   Funicle with three or less segments ....I. *Monarthrum* (p. 810)
3. Base of pronotum finely margined by a raised line; metepisterna largely covered by elytra, visible only anteriorly when elytra are closed ....III. *Gnathotrichus* (p. 810)
   Base of pronotum not margined; metepisterna distinct for their entire length 4
4. Protarsi strongly dilated apically; mouthparts with sparse, slender hairs; maxillary lobe pilose ....VI. *Xyleborus* (p. 814)
   Protarsi only moderately dilated apically; mouthparts clothed on ventral side with many stiff hairs; maxillary lobe spinose 5
5. Concavity of declivous portion of elytra separated from the apical margin of elytra by the strongly produced, horizontal, platelike, acute apical margin of declivity (Fig. 538); antennal club flattened, sutured on upper side ....IV. *Ips* (p. 812)
   Declivity of elytra with apical margin only feebly produced, at most forming an acute apical ridge (Fig. 539); antennal club widened basally, obliquely truncate apically on upper side ....
   ....V. *Orthotomicus* (p. 814)

Genus I. *MONARTHRUM* Kirsch

Very small, elongate, cylindrical; head concealed from above by pronotum; antennal funicle two-segmented; eyes not divided; pronotum elongate, tuberculate apically; protibiae not strongly produced on outer apical angle, widened distally; elytra emarginate at apex.

These are the "ambrosia beetles," so called because they feed on fungi. The female, assisted by the male, packs small chips of wood in pits they have excavated beneath the bark of trees and grow a fungus on the decaying chips. The larvae feed on the fungus.

Monarthrum mali (Fitch)   Plate LXXXI, No. 18, p. 801

Elongate, cylindrical; brown; pronotum, at base, and elytra lighter brown; antennae and legs brownish yellow; elytra covered with yellowish pubescence. Pronotum elongate, tuberculate and pubescent apically. Elytra with rows of very fine punctures; apex obliquely truncate, two small teeth near suture. Length 1.8–2 mm.

These beetles may be found on various coniferous and deciduous trees.

Genus II. *XYLOTERINUS* Swaine

Small, elongate-oblong, robust, cylindrical; head concealed from above by pronotum; antennal funicle four- or five-segmented, the first segment robust; club oval, solid, pubescent on both sides, not annulate; eyes completely divided; elytra rounded at apex; protibiae not strongly produced at outer apical angle, widened distally.

Xyloterinus politus (Say)   Plate LXXXI, No. 15, p. 801

Elongate-oblong, cylindrical; yellow to deep brown, shining. Pronotum quadrate; apical margin broadly rounded, fringed with hairs; disk convex, finely punctate at sides, more coarsely so anteriorly. Elytra with rows of fine punctures; intervals sparsely punctate, the punctures often confused with the rows of punctures. Male with metatibiae narrower than female. Length 3–3.5 mm.

This species is found in logs and stumps and in dying or injured trees, particularly white birch.

Genus III. *GNATHOTRICHUS* Eichhoff

Small, elongate-oblong, cylindrical, slender; head concealed from above by pronotum; funicle of antennae five-segmented; eyes emarginate, not divided; pronotum and elytra glabrous; elytra with apex rounded; protibiae widened apically, serrate on external margin.

Gnathotrichus materiarius (Fitch) The Pine Wood-stainer
Plate LXXXI, No. 16, p. 801

Elongate-oblong, slender, cylindrical; dark brown, shining; elytral base yellowish brown; underside sometimes black; antennae and legs yellowish. Pronotum elongate, rounded apically; feebly tuberculate and finely carinate near apex, smooth basally. Elytra with very indistinct rows of punctures, otherwise smooth; apex with scattered hairs. Head in male with longitudinal elevations on front, ending in an acute point just above base of mandibles; in female smooth and sparsely punctate. Length 2.8–3.2 mm.

This species makes galleries in pine and spruce.

Fig. 537

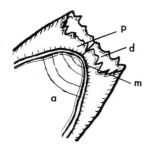

Fig. 538

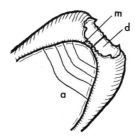

Fig. 539

Fig. 537. Left eye of *Xyloterinus*, divided into two lobes.
Fig. 538. Posterior end of body of *Ips calligraphus* viewed from beneath. *a*, abdominal sternites; *m*, apical margin of elytra; *p*, broad plate of elytra below declivity (*d*).
Fig. 539. Posterior end of body of *Orthotomicus* viewed from beneath. *a*, abdominal sternites; *m*, apical margin of elytra close to declivity (*d*), without a plate.

Genus IV. *IPS* DeGeer

Small, elongate-oblong, cylindrical, slender; head concealed from above by pronotum; antennal funicle five-segmented, club pubescent, flattened, widest medially; eyes broadly emarginate; pronotum and elytra covered with scales or pubescence; elytral declivity deeply excavated, margined externally and below by many coarse, prominent teeth; protibiae wider apically and with several fine, external teeth.

KEY TO SPECIES

1. Sutures of antennal club strongly angulated (Fig. 540) 2
   Sutures of antennal club not angulated, nearly straight, second bisinuate; elytral marginal declivity with four prominent tubercles (Fig. 541) ..c. *pini*
2. Elytral marginal declivity with three teeth behind the most prominent one (Fig. 542) ....a. *calligraphus*
   Elytral marginal declivity with two teeth behind the most prominent one (Fig. 543) ....b. *grandicollis*

a. *Ips calligraphus* (Germar)   Plate LXXXI, No. 7, p. 801

Elongate, subcylindrical; piceous or dark testaceous, feebly shining; clothed with long, yellowish or grayish pubescence; antennae yellow. Sutures of antennal club angulated, point of angle directed anteriorly. Pronotum elongate; anterior portion roughly tuberculate and with transverse rugosities; posteriorly finely, sparsely punctate; medially with a longitudinal smooth line. Elytral striae with large, transverse punctures; intervals subconvex, the ones nearest suture uniseriately punctate; sutural stria subsulcate; apices obliquely excavate-truncate, the margin of excavation with six teeth, the second and third from top larger, fourth and fifth small, sixth minute; apical margin produced (Fig. 542); tibiae strongly dentate. Length 4.5–6.4 mm.

This species mines under green bark of injured or dying pines.

b. *Ips grandicollis* (Eichhoff)   Plate LXXXI, No. 4, p. 801

Elongate, rather slender, cylindrical; bright orange-brown to fuscous, feebly shining; sparsely clothed with long, pale-yellowish or grayish hairs. Pronotum elongate; anterior portion roughly tuberculate, transversely rugose; posteriorly finely punctate, punctures gradually diminishing basally; median line narrow, smooth on posterior half. Elytral striae with subquadrate punctures; sutural striae deep, with dilated punctures; sutural intervals convex; apices obliquely excavate-truncate, margin of declivity five-toothed, the third tooth larger, first tooth minute, apical margin strongly elevated, entire (Fig. 543). Length 3.2–4.5 mm.

This species attacks pine and spruce.

c. *Ips pini* (Say)   Plate LXXXI, No. 8, p. 801

Elongate-oblong, rather slender, cylindrical; brown to deep brown, shining; sparsely covered with gray pubescence. Pronotum feebly elongate; rounded anteriorly, with apical margin very feebly sinuate each side; sparsely punctate at base, apically very rough, with raised points. Elytra with finely punctate striae; intervals flat, the ones near suture smooth; apical declivity with four teeth each side, the second and third ones large and coalescing (Fig. 544). Length 3.5–4.5 mm.

This species breeds in pine and spruce.

FIG. 540   FIG. 541

FIG. 542   FIG. 543   FIG. 544

Fig. 540. Antennal club of *Ips calligraphus,* with strongly angulate sutures.

Fig. 541. Antennal club of *Ips pini,* the sutures sinuate or nearly straight.

Fig. 542. Elytral apices of *Ips calligraphus,* with three teeth below largest one.

Fig. 543. Elytral apices of *Ips grandicollis,* with two teeth below largest one.

Fig. 544. Elytral apices of *Ips pini,* each with but a single tooth below two large ones.

SCOLYTIDAE

Genus V. *ORTHOTOMICUS* Ferris

Small, elongate-oblong, rather slender; covered with fine, erect hairs; head entirely concealed from above; antennae with funicle five-segmented, club pubescent, widened basally, obliquely truncate on upper surface; eyes broadly emarginate; elytral declivity scarcely excavated, margined with feeble teeth; protibiae wider apically and with several fine, external teeth.

Orthotomicus caelatus (Eichhoff)   Plate LXXXI, No. 9, p. 801
Elongate, cylindrical; fuscous to piceous; antennae and legs dark reddish yellow. Pronotum cylindrical; median line smooth; disk basally rugosely punctate. Elytral striae with coarse, quadrate punctures; intervals flat, with rows of sparse, fine punctures; declivity scarcely excavated, each side margin with about eight feeble teeth, which are widely separated and irregularly arranged; apical margin entire, feebly elevated (Fig. 539). Length 2.5–3 mm.
This species lives in spruce, pine, and fir.

Genus VI. *XYLEBORUS* Eichhoff

Very small, oblong species; head completely concealed by pronotum; antennal funicle five-segmented, the fifth segment short and broad; club short, broad, anterior face obliquely truncate, with one or two recurved sutures; pronotum longer than broad, sides nearly parallel; apical margin broadly rounded, not serrate.

Xyleborus pubescens Zimmermann   Plate LXXXI, No. 19, p. 801
Elongate-oblong; yellowish brown, shining; legs and antennae somewhat paler; entire upper surface thinly clothed with long, erect, pale-brownish pubescence. Pronotum elongate, gradually widened anteriorly; basal half medially nearly smooth, with fine, sparse punctures, anterior half and extreme sides of base coarsely and densely rugose. Elytra with rows of feebly impressed, rather coarse punctures; intervals flat, feebly rugose, and with scattered, fine punctures; declivity not excavated, simply truncate, and without teeth on margins; apical margin not elevated. Length 2–2.5 mm.

GLOSSARY

[The following definitions have largely been adapted from Torre-Bueno's *Glossary of Entomology* and from *Webster's New International Dictionary* to fit the usage in this book.]

Abbreviated. Shortened; not of usual length.

Acicular, aciculate. Needle-like; ending in a long, fine, sharp point.

Acuminate. Tapering to a slender point; pointed.

Acute. Sharp, pointed; forming less than a right angle.

Aëneous. Shining brassy or golden.

Alutaceous. With very minute cracks or wrinkles, resembling the grain of Morocco leather on a much smaller scale.

Angulate. Bent at an angle; forming an angle.

Annulate. Ringed or marked with colored bands.

Antennal groove. A groove or sulcus to receive and conceal the antennae, as in many Buprestidae and Elateridae.

Antennal scrobe. A groove in the beak of Curculionidae, to receive the scape (basal segment) of the antenna.

Antennal tubercle. An elevation on the head from which the antenna arises, as in the Cerambycidae.

Anterior. Situated in front; relatively nearer the head.

Apex. The tip, that portion furthest away from the body or from the base; apex of pronotum, that part nearest the head.

Apical. At, near, or going toward the apex.

Appendiculate. With an appendage or appendages; said of tarsal claws when they have a long, or rather long, straight base before the curved portion.

Appressed. Closely applied to.

Apterous. Not winged, without wings.

Arcuate. Curved or rounded; like a bow.

Attenuate, attenuated. Gradually becoming more slender; tapering.

Band. A marking running transversely, wider than a line; a fascia.

Basal. At, near, or going toward the base.

Base. That part nearest the main body; base of pronotum is that portion nearest the elytra; of abdomen, the region adjacent to the thorax.

Beak. A prolongation of the head, bearing the mouthparts.

Bidentate. With two teeth or toothlike projections.

Bifid. Split to the middle; with two equal lobes, narrowly separated.

Bifurcate. Divided into two branches, as veins, stripes, or lines; forked.

Bimaculate. With two spots, or maculae.

Bipectinate. With two opposite margins toothed like a comb.

Bisinuate. A line or edge with two broad incurves and two similar out-curves.

Blotch. A large, irregular marking.

Brassy. Yellowish with the lustre of metallic brass.

Callosity. A rather flattened elevation.

Campanulate. Bell-shaped.

Canaliculate. Channeled; longitudinally grooved, usually with a deeper, concave line medially.

Capitate. With a head; a type of antennae with a sudden, rounded knob at apex.

Carina (pl. *carinae*). A narrow, elevated ridge or keel.

Carinate. Having one or more carinae.

Channeled. Sulcate.

Chelate. Said of tarsal claws when retractile, i.e., capable of being drawn back upon the last segment.

Cicatrix. A scar or scarlike marking; in *Monochamus* and related Ceramby-cidae, a roughened area on the apex of the antennal scape.

Cilia (pl. *ciliae*). A long hair, many usually forming a fringe.

Ciliate. With cilia.

Clavate. Gradually thickened apically.

Cleft. Split, partially divided longitudinally.

Concave. Hollowed out.

Confluent. Running together or overlapping.

Confused. Irregular; without distinct pattern; disordered.

Conical. Cone-shaped.

Connate. Firmly united, along base or entire length.

Constricted. Narrowed and re-expanded.

Contiguous. Touching.

Converging. Gradually narrowing or tapering.

Convex. Evenly and broadly rounded.

Corbels. An ovate area at distal end of tibiae surrounded by a fringe of very small bristles or hairs.

Cordate. Heart-shaped, with base not necessarily emarginate.

Coriaceous. Leathery.

Corneous. Hornlike in texture.

Costa. A feebly elevated ridge, often running veinlike or riblike on elytra.

Coxal cavity. A cavity in which a coxa is articulated.

Crenate. Having the margin with rounded scallops.

Crenulate. With small scallops.

Crest. A ridge or ridgelike formation.

Cupreous. Coppery in color.

Cylindrical. Circular in cross section; resembling a cylinder.

Deflexed. Bent downward.

Dehiscent. Said of the elytra when they are separated toward the apex.

Dense. Thickly crowded together.

Dentate. Toothed; with acute teeth, the sides of which are equal, with the tip above the middle of the base.

Denticle. A very small tooth.

Depressed. Flattened vertically.

Dilated. Widened; expanded.

Disk. The central portion of the pronotum or elytra, in contrast to the margin.

Distal. The part of an appendage or section of an appendage farthest from the body.

Diurnal. Normally active during the day; the opposite of nocturnal.

Divaricate. Said of tarsal claws when the two members of a pair meet each other in a straight line, i.e., at an angle of 180°.

Divergent. Spread out from a common base; said of tarsal claws when they meet at a slight angle at base.

Dorsal. Upper surface, or belonging to the upper surface.

Elliptical. Resembling oval, but differing in having the two rounded ends equal.

Elongate. Longer than wide, usually distinctly so.

Emarginate. Notched at the margin.

Entire. Having the margin or line continuous; unbroken.

Epimeron (pl. *epimera*). Usually a small, narrow or triangular piece at the sides of a sternum, behind the episternum.

Epipleuron (pl. *epipleura*). The entire deflexed or inflexed part of the elytra beneath the side margins.

Episternum. A sclerite anteriorly at the sides of a sternum, usually larger than the epimeron.

Epistoma. The sclerite immediately behind the labrum, whether the clypeus or an intermediate piece; in rhynchophorous beetles, the reduced fronto-clypeal region.

Erect. Standing upright, not necessarily perpendicular.

Excavated. Hollowed out; broadly impressed.

Explanate. Spread out and flattened; applied to a margin.

Exserted. Not enclosed; not concealed; protruded.

Facet. The surface of one of the numerous small eyes that make up the compound eye.

Fascia (pl. *fasciae*). A transverse band or broad line.

Femur (pl. *femora*). In Coleoptera, the first elongate segment of the leg.

Ferruginous. Rusty red-brown.

Filiform. Threadlike; slender, of equal diameter.

Fimbriate. Fringed with hairs.

Flabellate. Said of an antenna that is pectinate with very long processes, giving it a fanlike appearance.

Foliaceous. Leaflike.

Fossa (pl. *fossae*). A groove; usually applied to the grooves which receive the antennae.

Fossorial. Adapted for digging, as the tibiae of some of the Scarabaeidae having teeth on the outer margin.

Fovea (pl. *foveae*). A pit; a rounded, small impression.

Foveate. Pitted; with foveae.

Free. Unrestricted in movement; not firmly united to another part.

Fulvous. Tawny; a light yellowish brown.

Funicle. The segments of an antenna between the club and the scape (first segment).

Fuscous. Brownish black.

Fusiform. Spindle-shaped; broad at the middle and narrowing toward the ends.

Geniculate. Elbowed; suddenly bent at an angle.

Gibbose. Raised or rounded to some extent, resembling the moon when more than half full.

Glabrous. Smooth, bald, without hairs.

Globose. Sphere-shaped; spherical.

Granulate. Covered with small grains; with numerous small, flattened elevations on the surface.

Granule. A small, grainlike elevation.

Gregarious. Living in a group but not social.

Griseous. Light gray.

Gular suture. Line of division between the throat (gula) and cheeks (genae).

Hibernate. To pass the winter in close quarters, in a dormant state.

Hirsute. Shaggy; with long hairs.

Hoary. Covered with fine, white or silvery pubescence.

Humeral. Near, or on, the shoulder or humerus.

Humerus (pl. *humeri*). The basal, external angle of the elytra.

Imbricate. Arranged like shingles.

Immaculate. Not spotted or marked.

Impressed. Lying below the general surface, as if stamped into it, as lines or dots.

Impression. An indentation on the surface.

Incised. Having the margin deeply and sharply notched.

Incurved. Curved toward the center.

Inferior. Beneath or below.

Infuscated. Smoky-gray-brown, with blackish tinge.

Insertion. The place of attachment.

Intercoxal process. A protrusion of the basal sternite between the meta-coxae.

Interocular. Between the eyes.

Interrupted. Broken in continuity, but the tips of the broken parts in the same line with each other.

Interval. The area between two elytral striae.

Iridescent. Reflecting colors of various hues.

Irregular. Unequal in distribution; bent or twisted or otherwise modified.

Labial. On or belonging to the labium.

Labium. The lower lip.

Labrum. The upper lip, which covers the base of the mandibles and forms the roof of the mouth.

Lacinia. A part of the maxilla.

Lamellate. Said of antennae which have some of the distal segments expanded laterally to form leaflike or platelike structures.

Lamelliform. Made up of, or resembling, plates or blades.

Lanceolate. Shaped like the head of a spear; narrowed and pointed at the apex.

Larva (pl. *larvae*). The second stage of insect development.

Laterad. Toward the side.

Lateral. On, toward, or near the sides.

Leathery. Having the appearance or texture of leather.

Linear. Straight; in the form of a line.

Lobe. Any prominent rounded process on a margin.

Longitudinal. In the direction of the long axis.

Lunule. A crescent-shaped mark.

Luteous. Pale clay-yellow.

Macula (pl. *maculae*). A spot or marking.

Maculate. Spotted or marked.

Mandible. One of the upper pair of jaws in a biting insect.

Margin. The border; the edge.

Marginal. Of or at the margin.

Margined. With a distinct border.

Maxilla (pl. *maxillae*). One of the lower pair of jaws.

Maxillary palpi. The upper pair of palpi; borne on the maxillae.

Membranous. Thin, skinlike, semitransparent, like parchment.

Medial. Refers to, or at, the middle.

Mentum. Part of the labium.

Mes- or *meso-*. A prefix meaning middle; refers to the middle segment of the thorax or its appendages.

Mesially. Pertaining to the middle portion.

Met- or *meta-*. A prefix meaning posterior; refers to the last segment of the thorax or its appendages.

Metallic. With a lustre or color like metals.

Moniliform. Beaded; made up of rounded segments.

Mucronate. Ending abruptly in a sharp point.

Muricate. Armed with sharp, rigid points; usually a surface-sculpture term.

Naked. Not clothed, without hairs or other vestiture.

Nocturnal. Active or flying at night.

Notched. Indented, usually on a margin.

Obconical. Cone-shaped, with the apex pointing downward.

Obcordate. Inversely heart-shaped.

Oblique. Any direction between vertical and horizontal.

Oblong. Essentially a four-sided figure with one dimension much longer than the other.

Obovate. Inversely egg-shaped, with the narrow end caudally or basally.

Obsolete. Nearly or entirely lost; inconspicuous.

Obtuse. Not pointed; with an angle greater than a right angle.

Occiput. The basal part of the head behind the vertex.

Ocellus. A simple eye, consisting of a beadlike lens, usually on the vertex.

Ochraceous. A brownish yellow.

Olivaceous. With a tinge of olive-green.

Onychium. A more or less retractile process between the tarsal claws of some beetles, for example in the Scarabaeidae.

Opaque. Dull, not shining.

Orbicular. Round and more or less flattened.

Ovipositor. Tubular structure on last segment of female abdomen by means of which eggs are laid; usually concealed.

Palpus (pl. *palpi*). A short, segmented appendage, found on the maxillae and labium.

Parapleuron (pl. *parapleura*). The undivided pleuron of the thorax, ventrally on each side of the sternum.

Pectinate. With elongated, equal processes, like the teeth of a comb.

Pedunculate. With a narrow part connecting two larger portions.

Penultimate. Next to the last.

Perfoliate. Divided into leaflike plates; applied to antennae with disklike expansions connected by a stalk passing nearly through their centers.

Persistent. Always present; remaining constantly.

Piceous. Pitch-colored.

Pilose. Covered with long, soft hairs.

Pleuron (pl. *pleura*). Lateral sclerite between abdominal sternites and tergites.

Poriferous. Densely and deeply punctate.

Porrect. Extending horizontally; stretched out.

Posterior. Situated in the rear; relatively nearer the hind end of the body.

Pro-. As a prefix, pertaining to the foremost division of the thorax or its appendages.

Process. Any marked prominence; an outgrowth or projection of surface, margin, or appendage.

Produced. Prolonged; elongated; extended.

Prolonged. Longer than usual.

Prominent. Elevated above the surface or produced beyond the margin; conspicuous.

Pronotum. Upper surface of the prothorax.

Propygidium. The next to the last dorsal segment of the abdomen.

Prosternal. Belonging to the sternum.

Prosternum. Area of prothorax anterior to and often between the procoxae.

Prothorax. First thoracic segment, bearing a pair of legs but no wings.

Protuberance. Any elevation above the surface.

Proximal. That part of an appendage nearest to the body.

Pruinose. Hoary, like the skin of a plum.
Pubescence. A covering of short, soft hairs.
Pubescent. Covered with soft, fine hairs.
Punctate. With impressed dots.
Puncture. A small depression, an impressed dot.
Punctured. Marked with small impressed dots; same as punctate.
Pygidium. The apical dorsal segment of the abdomen, sometimes not covered by the elytra.

Quadrate. Square or nearly so; sides of equal length.

Rectangular. In the form of a right angle or rectangle.
Rectilinear. In the form of a straight line.
Recumbent. Lying down; reclining.
Recurved. Curved in a direction opposite from the usual.
Reflex. Reflected light or color, e.g., a metallic-blue reflex.
Reflexed. Bent backward.
Reticulate. Resembling network; netted.
Retractile. Capable of being drawn back or in; said of the head when it can be withdrawn into the prothorax.
Rigid. Stiff, not flexible.
Robust. Thickened, stout.
Rudimentary. Undeveloped; represented by a vestige.
Rufous. Brownish red; yellowish red.
Ruga (pl. *rugae*). A fine wrinkle.
Rugose. With more or less parallel raised lines or wrinkles.
Rugulose. Finely rugose.

Saltatorial. Adapted for leaping; in saltatorial beetles, the metafemora are greatly thickened.
Scabrous. Rough; with irregular, close elevations.
Scale. A broad, flattened hair.
Scape. The first or basal segment of an antenna.
Scapiform. Shaftlike.
Sclerite. Any piece of the insect body wall surrounded by sutures.
Sclerotized. Hardened with a deposit of a material called sclerotin; most of the body integument of beetles is sclerotized.
Scrobe. A groove to receive or conceal an appendage.
Sculpture. The surface structure; surface markings except those of color and those formed by pubescence.
Scutellum. In beetles, the more or less triangular piece between the bases of the elytra (occasionally lacking).
Securiform. Hatchet-shaped; triangular and compressed.
Segment. A division marked by sutures or incisions.
Sericeous. Silky or satiny; with a silklike lustre.
Serrate. With notched edges, like the teeth of a saw.
Serrulate. With numerous little saw teeth.
Seta (pl. *setae*). A bristle or long, stiff hair.

Setaceous. Bristle-shaped; slender, gradually tapering toward the tip.

Setigerous. Bearing setae or bristles, e.g., setigerous punctures.

Setose. Bristly; bearing setae.

Sinuate. Said of lines or margins with undulations.

Sinuous. Sinuate; winding; curved in and out.

Sinus. A broad, shallow indentation in an otherwise straight margin; an excavation, as if scooped out.

Sparse. Scattered; set at some distance apart.

Spindleform. Elongate-cylindrical; thicker in the middle and tapering toward both ends.

Spine. A slender, sharp process.

Spiniform. Shaped like a spine.

Spinose. Armed with spines.

Spinule. A small spine.

Spiracle. A breathing pore, usually on the sides of the abdomen.

Spur. Usually a short, stiff process, not articulated at its base.

Sternum. The middle portion of the undersurface of the thorax, between the coxal cavities.

Stria (pl. *striae*). Usually a longitudinal impressed line on the elytra; a narrow sulcus; sometimes a marginal sulcus on pronotum.

Striate. Marked with fine, parallel impressed lines.

Striga (pl. *strigae*). A narrow, impressed line or streak.

Strigose. Rough with fine, closely set lines.

Style. A pointed appendage; when present, found on the terminal segment of the abdomen.

Sub-. Prefix designating moderately, more or less, near, or beneath.

Subocular. Beneath the eyes.

Sulcate. Grooved or furrowed; set with impressed lines.

Sulcus (pl. *sulci*). A groove or furrow.

Supraorbital. Above the eyes.

Suture. A line indicating the junction of two sections of the body wall; the line of the junction of the elytra.

Tarsal lobes. Sometimes, membranous appendages arising from the underside of the tarsal segments; often, the lobes formed by a cleft in the distal end of a segment.

Tarsus (pl. *tarsi*). The foot; the distal portion of the leg, attached to the tibia, composed of from two to five segments.

Tawny. Brownish yellow.

Terminal. At the tip; opposed to basal.

Tergite. A dorsal segment of the abdomen.

Testaceous. A dull yellow-brown.

Thorax. The second or middle region of an insect, bearing the legs and wings; made up of three sections, the pro-, meso-, and metathorax.

Tibia (pl. *tibiae*). The shank; the portion of the leg articulating with the femur and bearing the tarsus.

Tomentose. Covered with fine, matted hairs.

Tomentum. Dense, matted, prostrate hairs, lying in irregular fashion.

Tooth. A short, pointed process from an appendage or margin (cf. *Dentate*).

Translucent. Semitransparent, permitting the passing of light but not of vision.

Transverse. When the longest dimension is across the body.

Trochanter. A segment of the leg between the coxa and femur, often fused to the femur in beetles.

Trochantin. A piece sometimes present on the external side of a coxa, sometimes movable; the basal portion of the trochanter when it is divided.

Truncate. Having the end square or even, as if cut off; lacking the apex.

Tubercle. A small, knoblike prominence.

Tuberculate, tuberculose. Bearing tubercles.

Tumescent. Somewhat swollen or puffed up.

Ultimate. Last or final.

Umbilicate. Navel-shaped; a small depression with a raised portion in the middle.

Umbone (pl. *umbones*). An embossed, elevated knob situated on the humeral angle of elytra.

Unarmed. Without spines, teeth, or spurs.

Undulate. Wavy; bending in gradual curves.

Unguiculate. With a broad claw or nail.

Variegated. Varied in color; dappled; of several colors in indefinite patterns.

Ventral. Belonging to or pertaining to the undersurface.

Vertex. The tip portion of the head, between the eyes, front, and occiput.

Vestiture. The general surface covering, as hairs, scales, etc.

Vibrissa (pl. *vibrissae*). Curved bristles.

Violaceous. Violet-colored; purplish.

Vitta (pl. *vittae*). A longitudinal stripe.

Vittate. Striped longitudinally.

BIBLIOGRAPHY

General

Arrow, Gilbert J. 1951. Horned beetles. Ed. by W. D. Hincks. Dr. W. Junk Publishers, The Hague, 154 pp.

Beaulne, J. L. 1925. Les Coléoptères du Canada. Nat. Can., Vol. 52.

———. 1929. Les Coléoptères du Canada. Nat. Can., Vol. 56.

Blackwelder, R. E. 1939. Fourth supplement, 1933–1939 (inclusive), to the Leng Catalogue of Coleoptera of America, north of Mexico. John D. Sherman, N.Y., pp. 1–146.

——— and R. M. Blackwelder. 1948. Fifth supplement, 1939–1947 (inclusive), to Leng Catalogue of Coleoptera of America, north of Mexico. John D. Sherman, N.Y., pp. 1–87.

Blaisdell, F. E., Sr. 1925. Coleoptera of the Pacific Coast. Ent. News, 36:79–85.

Blatchley, W. S. The Coleoptera of Indiana. Ind. Dept. Geol. and N.R., Bull. No. 1, pp. 1–1386.

Böving, Adam G., and F. C. Craighead. 1931. An illustrated synopsis of larval forms of the order Coleoptera. Ent. Amer. (n.s.), 11(1–4):1–351.

Bradley, J. C. 1930. A manual of genera of beetles. Daw Illston & Co., Ithaca, 360 pp.

Bryson, H. R. 1939. The identification of soil insects by their burrow characteristics. Trans. Kan. Acad. Sci., 42:245–253.

Casey, T. L. 1924. Additions to known Coleoptera of North America. Mem. Col., 11:1–347.

Clausen, Curtis P. 1940. Entomophagous insects. McGraw-Hill Book Co., Inc., N.Y., 688 pp.

Craighead, F. C. 1950. Insect enemies of eastern forests. U.S.D.A., Misc. Pub. No. 657, 679 pp.

De la Torre-Bueno, J. R. 1937. A glossary of entomology. Brooklyn Ent. Soc., Brooklyn, N.Y., 336 pp.

Doane, R. W., E. C. Van Dyke, W. J. Chamberlain, and H. E. Burke. 1936. Forest insects. McGraw-Hill Book Co., Inc., N.Y.

Edwards, J. G. 1949. Coleoptera or beetles east of the Great Plains. Published by the author, Ann Arbor, Michigan, 181 pp.

Felt, E. P. 1905–1906. Insects affecting park and woodland trees. Mem. N.Y. State Mus., 8:1–877.

———. 1929. Popular guide to study of insects. N.Y. State Mus., Handbook, No. 6, 147 pp.

Forbes, W. T. M. 1922. The wing venation of Coleoptera. Ann. Ent. Soc. Amer., 15:328–351.

———. 1926. Wing folding patterns of Coleoptera. Jour. N.Y. Ent. Soc., 34:42–68, 91–115.

Forbes, W. T. M. 1947. Beetle wings. Coleop. Bull., 1:71–73.

Graham, S. A. 1922. Study of wing venation of Coleoptera. Ann. Ent. Soc. Amer., 15:191–200.

Hatch, Melville H. 1933. Studies on Leptodiridae (Catopidae), with descriptions of new species. Jour. N.Y. Ent. Soc., 41:187–239.

———. 1946. Beetles. The Biologist, 28:66–80.

———. 1953. The beetles of the Pacific Northwest, Pt. I: Introduction and Adephaga. Univ. Wash. Pub. Biol., Vol. 16, 340 pp.

———. 1957. The beetles of the Pacific Northwest, Pt. II: Staphyliniformia. Univ. Wash. Pub. Biol., Vol. 16, 384 pp.

Hinton, H. E. 1945. A monograph of the beetles associated with stored products. Brit. Mus. (Nat. Hist.), pp. 1–443.

Jacques, H. E. 1951. How to know the beetles. Wm. C. Brown Co., Dubuque, Ia., 372 pp.

Leng, C. W. 1920. Catalogue of Coleoptera of North America, north of Mexico. John D. Sherman, N.Y., 470 pp.

——— and A. J. Mutchler. 1927. Catalogue of Coleoptera of North America, north of Mexico. First supplement, 1919–24 (inclusive). John D. Sherman, N.Y., pp. 1–78.

———. 1933. Catalogue of Coleoptera of North America, north of Mexico. Second and third supplements, 1925–32 (inclusive). John D. Sherman, N.Y., 112 pp.

Moennich, H. 1939. List of Coleoptera found living in and on various fungi. Bull. Brooklyn Ent. Soc., 34:155–157.

Peterson, Alvah. 1951. Larvae of insects, Pt. II. (Coleoptera, pp. 2–218.) Pub. by the author, Columbus, Ohio.

Schenkling, S. (ed.). 1910–1940. Catalogus Coleopterorum. W. Junk, The Hague.

U.S.D.A. 1952. Insects. (Yearbook of Agr.). Washington, D.C., 798 pp.

Ecology

Balduf, Walter V. 1935. The bionomics of entomophagous Coleoptera. John S. Swift Co., Inc., N.Y.

———. 1939. The bionomics of entomophagous insects, Pt. 2. John S. Swift Co., Inc., N.Y.

Bedard, W. D. 1938. Annotated list of insects of Douglas fir. Can. Ent., 70:188–197.

Blackman, M. W., and H. H. Stage. 1924. On the succession of insects living in the bark of wood of dying, dead and decaying hickory. N.Y. State Coll. For., Tech. Bull. No. 17, pp. 1–269.

Chamberlin, W. J. 1939. Bark and timber beetles of North America. Ore. State Coll. Coop. Assoc., Corvallis, Ore., 512 pp.

Craighead, F. C., and W. Middleton. 1930. An annotated list of the North American forest insects. U.S.D.A., Pub. No. 74.

Dozier, H. L. 1920. Ecological study of hammock and piney woods insects in Florida. Ann. Ent. Soc. Amer., 13:325–380.

Edwards, J. Gordon. 1956. Entomology above the timberline. Mazamas, pp. 13–17.

Felt, E. P. 1928. Dispersal of insects by air currents. Bull. N.Y. State Mus., 274:59–129.

Graham, Samuel A. 1925. The felled tree trunk as an ecological unit. Ecology, 6:397–411.

Hatch, Mellville H. 1925. Outline of ecology of the Gyrinidae. Bull. Brooklyn Ent. Soc., 20:101–114.

Hendrickson, G. O. 1930. Studies on insect fauna of Iowa prairies. Iowa State Coll. Jour. Sci., 4:49–179.

Hinton, H. E. 1945. Monograph of beetles associated with stored products. Brit. Mus. (Nat. Hist.), 443 pp.

Hopkins, A. D. 1893. Catalogue of forest and shade tree insects. Bull. W.Va. Agr. Exp. Sta., 32:169–252.

Howden, Henry F., and George B. Vogt. 1951. Insect communities of standing dead pine (Pinus virginiana). Ann. Ent. Soc. Amer., 44(4):581–595.

McIndoo, N. E. 1931. Tropisms and sense organs of Coleoptera. Smiths. Misc. Col., 82(18):1–70.

Needham, J. G., S. W. Frost, and B. H. Tothill. 1928. Leafmining insects. Williams & Wilkins, Baltimore, 351 pp.

Packard, A. 1886. Cave fauna of North America. Mem. Nat. Acad. Sci., 4:1–156.

Park, Orlando, Stanley Auerbach, and Glenna Corley. 1950. The tree-hole habitat, with emphasis on the pselaphid beetle fauna. Chicago Acad. Sci. Bull., 9(2):19–45.

Pennack, R. W. 1953. Freshwater invertebrates of the United States. Ronald Press, N.Y., 769 pp.

Savely, Harvey E., Jr. 1939. Ecological relations of certain animals in dead pine and oak logs. Ecol. Monog., 9:321–385.

Shelford, Victor E. 1913. Animal communities in temperate America. Geog. Soc. of Chicago, Bull. 5. Univ. Chicago Press, 220 pp.

Voris, R. 1934. Biological investigations on Staphylinidae. Trans. Acad. Sci. St. Louis, 28:233–261.

Wolcott, A. B., and B. E. Montgomery. 1933. Ecological study of Coleoptera of a tamarack swamp. Amer. Midl. Nat., 14:113–169.

Wolcott, G. N. 1937. Animal census of pastures and meadows. Ecol. Monog., 7:1–90.

Baits and Trapping

Barber, H. S. 1931. Traps for cave-inhabiting insects. E. Mitchell Sci. Soc., 46:259–266.

Champlain, A. B., and J. N. Knull. 1932. Fermenting baits for trapping Elateridae and Cerambycidae. Ent. News, 43:253–257.

Frost, S. W. 1936. Summary of insect liquid baits. Ent. News, 47:64–68, 89–92.

———. 1937. New records from bait traps. Ent. News, 48:201–202.

——— and H. Dietrich. 1929. Coleoptera taken from bait traps. Ann. Ent. Soc. Amer., 22:427–437.

Gardinier, L. M. 1957. Collecting wood-boring beetle adults by turpentine and smoke. Bi-Month. Prog. Rept., Dept. Agr., Sci. Serv., For. Div., Canada, 13(1):2.

Hubbell, Theodore H. 1956. A new collecting method: The oatmeal trail. Ent. News, 67(2):49–51.

Turnock, W. J. 1957. A trap for insects emerging from the soil. Can. Ent., 89:455–456.

TECHNIQUES

Arnett, Ross H., Jr. 1947. A technique for staining, dissecting, and mounting male genitalia of beetles. Coleop. Bull., 1(7):63–66.

———. 1949. Locality labels. Coleop. Bull., 3(6):85–88.

Beer, Frank M. 1948. Winter collecting of Coleoptera. Coleop. Bull., 2(3):24–25.

———. 1949. The rearing of Buprestidae and delayed emergence of their larvae. Coleop. Bull., 3(6):81–84.

Duffy, E. A. J. 1949. The preservation of beetle larvae. Proc. Trans. South London Ent. Nat. Hist. Soc., 1948–49, pp. 146–147.

Gressitt, J. L. 1954. Notes on use of photography in taxonomic work. Bull. Brooklyn Ent. Soc., 49(4):105–106.

Hanson, J. F. 1954. Simple technique for improving and accelerating KOH cleaning of insects. Bull. Brooklyn Ent. Soc., 49(1):21.

Luginbill, Philip. 1948. Methods of collecting and preserving May beetles (*Phyllophaga*). Coleop. Bull., 2(4):31–32.

Nelson, Harry G. 1949. A method of cleaning insects for study. Coleop. Bull., 3(6):89–92.

Peterson, Alvah. 1944. A manual of entomological equipment and methods. Pts. I and II, 4th ed. Pub. by the author, Columbus, Ohio.

———. 1953. A manual of entomological techniques. 7th ed., 367 pp. Pub. by the author, Columbus, Ohio.

Valentine, J. Manson. 1942. On the preparation and preservation of insects, with particular reference to Coleoptera. Smiths. Misc. Col., 103(2):1–16.

Wagstaffe, Reginald, and J. Havelock Fidler. 1953. The preservation of natural history specimens, Vol. I: Invertebrates, pp. 49–117. Philos. Lib., New York.

BIBLIOGRAPHY ARRANGED BY FAMILIES

ALLECULIDAE

Casey, T. L. 1891. Synopsis of the Cistelidae of the United States. Ann. N.Y. Acad. Sci., 6:69–170.

Fall, H. C. 1931. North American species of the genus *Hymenorus*. Trans. Amer. Ent. Soc., 57:161–247.

Horn, G. H. 1894. Key for the genus *Lystronychus*. Proc. Calif. Acad. Sci., Ser. 2, 4:433.

Hopping, R. 1933. The genus *Pseudocistela,* with key to species. Can. Ent., 65:281–286.

ANOBIIDAE

Böving, A. G. 1927. Classification of Anobiidae larvae. Proc. Ent. Soc. Wash., 29:51–62.

Fall, H. C. 1905. Revision of the Ptinidae of boreal America. Trans. Amer. Ent. Soc., 31:127–296.

LeConte, J. L. 1865. Monograph of the tribe Anobiini of North America. Proc. Acad. Nat. Sci., Phila., pp. 222–244.

Linsley, E. G. 1943. Identification and control of the death watch beetles. Pests and Control, March, 1943.

Ruckes, H. 1957. A synopsis of the California death watch beetles of the genus *Ernobius*. Pan-Pac. Ent., 33:157–161.

ANTHICIDAE

Casey, T. L. 1895. Synopsis of the Anthicidae of the United States. Ann. N.Y. Acad. Sci., 8:624–809.

LeConte, J. L. 1852. Synopsis of the Anthicites of the United States. Proc. Acad. Nat. Sci., Phila., 6:91–104.

Werner, F. G. 1957. A revision of the nearctic species of *Tomoderus* (Anthicidae). Psyche, 64:51–59.

ANTHRIBIDAE

Blatchley, W. S., and C. W. Leng. 1916. Rhynchophora of northeastern America. Nature Pub. Co., Indianapolis, pp. 23–45.

Jordan, K. 1904. American Anthribidae. Nov. Zool., 11:242–309.

LeConte, J. L., and G. H. Horn. 1876. Rhynchophora. Proc. Amer. Phil. Soc., 15:391–409.

BELIDAE

Blatchley, W. S., and C. W. Leng. 1916. Rhynchophora of northeastern America. Nature Pub. Co., Indianapolis, pp. 91–93.

LeConte, J. L. 1883. The subfamily Ithycerinae. Smiths. Misc. Col., 26:459–462.

BOSTRICHIDAE

Anderson, W. H. 1939. Key to larval Bostrichidae. Jour. Wash. Acad. Sci., 29:382–391.

Fisher, W. S. 1950. Revision of the North American species of beetles belonging to the family Bostrichidae. U.S.D.A., Misc. Pub. No. 698, 157 pp.

Horn, G. H. 1878. Revision of the subfamily Bostrichidae of the United States. Proc. Amer. Phil. Soc., 17:540–555.

BRENTIDAE

Blatchley, W. S., and C. W. Leng. 1916. Rhynchophora of northeastern America. Nature Pub. Co., Indianapolis, pp. 18–23.

Schaeffer, Charles. 1915. Table of genera and species of North American Brenthidae. Jour. N.Y. Ent. Soc., 23:52–55.

BUPRESTIDAE

Barr, W. E. 1950. Revision of species of the genus *Polycesta* occurring in the United States. Amer. Mus. Nov., No. 1432, 42 pp.

Beer, F. M. 1950. The rearing of Buprestidae and delayed emergence of their larvae. Coleop. Bull., 3:81–84.

Burke, H. E. 1917. Flat-headed borers affecting forest trees. U.S.D.A., Bull. No. 437.

Chamberlin, W. J. 1926. Catalogue of Buprestidae of North America. Ore. State Coll. Pub., Corvallis, Ore., 289 pp.

Crotch, G. R. 1873. Notes on the species of Buprestidae found in the United States. Proc. Acad. Nat. Sci., Phila., 25:84–96.

Evans, D. 1957. A revision of the genus *Poecilonota* in America north of Mexico. Ann. Ent. Soc. Amer., 50:21–37.

Fall, H. C. 1899. Synopsis of the species of *Acmaeodera* of North America. Jour. N.Y. Ent. Soc., 7:1–37.

Fisher, W. S. 1928. A revision of the North American species of buprestid beetles belonging to the genus *Agrilus*. Bull. U.S.N.M., 145:1–347.

———. 1942. Revision of the North American species of buprestid beetles belonging to the tribe Chrysobothrini. U.S.D.A., Misc. Pub. No. 470, 274 pp.

Good, H. G. 1925. Wing venation of Buprestidae. Ann. Ent. Soc. Amer., 18:251–276.

Helfer, J. R. 1941. Revision of the genus *Buprestis* of North America north of Mexico. Ent. Amer., 21:123–199.

Horn, G. H. 1878. Revision of the *Acmaeodera* of the United States. Trans. Amer. Ent. Soc., 7:2–27.

———. 1882. Revision of some genera of Buprestidae. Trans. Amer. Ent. Soc., 10:101–112.

———. 1886. Monograph of the species of *Chrysobothris* of the United States. Trans. Amer. Ent. Soc., 13:65–124.

———. 1891. The species of *Agrilus* of boreal America. Trans. Amer. Ent. Soc., 18:277–336.

Knull, J. N. 1925. Buprestidae of Pennsylvania. Ohio State Univ. Stud., 2(11):1–71.

Nicolay, A. S., and H. B. Weiss. 1918. Review of the genus *Buprestis*. Jour. N.Y. Ent. Soc., 26:75–109.

BYRRHIDAE

Casey, T. L. 1890. Synopsis of *Limnichus*. Ann. N.Y. Acad. Sci., 5:145–160.

———. 1912. Descriptive catalogue of American Byrrhidae. Mem. Col., 3: 1–69.

Horn, G. H. 1879. Table of the species of *Limnichus*. U.S. Geol. Surv. Bull., 5:514.

LeConte, J. L. 1854. Synopsis of the Byrrhidae of the United States. Proc. Acad. Nat. Sci., Phila., 7:113–117.

CANTHARIDAE

Fall, H. C. 1928. A review of *Podabrus*. Ent. Amer., 8(n.s.):65–103.

Fender, K. M. 1943. Studies in the Cantharidae. Pan-Pac. Ent., 19:63–69.

———. 1945. Studies in the Cantharidae, II. Can. Ent., 77:37–39.

———. 1952. The Malthini of North America. Amer. Midl. Nat., 46:513–629.

Green, J. W. 1940. Taxonomic studies in *Cantharis*. Ent. Amer., 20:159–217.

———. 1947. New eastern American species of *Podabrus*. Trans. Amer. Ent. Soc., 73:63–76.

Green, J. W. 1948. New eastern American species of *Podabrus*, II. Trans. Amer. Ent. Soc., 74:75–82.

CARABIDAE

Ball, G. E. 1956. A revision of North American species of the genus *Helluomorphoides*. Proc. Ent. Soc. Wash., 58:67–91.

Banninger, M. 1950. The subtribe Pasimachina. Rev. de Ent., 21:481–511.

Böving, A. G., and F. C. Craighead. 1930. An illustrated synopsis of larval forms of Coleoptera. Ent. Amer., 11:1–351.

Burgess, A. F., and C. W. Collins. 1917. The genus *Calosoma*, with tables of both adults and larvae. U.S.D.A., Bull. No. 417, 134 pp.

Casey, T. L. 1913. Cicindelidae and Carabidae. Mem. Col., 4:1–192.

———. 1914. Revision of North American Harpalinae. Mem. Col., 5:45–305.

———. 1918. Review of North American Bembidiinae. Mem. Col., 8:1–223.

———. 1918. Studies in American Amarinae and Pterostichinae. Mem. Col., 8:224–393.

———. 1918. American Pogonini. Mem. Col., 8:394–412.

———. 1920. Revisional study of American Platyninae. Mem. Col., 9:1–529.

Chu, H. F. 1945. Larvae of Harpalinae. Ent. Amer., 25:1–71.

Darlington, P. J., Jr. 1938. The American Patrobini. Ent. Amer., 18(n.s.): 135–187.

Hayward, R. 1900. A study of the species of *Tachys* of boreal America. Trans. Amer. Ent. Soc., 26:191–238.

Horn, G. H. 1872. Revision of the species of *Lebia*. Trans. Amer. Ent. Soc., 4:130–142.

———. 1876. Revision of the species of *Chlaenius*. Trans. Amer. Ent. Soc., 5:253–276.

———. 1881. On the genera of Carabidae, with special reference to boreal America. Trans. Amer. Ent. Soc., 9:91–196.

LeConte, J. C. 1853. Notes on the classification of Carabidae of the United States. Trans. Amer. Phil. Soc., 10(n.s.):363–403.

Leng, C. W., and W. Beutenmüller. 1894–1896. Handbook of Carabidae of northeastern America. Jour. N.Y. Ent. Soc., Vols. 2 and 4.

VanDyke, E. C. 1944. Revision of North American species of the genus *Carabus*. Ent. Amer., 24:87–137.

CERAMBYCIDAE

Beutenmüller, W. 1896. Food habits of North American Cerambycidae. Jour. N.Y. Ent. Soc., 4:73–81.

Casey, T. L. 1912. Studies in Cerambycidae of North America. Mem. Col., 3:215–386.

———. 1913. Further studies in Cerambycidae of North America. Mem. Col., 4:193–400.

———. 1914. Cerambycidae of North America: Prioninae. Mem. Col., 11: 208–296.

Craighead, F. C. 1912. Contributions to the classification and biology of North American Cerambycidae: Larvae of Prioninae. U.S.D.A., Secretary's Rept., 107:1–24.

———. 1923. North American cerambycid larvae: A classification and biology of North American cerambycid larvae. Can. Dept. Agr., Ent. Br., Bull. No. 27, 238 pp.

Dillon, Lawrence S. 1956. The nearctic components of the tribe Acantho-cinini, I–III. Ann. Ent. Soc. Amer., 49:134–167, 207–235, and 332–355.

—— and Elizabeth S. Dillon. 1941. The Monochamini of the Western Hemisphere. Reading Pub. Mus. & Art Gal., Sci. Pub., No. 1, 135 pp.

—— and ——. 1945–1946. The tribe Onciderini, I and II. Reading Pub. Mus. & Art Gal., Sci. Pub., Nos. 5 and 6, 413 pp.

—— and ——. 1947. The tribe Dorcaschematini. Trans. Amer. Ent. Soc., 73:173–298.

Fall, H. C. 1910. New species of *Pogonocherus*, with synoptic table. Ent. News, 21:5–9.

Felt, E. P., and L. H. Joutel. 1904. Monograph of the genus *Saperda*. Bull. N.Y. State Mus., 74:3–86.

Hess, A. D. 1940. Biology and control of *Saperda candida*. N.Y. State Agr. Exp. Sta., Bull. No. 688, 93 pp.

Hopping, G. R. 1932. Review of Clytini. Ann Ent. Soc. Amer., 25:529–577.

——. 1937. Revision of Clytini of boreal America, II. Ann. Ent. Soc. Amer., 30:438–457.

Hopping, Ralph. 1937. Lepturini of America north of Mexico, II. Nat. Mus. Can. Bull., 85:1–42.

—— and G. R. Hopping. 1947. Lepturini of North America, III. Sci. Agr., 27:220–236.

Knull, J. N. 1946. The long-horned beetles of Ohio. Ohio Biol. Surv. Bull., 7:133–354.

Leng, C. W. 1884. Synopses of Cerambycidae. Bull. Brooklyn Ent. Soc., Vol. 7.

——. 1885–87. Synopses of Cerambycidae. Ent. Amer., Vols. 1, 2, and 3.

——. 1890. Synopses of Cerambycidae. Ent. Amer., Vol. 6.

—— and J. Hamilton. 1896. Lamiinae of North America. Trans. Amer. Ent. Soc., 23:101–178.

Linsley, E. G. 1934. Revision of Pogonocherini of North America. Ann. Ent. Soc. Amer., 28:73–103.

Swaine, J. M., and R. Hopping. 1928. The Lepturini of America north of Mexico, I. Nat. Mus. Can. Bull., 52:1–97.

CHRYSOMELIDAE

Barber, H. S. 1916. Revision of the tortoise beetles. Proc. Ent. Soc. Wash., 18:113–127.

Blake, Doris H. 1927. Revision of the beetles of the genus *Oedionychis* occurring in America north of Mexico. Proc. U.S.N.M., Vol. 70, art. 3, pp. 1–44.

——. 1931. Revision of the species of *Trirhabda* north of Mexico. Proc. U.S.N.M., Vol. 79, art. 2, pp. 1–36.

——. 1933. Revision of the beetles of the genus *Disonycha* occurring in America north of Mexico. Proc. U.S.N.M., Vol. 82, art. 28, pp. 1–66.

——. 1945. The genus *Galeruca* in the United States. Proc. Ent. Soc. Wash., 47:53–63.

——. 1951. A revision of beetles of the genus *Myochrous*. Proc. U.S.N.M., 101(3271):1–64.

——. 1953. The chrysomelid beetles of the genus *Strabala* Chevrolat. Proc. U.S.N.M., 103(3319):121–134.

Blake, Doris H. 1958. A review of some galerucine beetles with excised tibiae in the male. Proc. U.S.N.M., 108(3395):59–101.

Böving, A. G. 1910. Natural history of Donaciinae larvae. Internat. Rev. d. gesamten Hydrobiologie u. Hydrogr., 3(Biol. Supp. 1):1–108.

———. 1927. Larvae of *Diabrotica* and *Phyllobrotica*. Proc. Ent. Soc. Wash., 29(19):193–206.

———. 1929. Larvae of Galerucinae. Proc. U.S.N.M., Vol. 85, art. 2, pp. 1–48.

Chittenden, F. H. 1927. The species of *Phyllotreta*. Ent. Amer., 8:1–62.

Edwards, J. Gordon. 1953. Species of the genus *Syneta* of the world. Wasmann Jour. Biol., 11(1):23–82.

Fall, H. C. 1915. Revision of North American species of *Pachybrachys*. Trans. Amer. Ent. Soc., 41:291–486.

———. 1929. On the genus *Phaedon*. Pan-Pac. Ent., 5:145–152.

Gentner, L. G. 1928. Contributions to the North American Halticinae. Trans. Amer. Ent. Soc., 54:57–67.

Hatch, Melville H. 1928. The nearctic and European species of the subgenus *Phaedon* (Chrysomelinae). Pan-Pac. Ent., 5(1):44–47.

Horn, G. H. 1889. Synopsis of the Halticini of boreal America. Trans. Amer. Ent. Soc., 16:163–320.

———. 1892. Studies in the Chrysomelidae. Trans. Amer. Ent. Soc., 19:1–18.

———. 1892. Eumolpini of boreal America. Trans. Amer. Ent. Soc., 19:195–234.

———. 1893. Galerucini of boreal America. Trans. Amer. Ent. Soc., 20:57–136.

LeConte, J. L. 1865. On *Galeruca* and allied genera of North America. Proc. Acad. Nat. Sci., Phila., pp. 204–222.

Leng, C. W. 1891. Review of the Donaciae of boreal America. Trans. Amer. Ent. Soc., 18:159–176.

Marx, E. J. 1957. A review of the subgenus *Donacia* in the Western Hemisphere. Bull. Amer. Mus. Nat. Hist., 112:191–278.

Maulik, S. 1931. Structure of hispine larvae, I. Proc. Zool. Soc. London, 1931, pp. 1137–1162.

———. 1932. Larvae of hispine beetles, II. Proc. Zool. Soc. London, 1932, pp. 293–322.

McCauley, R. H., Jr. 1938. Revision of *Microrhopala*. Bull. Brooklyn Ent. Soc., 33(4):145–169.

Salisbury, M. B. 1943. Morphology and taxonomy of larval Criocerinae. Bull. Brooklyn Ent. Soc., 38:59–74, 128–139.

Sanderson, Milton W. 1948. Larval, pupal and adult states of North American *Physonota*. Ann. Ent. Soc. Amer., 41(4):468–477.

Schaeffer, C. 1925. Revision of Donaciini. Brooklyn Mus. Sci. Bull., 3:45–165.

———. 1933. Key to species of *Lema*. Jour. N.Y. Ent. Soc., 41:299–307.

VanDyke, E. C. 1938. Revision of *Chrysolina*. Bull. Brooklyn Ent. Soc., 33:45–58.

Wilcox, J. A. 1954. The leaf beetles of Ohio. Ohio Biol. Surv. Bull., 8:353–506.

Woods, W. S. 1918. Biology of the Maine species of *Altica*. Me. Agr. Exp. Sta., Bull. No. 273, pp. 149–204.

CICINDELIDAE

Blanchard, F. N. 1921. Tiger beetles of Michigan. Pap. Mich. Acad. Sci., Arts, and Letters, 1:396–417.

Cartwright, O. L. 1935. Tiger beetles of South Carolina. Bull. Brooklyn Ent. Soc., 30:69–77.

Casey, T. L. 1913. Cicindelidae and Carabidae. Mem. Col., 4:1–192.

——. 1914. *Omus* and *Cicindela*. Mem. Col., 5:1–24.

Cazier, Mont A. 1937. Review of groups of *Cicindela*. Bull. S. Calif. Acad. Sci., 35:156–163.

Cresson, E. T. 1861. Catalogue of Cicindelidae of North America. Proc. Ent. Soc. Phila., 1:7–20.

Criddle, N. 1907. Habits of some Manitoba tiger beetles. Can. Ent., 39:105–114.

Dawson, R. W., and W. Horn. 1928. Tiger beetles of Minnesota. Univ. Minn. Agr. Exp. Sta., Tech. Bull. No. 56, 13 pp.

Hamilton, C. C. 1925. Larvae of Cicindelidae. Proc. U.S.N.M., 65:1–87.

Hatch, Melville H. 1938. Coleoptera of Washington: Cicindelinae. Univ. Wash., Pub. Biol., 1(5):229–238.

Horn, G. H. 1868. The United States species of *Cicindela*. Trans. Amer. Ent. Soc., 1:2–3.

Horn, W. 1908–1915. Family Carabidae: Cicindelinae. Gen. Insect., Fasc. 82A, B, and C.

Knaus, W. 1900. Cicindelidae of Kansas. Can. Ent., 32:109–116.

Leng, C. W. 1902. Revision of the Cicindelidae of boreal America. Trans. Amer. Ent. Soc., 28:93–186.

—— and W. Beutenmüller. 1894–1896. Handbook of Cicindelidae of northeastern America. Jour. N.Y. Ent. Soc., Vols. 2 and 4.

Macnamara, Charles. 1922. Tiger beetle larvae. Can. Ent., 54:241–246.

Say, Thomas. 1818. Monograph of the North American *Cicindela*. Trans. Amer. Phil. Soc., 1:401–426.

Shelford, V. E. 1917. Color and color pattern mechanism of tiger beetles. Ill. Biol. Monog., 3(4):1–134.

Vaurie, Patricia. 1951. Notes on the habits of some North American tiger beetles. Jour. N.Y. Ent. Soc., 58:143–153.

CIIDAE
(Cioidae and Cisidae)

Casey, T. L. 1898. Studies in the Ptinidae, Cioidae, and Sphindidae of America. Jour. N.Y. Ent. Soc., 6:76–91.

Dury, C. 1917. Synopsis of Cisidae. Jour. Cin. Soc. Nat. Hist., 23:1–28.

CLERIDAE

Böving, A. G., and A. M. Champlain. 1920. Larvae of the North American beetles of the family Cleridae. Proc. U.S.N.M., 57:575–649.

Champlain, A. B. 1920. Biology of North American Cleridae. Proc. U.S.N.M., 58:624–639.

Chapin, E. A. 1922. New North American *Hydnocera*. Proc. Biol. Soc. Wash., 35:55–58.

Chapin, E. A. 1924. Classification of the Cleridae. Philippine Jour. Sci., 25:160–286.

Horn, G. H. 1876. Synopsis of the species of *Cymatodera* and *Trichodes* of the United States. Trans. Amer. Ent. Soc., 5:220–232.

Knull, Josef N. 1951. The checkered beetles of Ohio. Ohio Biol. Surv. Bull., 8:269–350.

LeConte, J. L. 1849. Synopsis of the group Cleridae of the United States. Ann. N.Y. Lyc. Nat. Hist., 5:9–35.

Linsley, E. G. 1936. Studies in the genus *Aulicus*. Univ. Calif. Pub. Ent., 6:249–262.

Wolcott, A. B. 1908. The North American species of *Chariessa*. Ent. News, 19:70–72.

———. 1910. The Cleridae. Field Mus. Nat. Hist., Zool. Ser., 7:339–401.

———. 1921. The tribe Tillini. Proc. U.S.N.M., 59:269–289.

———. 1922. The tribe Clerini. Trans. Amer. Ent. Soc., 48:67–78.

———. 1944. The American species of *Trichodes*. Pan-Pac. Ent., 20:54–60.

———. 1944. A generic review of the subfamily Phyllobaeninae. Jour. N.Y. Ent. Soc., 52:121–152.

———. 1947. Catalogue of North American beetles of the family Cleridae. Fieldiana: Zool., 32(2):61–105.

COCCINELLIDAE

Böving, A. G. 1917. Coccinellidae larvae and bibliography. Proc. U.S.N.M., 51:621–656.

Casey, T. L. 1899. A revision of American Coccinellidae. Jour. N.Y. Ent. Soc., 7:71–169.

Chapin, E. A. 1946. Revision of New World *Hippodamia*. Smiths. Misc. Col., 106(11):1–39.

Crotch, G. B. 1873. Revision of the Coccinellidae of the United States. Trans. Amer. Ent. Soc., 4:363–382.

Dobzhansky, T. 1931. The North American beetles of the genus *Coccinella*. Proc. U.S.N.M., 80(4):1–32.

———. 1941. *Hyperaspis* of the United States. Smiths. Misc. Col., 101(6): 1–92.

Gage, J. H. 1920. The larvae of Coccinellidae. Ill. Biol. Monog., 6(4):235–296.

Horn, G. H. 1895. Studies in Coccinellidae. Trans. Amer. Ent. Soc., 22: 81–114.

Kapur, A. P. 1950. The biology and external morphology of larvae of Epilachninae. Bull. Ent. Res., 41:161–208.

LeConte, J. L. 1852. Remarks upon the Coccinellidae of the United States. Proc. Acad. Nat. Sci., Phila., 6:129–145.

Leng, C. W. 1903. Notes on Coccinellidae. Jour. N.Y. Ent. Soc., 11:35–45, 193–211.

———. 1908. Notes on Coccinellidae. Jour. N.Y. Ent. Soc., 16:33–44.

Palmer, M. A. 1911. Notes on heredity in *Adalia*. Ann. Ent. Soc. Amer., 4:283–302.

———. 1914. Some notes on the life history of lady beetles. Ann. Ent. Soc. Amer., 7:213–237.

———. 1917. Additional notes on heredity in *Adalia*. Ann. Ent. Soc. Amer., 10:289–302.

Stehr, W. C. 1930. The Coccinellidae of Minnesota. Univ. Minn. Agr. Exp. Sta., Tech. Bull. No. 75, 54 pp.

Watson, W. Y. 1956. A study of the phylogeny of the genera of the tribe Coccinellini. Paleont. Contrib., Roy. Ontario Mus. Zool., 42:1–52.

Wheeler, W. M. 1911. Ant nest Coccinellid. Jour. N.Y. Ent. Soc., 19:169–174.

COLYDIIDAE

Craighead, F. C. 1920. Biology of the family Colydiidae. Proc. Ent. Soc. Wash., 22:1–13.

Horn, G. H. 1878. Synopsis of the Colydiidae of the United States. Proc. Amer. Phil. Soc., 17:555–592.

CRYPTOPHAGIDAE

Casey, T. L. 1900. Review of American Cryptophagidae. Jour. N.Y. Ent. Soc., 8:75–128.

Hinton, H. E. 1945. Beetles associated with stored products—keys to adults and larvae; biology and control. Brit. Mus. (Nat. Hist.), pp. 189–194, 201–233.

CUCUJIDAE

Böving, A. G. 1941. Larvae and pupae of Cucujidae. Zoologica, 3(7):197–222.

Casey, T. L. 1884. Revision of the Cucujidae of America north of Mexico. Trans. Amer. Ent. Soc., 11:69–112.

LeConte, J. L. 1854. Revision of the Cucujides of the United States. Proc. Acad. Nat. Sci., Phila., 7:73–79.

CUPESIDAE

Barber, G. W., and W. O. Ellis. 1920. The Cupesidae of America north of Mexico. Jour. N.Y. Ent. Soc., 28:197–208.

Casey, T. L. 1897. Synopsis of the genus *Cupes*. Ann. N.Y. Acad. Sci., 9:637–638.

Edwards, J. Gordon. 1951. Cupesid beetles attracted to soap in Montana. Coleop. Bull., 5:42–43.

LeConte, J. L. 1874. On the Cupesidae of North America. Trans. Amer. Ent. Soc., 5:87–88.

CURCULIONIDAE

Anderson, W. H. 1952. Larvae of some genera of Cossoninae. Ann. Ent. Soc. Amer., 45:281–308.

Blatchley, W. S. 1925. Notes on Rhynchophora, III. Jour. N.Y. Ent. Soc., 33:87–113.

———. 1928. Notes on Rhynchophora, IV. Jour. N.Y. Ent. Soc., 36:235–262.

——— and C. W. Leng. 1916. Rhynchophora of northeastern America. Nature Pub. Co., Indianapolis, pp. 1–682.

Buchanan, L. L. 1927. A review of *Panscopus*. Proc. Ent. Soc. Wash., 29: 25–36.

——. 1939. The species of *Pantomorus* of America north of Mexico. U.S.D.A., Misc. Pub. No. 341.

Casey, T. L. 1920. American species of Barinae. Mem. Col., 8:300–516.

Chittenden, F. H. 1927. Classification of nut curculios (*Balanius*) of boreal America. Ent. Amer., 7:129–206.

Davis, A. C. 1947. Review of weevils of the tribe Ophryastini of America north of Mexico. Proc. U.S.N.M., 96:483–551.

Dietz, W. G. 1891. Revision of the genera and species of Anthonomini. Trans. Amer. Ent. Soc., 18:177–276.

——. 1896. Revision of the genera and species of Ceutorhynchini. Trans. Amer. Ent. Soc., 23:387–480.

Fall, H. C. 1898. Revision of species of *Apion* of America north of Mexico. Trans. Amer. Ent. Soc., 25:105–184.

Henderson, L. S. 1939. Revision of *Listronotus,* I. Kan. Univ. Sci. Bull., 26:215–337.

Kiefer, H. H. 1932. Key to larvae of curculionid subfamilies. Ent. Amer., 13(2):48–49.

Kissinger, David G. 1957. Studies on North American *Apion*: The *Apion disparatum* group. Coleop. Bull., 10:69–80.

——. 1957. The *Apion nodicorne* group. Coleop. Bull., 11:71–78.

MacAloney, H. J. 1930. The biology and control of *Pissodes strobi* Peck, the white pine weevil. Bull. N.Y. State Coll. For., Tech. Pub. No. 28.

Pierce, W. D. 1907. Biologies of Rhynchophora of North America. Univ. Neb. Stud., 78:249–320.

——. 1941. Studies in Cyladinae. Bull. S. Calif. Acad. Sci., 39:205–228.

Schoof, H. F. 1942. *Conotrachelus* in north central United States. Ill. Biol. Monog., 19(3):1–170.

Taylor, R. L. 1929–30. Biology of the white pine weevil. Ann. Ent. Soc. Amer., 9:167–248; 10:1–86.

VanDyke, E. C. 1933. Revision of *Dyslobus*. Pan-Pac. Ent., 9:31–47.

Vaurie, P. 1954. Revision of genera *Anchylorhynchus* and *Petalochilus* of the Petalochilinae. Amer. Mus. Nov., No. 1651, 58 pp.

DASCILLIDAE

Blaisdell, F. E. 1934. The genus *Anorus,* with key to species of males. Trans. Amer. Ent. Soc., 60:319–325.

Horn, G. H. 1880. Synopsis of the Dascyllidae of the United States. Trans. Amer. Ent. Soc., 8:76–114.

LeConte, J. L. 1853. Synopsis of the Atopidae and Cyphonidae of the United States. Proc. Acad. Nat. Sci., Phila., 6:350–357.

DERMESTIDAE

Beal, R. S., Jr. 1954. Biology and taxonomy of nearctic species of *Trogoderma*. Univ. Cal. Pub. Ent., 10(2):35–102.

——. 1954. A revision of the species included in the genus *Novelsis*. Trans. Amer. Ent. Soc., 80:73–90.

Casey, T. L. 1900. A review of the American Dermestidae. Jour. N.Y. Ent. Soc., 8:138–165.

Jayne, H. F. 1882. Revision of the Dermestidae of the United States. Proc. Amer. Phil. Soc., 20:343–377.

LeConte, J. L. 1854. Synopsis of the Dermestidae of the United States. Proc. Acad. Nat. Sci., Phila., 7:106–113.

Mutchler, A. J., and H. B. Weiss. 1927. The dermestid beetles of New Jersey. N.J. Dept. Agr., Circ. No. 108.

Rees, B. E. 1943. Classification of larvae of American Dermestidae. U.S.D.A., Misc. Pub. No. 511, 18 pp.

DRYOPIDAE

Barthe, E. 1928. Dryopidae. Misc. Ent., 30:211–274.

Horn, G. H. 1870. Synopsis of the Parnidae of the United States. Trans. Amer. Ent. Soc., 3:29–42.

LeConte, J. L. 1852. Synopsis of the Parnidae of the United States. Proc. Acad. Nat. Sci., Phila., 6:41–45.

Sanderson, Milton W. 1938. Monographic revision of the North American species of *Stenelmis*. Kan. Univ. Sci. Bull., 25:635–717.

West, L. S. 1929. Larvae of Dryopidae. Ann. Ent. Soc. Amer., 22:691–727.

DYTISCIDAE

Crotch, G. B. 1873. Revision of the Dytiscidae of the United States. Trans. Amer. Ent. Soc., 4:383–424.

Fall, H. C. 1919. North American species of *Coelambus*. J. D. Sherman, Jr., Mt. Vernon, N.Y., 20 pp.

———. 1922. The genus *Agabus*. J. D. Sherman, Jr., Mt. Vernon, N.Y., 20 pp.

———. 1923. Revision of North American species of *Hydroporus* and *Agaporus*. Privately printed, 129 pp.

Hatch, Melville H. 1929. *Bidessus, Shantus, Colymbetes* and *Graphoderus*. Bull. Brooklyn Ent. Soc., 23:217–229.

Leech, Hugh B. 1940. Key to nearctic species of *Laccornis* and *Agaporus*. Can. Ent., 72:122–128.

———. 1942. Key to the nearctic genera of the tribe Agabini. Ann. Ent. Soc. Amer., 35(3):355–362.

Sharp, D. 1882. On aquatic carnivorous Coleoptera or Dytiscidae. Sci. Trans. Roy. Dublin Soc., 2(n.s.):179–1003.

Sherman, J. D. 1913. Some habits of the Dytiscidae. Jour. N.Y. Ent. Soc., 21:43–53.

Wallis, J. B. 1939. The genus *Ilybius* in North America. Can. Ent., 71:192–199.

ELATERIDAE

Arnett, R. H., Jr. 1952. A review of the nearctic *Adelocerina*. Wasmann Jour. Biol., 10:103–126.

Becker, E. C. 1956. Revision of the nearctic species of *Agriotes*. Can. Ent., 88(Suppl. 1):1–101.

Dietrich, Henry. 1945. The Elateridae of New York State. Cornell Univ. Mem. No. 269, 79 pp.

Glen, Robert. 1950. Larvae of elaterid beetles of the tribe Lepturiodini. Smiths. Misc. Col., 111(11):1–246.

Glen, Robert, K. M. King, and A. D. Arnason. 1943. Wire-worm identification. Can. Jour. Res., 21:358–387.

Hyslop, J. A. 1917. Phylogeny of the Elateridae based on larval characters. Ann. Ent. Soc. Amer., 10:241–263.

Lanchester, H. P. 1946. Larvae of six species of *Limonius*. Ann. Ent. Soc. Amer., 39:619–626.

LeConte, J. L. 1853. Revision of the Elateridae of the United States. Trans. Amer. Phil. Soc., 10(2):405–508.

VanDyke, E. C. 1932. Miscellaneous studies in Elateridae. Proc. Calif. Acad. Sci., 20(9):293–452.

ELMIDAE

Horn, G. J. 1870. Synopsis of the Parnidae of the United States. Trans. Amer. Ent. Soc., 3:29–42.

LeConte, J. L. 1852. Synopsis of the Parnidae of the United States. Proc. Acad. Nat. Sci., Phila., 6:41–45.

Matheson, R. 1914. Life history notes on *Stenelmis*. Can. Ent., 46:181–189.

Sanderson, Milton W. 1938. Monographic revision of the North American species of *Stenelmis*. Kan. Univ. Sci. Bull., 25:635–717.

———. 1953–1954. Revision of nearctic genera of Elmidae. Jour. Kan. Ent. Soc., 26(4):148–163; 27(1):1–13.

West, L. S. 1929. Larvae of Dryopidae. Ann. Ent. Soc. Amer., 22:691–727.

ENDOMYCHIDAE

Arrow, G. J. 1920. Contribution to the classification of Endomychidae. Trans. Ent. Soc. Lond., pp. 1–83.

Crotch, G. B. 1873. Synopsis of the Endomychidae of the United States. Trans. Amer. Ent. Soc., 4:359–363.

LeConte, J. L. 1853. Synopsis of the Endomychidae of the United States. Proc. Acad. Nat. Sci., Phila., 6:357–360.

Strohecker, H. F. 1953. The family Endomychidae. Gen. Insect., Fasc. 210, 140 pp.

EROTYLIDAE

Boyle, W. Wayne. 1956. A revision of Erotylidae of America north of Mexico. Bull. Amer. Mus. Nat. Hist., 110(2):67–172.

Casey, T. L. 1916. North American Erotylidae. Mem. Col., 7:146–172.

Crotch, G. B. 1873. Synopsis of the Erotylidae of boreal America. Trans. Amer. Ent. Soc., 4:349–358.

LeConte, J. L. 1854. Synopsis of the Erotylidae of the United States. Proc. Acad. Nat. Sci., Phila., 7:158–163.

GYRINIDAE

Abbott, C. E. 1941. Why does *Gyrinus* circle? Ent. News, 52:287–290.

Fall, H. C. 1922. The North American species of *Gyrinus*. Trans. Amer. Ent. Soc., 47:269–306.

Hatch, Melville H. 1925. Outline of ecology of Gyrinidae. Bull. Brooklyn Ent. Soc., 20:101–114.

Hatch, Melville H. 1926. Phylogeny and phylogenetic tendencies of Gyrinidae. Pap. Mich. Acad. Sci., Arts, and Letters, 5:429–467.

———. 1927. Morphology of Gyrinidae. Pap. Mich. Acad. Sci., Arts, and Letters, 7:311–350.

LeConte, J. L. 1868. Gyrinidae of America north of Mexico. Proc. Acad. Nat. Sci., Phila., pp. 365–373.

Roberts, C. H. 1895. Species of *Dineutes* of America north of Mexico. Trans. Amer. Ent. Soc., 22:279–288.

HALIPLIDAE

Chandler, H. P. 1943. Key to genera of Haliplidae. Pan-Pac. Ent., 19:157–158.

Crotch, G. B. 1873. Revision of the Dytiscidae of the United States. Trans. Amer. Ent. Soc., 4:383–424.

Hickman, J. R. 1931. Contributions to biology of Haliplidae. Ann. Ent. Soc. Amer., 24:129–142.

Matheson, R. 1912. The Haliplidae of America north of Mexico. Jour. N.Y. Ent. Soc., 20:156–193.

Roberts, C. N. 1913. Haliplidae of America north of Mexico. Jour. N.Y. Ent. Soc., 21(2):91–123.

Wallis, J. B. 1932. Revision of North American *Haliplus*. Tr. Roy. Can. Inst., 19:1–76.

HELMIDAE
(see ELMIDAE)

HELODIDAE

Good, H. G. 1924. Life history of *Prionocyphon*. Jour. N.Y. Ent. Soc., 8:98–110.

Horn, G. H. 1880. Synopsis of the Dascyllidae of the United States. Trans. Amer. Ent. Soc., 8:76–114.

LeConte, J. L. 1853. Synopsis of the Atopidae and Cyphonidae of the United States. Proc. Acad. Nat. Sci., Phila., 6:350–357.

HETEROCERIDAE

Horn, G. H. 1890. The species of *Heterocerus* of boreal America. Trans. Amer. Ent. Soc., 17:1–16.

HISTERIDAE

Carnochan, F. G. 1917. Hololeptinae of the United States. Ann. Ent. Soc. Amer., 10:367–398.

Casey, T. L. 1893. Descriptions of genera and species of Histeridae. Ann. N.Y. Acad. Sci., 7:533–578.

———. 1916. Keys and descriptions for North American Histeridae. Mem. Col., 7:201–292.

Hatch, Melville H. 1929. The genera *Hister* and *Saprinus*. Can. Ent., 61:76–83.

Horn, G. H. 1873. Synopsis of the Histeridae of the United States. Proc. Amer. Phil. Soc., 13:237–360.

LeConte, J. E. 1845. Monograph of North American Histeroides. Bost. Jour. Nat. Hist., 5:32–86.

Ross, E. S. 1940. Preliminary revision of North American *Dendrophilus*. Bull. Brooklyn Ent. Soc., 35:103–108.

Wenzel, R. L. 1944. On the classification of the histerid beetles. Field Mus. Nat. Hist., Zool. Ser., 28(2):1–151.

Hydrophilidae

Horn, G. H. 1873. Revision of the genera and species of the tribe Hydrobiini. Proc. Amer. Phil. Soc., 13:118–137.

———. 1890. Notes on some Hydrobiini of boreal America. Trans. Amer. Ent. Soc., 17:237–278.

———. 1890. A revision of the Sphaeridiini of boreal America. Trans. Amer. Ent. Soc., 17:279–314.

LeConte, J. L. 1855. Synopsis of the Hydrophilidae of the United States. Proc. Acad. Nat. Sci., Phila., 7:356–375.

Richmond, E. A. 1920. Studies on biology of Hydrophilidae. Bull. Amer. Mus. Nat. Hist., 42:1–94.

Winters, F. C. 1926. Notes on the Hydrobiini of boreal America. Pan-Pac. Ent., 3:49–58.

———. 1927. Key to *Helochares* of boreal America. Pan-Pac. Ent., 4(1):19–29.

Lagriidae

Horn, G. H. 1888. Synopsis of North American Lagriidae. Trans. Amer. Ent. Soc., 15:26–48.

Leng, C. W. 1923. The genus *Statira*. Jour. N.Y. Ent. Soc., 31:185–188.

Lampyridae

Allard, H. A. 1931. The photoperiodism of the firefly *Photinus pyralis:* Its relation to the evening twilight and other conditions. Proc. Ent. Soc. Wash., 33(3):49–58.

Barber, H. S. 1951. North American fireflies of the genus *Photuris*. Smiths. Misc. Col., 117(1):1–58.

Green, J. W. 1948. Generic revision of nearctic Lampyridae. Trans. Amer. Ent. Soc., 74(2):61–63.

———. 1956. Revision of the nearctic species of *Photinus*. Proc. Calif. Acad. Sci., 28:561–613.

Hess, W. N. 1920. Notes on the biology of the Lampyridae. Biol. Bull. Woods Hole, 38:39–76.

LeConte, J. L. 1881. Synopsis of the Lampyridae of the United States. Trans. Amer. Ent. Soc., 9:15–72.

Lund, E. J. 1911. Photogenic organs, with especial reference to the Lampyridae. Jour. Exp. Zool., 11:415–467.

McDermott, F. A. 1910. Light emissions of American Lampyridae. Can. Ent., 42:359–363.

———. 1911. Photogenic function in Photinini. Can. Ent., 43:399–406.

McDermott, F. A. 1912. Light emissions of American Lampyridae, IV. Can. Ent., 44:309–311.

——— and C. G. Crane. 1911. Photogenic organs of certain American Lampyridae. Amer. Nat., 45:306–313.

Rau, P. 1932. Rhythmic periodicity of *Photinus*. Ecology, 13:7–11.

Snell, P. A. 1931. The flashing in fireflies. Science, 73:372–373.

———. 1932. The control of luminescence. Jour. Cell. Comp. Physiol. Phila., 1:37–51.

Wenzel, H. W. 1896. Notes on Lampyridae. Ent. News, 7:294–296.

Williams, F. X. 1916. Photogenic organs of Lampyridae. Jour. Morph., 28:145–208.

———. 1917. Life history of North American Lampyridae. Jour. N.Y. Ent. Soc., 25:11–33.

LANGURIIDAE

Crotch, G. R. 1875. A revision of the coleopterous family Erotylidae. Cist. Ent., 1:377–561.

Lewis, G. 1894. Languriidae, a family. Jour. Lin. Soc. Lond., 17:347–361.

Schaeffer, C. 1904. Synoptic table of *Languria*. Jour. N.Y. Ent. Soc., 12:198–200.

Vaurie, Patricia. 1948. A review of the North American Languriidae. Bull. Amer. Mus. Nat. Hist., 92(3):123–155.

LATHRIDIIDAE

Fall, H. C. 1899. Revision of the Lathridiidae of boreal America. Trans. Amer. Ent. Soc., 26:101–190.

Horn, G. H. 1855. Synopsis of the Lathridiides of United States and Canada. Proc. Acad. Nat. Sci., Phila., 7:299–305.

Walkley, L. M. 1953. Revision of the Lathridiini of the state of Washington (Lathridiidae). Proc. Ent. Soc. Wash., 54:217–235.

LEIODIDAE

Brown, W. J. 1937. Key to species of *Neocyrtusa* and *Anistoma*. Can. Ent., 69:158–166, 193–203.

Hatch, Melville H. 1936. Studies on Leiodidae. Jour. N.Y. Ent. Soc., 44:33–41.

LUCANIDAE

Benesh, B. 1946. Systematic revision of holarctic *Platycerus*. Trans. Amer. Ent. Soc., 72:139–202.

Fuchs, C. 1882. Synopsis of the Lucanidae of the United States. Bull. Brooklyn Ent. Soc., 5:49–50, 57–60.

Hayes, W. P. 1928. Key to genera of lucanid larvae. Ann. Ent. Soc. Amer., 21:301.

Linsley, E. Gorton. 1932. *Diphyllostoma,* with key to species. Pan-Pac. Ent., 8(3):109–111.

LYCIDAE

Green, J. W. 1949. The Lycidae of the United States and Canada, I: The tribe Lycini. Trans. Amer. Ent. Soc., 75:53–70.

Green, J. W. 1950. The Lycidae of the United States and Canada, II: The tribe Lygistopterini. Trans. Amer. Ent. Soc., 76:13–25.

———. 1951. The Lycidae of the United States and Canada, III: The tribe Platerodini (in part). Trans. Amer. Ent. Soc., 77:1–20.

———. 1952. The Lycidae of the United States and Canada, IV: The tribe Calopterini. Trans. Amer. Ent. Soc., 78:1–19.

———. 1953. The Lycidae of the United States and Canada, V: *Plateros.* Trans. Amer. Ent. Soc., 78:149–181.

LeConte, J. L. 1851. Synopsis of the Lampyrides of temperate North America. Proc. Acad. Nat. Sci., Phila., 5(2):331.

———. 1881. Synopsis of the Lampyridae of the United States. Trans. Amer. Ent. Soc., 9:16–28.

LYCTIDAE

Casey, T. L. 1891. Coleopterological notes, III. Ann. N.Y. Acad. Sci., 6: 12–16.

Kraus, E. J., and A. D. Hopkins. 1911. Revision of holarctic Lyctidae. U.S.D.A., Bur. Ent. Tech. Bull. No. 20, pp. 111–138.

Gerberg, E. J. 1957. A revision of the new world species of the powder-post beetles (Lyctidae). U.S.D.A., Tech. Bull. No. 1157, 69 pp.

MELANDRYIDAE

Casey, T. L. 1900. Review of the tribe Tetratomini. Jour. N.Y. Ent. Soc., 8:166–172.

Hopping, R. 1935. Review of *Mycterus.* Pan-Pac. Ent., 11:75–78.

Horn, G. H. 1879. Notes on the Mycteridae and other Heteromera. Trans. Amer. Ent. Soc., 7:336–339.

———. 1888. Miscellaneous coleopterous studies. Trans. Amer. Ent. Soc., 15:32–44.

MELASIDAE

Hopping, R. 1926. The genus *Melasis.* Can. Ent., 58:225–228.

Horn, G. H. 1886. A monograph of the subfamilies Eucnemidae, Cerophytinae, and Perothopinae of the United States. Trans. Amer. Ent. Soc., 13:5–58.

LeConte, J. L. 1852. Synopsis of the Eucnemides of temperate North America. Proc. Acad. Nat. Sci., Phila., 6:45–49.

VanDyke, E. C. 1932. The genus *Hypocoelus,* with key to species. Proc. Calif. Acad. Sci., Ser. 4, 20:292–293.

VanHorn, R. W. 1909. Notes on some eastern Eucnemidae. Proc. Ent. Soc. Wash., 11:54–62.

MELOIDAE

Dillon, Lawrence S. 1952. The Meloidae of Texas. Amer. Midl. Nat., 48(2): 330–420.

Enns, Wilbur R. 1956. A revision of genera *Nemognatha, Zonitis,* and *Pseudozonitis* in North America north of Mexico. Kan. Univ. Sci. Bull., 37:685–909.

Fall, H. C. 1901. Notes on *Cantharis,* with synoptic table. Trans. Amer. Ent. Soc., 27:293–304.

Horn, G. H. 1873. Revision of several genera of Meloidae of the United States. Proc. Amer. Phil. Soc., 13:88–117.

———. 1885. Studies among the Meloidae. Trans. Amer. Ent. Soc., 12:107–116.

LeConte, J. L. 1853. Synopsis of the Meloides of the United States. Proc. Acad. Nat. Sci., Phila., 6:328–350.

MacSwain, J. W. 1953. A synopsis of the genus *Gnathium,* with description of new species. Wasmann Jour. Biol., 10:205–224.

———. 1958. Taxonomic and biological observations on the genus *Hornia.* Ann. Ent. Soc. Amer., 51:390–396.

Selander, R. B. 1955. The blister beetle genus *Linsleya.* Amer. Mus. Nov., No. 1730, 30 pp.

VanDyke, E. C. 1928. A reclassification of genera of North American Meloidae. Univ. Calif. Pub. Ent., 4:395–474.

Werner, F. G. 1945. Revision of the genus *Epicauta* in America north of Mexico. Bull. M.C.Z., 95:421–517.

———. 1955. Studies in the genus *Epicauta* of the North American continent, I: The *cavipes* group. Bull. Brooklyn Ent. Soc., 50(1):1–12.

Melyridae

Blaisdell, F. E. 1926. Studies in Melyridae, No. 5. Can. Ent., 58:8–13.

———. 1929. Studies in Melyridae, No. 7. Pan-Pac. Ent., 5:35–42.

———. 1938. Synopsis and revision of the tribe Dasytini of America north of Mexico. Trans. Amer. Ent. Soc., 64:1–31.

———. 1940. Monographic study of the genus *Trichochroides.* Trans. Amer. Ent. Soc., 66:283–306.

Casey, T. L. 1895. Synopsis of the Melyridae of North America. Ann. N.Y. Acad. Sci., 8:465–606.

Fall, H. C. 1912. Review of the North American species of *Collops.* Jour. N.Y. Ent. Soc., 20:249–274.

Horn, G. H. 1870. Synopsis of the genus *Collops.* Trans. Amer. Ent. Soc., 3:79–84.

———. 1872. Synopsis of the Malachiidae of the United States. Trans. Amer. Ent. Soc., 4:109–127.

Monotomidae

Horn, G. H. 1879. Synopsis of the Monotomidae of the United States. Trans. Amer. Ent. Soc., 7:257–267.

Mordellidae

LeConte, J. L. 1862. Synopsis of the Mordellidae of the United States. Proc. Acad. Nat. Sci., Phila., pp. 43–51.

Liljeblad, Emil. 1922. A revision of the genus *Mordella.* Can. Ent., 54:51–58.

———. 1945. Monograph of the family Mordellidae of North America north of Mexico. Mus. Zool., Univ. Mich., Misc. Pub. No. 62, pp. 1–229.

Ray, E. 1936. North American mordellids, I. Can. Ent., 68:124–129.

———. 1944. New mordellids of Western Hemisphere. Field Mus. Nat. Hist., Zool. Ser., 29(7):117–133.

———. 1946. North American Mordellidae, II, III, and IV. Pan-Pac. Ent., 22:41–50, 90–99, and 121–131.

———. 1947. North American Mordellidae, V. Pan-Pac. Ent., 23(3):121–131.

Smith, J. B. 1882. Synopsis of the Mordellidae of the United States. Trans. Amer. Ent. Soc., 10:73–100.

MYCETAEIDAE

Blaisdell, F. E. 1931. Revision of the tribe Liesthini. Trans. Amer. Ent. Soc., 56:375–390.

MYCETOPHAGIDAE

Casey, T. L. 1900. Review of American Tritomidae (Mycetophagidae). Jour. N.Y. Ent. Soc., 8:128–138.

Horn, G. H. 1878. Tables of the species of *Mycetophagus* and *Litargus*. Proc. Amer. Phil. Soc., 17:603–608.

LeConte, J. L. 1856. Synopsis of the Mycetophagidae of the United States. Proc. Acad. Nat. Sci., Phila., 8:12–15.

MYLABRIDAE

Back, E. A. 1922. Weevils in beans and peas. U.S.D.A., Farm. Bull. No. 1275, 35 pp.

Fall, H. C. 1910. The genus *Mylabris (Bruchus)*. Trans. Amer. Ent. Soc., 36:160–189.

Horn, G. H. 1873. Revision of the Bruchidae of the United States. Trans. Amer. Ent. Soc., 4:311–342.

NITIDULIDAE

Easton, A. M. 1955. A revision of nearctic species of beetles of the genus *Meligethes*. Proc. U.S.N.M., 104:87–103.

Horn, G. H. 1879. Revision of the Nitidulidae of the United States. Trans. Amer. Ent. Soc., 7:267–336.

Parsons, C. T. 1943. Revision of the nearctic Nitidulidae. Bull. M.C.Z., 92:121–278.

OEDEMERIDAE

Arnett, R. H., Jr. 1951. A revision of the nearctic Oedemeridae. Amer. Midl. Nat., 45(2):257–391.

Horn, G. H. 1896. Oedemeridae of boreal America. Proc. Calif. Acad Sci., 6(3):382–421.

LeConte, J. L. 1854. Synopsis of the Oedemeridae of the United States. Proc. Acad. Nat. Sci., Phila., 7:20–22.

OMOPHRONIDAE

Benschoter, C. A., and E. F. Cook. 1956. A revision of the genus *Omophron* of North America north of Mexico. Ann. Ent. Soc. Amer., 49:411–429.

ORTHOPERIDAE

Casey, T. L. 1900. Synopsis of the Corylophidae. Jour. N.Y. Ent. Soc., 8:60–75.

LeConte, J. L. 1852. Synopsis of the Corylophi. Proc. Acad. Nat. Sci., Phila., 6:141–145.

OSTOMATIDAE

Horn, G. H. 1862. Monograph of the species of *Trogosita* (*Tenebroides*) inhabiting the United States. Proc. Acad. Nat. Sci., Phila., pp. 82–88.

Mutchler, A. J., and H. B. Weiss. 1929. The Ostomidae of New Jersey. N.J. Dept. Agr., Circ. No. 154.

Schaeffer, C. F. A. 1918. The genera of Ostomidae. Jour. N.Y. Ent. Soc., 26:190–201.

PASSALIDAE

Gray, I. E. 1945. Observations on the life history of the horned *Passalus*. Amer. Midl. Nat., 35:728–746.

PHALACRIDAE

Casey, T. L. 1890. Synopsis of the Phalacridae. Ann. N.Y. Acad. Sci., 5:307–504.

LeConte, J. L. 1856. Synopsis of the Phalacridae of the United States. Proc. Acad. Nat. Sci., Phila., 8:15–17.

PSELAPHIDAE

Bowman, J. R. 1934. Pselaphidae of North America. Privately published, 149 pp.

Brendel, E. 1886. Synopsis of the genera and species of the family Pselaphidae. Proc. Ent. Soc. Phila., 6:31–38.

———. and H. F. Wickham. 1890. Pselaphidae of North America. Bull. Univ. Iowa, 1:216–304.

———. 1891. Pselaphidae of North America. Bull. Univ. Iowa, 2:1–84.

Casey, T. L. 1893. Coleopterological notices, V. Ann. N.Y. Acad. Sci., 7:433–509.

———. 1897. Coleopterological notices. Ann. N.Y. Acad. Sci., 9:550–630.

LeConte, J. L. 1850. On the Pselaphidae of the United States. Bost. Jour. Nat. Hist., 6:64–110.

Marsh, G. A., and R. O. Schuster. 1954. A preliminary revision of the genus *Pselaptrichus*. Trans. San Diego Soc. Nat. Hist., 12(2):3–28.

Park, Orlando. 1947. Observations on *Batrisodes,* with particular reference to the American species east of the Rocky Mountains. Bull. Chicago Acad. Sci., 8(3):45–132.

———. 1950. New species of nearctic pselaphid beetles and a revision of the genus *Cedius.* Bull. Chicago Acad. Sci., 8:315–343.

———. 1953. Discrimination of genera of pselaphid beetles of the United States. Bull. Chicago Acad. Sci., 9:229–331.

PSEPHENIDAE

Blaisdell, F. E. 1923. The genus *Psephenus*. Ent. News, 24:234–238.

Casey, T. L. 1894. Key to species of *Psephenus*. Ann. N.Y. Acad. Sci., 7:578.

Horn, G. H. 1870. Synopsis of Parnidae of the United States. Trans. Amer. Ent. Soc., 3:29–42.

Matheson, R. 1914. Life history notes on the genus *Psephenus*. Can. Ent., 46:185–188.

Pseudomorphidae

Notman, H. 1925. Revision of Pseudomorphidae. Proc. U.S.N.M., 67:1–34.

Ptinidae

Casey, T. L. 1898. Studies in the Ptinidae, Cicidae, and Sphindidae of America. Jour. N.Y. Ent. Soc., 6:61–93.

Fall, H. C. 1905. Revision of the Ptinidae of boreal America. Trans. Amer. Ent. Soc., 31:97–296.

Hinton, H. E. 1945. Monograph of beetles associated with stored grain. Brit. Mus. (Nat. Hist.), London, 443 pp.

Howe, R. W., and H. D. Burgess. 1952. Studies on beetles of the family Ptinidae, VII: Biology of five ptinid species found in stored products. Bull. Ent. Res., 43:153–186.

LeConte, J. L. 1865. Prodromus of a monograph of the tribe Anobiini of North America. Proc. Acad. Nat. Sci., Phila., pp. 222–244.

Pyrochroidae

Blair, K. G. 1914. A revision of Pyrochroidae. Ann. Mag. Nat. Hist., 13: 310–326.

Horn, G. H. 1888. Synopsis of *Dendroides*. Trans. Amer. Ent. Soc., 15:46–48.

LeConte, J. L. 1855. Synopsis of the pyrochroides of the United States. Proc. Acad. Nat. Sci., Phila., 7:270–277.

VanDyke, E. C. 1938. The genus *Ischalia,* with key to species. Ent. News, 49:192–194.

Pythidae

Hopping, R. 1935. Revision of the genus *Mycterus*. Pan-Pac. Ent., 11:75–78.

Horn, G. H. 1888. Synopsis of the genus *Pytho*. Trans. Amer. Ent. Soc., 15:45–46.

VanDyke, E. C. 1928. Key to species of *Cononotus* and *Lacconotus*. Bull. Brooklyn Ent. Soc., 23(5):257–259.

———. 1939. The genus *Cononotus*. Pan-Pac. Ent., 15:18–20.

Wickham, H. F. 1899. The Pythidae of Ontario and Quebec. Can. Ent., 31:57–61.

Rhipiphoridae

Horn, G. H. 1875. Notes on the species of *Rhipiphorus* of the United States. Trans. Amer. Ent. Soc., 5:121–125.

Linsley, E Gorton, and J. W. MacSwain. 1951. The Rhipiphoridae of California. Bull. Calif. Ins. Surv., 1(3):79–87.

Rivnay, E. 1929. Revision of the Rhipiphoridae of north and central America. Mem. Amer. Ent. Soc., 6:1–68.

RHYNCHOPHORIDAE

Anderson, W. H. 1948. Larvae of some genera of Calendrinae and Strombocerinae. Ann. Ent. Soc. Amer., 41:413–437.

Blatchley, W. S., and C. W. Leng. 1916. Rhynchophora of northeastern America. Nature Pub. Co., Indianapolis, pp. 547–576.

Cotton, R. T. 1924. Classification of Calendrinae larvae. Proc. U.S.N.M., Vol. 66, art. 5, 11 pp.

Horn, G. H. 1873. The subfamily Calendrinae. Proc. Amer. Phil. Soc., 13:407–430.

LeConte, J. L. 1876. Calendrinae. Proc. Amer. Phil. Soc., 15:328–341.

Satterthwait, A. F. 1931. *Calendra,* host plants, distribution, and pupal key. Ann. Ent. Soc. Amer., 24:143–172.

Vaurie, Patricia. 1952. Revision of the genus *Calendra* (formerly *Sphenophorus*) in the United States and Mexico. Bull. Amer. Mus. Nat. Hist., 98(2):31–186.

SALPINGIDAE

Spilman, T. J. 1952. The male genitalia of the nearctic Salpingidae. Coleop. Bull., 6(1):9–12.

SCAPHIDIIDAE

Casey, T. L. 1893. Synopsis of Scaphidiidae. Ann. N.Y. Acad. Sci., 7:510–533.

———. 1900. Synopsis of Scaphidiidae. Jour. N.Y. Ent. Soc., 8:55–60.

SCARABAEIDAE

Arrow, G. J. 1904. Sound production in the lamellicorn beetles. Trans. Ent. Soc. Lond., pp. 709–750.

———. 1951. Horned beetles. W. Junk, The Hague, 154 pp.

Beal, R. S. 1958. Synopsis of the economic species of *Trogoderma* occurring in the United States. Ann. Ent. Soc. Amer., 49:559–566.

Blaisdell, F. E., Sr. 1930. Revision of *Dinacoma*. Pan-Pac. Ent., 6:171–177.

Blanchard, F. 1885. On the species of *Canthon* and *Phanaeus* of the United States. Trans. Amer. Ent. Soc., 12:163–172.

———. 1888. Some account of our species of *Geotrupes*. Psyche, 5:103–110.

Blatchley, W. S. 1927–1930. Scarabaeidae of Florida. Fla. Ent., 11:44–46; 12:55–62; 13:69–77; and 14:25–35.

Bradley, J. C. 1944. Key to species of *Geotrupes* of America north of Mexico. Bull. Brooklyn Ent. Soc., 39:112–113.

Brown, W. J. 1927. A revision of *Aphodius,* group I, b. Can. Ent., 59:162–167.

Cartwright, O. L. 1948. The American species of *Pleurophorus*. Trans. Amer. Ent. Soc., 74:131–145.

— —. 1955. Scarab beetles of the genus *Psammodius* in the Western Hemisphere. Proc. U.S.N.M., 104:413–462.

Casey, T. L. 1915. Rutelinae, Dynastinae, and Cetoniinae. Mem. Col., 6:1–394.

Cazier, M. A. 1938. Generic revision of North American Cremastocheilini. Bull. S. Calif. Acad. Sci., 37:80–87.

———. 1940. Revision of the Phileurini of America. Bull. S. Calif. Acad. Sci., 38:169–171.

Chapin, E. A. 1935. Revision of *Chlaenobia*. Smiths. Misc. Col., 94(9):1–20.

Davis, A. C. 1934. Revision of the genus *Plecoma*. Bull. S. Calif. Acad. Sci., 33:123–130.

———. 1934. Revision of the genus *Plecoma*. Bull. S. Calif. Acad. Sci., 34:4–36.

Fall, H. C. 1909. Revision of the *Diplotaxis* of the United States. Trans. Amer. Ent. Soc., 35:1–97.

Forbes, S. A. 1916. General survey of *Phyllophaga* of Illinois. Univ. Ill. Agr. Exp. Sta., Bull. No. 186.

Hayes, W. P. 1925. A comparative study of the Scarabaeidae. Kan. State Agr. Coll., Bull. No. 16.

———. 1930. Morphology, taxonomy, and biology of larval Scarabaeoidea. Ill. Biol. Monog., 12:85–204.

Hoffman, C. H. 1939. Biology and taxonomy of nearctic *Osmoderma*. Ann. Ent. Soc. Amer., 32(3):510–525.

Horn, G. H. 1880. Synopsis of the *Geotrupes* of the United States. Trans. Amer. Ent. Soc., 8:145.

———. 1880. Synopsis of the Euphoriae of the United States. Proc. Amer. Phil. Soc., 18:397–408.

———. 1887. Monograph of Aphodiini of the United States. Trans. Amer. Ent. Soc., 14:1–110.

Howden, Henry F. 1955. Biology and taxonomy of North American beetles of the subfamily Geotrupinae, with revisions of genera *Bolboceroma, Eucanthus, Geotrupes,* and *Peltotrupes*. Proc. U.S.N.M., 104:151–319.

Langston, J. M. 1928. *Phyllophaga* of Mississippi. Miss. Agr. Exp. Sta., Tech. Bull. No. 15, 103 pp.

LeConte, J. L. 1856. Synopsis of the Melolonthidae of the United States. Jour. Acad. Nat. Sci., Phila., 3(2):225–288.

Luginbill, P. 1928. The *Phyllophaga* inhabiting South Carolina. Ann. Ent. Soc. Amer., 21:47–91.

——— and Henry R. Painter. 1953. May beetles of the United States and Canada. U.S.D.A., Tech. Bull. No. 1060, 102 pp.

Olson, Ada L., T. H. Hubbell, and H. F. Howden. 1954. The burrowing beetles of the genus *Mycotrupes*. Mus. Zool., Univ. Mich., Misc. Pub. No. 84, 59 pp.

Ritcher, P. O. 1943. Anomalini of eastern North America, with description of the larvae. Ky. Agr. Exp. Sta., Bull. No. 422, 27 pp.

———. 1944. Dynastinae of eastern North America, with description of larvae. Ky. Agr. Exp. Sta., Bull. No. 467, 56 pp.

———. 1945. Rutelinae of eastern North America, with description of larvae. Ky. Agr. Exp. Sta., Bull. No. 471, 19 pp.

———. 1945. North American Cetoniinae, with description of larvae. Ky. Agr. Exp. Sta., Bull. No. 476, 39 pp.

———. 1945. Coprinae of eastern North America, with description of larvae. Ky. Agr. Exp. Sta., Bull. No. 477, 23 pp.

———. 1947. Larvae of Geotrupinae. Ky. Agr. Exp. Sta., Bull. No. 506, 27 pp.

Robinson, Mark. 1948. Review of *Phanaeus*. Trans. Amer. Ent. Soc., 73:299–305.

———. 1948. Review of species of *Canthon* inhabiting the United States. Trans. Amer. Ent. Soc., 74:83–100.

Saylor, Lawrence W. 1940. Revision of the scarabaeid beetles of the phyllophagan subgenus *Listrochelus* of the United States with discussion and related subgenera. Proc. U.S.N.M., 89:59–130.

———. 1940. Revision of the genera *Cotalpa* and *Paracotalpa* of the United States. Proc. Ent. Soc. Wash., 42:190–200.

———. 1946. Revision of the genus *Dichelonyx*. Bull. Brooklyn Ent. Soc., 40:137–158.

———. 1948. Synoptic review of United States scarab beetles and subfamily Dynastinae, IV: Tribes Oryctini (in part), Dynastini, and Phileurini. Jour. Wash. Acad. Sci., 38:176–183.

Sim, R. J. 1928. *Phyllophaga* of the United States and Canada. N.J. Dept. Agr., Circ. No. 145, pp. 3–60.

Smith, J. B. 1888. Notes on the species of *Lachnosterna* of temperate North America. Proc. U.S.N.M., 11:481–525.

Wallis, J. B. 1928. Revision of the genus *Odontaeus*. Can. Ent., 60:119–128, 151–156, and 168–176.

Weiss, H. B. 1951. The death feint of *Diplotaxus liberata* Germ. Jour. N.Y. Ent. Soc., 59:245–247.

Vaurie, Patricia. 1956. *Diplotaxis* of the eastern United States. Coleop. Bull., 10:1–9.

———. 1958. A revision of the genus *Diplotaxis*, I. Bull. Amer. Mus. Nat. Hist., 115(5):269–396.

SCOLYTIDAE

Beal, James A., and Calvin L. Massey. 1945. Bark beetles and ambrosia beetles, with special reference to species occurring in North Carolina. Duke Univ. Sch. For., Bull. No. 10, 178 pp.

Blackman, M. W. 1922. Mississippi bark beetles. Miss. Agr. Exp. Sta., Tech. Bull. No. 11, 130 pp.

———. 1928. The genus *Pityophthorus*. N.Y. State Coll. For., Bull. No. 25, pp. 1–184.

———. 1928. Notes on Micracinae. N.Y. State Coll. For., Bull. No. 25, pp. 185–208.

———. 1934. Revisional study of *Scolytus* in North America. U.S.D.A., Tech. Bull. No. 431, 30 pp.

Blatchley, W. S., and C. W. Leng. 1916. Rhynchophora or weevils of northeastern America. Nature Pub. Co., Indianapolis, pp. 376–592.

Chapman, J. A. 1956. Flight-muscle changes during adult life in a scolytid beetle. Nature, 177:1183.

——— and J. M. Kinghorn. 1958. Studies of flight and attack activity of the ambrosia beetle, *Trypodendron lineatum* (Oliv.), and other scolytids. Can. Ent., 90:362–372.

Chamberlin, W. J. 1939. The bark and timber beetles of North America. Ore. State Coll. Coop. Assoc., pp. 105–273.

Swaine, J. W. 1909. Catalogue of North American Scolytidae. N.Y. State Ent. Rept. No. 24, pp. 76–159.

Swaine, J. W. 1917. Canadian bark-beetles, I. Can. Dept. Agr., Ent. Br. Bull. No. 14, 32 pp.

———. 1918. Canadian bark-beetles, II. Can. Dept. Agr., Ent. Br. Bull. No. 14, 143 pp.

Warren, G. L. 1958. A method of rearing bark- and cambium-feeding beetles, with particular reference to *Hylobius warreni* Wood. Can. Ent., 90:425–428.

SCYDMAENIDAE

Casey, T. L. 1897. Revision of the Scydmaenidae of the United States. Ann. N.Y. Acad. Sci., 9:351–548.

LeConte, J. L. 1852. Synopsis of the Scydmaenidae of the United States. Proc. Acad. Nat. Sci., Phila., 6:149–157.

SILPHIDAE

Arnett, R. H. 1944. A revision of the nearctic Silphini and Nicrophorini based upon female genitalia. Jour. N.Y. Ent. Soc., 52:1–25.

Bliss, R. Q. 1949. Studies on Silphidae, I: Secondary sexual differences in the genus *Nicrophorus*. Ent. News, 60:197–204.

Hatch, Melville H. 1927. Studies on Silphinae. Jour. N.Y. Ent. Soc., 35:331–370.

——— and W. Reuter. 1934. Silphidae of Washington State. Univ. Wash. Pub. Biol., 1(3):151–161.

Horn, G. H. 1880. Synopsis of the Silphidae of the United States. Trans. Amer. Ent. Soc., 8:219–322.

Milne, L. J. 1944. Biology of *Nicrophorus*. Jour. N.Y. Ent. Soc., 52:311–327.

SPHINDIDAE

Casey, T. L. 1898. Studies in the Ptinidae, Cicidae, and Sphindidae of America. Jour. N.Y. Ent. Soc., 6:61–93.

STAPHYLINIDAE

Blackwelder, R. E. 1936. Morphology of Staphylinidae. Smiths. Misc. Col., Vol. 94, art. 13, 102 pp.

———. 1936. Revision of North American *Tachyporus*. Proc. U.S.N.M., 84:39–54.

———. 1938. Revision of North American *Coproporus*. Proc. U.S.N.M., 86:1–10.

———. 1939. Generic revision of Paederini. Proc. U.S.N.M., 87:93–125.

Casey, T. L. 1884. Revision of the Stenini of America north of Mexico. Published by the author, Philadelphia, 206 pp.

———. 1905. Revision of the American Paederini. Trans. Acad. Sci. St. Louis, 15:17–248.

———. 1906. Observations on the groups Aleocharinae and Xantholinini. Trans. Acad. Sci. St. Louis, 16:125–434.

———. 1910. Myrmediniini. Mem. Col., 1:1–183.

———. 1910. Paederini and Pinophilini. Mem. Col., 1:184–205.

———. 1911. Aleocharinae and Myllaenini. Mem. Col., 2:1–245.

———. 1915. Staphylinidae. Mem. Col., 6:395–460.

Fenyes, A. 1908. A preliminary systematic arrangement of the Aleocharinae of the United States and Canada. Ent. News, 19:56–65.

Horn, G. H. 1877. Synopsis of the tribe Tachyporini of the United States. Trans. Amer. Ent. Soc., 6:81–128.

———. 1878. Synopsis of the Quedini of the United States. Trans. Amer. Ent. Soc., 7:149–167.

———. 1879. Synopsis of *Staphylinus* and allied genera of the United States. Trans. Amer. Ent. Soc., 7:185–200.

———. 1884. Synopsis of the Philonthi of boreal America. Trans. Amer. Ent. Soc., 11:177–244.

———. 1885. A study of the species of *Cryptobium* of North America. Trans. Amer. Ent. Soc., 12:85–106.

Mank, H. G. 1923. The biology of the Staphylinidae. Ann. Ent. Soc. Amer., 16:220–237.

Sanderson, Milton W. 1946. Nearctic *Stenus* of the *croceotus* group. Ann. Ent. Soc. Amer., 39(3):425–430.

Seevers, C. H. 1944. Staphylinidae of the subfamily Ambylopininae as parasites on mammals. Field Mus. Nat. Hist., Zool. Ser., 28(3):155–172.

———. 1952. A revision of the North American and European staphylinid beetles of the subtribe Gyrophaenae (Aleocharinae, Bolitocharinae). Fieldiana: Zoology, 32(10):659–762.

Voris, R. 1934. Biological investigations on Staphylinidae. Trans. Acad. Sci. St. Louis, 28:233–261.

Tenebrionidae

Blaisdell, F. E. 1925. Studies in Tenebrionidae, II. Proc. Calif. Acad. Sci., 14:369–390.

———. 1929. Revision of Usechini. Proc. U.S.N.M., 75:1–14.

———. 1933. Studies in Tenebrionidae, III. Trans. Amer. Ent. Soc., 59:191–210.

———. 1933. Monographic revision of *Centronopus*. Trans. Amer. Ent. Soc., 58:211–228.

———. 1936. Monographic revision of *Stibia*. Trans. Amer. Ent. Soc., 62:57–105.

———. 1939. Relationships of subfamilies and tribes of Tenebrionidae. Trans. Amer. Ent. Soc., 65:43–60.

Casey, T. L. 1912. Asidini. Mem. Col., 3:70–214.

Horn, G. H. 1870. Revision of the Tenebrionidae of America. Trans. Amer. Phil. Soc., 14:253–454.

LaRivers, I. 1946. The genus *Trogloderus*. Ent. News, 57(2):35–44.

Throscidae

Horn, G. H. 1885. Synopsis of the Throscidae of the United States. Trans. Amer. Ent. Soc., 12:198–208.

Trogidae

Horn, G. H. 1874. Revision of the species of *Trox* of the United States. Trans. Amer. Ent. Soc., 5:1–12.

LeConte, J. L. 1854. Descriptions of the species of *Trox* and *Omorgus* of the United States. Proc. Acad. Nat. Sci., Phila., 7:211–216.

Spector, W. 1943. Collecting beetles (*Trox*) with feather bait traps. Ent. News, 54:224–229.

Vaurie, Patricia. 1955. A revision of the genus *Trox* in North America. Bull. Amer. Mus. Nat. Hist., 106(1):1–90.

STATE AND CANADIAN LISTS

ALABAMA

Loding, H. P. 1933. Alabama Coleoptera not generally listed from the Gulf Coast states east of the Mississippi River, Florida, Georgia, and Mississippi. Bull. Brooklyn Ent. Soc., 27:139–151.

———. 1945. Catalogue of the beetles of Alabama. Geol. Surv. Ala., Mono. No. 11, 172 pp.

Park, Orlando. 1951. Cavernicolous pselaphid beetles of Alabama, with observations on taxonomy of family. Geol. Surv. Ala., Mus. Paper No. 31, 107 pp.

ALASKA

Fall, H. C. 1926. List of Coleoptera in Alaska. Pan.-Pac. Ent., 2:127–154, 191–208.

———. 1927. List of Coleoptera taken in Alaska. Pan.-Pac. Ent., 3:59–63.

Hamilton, J. 1894. Catalogue of the Coleoptera of Alaska. Trans. Amer. Ent. Soc., 21:1–38.

Hatch, Melville H. 1938. Report on Coleoptera collected by Mr. V. B. Scheffer on the Aleutian Islands in 1937. Pan.-Pac. Ent., 14(4):145–149.

———. 1939. List of Coleoptera taken by Mr. G. P. Engelhardt in Alaska in 1938. Bull. Brooklyn Ent. Soc., 34(1):45–50.

ARIZONA

Brisley, H. R. 1925. Notes on Chrysomelidae of Arizona. Trans. Amer. Ent. Soc., 51:167–182.

Griffith, H. G. 1900. Coleopterous fauna of Phoenix, Arizona. Ent. News, 11:561–570.

Schaeffer, C. 1908. List of longicorns collected in the Huachuca Mountains, Arizona. Sci. Bull. Brooklyn Inst. Arts Sci., 1:325–352.

———. 1908. List of Lampyridae from Arizona. Jour. N.Y. Ent. Soc., 16:61–67.

ARKANSAS

Hatch, Melville H. 1930. Records and new species of Coleoptera from Oklahoma and western Arkansas. Pub. Univ. Okla. Biol. Surv., 2:15–26.

Sanderson, Milton W. 1940. Arkansas Cyclocephalini. Ann. Ent. Soc. Amer., 33:377–384.

———. 1944. Distribution and hosts of Arkansas *Phyllophaga*. Jour. Kan. Ent. Soc., 17(1):1–7.

California

Dunn, G. W. 1891. Tiger beetles of California. Zoe, 2:152–154.

Fall, H. C. 1897. List of Coleoptera from southern Californian islands. Can. Ent., 29:233–244.

———. 1901. List of Coleoptera from southern California. Calif. Acad. Sci. Occ. Pap. No. 8, 282 pp.

Garnett, R. T. 1918. An annotated list of cerambycids of California. Can. Ent., 50:172–184.

Linsley, E. G., and J. W. MacSwain. 1951. The Rhipiphoridae of California. Bull. Calif. Insect Surv., 1(3):79–87.

——— and E. S. Ross. 1940. Coleoptera from San Jacinto Mountains, California. Pan.-Pac. Ent., 16:75–76.

Moore, I. 1937. List of beetles of San Diego County, California. San Diego Soc. Nat. Hist., Occ. Pap. No. 2, 109 pp.

Notman, H. 1929. Coleoptera from northern California. Bull. Brooklyn Ent. Soc., 24:222–223.

Okumura, G. T., and F. L. Blanc. 1955. Illustrated key to species of *Trogoderma* and to related genera of Dermestidae commonly encountered in stored grain in California. Calif. Dept. Agr., Admin. Bull. T-1, 5 pp.

Canada

Beaulieu, G. 1900–1929. Les Coléoptères du Canada. Nat. Can., Vols. 27–56.

Beaulne, J. L. 1940. Genera of Haliplidae in Canada. Le Naturaliste Canadien, 67:303–305.

Bell, J. T. 1885. List of Staphylinidae of Belleville, Ontario. Can. Ent., 17:49–50.

Brimley, J. F. 1930. Coleoptera from Rainy River district, Ontario. Can. Nat., 44:135–140.

———. 1941. Cerambycidae of Prince Edward County, Ontario. Univ. Toronto Stud. Biol., 48:120–123.

———. 1951. Mordellidae of Prince Edward County, Ontario. Can. Ent., 43:179–278.

Brown, W. J. 1940. Key to Ptinidae occurring in Canada. Can. Ent., 72:115–122.

———. 1945. Food plants and distribution of *Calligrapha* in Canada. Can. Ent., 77:117–133.

Chagnon, G. 1917. Preliminary list of insects of province of Quebec. Suppl. to Rept. Que. Soc. Prot. Plants, pp. 160–277.

Couper, W. 1882–1883. Coleoptera found in the province of Quebec. Can. Sports. Nat., Vols. 2 and 3.

Finnegan, R. J. 1957. Elm bark beetles in southwestern Ontario. Can. Ent., 89:275–280.

Germain, F. 1916. Histérides capturés à Ottawa. Nat. Can., 42:103–105.

———. 1917. Histérides d'Ottawa et environs. Nat. Can., 43:125–128, 136–138.

Hanham, A. W. 1894. List of Quebec Coleoptera. Can. Ent., 26:350.

Hardy, G. A. 1926. Buprestidae and Cerambycidae of Vancouver. Rept. Prov. Mus. Nat. Hist., 1925–1926, pp. C24–33.

———. 1927. Buprestidae and Cerambycidae of Vancouver. Rept. Prov. Mus. Nat. Hist., 1926–1927, pp. C32–37.

Harrington, W. H. 1883. List of Ottawa Coleoptera. Trans. Ottawa Field Nat. Club, 2:67–85.

———. 1899. Ottawa Cerambycidae. Ottawa Nat., 13:57–68.

Hausen, J. F. 1892. List of Coleoptera in vicinity of St. Jérome, Quebec. Can. Rec. Sci., Vol. 5.

Hicks, S. D. 1944. Coleoptera taken at Ojibway, Ontario. Can. Ent., 76:163.

———. 1946. Additional Coleoptera occurring in Ontario. Can. Ent., 77:214.

Keen, J. J. 1895. List of Coleoptera from Queen Charlotte Island, B.C. Can. Ent., 27:165–172, 217–220.

Notman, H. 1919. Coleoptera collected at Cochrane, northern Ontario. Jour. N.Y. Ent. Soc., 26:237.

Ouellet, C. J. 1902. Liste des Coléoptères du Québec. Le Nat. Can., 29:82–87, 103–105, 120–124, 139–141.

Swaine, J. M. 1917. Canadian bark beetles, I. Can. Dept. Agr., Ent. Br. Bull. No. 14, 1917, 32 pp.

———. 1918. Canadian bark beetles, II. Can. Dept. Agr., Ent. Br. Bull. No. 14, 1918, 143 pp.

Wickham, H. F. 1894–1899. Coleoptera of Canada. Can. Ent., Vols. 26–31.

COLORADO

Carpenter, W. L. 1874. Report on alpine insects of Colorado. Rept. U.S. Geol. Surv., pp. 539–542.

———. 1876. Report on alpine insects of Colorado and New Mexico. Ann. Rept. Chem. Eng., Pt. 3, pp. 521–525.

———. 1876. Report on alpine insects of Colorado and New Mexico. J. Chem. Eng., App. J, pp. 301–305.

Cockerell, T. D. A. 1893. The entomology of mid-alpine zone, Colorado. Trans. Amer. Ent. Soc., 20:305–370.

Pennak, R. W. 1947. Keys to the aquatic insects of Colorado. Univ. Colo. Stud., D 2:353–383.

Putnam, J. D. 1876. Lists of Coleoptera from Iowa, Colorado, Wyoming, and Utah. Proc. Davenport Acad. Sci., 1:169–207.

CONNECTICUT

Britton, W. E. 1914. Some common lady-beetles of Connecticut. Conn. Agr. Exp. Sta., Bull. No. 181, 24 pp.

———. 1920. Check list of the insects of Connecticut. Conn. Geol. Nat. Hist. Surv., Bull. No. 31, 397 pp.

Champlain, A. B. 1911. Coleoptera from Connecticut. Psyche, 18:35–36, 170–173.

Johnson, H. L. 1915. Coleoptera of Meriden, Connecticut. Ent. News, 26:307–319.

DELAWARE

McDermott, F. A. 1948. Common fireflies of Delaware. Privately printed. John D. Sherman, N.Y., 19 pp.

DISTRICT OF COLUMBIA

Ulke, H. 1902. List of beetles of District of Columbia. Proc. U.S.N.M., 25:1–57.

FLORIDA

Blatchley, W. S. 1919. Insects of Florida: The water beetles. Bull. Amer. Mus. Nat Hist., 41:305–322.

———. 1920. Notes on the Coleoptera from Florida, with descriptions. Can. Ent., 52:42–46, 68–72, 259–261.

———. 1924. Chrysomelidae of Florida. Fla. Ent., 7:33–39, 49–57.

———. 1924. Chrysomelidae of Florida. Fla. Ent., 8:1–7, 17–23, 39–46.

———. 1927–1930. Scarabaeidae of Florida. Fla. Ent., Vols. 11–14.

Dozier, H. L. 1920. Ecological study of hammock and piney woods insects in Florida. Ann. Ent. Soc. Amer., 13:325–380.

LeConte, J. L., and E. A. Schwarz. 1878. Coleoptera of Florida. Proc. Amer. Phil. Soc., 17:353–472.

Leng, C. W. 1915. List of Carabidae of Florida. Bull. Amer. Mus. Nat. Hist., 34:555–601.

Moznette, G. F. 1920. Luminous beetles of Florida. Fla. Ent., 4:17–18.

Notman, H. 1920. Staphylinidae from Florida. Bull. Amer. Mus. Nat. Hist., 42:693–732.

Wickham, H. F. 1910. List of VanDuzee collection of Florida beetles. Bull. Buffalo Soc. Nat. Sci., 9:399–405.

Young, F. N. 1951. Notes on habits and habitat of *Geotrupes chalybaeus* in Florida. Psyche, 57:88–92.

———. 1952. A new water beetle from Florida, with a key to the species of *Desmopachria* of the United States and Canada. Bull. Brooklyn Ent. Soc., 46:107–112.

———. 1954. Water beetles of Florida. Univ. Fla. Stud., Biol. Series, 5(1):1–238.

GEORGIA

Fattig, P. W. 1944. *Phyllophaga* or May beetles of Georgia. Emory Univ. Mus., Bull. No. 2, 32 pp.

———. 1947. The Cerambycidae or long-horned beetles of Georgia. Emory Univ. Mus., Bull. No. 5, 48 pp.

———. 1948. The Chrysomelidae or leaf beetles of Georgia. Emory Univ. Mus., Bull. No. 6, 47 pp.

———. 1949. The Carabidae or ground beetles of Georgia. Emory Univ. Mus., Bull. No. 7, 62 pp.

———. 1951. The Elateridae or click beetles of Georgia. Emory Univ. Mus., Bull. No. 10, 25 pp.

LeConte, J. L. 1849. List of Georgia Coleoptera. White's Statistics of Georgia, Atlanta, Ga.

ILLINOIS

Forbes, S. A. 1916. General survey of *Phyllophaga* of Illinois. Univ. Ill. Agr. Exp. Sta. Bull., 186:261–265.

INDIANA

Blatchley, W. S. 1910. The Coleoptera of Indiana. Ind. Dept. Geol. and Nat. Res., Bull. No. 1, 1386 pp.

———. 1921. Notes on Indiana Halticini. Jour. N.Y. Ent. Soc., 29:16–27.

Davis, J. J. 1933–1953. Insects of Indiana. Proc. Ind. Acad. Sci., Vols. 42–62.

Iowa

Bleasdell, C. G. 1937. Rhynchophora of Iowa. Ia. State Coll. Jour. Sci., 11: 405–445.

Eckoff, D. E. 1939. Cicindelidae of Iowa. Ia. State Coll. Jour. Sci., 13:201–230.

Hendrickson, G. O. 1930. Studies of insect fauna occurring in Iowa. Ia. State Coll. Jour. Sci., 4:49–179.

———. 1931. Studies of insect fauna of Iowa prairies. Ia. State Coll. Jour. Sci., 5:195–209.

———. 1934. Mordellidae of Iowa prairies. Bull. Brooklyn Ent. Soc. (1933), 28:193.

Jacques, H. E., and D. Gordner. 1940. List of Iowa Mordellidae. Proc. Ia. Acad. Sci., 46:427–428.

——— and L. Redlinger. 1946. Preliminary list of Carabidae from Iowa. Proc. Ia. Acad. Sci., 52:293–298.

Longnecker, K. 1930. A study of the Coccinellidae of Iowa. Proc. Ia. Acad. Sci., 35:307–311.

Owen, W., and H. E. Jacques. 1943. List of Elateridae of Iowa. Proc. Ia. Acad. Sci., 50:341–344.

Putnam, J. D. 1876. Lists of Coleoptera of Iowa, Colorado, Wyoming, and Utah. Proc. Davenport Acad. Sci., 1:169–207.

Schaffner, J. C., and D. D. Millspaugh. 1951. A preliminary list of Gyrinidae known to occur in Iowa. Proc. Ia. Acad. Sci., 57:531–532.

Travis, B. B. 1934. *Phyllophaga* of Iowa. Ia. State Coll. Jour. Sci., 8:313–365.

Wickham, H. F. 1911. List of Coleoptera of Iowa. Bull. Lab. Nat. Hist. Univ. Ia., No. 6, 40 pp.

Kansas

Douglass, J. R. 1929. Chrysomelidae of Kansas. Jour. Kan. Ent. Soc., 2:1–15, 26–38.

Gui, H. L. The Coccinellidae of Kansas. Jour. Kan. Ent. Soc., 1:2–13.

Hayes, W. P. 1922. Kansas Rhynchophora. Trans. Kan. Acad. Sci., 30:205–212.

Knaus, W. 1884–1908. Additions to list of Kansas Coleoptera. Trans. Kan. Acad. Sci., Vols. 9, 10, 14, 17, 19, 20, 21, 22.

———. 1900. Cicindelidae of Kansas. Can. Ent., 32:109–116.

———. 1915. Collecting notes on Kansas Coleoptera. Bull. Brooklyn Ent. Soc., 10:35–40.

———. 1918. Additions to Kansas Coleoptera. Trans. Kan. Acad. Sci., 28:261–263.

Popenoe, E. A. 1877. List of Kansas Coleoptera. Trans. Kan. Acad. Sci., 5:21–40.

———. 1878. Additions to Kansas Coleoptera. Trans. Kan. Acad. Sci., 6:77–86.

Smith, R. C., *et al.* 1943. Common insects of Kansas. Rept. Kan. State Bd. Agr., pp. 268–333.

Snow, F. H. 1878. The insects of Wallace County, Kansas. Trans. Kan. Acad. Sci., 6:61–70.

———. 1903. Lists of Coleoptera of Kansas. Kan. Univ. Sci. Bull., 2:191–203.

KENTUCKY

Jewett, H. H. 1946. Larval Elateridae in Kentucky. Ky. Agr. Exp. Sta., Bull. No. 489, 40 pp.

LOUISIANA

Shufeldt, R. W. 1884. Observations upon insects collected at New Orleans, Louisiana. Proc. U.S.N.M., 7:331–338.

Townsend, C. H. T. 1885. List of Coleoptera collected in Louisiana. Can. Ent., 17:66–73.

MAINE

Cloudman, A. M. 1925. A preliminary report on Cerambycidae on Mt. Desert, Maine. Jour. N.Y. Ent. Soc., 5:23–25.

Fall, H. C. 1924. *Galerucella* and some of its relatives. Maine Agr. Exp. Sta., Bull. No. 319, pp. 81–140.

Harris, E. D. 1901. Cicindelidae of Mt. Desert, Maine. Jour. N.Y. Ent. Soc., 9:27–28.

Johnson, C. W. 1927. Insect fauna of Mt. Desert. Wistar Inst. Anat. Biol., Philadelphia, 247 pp.

Nicolay, A. S. 1917. Buprestidae and Cerambycidae from Maine. Bull. Brooklyn Ent. Soc., 12:92–94.

Procter, W. 1938. The insect fauna from the Biological Survey of Mt. Desert Region, Pt. 6. Wistar Inst., Philadelphia, 496 pp.

———. 1946. Biological Survey of Mt. Desert Region, Pt. 7. Wistar Inst., Philadelphia, 566 pp.

Woods, W. S. 1918. Biology of Maine species of *Altica*. Me. Agr. Exp. Sta., Bull. No. 273, pp. 149–204.

MARYLAND

Duckett, A. B. 1920. Halticinae of Maryland. Univ. Md. Agr. Exp. Sta., Bull. No. 241, pp. 111–155.

MASSACHUSETTS

Gould, A. A. 1834. On the Cicindelae of Massachusetts. Bost. Jour. Nat. Hist., 1:41–54.

Harris, T. W. 1833. List of the insects of Massachusetts. Rept. on Geol., Min., Bot., and Zool. Mass. Amherst, pp. 566–595.

———. 1835. List of the insects of Massachusetts. Rept. on Geol., Min., Bot., and Zool. Mass. 2nd ed., Amherst, pp. 553–601.

Hawkins, D. C. 1915. List of Coleoptera collected at Concord, Massachusetts. Proc. Thoreau Mus. Nat. Hist., 1:44–47.

Heffenger, C. P. W. W., and J. B. Hopkins. 1910. A list of Coleoptera collected at Concord, Massachusetts. Proc. Thoreau Mus. Nat. Hist., 1:7–10.

Henshaw, S. 1874. List of Coleoptera of Cliftondale, Massachusetts. Psyche, 1:17–18, 22–23.

Johnson, C. W. 1930. List of insects occurring in Nantucket, Massachusetts. Pub. Nantucket M. Mitchell Assn., Vol. 3, No. 2.

MICHIGAN

Andrews, A. W. 1921. The Coleoptera of the Shiras Expedition in Michigan. Pap. Mich. Acad. Sci., Arts, and Letters, 1:293–370.

Blanchard, F. N. 1921. Tiger beetles of Michigan. Pap. Mich. Acad. Sci., Arts, and Letters, 1:396–417.

Hatch, Melville H. 1925. A list of Coleoptera from Charlevoix County, Michigan. Pap. Mich. Acad. Sci., Arts, and Letters, 4:543–586.

Hickman, J. R. 1930. Life histories of Michigan Haliplidae. Pap. Mich. Acad. Sci., Arts, and Letters, 11:399–424.

Hubbard, H. G., and E. A. Schwarz. 1878. Coleoptera of Michigan, Lake Superior. Proc. Amer. Phil. Soc., 17:627–643.

———. 1878. Coleoptera of Michigan, Lower Peninsula. Proc. Amer. Phil. Soc., 17:643–666.

MINNESOTA

Dawson, R. W., and W. Horn. 1928. Tiger beetles of Minnesota. Univ. Minn. Agr. Exp. Sta., Tech. Bull No. 56, 13 pp.

Dodge, H. R. 1938. Bark beetles of Minnesota. Univ. Minn. Agr. Exp. Sta., Tech. Bull. No. 132, 60 pp.

Hatch, Melville H. 1927. Studies on the carrion beetles of Minnesota. Univ. Minn. Agr. Exp. Sta., Tech. Bull. No. 48, 19 pp.

Lugger, O. 1899. Coleoptera of Minnesota. Minn. Agr. Exp. Sta., Bull. No. 66, pp. 85–331.

Stehr, W. C. 1930. The Coccinellidae of Minnesota. Univ. Minn. Agr. Exp. Sta., Tech. Bull. No. 75, 54 pp.

MISSISSIPPI

Blackman, M. W. 1922. Mississippi bark beetles. Miss. Agr. Exp. Sta., Tech. Bull. No. 11, 130 pp.

Dozier, H. L. 1921. An annotated list of Mississippi Chrysomelidae. Ohio Jour. Sci., 22:117–124.

Langston, J. M. 1927. *Phyllophaga* from Mississippi. Ann. Ent. Soc. Amer., 20:221–223.

———. 1928. *Phyllophaga* of Mississippi. Miss. Agr. Exp. Sta., Tech. Bull. No. 15, 103 pp.

MONTANA

Hatch, Melville H. 1933. Records of Coleoptera from Montana. Can. Ent., 65:5–15.

NEBRASKA

Bruner, L. 1901. The tiger beetles of Nebraska. Proc. Neb. Acad. Sci., 7:97–99.

Dawson, R. W. 1924. Synopsis of the Scarabaeidae of Nebraska. Univ. Neb. Stud., 22:163–244.

Meserve, F. G. 1936. Silphidae of Nebraska. Ent. News, 47:132–134.

———. 1936. Cicindelidae of Nebraska. Ent. News, 47:270–275.

Powell, E. F. 1932. The Chrysomelinae occurring in Nebraska. Ent. News, 43:92–97.

Whelan, D. B. 1936. Coleoptera of original prairie in east Nebraska. Jour. Kan. Ent. Soc., 9:111–115.

NEVADA

LaRivers, I. 1946. List of Cicindelidae occurring in Nevada. Pan.-Pac. Ent., 22:135–141.

LaRivers, I. 1946. Annotated list of Carabinae occurring in Nevada. Bull. S. Calif. Acad. Sci., 45:133–140.

———. 1947. Histeridae occurring in Nevada. Great Basin Nat., 7:7–9.

———. 1950. The Dryopidae known or expected to occur in the Nevada area. Wasmann Jour. Biol., 8:100–104.

———. 1951. The cerambycoid semi-aquatic Coleoptera of the Nevada area. Great Basin Nat., 11(3–4):97–104.

———. 1951. Nevada Dytiscidae. Amer. Midl. Nat., 45(2):392–406.

———. 1954. Nevada Hydrophilidae. Amer. Midl. Nat., 52(1):64–174.

New Hampshire

Austin, E. P. 1874. Coleoptera of Mt. Washington, New Hampshire. Proc. Bost. Soc. Nat. Hist., 16:265–272.

Harris, E. D. 1918. Cicindelidae of New Hampshire. Jour. N.Y. Ent. Soc., 26:237.

Slosson, A. T. 1894–1906. Lists of insects of alpine regions of Mt. Washington, New Hampshire. Ent. News, Vols. 5–17.

New Jersey

Malkin, B. 1941. Additions to New Jersey list of Coleoptera. Jour. N.Y. Ent. Soc., 49:285–291.

Mutchler, A. J., and H. B. Weiss. 1922. Wood-boring *Agrilus* occurring in New Jersey. N.J. Dept. Agr., Circ. No. 48, 20 pp.

——— and ———. 1923. Beetles of the genera *Saperda* and *Oberea* in New Jersey. N.J. Dept. Agr., Circ. No. 58, 26 pp.

——— and ———. 1924. The oil and blister beetles of New Jersey. N.J. Dept. Agr., Circ. No. 76, 19 pp.

——— and ———. 1925. *Conotrachelus* in New Jersey. N.J. Dept. Agr., Circ. No. 87, 22 pp.

——— and ———. 1926. Leaf beetles of the genus *Galerucella* occurring in New Jersey. N.J. Dept. Agr., Circ. No. 98, 16 pp.

——— and ———. 1927. The dermestid beetles of New Jersey. N.J. Dept. Agr., Circ. No. 108, pp. 16–26.

——— and ———. 1929. The Ostomidae of New Jersey. N.J. Dept. Agr., Circ. No. 154.

Nicolay, A. S. 1919. Additions to insects of New Jersey, No. 7. Ent. News, 30:276–279.

Sim, R. J. 1930. Scarabaeidae in New Jersey. Jour. N.Y. Ent. Soc., 38:139–147.

Smith, J. B. 1910. Catalogue of the insects of New Jersey. 3rd ed. Ann. Rept. N.J. State Mus. for 1909–10, 888 pp.

Weiss, H. B. 1915. Additions in insects of New Jersey. Ent. News, 26:101–107, 260–262.

———. 1916. Additions in insects of New Jersey. Ent. News, 27:9–13, 162–166.

New Mexico

Carpenter, W. L. 1876. Report on alpine insects of Colorado and New Mexico. Ann. Rept. Chem. Eng., Pt. 3, pp. 521–525.

Carpenter, W. L. 1876. Report on alpine insects of Colorado and New Mexico. J. Chem. Eng., App. J, pp. 301–305.

Cockerell, T. D. A. 1898. Life zones in New Mexico, II. N. Mex. Agr. Exp. Sta., Bull. No. 28, pp. 137–179.

Fall, H. C., and T. D. A. Cockerell. Coleoptera of New Mexico. Trans. Amer. Ent. Soc., 33:145–272.

Knaus, W. 1910. Coleoptera of New Mexico. Trans. Kan. Acad. Sci., 23:108.

——. 1911. Coleoptera of New Mexico. Trans. Kan. Acad. Sci., 26:89–93.

Skinner, H. 1903. List of the insects of Beulah, New Mexico. Trans. Amer. Ent. Soc., 29:35–117.

Snow, F. H. 1881. Lists of Coleoptera collected in New Mexico. Trans. Kan. Acad. Sci., 7:70–73.

——. 1885. Lists of Coleoptera of New Mexico. Trans. Kan. Acad. Sci., 9:65–69.

——. 1906. List of Coleoptera collected in New Mexico by the entomological expedition of the University of Kansas. Trans. Kan. Acad. Sci., 20(2): 165–189.

——. 1907. List of species collected in New Mexico. Trans. Kan. Acad. Sci., 20:41–65.

Townsend, C. H. T. 1895. On the Coleoptera of New Mexico and Arizona. Can. Ent., 27:39–51.

New York

Belkin, J. N. 1934. Addition to New York State list of insects. Bull. Brooklyn Ent. Soc., 28:220–222.

Cooper, K. W. 1932. Additions to New York State list. Bull. Brooklyn Ent. Soc., 27:189–195.

——. 1935. Supplement to New York State list of Coleoptera. Bull. Brooklyn Ent. Soc., 30:142–159.

Dietrich, H. 1945. Elateridae of New York State. Cornell Univ. Agr. Exp. Sta., Mem. No. 269, 79 pp.

Emmons, E. 1854. The natural history of New York: Agriculture, Vol. 5: Insects. Albany, 272 pp.

Felt, E. P. 1907. Insects affecting park and woodland trees. Mem. N.Y State Mus., Vol. 8, Pt. 142, 1905–1906, 877 pp.

Fitch, A. 1855. Insects of the State of New York. Trans. N.Y. State Agr. Soc., 14:742–753.

——. 1856–1858. Reports on . . . insects of the State of New York. Trans. N.Y. State Agr. Soc., 16:315–490; 17:687–753; and 18:781–854.

Fletcher, F. C. 1926. Coleoptera (at McLean, N.Y.). Bull. Lloyd Library, pp. 128–146.

Hatch, Melville H. 1924. A preliminary list of Coleoptera of Cranberry Lake, New York. N.Y. Coll. For., Tech. Bull. No. 17, pp. 273–312.

Houghton, C. O. 1902. List of Adirondack Mountains insects. Ent. News, 13:247–253.

Leng, C. W., and W. T. Davis. 1924. List of the Coleoptera of Staten Island. Proc. Staten Island Inst. Arts, Sci., 2:1–82.

Leonard, M. D. 1928. A list of insects of New York. Cornell Univ. Agr. Exp. Sta., Mem. No. 101.

Malkin, B. 1941. Additions to New York list, No. 5. Bull. Brooklyn Ent. Soc., 36:209–212.

Malkin, B. 1941. Addition to Staten Island Coleoptera. Proc. Staten Island Inst. Arts, Sci., 9:91–96.

———. 1945. Supplement to New York list, No. 6. Jour. N.Y. Ent. Soc., 53:91–116.

Nicolay, A. S. 1914. Mordellidae of New York. Bull. Brooklyn Ent. Soc., 9:29–32.

———. 1919. List of Buprestidae and Cerambycidae occurring on Long Island. Bull. Brooklyn Ent. Soc., 14:17–20, 63–72.

Notman, H. 1919. Coleoptera collected at Mooers, New York. Bull. Brooklyn Ent. Soc., 14:129–141.

NORTH CAROLINA

Beal, J. A., and C. L. Massey. 1945. Bark beetles and ambrosia beetles (Coleoptera: Scolytidae), with special reference to species occurring in North Carolina. Duke Univ. Sch. For., Bull. No. 10, 178 pp.

Beutenmüller, W. 1903. Beetles from the Black Mountains, North Carolina. Bull. Amer. Mus. Nat. Hist., 19:511–519.

Brimley, C. S. 1938. The insects of North Carolina. N.C. Dept. Agr., Raleigh, 560 pp.

———. 1942. Supplement to The insects of North Carolina. N.C. Dept. Agr., Raleigh, 39 pp.

Coues, E., and H. C. Yarrow. 1878. List of Coleoptera from Ft. Macon, North Carolina. Proc. Acad. Nat. Sci., Phila., pp. 313–314.

Sherman, F. 1904. List of Cicindelidae of North Carolina. Ent. News, 15:26–31.

OHIO

Dury, C. 1879. List of Coleoptera of Cincinnati. Jour. Cin. Soc. Nat. Hist., 2:162–178.

———. 1882. List of Coleoptera of Cincinnati. Jour. Cin. Soc. Nat. Hist., 5:218–220.

———. 1888. Elateridae of Cincinnati. Ent. Amer., 4:163–164.

———. 1892. Mordellidae in the vicinity of Cincinnati. Jour. Cin. Soc. Nat. Hist., 15:123–126.

———. 1902. Revised list of Cincinnati Coleoptera. Jour. Cin. Soc. Nat. Hist., 20:107–196.

Easterling, G. R. 1934. Study of insect fauna of Ohio. Ohio Jour. Sci., 34:129–146.

Everly, R. T. 1927. A check-list of the Carabidae of Columbus, Ohio. Ohio Jour. Sci., 27:155–156.

Hughes, J. H. 1944. List of Chrysomelidae in Ohio. Ohio Jour. Sci., 44(3): 129–142.

Knull, J. N. 1946. The long-horned beetles of Ohio (Coleoptera: Cerambycidae). Ohio Biol. Surv. Bull., 7:133–354.

———. 1951. The checkered beetles of Ohio (Coleoptera: Cleridae). Ohio Biol. Surv. Bull., 8:269–350.

Miskimen, G. W. 1956. A faunal list of Cantharidae of Ohio. Ohio Jour. Sci., 56:129–134.

Wilcox, J. A. 1954. Leaf beetles of Ohio. Ohio Biol. Surv. Bull., 8:353–506.

Wright, J. F., and J. Whitehouse. 1941. Additions to list of Cincinnati Coleoptera. Bull. Brooklyn Ent. Soc., 36:69–73.

OKLAHOMA

Brown, W. J. 1927. An annotated list of the coprophagous Scarabaeidae known to occur in Oklahoma. Proc. Okla. Acad. Sci., 7:24–28.

Hatch, M. H. 1926. Coleoptera from southeastern Oklahoma. Proc. Okla. Acad. Sci., 6:142–148.

———. 1930. Records and new species of Coleoptera from Oklahoma and western Arkansas. Pub. Univ. Okla. Biol. Surv., 2:15–26.

——— and A. I. Ortenburger. 1930. Records and new species of Coleoptera from Oklahoma. Pub. Univ. Okla. Biol. Surv., 2:7–14.

OREGON

Beer, F. M. 1940. Buprestidae of southwestern Oregon. Pan-Pac. Ent. 16:13–16.

Canova, M. F. 1936. Annotated list of Lepturini of Oregon. Pan-Pac. Ent., 12:126–132.

Chamberlin, W. J. 1917. Annotated list of Scolytidae of Oregon. Can. Ent., 49:321–323.

———. 1924. Notes on the Buprestidae of Oregon. Jour. N.Y. Ent. Soc., 32:186–195.

Fender, K. M. 1945. Oregon Chrysomelidae. Pan-Pac. Ent., 21:72–73.

Hatch, M. H., and Samuel Beller. 1932. A preliminary catalogue of Chrysomelidae of Oregon. Pan-Pac. Ent., 8:102–108.

Malkin, B. 1943. Catalogue of Oregon Coccinellidae. Jour. N.Y. Ent. Soc., 51:191–198.

PENNSYLVANIA

Champlain, A. B., and H. B. Kirk. 1910. Carabidae from Harrisburg. Ent. News, 21:201–210.

Fisher, W. S. 1912. Cerambycidae from Harrisburg, Pennsylvania. Ent. News, 23:308–316.

Gamble, J. T. 1932. List of aquatic beetles occurring in Pennsylvania. Ent. News, 43:122–124.

Haldeman, S. S. 1842. Catalogue of the Carabidae of southeastern Pennsylvania. Proc. Acad. Nat. Sci., Phila., 1:295–298.

Hamilton, J. 1895. Catalogue of the Coleoptera of southwestern Pennsylvania. Trans. Amer. Ent. Soc., 22:317–381.

Klages, H. G. 1901. Supplement to Hamilton's list of Pennsylvania Coleoptera. Ann. Carn. Mus., 1:265–294.

Knull, J. N. 1922. Annotated list of Buprestidae of Pennsylvania. Can. Ent., 54:79–86.

———. 1925. Buprestidae of Pennsylvania. Ohio State Univ. Stud., 2(11):1–11.

———. 1926. Annotated list of Cerambycidae of Pennsylvania. Can. Ent., 58:21–26, 39–46.

———. 1929. Additions to lists of Pennsylvania. Ent. News, 40:144–145.

Melsheimer, F. V. 1806. Catalogue of the insects (beetles) of Pennsylvania. 66 pp. Published by the author, Hanover, Pa. (First separate publication in America referring to insects.)

Thomas, C. A. 1941. Elateridae of Pennsylvania. Jour. N.Y. Ent. Soc., 49:233–263.

RHODE ISLAND

Davis, C. A. 1903. The Cicindelidae of Rhode Island. Ent. News, 14:270–273.

———. 1904. Check list of Coleoptera from Rhode Island. 3rd ed. Bull. Roger Williams Park Mus., Prov., 1:1–47.

———. 1905. Additions to check list. Apteryx, 1:13–17.

———. 1910. The beetles of Rhode Island. Bull. Roger Williams Park Mus., Prov., 11:113–120.

SOUTH CAROLINA

Cartwright, O. L. 1935. Tiger beetles of South Carolina. Bull. Brooklyn Ent. Soc., 30:69–77.

Luginbill, P. 1928. The *Phyllophaga* inhabiting South Carolina. Ann. Ent. Soc. Amer., 21:47–91.

SOUTH DAKOTA

Carruth, K. A. 1931. The Meloidae of South Dakota. Ent. News, 42:50–55.

Gilbertson, G. I. 1929. The Cicindelidae of South Dakota. Proc. S. Dakota Acad. Sci., 29:22–26.

Johnson, P. H. 1941. Eumolpinae and Chrysomelidae in South Dakota. Ent. News, 52:9–14.

Severin, H. C. 1949. Wireworms of South Dakota. S. Dakota State Coll. Agr. Exp. Sta., Tech. Bull. No. 8, 18 pp.

TENNESSEE

Doran, E. W. 1888. Report on the insects of Tennessee. Biennial Rept. Agr. Sta., Tenn., 1887–1888, pp. 38–39.

TEXAS

Dillon, L. S. 1952. The Meloidae of Texas. Amer. Midl. Nat., 48:330–420.

Mitchell, J. D., and W. D. Pierce. 1911. Weevils of Victoria County, Texas. Proc. Ent. Soc. Wash., 13:45–62.

Reinhard, H. J. 1939. New *Phyllophaga* from Texas. Jour. Kan. Ent. Soc., 12:47–63.

———. 1950. The *Phyllophaga* of Texas. Jour. Kan. Ent. Soc., 23(1):27–51.

Schaeffer, C. 1908. List of longicorns collected at Brownsville, Texas. Brooklyn Inst. Arts, Sci., 1:325–352.

Townsend, C. H. T. 1903. Brownsville, Texas, Coleoptera. Trans. Tex. Acad. Sci., 10:82–84.

Valentine, B. D. 1947. Cicindelidae collected in Texas. Coleop. Bull., 1:61–62.

Vogt, G. B. 1949. A biologically annotated list of the Buprestidae of the Lower Rio Grande Valley, Texas. Ann. Ent. Soc. Amer., 42:192–202.

UTAH

Engelhardt, G. P. 1918. Faunal zones in southwestern Utah. Jour. N.Y. Ent. Soc., 26:230.

Knowlton, G. F. 1930. Notes on Utah Coleoptera. Fla. Ent., 14:36–37, 75–77.

———. 1931. Notes on Utah Coleoptera. Fla. Ent., 15:10.

———. 1939. Utah insects, III: Coleoptera. Utah Agr. Exp. Sta., Mimeo. Ser., No. 200, 25 pp.

——— and S. L. Wood 1948. Utah Buprestidae. Ent. News, 59:41–43.

——— and ———. 1950. An annotated list of Utah Cerambycidae. Bull. Brooklyn Ent. Soc., 45:10–13.

Putnam, J. D. 1876. Lists of Coleoptera from Iowa, Colorado, Wyoming, and Utah. Proc. Davenport Acad. Sci., 1:169–207.

Schwarz, E. A. 1891. Insect fauna of Great Salt Lake. Can. Ent., 23:233–241.

Tanner, V. M. 1928. Coleoptera of Zion National Park, Utah. Ann. Ent. Soc. Amer., 21:269–280.

———. 1929. Coleoptera of Utah: Cicindelidae. Pan-Pac. Ent., 6:78–87.

———. 1934. List of Coleoptera of Zion National Park, Utah. Ann. Ent. Soc. Amer., 27:43–49.

VIRGINIA

Horn, G. H. 1868. Catalogue of Coleoptera from southwestern Virginia. Trans. Amer. Ent. Soc., 2:123–128.

Uhler, P. A. 1879. List of animals observed at Fort Wool, Virginia. Stud. Biol. Lab., Johns Hopkins Univ., 1:17–34.

WASHINGTON

Beer, F. M., and Melville H. Hatch. 1941. Coleoptera of Washington: Buprestidae. Univ. Wash. Pub. Biol., 10:93–142.

Beller, Samuel, and Melville H. Hatch. 1932. Coleoptera of Washington: Chrysomelidae. Univ. Wash. Pub. Biol., 1(2):69–144.

Gray, B., and Melville H. Hatch. 1941. Coleoptera of Washington: Carabidae, Agonini. Univ. Wash. Pub. Biol., 10:5–45.

Hatch, Melville H. 1938. Coleoptera of Washington: Cicindelinae. Univ. Wash. Pub. Biol., 1:229–238.

———. 1948. On collecting beetles in Washington. Coleop. Bull., 2(5):45–46.

——— and Trevor Kincaid. 1958. A list of Coleoptera from the vicinity of Willapa Bay, Washington. The Calliostoma Co., 1904 E. 52nd, Seattle 5, Wash.

——— and W. Reuter. 1934. Coleoptera of Washington: Silphidae. Univ. Wash. Pub. Biol., 1:147–162.

McGrath, R. M., and Melville H. Hatch. 1941. Coleoptera of Washington: Sphaeritidae, Histeridae. Univ. Wash. Pub. Biol., 10:47–91.

Melander, A. L. 1922. Collecting insects on Mt. Rainier. Ann. Rept. Smiths. Inst. (1921), pp. 415–522.

Patterson, G. K., and Melville H. Hatch. 1945. List of Scolytoidea of Washington. Univ. Wash. Pub. Biol., 10:145–156.

Walkley, L. M. 1953. Revision of the Lathridiini of the state of Washington (Lathridiidae). Proc. Ent. Soc. Wash., 54:217–235.

WEST VIRGINIA

Hopkins, A. D. 1893. Catalogue of West Virginia Scolytidae and their enemies. Bull. W.Va. Agr. Exp. Sta., 31:154–157.

Hopkins, A. D. 1893. Catalogue of West Virginia forest and shade tree insects. Bull. W.Va. Agr. Exp. Sta., 32(3):171–251.

WISCONSIN

Rauterberg, F. 1885–1888. Coleoptera of Wisconsin. Proc. Nat. Hist. Soc. Wis., 1885, pp. 10–25, 48–62; 1888, pp. 145–153, 222–228.

Snyder, W. E. 1897. Scarabaeidae of Dodge County, Wisconsin. Ent. News, 8:129–131.

WYOMING

Putnam, J. D. 1876. Lists of Coleoptera from Iowa, Colorado, Wyoming, and Utah. Proc. Davenport Acad. Sci., 1:169–207.

———. 1876. List of Wyoming Coleoptera. Reconn. of N.W. Wyo., U.S. War Dept., Washington, D.C., pp. 315–318.

APPENDIX

SOURCES OF SUPPLIES

Books

Adams, L. C., Jr., Box 158, Columbia, Mo.
Antiquariaat Junk, Lochem (G), Netherlands.
Bassett, F. N., 722 N. Orange Dr., Los Angeles 38, Calif.
Botanical Books, 3066 Georgia St., Oakland 2, Calif.
Burch, John Q., 1584 W. Vernon Ave., Los Angeles 37, Calif.
Gottschalk, Paul, Inc., 21 Pearl St., New York 4, N.Y.
Natural History Books, 6843 Hobart Ave., Chicago, Ill.
Pierce Book Co., Winthrop, Ia.
Schmidt, G., 460 Broad Ave., Palisades Park, N.J.
Stechert-Hafner, Inc., 31 E. 10th St., New York 3, N.Y.
Tripp, Henry, 31 E. 10th St., New York 3, N.Y.
Ward's Natural Science Establishment, Inc., 3000 Ridge Road E., Rochester, N.Y.

Equipment

Bio Metal Associates, Box 346, Beverly Hills, Calif.
Carolina Biological Supply Co., Elon College, N.C.
College Biological Supply Co., 9230 Woodlawn Ave., Seattle 3, Wash.
General Biological Supply House, Inc., 8200 S. Hoyne, Chicago, Ill.
Lane, Chas. J., Corp., 46 W. Broadway, New York 7, N.Y.
Nushawg Biological Supply, Inc., Buffalo Division, 110 Ivyhurst Rd., Buffalo 21, N.Y.
Quivira Specialties Co., 4204 W. 21st St., Topeka, Kans.
Ward's Natural Science Establishment, Inc., 3000 Ridge Road E., Rochester, N.Y.
Wind, Robert G., Route 1, Box 145, Buena Vista, Livermore, Calif.

INDEX

[The principal reference in each case is printed in boldface type.]

875

884

Date Due